ACTIVE NETWORK DESIGN

with Signal Filtering Applications

International Series in Signal Processing and Filtering

LINDQUIST: Active Network Design with Signal Filtering Applications

LINDQUIST: Digital Signal Processing with Signal Filtering Applications

ACTIVE NETWORK DESIGN

with Signal Filtering Applications

CLAUDE S. LINDQUIST

Professor of Electrical Engineering
California State University
Long Beach, California

STEWARD & SONS

ACTIVE NETWORK DESIGN

Printed in the United States of America
Second Printing

Published by Steward & Sons
P. O. Box 15282
Long Beach, CA 90815

Library of Congress Catalog Card Number 76-14238
ISBN 0-917144-01-5

To Todd and Tad

Always remember,
"What I gave, I held;
What I spent, I had;
What I kept, I lost."

PREFACE

Bacon observed that "some books are to be tasted, others to be swallowed and some few to be chewed and digested." This book is certainly to be digested since we are convinced that both student and design engineer will find it to be his most useful compendium of active network design results.

The book has been written as a text for undergraduate and graduate level courses in the design of active networks and especially active filters. It is also intended to serve as a reference and self-learning text for practicing engineers. The material has been developed, tested, and used for several years in undergraduate and graduate courses at California State University, Long Beach. It has won great acclaim from students who have used it, the majority of whom are practicing engineers.

A perusal of the Table of Contents, however, will show that this book is much more than a study in active network design. Broadly speaking, it is a complete theoretical and applied guide to all linear system design with emphasis on signal filtering and processing. The theory presented has been carefully selected on the basis of industrial usefulness. All theory is rigorously derived and thoroughly interpreted using a myriad of practical design examples. A number of standard, yet not widely available, design curves have been collected for ready reference. Many new concepts and design techniques are introduced. A multitude of useful references are included to lend historical insight and cohesiveness, and to provide a springboard for independent study by the engineer.

Our approach is to begin with the basic theory applicable to active networks and filters, to develop it, and to have it culminate in practical hardware design. The book is unique in that it is a blend of rigorous theory (e.g., Blackman's immittance relation seldom found in current books on electrical engineering) and practical results (e.g., Touch-Tone decoding filters used by the telephone company). Even the important topic of component selection, neglected in almost every other text, is thoroughly covered. Much of the material in the book is the result of original research which has never been published. Many of the topics covered are unique, both in scope and depth.

Each chapter contains complete problem sets with selected problem solutions tabulated at the end of the book. The problems have been chosen very carefully. Most contain useful and often necessary design information for solving current industrial problems (e.g., tape recorder equalizers, audiometers, sound level meters, EEG filters, SF and MF filters, C2 line conditioners, etc.). Thus, the problems form an encylopedia of terminology, specifications, and diverse filter applications. For easy reference, these topics have been listed in the Index.

The book is divided into two parts—analysis (Chapters 1–6) and synthesis (Chapters 7–14). We begin by summarizing the theory which is useful in linear system analysis and design (Chapter 1). Then we discuss general frequency and time domain analyses, approximations, and design using trial-and-error (Chapters 2–3). Next, systematic designs are introduced using classical and optimum filter responses (Chapters 4–5). The mathematical means to extend these low-pass filter results to high-pass, band-pass, band-stop, and all-pass filters are then developed (Chapter 6). These chapters describe the analysis phase required for any filter design, but there is much more to come. As Churchill said, "This is not the end. It is not even the beginning of the end. But it is, perhaps, the end of the beginning."

Now the designs are implemented with hardware. We first derive a classification system to describe the hundreds of active filters known and available. Bounds on gain and sensitivity are established (Chapter 7). The hardware implementations of filters are discussed in the succeeding chapters for low-pass (Chapter 8), high-pass (Chapter 9), band-pass (Chapter 10), band-stop (Chapter 11), and all-pass filters (Chapter 12). The related area of oscillators is also considered and their theory and implementation is developed (Chapter 13). Finally, the active filter and oscillator designs are completed by proper selection of components (Chapter 14).

The book can be used for both one- and two-semester courses as:

Analysis (Chapters 1–6), Synthesis (Chapters 7–14)

or

Design 1 (Chapters 2–4, 7, 8, 14), Design 2 (Chapters 1, 5,6,9–13)

Graduate courses cover the material in detail; undergraduate courses cover the material in abbreviated form. Although this is the sequence we use, other professors may wish to cover the chapters sequentially. Practicing engineers using the book as a self-learning text may cover it in the order listed above or sequentially as best suits their needs.

In covering Chapter 6, we have found it useful to follow each of its various sections (high-pass, band-pass, band-stop, and all-pass) with its appropriate design chapter (Chapters 9–12). Since transformation theory tends to be rather tedious mathematically and its topics heavily interrelated, we chose to collect it in a single chapter rather than distribute it throughout later chapters. The reader will see the benefits of this arrangement when he uses the material.

We should make one other comment concerning equations. For ease of reading and simplicity, we have sometimes grouped several related equations together and referred to them with a single equation number (e.g., see Eq. 1.3.2). In discussions, we use letters to explicitly denote the particular equation with the group to which we are referring (e.g., Eq. 1.3.2b refers to the B_{ij} equation).

As Colton noted, the consequences of things are not always proportionate to the apparent magnitude of any one event which produced them. For this reason, I am indebted to a number of students, colleagues, and practicing engineers who encouraged me during the development of this book. I am particularly grateful to Mr. J. S. Turnbull, Jr. of Collins Radio Company for providing me with an invaluable experience. Also, my personal thanks go to Professors J. H. Mulligan, Jr., M. S. Ghausi, and S. S. Shamis of New York University, P. C. Magnusson of Oregon State University, R. J. Smith of Stanford University, and J. H. Johnson of the University of Redlands for their influence through many years of study and development. Special thanks are also due to the various people who assisted in typing and proofreading at different stages of writing.

But most especially, I am indebted to my family and to my wife Diana who have assisted me continually for several years in preparing this book. We are pleased and relieved to complete this undertaking.

Claude S. Lindquist

Huntington Beach, California
September, 1976.

CONTENTS

1 GENERAL CONCEPTS

Nature, to be commanded, must be obeyed
Bacon

This book presents a thorough study of active networks emphasizing the active filter. Although active networks have been utilized for decades, active filters are a relatively new area of application for this classical subject. They not only obey and vividly illustrate active network theory, but have led to new design approaches and concepts having many industrial applications. Active filters in the modern sense are composed of resistors, capacitors, and operational amplifiers. With the advent of integrated circuit technology, the bulky discrete-component type op amp was miniaturized onto a tiny chip. The chip was packaged in a metal can smaller than a thimble, and the integrated operational amplifier resulted. Not only was it small, but it had almost ideal characteristics–infinite input impedance, zero output impedance, and infinite gain. This development is essentially responsible for today's explosive interest in active filters. Not only will this be known as the era of the integrated circuit, but in addition, the active filter.

A number of different filter types are available to the design engineer. These include:

1. *Active filters*: Composed of resistors, capacitors, and operational amplifiers.
2. *LC filters*: Composed of inductors and capacitors.
3. *Mechanical filters*: Composed of mechanical resonators (bars or discs) coupled by rods or wires and driven by electromechanical transducers (magnetostrictive ferrite or piezoelectric ceramic).
4. *Crystal or ceramic filters*: Composed of crystals, inductors, and capacitors; or of crystals (electroacoustic) or ceramic (piezoelectric) resonators and driven directly.
5. *Monolithic crystal or ceramic filters*: Composed of metallic electrodes deposited on a single crystal or ceramic substrate and driven directly.

Each filter type has its particular frequency band and fractional bandwidth (or Q) range where it excels. These are shown in Fig. 1.0.1. It is clear that active filters are useful in frequency ranges up to 1 MHz and Q's over 100 at lower frequencies. This is the frequency and Q range where the bulk of industrial applications exist. Thus, active filters are invaluable to the design engineer.

However, this book is much more than simply a study of active networks and filters as a perusal of the index will show. Broadly speaking, it is a complete theoretical and applied guide to all linear system design with emphasis on signal filtering and processing. The theory presented has been carefully selected on the basis of industrial usefulness. All theory is rigorously derived and thoroughly interpreted using a myriad of practical and current design examples. A number of standard, yet not widely available, design curves have been collected for ready reference by the

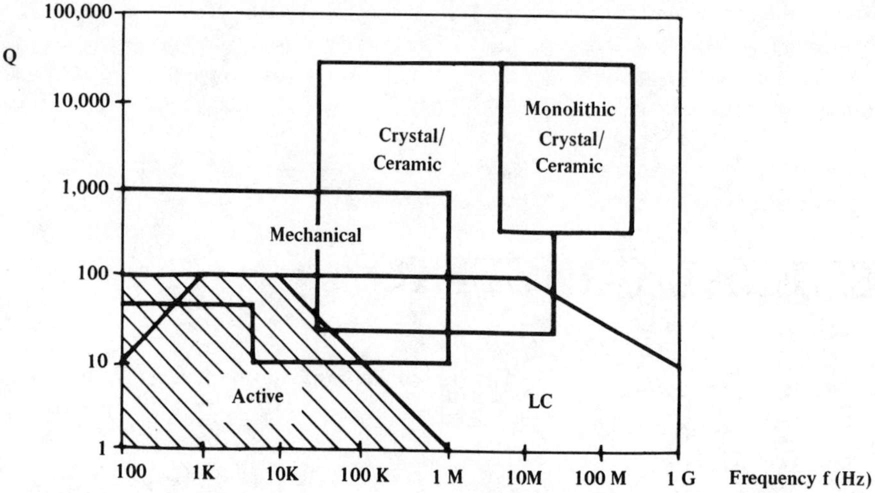

Fig. 1.0.1 Frequency and Q range for various filter types.[1]

engineer. Many new concepts and design techniques are introduced. A multitude of useful references are included to lend historical insight and cohesiveness to this book, and to serve as a springboard for independent study by the engineer. As we will say several times, the design engineer will find this book to be one of his most (if not the most) useful compendiums of filter design results.

This first chapter is a collection of ideas and concepts upon which we will base much of our later work. Some of the material may appear to be of only theoretical interest; however, this is not the case as later development will show. The material of Chap. 1 is self-contained, and we assume it will be primarily a conceptual review for the engineer.

1.1 SYSTEM CLASSIFICATIONS

Systems may be classified in a variety of ways: (1) continuous time versus discrete time, (2) deterministic versus probabilistic, (3) lumped versus distributed, (4) linear versus nonlinear, (5) time-invariant versus time-varying, (6) memoryless versus memory, (7) causal versus noncausal, and (8) stable versus unstable. Each category characterizes the system from a different viewpoint.

Continuous time (or analog) systems process signals continuously in time. Generally the signals have a continuum of values. However, *discrete time* systems process signals at discrete times. Very often, the signals have only particular (i.e., quantized) values.

Deterministic systems are systems whose parameters are known. However, there are many systems whose parameters are not known exactly, and must instead be described statistically or probabilistically. These are called *probabilistic* or nondeterministic systems. Communication links involving the atmosphere, large switching systems, or random interference sources are examples of such systems.

Lumped systems are systems which are composed of lumped circuit elements such as resistors, capacitors, amplifiers, etc. *Distributed* systems are systems which are composed of distributed elements such as transmission lines, etc. The distinction may appear somewhat artificial since all circuit elements are physically or spatially distributed. However, the test for distinguishing these systems is whether the elements can be adequately described by ordinary differential equations or whether partial differential equations involving the spatial (distance) variables must be used. Invariably, this reduces to a question of the relative wavelengths of the electrical signals being processed by the system, and the physical dimensions of the system itself. If the circuit element and system dimensions are a small fraction of the wavelength, then they can be treated as lumped. Otherwise, the spatial effects must be considered and they become distributed.

Linear systems are systems in which the superposition principle can be applied. In *nonlinear* systems, superposition cannot be applied. Nonlinear system theory is, for the most part, mathematically untractable. Approximation methods are generally used when necessary. Nonlinear systems can also be analyzed using computer simulation.

Time-varying systems are systems whose parameters vary with time, while *time-invariant* systems have constant parameters. Contrast these systems with the probabilistic system whose parameters can only be described statistically, and whose parameter distributions may or may not vary with time.

Memoryless systems are systems which have no recollection of past inputs. They only process present inputs. However, systems with *memory* store a portion of the inputs as they are received. For example, the inductor and capacitor are memory elements since their current and voltage values at any time depend upon the past voltages and currents which they have processed, respectively. In digital systems, the shift register is a memory element since it stores a number of preceding inputs. However, the resistor is not a memory element since its voltage-current relation depends only upon their instantaneous values.

Causal systems are systems which exhibit outputs in response to inputs. However, in *noncausal* systems, outputs occur before any input. Since an input cannot be used to control a future output, noncausal systems are of limited usefulness.

Stable systems are systems whose impulse response is bounded and decays to zero as time becomes infinite. *Unstable* systems are systems whose impulse response grows without bound. *Conditionally stable* systems are systems whose impulse responses neither grow nor decay. Examples of conditionally stable systems are oscillators and astable multivibrators.

We shall discuss linearity, causality, and stability at greater length later in the chapter. They are especially important to our study of active filters.

1.2 PASSIVE ELEMENTS

The devices which make up electronic systems are called *circuit elements* or *circuit components.* Circuit components are realizations of idealized passive and active elements. In constructing models of devices and systems, the ideal elements are utilized. Roughly speaking, active elements provide unilateral signal coupling while passive elements provide bilateral coupling.

In the physical sense, passive elements describe (or provide) the basic processes of energy dissipation and storage in either electric or magnetic fields. The behavior of passive elements is completely described by their voltage-current relations. However, active elements describe (or provide) the basic process of remote signal transfer and energy generation as will be discussed in the next section. Now we shall describe passive elements from a modelling theory viewpoint.[2]

The passive elements are the (1) resistor and conductor, (2) inductor and inverse inductor, and (3) capacitor and inverse capacitor. Historically, no standard names have been assigned to describe the "inverse" elements. The passive elements are two-terminal devices as shown in Fig. 1.2.1. They are characterized graphically by their relation between (1) voltage V-current I (electromagnetic field phenomena), (2) flux linkage λ-current I (magnetic field phenomena), and (3) charge Q-voltage V (electric field phenomena), respectively. The curves which describe these relations are also shown in Fig. 1.2.1. Although it may appear redundant to introduce two elements of each type, it is convenient to have these available for general analysis. The choice of which of the two elements to use is determined by the variable in its characteristic which is considered to be independent. For example, in the resistor, voltage and current are considered to be the dependent and independent variables, respectively. For the conductor, the situation is reversed. We see that both single-valued and multiple-valued functions are possible, as demonstrated by the resistor and conductor characteristics, respectively. Examples of such multiple-valued

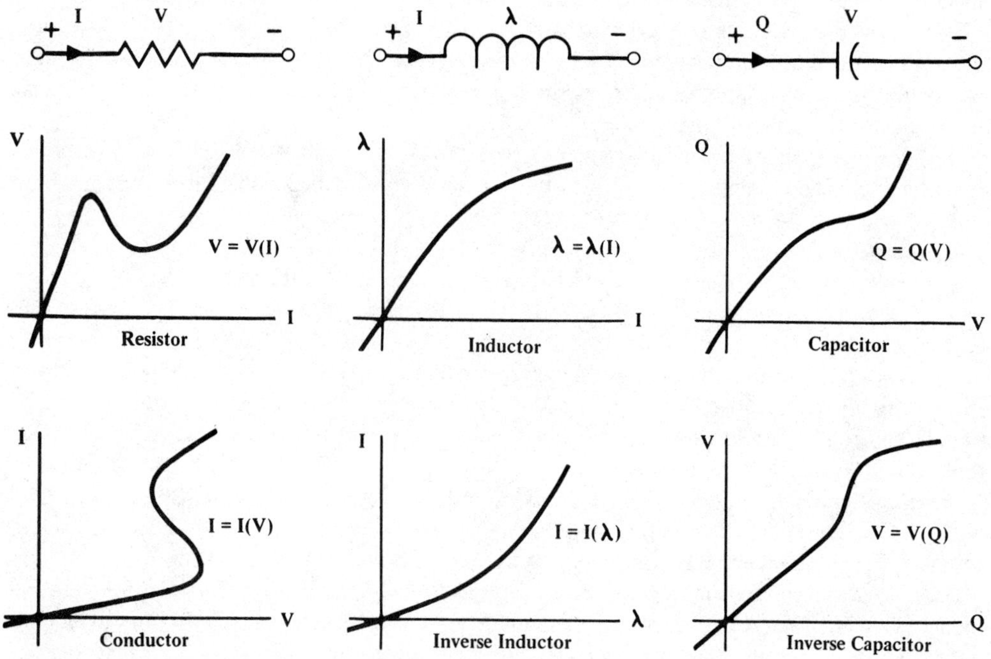

Fig. 1.2.1 Graphical descriptions of passive elements.

characteristics are the V-I characteristic of a tunnel diode and the B-H characteristic of a square-loop magnetic core. Passive elements that have linear characteristics which pass through the origin are said to be *linear*.

For design and analysis purposes, we are generally interested in the numerical values of the passive elements rather than their graphical descriptions shown in Fig. 1.2.1. For dc analysis (such as biasing), we are interested in their dc values. However, for ac analysis, we are interested in their small-signal values which we shall presently discuss.

The dc parameter values (equivalently referred to as their quiescent values) are determined directly from Fig. 1.2.1. These values relate the dependent and independent variables of the graphs as (1) resistance R(I) and conductance G(V), (2) inductance L(I) and inverse inductance Γ(λ), and (3) capacitance C(V) and inverse capacitance S(Q) where

$$\begin{aligned} &V = R(I)I \qquad \lambda = L(I)I \qquad Q = C(V)V \\ &I = G(V)V \qquad I = \Gamma(\lambda)\lambda \qquad V = S(Q)Q \end{aligned} \tag{1.2.1}$$

By convention, upper case (capital) letters denote dc parameters. At some particular dc condition or operating point, denoted by subscript "o", the dc parameter values equal

$$\begin{aligned} &R(I_o) = V_o/I_o \qquad L(I_o) = \lambda_o/I_o \qquad C(V_o) = Q_o/V_o \\ &G(V_o) = I_o/V_o \qquad \Gamma(\lambda_o) = I_o/\lambda_o \qquad S(Q_o) = V_o/Q_o \end{aligned} \tag{1.2.2}$$

The *dc parameter value* equals the slope of the line connecting the origin to the dc bias point of its characteristic as shown in Fig. 1.2.2. Although the dc values are not of general interest, they sometimes are given in specifications. We shall find them of great use.

Whenever the dc operating point is disturbed or perturbed by a signal, the dc level must move along its characteristic curve. For example, consider Fig. 1.2.2 where a perturbation Δx in the independent variable x causes a change Δy in the dependent variable y of

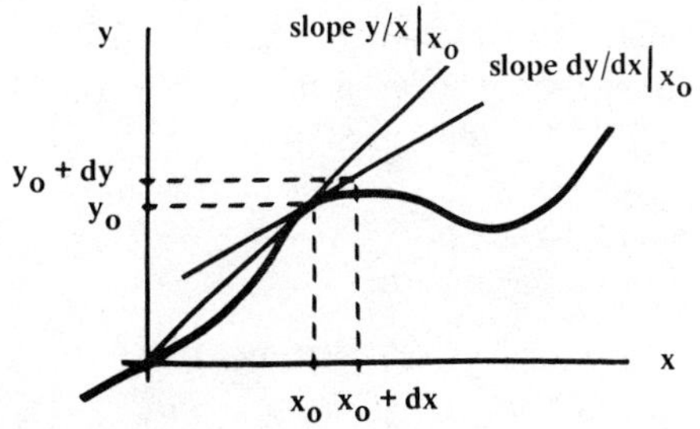

Fig. 1.2.2 Movement along characteristic curve resulting from change of bias point.

$$\begin{aligned} y_o + \Delta y &= y(x_o) + dy/dx|_{x_o} \Delta x + d^2y/dx^2|_{x_o} \Delta x^2/2! + \ldots \\ \Delta y &= (y_o + \Delta y) - y_o = dy/dx|_{x_o} \Delta x + d^2y/dx^2|_{x_o} \Delta x^2/2! + \ldots \end{aligned} \tag{1.2.3}$$

Therefore, the relation between changes in the dependent variable y due to changes in the independent variable x equals

$$\Delta y/\Delta x = dy/dx|_{x_o} + d^2y/dx^2|_{x_o} \Delta x/2! + \ldots \tag{1.2.4}$$

Establishing a new operating point at (y_o + dy, x_o + dx) requires initial movement (of differential length ds) along the line having slope $dy/dx|_{x_o}$ beginning at y_o, calculation of the new trajectory's slope $dy/dx|_{x_o+dx}$, and so forth. This differential movement along tangents to establish new operating points is of paramount importance since it forms the essential distinction between ac and dc parameter values.

The *effective* or *ac parameter value* under a transient or ac excitation is the slope of the characteristic at the quiescent level. The slope is usually different from the slope of the line joining the origin to the operating point of the characteristic. Failure to clearly distinguish between these two values is often responsible for obtaining seemingly erroneous results. From Eq. 1.2.1, the ac parameter values equal

$$\begin{aligned} r(I_o) &= dV/dI\,|_{I_o} \qquad l(I_o) = d\lambda/dI|_{I_o} \qquad c(V_o) = dQ/dV|_{V_o} \\ g(V_o) &= dI/dV\,|_{V_o} \qquad \gamma(\lambda_o) = dI/d\lambda|_{\lambda_o} \qquad s(Q_o) = dV/dQ|_{Q_o} \end{aligned} \tag{1.2.5}$$

The lower case letters are reserved for ac parameter values. The ac parameter values can be related to the dc parameter values in the following manner. Consider, for example, the resistor where V = R(I)I. Its ac resistance must equal

$$r(I_o) = dV/dI|_{I_o} = R(I_o) + I_o\, dR(I)/dI\,|_{I_o} = R(I_o) + I_o\, dR(I_o)/dI \tag{1.2.6}$$

Normalizing the ac resistance by the dc resistance gives

$$r_n(I_o) = r(I_o)/R(I_o) = 1 + d \ln R(I_o)/d \ln I \tag{1.2.7}$$

Similarly, the other normalized ac passive element values equal

$$\begin{aligned} g(V_o) &= G(V_o) + V_o\, dG(V_o)/dV & g_n(V_o) &= 1 + d \ln G(V_o)/d \ln V \\ l(I_o) &= L(I_o) + I_o\, dL(I_o)/dI & l_n(I_o) &= 1 + d \ln L(I_o)/d \ln I \\ \gamma(\lambda_o) &= \Gamma(\lambda_o) + \lambda_o\, d\Gamma(\lambda_o)/d\lambda & \gamma_n(\lambda_o) &= 1 + d \ln \Gamma(\lambda_o)/d \ln \lambda \\ c(V_o) &= C(V_o) + V_o\, dC(V_o)/dV & c_n(V_o) &= 1 + d \ln C(V_o)/d \ln V \\ s(Q_o) &= S(Q_o) + Q_o\, dS(Q_o)/dQ & s_n(Q_o) &= 1 + d \ln S(Q_o)/d \ln Q \end{aligned} \tag{1.2.8}$$

These equations show that the ac and dc parameter values differ by the right-most terms. They also show that the error incurred in failing to distinguish the ac and dc values is d ln $R(I_o)$/d ln I, etc. Graphically, the (decimal) error is equal to the slope of the dc parameter curve at the bias point, when plotted on log-log paper. Thus, if the error is small, one may not wish to bother distinguishing between the two values. These errors are the sensitivity coefficients which we shall discuss later in the chapter.

EXAMPLE 1.2.1 From one viewpoint, a semiconductor diode is a nonlinear resistor which is described by the equation[3]

$$I = I_s\,[\exp(qV/mkT) - 1] \tag{1.2.9}$$

where I_s is the reverse saturation current, q/kT equals 40 at a room temperature T of 300°K, and m equals an empirical constant where $1 \leqslant m \leqslant 2$. Its I-V characteristic is drawn in Fig. 1.2.3. Determine the small-signal resistance of the diode in its various operating regions.

Solution Since we have a current equation, we shall first determine the ac conductance g of the diode where g is given by Eq. 1.2.5. Substituting the diode equation into this equation yields

$$g(V_o) = (qI_s/mkT)\exp(qV_o/mkT) \tag{1.2.10}$$

for any dc bias point V_o. Since the I-V characteristic is single-valued and has a unique inverse, then ac resistance r equals the reciprocal of g as

$$r(V_o) = dV/dI\Big|_{I_o} = (dI/dV\Big|_{V_o})^{-1} = g(V_o)^{-1} = (mkT/qI_s)\exp(-qV_o/mkT) \tag{1.2.11}$$

Defining the constants r_o and V_r as

$$\begin{aligned} r_o &= mkT/qI_s = \text{small-signal resistance for } V_o = 0 \\ V_r &= mkT/q = \text{reference voltage } (0.025 \leqslant V_r \leqslant 0.05 \text{ volts}) \end{aligned} \tag{1.2.12}$$

then the small-signal resistance given by Eq. 1.2.11 can be expressed as

$$r(V_o) = r_o \exp(-V_o/V_r) \tag{1.2.13}$$

Thus, the ac resistance varies exponentially with dc bias voltage V_o. This is shown in Fig. 1.2.4. If for instance $I_s = 1\ \mu A$ and m = 1, then $r_o = 0.025\ V/1\ \mu A = 25\ K\Omega$. Therefore, we see from Fig. 1.2.4 that $r_o = 25\ \Omega$ for $V_o = 6.91(0.025) = 0.17$ volt, and $r_o = 25\ G\Omega$ for $V_o = -0.17$ volt.

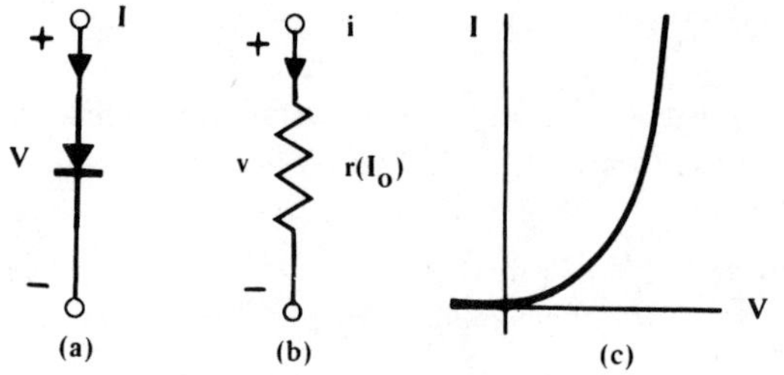

Fig. 1.2.3 (a) Semiconductor diode, its (b) simplest ac model, and its (c) I-V characteristic.

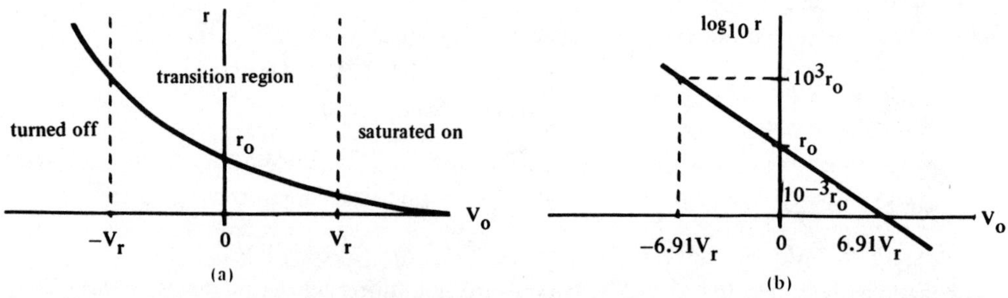

Fig. 1.2.4 Small-signal diode resistance plotted on (a) linear and (b) semi-log paper.

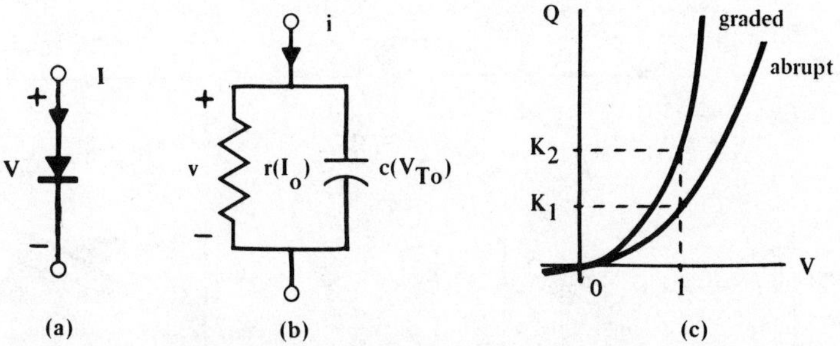

Fig. 1.2.5 (a) Semiconductor diode, its (b) complete ac model, and its (c) Q-V junction characteristics.

EXAMPLE 1.2.2 Semiconductor diodes also store charge in the depletion regions which exist around their junctions. It can be shown that stored charge Q in a junction diode equals[3]

$$Q = K_1 V_T^{1/2} \text{ (abrupt)} \quad \text{or} \quad K_2 V_T^{2/3} \text{ (graded)} \tag{1.2.14}$$

where constants K_1 and K_2 depend upon the geometry of the junction and the electrical properties of the semiconductor. V_T is the junction voltage which is always nonnegative. Determine the dc and ac capacitances of the junction. Draw the complete ac model for the diode.

Solution The large-signal junction capacitances equal

$$C(V_{To}) = Q/V_T \Big|_{V_{To}} = K_1 V_{To}^{-1/2} \text{ (abrupt)} \quad \text{or} \quad K_2 V_{To}^{-1/3} \text{ (graded)} \tag{1.2.15}$$

However, the small-signal junction capacitances equal

$$c(V_{To}) = dQ/dV_T \Big|_{V_{To}} = \tfrac{1}{2} K_1 V_{To}^{-1/2} \text{ (abrupt)} \quad \text{or} \quad \tfrac{2}{3} K_2 V_{To}^{-1/3} \text{ (graded)} \tag{1.2.16}$$

Thus, the ac and dc capacitances differ only by 1/2 and 2/3, respectively. If $C(V_{To})$ is plotted on log-log paper, the two curves will have slopes of −1/2 and −1/3, respectively, since $C(V_{To})$ obeys a power law relation. The complete ac model for the semiconductor diode is shown in Fig. 1.2.5. It is useful to recall that the voltage controlled capacitance characteristic of diodes is used in certain high-frequency applications. When diodes are designed especially for this purpose, they are called *varactors* or *varicaps*. Such devices are used for voltage-controlled tuning of hf systems, harmonic generation, and parametric amplification.

1.3 INDEPENDENT AND DEPENDENT SOURCES

In the last section, we discussed ideal passive elements. We shall now discuss ideal active elements. Active elements or active sources are sometimes called dependent sources. Another type of source is the independent source which differs from the dependent source as we shall now discuss.

There are only two types of ideal sources in electrical engineering—voltage sources and current sources. *Voltage sources* provide a source of constant voltage regardless of the current drawn from or delivered to that source. Conversely, *current sources* provide a source of constant current regardless of the magnitude and polarity of the voltage created or imposed across its terminals.

If the output of the voltage and current sources are independent of any voltage or current within the system for which they provide signals or energize, they are called *independent sources.* These include dc power supplies which provide constant levels, and various types of signal generators which provide prescribed time-varying levels (e.g., sine, square, and sawtooth generators).

However, *dependent sources* provide voltage or current levels which depend upon other voltage or current levels in the system. There are four types of ideal dependent sources: (1) voltage-controlled voltage sources (VCVS), (2) current-controlled voltage sources (ICVS), (3) current-controlled current sources (ICIS), and (4) voltage-controlled current sources (VCIS). Thus,

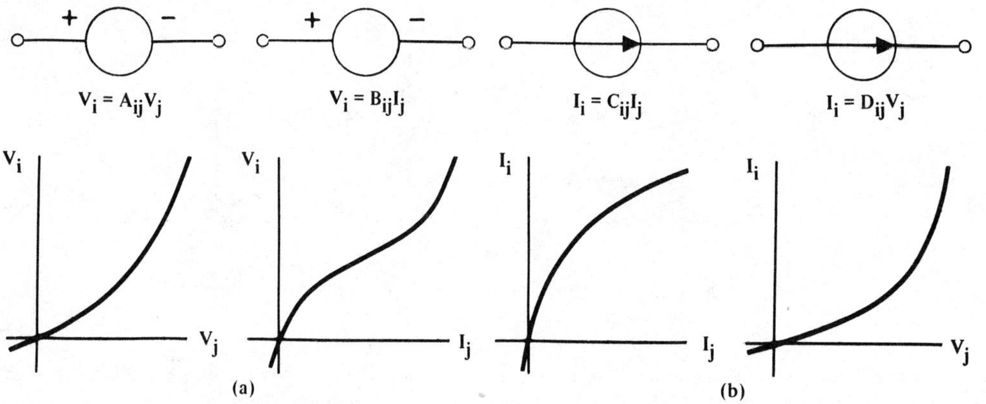

Fig. 1.3.1 (a) Dependent voltage and (b) current sources and their characteristics.

these are voltage or current sources which are controlled by either a voltage or current somewhere else in the system. Mathematically, they are described by

$$V_i = A_{ij}(V_j)V_j \qquad V_i = B_{ij}(I_j)I_j \qquad I_i = C_{ij}(I_j)I_j \qquad I_i = D_{ij}(V_j)V_j \tag{1.3.1}$$

respectively, where A_{ij}. B_{ij}, C_{ij}. and D_{ij} are referred to as the source *strengths.* The sources and their dependencies are shown in Fig. 1.3.1. The graphical interpretations are identical to those made for the passive elements with the exception now to be discussed.

We mentioned earlier that passive elements have bilateral coupling, but active elements provide only unilateral coupling. This is equivalent to saying the graphical characteristic of a passive element can be inverted (assuming it is well-defined), but that of an active element *cannot* be inverted. For example, consider a resistor having $V = R(I)I$. Since $I = R(I)^{-1}V = G(V)V$, then the resistance characteristic is the inverse (assuming an inverse exists) of the conductance characteristic where $R(I)^{-1} = G(V)$. However, the active element graphs do *not* have inverses. Even though $V_i = B_{ij}(I)I_j$, the nature of the source *prohibits* one from saying $I_j = B_{ij}(I_j)^{-1}V_i$. The proper interpretation is that current I_j through the *j*th branch of the system controls the output V_i of the voltage source in the *i*th branch. However, the output voltage V_i serves to modify its controlling current I_j only in so much as there may be signal coupling between branches i and j due to the presence of other passive and/or active elements.

The dc strengths of the signal sources equal

$$A_{ij}(V_{jo}) = V_i/V_j \qquad B_{ij}(I_{jo}) = V_i/I_j \qquad C_{ij}(I_{jo}) = I_i/I_j \qquad D_{ij}(V_{jo}) = I_i/V_j \tag{1.3.2}$$

As before, the dc strength equals the slope of the line connecting the origin to the dc bias or quiescent point of its characteristic.

Again, any transient or ac excitation moves the operating point along the curve. For differential changes, the ac source strengths equal

$$\begin{aligned} a_{ij}(V_{jo}) &= dV_i/dV_j\,|_{V_{jo}} & c_{ij}(I_{jo}) &= dI_i/dI_j\,|_{I_{jo}} \\ b_{ij}(I_{jo}) &= dV_i/dI_j\,|_{I_{jo}} & d_{ij}(V_{jo}) &= dI_i/dV_j\,|_{V_{jo}} \end{aligned} \tag{1.3.3}$$

As before, the unnormalized and normalized ac source strengths equal

$$\begin{aligned} a_{ij}(V_{jo}) &= A_{ij}(V_{jo}) + V_{jo}\, dA_{ij}(V_{jo})/dV_j & a_{nij}(V_{jo}) &= 1 + d\ln A_{ij}(V_{jo})/d\ln V_j \\ b_{ij}(I_{jo}) &= B_{ij}(I_{jo}) + I_{jo}\, dB_{ij}(I_{jo})/dI_j & b_{nij}(I_{jo}) &= 1 + d\ln B_{ij}(I_{jo})/d\ln I_j \end{aligned} \tag{1.3.4}$$

$$c_{ij}(I_{jo}) = C_{ij}(I_{jo}) + I_{jo}\, dC_{ij}(I_{jo})/dI_j \qquad c_{nij}(I_{jo}) = 1 + d\ln C_{ij}(I_{jo})/d\ln I_j$$
$$d_{ij}(V_{jo}) = D_{ij}(V_{jo}) + V_{jo}\, dD_{ij}(V_{jo})/dV_j \qquad d_{nij}(V_{jo}) = 1 + d\ln D_{ij}(V_{jo})/d\ln V_j \qquad (1.3.4)$$

and the error incurred in failing to differentiate the ac and dc values is $d \ln A_{ij}(V_{jo})/d \ln V_j$, etc. Again, the graphical interpretation is that the (decimal) error is equal to the slope of the dc source strength curve at the bias point, when plotted on log-log paper.

Active sources which have linear characteristics passing through the origin are said to be *linear*. For example, a VCVS source having $V_i = A_{ij}V_j$ is linear when the source strength A_{ijo} is independent of signal level V_{jo}. Mathematically, this is equivalent to $dA_{ij}(V_{jo})/dV_j = 0$. Therefore, the ac source strength a_{ij} equals the dc source strength A_{ij} in such cases.

Active devices are used to realize active elements or sources. Several are shown in Table 1.3.1 Of these devices, the operational amplifier is closest to the ideal. Since it usually has input resistance $R_i > 10^6\ \Omega$, output resistance $R_o < 10\ \Omega$, and gain $K > 80$ dB, it *can* be considered ideal in many applications. It is the active element which we use for constructing active filters. Their characteristics will be extensively discussed in Chap. 14.

A *nonideal source* is an ideal source which has one or more passive elements in some way connected to its terminals. A number of examples of such nonideal sources are shown in Table 1.3.1. The engineer merely needs to compare the ideal and actual models to see the difference. This illustrates what is meant by the phrase "nonidealness of devices". In both analysis and design, these "parasitic" elements which make the source nonideal can be accounted for. The techniques involve the concept of impedance, two-port theory, and Thevenin and Norton equivalents all of which we shall later discuss in this chapter. Thus, we delay further discussion of characterizing nonideal sources until later sections.

EXAMPLE 1.3.1 A 2N2432 high-speed chopper transistor has the dc current gain h_{FE} characteristic of Fig. 1.3.2. Determine its ac current gain h_{fe} at room temperature when $V_{CE} = 5$ volt.
Solution The h_{FE}-I_C plot is on log-log paper. Since the ac and dc current gains are related by Eq. 1.3.4 as

$$h_{fe}(I_{Co}) / h_{FE}(I_{Co}) = 1 + \frac{d \ln h_{FE}(I_{Co})}{d \ln I_C} = 1 + \frac{d \log_{10} h_{FE}(I_{Co})}{d \log_{10} I_C} \qquad (1.3.5)$$

we simply require the slope of the characteristic if we are to relate h_{FE} to h_{fe}. Linearizing the characteristic over $0.001 \leq I_C \leq 10$ mA, we see that

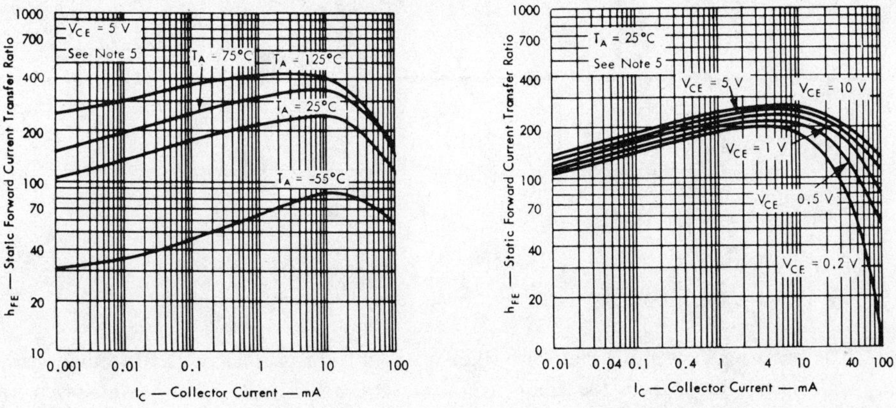

Fig. 1.3.2 h_{FE}-I_C **characteristic of a 2N2432 transistor. (From the Transistor and Diode Data Book, 1st ed., p. 5–79, Texas Instruments, Inc., Dallas, TX, 1973.)**

Table 1.3.1 Compilation of active devices and their models.

Source Type	Ideal Model	Device	Symbol	Actual Model
VCVS	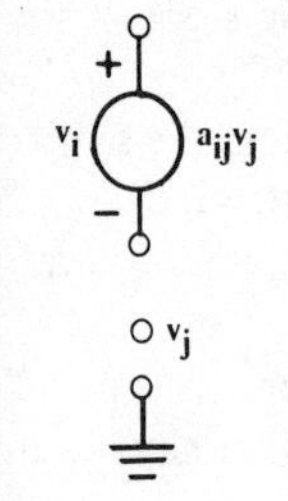	Operational Amplifier	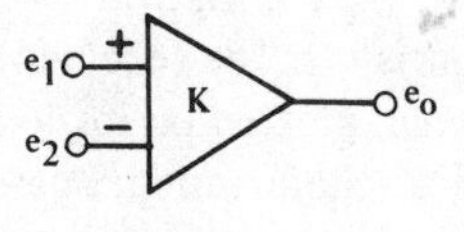	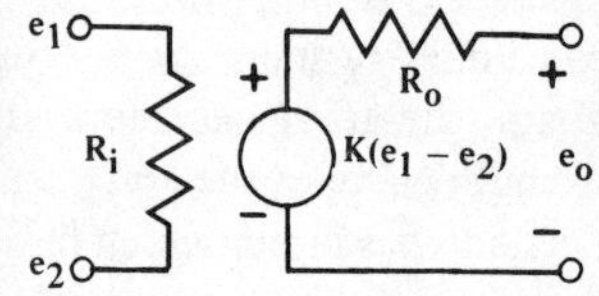
		Triode	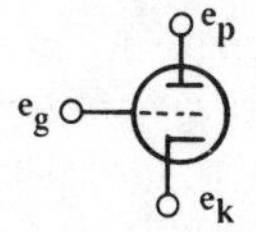	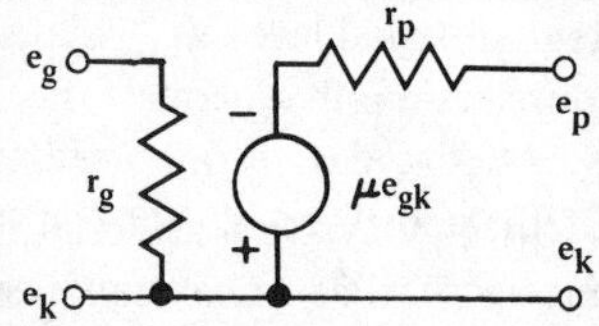
ICVS	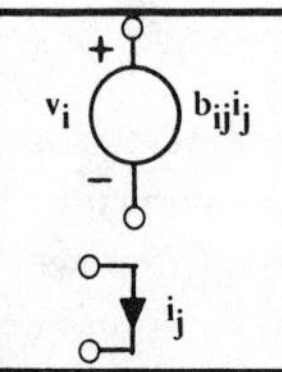	Norton Operational Amplifier	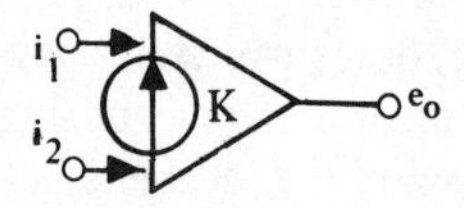	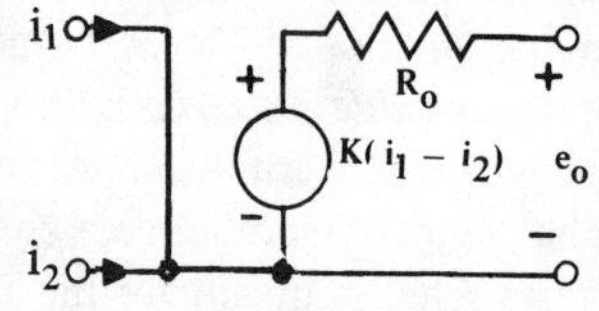
ICIS	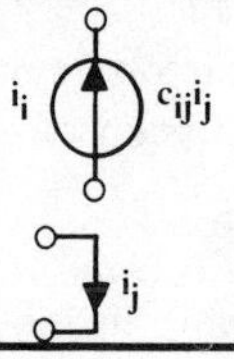	Bipolar Transistor	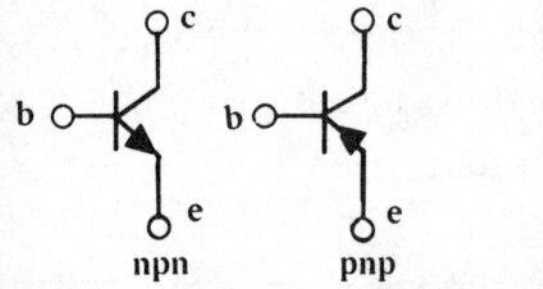	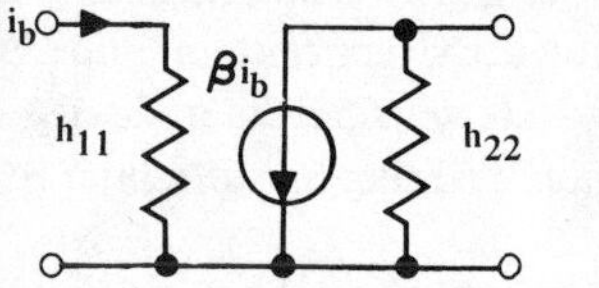
VCIS	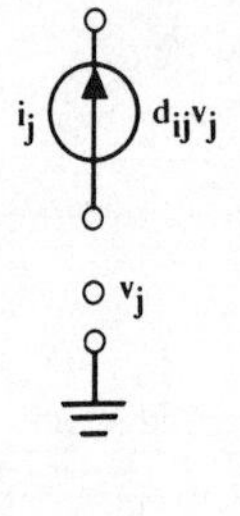	Field-Effect Transistor	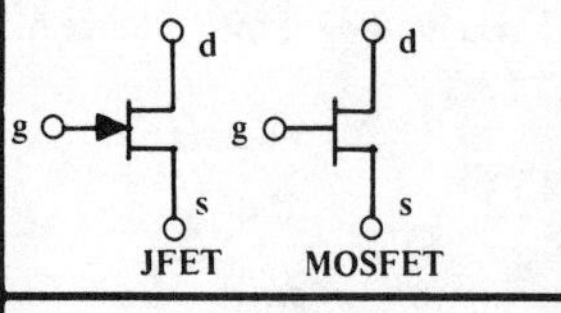	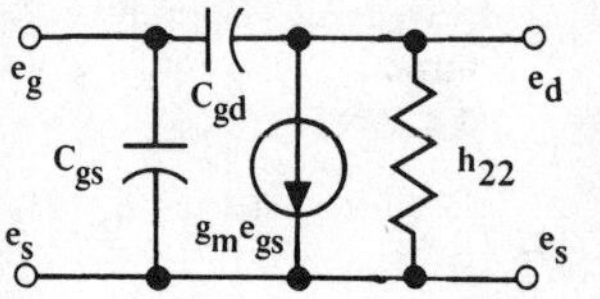
		Pentode	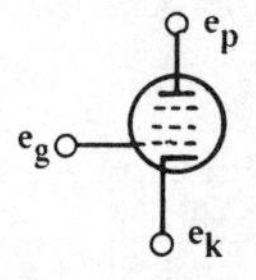	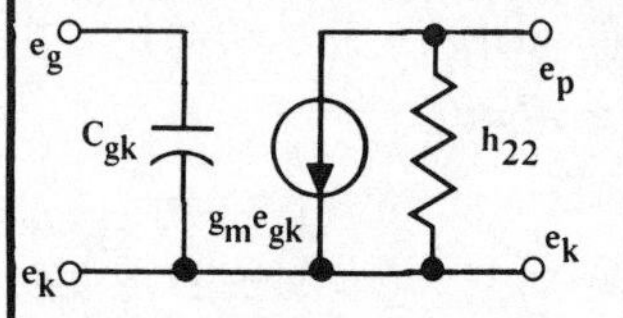

$$\frac{d \log_{10} h_{FE}(I_{Co})}{d \log_{10} I_C} = \frac{\log_{10}(250/100)}{\log_{10}(10/0.001)} = \frac{0.4}{4} = 0.1 \tag{1.3.6}$$

Therefore, the ac gain equals

$$h_{fe}(I_{Co}) = 1.1\, h_{FE}(I_{Co}), \qquad 0.001 \leq I_C \leq 10 \text{ mA} \tag{1.3.7}$$

and the ac and dc gains at any level are virtually identical.

The engineer may also inquire whether we could not also account for temperature effects in h_{fe} which are evident from the graph using the same technique. The answer is yes, we can. We shall pursue this later in the chapter when we discuss general two-ports and again in Chap. 14 when we discuss components.

Let us reiterate what we have said in the last two sections from the viewpoint of design usefulness. The components which make up electronic systems are called devices or circuit components. These devices include resistors, capacitors, inductors, transformers, transistors, operational amps, amplifiers, etc. However, the components which the design engineer uses to *analyze* electronic systems are idealized passive and active circuit elements. The components mentioned above which he uses to actually implement or manufacture the electronic systems are modelled using these passive and active elements. The successful engineer uses only as complex a model as needed to adequately describe the actual component which he shall ultimately specify. By so doing, he accounts for component "nonidealness" with minimum complexity.

1.4 LINEARITY

Electronic systems are basically interconnections of passive and active elements configured in such a way that electrical signals are properly processed. A general electronic system having multiple inputs and outputs is shown in Fig. 1.4.1a. The inputs to the system (independent variables) are $x_1, x_2, \ldots, x_n$. The system outputs (dependent variables) are $y_1, y_2, \ldots, y_m$. The simplest case of course, is the single input and output system shown in Fig. 1.4.1b. Suppose that the system transforms inputs into outputs using the transformation **H** where

$$[y_1 \ \ldots \ y_m]^T = \mathbf{H}[x_1 \ \ldots \ x_n]^T \quad \text{or} \quad \mathbf{y} = \mathbf{Hx} \tag{1.4.1}$$

H is an n x m matrix containing operators. Note that in the single input/output case, y = Hx, so that the vector equation, Eq. 1.4.1, reduces to a scalar equation. The system is *linear* if **H** is a *linear transformation*. **H** is a linear transformation if it satisfies the homogeneity and superposition condition. Transformation **H** satisfies the *homogeneity condition* if for an input **ax**, then

$$\mathbf{y} = \mathbf{H}[\mathbf{ax}] = \mathbf{a\,Hx} \tag{1.4.2}$$

Transformation **H** satisfies the *superposition condition* if for an input $\mathbf{x} + \Delta\mathbf{x}$, then

$$\mathbf{y} = \mathbf{H}[\mathbf{x} + \Delta\mathbf{x}] = \mathbf{Hx} + \mathbf{H}\Delta\mathbf{x} \tag{1.4.3}$$

This transformation or operator notation is especially convenient for mathematically defining some other system categories we discussed earlier.

A system is *time-invariant* if for all inputs $\mathbf{x}(t + \tau)$, then

$$\mathbf{y}(t + \tau) = \mathbf{H}[\mathbf{x}(t + \tau)] \tag{1.4.4}$$

for any time t and time delay τ. Thus, delaying an input by time τ simply delays the output by time τ in time-invariant systems. In other words, the output is independent of the time origin and depends only upon the input shape.

A system is *memoryless* if for all inputs $\mathbf{x}(t)$, then the outputs can be expressed as

$$\mathbf{y}(t) = \mathbf{H}[\mathbf{x}(t), t] \tag{1.4.5}$$

This equation stipulates that the output at time t of a memoryless system depends only upon the input at that instant of time, and not upon any other. We will use these terms to describe several examples in a moment.

Fig. 1.4.1 (a) Multiple input/output system and (b) single input/output system.

1.5 CAUSALITY

A system is *causal* if its response to an input at time t does not depend on future input values. Thus mathematically, a causal system satisfies

$$y(t_o) = H[x(t)], \qquad t \leq t_o \tag{1.5.1}$$

Noncausal or anticipatory systems are said to be *physically nonrealizable*. Such systems generate outputs before inputs are applied. The name stems from the fact that noncausal systems cannot perform controlled functions in the usual sense.

EXAMPLE 1.5.1 A variety of systems are described by their operators in Fig. 1.5.1. Classify the systems in terms of linearity, time-invariance, memory, and causality.

Solution In the first system where the operator H[ ] = k(t)[ ], the input/output relation equals

$$y(t) = k(t)x(t) \tag{1.5.2}$$

Setting $x = ax_1$, we see $y = kax_1$. Setting $x = bx_1 + cx_2$, we find

$$y = kx = k(bx_1 + cx_2) = k(bx_1) + k(cx_2) = bk(x_1) + ck(x_2) = by_1 + cy_2 \tag{1.5.3}$$

so the system is linear since Eqs. 1.4.2 and 1.4.3 are satisfied. We test for time-invariance by setting $t = t + \tau$ in Eq. 1.5.2 and comparing the results. Since

$$y(t + \tau) = k(t + \tau)x(t + \tau) \tag{1.5.4}$$

the gain k clearly depends upon time. Thus, the system is time-varying since Eq. 1.4.4 is not satisfied. Testing for memory, we see that an instantaneous input/output exists. Thus, the system is memoryless since Eq. 1.4.5 is satisfied. Testing for causality, we input an x(t) beginning at time t = 0. Since no output occurs for $t < 0$, the system is causal since Eq. 1.5.1 is satisfied. These system characteristics are listed in Fig. 1.5.1a. The other examples follow in the same way so we shall not discuss them in detail.

Now consider a single input/output linear system having a transform function H(s). We will show how it is derived after we discuss Laplace transforms. Let us now simply accept its existence. The Laplace transformed output of the system Y(s) equals

$$Y(s) = H(s)X(s) \tag{1.5.5}$$

where X(s) is the Laplace transformed input. A convenient analytical input for testing the system is the impulse where $x(t) = U_0(t)$. We shall later see its Laplace transform X(s) = 1. Thus, the system output Y(s) = H(s) or

$$y(t) = \mathcal{L}^{-1}[Y(s)] = \mathcal{L}^{-1}[H(s)] = h(t) \tag{1.5.6}$$

h(t) is said to be the *impulse response* of the system. It depends strictly on the H(s) of the system. Since the input occurs at t = 0, causal systems must have impulse responses which satisfy

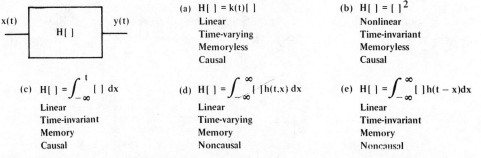

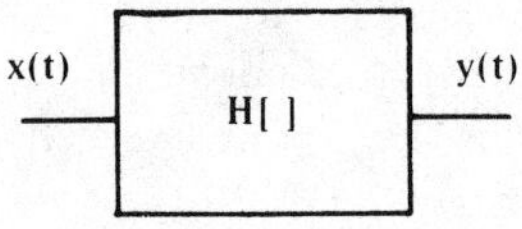

(a) H[ ] = k(t)[ ]
Linear
Time-varying
Memoryless
Causal

(b) $H[\ ] = [\ ]^2$
Nonlinear
Time-invariant
Memoryless
Causal

(c) $H[\ ] = \int_{-\infty}^{t} [\ ]\, dx$
Linear
Time-invariant
Memory
Causal

(d) $H[\ ] = \int_{-\infty}^{\infty} [\ ]h(t,x)\, dx$
Linear
Time-varying
Memory
Noncausal

(e) $H[\ ] = \int_{-\infty}^{\infty} [\ ]h(t-x)dx$
Linear
Time-invariant
Memory
Noncausal

Fig. 1.5.1 A variety of systems and their classification.

$$h(t) = 0, \qquad t < 0 \tag{1.5.7}$$

This is an alternative causality definition which allows h(t) to be used directly for testing.

EXAMPLE 1.5.2 Consider the following transfer functions and their inverses.[4] Do they represent physically realizable systems?

$$\text{(a)}\ |H_1(j\omega)| = 1, \quad |\omega| < \omega_o; \quad = 0, \quad |\omega| > \omega_o \qquad \text{(b)}\ |H_2(j\omega)| = e^{-\omega^2} \qquad \text{(c)}\ H_3(j\omega) = \frac{\sin\omega}{\omega} \tag{1.5.8}$$

Solution H_1 represents the gain of an ideal low-pass filter while H_2 is that of an ideal Gaussian filter. We will later show that their corresponding impulse responses equal

$$\text{(a)}\ h_1(t) = \frac{\omega_o}{\pi}\frac{\sin\omega_o t}{\omega_o t} \qquad \text{(b)}\ h_2(t) = \frac{1}{\sqrt{2\pi}}e^{-t^2} \qquad \text{(c)}\ h_3(t) = 1, \quad |t| < 1; \quad = 0, \quad \text{elsewhere} \tag{1.5.9}$$

These impulse responses are drawn in Fig. 1.5.2. Since they are all nonzero for some negative time, all the transfer functions describe physically nonrealizable systems.

Transfer functions can be tested directly for causality (rather than their impulse responses) using the *Paley-Wiener criterion.*[5] For a magnitude function $|H(j\omega)|$ to be realizable, a necessary and sufficient condition is that

$$\text{PWC} = \int_{-\infty}^{\infty} \frac{|\log|H(j\omega)||}{1+\omega^2}\,d\omega = 2\int_0^{\infty} \frac{|\log|H(j\omega)||}{1+\omega^2}\,d\omega < \infty \tag{1.5.10}$$

Thus, not only must $H(j\omega)$ exist (i.e., the area under the magnitude curve must be finite, at least), the area under a plot of $|\log|H||/(1+\omega^2)$ must be finite. This further implies that the magnitude characteristics $|H|$ cannot be zero over any band of frequencies. However, $|H|$ may possess a countably infinite number of zeros along the $j\omega$-axis without violating the test condition.

EXAMPLE 1.5.3 Verify that $|H_1|$ and $|H_2|$ describe nonrealizable filters, but that $|H_3|$ describes a realizable filter using the Paley-Wiener criterion.
Solution To test $|H_1|$, we must evaluate

$$\text{PWC}_1 = 2\int_0^{\infty} \frac{|\log|H||}{1+\omega^2}\,d\omega = 2\left[|\log 1|\int_0^{\omega_o}\frac{1}{1+\omega^2}\,d\omega + |\log 0|\int_{\omega_o}^{\infty}\frac{1}{1+\omega^2}\,d\omega\right] \tag{1.5.11}$$

Noting that the integral equals

$$\int_a^b \frac{1}{1+\omega^2}\,d\omega = \tan^{-1}\omega\Big|_{\omega=a}^{b} \tag{1.5.12}$$

then

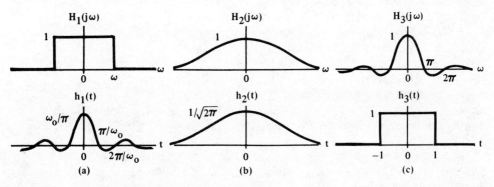

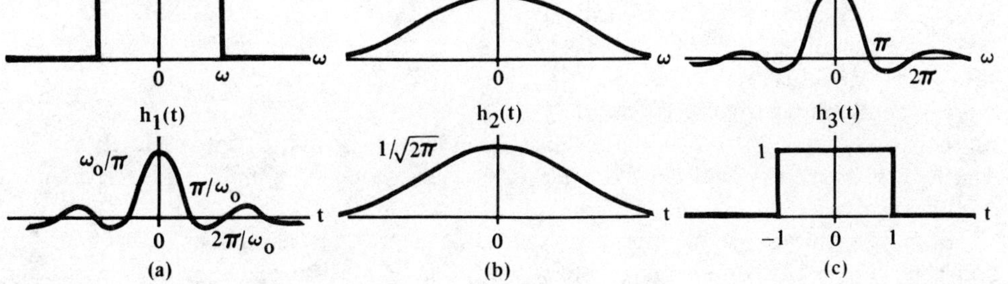

Fig. 1.5.2 Several examples of noncausal systems.

$$\text{PWC}_1 = 2[\,|\log 1|\,(\tan^{-1}\omega_0) + |\log 0|\,(\pi/2 - \tan^{-1}\omega_0)] = 0 + |\log 0| = \infty \tag{1.5.13}$$

Thus, $|H_1|$ does not describe a realizable filter. Testing $|H_2|$ in the same manner gives

$$\text{PWC}_2 = 2\int_0^\infty \frac{|\log e^{-\omega^2}|}{1+\omega^2}\,d\omega = 2\int_0^\infty \frac{\omega^2}{1+\omega^2}\,d\omega = 2[\omega - \tan^{-1}\omega]\Big|_{\omega=0}^{\infty}$$

$$= 2\lim_{\omega\to\infty}[\omega - \tan^{-1}\omega] = \infty \tag{1.5.14}$$

Thus, $|H_2|$ also does not describe a realizable filter. Finally, testing $|H_3|$ gives

$$\text{PWC}_3 = 2\int_0^\infty \left|\log\left|\frac{\sin\omega}{\omega}\right|\right| \frac{1}{1+\omega^2}\,d\omega = 2.63 < \infty \tag{1.5.15}$$

Thus, $|H_3|$ does describe a realizable filter. In fact, it is clear from the Paley-Wiener test that any $|\sin \omega/\omega|^n$ magnitude function describes a realizable filter ($n \geqslant 1$). We found in Example 1.5.2 that H_3 described a nonrealizable filter, and therefore, we are faced by an apparent conflict and dilemma. There is no conflict, however, when we note that an appropriate phase arg H must be chosen for H if it is to be realizable. Recall that gain H equals

$$H(j\omega) = |H(j\omega)|\, e^{j\arg H(j\omega)} \tag{1.5.16}$$

and that phase arg H does not affect magnitude. We shall later see that choosing a linear phase $\arg H = \omega$ is sufficient to make H_3 realizable. This has the effect of delaying $h_3(t)$ in Fig. 1.5.2 by one second, which forces $h_3(t) = 0$ for $t < 0$.

The converse of the Paley-Wiener condition says that $h(t) = 0$ for $t < 0$ if the condition of Eq. 1.5.10 is satisfied. This corresponds to Eq. 1.5.7. Thus, we may test realizability in either the time domain or the frequency domain depending upon which is more convenient.

1.6 STABILITY

In assessing system behavior, we are often interested in its stability. System stability depends upon its time domain response. Several definitions of stability exist. Roughly speaking, a system is stable if its output is bounded for every bounded input. The following is a precise definition that can be tested mathematically.

Absolutely stable system: A system whose impulse response $|h(t)| \to 0$ as $|t| \to \infty$

Conditionally stable system: A system whose impulse response $|h(t)|$ is bounded (by a constant) as $|t| \to \infty$

Unstable system: A system whose impulse response $|h(t)| \to \infty$ as $|t| \to \infty$

It should be noted that stability and causality are different concepts and independent of one another. Let us investigate the stability of the systems whose impulse response is shown in Fig. 1.6.1. The systems can be classified in terms of stability and causality as:

a. Conditionally stable, causal
b. Conditionally stable, noncausal
c. Conditionally stable, noncausal
d. Absolutely stable, causal
e. Absolutely stable, noncausal
f. Unstable, noncausal
g. Conditionally stable, causal
h. Conditionally stable, noncausal
i. Unstable, causal

We see that systems (f) and (i) are unstable, and systems (d) and (e) are absolutely stable. The remaining systems are conditionally stable since their impulse responses approach bounded levels rather than zero.

From the causality standpoint, the systems of (a), (d), (g), and (i) are causal and therefore realizable. However, the remaining systems are noncausal. Therefore, these responses cannot be generated using real systems.

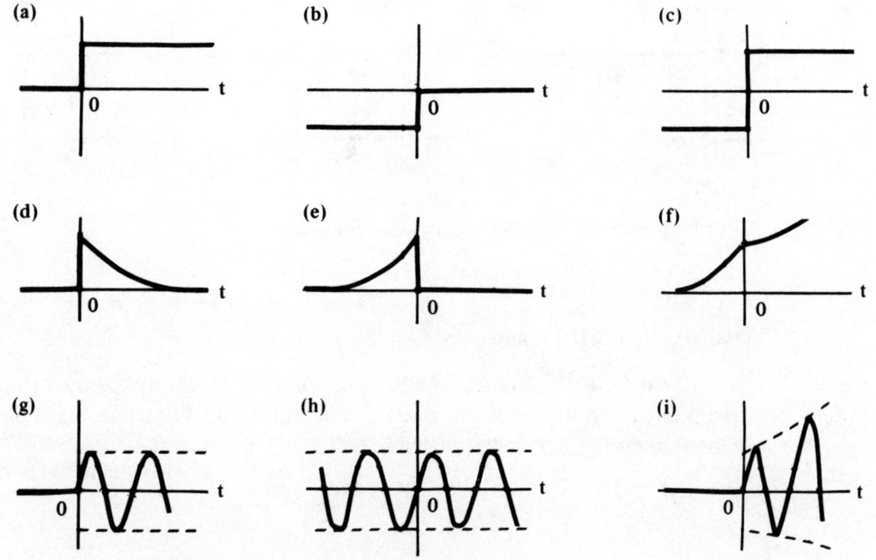

Fig. 1.6.1 Assorted impulse response functions.

We shall see in Chap. 3 that if we are concerned with *causal* systems, then such systems are *absolutely stable* if all their poles lie in the left-half s-plane. They will be *conditionally stable* if they have any additional simple poles on the jω-axis. They will be *unstable* if they have multiple-order poles on the jω-axis or any poles in the right-half s-plane. The system zeros have no effect on system stability. The statement that stable systems are systems whose transfer function poles lie only in the left-half s-plane is incorrect unless realizability is also required.

An alternative test for stability uses the magnitude function $|H(j\omega)|$ and the final value theorem to be discussed later. Since the final value of the impulse response h(t) satisfies

$$h(+\infty) - h(-\infty) = \lim_{s\to 0} s|H(s)| = \lim_{\omega\to 0} \omega|H(j\omega)| \tag{1.6.1}$$

then we can test $|H(j\omega)|$ directly. It must be remembered however, that this limit can only be performed if the region of convergence of H includes the s-plane origin (s = 0 or ω = 0).

EXAMPLE 1.6.1 Three transfer functions were tested for causality in Example 1.5.2. Now test them for stability directly in the frequency domain.

Solution Since all three transfer functions approach unity as $\omega \to 0$ as shown in Fig. 1.5.2, they all have impulse responses $|h(\pm\infty)|$ which equal 0. This is confirmed by h(t) in Fig. 1.5.2 and therefore all three filters are absolutely stable. We will discuss stability at greater length later in the chapter when we review passivity and activity.

1.7 SINGULARITY FUNCTIONS

A number of convenient input signals are often used to test system behavior. These include both nonperiodic and periodic functions. A set of nonperiodic functions which is standard are the so-called *singularity functions.* These include the impulse, step, ramp, and other related time functions. Singularity functions derive their name from the fact that some have Laplace transforms which are nonanalytic at the origin of the s-plane. These points are called singularity points. We shall discuss this in depth.

Perhaps the most commonly encountered singularity function is the *unit step* which is de-

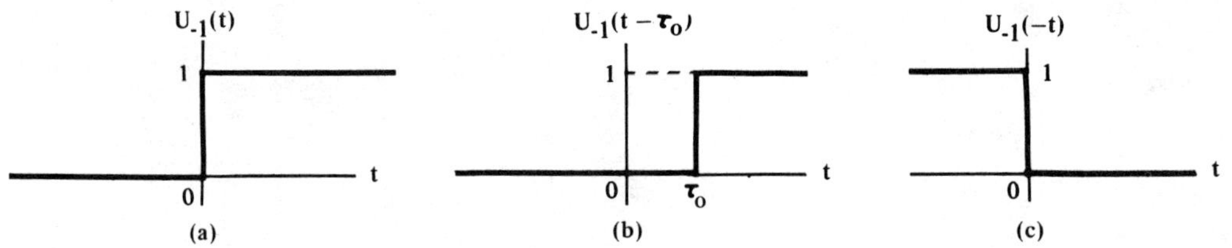

Fig. 1.7.1 Unit step function having various arguments.

noted as $U_{-1}(t)$. It is defined as

$$U_{-1}(t) = 0, \quad t<0 \quad \text{and} \quad 1, \quad t>0 \tag{1.7.1}$$

which is equal to zero for a negative argument t and unity for a positive argument. It is undefined at the transition point when the argument is zero. The unit step is shown in Fig. 1.7.1a.

Consider the function in Fig. 1.7.1b, where

$$\begin{aligned} U_{-1}(t-\tau_0) &= 0, \quad t-\tau_0<0 \quad \text{or} \quad t<\tau_0 \\ &= 1, \quad t-\tau_0>0 \quad \text{or} \quad t>\tau_0 \end{aligned} \tag{1.7.2}$$

This is a unit step delayed by τ_0 seconds. It is equal to zero for a negative argument, unity for a positive argument, and makes its unit transition for a zero argument. If τ_0 is positive, the step is delayed; while if τ_0 is negative, the step is advanced relative to time zero.

If we change the sign of its argument, this inverts the unit step function. This is demonstrated in Fig. 1.7.1c where

$$\begin{aligned} U_{-1}(-t) &= 0, \quad -t<0 \quad \text{or} \quad t>0 \\ &= 1, \quad -t>0 \quad \text{or} \quad t<0 \end{aligned} \tag{1.7.3}$$

It is important to note that one simply manipulates the basic unit step function definition to obtain the results shown in Figs. 1.7.1b and c.

An infinite number of other singularity functions can be generated from $U_{-1}(t)$ using recursion formulas. These formulas involve either integration or differentiation. The recursion formulas are given by

$$U_{n-1}(t) = \int_{-\infty}^{t} U_n(x)\,dx \quad \text{and} \quad U_{n+1}(t) = dU_n(t)/dt \tag{1.7.4}$$

Let us first consider the integral equation. When n = - 1, then

$$U_{-2}(t) = \int_{-\infty}^{t} U_{-1}(x)\,dx = 0, \quad t<0 \quad \text{and } t, \quad t>0 \tag{1.7.5}$$

This is called the *unit ramp* function since it increases linearly with unit slope for positive t. It is zero for negative t. To simplify expressing this function, we can use the "gating" property of the unit step function, and write

$$U_{-2}(t) = tU_{-1}(t) \tag{1.7.6}$$

The unit step forces $U_{-2}(t)$ to equal zero for negative t. $U_{-1}(t)$ is often used for this purpose.

We can continue to generate lower-order (more negative subscript n) singularity functions in this manner. For instance,

$$U_{-3}(t) = \int_{-\infty}^{t} U_{-2}(x)\,dx = \int_{-\infty}^{t} xU_{-1}(x)\,dx = \int_{0}^{t} x\,dx\,U_{-1}(t) = (t^2/2)U_{-1}(t) \tag{1.7.7}$$

which is the *unit parabola* function. The general *n*th-order function equals

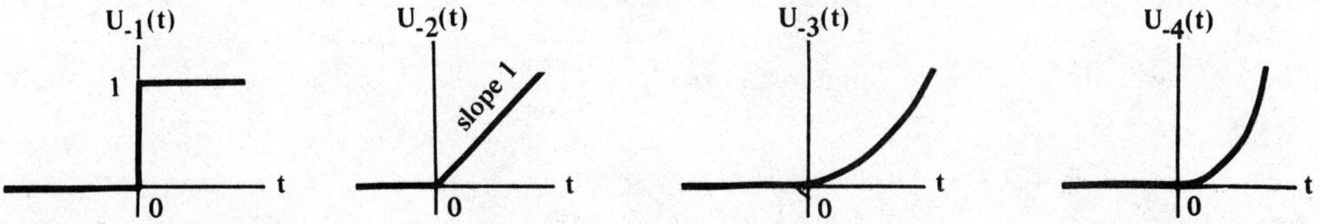

Fig. 1.7.2 Lower-order singularity functions.

$$U_{-n}(t) = (t^{n-1}/(n-1)!)U_{-1}(t) \tag{1.7.8}$$

Several of these functions are shown in Fig. 1.7.1. Now let us consider higher-order singularity functions.

Using the derivative equation, we have

$$U_{n+1}(t) = dU_n(t)/dt \tag{1.7.9}$$

so we increase the order of the singularity function by one for every differentiation. This requires that the function in question be differentiable. It is clear from Fig. 1.7.2 that U_{-3} can be easily obtained from U_{-4}, and that U_{-2} can likewise be obtained from U_{-3}. However, U_{-2} has a discontinuous slope at t = 0. It has different derivative values on each side of t = 0 with an undefined derivative at t = 0. Since U_{-1} is discontinuous at t = 0, it likewise has an undefined derivative at t = 0. Thus, we are faced by an apparent inability to apply the derivative formula.

The dilemma disappears when we enlarge our understanding and definition of the derivative and integral. Let us introduce this notion by evaluating $U_0(t)$ as

$$U_0(t) = dU_{-1}(t)/dt = 0, \quad t \neq 0 \quad \text{and} \quad \text{undefined}, \quad t = 0 \tag{1.7.10}$$

$U_0(t)$ is called the *unit impulse* function. This is not a proper mathematical definition of $U_0(t)$ since it must be well-defined and finite for all values of t. Using the integral formula, U_0 satisfies

$$U_{-1}(t) = \int_{-\infty}^{t} U_0(x)\,dx = \lim_{\epsilon \to 0} \int_{-\epsilon}^{\epsilon} U_0(x)\,dx = \lim_{\epsilon \to 0} \int_{-\epsilon}^{\epsilon} dU_{-1}(t) \tag{1.7.11}$$

Interpreting this as either Riemann or Lebesque integration, $U_{-1}(t)$ must be zero since the integral of any function over a zero interval must be zero. However, if we interpret this as a Stieltjes integration, then the value of the integral at a point (i.e., an interval of zero width) is equal to whatever instantaneous jump $U_{-1}(t)$ may take at that point. The usual definition for $U_0(t)$ assumes this viewpoint where

$$U_0(t) = 0, \quad t \neq 0 \quad \text{and} \quad \infty, \quad t = 0 \tag{1.7.12}$$

such that

$$\lim_{\epsilon \to 0} \int_{-\epsilon}^{\epsilon} U_0(x)\,dx = 1 \tag{1.7.13}$$

U_0 is an impulse having unit area. Although this is a conceptually proper signal to the engineer and is almost mathematically proper from the Stieltjes standpoint, it cannot be immediately generalized for the higher order singularity functions $U_1(t)$, $U_2(t)$, . . . , etc.

The proper mathematical viewpoint required for rigorous notation and manipulation is *generalized function theory*, or the *theory of distributions* as it is sometimes called.[6] The historical development for this theory is summarized in Lighthill's dedication of his book to "Paul Dirac, *who saw it must be true*, Laurent Schwartz, *who proved it*, and George Temple, *who showed how simple it could be made*." Generalized function theory enlarges the classes of functions which can be operated upon, and generalizes the concept of basic differentiation, integration, and limiting operations. Unfortunately, we do not have the time to devote to this powerful analytic tool, but the interested engineer will be well-rewarded for investigating it on his own.[7] However, we will incorporate some of the results when discussing Laplace and Fourier transforms.

1.8 LAPLACE TRANSFORMATION

The Laplace transformation is a mathematical operation that transforms a time domain function f(t) into a frequency domain function F(s). Mathematically, the *Laplace transformation* is defined as

$$F(s) = \mathcal{L}[f(t)] = \int_{-\infty}^{\infty} f(t)e^{-st}\,dt, \qquad s \in R \tag{1.8.1}$$

where $\mathcal{L}[\ ]$ denotes the Laplace transform operation. Thus, a function f of time t is converted to a function F of complex frequency $s = \sigma + j\omega$ using this transformation. The complex frequency variable s has a real part σ and an imaginary part ω. A particular complex frequency s_o represents a point in the so-called *s-plane*. Thus, although f(t) is depicted in a 2-dimensional plot (i.e., f versus t), F(s) must be depicted in one 4-dimensional plot (i.e., |F| and arg F versus σ and ω; or Re F and Im F versus σ or ω) or two 3-dimensional plots. In general, F(s) will only exist (i.e., be defined) over some restricted region R (i.e., values of s) of the s-plane. This is the so-called *region of convergence R* which we shall soon discuss. Within this region, F is analytic.

When F(s) is known, f(t) is obtained using the *inverse Laplace transformation* which equals

$$f(t) = \mathcal{L}^{-1}[F(s)] = \frac{1}{2\pi j}\int_{c-j\infty}^{c+j\infty} F(s)e^{st}\,ds, \qquad c \in R \tag{1.8.2}$$

Here $\mathcal{L}^{-1}[\ ]$ denotes the inverse Laplace transform operation. Thus, a function F of complex frequency s is converted to a function f of time t using this transformation. The integration takes place along a vertical line Re s = c in the s-plane. This line must lie in the region of convergence R of F. To minimize notational confusion, lower-case (small) letters are reserved for time domain functions and upper-case (capital) letters are reserved for frequency domain functions. Thus, f represents a time domain function and F represents a frequency domain function.

EXAMPLE 1.8.1 Determine the Laplace transform for a unit step function $U_{-1}(t)$ given by Eq. 1.7.1. Carefully determine its region of convergence. Sketch f(t) and F(s).

Solution Substituting Eq. 1.7.1 into Eq. 1.8.1, the Laplace transform F(s) of f(t) must equal

$$F(s) = \int_{-\infty}^{\infty} U_{-1}(t)e^{-st}\,dt = \int_{0}^{\infty} e^{-st}\,dt = -\frac{e^{-st}}{s}\Big|_{t=0}^{\infty} = \frac{1}{s}[1 - \lim_{t\to\infty} e^{-st}] \tag{1.8.3}$$

Since $s = \sigma + j\omega$, the second term can be bounded by

$$|e^{-st}| = |e^{-(\sigma + j\omega)t}| = |e^{-\sigma t}|\,|e^{-j\omega t}| = e^{-\sigma t} \tag{1.8.4}$$

The limit is therefore

$$\lim_{t\to\infty} |e^{-st}| = \lim_{t\to\infty} e^{-\sigma t} = 0, \qquad \sigma > 0 \tag{1.8.5}$$

The limit is zero only if Re $s = \sigma > 0$. Otherwise the limit is undefined. This establishes the region of convergence in the s-plane where the Laplace transform exists. Thus, the Laplace transform equals

$$F(s) = \mathcal{L}[U_{-1}(t)] = 1/s, \qquad \text{Re } s > 0 \tag{1.8.6}$$

In any other region, F(s) is undefined. Since

$$|F(s)| = 1/|s| \quad \text{and} \quad \arg F(s) = -\arg s, \qquad \text{Re } s > 0 \tag{1.8.7}$$

the magnitude and angle of F are shown in Fig. 1.8.1. Since we cannot draw a 4-dimensional sketch to

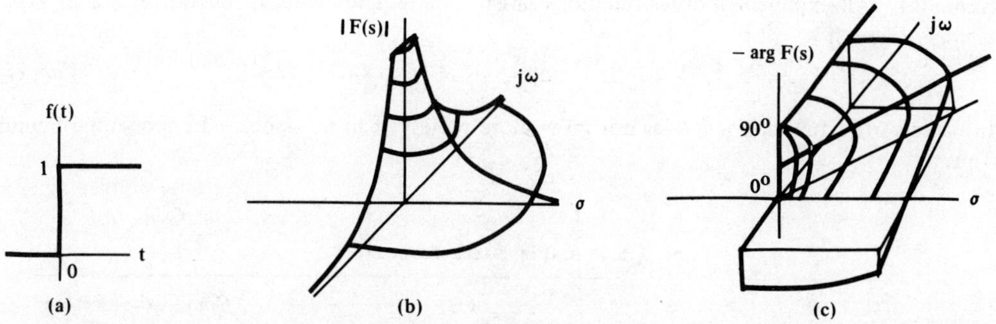

Fig. 1.8.1 (a) f(t), (b) F(s), and (c) arg F(s) of Example 1.8.1.

characterize F, we must use two 3-dimensional sketches instead. Notice the Laplace transform is only defined (or exists) in the right-half s-plane (or simply right-half-plane) which is its region of convergence.

EXAMPLE 1.8.2 Determine the Laplace transform for the f(t) shown in Fig. 1.8.2a. Compare its region of convergence with that in Example 1.8.1.

Solution Note that we can express f(t) as $-U_{-1}(-t)$ using Eq. 1.7.3. Its Laplace transform equals

$$F(s) = -\int_{-\infty}^{\infty} U_{-1}(-t)e^{-st}\,dt = -\int_{\infty}^{0} e^{st}\,dt = \frac{e^{st}}{s}\Big|_{t=\infty}^{0} = \frac{1}{s}[1 - \lim_{t\to\infty} e^{st}] \tag{1.8.8}$$

Evaluating the limit as before in Eq. 1.8.5,

$$\lim_{t\to\infty} e^{st} \leqslant \lim_{t\to\infty} |e^{st}| = \lim_{t\to\infty} e^{\sigma t} = 0, \qquad \sigma < 0 \tag{1.8.9}$$

it is equal to zero only if Re s = $\sigma < 0$. Thus, the Laplace transform equals

$$F(s) = \mathcal{L}[-U_{-1}(-t)] = 1/s, \qquad \text{Re } s < 0 \tag{1.8.10}$$

It is important to note that the only difference between this transform and that in Example 1.8.1 is its region of convergence. The region of convergence is often denoted by shading the appropriate region of the s-plane as shown in Fig. 1.8.2b. This transform converges only in the left-half-plane, while that of the previous example converged only in the right-half-plane.

A number of Laplace transforms are tabulated in Table 1.8.1 for future reference. These are derived using the definition of the Laplace transform. Several noncausal functions are included as a matter of interest.

The Laplace transform exists for those values of s for which F(s) is finite. Since

$$|F(s)| = \left|\int_{-\infty}^{\infty} f(t)e^{-st}\,dt\right| \leqslant \int_{-\infty}^{\infty} |f(t)e^{-st}|\,dt \leqslant \int_{-\infty}^{\infty} |f(t)|e^{-\sigma t}\,dt \tag{1.8.11}$$

it is sufficient for F(s) to exist if

$$\int_{-\infty}^{\infty} |f(t)|e^{-\sigma t}\,dt < \infty \tag{1.8.12}$$

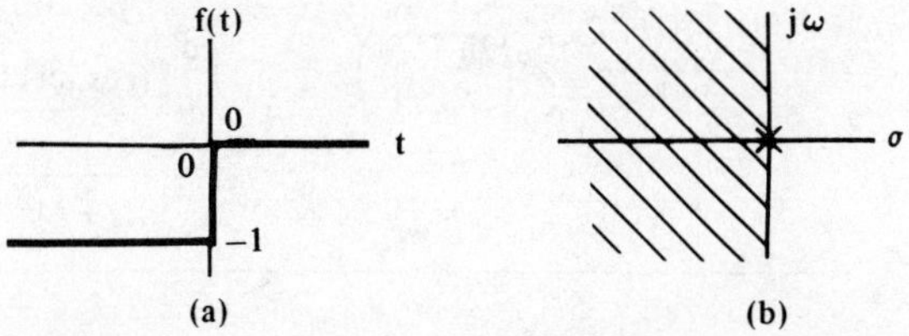

Fig. 1.8.2 (a) Time function and its (b) region of convergence for Example 1.8.2.

(is finite). All exponential-order functions satisfy this requirement. A function f(t) is of *exponential order* k if[8]

$$|f(t)| < M_1 \exp k_1 t, \quad t > 0 \quad \text{and} \quad < M_2 \exp k_2 t, \quad t < 0 \tag{1.8.13}$$

In other words, function f(t) does not grow more rapidly than its associated exponential bound. Thus,

Table 1.8.1 Laplace transform table.

	f(t)	F(s)	Convergence Region
1.	$U_0(t)$	1	all s
2.	$U_1(t)$	s	all s
3.	$U_n(t)$	s^n	all s
4.	$U_{-1}(t)$	$\frac{1}{s}$	Re s > 0
5.	$tU_{-1}(t) = U_{-2}(t)$	$\frac{1}{s^2}$	Re s > 0
6.	$(t^{n-1}/(n-1)!)U_{-1}(t) = U_{-n}(t)$	$\frac{1}{s^n}$	Re s > 0
7.	$\operatorname{sgn} t$	$\frac{2}{s}$	Re s = 0
8.	$-U_{-1}(-t)$	$\frac{1}{s}$	Re s < 0
9.	$e^{-\sigma t}U_{-1}(t)$	$\frac{1}{s+\sigma}$	Re s > – Re σ
10.	$te^{-\sigma t}U_{-1}(t)$	$\frac{1}{(s+\sigma)^2}$	Rc s > – Re σ
11.	$(t^n/n!)e^{-\sigma t}U_{-1}(t)$	$\frac{1}{(s+\sigma)^{n+1}}$	Re s > – Re σ
12.	$(1-e^{-\sigma t})U_{-1}(t)$	$\frac{\sigma}{s(s+\sigma)}$	Re s > max (0, – Re σ)
13.	$e^{-\sigma\|t\|}$	$\frac{2\sigma}{\sigma^2 - s^2}$	– Re σ < Re s < Re σ
14.	$2 \sinh \sigma t\, U_{-1}(t)$	$-\frac{2\sigma}{\sigma^2 - s^2}$	Re s > max (Re σ, – Re σ)
15.	$\cos \omega t\, U_{-1}(t)$	$\frac{s}{s^2+\omega^2}$	Re s > 0
16.	$\sin \omega t\, U_{-1}(t)$	$\frac{\omega}{s^2+\omega^2}$	Re s > 0
17.	$e^{-\sigma t}\cos \omega t\, U_{-1}(t)$	$\frac{s+\sigma}{(s+\sigma)^2+\omega^2}$	Re s > – Re σ
18.	$e^{-\sigma t}\sin \omega t\, U_{-1}(t)$	$\frac{\omega}{(s+\sigma)^2+\omega^2}$	Re s > – Re σ
19.	$\frac{e^{-\sigma t}}{4^{n-1}\omega^{2n}} \sum_{r=1}^{n} \binom{2n-r-1}{n-1} (-2t)^{r-1} \frac{d^r}{dt^r}(\cos \omega t)\, U_{-1}(t)$	$\frac{1}{[(s+\sigma)^2+\omega^2]^n}$	Re s > max (0, – Re σ)

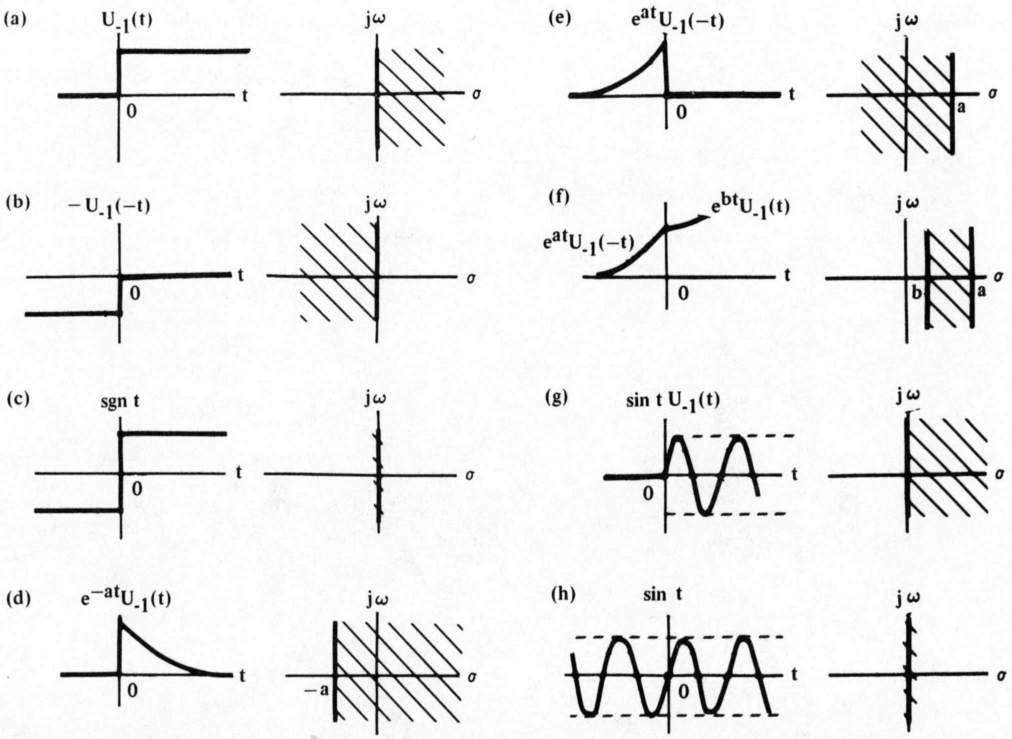

Fig. 1.8.3 Associated time domain functions and their (minimum) regions of convergence.

$$\int_{-\infty}^{\infty} |f(t)|e^{-\sigma t}\, dt < \int_{-\infty}^{0} M_2 \exp{(k_2 - \sigma)t}\, dt + \int_{0}^{\infty} M_1 \exp{(k_1 - \sigma)t}\, dt$$
$$= \frac{M_2}{k_2 - \sigma} - \frac{M_1}{k_1 - \sigma} < \infty \quad \text{for } k_1 < \sigma \text{ and } k_2 > \sigma \tag{1.8.14}$$

Therefore, the Laplace transform F(s) for f(t) has a region of convergence *no less* than

$$k_1 < \text{Re } s < k_2 \tag{1.8.15}$$

and which may be even greater. A number of examples are shown in Fig. 1.8.3 which the engineer should verify.

Note that when f(t) is zero for $t < 0$, it is bounded by e^{kt} where $k = \infty$. Thus, Re $s = \infty$ forms the right-hand boundary on the region of convergence R. The left-hand boundary is determined by the form of f(t) for $t > 0$. Conversely, when f(t) is zero for $t > 0$, it is bounded by e^{kt} where $k = -\infty$. Thus, Re $s = -\infty$ forms the left-hand boundary of R. The right-hand boundary then depends upon the form of f(t) for $t < 0$. Of course, there is an infinite variety of functions which are not of exponential order such as t^t, $\exp{(t^2)}$, and $1/t$. They simply vary too rapidly to be bounded by an exponential. However, they are of little practical interest.

The Laplace transform satisfies a number of interesting properties. These properties are listed in Table 1.8.2 for the two-sided Laplace transform. They are easily proved using the transformation definition. The engineer will find it interesting to see how many of the entries in the Laplace transform table (Table 1.8.1) he can derive using these properties and the unit step transform. He will find that they can *all* be written very simply. This exercise shows the great utility of Table 1.8.2.

Table 1.8.2 Properties of Laplace transforms.

Definition	f(t)	$\mathcal{L}[f(t)] = F(s) = \int_{-\infty}^{\infty} f(t)e^{-st}\,dt$	Region of Convergence
Linear Operations			$\alpha < \text{Re } s < \beta$
Homogeneity	$Kf(t)$	$KF(s)$	$\alpha < \text{Re } s < \beta$
Superposition	$f_1(t) \pm f_2(t)$	$F_1(s) \pm F_2(s)$	$\max(\alpha_1, \alpha_2) < \text{Re } s < \min(\beta_1, \beta_2)$ (for both rows)
Both operations	$a_1f_1(t) \pm a_2f_2(t)$	$a_1F_1(s) \pm a_2F_2(s)$	(for both rows above)
Symmetry	$F(t)$	$2\pi f(-s)$	$\alpha < \text{Re } s = 0 < \beta$
Scaling			
Time scaling	$f(at)$	$\frac{1}{\lvert a \rvert} F(\frac{s}{a})$	$a\alpha < \text{Re } s < a\beta$
Magnitude scaling	$af(t)$	$aF(s)$	$\alpha < \text{Re } s < \beta$
Shifting			
Time shifting	$f(t-a)$	$e^{-as}F(s)$	$\alpha < \text{Re } s < \beta$
Frequency shifting	$e^{-at}f(t)$	$F(s+a)$	$\alpha - \text{Re } a < \text{Re } s < \beta - \text{Re } a$
Periodic Functions (for $t > 0$ only)	$f(t) = \sum_{n=0}^{\infty} f(t+nT)$	$\frac{F_1(s)}{1-e^{-Ts}} = F_1(s) \sum_{n=0}^{\infty} e^{-nTs}$	$\alpha < \text{Re } s$
		where $F_1(s) = \int_0^T f(t)e^{-st}\,dt$	$\alpha < \text{Re } s$
Convolution			
Time convolution (Frequency product)	$f_1(t)*f_2(t) = \int_{-\infty}^{\infty} f_1(\tau)f_2(t-\tau)\,d\tau$	$F_1(s)F_2(s)$	$\max(\alpha_1, \alpha_2) < \text{Re } s < \min(\beta_1, \beta_2)$
Frequency convolution (Time product)	$f_1(t)f_2(t)$	$F_1(s)*F_2(s) = \frac{1}{2\pi j}\int_{c-j\infty}^{c+j\infty} F_1(p)F_2(s-p)\,dp$	$\alpha_1 + \alpha_2 < \text{Re } s < \beta_1 + \beta_2$; $\alpha_1 < c < \alpha_2$
Time Differentiation*&			
First derivative	$df(t)/dt$	$sF(s) - f(0^+)$	$\alpha < \text{Re } s < \beta$
Second derivative	$d^2f(t)/dt^2$	$s^2F(s) - sf(0^+) - df(0^+)/dt$	$\alpha < \text{Re } s < \beta$
*n*th derivative	$d^nf(t)/dt^n$	$s^nF(s) - s^{n-1}f(0^+) - s^{n-2}df(0^+)/dt - \ldots - d^{n-1}f(0^+)/dt^{n-1}$	$\alpha < \text{Re } s < \beta$
Time Integration*&			
First integral	$\int_{-\infty}^{t} f(t)\,dt = f^{(-1)}(t)$	$F(s)/s + f^{(-1)}(0^+)/s$	$\max(\alpha, 0) < \text{Re } s < \beta$ (for the three integral rows)
Second integral	$\int_{-\infty}^{t}\int_{-\infty}^{t} f(t)\,dt\,dt = f^{(-2)}(t)$	$F(s)/s^2 + f^{(-1)}(0^+)/s^2 + f^{(-2)}(0^+)/s$	(for the three rows above)
*n*th integral	$f^{(-n)}(t)$	$F(s)/s^n + f^{(-1)}(0^+)/s^n + f^{(-2)}(0^+)/s^{n-1} + \ldots + f^{(-n)}(0^+)/s$	(for the three rows above)
Frequency Differentiation			
First derivative	$tf(t)$	$-dF(s)/ds$	$\alpha < \text{Re } s < \beta$
*n*th derivative	$t^nf(t)$	$(-1)^n d^nF(s)/ds^n$	$\alpha < \text{Re } s < \beta$
Frequency Integration			
*n*th integral	$t^{-n}f(t)$	$(-1)^n F^{(-n)}(s)$	$\alpha < \text{Re } s < \beta$
Initial Value *	$f(0^+) = \lim_{t \to 0} f(t)$	$= \lim_{s \to \infty} sF(s)$	
Final Value *	$f(\infty) = \lim_{t \to \infty} f(t)$	$= \lim_{s \to 0} sF(s)$	providing poles of sF(s) in left-half-plane
Initial Slopes*	$d^{m-1}f(0+)/dt^{m-1}$	$= \lim_{s \to \infty} s^mF(s)$	

*For one-sided transforms. &In two-sided case, drop all terms involving $f^{(i)}(0+)$ in F(s) and retain only first term.

When describing the properties of Laplace transforms F(s), and simply functions in general, several mathematical definitions are used.[9] Recall that a function F(s) is *analytic* at a point s_o if it is single-valued and has a unique finite derivative at s_o and in the neighborhood surrounding s_o. Any analytic function can be described by a Taylor series about s_o. If $s_o = 0$ which is the origin of the s-plane, then such a series is called the Maclaurin series. The *Taylor* and *Maclaurin series* have the respective forms

$$\left.\begin{aligned} F(s) &= F(s_o) + F'(s_o)(s - s_o) + F''(s_o)(s - s_o)^2/2! + \dots \\ F(s) &= F(0) + sF'(0) + (s^2/2!)F''(0) + \dots \end{aligned}\right\} \quad |s| < \infty \tag{1.8.16}$$

Singularities or, more precisely, *singular points* are points in the s-plane (i.e., values of s) where F(s) fails to be analytic. *Isolated singularities* are singular points around which nonlapping circles can be drawn. Every F(s) having isolated singularities can be described by a *Laurent series* which has the form

$$F(s) = \sum_{n=N}^{1} \frac{F^n(s_o)}{(s - s_o)^n} + \sum_{n=0}^{\infty} \frac{(s - s_o)^n}{n!} F^n(s_o), \qquad |s - s_o| \leq c \tag{1.8.17}$$

in the vicinity of every isolated singularity s_o. The vicinity or region where F(s) is so defined, is a circle with center s_o and radius c. The radius is equal to the distance between s_o and its nearest isolated singularity. To further classify such F(s), we consider the descending part of the series. If N is finite, then the isolated singular point s_o of F(s) is said to be a *pole* of order N. When N is infinite, the singularity s_o is said to be an *essential singularity* or an *accumulation point* of F(s). If F(s) has only poles as singularities, it is said to be a *rational function*. Alternatively, it is sometimes called a *meromorphic function*. However, meromorphic functions may have an infinite number of poles, while rational functions may have only a finite number.

When the reciprocal function 1/F(s) is considered, the same terminology is used. When poles of 1/F(s) are established, these are said to be *zeros* of F(s). Usually the functions which we shall consider will have only poles and zeros with no other types of singularities.

EXAMPLE 1.8.3 Classify the following functions by their analyticity or by the type of singularities they possess. Identify poles and zeros when possible.

$$\text{(a) } 1/s \qquad \text{(d) } [\cosh \pi\sqrt{s}\,]^{-1} = \prod_{n=1}^{\infty} \left[1 + \frac{4s}{(2n-1)^2}\right]^{-1}$$

$$\text{(b) } 1/(s + a)^n \qquad \text{(e) } [\sin(\pi/s)]^{-1} = \prod_{n=1}^{\infty} \left[1 + \frac{s}{1/n}\right]^{-1} \tag{1.8.18}$$

$$\text{(c) } s/(s + a)(s - a) \qquad \text{(f) } e^{-as}$$

Solution Of all the functions listed, only (f) is analytic everywhere. We can classify these functions as: (a) poles: $s = 0$; zeros: $|s| = \infty$, (b) poles: $s = -a$ (nth-order); zeros: $|s| = \infty$ (nth-order), (c) poles: $s = \pm a$; zeros: $s = 0$, $|s| = \infty$, (d) poles: $s = -(2n - 1)^2/4$, $n = 1, 2, \dots$, (e) poles: $s = -1/n$, $n = 1, 2, \dots$ with essential singularity at origin, and (f) analytic function with no finite zeros.

In situations where the Laplace transform appears to be undefined, generalized function theory is used. Often integrals that do not exist in the classical sense do exist in the generalized sense.[7] Several examples are tabulated in Table 1.8.3. They are extremely useful as we shall see in the next section, when we shall interpret their physical meaning. It is useful to note that these transforms can be combined with those from Table 1.8.1 using superposition to extend their region of convergence.

Table 1.8.3 Additional Laplace transforms.

	f(t) (all t)	F(s)	Convergence Region
1.	1	$2\pi U_0(-js)$	Re s = 0
2.	t^n	$2\pi j^n U_n(-js)$	Re s = 0
3.	$e^{j\omega_o t}$	$2\pi U_0(-js - \omega_o)$	Re s = 0
4.	$\cos \omega_o t$	$\pi[U_0(-js + \omega_o) + U_0(-js - \omega_o)]$	Re s = 0
5.	$\sin \omega_o t$	$j\pi[U_0(-js + \omega_o) - U_0(-js - \omega_o)]$	Re s = 0
6.	sgn t	2/s	Re s = 0

1.9 FOURIER TRANSFORMATION

The Fourier transform is a special case of the Laplace transform. Mathematically, the *Fourier transform* and the *inverse Fourier transform* equal

$$\begin{aligned} F(j\omega) &= F[f(t)] = \int_{-\infty}^{\infty} f(t)e^{-j\omega t}\,dt \\ f(t) &= F^{-1}[F(j\omega)] = \frac{1}{2\pi}\int_{-\infty}^{\infty} F(j\omega)e^{j\omega t}\,d\omega \end{aligned} \qquad \omega \in (-\infty, \infty) \tag{1.9.1}$$

F[ ] and F^{-1}[ ] denote the Fourier and inverse Fourier transform operations, respectively. Thus, a function f of time t is converted to a function F of frequency ω, and vice versa, using these transformations. Interpreting this transformation physically, if f(t) describes an input or output signal, then F(jω) describes the ac steady-state frequency content or *spectrum* which make up the signal. However, if F(jω) describes the ac steady-state gain of a system, then F(jω) describes its output spectrum in response to a "flat" input spectrum (which is an impulse in time).

Comparing the Laplace and Fourier transforms, we see that the Fourier transform is indeed a special case of the Laplace transform where

$$F(j\omega) = F(s)\,|_{s=j\omega} \qquad \text{and} \qquad f(t) = F^{-1}[\mathcal{L}[f(t)]\,_{s=j\omega}] \tag{1.9.2}$$

Recall, in general, that the complex frequency $s = \sigma + j\omega$ where σ is the real part of s (nepers/sec) and ω is the imaginary part of s (radians/sec) or the ac steady-state frequency. Since we set $s = j\omega$ in relating the two transforms, this is equivalent to investigating only the ac steady-state behavior of a system. In terms of the s-plane, this corresponds to investigating system behavior only along the jω-axis where σ = Re s = 0. Thus, if we vertically slice the F(s) plot (or alternatively, the |F(s)| and arg F(s) plots) along the jω-axis, we obtain the F(jω) plot (or the |F(jω)| and arg F(jω) plots, respectively). This viewpoint emphasizes that F(jω) is less general than F(s).

It is also important to investigate convergence of these two transforms. There are many functions which possess an F(s) but do not possess an F(jω) due to the $e^{-\sigma t}$ convergence factor which occurs in F(s) but does not occur in F(jω). This is seen by comparing the absolute value of the two transforms:

$$\begin{aligned} |F(s)| &= \left|\int_{-\infty}^{\infty} f(t)e^{-st}\,dt\right| \leq \int_{-\infty}^{\infty} |f(t)|e^{-\sigma t}\,dt < \infty \\ |F(j\omega)| &= \left|\int_{-\infty}^{\infty} f(t)e^{-j\omega t}\,dt\right| \leq \int_{-\infty}^{\infty} |f(t)|\,dt < \infty \end{aligned} \tag{1.9.3}$$

In F(s), we usually have the ability to force F(s) to converge absolutely even though F(jω) does not converge absolutely. This is one of the great advantages of the Laplace transform. However, for physical interpretation and measurements, the Fourier transform is necessary. Note that sometimes, even the presence of the convergence factor $e^{-\sigma t}$ cannot overcome the rapid variations of functions such as t^t, exp (t^2), and 1/t to force F(s) to converge.

We can obtain F(jω) directly from F(s) by substituting s = jω whenever the region of convergence R for F(s) contains the jω-axis, i.e., $\sigma = 0 \in R$. If R does not contain the jω-axis, then F(jω) does not exist in the classical sense although it may exist in the generalized sense. In the previous section, we tabulated in Table 1.8.3 some Laplace transforms that only existed along the jω-axis. Thus, in this case, the two transforms are equivalent.

A number of Fourier transforms are listed in Table 1.9.1. Fourier transforms satisfy a number of properties which are analogous to those for the Laplace transform. These are listed in Table 1.9.2 for the one-sided case. They allow the engineer to easily expand a Fourier transform table. We will interpret some of these results in Chaps. 2 and 3.

EXAMPLE 1.9.1 Determine the Fourier transform for a dc signal of unity. Interpret the result.

Solution We find from Table 1.8.3 that the Laplace transform of unity equals

$$F(s) = \mathcal{L}[1] = 2\pi U_0(-js), \qquad \text{Re } s = 0 \tag{1.9.4}$$

Since the Fourier transform is evaluated letting s = jω, the jω-axis must be included in the region of convergence R for F(s). Indeed it is, so the Fourier transform of the dc signal equals

$$F(j\omega) = F(s)\Big|_{s=j\omega} = 2\pi U_0(\omega) \tag{1.9.5}$$

The spectrum is zero everywhere except at the origin as shown in Fig. 1.9.1. This must be the case since the signal contains only a dc frequency (i.e., ω = 0). We shall justify the 2π factor later.

EXAMPLE 1.9.2 Determine the Fourier transform for a signum function sgn t where from Table 1.8.3,

$$F(s) = 2/s, \qquad \text{Re } s = 0 \tag{1.9.6}$$

Solution The region of convergence for F(s) contains the jω-axis (actually it consists only of the jω-axis). Thus, letting s = jω, then

$$F(j\omega) = F(s)\Big|_{s=j\omega} = 2/j\omega, \qquad \text{all } \omega \tag{1.9.7}$$

The spectrum of the signum function is plotted in Fig. 1.9.2. Its magnitude varies as 1/ω. It is composed of all frequencies from 0 to +∞ (and image frequencies from −∞ to 0). Notice that although $|F| \to \infty$ as $\omega \to 0$, f(t) contains no dc component, i.e., it has zero average value since F contains no $U_o(\omega)$.

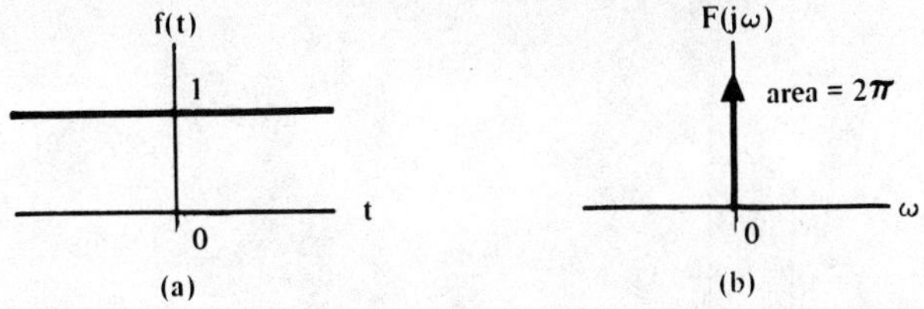

Fig. 1.9.1 (a) DC signal and its (b) spectrum.

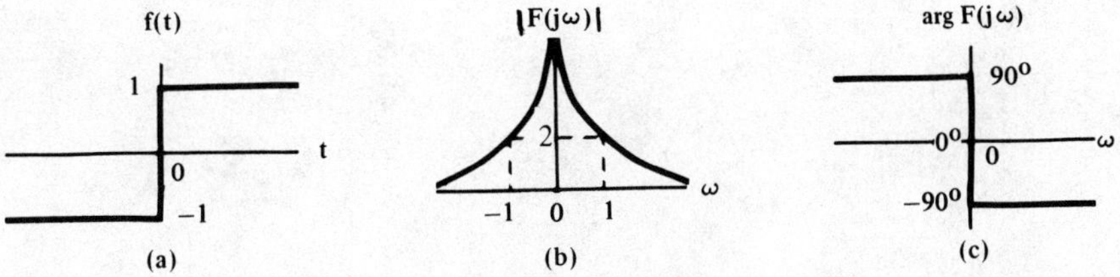

Fig. 1.9.2 (a) Signum function and its (b) magnitude and (c) phase spectrums.

Table 1.9.1 Fourier transform table.

	f(t)	F(jω)		f(t)	F(jω)
1.	$U_0(t)$	1	14.	$e^{-\sigma\|t\|}$	$\frac{2\sigma}{\sigma^2+\omega^2}$
2.	$U_1(t)$	$j\omega$	15.	$e^{-\sigma t^2}$	$\frac{\pi}{\sigma}e^{-\omega^2/4\sigma}$
3.	$U_n(t)$	$(j\omega)^n$	16.	$\frac{1}{\sigma^2+t^2}$	$\frac{\pi}{\sigma}e^{-\sigma\|\omega\|}$
4.	$U_{-1}(t)$	$\pi U_o(\omega) + 1/j\omega$	17.	$U_{-1}(t+T/2) - U_{-1}(t-T/2)$	$T\,\frac{\sin(\omega T/2)}{\omega T/2}$
5.	$tU_{-1}(t) = U_{-2}(t)$	$j\pi U_1(\omega) - 1/\omega^2$	18.	$\cos\omega_o t$	$\pi[U_o(\omega+\omega_o) + U_0(\omega-\omega_o)]$
6.	$t^nU_{-1}(t)$	$\pi j^nU_n(\omega) + n!/(j\omega)^{n+1}$	19.	$\sin\omega_o t$	$j\pi[U_o(\omega+\omega_o) - U_0(\omega-\omega_o)]$
7.	1	$2\pi U_o(\omega)$	20.	$\cos\omega_o t\,U_{-1}(t)$	$\frac{\pi}{2}[U_o(\omega+\omega_o) + U_0(\omega-\omega_o)] + \frac{j\omega}{\omega_o^2-\omega^2}$
8.	t^n	$2\pi j^nU_n(\omega)$	21.	$\sin\omega_o t\,U_{-1}(t)$	$\frac{j\pi}{2}[U_o(\omega+\omega_o) - U_0(\omega-\omega_o)] + \frac{\omega_o}{\omega_o^2-\omega^2}$
9.	$\|t\|$	$-2/\omega^2$	22.	$e^{-\sigma t}\cos\omega_o t\,U_{-1}(t)$	$\frac{\sigma+j\omega}{(\sigma+j\omega)^2+\omega_o^2}$
10.	sgn t	$2/j\omega$	23.	$e^{-\sigma t}\sin\omega_o t\,U_{-1}(t)$	$\frac{\omega_o}{(\sigma+j\omega)^2+\omega_o^2}$
11.	$e^{-\sigma t}U_{-1}(t)$	$\frac{1}{\sigma+j\omega}$			
12.	$te^{-\sigma t}U_{-1}(t)$	$\frac{1}{(\sigma+j\omega)^2}$			
13.	$(t^n/n!)e^{-\sigma t}U_{-1}(t)$	$\frac{1}{(\sigma+j\omega)^{n+1}}$			

Table 1.9.2 Properties of Fourier transforms.

Definition	$f(t)$	$F(j\omega) = \int_{-\infty}^{\infty} f(t)e^{-j\omega t}\,dt$
Linear Operations		
Homogeneity	$Kf(t)$	$KF(j\omega)$
Superposition	$f_1(t) \pm f_2(t)$	$F_1(j\omega) \pm F_2(j\omega)$
Both operations	$a_1f_1(t) \pm a_2f_2(t)$	$a_1F_1(j\omega) \pm a_2F_2(j\omega)$
Symmetry	$F(t)$	$j\,2\pi f(-j\omega)$
Scaling		
Time scaling	$f(at)$	$\frac{1}{\lvert a\rvert} F\left(\frac{j\omega}{a}\right)$
Magnitude scaling	$af(t)$	$aF(j\omega)$
Shifting		
Time shifting	$f(t-a)$	$e^{-ja\omega}F(j\omega)$
Frequency shifting	$e^{-at}f(t)$	$F(j\,\omega + a)$
Periodic Functions (for $t > 0$ only)	$f(t) = \sum_{n=0}^{\infty} f(t+nT)$	$\frac{F_1(j\omega)}{1-e^{-j\omega T}} = F_1(j\omega) \sum_{n=0}^{\infty} e^{-jn\omega T}$ where $F_1(j\omega) = \int_0^T f(t)e^{-j\omega t}dt$
Convolution		
Time convolution (Frequency product)	$f_1(t)*f_2(t) = \int_{-\infty}^{\infty} f_1(\tau)f_2(t-\tau)\,d\tau$	$F_1(j\omega)F_2(j\omega)$
Frequency convolution (Time product)	$f_1(t)f_2(t)$	$F_1(j\omega)*F_2(j\omega) = \frac{1}{2\pi j}\int_{-j\infty}^{j\infty} F_1(p)F_2(j\omega - p)\,dp$
Time Differentiation		
First derivative	$df(t)/dt$	$j\omega F(j\omega)$
Second derivative	$d^2f(t)/dt^2$	$(j\omega)^2F(j\omega)$
*n*th derivative	$d^nf(t)/dt^n$	$(j\omega)^nF(j\omega)$
Time Integration		
First integral	$\int_{-\infty}^{t} f(t)\,dt = f^{(-1)}(t)$	$F(j\omega)/j\omega$
Second integral	$\int_{-\infty}^{t}\int_{-\infty}^{t} f(t)\,dt\,dt = f^{(-2)}(t)$	$F(j\omega)/(j\omega)^2$
*n*th integral	$f^{(-n)}(t)$	$F(j\omega)/(j\omega)^n$
Frequency Differentiation		
First derivative	$tf(t)$	$-dF(j\omega)/d(j\omega)$
*n*th derivative	$t^nf(t)$	$(-1)^n\, d^nF(j\omega)/d(j\omega)^n$
Frequency Integration		
*n*th integral	$t^{-n}f(t)$	$(-1)^n\, F^{(-n)}(j\omega)$
Initial Value *	$f(0^+) = \lim_{t \to 0} f(t)$	$= \lim_{\omega \to \infty} j\omega F(j\omega)$
Final Value *	$f(\infty) = \lim_{t \to \infty} f(t)$	$= \lim_{\omega \to 0} j\omega F(j\omega)$ providing poles of $sF(s)$ in in left-half-plane
Initial Slopes *	$d^{m-1}f(0+)/dt^{m-1}$	$= \lim_{\omega \to \infty} (j\omega)^mF(j\omega)$

*For one-sided transforms.

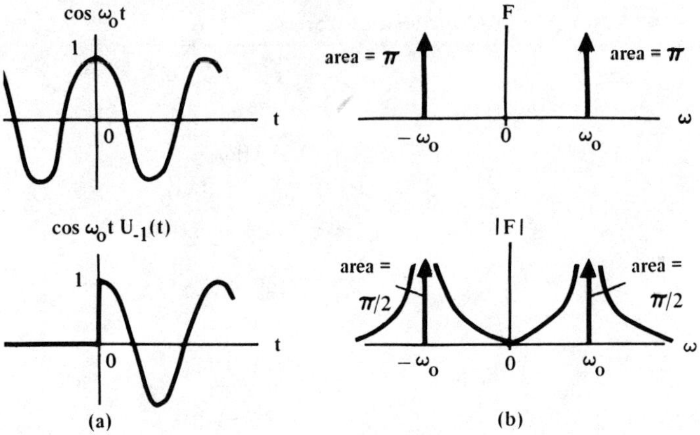

Fig. 1.9.3 **(a) Cosine signals and their (b) magnitude spectrums.**

EXAMPLE 1.9.3 Determine the Fourier transform for a unit step function $U_{-1}(t)$ where

$$F(s) = \mathcal{L}[f(t)] = 1/s, \qquad \text{Re } s > 0 \tag{1.9.8}$$

Interpret the result.

Solution Since the region of convergence R for F(s) does not include the jω-axis, we cannot evaluate F(jω) from this result. However, we can re-express f(t) as

$$f(t) = U_{-1}(t) = \tfrac{1}{2} + \tfrac{1}{2}\,\text{sgn } t \tag{1.9.9}$$

The Laplace transforms for each term are found in Table 1.8.3. Using these results, we can write that

$$F(s) = \mathcal{L}[\tfrac{1}{2}] + \mathcal{L}[\tfrac{1}{2}\,\text{sgn } t] = \pi U_0(-js) + 1/s, \qquad \text{Re } s \geqslant 0 \tag{1.9.10}$$

Interpreting this result, the first term is the transform along the jω-axis only, and the second term is the transform in the right-half-plane. Summing the two gives the transform over both regions. Therefore, the Fourier transform of the unit step equals

$$F(j\omega) = \pi U_0(\omega) + 1/j\omega \tag{1.9.11}$$

The first term corresponds to a dc value of ½ which agrees with the dc (average) value of f(t). Thus, |F| contains an impulse of area π at ω = 0. The remaining spectrum allows f(t) to make a unit transition at t = 0.

In obtaining the proper F(s), we extend the definition of F(s) to include the jω-axis. This process of enlarging the region to convergence is called *analytic continuation* and will be used extensively in Chap. 4 for deriving classical filters.[10]

EXAMPLE 1.9.4 Describe the difference in spectrums between the cosine signal and the gated-cosine signal whose Laplace transforms equal

$$\begin{aligned} \mathcal{L}[\cos\omega_0 t] &= \pi[U_0(-js+\omega_0) + U_0(-js-\omega_0)], \qquad \text{Re } s = 0 \\ \mathcal{L}[\cos\omega_0 t\, U_{-1}(t)] &= \frac{\pi}{2}[U_0(-js+\omega_0) + U_0(-js-\omega_0)] + \frac{s}{s^2+\omega_0^2}, \qquad \text{Re } s \geqslant 0 \end{aligned} \tag{1.9.12}$$

Solution The Fourier transforms equal

$$\begin{aligned} F[\cos\omega_0 t] &= \pi[U_0(\omega+\omega_0) + U_0(\omega-\omega_0)] \\ F[\cos\omega_0 t\, U_{-1}(t)] &= \frac{\pi}{2}[U_0(\omega+\omega_0) - U_0(\omega-\omega_0)] + \frac{j\omega}{\omega_0^2-\omega^2} \end{aligned} \tag{1.9.13}$$

The continuous cosine signal exists for all time. It therefore consists of only a single frequency at $\omega = \pm\omega_o$. However, although the gated-cosine has one discrete frequency component at $\pm\omega_o$, it has all other frequencies besides. This is shown in Fig. 1.9.3.

These examples illustrate the general result that signals which are repetitive or periodic consist of a countably infinite number of *discrete* frequencies. (A countably infinite number means that every number has a one-to-one correspondence with an integer n, such as $\omega_n = n^2\omega_o$.) Thus, their spectra consist entirely of lines or impulses at distinct frequencies. Nonrepetitive signals consist of a continuum or band of frequencies (in addition perhaps, to discrete frequencies). If the signal lasts only for a finite time, then it contains all frequencies from $\omega = -\infty$ to $+\infty$. However, if it exists for all time, then it *may* contain only a finite band of frequencies. This is called a *band-limited* signal.

The energy E contained in signal f(t) is defined to equal

$$E = \int_{-\infty}^{\infty} f^2(t)\, dt \tag{1.9.14}$$

The power P contained in a signal f(t) is defined to equal

$$P = \lim_{T\to\infty} \frac{1}{T}\int_{-T/2}^{T/2} f^2(t)\, dt \tag{1.9.15}$$

Parseval's theorem relates the energy contained within a signal to that contained within its spectrum.[11] Since

$$\begin{aligned} E &= \int_{-\infty}^{\infty} f^2(t)\, dt = \int_{-\infty}^{\infty} f(t)\left(\frac{1}{2\pi}\int_{-\infty}^{\infty} F(j\omega)e^{j\omega t}\, d\omega\right) dt \\ &= \frac{1}{2\pi}\int_{-\infty}^{\infty} F(j\omega)\left(\int_{-\infty}^{\infty} f(t)e^{j\omega t}\, dt\right) d\omega = \frac{1}{2\pi}\int_{-\infty}^{\infty} F(j\omega)F(-j\omega)\, d\omega \end{aligned} \tag{1.9.16}$$

then the energy equals

$$\begin{aligned} E &= \int_{-\infty}^{\infty} f^2(t)\, dt = \frac{1}{2\pi}\int_{-\infty}^{\infty} |F(j\omega)|^2\, d\omega = \int_{-\infty}^{\infty} |F(jf)|^2\, df \\ &= \int_0^{\infty} 2\, S(\omega)\, d\omega = \int_0^{\infty} 2\, S(f)\, df \end{aligned} \tag{1.9.17}$$

$S(\omega)$ is called the energy density spectrum of f(t) where

$$S(\omega) = \frac{1}{2\pi}|F(j\omega)|^2 = \frac{1}{2\pi}F(j\omega)F(-j\omega), \qquad S(f) = |F(jf)|^2 = F(jf)F(-jf) \tag{1.9.18}$$

$S(\omega)$ has the units of (rms volts)^2/(rad/sec) when f(t) represents a voltage signal. We should also note that the energy contained in the product of two signals f_1 and f_2 equals

$$\begin{aligned} \int_{-\infty}^{\infty} f_1(t)f_2(t)\, dt &= \frac{1}{2\pi}\int_{-\infty}^{\infty} F_1^*(j\omega)F_2(j\omega)\, d\omega = \int_{-\infty}^{\infty} F_1^*(jf)F_2(jf)\, df \\ &= \int_0^{\infty} 2S_{12}(\omega)\, d\omega = \int_0^{\infty} 2S_{12}(f)\, df \end{aligned} \tag{1.9.19}$$

$S_{12}(\omega)$ is called the cross-energy spectrum of f_1 and f_2.

The energy in a signal f(t) contained within a band of frequencies between ω_1 and ω_2 equals

$$E(\omega_1, \omega_2) = E(f_1, f_2) = \int_{\omega_1}^{\omega_2} 2\, S(\omega)\, d\omega = \int_{f_1}^{f_2} 2S(f)\, df \tag{1.9.20}$$

When E is continuous, the energy spectrum of the signal contains no impulses. That is, it contains no discrete frequencies. Thus, in a bandwidth of zero,

$$\lim_{\epsilon\to 0} E(\omega_1, \omega_1 + \epsilon) = \lim_{\epsilon\to 0} \int_{\omega_1}^{\omega_1+\epsilon} 2\, S(\omega)\, d\omega = 0 \tag{1.9.21}$$

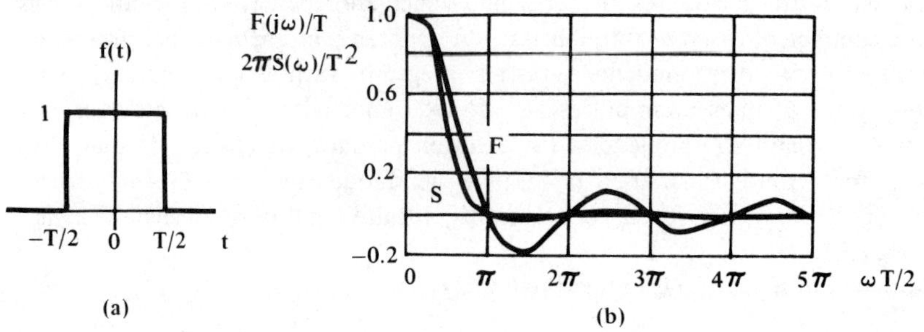

Fig. 1.9.4 (a) Pulse signal and its (b) spectrum.

EXAMPLE 1.9.5 Determine the energy spectrum of a unit pulse of duration T seconds centered about t = 0. The unit pulse can be expressed as

$$f(t) = U_{-1}(t + T/2) - U_{-1}(t - T/2) \tag{1.9.22}$$

Solution Using Eq. 1.9.22, its Laplace transform must therefore equal

$$F(s) = [\pi U_0(-js) + 1/s]\,[e^{sT/2} - e^{-sT/2}], \qquad \text{Re } s \geqslant 0 \tag{1.9.23}$$

from Example 1.9.3 and the time-shifting theorem of Table 1.8.2. Therefore, its Fourier transform equals

$$F(j\omega) = F(s)\big|_{s=j\omega} = [\pi U_0(\omega) + 1/j\omega]\,[e^{j\omega T/2} - e^{-j\omega T/2}] = [e^{j\omega T/2} - e^{-j\omega T/2}]/j\omega \tag{1.9.24}$$

where the $U_o(\omega)$ term is zero unless $T \to \infty$. We can then re-express $F(j\omega)$ as

$$F(j\omega) = \frac{2}{\omega}\,\frac{e^{j\omega T/2} - e^{-j\omega T/2}}{j2} = \frac{2}{\omega}\sin\frac{\omega T}{2} = T\,\frac{\sin \omega T/2}{\omega T/2} = T \text{ sinc } (\omega T/2) \tag{1.9.25}$$

which has a sin x/x (denoted as sinc x) variation with frequency as shown in Fig. 1.9.4b. The energy density spectrum of the pulse equals

$$S(\omega) = \frac{1}{2\pi}\,|F(j\omega)|^2 = \frac{T^2}{2\pi}\,\text{sinc}^2(\omega T/2) \tag{1.9.26}$$

which is also plotted in Fig. 1.9.4b. We see that the bulk of the energy in the signal is contained in the range $0 \leqslant f \leqslant 1/T$. Using Eq. 1.9.20, numerical integration shows that 92.2% of the total output energy lies within the main lobe, and 4.8, 1.7, 0.8, and 0.5% within the first, second, third, and fourth side-lobes, respectively. The total energy contained within the pulse equals

$$E(\infty) = \int_{-\infty}^{\infty} f^2(t)\,dt = \int_{-T/2}^{T/2} dt = T \tag{1.9.27}$$

EXAMPLE 1.9.6 Now determine the energy spectrum of a gated-cosine or unit cosine pulse given by

$$f(t) = \cos \omega_o t\,[U_{-1}(t + T/2) - U_{-1}(t - T/2)] \tag{1.9.28}$$

Solution The spectrum of the gated-cosine is easily determined using the frequency convolution theorem of Table 1.9.2 as

$$F(j\omega) = F(\cos \omega_o t) * T \text{ sinc } (\omega T/2) \tag{1.9.29}$$

From Example 1.9.4, the Fourier transform of the cosine signal was given by Eq. 1.9.13, so

$$F(j\omega) = \frac{T\pi}{2}\Big[\text{sinc } [(\omega + \omega_o)T/2] + \text{sinc } [(\omega - \omega_o)T/2]\Big] \tag{1.9.30}$$

Thus, the signal spectrum still has the sin x/x characteristic, but it is recentered about $\pm\omega_o$. Now the energy is concentrated in the frequency band $|\Delta f| \leqslant 1/T$ centered about ω_o. The total energy with the gated-cosine equals

Table 1.9.3 Spectral characteristics of signals (2β = reciprocal of signal length). (From Monograph No. 3, "Real signal processing in the frequency domain," p. 8, Nicolet Scientific Corp. (formerly Federal Scientific Corp.), Northvale, NJ, 11-70.)

WEIGHTING FUNCTION		Hz 3-dB BANDWIDTH	Hz NOISE BANDWIDTH	HIGHEST SIDELOBE LEVEL (dB)	ASYMPTOTIC ROLL-OFF (dB/OCTAVE)
RECTANGLE	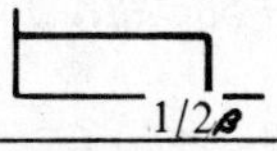	$0.85\,\beta$	$1\,\beta$	−13	6
TRIANGLE	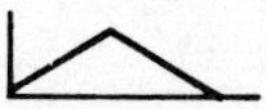	$1.25\,\beta$	$1.35\,\beta$	−26	12
COSINE		$1.17\,\beta$	$1.26\,\beta$	−23	12
$(\text{COSINE})^2$ = HANNING	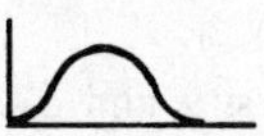	$1.4\,\beta$	$1.5\,\beta$	−32	18
$(\text{COSINE})^3$	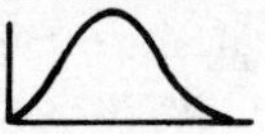	$1.61\,\beta$	$1.73\,\beta$	−39	24
$(\text{COSINE})^4$	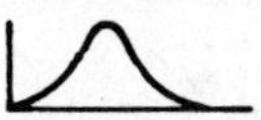	$1.88\,\beta$	$1.9\,\beta$	−48	30
HAMMING = $(\text{COSINE})^2$ + 8% PEDESTAL	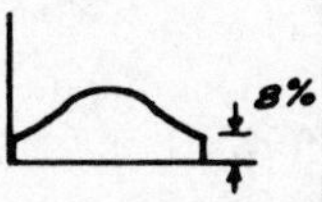	$1.3\,\beta$	$1.36\,\beta$	−42	6 dB/OCT BEYOND 5β
TRIPLET = $(\text{COSINE})^2$ X EXPONENTIAL	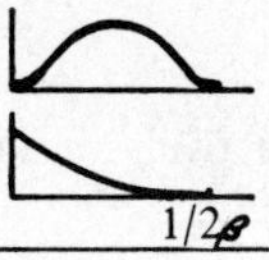	$1.5\,\beta$	$1.6\,\beta$	NONE	18 MONOTONIC

$$E(\infty) = \frac{T}{2}\left[1 + \sin\frac{\omega_0 T}{2}\right] \tag{1.9.31}$$

after some calculation.

Signals and impulse response functions f(t) are often described in terms of 3 dB bandwidth, asymptotic rolloff, highest side-lobe level, and noise bandwidth of their magnitude spectrums $|F(j\omega)|$. Several are listed in Table 1.9.3. The *3 dB bandwidth* of the spectrum is the frequency where $|F(j\omega)|$ is reduced 3 dB from its maximum value. The *asymptotic rolloff* of the spectrum is the high-frequency slope of $|F(j\omega)|$ and is measured in dB/dec or dB/oct. The *highest side-lobe level* is the maximum level attained by $|F(j\omega)|$ in its side-lobes (i.e., excluding the main lobe). The *noise bandwidth* is equal to the total energy E contained within the signal, or equivalently, the bandwidth B of an ideal rectangular filter (i.e., having $|H(j\omega)| = 1$ for $|\omega| < B$ and zero elsewhere) whose impulse response contains the same energy. The engineer can apply these definitions to the pulse in Example 1.9.5 and verify the corresponding entries in Table 1.9.3. We will discuss these results at length in Chaps. 2–4.

There are certain situations when signal parameters are not known exactly and must be described statistically. In these cases, a signal v(t) is viewed as a random variable which is described by a probability density function f(v(t)). When the probability density functions are time-invariant, the statistical process is said to be *stationary*. The probability that a signal v(t) does not exceed V_o is determined using the *probability density function* f(v) as

$$\Pr(v \leqslant V_o) = \int_{-\infty}^{V_o} f(v)\, dv = F(V_o) \tag{1.9.32}$$

F(v) is called the cumulative probability density function or the *probability distribution function* of v. F(v) and f(v) are related as

$$F(v) = \int_{-\infty}^{v} f(v)\, dv, \qquad f(v) = dF(v)/dv \tag{1.9.33}$$

The probability that a signal v(t) lies between two levels V_1 and V_2 therefore equals

$$\Pr(V_1 \leqslant v \leqslant V_2) = \int_{V_1}^{V_2} f(v)\, dv = F(V_2) - F(V_1) \tag{1.9.34}$$

using Eq. 1.9.32. A variety of signals and their probability density and distribution functions are shown in Table 1.9.4.

Certain statistics are usually used to describe random signals. These often involve a so-called "expected value" of some function g(v) of a random variable v. *Expected values* are denoted as E[ ] and are defined to equal

$$E[g(v)] = \int_{-\infty}^{\infty} g(v) f(v)\, dv \tag{1.9.35}$$

We shall now discuss several important statistics.[13] Consider $v_1(t)$ and $v_2(t)$ which are random variables and are described by probability density functions $f(v_1, t)$ and $f(v_2, t)$. The *mean*, average, or dc values of the signals equal

$$\eta_1 = E[v_1(t)], \qquad \eta_2 = E[v_2(t)] \tag{1.9.36}$$

Their *mean square* values equal $E[v_1^2(t)]$ and $E[v_2^2(t)]$, respectively. Their *variances* equal $E[v_1(t) - \eta_1)^2]$ and $E[(v_2(t) - \eta_2)^2]$, respectively.

The *autocorrelations* of the signals equal

$$R_{11}(\tau) = E[v_1(t+\tau)v_1(t)], \qquad R_{22}(\tau) = E[v_2(t+\tau)v_2(t)] \tag{1.9.37}$$

while their *cross-correlation* equals

$$R_{12}(\tau) = E[v_1(t+\tau)v_2(t)] \tag{1.9.38}$$

We find the *power spectrum* or *spectral density* S of $v_1(t)$ and $v_2(t)$ by taking the Fourier transform of their autocorrelations. Thus,

$$S_1(\omega) = \int_{-\infty}^{\infty} R_{11}(\tau) e^{-j\omega\tau}\, d\tau, \qquad S_2(\omega) = \int_{-\infty}^{\infty} R_{22}(\tau) e^{-j\omega\tau}\, d\tau \tag{1.9.39}$$

while the spectral density of their product equals

$$S_{12}(\omega) = \int_{-\infty}^{\infty} R_{12}(\tau) e^{-j\omega\tau}\, d\tau \tag{1.9.40}$$

S is the mean square voltage (volts^2/Hz) at frequency ω. Examples of autocorrelation and power spectrums are also shown in Table 1.9.4. The correlation between the two signals is

$$C(\omega) = S_{12}(\omega)/\sqrt{S_1(\omega) S_2(\omega)} \tag{1.9.41}$$

Table 1.9.4 Statistical characteristics of signals.
(From Monograph No. 1, "An introduction to correlation," pp. 6–7, Nicolet Scientific Corp. (formerly Federal Scientific Corp.), Northvale, NJ, 5-1-72.)

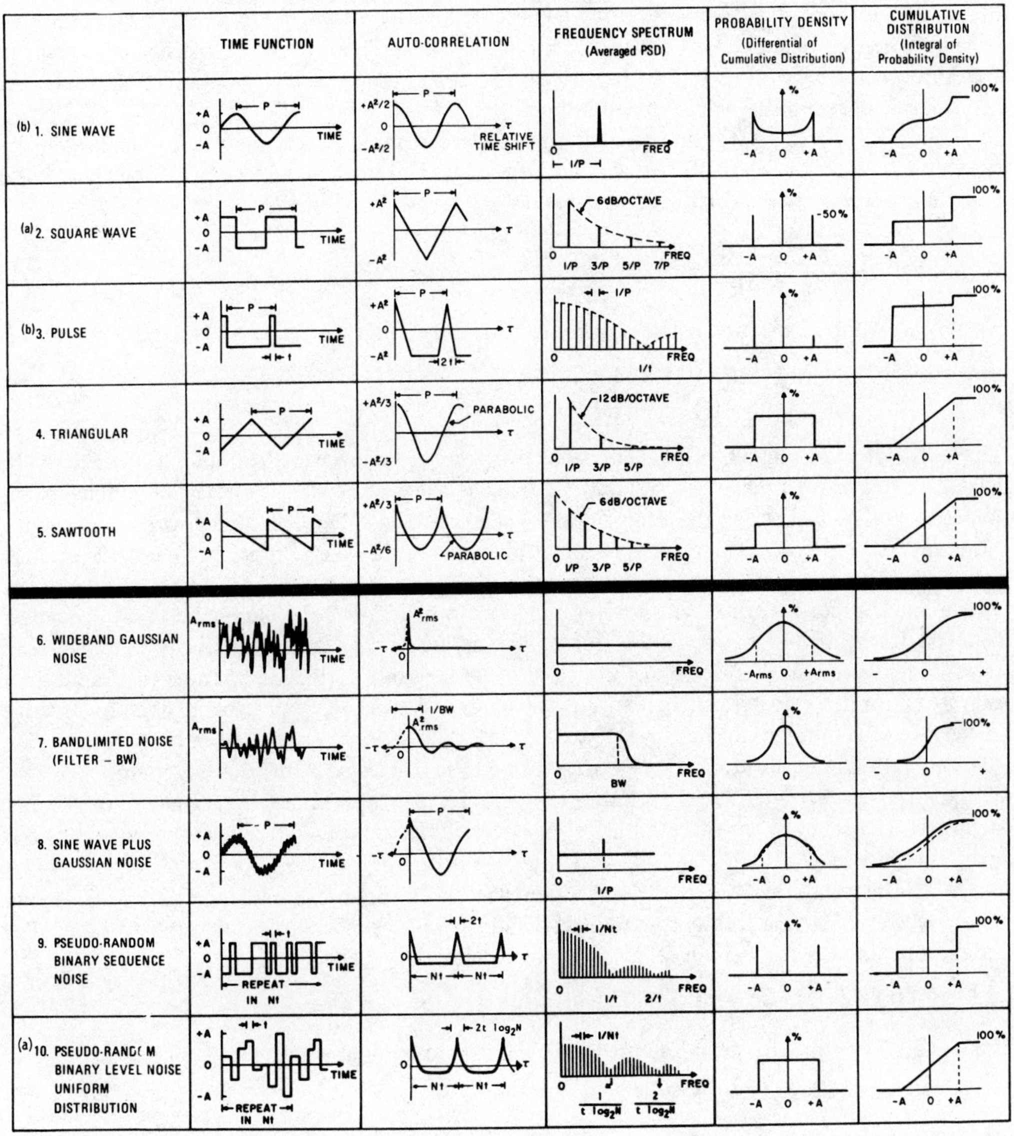

which in general varies with frequency and is bounded as $-1 \leqslant C(\omega) \leqslant 1$. Very often in analysis, we are concerned only with the rms signal contained between frequencies ω_1 and ω_2 with bandwidth $B = \omega_2 - \omega_1$. In this situation, the rms signal values equal

$$V_1 = \frac{1}{\pi}\left[\int_{\omega_1}^{\omega_1+B} S_1(\omega)\, d\omega\right]^{1/2}, \qquad V_2 = \frac{1}{\pi}\left[\int_{\omega_2}^{\omega_2+B} S_2(\omega)\, d\omega\right]^{1/2} \tag{1.9.42}$$

1.10 ONE-PORT ANALYSIS

We have discussed the modelling of passive and active elements. Now we shall be concerned with the larger problem of analyzing a group of interconnected elements which form a network or system. The electrical point of entry into a system is called a *port*. When there is only a single access point, the network is said to be a *one-port*. When there are two access points, it then becomes a *two-port* and so-forth as shown in Fig. 1.10.1.

Electrically, voltage v(t) and current i(t) can be measured in real time at a port. When the system is linear, time-invariant, contains no independent sources, and no initial stored energy, the Laplace transforms of the voltage and current are related as

$$Z(s) = \frac{V(s)}{I(s)} = \frac{\mathcal{L}[v(t)]}{\mathcal{L}[i(t)]} \tag{1.10.1}$$

where Z(s) is the *input impedance* of the one-port. The *input admittance* Y(s) to the two-port is

$$Y(s) = \frac{I(s)}{V(s)} = \frac{\mathcal{L}[i(t)]}{\mathcal{L}[v(t)]} = \frac{1}{Z(s)} \tag{1.10.2}$$

The one-port may contain dependent or active sources. However, V(s) and I(s) can only be related in this manner when the system is initially relaxed, and when it contains no independent sources. We shall consider the general case when we discuss Thevenin and Norton equivalents. Note that the ratio of v(t) and i(t) is meaningless except in the case of resistance networks, such as voltage dividers, attenuators, etc.

In making measurements, any forcing function form for v(t) or i(t) may be used. The most common form used is the sinusoidal signal; measurements are made in ac steady-state. In such cases, $s = j\omega$ and the Fourier transform ratio is used. Table 1.10.1 summarizes the immittance properties for the resistor, inductor, and capacitor. *Immittance* is the term used to describe impedance or admittance interchangeably.

Very often in ac steady-state measurements, we are interested in the limiting immittance conditions. We recall from Table 1.10.1 that the inductor is a short circuit at dc and an open-circuit at infinite frequency. The situation is reversed for the capacitor. Of course, the resistor is frequency-insensitive.

When analyzing one-port networks, either Kirchhoff's loop or node equations are generally used. However, we can often combine series and parallel elements directly to save time. For series elements each having impedance $Z_i(s)$, the total input impedance equals

$$Z(s) = Z_1(s) + Z_2(s) + \ldots + Z_n(s) \tag{1.10.3}$$

For parallel elements each having admittance $Y_i(s)$, the total input admittance equals

$$Y(s) = Y_1(s) + Y_2(s) + \ldots + Y_n(s) \tag{1.10.4}$$

Kirchhoff's equations are used for obtaining these two results.

EXAMPLE 1.10.1 The equivalent circuit for an actual resistor is shown in Fig. 14.1.7. Determine its input impedance. Find the limiting impedance at low and high frequencies, and identify the poles and zeros of the impedance.

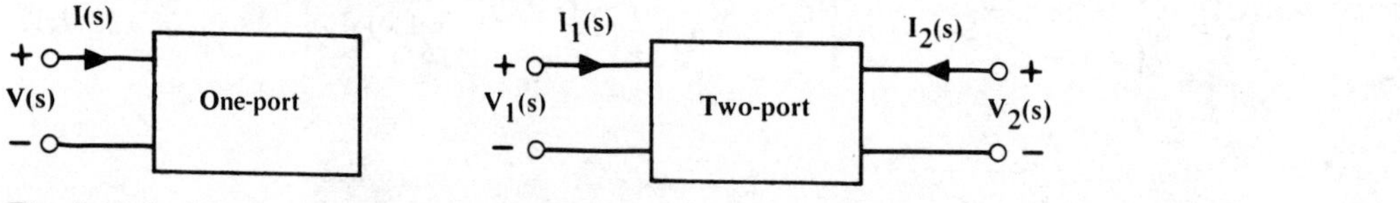

Fig. 1.10.1 One-port and two-port networks.

Table 1.10.1 Summary of immittance properties of passive elements.

	Impedance $Z(s)$	Admittance $Y(s)$	AC Impedance $Z(j\omega)$	AC Admittance $Y(j\omega)$	$Z(j\omega)$ at $\omega = 0$	$Z(j\omega)$ at $\omega = \infty$
Resistor	R	$G = 1/R$	R	$G = 1/R$	R	R
Inductor	sL	$1/sL$	$j\omega L$	$1/j\omega L$	0	∞
Capacitor	$1/sC$	sC	$1/j\omega C$	$j\omega C$	∞	0

Solution The impedance of the RL series branch equals $(R + sL)$ while that of the capacitive branch equals $1/sC$. Combining the parallel admittances gives the total input admittance, and taking the reciprocal gives the input impedance which equals

$$Z(s) = Y(s)^{-1} = \left[sC + \frac{1}{R + sL}\right]^{-1} = \frac{R + sL}{s^2LC + sRC + 1} \tag{1.10.5}$$

In ac steady-state, $s = j\omega$. At low frequencies when $\omega \to 0$, or equivalently $s \to 0$, then $Z(s) \sim R$. Thus, the resistor appears to be ideal at low frequencies. This is obvious since the capacitor becomes an open-circuit and the inductor a short-circuit. At high frequencies when $\omega \to \infty$ or $s \to \infty$, then $Z(s) \sim 1/sC$. Thus, the input impedance appears to be capacitive. This is obvious since the inductor becomes an open-circuit leaving only the capacitive branch. The zeros of $Z(s)$ are located at

$$s = -R/L, \quad \infty \tag{1.10.6}$$

while the poles are located at

$$s = \frac{-RC \pm \sqrt{(RC)^2 - 4LC}}{2LC} = -\frac{R}{2L} \pm \sqrt{\left[\frac{R}{2L}\right]^2 - \frac{1}{LC}} \tag{1.10.7}$$

We shall discuss the pole and zero variation with element values later. In Chap. 4, we thoroughly investigate the characteristics of resistors as well as capacitors and operational amplifiers.

A convenient aid in one-port analysis and design is the concept of magnitude and frequency scaling. This concept allows readily manipulated or normalized immittance values to be used for preliminary analysis, after which they are transformed or denormalized to their proper design values. If the impedance magnitude is to be scaled (or increased) by a factor a, and the critical frequencies scaled (or increased) by a factor b, then

$$Z(s) = aZ_n(s/b) \tag{1.10.8}$$

where $Z_n(s_n)$ is the normalized impedance and $Z(s)$ is the denormalized impedance. Denote the normalized impedance values for the resistor, inductor, and capacitor as

$$Z_n(s_n) = R_n, \quad Z_n(s_n) = s_nL_n, \quad Z_n(s_n) = 1/s_nC_n \tag{1.10.9}$$

respectively. Substituting into Eq. 1.10.8, then their denormalized values equal

$$Z(s) = R = aR_n, \quad Z(s) = sL = s(aL_n/b), \quad Z(s) = 1/sC = ab/sC_n \tag{1.10.10}$$

Therefore, the denormalized component values equal

$$R = aR_n, \quad L = aL_n/b, \quad C = C_n/ab \tag{1.10.11}$$

Since the resistor is frequency-insensitive, it is insensitive to frequency scaling.

EXAMPLE 1.10.2 The (normalized) input impedance to the RC network in Fig. 1.10.2a equals

$$Z_n(s) = 10\frac{s + 10}{(s + 1)(s + 100)} = \frac{0.91}{s + 1} + \frac{9.1}{s + 100} \tag{1.10.12}$$

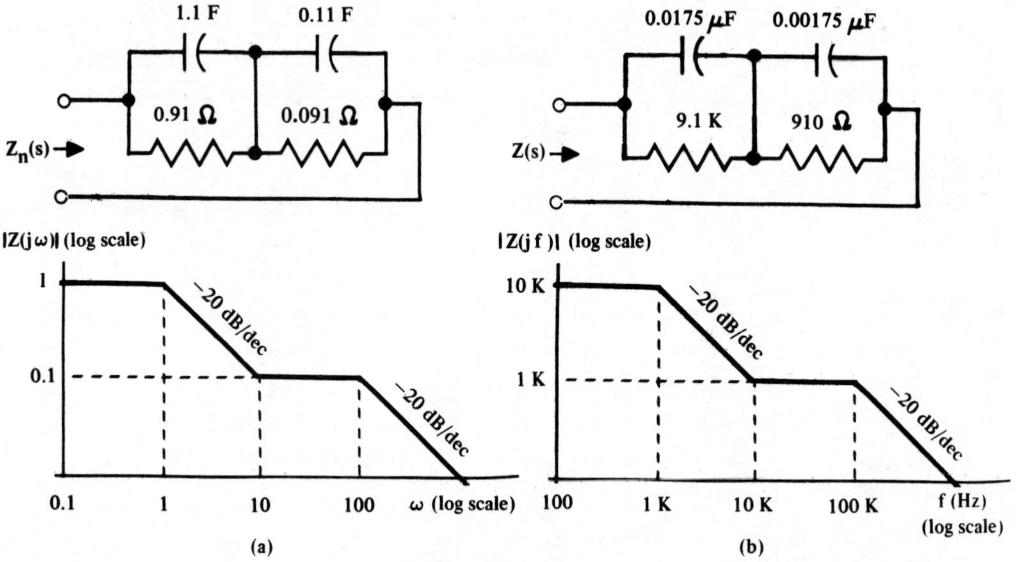

Fig. 1.10.2 (a) Normalized and (b) denormalized RC network and its ac steady-state magnitude characteristic.

Its magnitude characteristic in ac steady-state is also shown. Such plots are called Bode plots which we shall study in Chap. 2. Denormalize the impedance function so the dc impedance Z(0) equals 10 KΩ and the first corner frequency f_1 equals 1 KHz. Draw and label the denormalized network.

Solution Since the denormalized and normalized impedances are related by Eq. 1.10.9, we must determine the magnitude normalization constant a and the frequency normalization constant b. Noting that this equation at dc equals $Z(0) = aZ_n(0)$, we see that constant a equals

$$a = Z(0)/Z_n(0) = 10\ K\Omega/1\ \Omega = 10^4 \tag{1.10.13}$$

Since the first corner frequency must occur at $2\pi \times 10^3$ rad/sec rather than 1 rad/sec, then constant b equals

$$b = 2\pi \times 10^3 \tag{1.10.14}$$

Therefore, since the denormalized resistor values equal $R = aR_n$, then

$$R_1 = 0.91 \times 10^4 = 9.1\ K\Omega, \qquad R_2 = 0.091 \times 10^4 = 910\ \Omega \tag{1.10.15}$$

The denormalized capacitor values equal $C = C_n/ab$, so

$$C_1 = 1.1/(2\pi \times 10^7) = 0.0175\ \mu F, \qquad C_2 = 0.11/(2\pi \times 10^7) = 0.00175\ \mu F \tag{1.10.16}$$

The resulting circuit is shown in Fig. 1.10.2b.

Two parenthetical observations should be made. First, the design engineer will notice that although the mathematics show the exact values needed for the denormalization, the capacitors are not standard values which are commercially available. Such practical matters as standard values are discussed extensively in Chap. 14. Second, the effects of using inexact values are analyzed using sensitivity concepts which we shall later discuss in this chapter.

Duality is another concept useful in design. Two networks or systems are said to be *duals* or analogs if they are described by equations having the same *form*. Thus, when one electrical system has been analyzed and designed, the principle of duality allows another electrical system to be immediately specified. Everything that is known about the first system can be applied directly to the second system.

In electrical systems, duality consists essentially of interchanging the roles of voltage and

Table 1.10.2 Dual quantities.

Quantity	Dual Quantity	Quantity	Dual Quantity
Voltage	Current	Loop	Node
Impedance	Admittance	Short Circuit	Open Circuit
Resistance	Conductance	Series Connection	Parallel Connection
Inductance	Capacitance		

current. These interchanges are listed in Table 1.10.2. When a circuit is planar (i.e., it can be drawn with no crossing wires), its dual can be drawn immediately. This consists essentially of placing a node in every loop, and then drawing a dual element through every branch to connect these nodes.[14]

The concept of duality allows many nonelectrical or partially nonelectrical systems to be analyzed using pure electrical analogs. For example, mechanical (translational or rotational), hydraulic (or acoustical), and thermal systems can be readily described using this approach.[15] Such an approach is an invaluable analysis tool for all areas of engineering. Duality allows large, complex, and expensive systems to be analyzed in the laboratory using relatively small, simple, and inexpensive electrical analogs. Therefore, nonelectrical or only partially electrical engineering systems can be "simulated" using pure electrical analogs. They can be independently adjusted electronically without recourse to fabrication of new mechanical assemblies, etc.

A different approach to simulation utilizes analog and/or digital computers. When electrical analogs are formed as previously discussed, there is always a one-to-one correspondence between elements in the engineering system and the analogous electrical system. However, when the analog or digital computer is used for analysis, the engineering system is usually described in block diagram form where the individual element detail is suppressed. This block diagram can be viewed as a signal flow graph which we will soon discuss.

EXAMPLE 1.10.3 Determine the dual of the RC network in Example 1.10.2 which is drawn in Fig. 1.10.3a.

Solution Because of duality, we can write the Y(s) expression for the dual circuit directly from the Z(s) expression of Eq. 1.10.12 as

$$Y_{RL}(s) = 10\frac{s+10}{(s+1)(s+100)} = \frac{0.91}{s+1} + \frac{9.1}{s+100} \tag{1.10.17}$$

The magnitude characteristic in ac steady-state $|Y(j\omega)|$ is identical to that shown in Fig. 1.10.2a. The dual is easily drawn by placing a node inside and outside of each loop in Fig. 1.10.3a and connecting the nodes with the dual elements that pass through the individual branches. The result is shown in Fig. 1.10.3b. It is important to note that the dual elements have the *same numerical values* as the original elements. This is a fact which is often overlooked or confused in drawing duals.

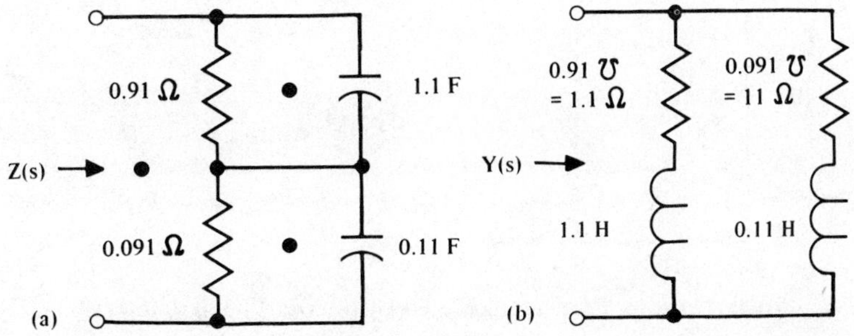

Fig. 1.10.3
(a) RC network
and its (b) dual.

In calculating the input immittance of networks, it is often convenient to utilize *Blackman's immittance relation.*[16] These relations state that

$$Z^{(k)} = Z^{(0)}\frac{1-T_s}{1-T_\infty}, \qquad Y^{(k)} = Y^{(0)}\frac{1-T_\infty}{1-T_s} \tag{1.10.18}$$

where

$Z^{(k)}, Z^{(0)}$ = impedances measured at a port when a controlled source y = kx has its normal strength k and the strength zero, respectively.

T_s = return ratio for k when the port at which $Z^{(k)}$ is measured is short-circuited.

T_∞ = return ratio for k when the port at which $Z^{(k)}$ is measured is open-circuited.

The *return ratio T(s)* is defined as the value of the variable x which is produced when the controlled source y = kx is replaced by an independent source (of the same type) of value k. All independent sources are set to zero (i.e., replaced with their internal impedances), and all other system conditions are unchanged from their normal operating state. For simplicity, T is often said to be the return ratio for k. Note, however, that T depends upon the model of the device or element in combination with the environment in which it is embedded. The return ratio is not a quantity associated with a particular device or circuit element.[17]

Sometimes, the immittance relations are expressed as

$$Z^{(k)} = Z^{(0)}(F_s/F_\infty), \qquad Y^{(k)} = Y^{(0)}(F_\infty/F_s) \tag{1.10.19}$$

where the F's are called the *return differences* under the measurement conditions indicated. F is simply equal to

$$F = 1 - T \tag{1.10.20}$$

EXAMPLE 1.10.4 Calculate the input impedance to a network having a load Z_L and the equivalent circuit shown in Fig. 1.10.4b. Use Blackman's impedance relation.

Solution Inspecting the equivalent circuit, we can choose either of the two dependent sources for calculating its respective return ratio. Let us arbitrarily select the z_{21} source. First, we calculate the input impedance in the zero state where z_{21} = 0 in Fig. 1.10.5a. Since there is no coupling to the output circuit, $I_2 = 0$. Thus,

$$Z^{(0)} = z_{11} \tag{1.10.21}$$

Now we calculate the return ratio T_s for the z_{21} source. The input port is short-circuited, and the $z_{21}I_1$ dependent source is replaced by an independent source of strength z_{21}. From Fig. 1.10.5b, we see the return ratio equals

$$T_s = I_1 = -\frac{z_{12}I_2}{z_{11}} = \frac{z_{12}}{z_{11}}\frac{z_{21}}{z_{22}+Z_L} \tag{1.10.22}$$

Finally, we calculate the return ratio T_∞ for the z_{21} source. In this case, the input port is open-circuited. Thus,

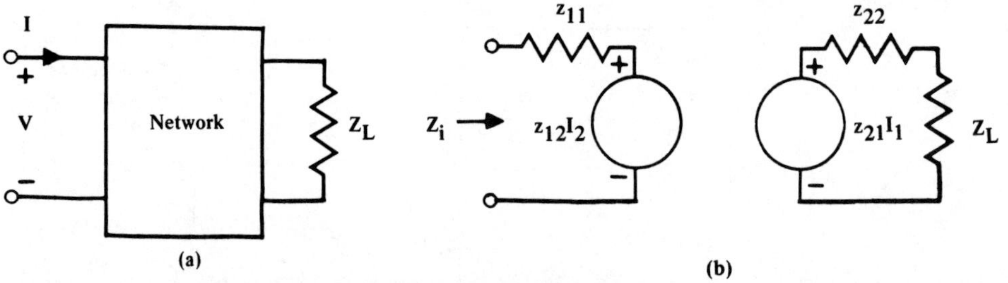

Fig. 1.10.4 (a) A terminated network and (b) an equivalent circuit.

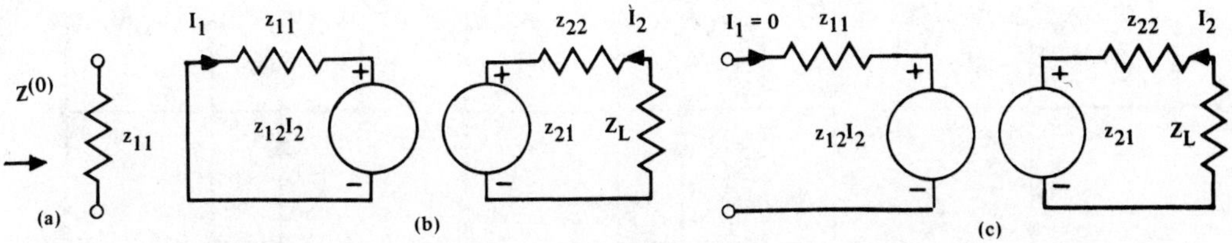

Fig. 1.10.5 Calculation of (a) $Z^{(0)}$, (b) T_s, and (c) T_∞ for the z_{21} source in Example 1.10.4.

$$T_\infty = I_1 = 0 \tag{1.10.23}$$

Substituting Eqs. 1.10.21–1.10.23 in Eq. 1.10.18, the input impedance under normal operating conditions equals

$$Z_i = Z^{(0)}\frac{1 - T_s}{1 - T_\infty} = z_{11}\left[1 - \frac{z_{12}z_{21}}{z_{11}(z_{22} + Z_L)}\right] = \frac{\Delta_z + Z_L z_{11}}{z_{22} + Z_L} \tag{1.10.24}$$

It is extremely useful that such a result can be found with relative ease.

EXAMPLE 1.10.5 Calculate the input impedance to the transistor network shown in Fig. 1.10.6a.[18] Use the ideal transistor model of Table 1.3.1 where $1/h_{11} = h_{22} = 0$.

Solution The equivalent circuit using the ideal transistor model is shown in Fig. 1.10.6b. Let us select the $\beta_1 i_{b1}$ source for the return ratio calculation. The equivalent circuit when β_1 is set to zero is shown in Fig. 1.10.7a. The input impedance equals

$$Z^{(0)} = Z_L \tag{1.10.25}$$

The return ratio T_s for β_1 under short-circuit input conditions is determined from Fig. 1.10.7b. Since we essentially have two independent sources driving the network, we can use superposition and write directly that

$$T_s = i_{b1} = -\beta_1\frac{R_2}{R_1 + R_2} + \beta_1\beta_2\frac{R_1}{R_1 + R_2} = \frac{\beta_1}{R_1 + R_2}(-R_2 + \beta_2 R_1) \tag{1.10.26}$$

The return ratio T_∞ for β_1 under open-circuit input conditions is determined from Fig. 1.10.7c. Again using superposition, then

$$T_\infty = i_{b1} = -\beta_1\frac{R_2}{R_1 + R_2} - \beta_1\beta_2\frac{R_2}{R_1 + R_2} = -\frac{\beta_1}{R_1 + R_2}(R_2 + \beta_2 R_2) \tag{1.10.27}$$

Thus, from Eq. 1.10.18, the input impedance to this network equals

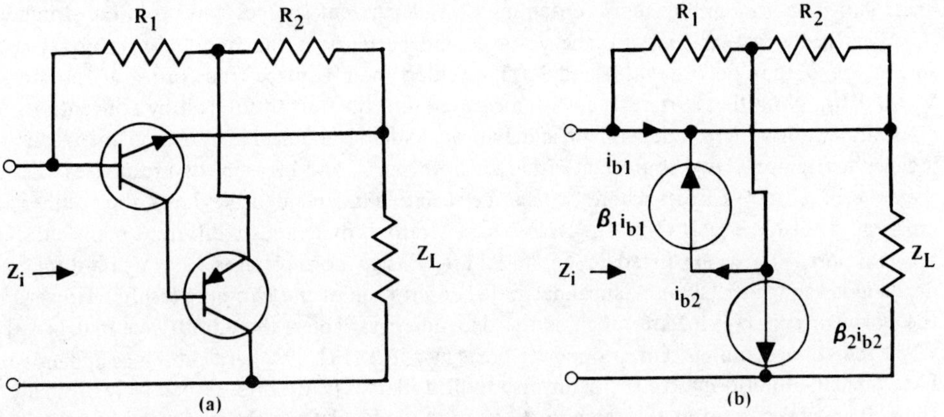

Fig. 1.10.6 (a) Transistor network and (b) ideal equivalent.

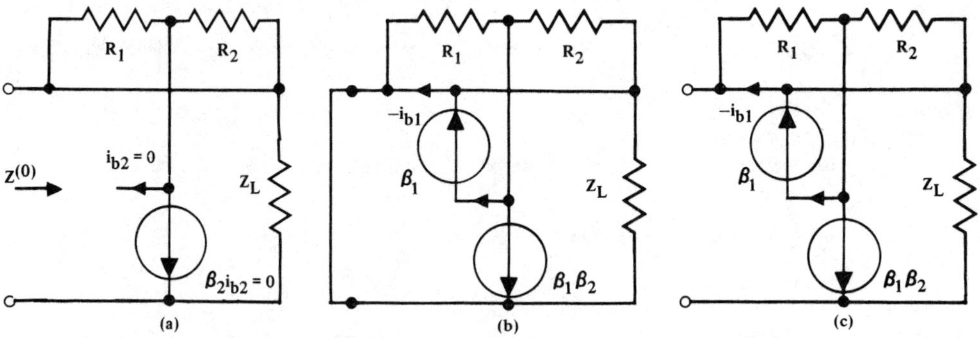

Fig. 1.10.7 Calculation of (a) $Z^{(0)}$, (b) T_s, and (c) T_∞ for the β_1 source in Example 1.10.5.

$$Z_i = Z^{(0)} \frac{1 - T_s}{1 - T_\infty} = Z_L \frac{1 + \dfrac{\beta_1}{R_1 + R_2}(R_2 - \beta_2 R_1)}{1 + \dfrac{\beta_1}{R_1 + R_2}(R_2 + \beta_2 R_1)} = -Z_L \frac{\beta_1\beta_2 R_1 - (R_1 + R_2 + \beta_1 R_2)}{\beta_1\beta_2 R_2 + (R_1 + R_2 + \beta_1 R_2)} \tag{1.10.28}$$

Therefore, when the transistor gains $\beta_1, \beta_2 \gg 1$,

$$\lim_{\beta_1, \beta_2 \to \infty} Z_i = -Z_L \frac{R_1}{R_2} \tag{1.10.29}$$

This device is called a negative impedance converter (NIC). This form was proposed by Larky.[19]

We note in passing that the input impedance to multiple active-source networks can sometimes be more easily analyzed using a generalized form of Blackman's immittance relation described by Mulligan.[18] Also since a passive element can be represented using a dependent source, Blackman's immittance relation can also be applied to networks which appear to contain no controlled sources.

1.11 TWO-PORT ANALYSIS

We have described the modelling of passive and active elements in one-port networks. Now we consider two-ports or two-terminal pair networks as shown in Fig. 1.10.1. Again we describe linear and time-invariant systems containing no independent sources and no initial stored energy.

Electrically we can measure the voltages and currents at the input port as $v_1(t)$ and $i_1(t)$ and at the output port as $v_2(t)$ and $i_2(t)$. Taking their Laplace transforms, we obtain V_1, I_1, V_2, and I_2. Note that current is always measured *into* the port of interest by convention. Mathematically, we have two independent and two dependent variables. Physically this means we can independently apply two sources at either or both ports, and measure two responses. Essentially then, we have four variables where two can be specified independently. Thus, the number of combinations available equals $C_2^4 = 4!/(2!2!) = 6$. Therefore, there are six different representations for the two-port. These are listed in Table 1.11.1. When port voltages (V_1, V_2) are taken as the dependent variables, the impedance matrix [z] description of the two-port results. However, when the port currents (I_1, I_2) are taken as the dependent variables, the admittance matrix [y] arises. When the voltage and current at opposite ports (V_1, I_2) or (I_1, V_2) are chosen as dependent variables, then the hybrid matrix [h] or inverse hybrid matrix [g] results, respectively. Finally, when the voltage and current at the same port (V_1, I_1) or (V_2, I_2) are chosen, the chain matrix [A] or inverse chain matrix [a] results, respectively. The particular description which is used in a prob-

Table 1.11.1 Two-port descriptions.

1. Impedance matrix [z]

$$\begin{bmatrix} V_1 \\ V_2 \end{bmatrix} = \begin{bmatrix} z_{11} & z_{12} \\ z_{21} & z_{22} \end{bmatrix} \begin{bmatrix} I_1 \\ I_2 \end{bmatrix}$$

2. Admittance matrix [y]

$$\begin{bmatrix} I_1 \\ I_2 \end{bmatrix} = \begin{bmatrix} y_{11} & y_{12} \\ y_{21} & y_{22} \end{bmatrix} \begin{bmatrix} V_1 \\ V_2 \end{bmatrix}$$

3. Hybrid matrix [h]

$$\begin{bmatrix} V_1 \\ I_2 \end{bmatrix} = \begin{bmatrix} h_{11} & h_{12} \\ h_{21} & h_{22} \end{bmatrix} \begin{bmatrix} I_1 \\ V_2 \end{bmatrix}$$

4. Inverse hybrid matrix [g]

$$\begin{bmatrix} I_1 \\ V_2 \end{bmatrix} = \begin{bmatrix} g_{11} & g_{12} \\ g_{21} & g_{22} \end{bmatrix} \begin{bmatrix} V_1 \\ I_2 \end{bmatrix}$$

5. Chain matrix [A]

$$\begin{bmatrix} V_1 \\ I_1 \end{bmatrix} = \begin{bmatrix} A & B \\ C & D \end{bmatrix} \begin{bmatrix} V_2 \\ -I_2 \end{bmatrix}$$

6. Inverse chain matrix [a]

$$\begin{bmatrix} V_2 \\ I_2 \end{bmatrix} = \begin{bmatrix} a & b \\ c & d \end{bmatrix} \begin{bmatrix} V_1 \\ -I_1 \end{bmatrix}$$

lem depends upon the excitation sources, their placement, and the desired responses. Two-port representations are a way of succinctly and completely describing the system while suppressing all detail of internal structure.

It is useful to determine the equivalent circuits under these different representations. These are easily drawn by simply drawing the circuit from the two-port equations. Each equation is viewed either as a Kirchhoff node or loop equation. For example, consider the impedance description where

$$\begin{aligned} V_1 &= z_{11}I_1 + z_{12}I_2 \\ V_2 &= z_{21}I_1 + z_{22}I_2 \end{aligned} \tag{1.11.1}$$

The first equation simply says that the voltage at the input port equals the voltage drop $z_{11}I_1$ due to input impedance z_{11} plus the voltage contribution $z_{12}I_2$ due to output current flow. Thus, we may draw the input circuit equivalent as shown in Fig. 1.11.1. The output circuit follows in the same manner. A slightly different equivalent circuit arises when we rearrange the two-port equations as

$$\begin{aligned} V_1 &= (z_{11} - z_{12})I_1 + z_{12}(I_1 + I_2) \\ V_2 &= (z_{22} - z_{12})I_2 + z_{12}(I_1 + I_2) + (z_{21} - z_{12})I_1 \end{aligned} \tag{1.11.2}$$

Then the second equivalent circuit in Fig. 1.11.1 results. The difference is that the second representation must be used in systems having a common ground between input and output. The first representation is used for systems not having a common ground. Notice that the chain and inverse chain parameters do not have an equivalent circuit.

It is a simple matter to determine any of the two-port parameters by arbitrarily setting a port voltage to zero (by shorting the port) or a port current to zero (by opening the port) and calculating an immittance or gain. For example, we see by inspection that the impedance parameters equal

$$z_{11} = V_1/I_1 \big|_{I_2=0} = \text{open-circuit input impedance} \qquad z_{12} = V_1/I_2 \big|_{I_1=0} = \text{open-circuit reverse transfer impedance}$$

$$z_{21} = V_2/I_1 \big|_{I_2=0} = \text{open-circuit forward transfer impedance} \qquad z_{22} = V_2/I_2 \big|_{I_1=0} = \text{open-circuit output impedance} \tag{1.11.3}$$

The admittance parameters are determined in the same fashion as the impedance parameters, but with the ports short-circuited. The remaining parameters are determined under various combinations of open- and short-circuits.

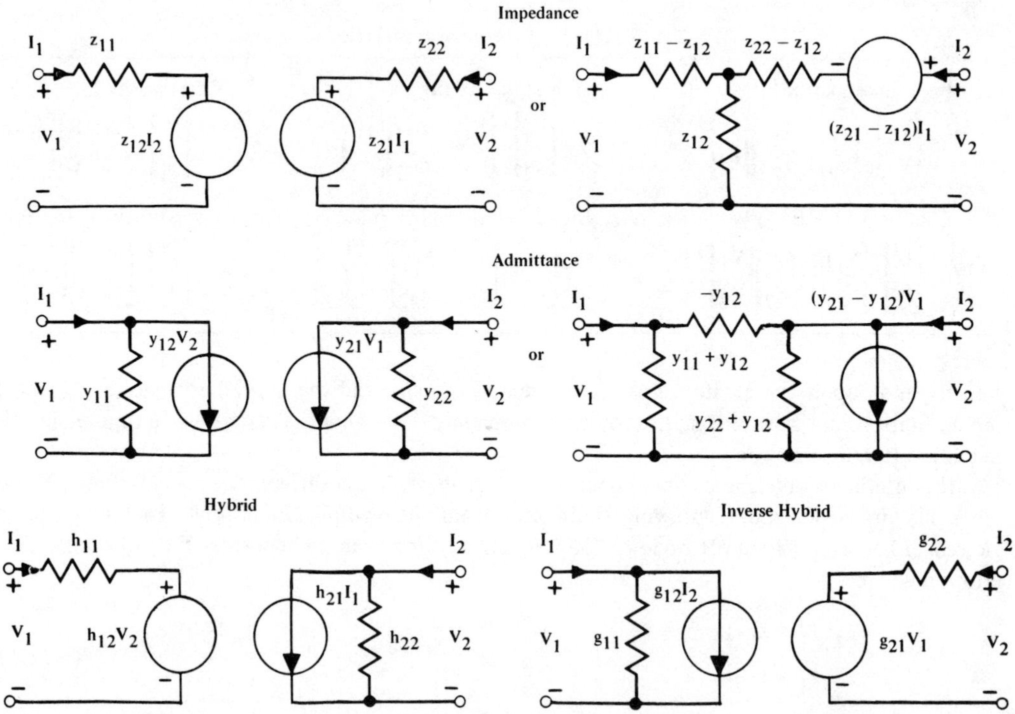

Fig. 1.11.1 Equivalent circuits for various two-port representations.

EXAMPLE 1.11.1 Determine the impedance parameters for the T network of Fig. 1.11.2 using the basic two-port descriptions, and then the equivalent circuit. Is the network reciprocal?

Solution Applying the impedance parameter definitions directly, we see that

$$z_{11} = V_1/I_1 \big|_{I_2=0} = Z_1 + Z_3, \quad z_{22} = V_2/I_2 \big|_{I_1=0} = Z_2 + Z_3$$
$$z_{12} = V_1/I_2 \big|_{I_1=0} = Z_3, \quad z_{21} = V_2/I_1 \big|_{I_2=0} = Z_3 \tag{1.11.4}$$

Since $z_{12} = z_{21}$, the network is reciprocal by definition as we shall discuss in a moment. Alternatively, simply matching coefficients using the z-parameter equivalent circuit of Fig. 1.11.1 gives

$$z_{11} - z_{12} = Z_1, \quad z_{22} - z_{12} = Z_2, \quad z_{12} = z_{21} = Z_3 \tag{1.11.5}$$

so that solving Eq. 1.11.5 for z_{11} and z_{22} gives

$$z_{11} = Z_1 + Z_3, \quad z_{22} = Z_2 + Z_3 \tag{1.11.6}$$

Now let us review the ways in which the two-port parameters are determined. We can either manipulate a system of node or loop equations into the proper form,[20] or determine the parameters using circuit theory. Often, when the networks are simple, the parameters can be written by inspection. When these parameters are determined experimentally, we inject a voltage or a current at the appropriate port and measure the required response. Usually sinusoidal signals are used and measurements are made in ac steady-state. The magnitude and angle of the output/input phasor ratio is plotted versus frequency on log-log paper which forms a Bode plot of the response. We then fit asymptotic approximations to the response using the techniques to be discussed in Chap. 2. In this way, we obtain an expression for the immittance or gain in ac steady-state. By setting $\omega = s/j$ (analytic continuation), we obtain the corresponding matrix element $x_{ij}(s)$.

As mentioned earlier, the particular description which is used to describe a device depends

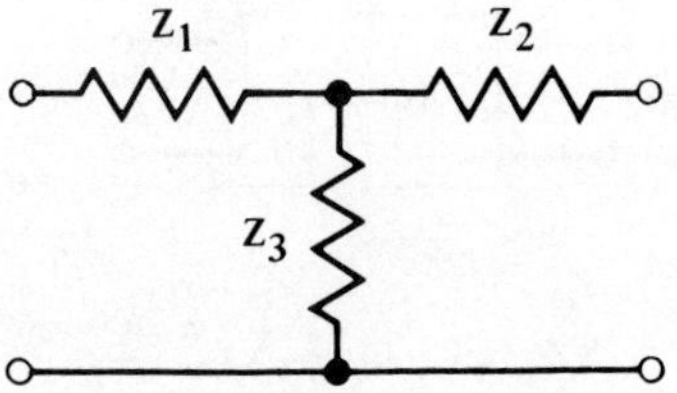

Fig. 1.11.2 T network.

upon its model. For example, consider the devices used to obtain the controlled sources listed in Table 1.3.1. Comparing their models with the two-port equivalent circuits of Fig. 1.11.1, we see that bipolar transistors (ICIS) have h models, FET's and pentodes (VCIS) have y models, and operational amplifiers and triodes (VCVS) have g models.

EXAMPLE 1.11.2 An operational amplifier (or simply op amp) is often used for constructing active filters. Determine the equivalent circuit of a 741 op amp having the following typical parameters:

Input resistance = 2 MΩ	Forward voltage gain = 106 dB
Output resistance = 75 Ω	Reverse voltage gain = Negligible

Solution Comparing the specifications with the two-port representations, the g-parameters appear to be the best suited. Calculating the g-parameters for the op amp gives

$$g_{11} = 1/2\ \text{M}\Omega = 0.5\ \mu\mho, \quad g_{12} = 0, \quad g_{21} = 200{,}000, \quad g_{22} = 75\ \Omega \tag{1.11.7}$$

The two-port representation is shown in Fig. 1.11.3b. Note that it is permissible (and sometimes standard) to invert admittances to form impedances for labelling purposes. We will study op amps extensively in Chap. 14.

When the two-port is such that its responses to the same excitation applied at either end are identical, the network is said to be *reciprocal*. Otherwise, it is said to be *nonreciprocal*. In terms of two-port parameters, reciprocal networks have

$$z_{21} = z_{12}, \quad y_{21} = y_{12} \tag{1.11.8}$$

We will see in a moment that this further implies

$$h_{21} = -h_{12}, \quad g_{21} = -g_{12}, \quad \Delta_A = 1, \quad \Delta_a = 1 \tag{1.11.9}$$

In general, networks containing passive elements are reciprocal. The addition of active sources to such networks usually makes them nonreciprocal.

Networks are sometimes also classified as symmetrical/unsymmetrical and balanced/unbalanced. *Symmetrical networks* are networks whose inputs and outputs can be interchanged (i.e., turned end for end) without changing their characteristics. Alternatively stated, symmetrical networks are composed of identical halves. The halves are mirror images about the vertical line that bisects the two-port. This is illustrated in Fig. 1.11.4a with a T network. However, *balanced networks* are composed of identical halves appearing as mirror images about the horizontal line

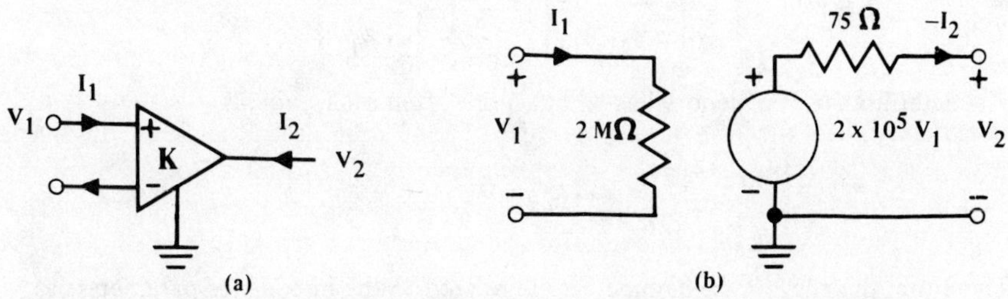

Fig. 1.11.3 (a) Operational amplifier and its (b) g-parameter representation.

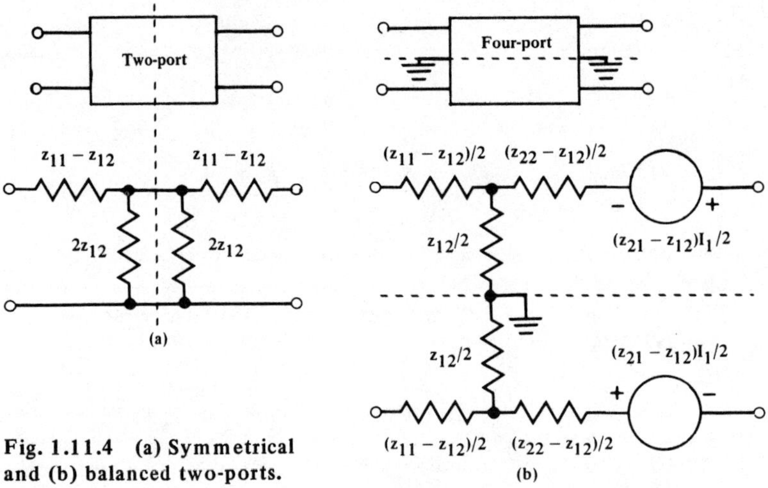

Fig. 1.11.4 (a) Symmetrical and (b) balanced two-ports.

which bisects the network. Thus, they may be viewed as four-port networks whose two input ports and output ports have identical characteristics. Note, however, that since no ground current flows (they are perfectly balanced), the ground can be removed which reduces it to a two-port. Symmetrical networks are always reciprocal and have parameters which satisfy

$$\begin{array}{lllll} z_{11} = z_{22}, & z_{12} = z_{21}; & h_{21} = -h_{12}; & A = D, & \Delta_A = 1 \\ y_{11} = y_{22}, & y_{12} = y_{21}; & g_{21} = -g_{12}; & a = d, & \Delta_a = 1 \end{array} \tag{1.11.10}$$

Balanced networks may or may not be reciprocal.

It should be clear that the various two-port representations are not independent; in fact, they can all be interrelated. For example, let us say we are given the impedance matrix [z] where

$$\begin{bmatrix} V_1 \\ V_2 \end{bmatrix} = [z] \begin{bmatrix} I_1 \\ I_2 \end{bmatrix} \tag{1.11.11}$$

Let us convert it to an admittance matrix representation by solving for (I_1, I_2) using Cramer's rule, or simply by algebraic manipulation. We then obtain

$$\begin{bmatrix} I_1 \\ I_2 \end{bmatrix} = [y] \begin{bmatrix} V_1 \\ V_2 \end{bmatrix} = [z]^{-1} \begin{bmatrix} V_1 \\ V_2 \end{bmatrix} \tag{1.11.12}$$

where the admittance matrix equals

$$[y] = [z]^{-1} = \frac{1}{|z|} \begin{bmatrix} z_{22} & -z_{12} \\ -z_{21} & z_{11} \end{bmatrix}^T = \frac{1}{\Delta_z} \begin{bmatrix} z_{22} & -z_{12} \\ -z_{21} & z_{11} \end{bmatrix} \tag{1.11.13}$$

The determinant of z, denoted as |z| but more often as Δ_z, equals

$$\Delta_z = |z| = \begin{vmatrix} z_{11} & z_{12} \\ z_{21} & z_{22} \end{vmatrix} = z_{11}z_{22} - z_{12}z_{21} \tag{1.11.14}$$

Therefore, the admittance parameters are related to the impedance parameters as

Table 1.11.2 Relations between the various two-port parameters. (From M. S. Ghausi, "Principles and Design of Linear Active Circuits," p. 50, Table 3-3, McGraw-Hill, NY, 1965.)

	$[z_{ij}]$	$[y_{ij}]$	$[g_{ij}]$	$[h_{ij}]$	$\begin{bmatrix} A & B \\ C & D \end{bmatrix}$	$\begin{bmatrix} \mathcal{A} & \mathcal{B} \\ \mathcal{C} & \mathcal{D} \end{bmatrix}$
$[z_{ij}]$	$\begin{matrix} z_{11} & z_{12} \\ z_{21} & z_{22} \end{matrix}$	$\begin{matrix} \frac{y_{22}}{\Delta_y} & -\frac{y_{12}}{\Delta_y} \\ -\frac{y_{21}}{\Delta_y} & \frac{y_{11}}{\Delta_y} \end{matrix}$	$\begin{matrix} \frac{1}{g_{11}} & -\frac{g_{12}}{g_{11}} \\ \frac{g_{21}}{g_{11}} & \frac{\Delta_g}{g_{11}} \end{matrix}$	$\begin{matrix} \frac{\Delta_h}{h_{22}} & \frac{h_{12}}{h_{22}} \\ -\frac{h_{21}}{h_{22}} & \frac{1}{h_{22}} \end{matrix}$	$\begin{matrix} \frac{A}{C} & \frac{\Delta_A}{C} \\ \frac{1}{C} & \frac{D}{C} \end{matrix}$	$\begin{matrix} \frac{\mathcal{D}}{\mathcal{C}} & \frac{1}{\mathcal{C}} \\ \frac{\Delta_{\mathcal{A}}}{\mathcal{C}} & \frac{\mathcal{A}}{\mathcal{C}} \end{matrix}$
$[y_{ij}]$	$\begin{matrix} \frac{z_{22}}{\Delta_z} & -\frac{z_{12}}{\Delta_z} \\ -\frac{z_{21}}{\Delta_z} & \frac{z_{11}}{\Delta_z} \end{matrix}$	$\begin{matrix} y_{11} & y_{12} \\ y_{21} & y_{22} \end{matrix}$	$\begin{matrix} \frac{\Delta_g}{g_{22}} & \frac{g_{12}}{g_{22}} \\ -\frac{g_{21}}{g_{22}} & \frac{1}{g_{22}} \end{matrix}$	$\begin{matrix} \frac{1}{h_{11}} & -\frac{h_{12}}{h_{11}} \\ \frac{h_{21}}{h_{11}} & \frac{\Delta_h}{h_{11}} \end{matrix}$	$\begin{matrix} \frac{D}{B} & -\frac{\Delta_A}{B} \\ -\frac{1}{B} & \frac{A}{B} \end{matrix}$	$\begin{matrix} \frac{\mathcal{A}}{\mathcal{B}} & -\frac{1}{\mathcal{B}} \\ -\frac{\Delta_{\mathcal{A}}}{\mathcal{B}} & \frac{\mathcal{D}}{\mathcal{B}} \end{matrix}$
$[g_{ij}]$	$\begin{matrix} \frac{1}{z_{11}} & -\frac{z_{12}}{z_{11}} \\ \frac{z_{21}}{z_{11}} & \frac{\Delta_z}{z_{11}} \end{matrix}$	$\begin{matrix} \frac{\Delta_y}{y_{22}} & \frac{y_{12}}{y_{22}} \\ -\frac{y_{21}}{y_{22}} & \frac{1}{y_{22}} \end{matrix}$	$\begin{matrix} g_{11} & g_{12} \\ g_{21} & g_{22} \end{matrix}$	$\begin{matrix} \frac{h_{22}}{\Delta_h} & -\frac{h_{12}}{\Delta_h} \\ -\frac{h_{21}}{\Delta_h} & \frac{h_{11}}{\Delta_h} \end{matrix}$	$\begin{matrix} \frac{C}{A} & -\frac{\Delta_A}{A} \\ \frac{1}{A} & \frac{B}{A} \end{matrix}$	$\begin{matrix} \frac{\mathcal{C}}{\mathcal{D}} & -\frac{1}{\mathcal{D}} \\ \frac{\Delta_{\mathcal{A}}}{\mathcal{D}} & \frac{\mathcal{B}}{\mathcal{D}} \end{matrix}$
$[h_{ij}]$	$\begin{matrix} \frac{\Delta_z}{z_{22}} & \frac{z_{12}}{z_{22}} \\ -\frac{z_{21}}{z_{22}} & \frac{1}{z_{22}} \end{matrix}$	$\begin{matrix} \frac{1}{y_{11}} & -\frac{y_{12}}{y_{11}} \\ \frac{y_{21}}{y_{11}} & \frac{\Delta_y}{y_{11}} \end{matrix}$	$\begin{matrix} \frac{g_{22}}{\Delta_g} & -\frac{g_{12}}{\Delta_g} \\ -\frac{g_{21}}{\Delta_g} & \frac{g_{11}}{\Delta_g} \end{matrix}$	$\begin{matrix} h_{11} & h_{12} \\ h_{21} & h_{22} \end{matrix}$	$\begin{matrix} \frac{B}{D} & \frac{\Delta_A}{D} \\ -\frac{1}{D} & \frac{C}{D} \end{matrix}$	$\begin{matrix} \frac{\mathcal{B}}{\mathcal{A}} & \frac{1}{\mathcal{A}} \\ -\frac{\Delta_{\mathcal{A}}}{\mathcal{A}} & \frac{\mathcal{C}}{\mathcal{A}} \end{matrix}$
$\begin{bmatrix} A & B \\ C & D \end{bmatrix}$	$\begin{matrix} \frac{z_{11}}{z_{21}} & \frac{\Delta_z}{z_{21}} \\ \frac{1}{z_{21}} & \frac{z_{22}}{z_{21}} \end{matrix}$	$\begin{matrix} -\frac{y_{22}}{y_{21}} & -\frac{1}{y_{21}} \\ -\frac{\Delta_y}{y_{21}} & -\frac{y_{11}}{y_{21}} \end{matrix}$	$\begin{matrix} \frac{1}{g_{21}} & \frac{g_{22}}{g_{21}} \\ \frac{g_{11}}{g_{21}} & \frac{\Delta_g}{g_{21}} \end{matrix}$	$\begin{matrix} -\frac{\Delta_h}{h_{21}} & -\frac{h_{11}}{h_{21}} \\ -\frac{h_{22}}{h_{21}} & -\frac{1}{h_{21}} \end{matrix}$	$\begin{matrix} A & B \\ C & D \end{matrix}$	$\begin{matrix} \frac{\mathcal{D}}{\Delta_{\mathcal{A}}} & \frac{\mathcal{B}}{\Delta_{\mathcal{A}}} \\ \frac{\mathcal{C}}{\Delta_{\mathcal{A}}} & \frac{\mathcal{A}}{\Delta_{\mathcal{A}}} \end{matrix}$
$\begin{bmatrix} \mathcal{A} & \mathcal{B} \\ \mathcal{C} & \mathcal{D} \end{bmatrix}$	$\begin{matrix} \frac{z_{22}}{z_{12}} & \frac{\Delta_z}{z_{12}} \\ \frac{1}{z_{12}} & \frac{z_{11}}{z_{12}} \end{matrix}$	$\begin{matrix} -\frac{y_{11}}{y_{12}} & -\frac{1}{y_{12}} \\ -\frac{\Delta_y}{y_{12}} & -\frac{y_{22}}{y_{12}} \end{matrix}$	$\begin{matrix} -\frac{\Delta_g}{g_{12}} & -\frac{g_{22}}{g_{12}} \\ -\frac{g_{11}}{g_{12}} & -\frac{1}{g_{12}} \end{matrix}$	$\begin{matrix} \frac{1}{h_{12}} & \frac{h_{11}}{h_{12}} \\ \frac{h_{22}}{h_{12}} & \frac{\Delta_h}{h_{12}} \end{matrix}$	$\begin{matrix} \frac{D}{\Delta_A} & \frac{B}{\Delta_A} \\ \frac{C}{\Delta_A} & \frac{A}{\Delta_A} \end{matrix}$	$\begin{matrix} \mathcal{A} & \mathcal{B} \\ \mathcal{C} & \mathcal{D} \end{matrix}$

$\Delta_z = z_{11}z_{22} - z_{12}z_{21}$ $\Delta_h = h_{11}h_{22} - h_{12}h_{21}$ $\Delta_A = AD - BC$

$\Delta_y = y_{11}y_{22} - y_{12}y_{21}$ $\Delta_g = g_{11}g_{22} - g_{12}g_{21}$ $\Delta_a = ad - bc$

(All matrices appearing in the same row are equivalent. Note that lower case letters and script letters are also equivalent in the inverse chain parameter description.)

$$\begin{bmatrix} y_{11} & y_{12} \\ y_{21} & y_{22} \end{bmatrix} = \begin{bmatrix} z_{22}/\Delta_z & -z_{12}/\Delta_z \\ -z_{21}/\Delta_z & z_{11}/\Delta_z \end{bmatrix} \tag{1.11.15}$$

In like fashion, all of the two-port parameters can be related to one another. The equivalences are listed in Table 1.11.2.

Care must be exercised when converting from one parameter set to another using this table. For example, note that

$$z_{11} = V_1/I_1 \Big|_{I_2=0} = \text{open-circuit input impedance} \qquad h_{11} = V_1/I_1 \Big|_{V_2=0} = \text{short-circuit input impedance} \tag{1.11.16}$$

are not in general equal. This is because z_{11} and h_{11} are defined and measured under different conditions at the output port. Since

$$h_{11} = \Delta_z/z_{22} = z_{11} - z_{12}z_{21}/z_{22} \tag{1.11.17}$$

from Table 1.11.2, they are equal only when z_{12} and/or z_{21} equal zero.

A common error involves reciprocal quantities. For example, since

$$z_{11} = V_1/I_1 \Big|_{I_2=0} = \text{open-circuit input impedance} \qquad g_{11} = I_1/V_1 \Big|_{I_2=0} = \text{open-circuit input admittance} \tag{1.11.18}$$

then $z_{11} = 1/g_{11}$. However, since

$$z_{11} = y_{22}/\Delta_y = [y_{11} - y_{12}y_{21}/y_{22}]^{-1} \tag{1.11.19}$$

then $z_{11} = 1/y_{11}$ only when y_{12} and/or y_{21} equal zero.

It is interesting that some networks are degenerate in the sense that they can be described by only one or more of the two-port descriptions. For example, a two-port having a zero output impedance under the appropriate measurement conditions cannot be described by either a y- or h-matrix. This is because its output admittance becomes infinite.

EXAMPLE 1.11.3 Determine the two-port representation for the ideal transformer. It has zero power loss so that $V_1I_1 = -V_2I_2$, and an output voltage $V_2 = nV_1$ where n is the turns ratio.

Solution The port equations which describe the transformer are $V_2 = nV_1$ and $I_2 = -I_1/n$. The voltages and currents which occur at the ports must simultaneously satisfy these equations so that

$$\begin{bmatrix} V_2 \\ I_2 \end{bmatrix} = \begin{bmatrix} n & 0 \\ 0 & 1/n \end{bmatrix}\begin{bmatrix} V_1 \\ -I_1 \end{bmatrix} = [a]\begin{bmatrix} V_1 \\ -I_1 \end{bmatrix}, \qquad \begin{bmatrix} V_1 \\ I_1 \end{bmatrix} = \begin{bmatrix} 1/n & 0 \\ 0 & n \end{bmatrix}\begin{bmatrix} V_2 \\ -I_2 \end{bmatrix} = [A]\begin{bmatrix} V_2 \\ -I_2 \end{bmatrix} \tag{1.11.20}$$

Therefore, the ideal transformer has the chain or inverse matrix description shown in Eq. 1.11.20. Investigating the other representations of Table 1.11.2, we see that the h- and g-matrix equal

$$[h] = \begin{bmatrix} 0 & 1/n \\ -1/n & 0 \end{bmatrix}, \qquad [g] = \begin{bmatrix} 0 & -n \\ n & 0 \end{bmatrix} \tag{1.11.21}$$

However, no z- or y-matrix representation is possible.

EXAMPLE 1.11.4 A gyrator is an active network which is analogous to a transformer. Its transfer impedance a satisfies $a = V_2/I_1 = -V_1/I_2$, so its power loss is zero. A gyrator is represented as shown in Fig. 1.11.5. Determine the two-port representations which can be used to describe it.

Solution Since $V_2 = aI_1$ and $V_1 = -aI_2$, then the z-matrix equals

$$\begin{bmatrix} V_1 \\ V_2 \end{bmatrix} = \begin{bmatrix} 0 & -a \\ a & 0 \end{bmatrix}\begin{bmatrix} I_1 \\ I_2 \end{bmatrix} = [z]\begin{bmatrix} I_1 \\ I_2 \end{bmatrix} \tag{1.11.22}$$

Here $z_{11} = z_{22} = 0$ so that the open-circuit input and output impedances are zero. Returning to Table 1.11.2, we see that a gyrator cannot be represented by a g- or h-matrix. However, it can be represented in y-, A-, and a-matrix forms as

$$[y] = \begin{bmatrix} 0 & 1/a \\ -1/a & 0 \end{bmatrix}, \qquad [A] = \begin{bmatrix} 0 & a \\ 1/a & 0 \end{bmatrix}, \qquad [a] = \begin{bmatrix} 0 & -a \\ -1/a & 0 \end{bmatrix} \tag{1.11.23}$$

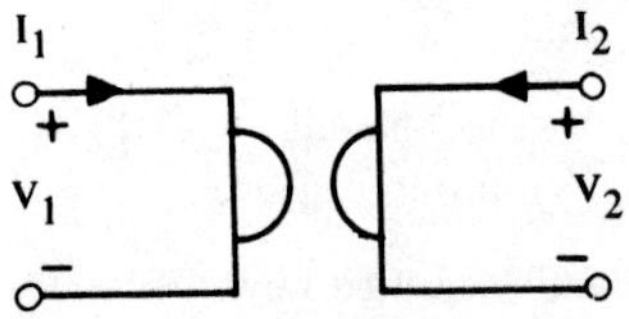

Fig. 1.11.5 Gyrator representation in Example 1.11.4.

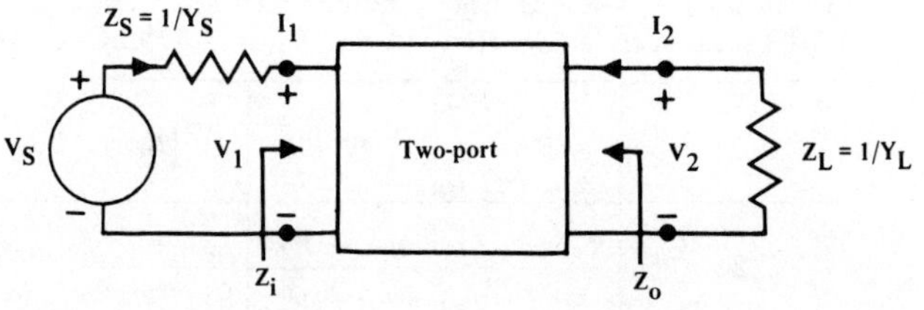

Fig. 1.11.6 Two-port with source and load terminations.

As we mentioned previously, two-port representations are system level descriptions of two-ports. For design purposes we are concerned, among other things, with the input and output impedances under particular loading conditions, and with the voltage and current gains in the system. We can easily manipulate the two-port equations to obtain this information. A general two-port having source and load terminations is shown in Fig. 1.11.6. The source voltage is V_s, the source impedance is Z_S, and the source load is Z_L. Since the source and load impedances are no longer zero or infinite, the input impedance Z_i and output impedance Z_o will be different from the driving-point impedances involved in the two-port parameters. We shall denote the voltage gain as A_v and the current gain as A_i in the loaded conditions.

Let us derive Z_i, Z_o, A_v, and A_i assuming the two-port is described by the impedance parameters $[z_{ij}]$. Since the two-port equations and port constraint equations equal

$$\begin{aligned} V_1 &= z_{11}I_1 + z_{12}I_2 \qquad & V_1 &= V_S - Z_S I_1 \\ V_2 &= z_{21}I_1 + z_{22}I_2 \qquad & V_2 &= -Z_L I_2 \end{aligned} \tag{1.11.24}$$

we must solve these equations simultaneously for the parameters listed above. Since

$$-Z_L I_2 = z_{21}I_1 + z_{22}I_2 \tag{1.11.25}$$

then the current gain A_i equals

$$A_i = \frac{-I_2}{I_1} = \frac{z_{21}}{z_{22} + Z_L} \tag{1.11.26}$$

Therefore, the voltage gain A_v equals

$$A_v = \frac{V_2}{V_1} = \frac{z_{21} - z_{22}A_i}{z_{11} - z_{12}A_i} = \frac{z_{21}Z_L}{\Delta_z + z_{11}Z_L} \tag{1.11.27}$$

while the overall voltage gain A_v' equals

$$A_v' = \frac{V_2}{V_S} = \frac{V_2}{V_1}\frac{V_1}{V_S} = \frac{Z_i}{Z_i + Z_S}A_v = \frac{z_{21}Z_L}{\Delta_z + z_{11}Z_L + Z_S(z_{22} + Z_L)} \tag{1.11.28}$$

The input impedance Z_i is

$$Z_i = \frac{V_1}{I_1} = z_{11} - z_{12}A_i = \frac{\Delta_z + z_{11}Z_L}{z_{22} + Z_L} \tag{1.11.29}$$

The output impedance Z_o is

$$Z_o = \frac{V_2}{I_2} = \frac{\Delta_z + z_{22}Z_S}{z_{11} + Z_S} \tag{1.11.30}$$

by analogy with Z_i where the input/output roles are interchanged.

The complete set of gain and impedance relations for all the parameter sets are listed in Table 1.11.3. These allow rapid calculations to be made for the system under different loading conditions. It is rather remarkable that such important design parameters can be obtained so

Table 1.11.3 Gain and impedance relations. (From M. S. Ghausi, "Principles and Design of Linear Active Circuits," p. 52, Table 3-5, McGraw-Hill, NY, 1965. (Excluding A_v'.))

	$[z_{ij}]$	$[y_{ij}]$	$[g_{ij}]$	$[h_{ij}]$	$\begin{bmatrix} A & B \\ C & D \end{bmatrix}$	$\begin{bmatrix} \mathcal{A} & \mathcal{B} \\ \mathcal{C} & \mathcal{D} \end{bmatrix}$
Z_i	$\dfrac{\Delta_z + z_{11}Z_L}{z_{22} + Z_L}$	$\dfrac{y_{22} + Y_L}{\Delta_y + y_{11}Y_L}$	$\dfrac{g_{22} + Z_L}{\Delta_g + g_{11}Z_L}$	$\dfrac{\Delta_h + h_{11}Y_L}{h_{22} + Y_L}$	$\dfrac{AZ_L + B}{CZ_L + D}$	$\dfrac{\mathcal{D}Z_L + \mathcal{B}}{\mathcal{C}Z_L + \mathcal{A}}$
Z_0	$\dfrac{\Delta_z + z_{22}Z_s}{z_{11} + Z_s}$	$\dfrac{y_{11} + Y_s}{\Delta_y + y_{22}Y_s}$	$\dfrac{\Delta_g + g_{22}Y_s}{g_{11} + Y_s}$	$\dfrac{h_{11} + Z_s}{\Delta_h + h_{22}Z_s}$	$\dfrac{DZ_s + B}{CZ_s + A}$	$\dfrac{\mathcal{A}Z_s + \mathcal{B}}{\mathcal{C}Z_s + \mathcal{D}}$
$A_i = -\dfrac{I_2}{I_1}$	$\dfrac{z_{21}}{z_{22} + Z_L}$	$\dfrac{-y_{21}Y_L}{\Delta_y + y_{11}Y_L}$	$\dfrac{g_{21}}{\Delta_g + g_{11}Z_L}$	$\dfrac{-h_{21}Y_L}{h_{22} + Y_L}$	$\dfrac{1}{D + CZ_L}$	$\dfrac{\Delta_{\mathcal{A}}}{\mathcal{A} + \mathcal{C}Z_L}$
$A_v = \dfrac{V_2}{V_1}$	$\dfrac{z_{21}Z_L}{\Delta_z + z_{11}Z_L}$	$\dfrac{-y_{21}}{y_{22} + Y_L}$	$\dfrac{g_{21}Z_L}{g_{22} + Z_L}$	$\dfrac{-h_{21}}{\Delta_h + h_{11}Y_L}$	$\dfrac{Z_L}{B + AZ_L}$	$\dfrac{\Delta_{\mathcal{A}}}{\mathcal{B} + \mathcal{D}Z_L}$

$A_v' = \dfrac{V_2}{V_S}$	$\dfrac{z_{21}Z_L}{\Delta_z + z_{11}Z_L + Z_S(z_{22} + Z_L)}$	$\dfrac{-y_{21}}{y_{22} + Y_L + Z_S(\Delta_y + y_{11}Y_L)}$
	$\dfrac{-h_{21}}{Z_S(h_{22} + Y_L) + (\Delta_h + h_{11}Y_L)}$	$\dfrac{g_{21}Z_L}{g_{22} + Z_L + Z_S(\Delta_g + g_{11}Z_L)}$
	$\dfrac{Z_L}{Z_S(D + CZ_L) + (AZ_L + B)}$	$\dfrac{\Delta_a}{b + dZ_L + Z_S(cZ_L + a)}$

rapidly once the basic two-port description is known.

Often two-ports are interconnected in certain standard arrangements. These series and parallel arrangements are shown in Fig. 1.11.7.[21] There are $2^2 = 4$ possibilities for such interconnections. In such arrangements, the individual two-port parameters of each network can be added directly. For example, in the series-series arrangement, the overall impedance matrix is the sum of the two individual impedance matrices, or

$$[z] = [z^a] + [z^b] \tag{1.11.31}$$

One must be careful that such interconnections do not disturb the individual parameter sets (e.g., form ground loops). The validity of tests to insure that this is true are called the *Brune tests*. If either of the individual two-port parameters are modified, an ideal transformer having unity turns ratio must be used on the input or output of one network to provide the necessary isolation. We shall not pursue this further.[22] Note that the individual chain and inverse chain matrices multiply in the cascade connection which is a useful result.

EXAMPLE 1.11.5 Derive the admittance matrix for the twin-T network of Fig. 1.11.8a. Determine the admittance matrix for the symmetrical twin-T which has $R_1 = R_2 = R$, $R_3 = R/2$, $C_1 = C_2 = C$, and $C_3 = 2C$. Find its gain.

Solution The twin-T is composed of two T's in parallel. Thus, if we find the y-parameters for each individual T network, then we simply add them to find the y-parameters of the twin-T. The individual T networks are shown in Fig. 1.11.8b. Using the results of Example 1.11.1, their matrices are

$$[z'] = \begin{bmatrix} R_1 + \dfrac{1}{sC_3} & \dfrac{1}{sC_3} \\ \dfrac{1}{sC_3} & R_2 + \dfrac{1}{sC_3} \end{bmatrix} = \begin{bmatrix} \dfrac{1 + sR_1C_3}{sC_3} & \dfrac{1}{sC_3} \\ \dfrac{1}{sC_3} & \dfrac{1 + sR_2C_3}{sC_3} \end{bmatrix} \tag{1.11.32a}$$

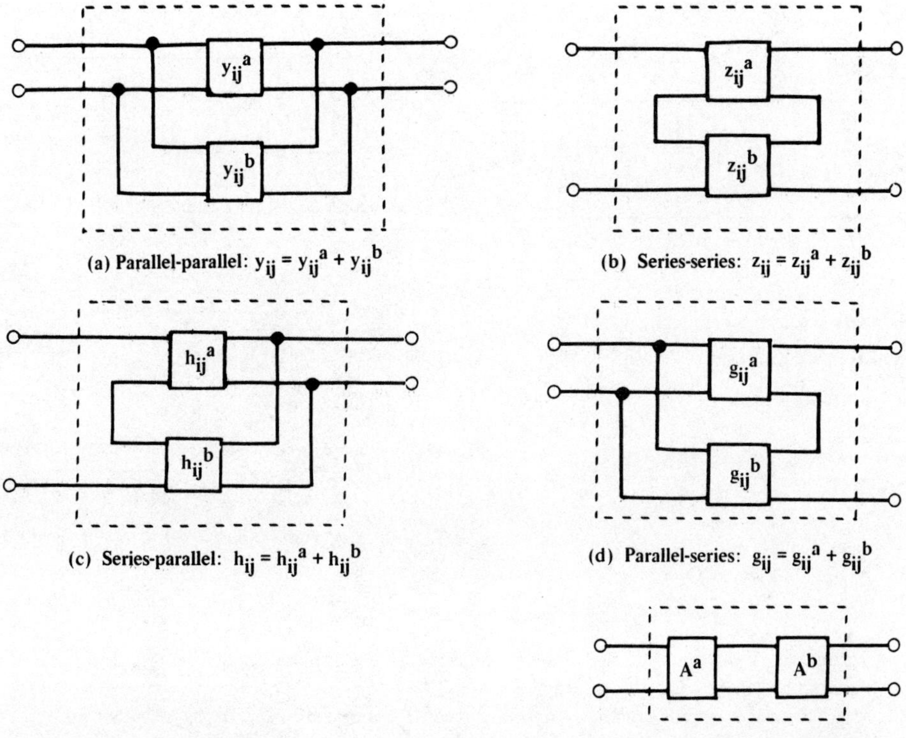

(e) Cascade: $[A] = [A^a][A^b]$

$[a] = [a^a][a^b]$

Fig. 1.11.7 Some standard two-port interconnections.

$$[z''] = \begin{bmatrix} R_3 + \dfrac{1}{sC_1} & R_3 \\ R_3 & R_3 + \dfrac{1}{sC_2} \end{bmatrix} = \begin{bmatrix} \dfrac{1 + sR_3C_1}{sC_1} & R_3 \\ R_3 & \dfrac{1 + sR_3C_2}{sC_2} \end{bmatrix} \tag{1.11.32b}$$

The determinants of the z-matrices equal

$$\begin{aligned} \Delta_{z'} &= \left(\frac{1}{sC_3}\right)^2 [(1 + sR_1C_3)(1 + sR_2C_3) - 1] = \frac{1}{sC_3} [sR_1R_2C_3 + (R_1 + R_2)] \\ \Delta_{z''} &= \frac{1}{s^2C_1C_2} [(1 + sR_3C_1)(1 + sR_3C_2) - s^2R_3^2C_1C_2] = \frac{s(R_3C_1 + R_3C_2) + 1}{s^2C_1C_2} \end{aligned} \tag{1.11.33}$$

Therefore, from Table 1.11.2, we can write the y-matrices of the individual T networks as

$$\begin{aligned} [y'] &= \frac{1}{\Delta_{z'}} \begin{bmatrix} z'_{22} & -z'_{12} \\ -z'_{21} & z'_{11} \end{bmatrix} = \frac{1}{sR_1R_2C_3 + (R_1 + R_2)} \begin{bmatrix} 1 + sR_2C_3 & -1 \\ -1 & 1 + sR_1C_3 \end{bmatrix} \\ [y''] &= \frac{1}{sR_3(C_1 + C_2) + 1} \begin{bmatrix} sC_1(1 + sR_3C_2) & -s^2R_3C_1C_2 \\ -s^2R_3C_1C_2 & sC_2(1 + sR_3C_1) \end{bmatrix} \end{aligned} \tag{1.11.34}$$

The y-matrix of the twin-T network must therefore equal the sum of $[y']$ and $[y'']$ which is

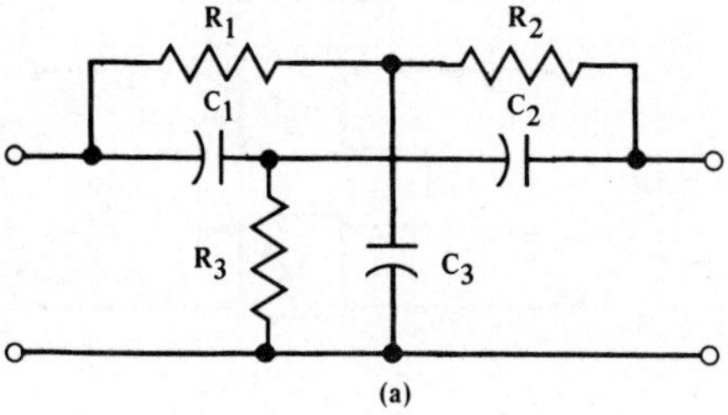

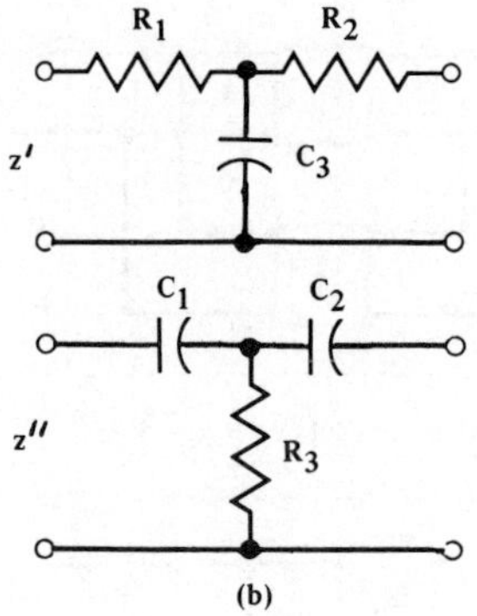

Fig. 1.11.8 (a) General twin-T network and its (b) individual T's.

$$\begin{bmatrix} \dfrac{1 + sR_2C_3}{sR_1R_2C_3 + (R_1 + R_2)} + \dfrac{sC_1(1 + sR_3C_2)}{sR_3(C_1 + C_2) + 1} & \dfrac{-1}{sR_1R_2C_3 + (R_1 + R_2)} - \dfrac{s^2R_3C_1C_2}{sR_3(C_1 + C_2) + 1} \\ \dfrac{-1}{sR_1R_2C_3 + (R_1 + R_2)} - \dfrac{s^2R_3C_1C_2}{sR_3(C_1 + C_2) + 1} & \dfrac{1 + sR_1C_3}{sR_1R_2C_3 + (R_1 + R_2)} + \dfrac{sC_2(1 + sR_3C_1)}{sR_3(C_1 + C_2) + 1} \end{bmatrix} \tag{1.11.35}$$

from Fig. 1.11.8a. Although this result has required considerable algebra, this is still one of the shortest methods for obtaining these parameters.

Now the y-matrix of the symmetrical twin-T can be easily determined. Substituting $R_1 = R_2 = 2R_3 = R$ and $C_1 = C_2 = C_3/2 = C$ into Eq. 1.11.35, then

$$[y] = \frac{1}{1 + sRC}\begin{bmatrix} (1/2R)(1 + s2RC) + sC(1 + sRC/2) & -(1/2R) - (sRC/2)^2 \\ -(1/2R) - (sRC/2)^2 & (1/2R)(1 + s2RC) + sC(1 + sRC/2) \end{bmatrix}$$

$$= \frac{1/2R}{1 + s_n}\begin{bmatrix} 1 + 4s_n + s_n^2 & -(1 + s_n^2) \\ -(1 + s_n^2) & 1 + 4s_n + s_n^2 \end{bmatrix} \tag{1.11.36}$$

where $s_n = sRC$. The open-circuit voltage gain and short-circuit current gain of the symmetrical twin-T equal

$$A_v = A_i = -\frac{y_{21}}{y_{22}} = \frac{1 + s_n^2}{1 + 4s_n + s_n^2} \tag{1.11.37}$$

In Chap. 2, we will see that the twin-T is a notch filter having $\omega_o = 1/RC$ and $\gamma = 2$ or $Q = ¼$.

1.12 THEVENIN AND NORTON EQUIVALENTS

In discussing one-port and two-port representations, we specified that the systems being considered were linear, time-invariant, and contained no independent sources or initial stored energy. Recall that initial stored energy in capacitors and inductors can be accounted for by including initial condition generators in their models, and that these generators are also independent sources. In the most general sense then, the one- and two-port representations previously discussed apply to linear and time-invariant systems containing no independent sources. We can remove this restriction by considering one-ports and two-ports from a more general standpoint. This generalization, although conceptually simple, has historically been overlooked except in the one-port case. In this situation, the more general representation has been called the *Thevenin* and *Norton* equivalents. From here on, we will refer to this generalized case when we speak of one- and two-ports.

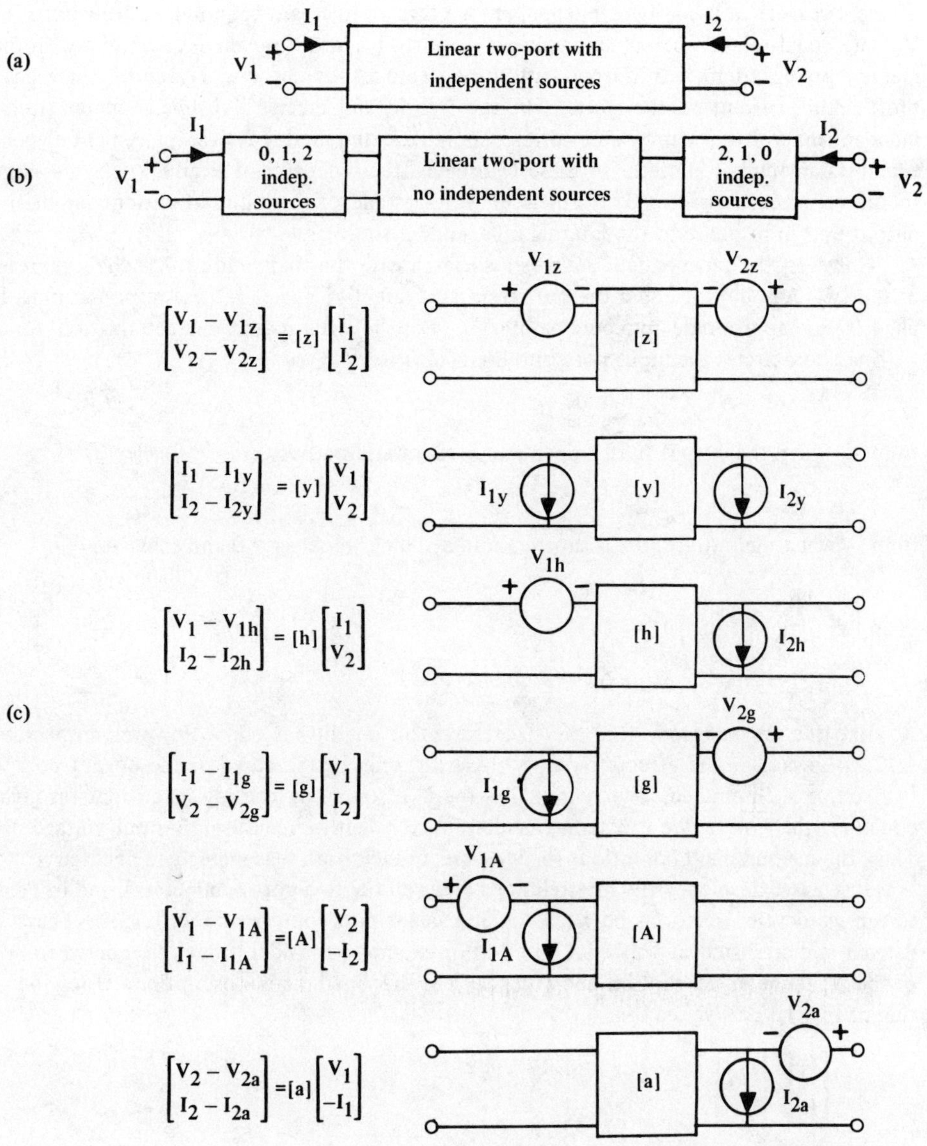

Fig. 1.12.1 Various characterizations of two-ports containing independent sources.

Let us consider the two-port case first.[23] Assume that the two-port network contains n independent sources as shown in Fig. 1.12.1a. Alternatively, we may view the network as an (n + 2)-port containing no independent sources. Since the system is linear and time-invariant, superposition can be applied. Thus, the effects of the n independent voltage and current sources at the n ports superimpose at ports 1 and 2. However, the same effects can be *produced* at ports 1 and 2 by inserting two independent sources at ports 1 and/or 2 and setting the n independent voltage and current sources at the remaining n ports to zero. This is shown in Fig. 1.12.1b. The type and placement of the two sources depend upon the parameter set chosen to characterize the two-port network. The matrix describing the two-port is found with the n internal independent sources set to zero.

The various representations are shown in Fig. 1.12.1c. When the z-parameter representation of the two-port is used, two independent voltage sources are required at both ports. V_{1z} and V_{2z} are equal to the open-circuit voltages at ports 1 and 2, respectively. Similarly, in the y-parameter representation, two independent current sources are needed. I_{1y} and I_{2y} are equal to the short-circuit current at the ports. In the hybrid and inverse hybrid parameter situations, an independent voltage source and current source are required. Source placement depends upon which parameter set is used. In these four cases, the independent source values are simply equal to the (Laplace transformed) open-circuit voltages and/or short-circuit currents at the input and output port in response to the internal independent sources.

However, the independent sources associated with the chain and inverse chain representations of the two-port do not equal the port responses directly. Instead, these responses must be multiplied by the appropriate two-port parameter. For the chain matrix characterization, for example, we first short-circuit the input port, and then calculate V_{1A} as

$$V_{1A} = -AV_2, \qquad I_2 = 0 \tag{1.12.1}$$

from V_2 when the output port is open-circuited, or alternatively,

$$V_{1A} = BI_2, \qquad V_2 = 0 \tag{1.12.2}$$

from I_2 when the output port is short-circuited. Then we set $I_1 = 0$ and calculate

$$I_{1A} = -CV_2, \qquad I_2 = 0 \tag{1.12.3}$$

or alternatively,

$$I_{1A} = DI_2, \qquad V_2 = 0 \tag{1.12.4}$$

At first, the engineer may find these measurement conditions odd. However, inspection of Fig. 1.12.1 shows that the effects of V_{1A} alone can only be measured at the output port when the I_{1A} source is eliminated. We "eliminate" the I_{1A} source by routing its current through a short-circuit at the input. We can then calculate V_{1A} by either measuring output voltage or current. Thus, the measurement conditions for V_{1A} are, in fact, both reasonable and necessary.

Just as we developed the interrelations between the two-port parameters listed in Table 1.11.2 so can we develop relations between the equivalent port sources of Fig. 1.12.1. These are easily derived and are listed in Table 1.12.1.[24] For example, consider the relation between (V_{1z}, V_{2z}) of the z-parameter description and (I_{1y}, I_{2y}) of the y-parameter description. Using the y-description of Fig. 1.12.1, we see that

$$\begin{bmatrix} I_1 \\ I_2 \end{bmatrix} = \begin{bmatrix} I_{1y} \\ I_{2y} \end{bmatrix} \tag{1.12.5}$$

when the input ports are shortened (where $V_1 = V_2 = 0$). Under this condition, the z-description of Fig. 1.12.1 gives

$$\begin{bmatrix} -V_{1z} \\ -V_{2z} \end{bmatrix} = [z]\begin{bmatrix} I_1 \\ I_2 \end{bmatrix} = \begin{bmatrix} z_{11} & z_{12} \\ z_{21} & z_{22} \end{bmatrix}\begin{bmatrix} I_{1y} \\ I_{2y} \end{bmatrix} \tag{1.12.6}$$

or

$$\begin{bmatrix} V_{1z} \\ V_{2z} \end{bmatrix} = \begin{bmatrix} -z_{11} & -z_{12} \\ -z_{21} & -z_{22} \end{bmatrix}\begin{bmatrix} I_{1y} \\ I_{2y} \end{bmatrix} \tag{1.12.7}$$

This matrix equation relates the two sets of port sources.

The independent port generators in Fig. 1.12.1 arise because of the presence of independent sources within the two-port itself. These port generators may be a variety of types. For

Table 1.12.1 Matrix relations between the various pairs of independent sources in Fig. 1.12.1.

	$\begin{bmatrix}V_{1z}\\V_{2z}\end{bmatrix}$	$\begin{bmatrix}I_{1y}\\I_{2y}\end{bmatrix}$	$\begin{bmatrix}V_{1h}\\I_{2h}\end{bmatrix}$	$\begin{bmatrix}I_{1g}\\V_{2g}\end{bmatrix}$	$\begin{bmatrix}V_{1A}\\I_{1A}\end{bmatrix}$	$\begin{bmatrix}V_{2a}\\I_{2a}\end{bmatrix}$
$\begin{bmatrix}V_{1z}\\V_{2z}\end{bmatrix}$	$\begin{matrix}1 & 0\\0 & 1\end{matrix}$	$\begin{matrix}-z_{11} & -z_{12}\\-z_{21} & -z_{22}\end{matrix}$	$\begin{matrix}1 & -z_{12}\\0 & -z_{22}\end{matrix}$	$\begin{matrix}-z_{11} & 0\\-z_{21} & 1\end{matrix}$	$\begin{matrix}1 & -z_{11}\\0 & -z_{21}\end{matrix}$	$\begin{matrix}0 & -z_{12}\\1 & -z_{22}\end{matrix}$
$\begin{bmatrix}I_{1y}\\I_{2y}\end{bmatrix}$	$\begin{matrix}-y_{11} & -y_{12}\\-y_{21} & -y_{22}\end{matrix}$	$\begin{matrix}1 & 0\\0 & 1\end{matrix}$	$\begin{matrix}-y_{11} & 0\\-y_{21} & 1\end{matrix}$	$\begin{matrix}1 & -y_{12}\\0 & -y_{22}\end{matrix}$	$\begin{matrix}-y_{11} & 1\\-y_{21} & 0\end{matrix}$	$\begin{matrix}-y_{12} & 0\\-y_{22} & 1\end{matrix}$
$\begin{bmatrix}V_{1h}\\I_{2h}\end{bmatrix}$	$\begin{matrix}1 & -h_{12}\\0 & -h_{22}\end{matrix}$	$\begin{matrix}-h_{11} & 0\\-h_{21} & 1\end{matrix}$	$\begin{matrix}1 & 0\\0 & 1\end{matrix}$	$\begin{matrix}-h_{11} & -h_{12}\\-h_{21} & -h_{22}\end{matrix}$	$\begin{matrix}1 & -h_{11}\\0 & -h_{21}\end{matrix}$	$\begin{matrix}-h_{12} & 0\\-h_{22} & 1\end{matrix}$
$\begin{bmatrix}I_{1g}\\V_{2g}\end{bmatrix}$	$\begin{matrix}-g_{11} & 0\\-g_{21} & 1\end{matrix}$	$\begin{matrix}1 & -g_{12}\\0 & -g_{22}\end{matrix}$	$\begin{matrix}-g_{11} & -g_{12}\\-g_{21} & -g_{22}\end{matrix}$	$\begin{matrix}1 & 0\\0 & 1\end{matrix}$	$\begin{matrix}-g_{11} & 1\\-g_{21} & 0\end{matrix}$	$\begin{matrix}0 & -g_{12}\\1 & -g_{22}\end{matrix}$
$\begin{bmatrix}V_{1A}\\I_{1A}\end{bmatrix}$	$\begin{matrix}1 & -A\\0 & -C\end{matrix}$	$\begin{matrix}0 & B\\1 & D\end{matrix}$	$\begin{matrix}1 & B\\0 & D\end{matrix}$	$\begin{matrix}0 & -A\\1 & -C\end{matrix}$	$\begin{matrix}1 & 0\\0 & 1\end{matrix}$	$\begin{matrix}-A & B\\-C & D\end{matrix}$
$\begin{bmatrix}V_{2a}\\I_{2a}\end{bmatrix}$	$\begin{matrix}-a & 1\\-c & 0\end{matrix}$	$\begin{matrix}b & 0\\d & 1\end{matrix}$	$\begin{matrix}-a & 0\\-c & 1\end{matrix}$	$\begin{matrix}b & 1\\d & 0\end{matrix}$	$\begin{matrix}-a & b\\-c & d\end{matrix}$	$\begin{matrix}1 & 0\\0 & 1\end{matrix}$

example, they could be dc sources whose levels correspond to those of the system in its dc quiescent state. Thus, if V_1 is the input voltage and V_{1z} the dc level, then $(V_1 - V_{1z})$ is the input port voltage fluctuation. The port generators might correspond to the input and output port responses due to initial conditions within the two-port; or they may correspond to contaminating signals due to imperfect power supply filtering (i.e., hum) or pickup of stray signals. It might be that the sources are equivalent noise generators for the two-port and have a statistical nature; the sources may even arise from temperature changes, aging effects, radiation, and other environmental causes. Thus, there are a variety of ways that such generators may arise. In any event, they account for the fluctuations of the signals at the ports due to causes other than input and/or output signal variations in the independent variables associated with the two-port (e.g., I_1 and I_2 in the z-representation).

Let us view the general two-port representation from a different viewpoint. Assume that dependent variable y_i is analytic, and therefore, has a Taylor series representation as

$$y_i(x_1, x_2, \ldots, x_n) = y_i(x_{1o}, x_{2o}, \ldots, x_{no}) + [(x_1 - x_{1o})\partial/\partial x_1 + \ldots + (x_n - x_{no})\partial/\partial x_n]y_i + [(x_1 - x_{1o})\partial/\partial x_1 + \ldots + (x_n - x_{no})\partial/\partial x_n]^2 y_i/2! + \ldots \tag{1.12.8}$$

where $x_{1o}, x_{2o}, \ldots, x_{no}$ are the quiescent values of the independent variables $x_1, x_2, \ldots, x_n$. Then the variation Δy_i in y_i equals

$$\Delta y_i = y_i(x_1, x_2, \ldots, x_n) - y_i(x_{1o}, x_{2o}, \ldots, x_{no}) = [\Delta x_1 \partial/\partial x_1 + \ldots + \Delta x_n \partial/\partial x_n]y_i + \ldots \tag{1.12.9}$$

If the products of the Δx_i^n perturbations and $\partial^n y/\partial x_i^n$ are negligible, then

$$\Delta y_i = \Delta x_1 \partial y/\partial x_1 + \Delta x_2 \partial y/\partial x_2 + \ldots + \Delta x_n \partial y/\partial x_n \tag{1.12.10}$$

This is the linear approximation for the change Δy_i in y_i given the changes Δx_i in all of the independent variables x_i. Comparing this equation with the two-port equation in Fig. 1.12.1 using the impedance representation, we see that Δy_1 and Δx_1 (Δy_2 and Δx_2) correspond to the input (output) port voltage and current, respectively. Notice that Eq. 1.12.8 can be re-expressed as

$$\begin{bmatrix} V_1 \\ V_2 \end{bmatrix} = \begin{bmatrix} z_{11} & z_{12} \\ z_{21} & z_{22} \end{bmatrix} \begin{bmatrix} I_1 \\ I_2 \end{bmatrix} + \begin{bmatrix} \partial y_1/\partial x_3 & \ldots & \partial y_1/\partial x_n \\ \partial y_2/\partial x_3 & \ldots & \partial y_2/\partial x_n \end{bmatrix} \begin{bmatrix} \Delta x_3 \\ \vdots \\ \Delta x_n \end{bmatrix} \tag{1.12.11}$$

where the port generators equal

$$\begin{bmatrix} V_{1z} \\ V_{2z} \end{bmatrix} = \begin{bmatrix} \partial y_1/\partial x_3 & \ldots & \partial y_1/\partial x_n \\ \partial y_2/\partial x_3 & \ldots & \partial y_2/\partial x_n \end{bmatrix} \begin{bmatrix} \Delta x_3 \\ \vdots \\ \Delta x_n \end{bmatrix} \tag{1.12.12}$$

$\Delta x_3, \ldots, \Delta x_n$ are the other independent variables (other than I_1 and I_2) that cause variations in the port voltages V_1 and V_2. Thus, the general two-port may be viewed as a general n-port having (n − 2) additional inputs. This viewpoint allows us to gain another perspective of two-port equivalents.

EXAMPLE 1.12.1 Consider the simple RC low-pass filter shown in Fig. 1.12.2a. Assume that the capacitor has an initial condition $v_c(0) = 1$ volt. Determine the complete z-parameter representation of the two-port.

Solution We can write the z-parameters for the network as

$$[z] = \begin{bmatrix} R_1 + \dfrac{R_2}{1 + sR_2C} & \dfrac{R_2}{1 + sR_2C} \\ \dfrac{R_2}{1 + sR_2C} & \dfrac{R_2}{1 + sR_2C} \end{bmatrix} \tag{1.12.13}$$

by inspection or by using the results of Example 1.11.1. The general description of the two-port is

$$\begin{bmatrix} V_1 - V_{1z} \\ V_2 - V_{2z} \end{bmatrix} = [z] \begin{bmatrix} I_1 \\ I_2 \end{bmatrix} \tag{1.12.14}$$

from Fig. 1.12.1. Thus, we can evaluate V_{1z} and V_{2z} by observing that the port voltages $V_1 = V_{1z}$ and $V_2 = V_{2z}$ when $I_1 = I_2 = 0$ (i.e., under open-circuit conditions). We must therefore calculate the port voltage responses under this condition. Since $v_c(0) = 1$ volt, then we can write that

$$v_1(t) = v_2(t) = v_c(0) \exp(-t/R_2C)\, U_{-1}(t) \tag{1.12.15}$$

or

$$V_{1z}(s) = V_{2z}(s) = \frac{R_2C}{1 + sR_2C} \tag{1.12.16}$$

Therefore, the complete two-port description is shown in Fig. 1.12.2b. It is important to remember that the capacitor now has a *zero* initial condition.

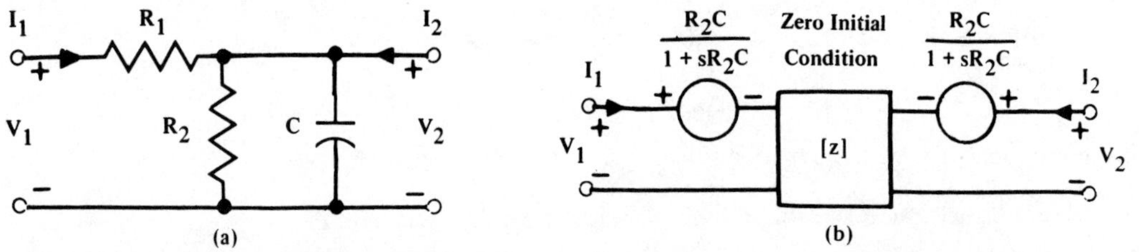

Fig. 1.12.2 (a) RC network with initial condition and its (b) two-port representation.

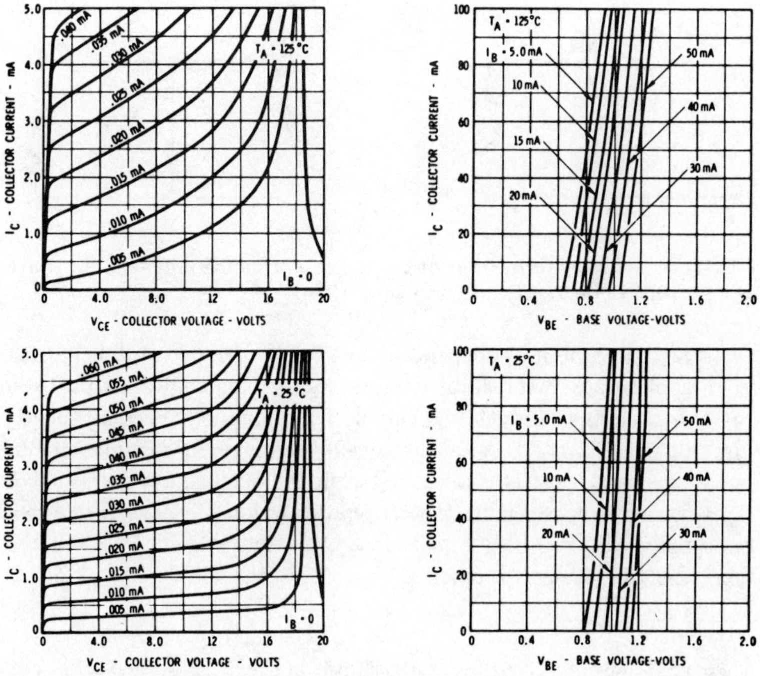

Fig. 1.12.3 Characteristics of a 2N2369A transistor for Example 1.12.2. (From 1970 Fairchild Semiconductor Transistor and Diode Data Catalog, BR-BR-0015-29, p. 2–112, Fairchild Semiconductor, Mt. View, CA, 1970.)

EXAMPLE 1.12.2 The collector characteristics of a 2N2369A high-speed transistor are shown in Fig. 1.12.3 at 25°C and 125°C. Determine the complete h-parameter representation for the transistor including temperature effects. Assume the bias points are $(I_C, V_{CE}, T_o) = (1.5\text{ mA}, 10\text{ V}, 25°\text{C})$ and $(I_B, V_{BE}, T_o) = (0.02\text{ mA}, 0.8\text{ V}, 25°\text{C})$.

Solution The h-parameter set equals

$$\begin{bmatrix} V_1 \\ I_2 \end{bmatrix} = \begin{bmatrix} h_{11} & h_{12} \\ h_{21} & h_{22} \end{bmatrix} \begin{bmatrix} I_1 \\ V_2 \end{bmatrix} + \begin{bmatrix} k_1 \\ k_2 \end{bmatrix} (T - 25^\circ\text{C}) \tag{1.12.17}$$

We can easily determine the parameters as follows. The hybrid parameters equal

$$\begin{aligned} h_{21} &= I_2/I_1 \Big|_{V_{2o},\, T_o} = \frac{1.9 - 1.1\text{ mA}}{0.025 - 0.015\text{ mA}} = \frac{0.8}{0.01} = 80 \\ h_{22} &= I_2/V_2 \Big|_{I_{1o},\, T_o} = \frac{1.6 - 1.4\text{ mA}}{12 - 8\text{ V}} = \frac{0.2\text{ mA}}{4\text{ V}} = 50\mu\mho \end{aligned} \tag{1.12.18}$$

Note that we cannot determine h_{11} or h_{12} from the data shown; h_{11} because we do not have the (V_1, I_1) curves, and h_{12} because we do not have the (V_1, V_2) curves. The temperature effects are included in the two-port by using

$$k_2 = I_2/\Delta T \Big|_{I_{1o},\, V_{2o}} = \frac{3.25 - 1.5\text{ mA}}{125 - 25\,^\circ\text{C}} = \frac{1.75\text{ mA}}{100^\circ\text{C}} = 17.5\ \mu\text{A}/^\circ\text{C} \tag{1.12.19}$$

Again k_1 cannot be evaluated since we do not have the (V_1, I_1) curves.

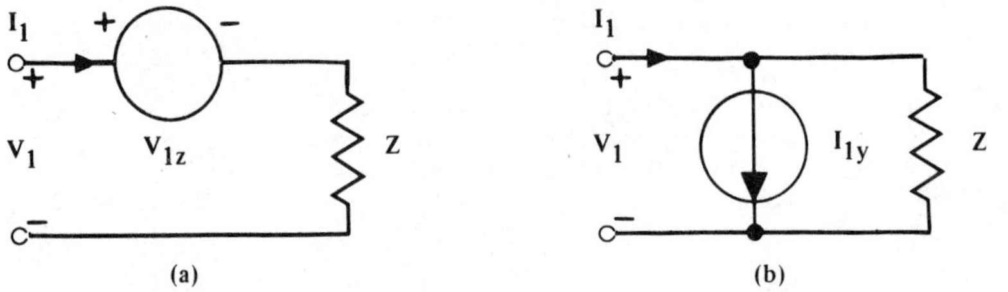

Fig. 1.12.4 Characterizations of one-ports containing independent sources using (a) Thevenin and (b) Norton equivalents.

When the internal independent sources of the two-port have statistical natures such as in noise applications, a statistical interpretation of the equivalent port sources is required. In such cases, conversions between the various representations become slightly more involved and will not be pursued here.[25] A third source, which is useful in some analyses, can be added such that one source pair is perfectly correlated while the other source pair is uncorrelated.[26]

Now let us consider the general representation of one-port networks. Using Fig. 1.12.1, we can simply set $I_2 = 0$ in the impedance characterization or $V_2 = 0$ in the admittance characterization. Then the one-port is described by

$$V_1 - V_{1z} = ZI_1 \quad \text{or} \quad I_1 - I_{1y} = YV_1 \tag{1.12.20}$$

These equations describe the circuits shown in Fig. 1.12.4. The series circuit is called the *Thevenin equivalent* and the shunt circuit is called the *Norton equivalent*. Any one-port network which is linear, time-invariant, and contains independent sources can be represented in this form. It is easy to see that V_{1z} and I_{1y} are related as

$$V_{1z} = -ZI_{1y}, \quad I_{1y} = -YV_{1z} \tag{1.12.21}$$

Referring back to Fig. 1.12.1, we can view the z-, y-, h-, and g-parameter two-port representations as consisting essentially of a pair of Thevenin and/or Norton equivalents. However, each independent source must become a pair of dependent and independent sources. The dependent sources account for signal coupling between the two equivalent circuits. We shall often speak of the Thevenin or Norton equivalent of the port of interest. In such cases, this is the viewpoint we are using.

EXAMPLE 1.12.3 Determine the Thevenin and Norton equivalents for the inductor and capacitor. Interpret the results in the s-domain and the t-domain.

Solution The capacitor is described by the equation $i = Cdv/dt$. From Table 1.8.2, the Laplace transformed equation equals

$$I(s) = sCV(s) - Cv(0) \tag{1.12.22}$$

where $v(0)$ is the initial capacitor voltage. Solving for $V(s)$ yields

$$V(s) = I(s)/sC + v(0)/s \tag{1.12.23}$$

Comparing the V and I equations with the one-port equations, we can draw the Thevenin and Norton equivalents in the s-domain as shown in Fig. 1.12.5. Thus, a capacitor having an initial condition $v(0)$ can be represented as a capacitor with a zero initial condition in series with a step voltage generator $v(0)/s$. Alternatively, it can be represented as a capacitor with a zero initial condition in parallel with an impulse current generator $Cv(0)$. The charge transferred to the capacitor at $t = 0$ equals $Cv(0)$ coulombs which *produces* an initial voltage of $Cv(0)/C = v(0)$. Note that by convention, we label both circuits in terms of *impedance*. The engineer may find the t-domain representation just as useful. Here, we simply take the inverse transform of the $V(s)$ and $I(s)$ equations to obtain the $v(t)$ and $i(t)$ equations, respectively. These equivalents emphasize the presence of the step and impulse initial condition generators.

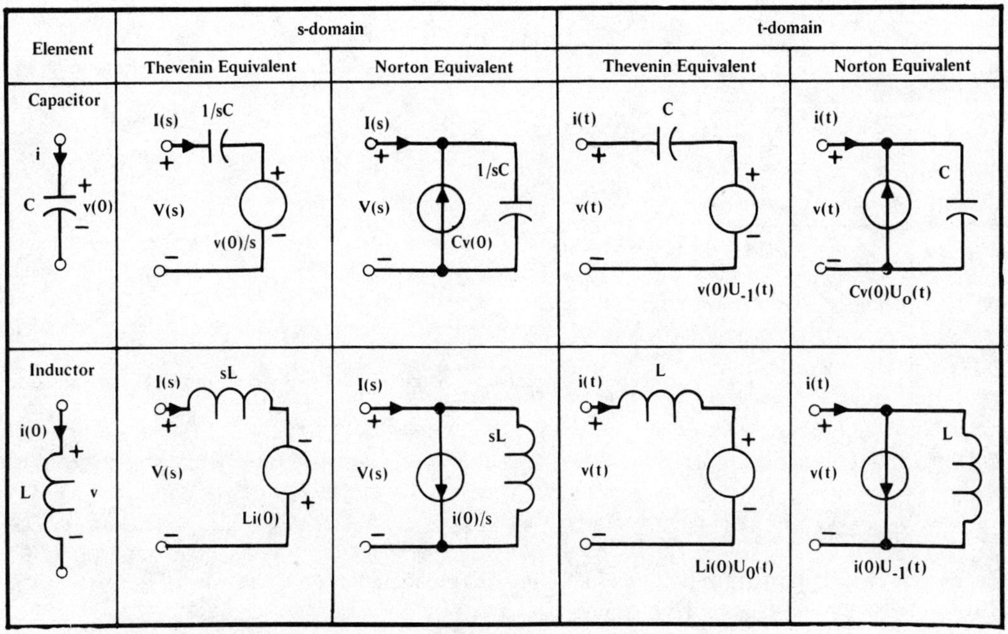

Fig. 1.12.5 Thevenin and Norton equivalents for the capacitor and inductor.

Since the inductor is the dual of the capacitor, we merely need to draw the dual circuits in Fig. 1.12.5 and relabel. Note that in this case, the impulse generator equals Li(0) which represents the flux linkages λ in webers.

When the independent source of the Thevenin or Norton equivalent circuit has a statistical nature, a statistical interpretation of V_{1z} and I_{1y} is required. For example, consider the thermal noise generated by a resistance R, where rms noise voltage equals

$$V_{1z} = e_n = \sqrt{4kTRB} \tag{1.12.24}$$

We shall discuss this result in Chap. 14 when we consider resistors. Equivalently, the rms noise current equals

$$I_{1y} = i_n = \sqrt{4kTGB} = \sqrt{4kTB/R} \tag{1.12.25}$$

The Thevenin and Norton representation of the resistor is shown in Fig. 1.12.4. As with two-ports we may use two sources in a single representation if correlation results are desired.[27]

1.13 PASSIVITY AND ACTIVITY

A network is said to be *passive* if the total energy flowing into the network is nonnegative for all excitations. Any network which is not passive is said to be *active*. For a one-port, the passivity condition is mathematically expressed as

$$E(t) = \int_{-\infty}^{t} v(\tau)i(\tau)\, d\tau \geqslant 0, \qquad \text{all } t \tag{1.13.1}$$

For a two-port,

$$E(t) = \int_{-\infty}^{t} [v_1(\tau)i_1(\tau) + v_2(\tau)i_2(\tau)]\, d\tau \geqslant 0, \qquad \text{all } t \tag{1.13.2}$$

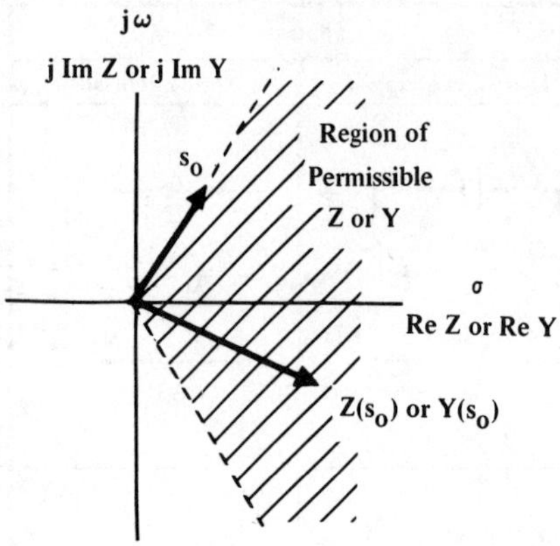

Fig. 1.13.1 Angle requirement for positive-real function.

while for an n-port

$$E(t) = \sum_{i=1}^{n} \int_{-\infty}^{t} v_i(\tau) i_i(\tau)\, d\tau \geq 0, \qquad \text{all } t \tag{1.13.3}$$

We can deduce important relations which the port parameters must satisfy if the network is passive. Begin by considering the one-port.

Brune established the passivity conditions for the one-port.[28] For a one-port to be passive, i.e., to be realizable using passive elements, its input immittance Z(s) or Y(s) must satisfy[29]

$$\text{Re } Z(s) \text{ or } \text{Re } Y(s) \geq 0 \qquad \text{for} \qquad \text{Re } s \geq 0 \tag{1.13.4}$$

An equivalent, but not readily apparent, requirement established by Brune is that

$$|\arg Z(s)| \text{ or } |\arg Y(s)| \leq |\arg s| \leq \pi/2 \tag{1.13.5}$$

The Re F or arg F requirements may be used interchangeably. The angle requirement has a ready graphical interpretation. This is shown in Fig. 1.13.1. The magnitude of the angle of the one-port immittance at a complex frequency s_o must always be less than the magnitude of the angle of s_o itself, for any s_o not in the left-half-plane. When arg s = 0 so that this frequency lies on the positive-real axis, the immittance must also lie on the positive-real axis (i.e., must be real and positive). Thus, immittance functions satisfying this criteria were named *positive-real functions* by Brune.

In testing an immittance function F(s), all values of s in the right-half-plane and its boundary must be used. We can reduce these values to those falling on the boundary itself (the jω-axis) using the maximum modulus theorem when F(s) is rational. Recall that F(s) is *rational* if it has a finite number of pole singularities and no other singularity types. Then the maximum modulus theorem says that F(s) attains its maximum magnitude on the boundary of a region within which and on whose boundary it is analytic.[30] Similarly, F(s) attains its minimum magnitude on the boundary when 1/F(s) has no poles within or on the boundary. A corollary of the maximum modulus theorem says that minimum value of Re F(s) also occurs on the boundary. This corollary allows us to test immittance functions simply along the jω-axis rather than along the closed right-half-plane. When F has poles along the jω-axis, we by-pass them with semicircles of zero radius so that F remains analytic in the region of interest. Thus, the passivity test for a one-port immittance function becomes:

1. F(s) has no poles or zeros in the right-half-plane.
2. Any pole of F(s) on the jω-axis must be simple, with real and positive residue.
3. $\text{Re } F(j\omega) \geq 0$ for $0 \leq \omega \leq \infty$.

Since Re F is an even function, we need not test over the entire $-\infty < \omega < \infty$ range in (3). If all of these conditions are satisfied, the one-port is said to be *passive*. Otherwise, the one-port is said

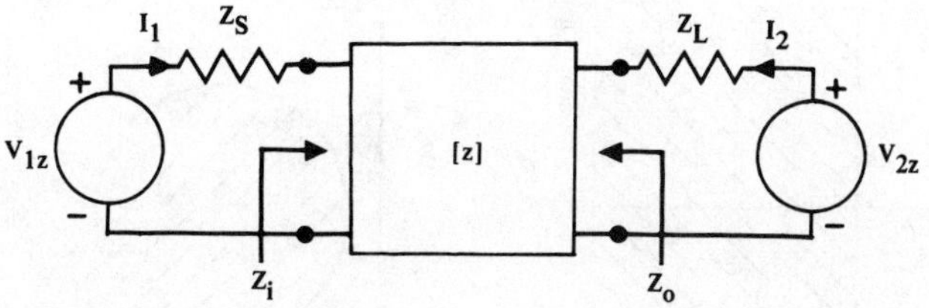

Fig. 1.13.2 Two-port network.

to be *active*. Most functions which the engineer might write at random fail to be positive-real.[31] Brune's condition is very stringent indeed.

These results can be generalized for two-ports. The passivity condition for a two-port described by a z- or y-matrix is:[32]

1. The driving-point immittance functions (z_{11} and z_{22} or y_{11} and y_{22}) have no poles or zeros in the right-half-plane.
2. Any pole of these immittances on the $j\omega$-axis must be simple, with real and positive residues.
3. $\text{Re}\, z_{11}(j\omega)\,\text{Re}\, z_{22}(j\omega) - \text{Re}\, z_{12}(j\omega)\,\text{Re}\, z_{21}(j\omega) \geq |z_{21}(j\omega) - z_{12}(j\omega)|^2/4$, or
$\text{Re}\, y_{11}(j\omega)\,\text{Re}\, y_{22}(j\omega) - \text{Re}\, y_{12}(j\omega)\,\text{Re}\, y_{21}(j\omega) \geq |y_{21}(j\omega) - y_{12}(j\omega)|^2/4$
for $0 \leq \omega \leq \infty$ (1.13.6)

As before, if any of these conditions are violated, the two-port is said to be *active.*

It is important to remember that passivity and activity refer to realizability. Passive networks can be realized using resistors, inductors, capacitors, and transformers. However, active networks require that an active element such as a transistor also be used *and* that it be capable of delivering energy. The use of active elements is necessary but not sufficient to insure activity.

Now that we have reviewed the conditions for passivity and activity, let us reconsider stability which was introduced in Sec. 1.6. We choose to discuss stability here because certain stability tests permit us to consider the network directly rather than the network responses as was done in Sec. 1.6. This discussion will enlarge our viewpoint of both the network and its responses. Sometimes, the concept of activity and instability are confused. Passivity implies inherent stability, but inherent stability does not imply passivity. Instability implies activity, but activity does not imply instability. Finally, potential instability implies activity, but activity does not imply instability.

A two-port is potentially unstable if there is a set of passive loads which, when connected to the two-port, produce an unstable system. Consider the two-port network shown in Fig. 1.13.2 which is driven by voltage sources and terminated in impedances Z_S and Z_L. The input and output impedances equal

$$Z_i = z_{11} - \frac{z_{12}z_{21}}{z_{22} + Z_L} = \frac{z_{11}Z_L + (z_{11}z_{22} - z_{12}z_{21})}{Z_L + z_{22}}$$
$$Z_o = z_{22} - \frac{z_{12}z_{21}}{z_{11} + Z_S} = \frac{z_{22}Z_S + (z_{11}z_{22} - z_{12}z_{21})}{Z_S + z_{11}} \tag{1.13.7}$$

from Table 1.11.3. The port currents equal

$$\begin{bmatrix} I_1 \\ I_2 \end{bmatrix} = \frac{1}{|z|}\begin{bmatrix} z_{11} + Z_S & z_{12} \\ z_{21} & z_{22} + Z_L \end{bmatrix}^T \begin{bmatrix} V_1 \\ V_2 \end{bmatrix} \tag{1.13.8}$$

If the system is to be absolutely stable, then

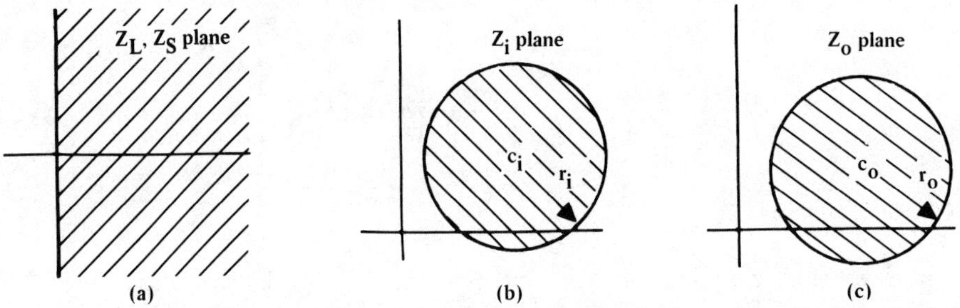

Fig. 1.13.3 Transformation of (a) Z_L and Z_S test values into resulting (b) Z_i and (c) Z_o values.

$$|z| = \begin{vmatrix} z_{11} + Z_S & z_{12} \\ z_{21} & z_{22} + Z_L \end{vmatrix} \neq 0 \tag{1.13.9}$$

for all $s = j\omega$ and passive Z_S and Z_L. This condition is satisfied if and only if

$$\text{Re } Z_i > 0, \text{ all } Z_L \quad \text{and} \quad \text{Re } Z_o > 0, \text{ all } Z_S \tag{1.13.10}$$

so the Brune condition (but without the equality condition) must be satisfied at both the input and output ports. To determine the limitations on the two-port parameters themselves, let us consider Z_i and Z_o. Eq. 1.13.7 is a bilinear transformation between Z_L and Z_i, and Z_S and Z_o, respectively, having the form[33]

$$w = \frac{az + b}{cz + d} \tag{1.13.11}$$

The bilinear transformation always maps circles in the z-plane into circles in the w-plane with straight lines as limiting cases. This is shown in Fig. 1.13.3. Thus, for any passive termination, the input and output impedances must fall within circles having centers

$$c_i = z_{11} - \frac{z_{12}z_{21}}{2 \text{ Re } z_{22}}, \qquad c_o = z_{22} - \frac{z_{12}z_{21}}{2 \text{ Re } z_{11}} \tag{1.13.12}$$

and radii of

$$r_i = |z_{12}z_{21}|/2 \text{ Re } z_{22}, \qquad r_o = |z_{12}z_{21}|/2 \text{ Re } z_{11} \tag{1.13.13}$$

respectively.[34] By inspection of Fig. 1.13.3, the impedances have minimum real parts equalling

$$\text{Re } Z_{i_{min}} = \text{Re } c_i - r_i, \qquad \text{Re } Z_{o_{min}} = \text{Re } c_o - r_o \tag{1.13.14}$$

For the absolute stability conditions of Eq. 1.13.10, then from Eq. 1.13.14,

$$\text{Re } c_i - r_i > 0, \qquad \text{Re } c_o - r_o > 0 \tag{1.13.15}$$

Substituting Eqs. 1.13.12 and 1.13.13 into Eq. 1.13.15 gives

$$\frac{2 \text{ Re } z_{11} \text{ Re } z_{22} - \text{Re } (z_{12}z_{21}) - |z_{12}z_{21}|}{2 \text{ Re } z_{22}} > 0 \tag{1.13.16}$$

or after rearranging

$$\begin{aligned} \text{Re } z_{11} \text{ Re } z_{22} &> \tfrac{1}{2}[|z_{12}z_{21}| + \text{Re } (z_{12}z_{21})] = \tfrac{1}{2}|z_{12}z_{21}|[1 + \cos(\arg z_{12}z_{21})] \\ &= |z_{12}z_{21}| \cos^2 (\tfrac{1}{2} \arg z_{12}z_{21}) \end{aligned} \tag{1.13.17}$$

We see that in addition, when $Z_S = Z_L = \infty$, then from Eqs. 1.13.7 and 1.13.10,

$$\text{Re } z_{11} > 0, \qquad \text{Re } z_{22} > 0 \tag{1.13.18}$$

for the Brune conditions. These three equations given by Eqs. 1.13.17 and 1.13.18 are *Llewellyn's criterion* for the absolute stability of linear active two-ports.[35] If these equations are satisfied, the two-port will be absolutely stable regardless of the passive terminations Z_L and Z_S. If they are not satisfied at any frequency, the two-port is potentially unstable and by a suitable choice in Z_L and Z_S, instability will result.

1.14 SIGNAL FLOW GRAPHS

We saw that one-port and two-port analysis suppressed the internal detail of a network, and allowed us to simply represent its terminal characteristics. This greatly facilitates analysis. Another immensely useful analysis technique is the use of signal flow graphs. From one viewpoint, a signal flow graph is a pictorial representation of a network. Once the equations describing the network have been written, they are represented in signal flow graph form. The flow graph can be easily manipulated and simplified using standard rules. Much greater insight is gained by manipulating the graph of the equations, rather than the equations themselves, as we shall see.

Mason introduced signal flow graph theory.[36] A *signal flow graph* is a graphical representation of the relationships between the variables of a set of linear algebraic equations. The graph consists of oriented branches connected to nodes. The nodes represent the signals or variables of the system. A branch leaving node x_i and terminating on node x_j represents the linear dependance of variable x_j on variable x_i, but not visa versa. Each branch has a unidirectional gain or transmittance T_{ij}. The direction is denoted by an arrowhead. A signal is transmitted through a branch in the arrowhead direction and is multiplied by the branch gain. Each node algebraically sums the incoming signals, and then transmits the resulting signal to every outgoing branch. A number of standard definitions and terminologies are used in signal flow graph theory. The most important for our uses are the following:

1. *Signal Flow Graph*: A network of nodes connected by (directed) branches.
2. *Node*: Represents a signal or variable (dependent/independent) in the system.
3. *Branch*: Represents the dependence of a dependent variable upon an independent variable.
4. *Input (Source) Node*: A node having only outgoing branches. This represents a signal input or excitation.
5. *Output (Sink) Node*: A node having only incoming branches. This represents a signal output or response.
6. *Path*: Any continuous succession or connected set of branches transversed in their indicated directions.
7. *Forward Path (Open Path)*: Any path connecting an input node to an output node, along which no node is encountered more than once.
8. *Feedback Path (Loop, Closed Path)*: Any path which originates and terminates on the same node, in which no node is transversed more than once.
9. *Path Gain*: The product of the transmittances (branch gains) of the branches forming the path.
10. *Loop Gain*: The product of the branch gains forming the loop.
11. *Residual Graph*: A graph containing only sources and sinks. Residual graphs are obtained from the original signal flow graph using reduction techniques.
12. *Signal Flow Graph Gain*: The signal appearing at the sink per unit signal applied at the source. For multiple input/output graphs, every sink-source combination has its own gain.
13. *Essential Nodes*: Those nodes which must be removed to eliminate all feedback loops.
14. *Flow Graph Order (Index)*: Equals the minimum number of essential nodes.
15. *Node Splitting*: A node that has been separated into a source node and a sink node. Con-

sists of grouping input branches on one side of a node, output branches on the opposite side, and splitting the node in half.

16. *Loop Gain of Node:* Signal returned to node per unit signal transmitted by that node; or gain between the source and sink created by splitting the node.
17. *Loop Difference (Return Difference)*: Difference between a unit signal injected at a node and the signal returned to the node; or one minus the loop gain of the node.
18. *Nontouching Loops*: Loops having no common nodes.

One of the great benefits of signal flow graphs is the ease with which gain expressions can be determined. In fact, Mason described signal flow graphs by saying, "A way to enhance, writing gain at a glance, . . .". The general expression for the gain between any two sink and source nodes of a graph is

$$H = \frac{\Sigma\, T_k \Delta_k}{\Delta} \tag{1.14.1}$$

where

$$\begin{aligned} T_k &= \text{gain of the } k\text{th forward path} \\ \Delta &= 1 - \sum_m P_{m1} + \sum_m P_{m2} - \sum_m P_{m3} + \ldots \\ P_{mr} &= \text{gain product of the } m\text{th possible combination of r nontouching loops} \\ \Delta_k &= \text{the value of } \Delta \text{ for that part of the graph not touching the } k\text{th forward path} \end{aligned} \tag{1.14.2}$$

Sometimes Δ is called the determinant of the graph, and Δ_k is called the cofactor of the T_k path. The engineer may prefer to express the determinant Δ as

$$\begin{aligned} \Delta = 1 &- (\text{sum of all loop gains}) \\ &+ (\text{sum of loop gain products of all combinations of 2 nontouching loops}) \\ &- (\text{sum of loop gain products of all combinations of 3 nontouching loops}) + \ldots \end{aligned} \tag{1.14.3}$$

Recall that two loops are nontouching if they have no common nodes. After some practice, Mason's gain formula can be written by inspection so it is an especially convenient analysis tool.

Signal flow graphs can be easily reduced or simplified using a set of basic operations. These are listed in Table 1.14.1, and are established by simply writing and re-expressing the algebraic expression represented by the graph. The cascade graph consisting of two cascaded branches with gains T_1 and T_2 has an overall gain $T = T_1 T_2$, since

$$x_3 = T_2 x_2 = T_2(T_1 x_1) = T_1 T_2 x_1 = T x_1 \tag{1.14.4}$$

The parallel graph has a gain $T = T_1 + T_2$ since

$$x_2 = T_1 x_1 + T_2 x_1 = (T_1 + T_2) x_1 = T x_1 \tag{1.14.5}$$

The star-mesh graph involves superposition of signals where an intermediate node is eliminated as

$$x_4 = T_3 x_3 = T_3(T_1 x_1 + T_2 x_2) = T_1 T_3 x_1 + T_2 T_3 x_2 \tag{1.14.6}$$

Path inversion in a graph is often used. Since

$$x_3 = T_1 x_1 + T_2 x_2 \tag{1.14.7}$$

we may solve for x_1 as

$$x_1 = \frac{1}{T_1} x_3 - \frac{T_2}{T_1} x_2 \tag{1.14.8}$$

Here, x_1 and x_2 were the independent variables and x_3 the independent variable in the original graph. By solving for x_1, x_1 becomes the dependent variable, and x_2 and x_3 the independent

Table 1.14.1 Basic operations for signal flow graphs.

Description	Original Graph	Reduced Graph
(a) Cascade Transformation	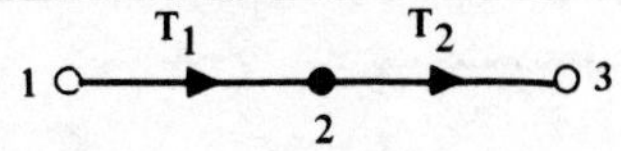	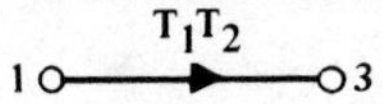
(b) Parallel Transformation	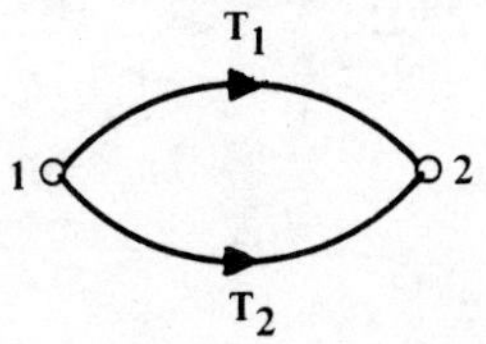	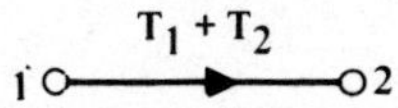
(c) Star/Mesh Transformation	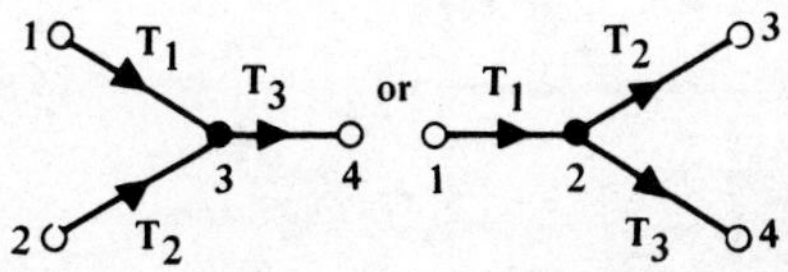	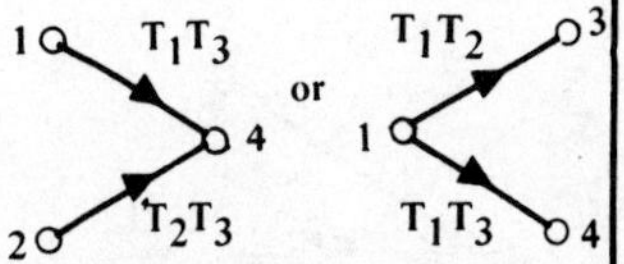
(d) Path Inversion	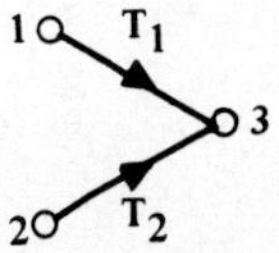	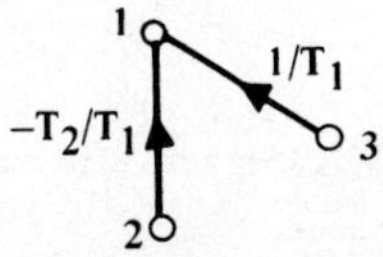
(e) Feedback Loop Equivalence	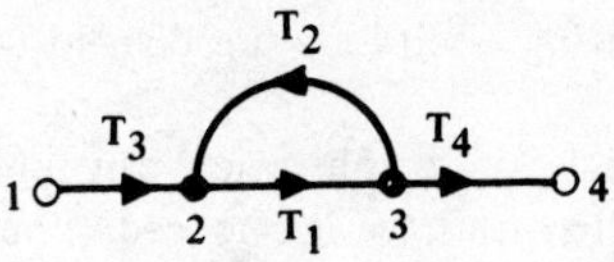	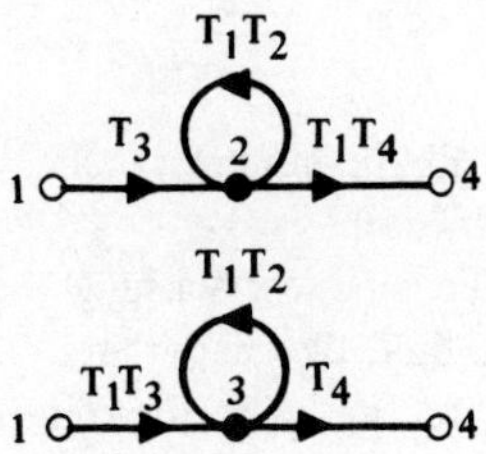
(f) Feedback Loop Removal	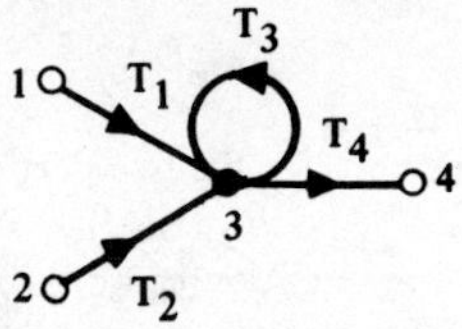	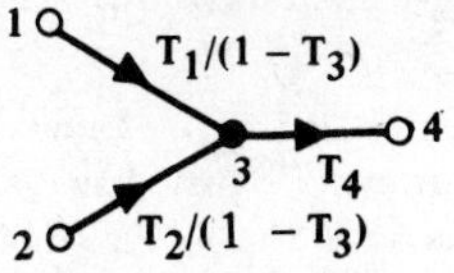

variables in the new graph.

Feedback loops are also easily manipulated. Note in Table 1.14.1e that the feedback loop can be formed into a self-loop by eliminating a node. Feedback loops can be eliminated as shown in Fig. 1.14.1f. Assuming $x_2 = 0$, then

$$x_3 = T_1x_1 + T_3x_3, \qquad x_4 = T_4x_3 \tag{1.14.9}$$

Combining these two equations and solving for x_3 gives

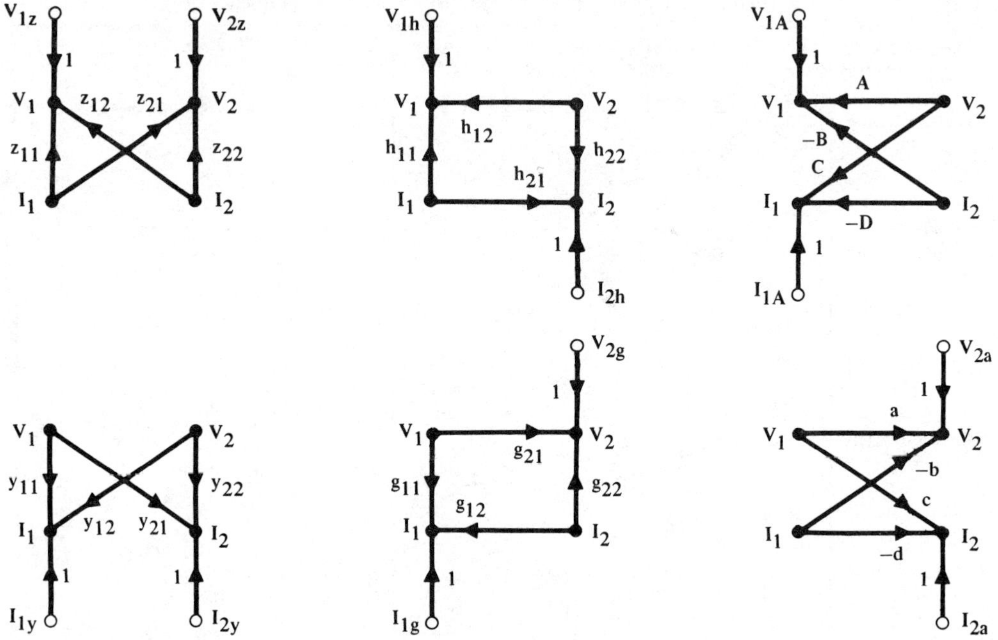

Fig. 1.14.1 Signal flow graph description for general two-ports.

$$x_3 = \frac{T_1}{1 - T_3} x_1 \tag{1.14.10}$$

Thus, all incoming branches to a node having a self-loop are divided by the return difference of the self-loop.

The engineer wishing a complete signal flow graph review can find no better reference than the original two papers by Mason. Now that we have introduced some useful terminology, let us illustrate the basic flow graph operations of Table 1.14.1.[37] We found that the two-port parameters could be defined as shown in Figs. 1.11.1 and 1.12.1, and interrelated as listed in Tables 1.11.2 and 1.12.1. These relationships can be easily established by simple flow graph manipulations as we shall now illustrate.

EXAMPLE 1.14.1 Draw the flow graph descriptions for the two-port representations of Fig. 1.12.1.
Solution We first draw and label four nodes V_1, I_1, V_2, and I_2. We arrange them in input/output pairs as shown in Fig. 1.14.1. We must also draw two source nodes for the independent port generators. Their placement depends upon the two-port description used. In the impedance representation, the voltages (V_1, V_2) are sinks, and the currents (I_1, I_2) and independent voltages (V_{1z}, V_{2z}) are sources. Since the port equations equal

$$\begin{aligned} V_1 &= V_{1z} + z_{11}I_1 + z_{12}I_2 \\ V_2 &= V_{2z} + z_{21}I_1 + z_{22}I_2 \end{aligned} \tag{1.14.11}$$

we simply draw directed branches from the source nodes V_{1z}, I_1, and I_2 to the sink node V_1; the branch gains equal 1, z_{11}, and z_{12}, respectively. We do the same for the output circuit. The complete flow graph is shown in Fig. 1.14.1. The other representations follow in the same manner. Figuratively speaking, the z- and y-parameters have graphs shaped as bow ties, the h- and g-parameters have graphs shaped as squares, and the A- and a-parameters have graphs shaped as hourglasses.

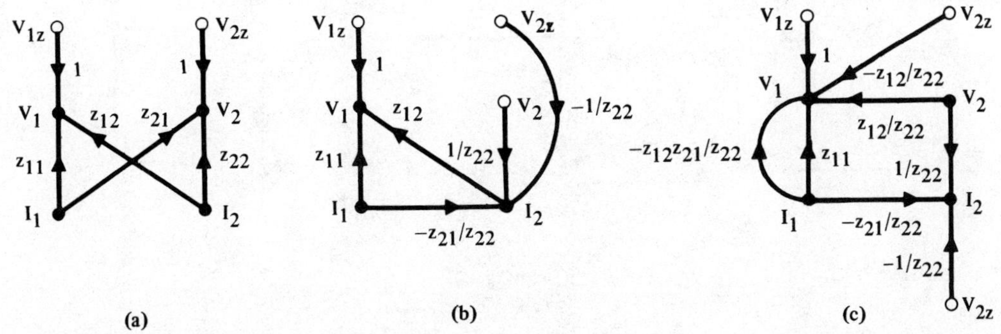

Fig. 1.14.2 Manipulations of a z-graph into an h-graph.

EXAMPLE 1.14.2 Convert the z-representation to the h-representation using signal flow graph manipulations.

Solution These representations are shown in Fig. 1.14.1. To convert from the z- to the h-form, we need to reorient the z-graph to look like the h-graph. Comparing the two graphs, we see that V_2 is a sink in the z-graph, but I_2 is a sink in the h-graph. This is essentially the only difference. Thus, let us invert the path from I_2 to V_2 in the z-graph. This is shown in Fig. 1.14.2b. Recall from Table 1.14.1 that this consists of reversing the branch direction and assigning it a reciprocal gain. All other branches terminating on the original node now terminate on the new node and have new gains which equal their original gains divided by the negative gain of the branch being inverted. From this intermediate graph, we now see that we must eliminate the (I_2, V_1) branch and replace it with a (V_2, V_1) branch. This is easily accomplished by using the star-mesh transform of Table 1.14.1. The result is shown in Fig. 1.14.2c. This consists essentially of identifying all incoming branches to node I_2 and moving them so they each terminate on node V_1. Then the (I_2, V_1) branch can be omitted. This new graph now has the desired form of the h-graph in Fig. 1.14.1. Thus, we can write by inspection that

$$[h] = \begin{bmatrix} h_{11} & h_{12} \\ h_{21} & h_{22} \end{bmatrix} = \begin{bmatrix} z_{11} - z_{12}z_{21}/z_{22} & z_{12}/z_{22} \\ -z_{21}/z_{22} & 1/z_{22} \end{bmatrix} = \begin{bmatrix} \Delta_z/z_{22} & z_{12}/z_{22} \\ -z_{21}/z_{22} & 1/z_{22} \end{bmatrix} \tag{1.14.12}$$

and

$$\begin{bmatrix} V_{1h} \\ I_{2h} \end{bmatrix} = \begin{bmatrix} 1 & -z_{12}/z_{22} \\ 0 & -1/z_{22} \end{bmatrix} \begin{bmatrix} V_{1z} \\ V_{2z} \end{bmatrix} = \begin{bmatrix} 1 & -h_{12} \\ 0 & -h_{22} \end{bmatrix} \begin{bmatrix} V_{1z} \\ V_{2z} \end{bmatrix} \tag{1.14.13}$$

These results are identical to those listed in Tables 1.11.2 and 1.12.1. It may appear remarkable that the conversion was so simple. This helps to re-emphasize our earlier statement that greater insight is often gained by manipulating the flow graph of equations rather than the equations themselves.

We have illustrated flow graph manipulations and now want to apply Mason's gain formula. To do so, let us again consider two-port examples. In Table 1.11.3, we listed the input and output impedances and the voltage and current gains of general two-ports. These results can easily be obtained using signal flow graph theory. Let us determine the input/output impedances and the voltage and current gains of the two-port shown in Fig. 1.14.3 which is characterized by its z-parameters using Mason's gain formula.

The flow graph of the two-port is shown in Fig. 1.14.3b. Since the port conditions require

$$I_1 = \frac{V_S - V_1}{Z_S} = \frac{V_S}{Z_S} - \frac{V_1}{Z_S}, \qquad I_2 = -\frac{V_2}{Z_L} \tag{1.14.14}$$

we must include these conditions in the flow graph as shown. We have "turned over" the output portion of the graph to simplify its appearance. Now let us calculate Z_i, Z_o, A_i, A_v, and A_v'.

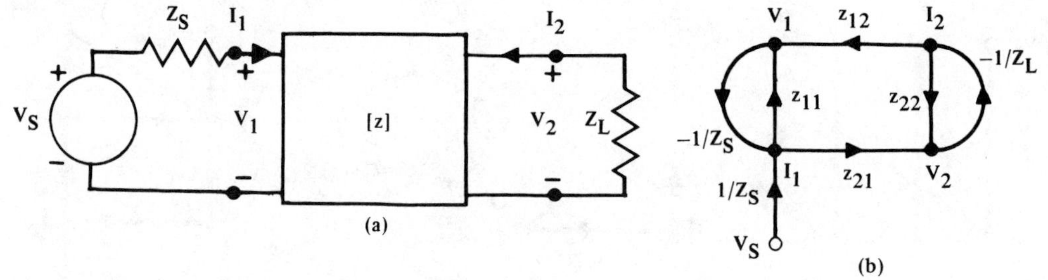

Fig. 1.14.3 (a) Loaded two-port and its (b) flow graph.

By definition, the two-port impedance $Z_i = V_1/I_1$. Thus, we can inject $I_1 = 1$ and measure V_1. Conceptually I_1 is a source and V_1 is a sink. To show this in the signal flow graph of Fig. 1.14.4a, we split the I_1 node to obtain a source node. Notice that since we have split the I_1 node, its incoming branches have no effect on its value. Thus, we can constrain the node to have any desired value. Equivalently, we could have eliminated or deleted all incoming branches to the I_1 node as shown in Fig.1.14.4b. Let us also introduce a V_1' node to obtain a sink. The V_1 node is connected to the V_1' by a unity gain branch. To apply Mason's gain formula, we identify the forward paths which connect I_1' to V_1'. There are two such paths as shown in Fig. 1.14.4c. These paths pass through nodes (I_1', I_1, V_1, V_1') and $(I_1', I_1, V_2, I_2, V_1, V_1')$. Thus the forward path gains equal

$$T_1 = z_{11}, \quad T_2 = -z_{12}z_{21}/Z_L \tag{1.14.15}$$

Now we identify the feedback loops of the graph. We see there is only one loop around nodes (I_2, V_2, I_2). Thus, the system determinant equals

$$\Delta = 1 + z_{22}/Z_L \tag{1.14.16}$$

Next, we identify the feedback loops which touch the forward path. To form the path cofactors, we delete the loop gains of the touching feedback loops from the system determinant Δ. Here

$$\Delta_1 = 1 + z_{22}/Z_L, \quad \Delta_2 = 1 \tag{1.14.17}$$

since the outer feedback loop (I_2, V_2, I_2) fails to touch the first forward path, and the feedback loop touches the second forward path. Therefore, the two-port input impedance can be written as

$$Z_i = \frac{V_1}{I_1} = \frac{T_1\Delta_1 + T_2\Delta_2}{\Delta} = \frac{z_{11}(1 + z_{22}/Z_L) - z_{12}z_{21}/Z_L}{1 + z_{22}/Z_L} = \frac{\Delta_z + z_{11}Z_L}{z_{22} + Z_L} \tag{1.14.18}$$

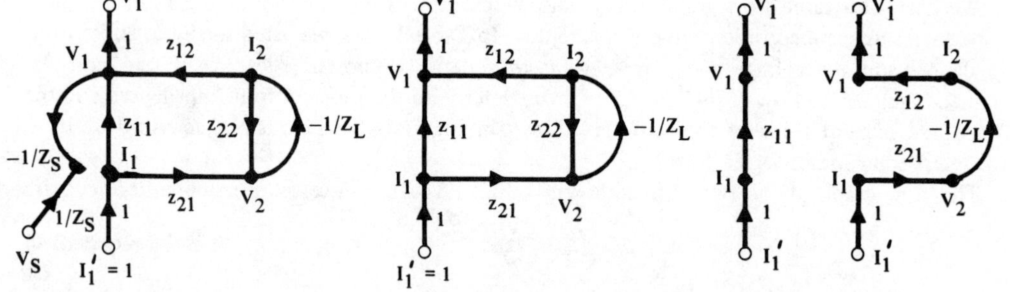

Fig. 1.14.4 Flow graphs and identification of forward paths for Z_i calculation.

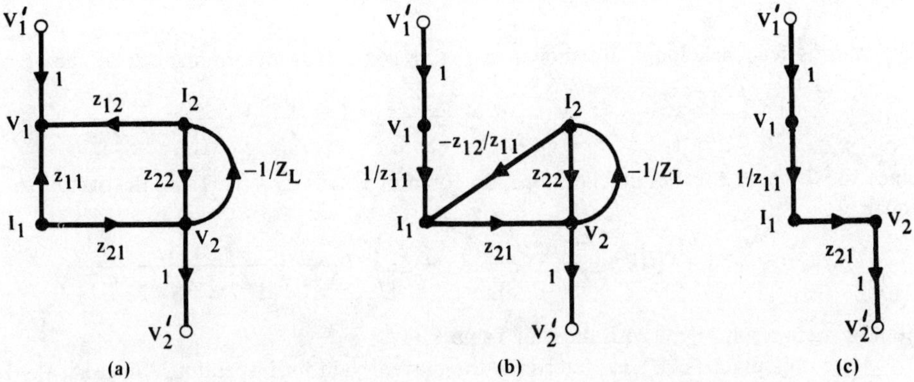

Fig. 1.14.5 Flow graphs and identification of forward path for A_v calculation.

This agrees with the result of Table 1.11.3. Using the same approach at the output, we can write

$$Z_o = \frac{V_o}{I_o} = \frac{\Delta_z + z_{22}Z_S}{z_{11} + Z_S} \tag{1.14.19}$$

Alternatively, we can simply note two-port symmetry, reverse the input/output roles, and interchange parameters (i.e., z_{11} and z_{22}, z_{12} and z_{21}, and Z_S and Z_L) in Z_i. This results in Z_o.

The forward voltage gain of the two-port equals $A_v = V_2/V_1$. Thus, we inject $V_1 = 1$ and measure V_2. Here V_1 is a source and V_2 a sink. We must set $Z_S = \infty$ since I_1 is independent of Z_S in Fig. 1.14.3. This eliminates the $1/Z_S$ branches since $1/Z_S = 0$. We introduce nodes V_1' and V_2' into the flow graph for analysis purposes as shown in Fig. 1.14.5a. The z_{11} branch is inverted to allow signal flow in the graph as shown in Fig. 1.14.5b. There is only a single forward path connecting V_1' to V_2'. Its gain equals

$$T_1 = z_{21}/z_{11} \tag{1.14.20}$$

This path touches the feedback loops around nodes (I_2, V_2, I_2) and (I_1, V_2 I_2, I_1), so their cofactors equal $\Delta_1 = \Delta_2 = 1$ where

$$\Delta = 1 + (z_{22} - z_{12}z_{21}/z_{11})/Z_L = 1 + \Delta_z/z_{11}Z_L \tag{1.14.21}$$

Therefore, the forward voltage gain equals

$$A_v = \frac{V_2}{V_1} = \frac{T_1\Delta_1}{\Delta} = \frac{z_{21}/z_{11}}{1 + \Delta_z/z_{11}Z_L} = \frac{z_{21}Z_L}{\Delta_z + z_{11}Z_L} \tag{1.14.22}$$

The overall voltage gain from the source to the two-port output is slightly more complicated. Here V_S is a source node and V_2' a sink referring to Fig. 1.14.3. Note there is only one forward path from input to output having gain

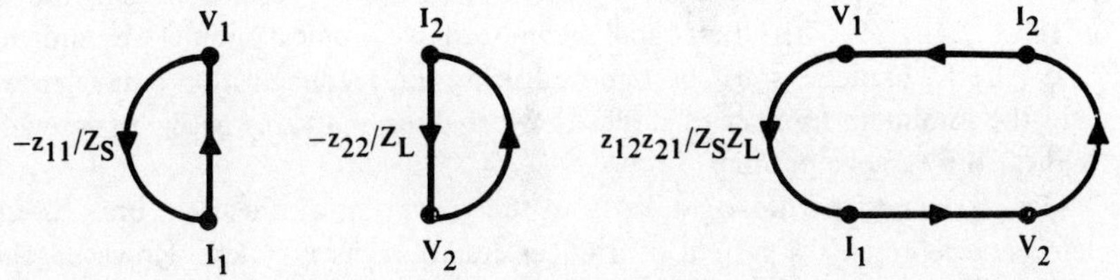

Fig. 1.14.6 Identification of feedback loops in signal flow graph of Fig. 1.14.3b.

$$T_1 = z_{21}/Z_S \tag{1.14.23}$$

The various feedback loops are shown in Fig. 1.14.6. The determinant Δ of the graph equals

$$\Delta = 1 - \left(\frac{z_{12}z_{21}}{Z_SZ_L} - \frac{z_{11}}{Z_S} - \frac{z_{12}}{Z_L}\right) + \frac{z_{11}z_{22}}{Z_SZ_L} = 1 + \frac{z_{11}}{Z_S} + \frac{z_{22}}{Z_L} + \frac{\Delta_z}{Z_SZ_L} \tag{1.14.24}$$

Since the T_1 path touches all the loops, its cofactor equals $\Delta_1 = 1$. Thus, the overall voltage gain equals

$$A_v = \frac{V_2}{V_S} = \left(\frac{z_{21}}{Z_S}\right) \Big/ \left(1 + \frac{z_{11}}{Z_S} + \frac{z_{22}}{Z_L} + \frac{\Delta_z}{Z_SZ_L}\right) = \frac{z_{21}Z_L}{\Delta_z + z_{11}Z_L + Z_S(z_{22} + Z_L)} \tag{1.14.25}$$

Both of these results agree with those of Table 1.11.3.

After this practice, let us determine the current gain by inspection. Since $A_i = -I_2/I_1$, we split the I_1 node, introduce I_1' and I_2' nodes, and calculate the gain between them. The single forward path has gain

$$T_1 = -z_{21}/Z_L \tag{1.14.26}$$

The graph determinant equals

$$\Delta = 1 + z_{22}/Z_L \tag{1.14.27}$$

Since the forward path touches the feedback path, $\Delta_1 = 1$ and the current gain equals

$$A_i = -\frac{I_2}{I_1} = \frac{z_{21}/Z_L}{1 + z_{22}/Z_L} = \frac{z_{21}}{z_{22} + Z_L} \tag{1.14.28}$$

These examples show that not only can two-ports be conveniently represented by signal flow graphs, but that the flow graph transmittances are easily determined by physical measurement. The concept of independent forcing functions injecting signals into flow graph source nodes parallels that of injecting signals into networks. Similarly, the responses at flow graph sinks correspond to a physical measurement of responses at network ports. Note that we shall "clamp" flow graph node signals to zero symbolically using a ground. Physically, this will correspond to opening a port if the node variable is current, so proper interpretation is necessary.

We introduced Blackman's impedance relation when we discussed two-ports. We derived the input impedance directly for the network in two examples. It should be clear that we can likewise apply the relation to flow graphs and derive impedance. Recall that Blackman's impedance relation was given by Eq. 1.10.18 where $Z^{(k)}$ and $Z^{(0)}$ were the normal and reference port impedances and the T's were the return ratios of some $y = kx$ controlled source within the network. In terms of the flow graph, $Z^{(k)}$ and $Z^{(0)}$ represent gains between the I and V nodes. The return ratios equal the loop gain of a node which is inserted into the branch between the x and y node, under the appropriate V or I condition. Thus, the two interpretations are equivalent.

Recall from our flow graph definitions that the graph order is equal to the minimum number of nodes, which if removed, eliminate all feedback loops. Any flow graph of order n can be reduced to a so-called *canonical flow graph* having $(n + 1)^2$ branches using the reduction operations of Table 1.14.1.[38] The first- and second-order canonical graphs are shown in Figs. 7.1.1 and 7.1.5 (the K_i branches must be removed using the feedback loop equivalence of Table 1.14.1 to yield the minimum number of nodes). We shall be analyzing active filters which can be described by these flow graphs in Chap. 7.

Let us view signal flow graphs from the viewpoint of linear algebra. Essentially, a flow graph pictorially represents a system of n linear equations as $\mathbf{x} = \mathbf{kx}$. However, the flow graph is not unique. There are n! signal flow graphs which describe the same set of n equations. The particular graph obtained depends upon the order in which we choose the dependent variables. Never-

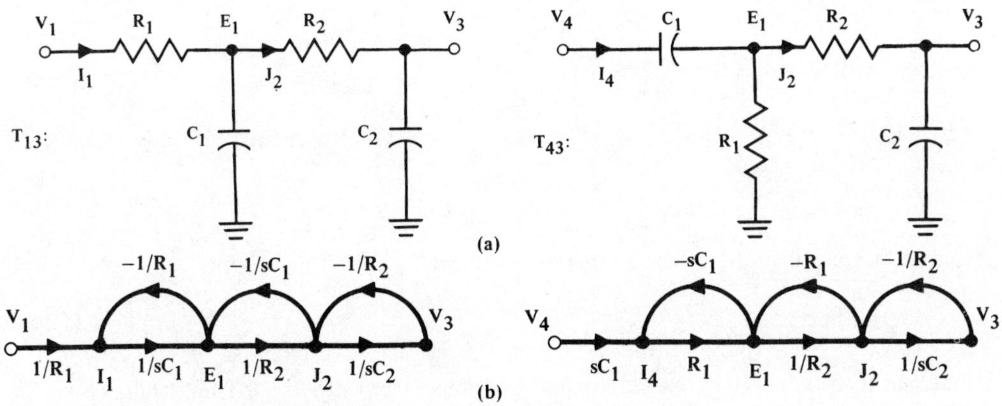

Fig. 1.14.7 (a) Ladder networks and (b) their flow graphs.

theless, all the graphs contain the same information although they have different signal flows. It is extremely fortunate to have this flexibility. In fact, in later chapters when we analyze active filters, we will choose to use a graph which has the physical shape or topology of the network.

Some networks have topologies which facilitate signal flow graph analysis. Perhaps the simplest is the ladder network.[39] Many active filters are composed of operational amplifiers embedded in such networks, so it will be extremely useful to review the best flow graph formulation for the case with an example.

EXAMPLE 1.14.3 Draw a signal flow graph to describe the two ladder networks of Fig. 1.14.7. Determine their voltage transfer functions.

Solution We begin by labelling internal node voltages by E and series branch currents by J. We then simply express node voltages and series currents successively in flow graph form. This is shown in Fig. 1.14.7b. Then using Kirchhoff's equations, we can write

$$I_1 = (V_1 - E_1)/R_1, \qquad E_1 = (I_1 - J_2)/sC_1 \tag{1.14.29}$$

and so forth for the first ladder. Thus, we insert and label the flow graph branches as shown in the figure. Then using Mason's gain formula, we can write the gains as

$$\begin{aligned} T_{13} &= \frac{1/s^2R_1C_1R_2C_2}{1 + [1/sR_1C_1 + 1/sR_2C_1 + 1/sR_2C_2] + 1/s^2R_1C_1R_2C_2} \\ &= \frac{1}{s^2R_1C_1R_2C_2 + s[R_1C_1 + R_2C_2 + R_1C_2] + 1} \\ T_{43} &= \frac{R_1C_1/R_2C_2}{1 + [sR_1C_1 + R_1/R_2 + 1/sR_2C_2] + R_1C_1/R_2C_2} \\ &= \frac{sR_1C_1}{s^2R_1C_1R_2C_2 + s[R_1C_1 + R_2C_2 + R_1C_2] + 1} \end{aligned} \tag{1.14.30}$$

The engineer will appreciate the power of this approach when we begin to derive active filter gains.

1.15 SENSITIVITY

Sensitivity is used to estimate the percentage drift of a dependent variable y which results from some percentage drift of an independent variable x. Mathematically, the *sensitivity* of y with respect to x equals

$$S_x^y = \frac{dy/y}{dx/x} = \frac{dy/dx}{y/x} = \frac{d \ln y}{d \ln x} \tag{1.15.1}$$

For a change of Δy in y due to a drift of Δx in x, then the percentage drifts or tolerances in y and x equal

$$T_y = \Delta y/y, \qquad T_x = \Delta x/x \tag{1.15.2}$$

Therefore, the sensitivity S_x^y can be related to tolerances T_x and T_y as

$$S_x^y = \lim_{\Delta x \to 0} T_y/T_x \tag{1.15.3}$$

so that sensitivity is equal to the ratio of the two percentage drifts for differential drift in x. For small percentage drifts in x

$$T_x^y \cong S_x^y T_x \tag{1.15.4}$$

Thus, when some percentage drift in x occurs, and the sensitivity of y with respect to x is known, the resulting percentage drift in y can be found.

Greater insight into the relation between tolerance and sensitivity can be gained by considering the dependent variable $y(x + \Delta x)$ expressed in its Taylor series representation as given by Eq. 1.2.3a. Then the change Δy in y due to a change Δx in x is given by Eq. 1.2.3b. Thus, the ratio of changes is given by Eq. 1.2.4 which can be re-expressed as

$$\Delta y(x)/\Delta x = y'(x) + y''(x)\Delta x/2! + y'''(\ddot{x})\Delta x^2/3! + \ldots \tag{1.15.5}$$

Forming the ratio T_y to T_x, substituting in Eq. 1.15.5, and manipulating gives

$$\frac{T_y}{T_x} = \frac{\Delta y/\Delta x}{y/x} = S_x^y + \frac{1}{2!}\frac{y''\Delta x}{y/x} + \frac{1}{3!}\frac{y'''\Delta \ddot{x}^2}{y/x} + \ldots \tag{1.15.6}$$

Eq. 1.15.6 reduces to Eq. 1.15.3 when $\Delta x \to 0$. This shows that the sensitivity is equal to the tolerance ratio only for very small Δx and for small second-order (and higher-order) derivatives of y.

When dependent variable y is a function of two or more independent variables x_i (for $i = 2, \ldots, n$), then the sensitivity of y with respect to x_i equals

$$S_{x_i}^y = \frac{\partial y/y}{\partial x_i/x_i} = \frac{\partial y/\partial x_i}{y/x_i} = \frac{\partial \ln y}{\partial \ln x}, \qquad i = 2, \ldots, n \tag{1.15.7}$$

Thus, when more than a single independent variable is present, partial differentiation replaces normal differentiation. All independent variable values are held constant except the one being considered for differentiation. The change Δy in y due to changes Δx_i in the x_i is given by Eq. 1.12.9.[40] The tolerance of y can, therefore, be expressed as

$$\begin{aligned} T_y = \frac{\Delta y(x)}{y(x)} &= \left(\frac{\partial y}{\partial x_1}\frac{\Delta x_1}{y} + \frac{\partial y}{\partial x_2}\frac{\Delta x_2}{y} + \ldots + \frac{\partial y}{\partial x_n}\frac{\Delta x_n}{y}\right) \\ &+ \frac{1}{2!}\left(\frac{\partial^2 y}{\partial x_1^2}\frac{\Delta x_1^{\,2}}{y} + \ldots + \frac{\partial^2 y}{\partial x_n^2}\frac{\Delta x_n^{\,2}}{y} + n\frac{\partial^2 y}{\partial x_1 \partial x_n}\frac{\Delta x_1 \Delta x_2}{y} + \text{etc.}\right) + \ldots \\ &= S_{x_1}^y T_{x_1} + \ldots + S_{x_n}^y T_{x_n} + \text{higher order terms} \end{aligned} \tag{1.15.8}$$

Thus, for sufficiently small drifts in the independent variables ($\Delta x_i \ll 1$), the first-order terms dominate and

Table 1.15.1 Some convenient sensitivity relations.[41]

$S_x^{kx} = 1$	$S_x^{y+k} = \dfrac{y}{y+k} S_x^y$
$S_x^{kx^n} = n$	$S_x^{k-y} = -\dfrac{y}{k-y} S_x^y$
$S_x^{y(x)} = S_x^y$	$S_x^{yz} = S_x^y + S_x^z$
$S_x^{1/y} = -S_x^y$	$S_x^{y/z} = S_x^y - S_x^z$
$S_x^{y^n} = nS_x^y$	$S_x^{y+z+\ldots} = \dfrac{1}{y+z+\ldots}(yS_x^y + zS_x^z + \ldots)$
$S_x^{ky} = S_x^y$	$S_x^z = S_x^y S_y^z$

$$T_y = S_{x_1}^y T_{x_1} + S_{x_2}^y T_{x_2} + \ldots + S_{x_n}^y T_{x_n} \tag{1.15.9}$$

If in general the x_i tolerances are uncorrelated, then the maximum and minimum tolerances equal

$$\begin{aligned} T_{y\,max} &= |S_{x_1}^y| T_{x_1\,max} + |S_{x_2}^y| T_{x_2\,max} + \ldots + |S_{x_n}^y| T_{x_n\,max} \\ T_{y\,min} &= |S_{x_1}^y| T_{x_1\,min} + \ldots + |S_{x_n}^y| T_{x_n\,min} \end{aligned} \tag{1.15.10}$$

When all the x_i tolerances have equal positive and negative values, then Eq. 1.15.10 reduces to

$$\pm T_y = \pm[|S_{x_1}^y||T_{x_1}| + |S_{x_2}^y||T_{x_2}| + \ldots + |S_{x_n}^y||T_{x_n}|] \tag{1.15.11}$$

Eq. 1.15.11 is used for worst-case analysis for drifts in y as will be discussed momentarily.

A number of useful relationships involving the sensitivities of various functions of x can be easily derived using the sensitivity definition. These are listed in Table 1.15.1 for easy reference. Here k and n are constants and y and z are differentiable functions of x. The reader should verify these relations for they shall be extensively utilized in later chapters.

Now let us apply the sensitivity concepts we have developed to solve two component drift problems. Drifts from nominal values in components occur because of temperature, aging, moisture, radiation, and other environmental effects. These component drifts, in turn, cause drifts in variables dependent upon their values such as gain, corner frequencies, Q, etc.

In addition to drifts, components have initial tolerances. Tolerance is equal to the maximum possible percentage variation or uncertainty from nominal value and is specified by the manufacturer. For example, most resistors are commercially available with (±) 1, 5, 10, and 20% tolerances while most capacitors have (±) 5, 10, and 20% tolerances. In practice, because statistical sampling techniques are used to determine mean values, the engineer has no assurance that any particular component value will lie within its tolerance bounds. Usually, actual component values are grouped close to, but within, their tolerance bounds.

We shall define the maximum possible tolerance T_x to be the sum of the initial tolerance (maximum uncertainty in component value) and drifts. However, we shall generally refer to T_x as tolerance.

EXAMPLE 1.15.1 An RC network has a 3 db frequency ω_o equalling 1/RC. If the R and C components have initial tolerances of 10 and 20%, respectively, and uncorrelated drifts due to temperature of 10%, determine the approximate and exact tolerances of ω_o.

Solution Since $\omega_o = 1/RC$, then using the $S_x^{1/y}$ identity from Table 1.15.1, gives

$$S_R^{\omega_o} = S_C^{\omega_o} = -1 \qquad (1.15.12)$$

The tolerances T_R of R and T_C of C equal

$$T_R = \pm(10 + 10) = \pm\ 20\%, \qquad T_C = \pm(20 + 10) = \pm\ 30\% \qquad (1.15.13)$$

From Eq. 1.15.11, the tolerance T_{ω_o} of ω_o therefore equals

$$T_{\omega_o} = \pm[\ |S_R^{\omega_o}|\ |T_R| + |S_C^{\omega_o}|\ |T_C|\ ] = \pm(20 + 30) = \pm\ 50\% \qquad (1.15.14)$$

assuming second-order effects are negligible.

The exact tolerance of ω_o is calculated from the ω_o expression. Using the form

$$\omega_o(1 + T_{\omega_o}) = \frac{1}{R(1 + T_R)\,C(1 + T_C)} = \frac{1}{RC\,(1 + T_R)(1 + T_C)} \qquad (1.15.15)$$

and solving for tolerance T_{ω_o} gives

$$T_{\omega_o} = \frac{1}{(1 + T_R)(1 + T_C)} - 1 \qquad (1.15.16)$$

Calculating minimum and maximum T_{ω_o} tolerances using Eqs. 1.15.16 and 1.15.13 yields

$$T_{\omega_{omin}} = \frac{1}{(1 + 0.2)(1 + 0.3)} - 1 = \frac{1}{1.56} - 1 = -\ 36\%$$

$$T_{\omega_{omax}} = \frac{1}{(1 - 0.2)(1 - 0.3)} - 1 = \frac{1}{0.56} - 1 = +\ 79\% \qquad (1.15.17)$$

The maximum T_{ω_o} differs greatly from that determined using the sensitivity results (first-order effects only). Thus, second-order (and higher-order) effects cannot be neglected.

EXAMPLE 1.15.2 An attenuator network made up of two resistors R_1 and R_2 has a gain of

$$H(s) = R_2/(R_1 + R_2) \qquad (1.15.18)$$

Determine the gain tolerance over a 100°C temperature range if the resistors have initial 5% tolerances and uncorrelated drifts of 1%.

Solution The gain tolerance approximately equals

$$T_H = S_{R_1}^H T_{R_1} + S_{R_2}^H T_{R_2} = -\frac{R_1}{R_1 + R_2} T_{R_1} + \left(1 - \frac{R_2}{R_1 + R_2}\right) T_{R_2} \qquad (1.15.19)$$

using the S_x^{y+k} identity of Table 1.15.1. Since the temperature drifts are uncorrelated, then the worst-case tolerance equals

$$T_H = \pm \frac{R_1}{R_1 + R_2}(|T_{R_1}| + |T_{R_2}|) = \pm \frac{R_1}{R_1 + R_2} 2(5 + 1) = \pm\ 12(1 - H) \leqslant \pm\ 12\% \qquad (1.15.20)$$

The exact gain tolerance is found by expressing Eq. 1.15.18 as

$$H(1 + T_H) = \frac{R_2(1 + T_{R_2})}{R_1(1 + T_{R_1}) + R_2(1 + T_{R_2})} = \left[1 + \frac{R_1}{R_2}\frac{1 + T_{R_1}}{1 + T_{R_2}}\right]^{-1} = \left[1 + \frac{1 - H}{H}\frac{1 + T_{R_1}}{1 + T_{R_2}}\right]^{-1} \qquad (1.15.21)$$

and solving Eq. 1.15.21 for T_H which gives

$$T_H = \left[\frac{1 + T_{R_1} + H(T_{R_2} - T_{R_1})}{1 + T_{R_2}}\right]^{-1} - 1 = \frac{1 + T_{R_2}}{1 + T_{R_1} + H(T_{R_2} - T_{R_1})} - 1 \qquad (1.15.22)$$

The tolerance of H will be maximum when H = 0 in which case Eq. 1.15.22 becomes

$$T_H = \frac{1 + T_{R_2}}{1 + T_{R_1}} - 1 = \frac{T_{R_2} - T_{R_1}}{1 + T_{R_1}} \tag{1.15.23}$$

Substituting 6% resistor tolerances into Eq. 1.15.23 gives

$$\begin{aligned} T_{H_{max}} &= \frac{1 + 0.06}{1 - 0.06} - 1 = \frac{1.06}{0.94} - 1 = +13\% \\ T_{H_{min}} &= \frac{1 - 0.06}{1 + 0.06} - 1 = \frac{0.94}{1.06} - 1 = -11.5\% \end{aligned} \tag{1.15.24}$$

Thus, the tolerances based upon sensitivities in Eq. 1.15.20 are almost exact. This is almost always the case for very small tolerances on the independent variables.

This classical approach for analyzing maximum changes in a dependent variable resulting from the worst possible combination of allowable independent variables is called *worst-case analysis*. Although worst-case analysis is generally pessimistic and unrealistic from the standpoint that worst possible element combinations rarely occur, it is the most universal quality assurance measure for electronic design used today. It is relatively easy to apply and lends great insight into the factors that dominate, or largely control, variations in system performance.

As an alternative to worst-case analysis, computerized methods are being developed for obtaining statistical descriptions of system behavior. Of these, *Monte Carlo analysis* is one of the most promising.[42] Here component values are selected according to their distributions, rather than their distribution limits. This will be discussed extensively in Sec. 8.5.

1.16 ROOT LOCUS

The Laplace transform allowed us to transform integrodifferential equations in time to algebraic equations in s. Signal flow graphs gave us a convenient tool for simply representing these equations and the means by which to calculate the gain of networks. We saw that (rational) gain expressions were characterized by their pole and zero locations in the s-plane. Generally, when system parameters are changed, its pole and zero locations also change. The *root locus* is simply a plot of the pole or zero locations of system gain as a system parameter k varies continuously from $-\infty$ to ∞. Thus, the root locus allows the engineer to predict how system poles and zeros change when a given parameter changes. Then using the frequency-domain and time-domain results to be developed in Chaps. 2 and 3, respectively, he can assess how these root changes effect system performance. Therefore, the root locus concept is of prime importance to the designer.

Let us express the general gain (impedance or whatever) expression as

$$H(s) = C(s)/R(s) \tag{1.16.1}$$

To determine the finite zeros and poles of H(s), we find the s values which satisfy

$$C(s) = 0 \qquad \text{and} \qquad R(s) = 0 \tag{1.16.2}$$

respectively. Very often, we can express these equations in the simple linear form

$$N(s) + KM(s) = 0 \tag{1.16.3}$$

K is a system parameter of interest which may take on values in the range $(-\infty, \infty)$. Note that we can rearrange this equation as

$$1 + K\frac{M(s)}{N(s)} = 1 + KG(s) = 0 \tag{1.16.4}$$

Table 1.16.1 Construction rules for root locus.

1. *Number of loci*: The number of separate loci equals the number of poles or zeros of G(s) when critical frequencies at infinity are included.
2. *Loci end points*: Each branch of the loci starts at a zero (for $k = -\infty$), passes through a pole (for $k = 0$), and terminates at a zero ($k = +\infty$).
3. *Symmetry of loci*: The root loci are symmetrical about the real axis (i.e., complex roots exist in conjugate pairs).
4. *Loci on real axis*: The parts of the real axis which comprise sections of the loci are to the left of an *even* number of poles and zeros for $k < 0$, and to the left of an *odd* number of poles and zeros for $k > 0$.
5. *Loci near infinity (asymptotes of loci)*:
   a. The loci near infinity (where $|s| \to \infty$) approach asymptotic lines having angle

   $$\theta_A = \pm \frac{p\pi}{n - m}, \quad \text{p an odd integer for } k>0 \text{ and even integer for } k<0$$

   b. The asymptotes intersect the real axis at σ_A where

   $$\sigma_A = \Big(\sum_n \text{poles} - \sum_m \text{zeros} \Big)/(n - m)$$

   where $n - m$ is the difference between the number of finite poles and zeros of G(s).
6. *Loci intersecting real axis*: The points of intersection of the loci with the real axis (breakaway points) are determined by solving

   $$\frac{dK}{ds} = \frac{d}{ds}\left(-\frac{1}{G(s)} \right) = 0$$

   The tangents to the loci at the breakaway points are equally spaced over 360°.
7. *Loci intersecting imaginary axis*: The points of intersection of the loci with the imaginary axis is determined using the Routh-Hurwitz test.
8. *Loci near poles and zeros*:
   a. The angle of departure ψ_d from a zero z_x equals

   $$\psi_d = \sum_{i=1}^{n} \arg(z_x - p_i) - \sum_{\substack{j=1 \\ j \neq x}}^{m} \arg(z_x - z_j)$$

   b. The angle of arrival ψ_a to a zero z_x equals $\psi_a = \psi_d \pm 180°$.

   c. The angle of arrival ϕ_a to a pole p_x equals

   $$\phi_a = \sum_{j=1}^{m} \arg(p_x - z_j) - \sum_{\substack{i=1 \\ i \neq x}}^{n} \arg(p_x - p_i)$$

   d. The angle of departure ϕ_d from a pole p_x equals $\phi_d = \phi_a \pm 180°$.

which will prove useful. Whenever we can rearrange an equation into this form, we can readily construct the locus of its roots as K varies from $-\infty$ to ∞ using a set of well-known rules.

The root locus construction rules are listed in Table 1.16.1. Although these rules are usually developed only for $k \in (0, \infty)$,[43] we have generalized them for $k \in (-\infty, \infty)$. We should re-emphasize that we are concerned with determining the roots of Eq. 1.16.3, or equivalently, Eq. 1.16.4. In Eq. 1.16.4, we have defined $G(s) = M(s)/N(s)$. Thus, the m finite zeros of G(s) satisfy

$$M(s) = 0 \tag{1.16.5}$$

while the n finite poles of G(s) satisfy

$$N(s) = 0 \tag{1.16.6}$$

The poles and zeros of G are easily located and facilitate the drawing of root locus. Generally, they bear no relation (in themselves) to the poles and zeros of H(s) in Eq. 1.16.1, except when K or 1/K = 0.

EXAMPLE 1.16.1 In Example 1.10.1, we determined the impedance expression Z(s) for the actual resistor as

$$Z(s) = \frac{R + sL}{s^2LC + sRC + 1} \tag{1.16.7}$$

Assume that L and C remain constant while R is allowed to vary from 0 to ∞. Determine the root locus of the poles and zeros of Z(s).

Solution Let us first consider the poles of Z(s). These are the values of s for which 1/Z(s) = 0. Thus, they satisfy

$$s^2LC + sRC + 1 = 0 \tag{1.16.8}$$

Since R is the parameter of interest, we rearrange the equation to isolate R as

$$(s^2LC + 1) + R(sC) = 0 \quad \text{or} \quad 1 + R\frac{sC}{s^2LC + 1} = 0 \tag{1.16.9}$$

The equation has the proper form for applying the root locus rules of Table 1.16.1. Here G(s) equals

$$G(s) = \frac{sC}{s^2LC + 1} \tag{1.16.10}$$

which has poles at $s = \pm j/\sqrt{LC}$ and zeros at $|s| = 0, \infty$. We can summarize the root locus characteristics as: 2 loci; begin at $s = \pm j/\sqrt{LC}$ and end at $|s| = 0, \infty$; negative σ-axis part of root loci; $\theta_A = -\pi$ and σ_A = real axis; breakaway point at $s = -1/\sqrt{LC}$ when $R = 2\sqrt{L/C}$; jω-axis intersections at $\omega = \pm 1/\sqrt{LC}$ when R = 0; $\phi_d = \pm 180°$. The root locus for the poles of Z(s) is shown in Fig. 1.16.1a. Figuratively speaking, the poles originate on the jω-axis, travel about a semicircle and break into the −σ-axis, where they collide; one travels to the origin and the other to −∞.

The zeros of Z(s) are the values of s for which Z(s) = 0. One is located at |s| = ∞, while the finite zero satisfies

$$sL + R = 0 \quad \text{or} \quad 1 + R\frac{1}{sL} = 0 \tag{1.16.11}$$

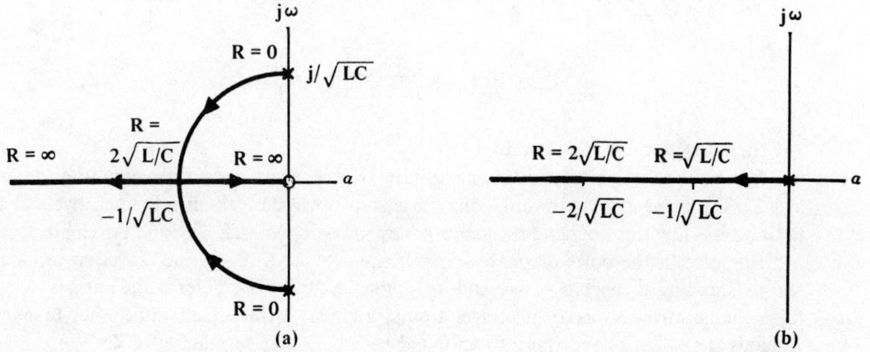

Fig. 1.16.1 Root locus for (a) pole and (b) zero locations for Z(s) as a function of R.

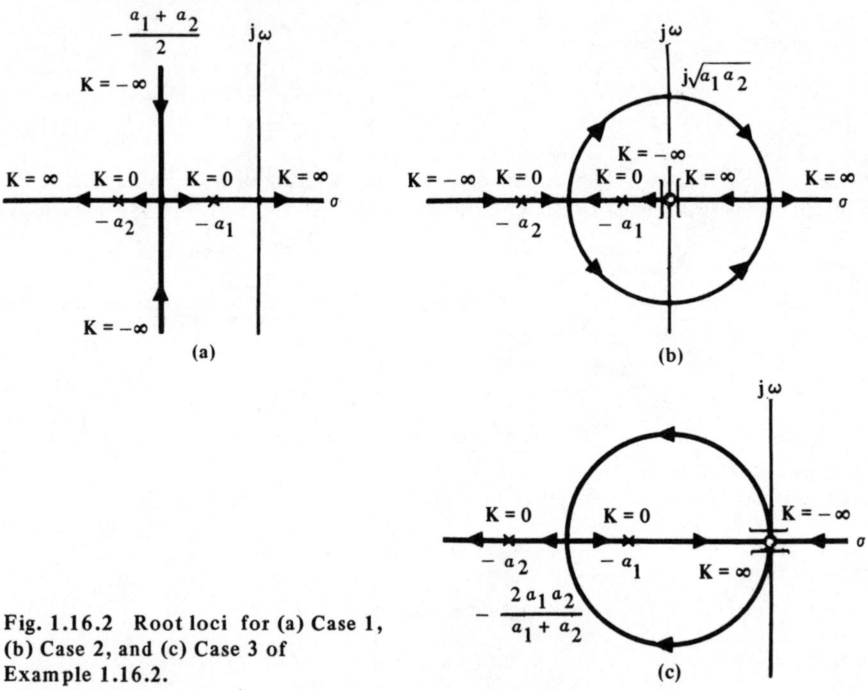

Fig. 1.16.2 Root loci for (a) Case 1, (b) Case 2, and (c) Case 3 of Example 1.16.2.

The equation has the proper root locus form, but it is sufficiently simple so we can draw its root locus by inspection in Fig. 1.16.1b. Note that the zero always has a more negative value than the real part of the poles. The pole-zero diagram for Z(s) will be fully interpreted in Chap. 14 when we discuss the resistor. This example shows the great ease and utility of the root locus concept and how tremendous insight can be gained for pole-zero variations under parameter variations.

EXAMPLE 1.16.2 In many active filter applications, the denominator of their voltage gain function has one of three forms:

$$D_1(s) = (s + a_1)(s + a_2) - K, \qquad D_2(s) = (s + a_1)(s + a_2) - Ks,$$
$$D_3(s) = (s + a_1)(s + a_2) - Ks^2 \tag{1.16.12}$$

We shall see this in Chap. 7 when we classify active filters. Draw and compare the root loci for these three cases for K varying from $-\infty$ to $+\infty$.

Solution These equations are already in proper locus form. They may be equivalently expressed as:

$$\text{Case 1: } 1 - K\frac{1}{(s + a_1)(s + a_2)} = 0, \qquad \text{Case 2: } 1 - K\frac{s}{(s + a_1)(s + a_2)} = 0,$$
$$\text{Case 3: } 1 - K\frac{s^2}{(s + a_1)(s + a_2)} = 0 \tag{1.16.13}$$

The three root loci are drawn in Fig. 1.16.2.

For case 1, the poles originate at infinity ($K = -\infty$) on a vertical asymptote centered at $s = -(a_1 + a_2)/2$. The poles migrate inward along the asymptote and break onto the negative-real axis. They travel in opposite directions passing through $s = -a_1$ and $-a_2$ when $K = 0$, and terminate at infinity ($K = +\infty$).

For case 2, the poles originate at $s = 0$ and $-\infty$ for $K = -\infty$ and travel inward along the negative-real axis passing through $s = -a_1$ and $-a_2$ when $K = 0$. The poles collide at $s = -\sqrt{a_1 a_2}$, break away from the negative-real axis, and travel around a circle of the same radius. They break into the positive-real axis at $s = \sqrt{a_1 a_2}$ and travel to $s = 0$ and $+\infty$ where they terminate for $K = +\infty$.

For case 3, the poles originate at the origin for $K = -\infty$, and travel around a circle of radius $a_1 a_2/$

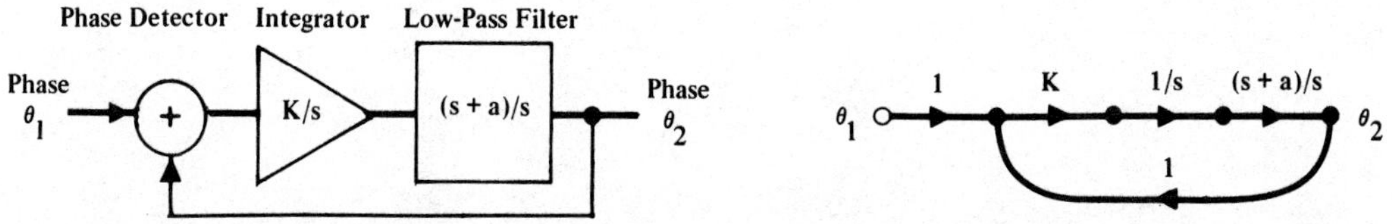

Fig. 1.16.3 Type 2 second-order phase-locked loop model and flow graph.

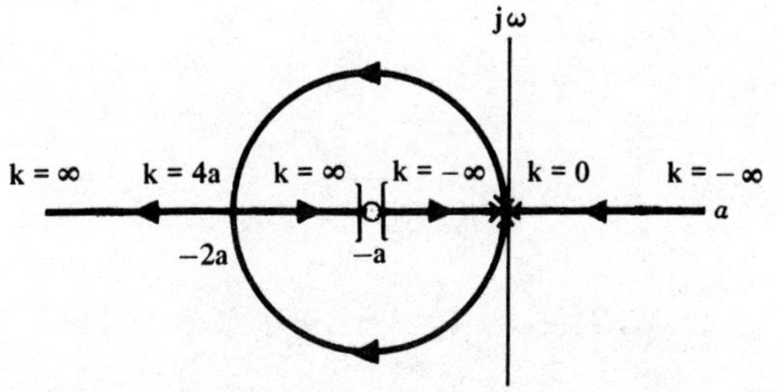

Fig. 1.16.4 Root locus for phase-locked loop poles in Example 1.16.3.

$(a_1 + a_2)$ centered at $s = -a_1a_2/(a_1 + a_2)$. They break onto the negative-real axis at $s = -2a_1a_2/(a_1 + a_2)$ and pass through $s = -a_1$ and $-a_2$ when K = 0. The $s = -a_1$ pole travels directly to the origin. The other pole migrates along the positive-real axis to $s = +\infty$, and terminates at the origin.

This example further illustrates the insight gained by utilizing root locus plots. Recall in describing systems, we often assessed their stability. Fig. 1.16.2 shows that for positive σ_1 and σ_2 (the usual case), and $K \leqslant 0$, case 1 systems are absolutely stable, case 2 systems are potentially unstable (possible pole at origin) and case 3 systems are potentially unstable (possible double poles at origin). For $K > 0$, case 1 and 2 systems are potentially unstable and case 2 systems are unstable.

EXAMPLE 1.16.3 A phase-locked loop model and flow graph are shown in Fig. 1.16.3.[44] Determine the closed-loop filter function. Investigate the effects on the system poles and zero due to variable k.
Solution Using Mason's gain equation given by Eq. 1.14.1, the closed-loop gain equals

$$\frac{\theta_2}{\theta_1} = H(s) = \frac{k(s + a)}{s^2 + ks + ak} \tag{1.16.14}$$

The system zero is located at s = −a and is unaffected by k. The system poles satisfy

$$s^2 + k(s + a) = 0 \qquad \text{or} \qquad 1 + k\frac{s + a}{s^2} = 0 \tag{1.16.15}$$

which is in proper root locus form. The root locus is easily drawn in Fig. 1.16.4. To obtain a stable system, $0 < k < \infty$. If complex poles are required, then $0 < k < 4a$ which is the usual case of interest.

EXAMPLE 1.16.4 We can re-express the gain of the phase-locked loop given by Eq. 1.16.14 as

$$H(s) = \frac{2\zeta\omega_n(s + \omega_n/2\zeta)}{s^2 + 2\zeta\omega_n s + \omega_n^2} \tag{1.16.16}$$

Now draw the root locus of the poles and zero for various ζ or damping factors.
Solution Comparing Eq. 1.16.16 with Eq. 1.16.14, we see that the poles have $\omega_n = \sqrt{ak}$ and $\zeta = 1/2\sqrt{k/a}$, and the zero equals $-\omega_n/2\zeta$. The root loci for the closed-loop poles and zero can be easily drawn as shown in Fig. 1.16.5 as a function of ζ. We see that for $\zeta = 0$, the zero is at $-\infty$ and the poles are at $s = \pm j\omega_n$. As ζ is increased from zero, the poles move around the circle to $s = -\omega_n$ for $\zeta = 1$. The zero moves inward towards the origin and passes through $s = -\omega_n$ for $\zeta = ½$. The pole traveling towards the origin for $\zeta \geqslant 1$ always trails behind the zero. As $\zeta \to \infty$, this pole effectively cancels the zero so that H(s) behaves as though it has only a single pole at $s = -2\zeta$.

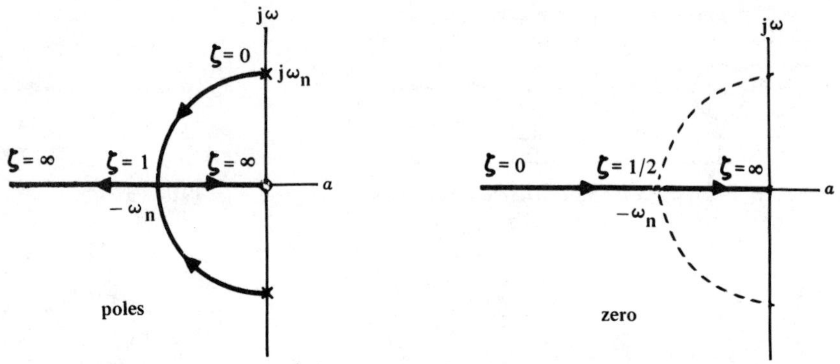

Fig. 1.16.5 Closed-loop poles and zero of phase-locked loop in Example 1.16.4.

1.17 MINIMUM-PHASE FUNCTIONS

We saw in Sec. 1.6 that the gain function H(s) of stable, causal systems had no poles in the right-half-plane (RHP) and that jω-axis poles could only be simple. However, there were no restrictions on the zeros of H(s). Classical terminology categorized such systems as being of two types:[45]

Minimum-phase: H(s) has no RHP zeros

Nonminimum-phase: H(s) has one or more RHP zeros

This was due to the fact that the phase characteristic of a minimum-phase gain function H(s) had the least possible phase for the given amplitude function. A nonminimum-phase gain function had more phase although it had the same amplitude function. We shall investigate this at length in Chap. 2. It can be shown that if a minimum phase gain function H(s) is expressed as

$$H(j\omega) = \exp\left[-a(\omega) - j\theta(\omega)\right] \tag{1.17.1}$$

in ac steady-state, then its *attenuation function* $a(\omega)$ and its *phase function* $\theta(\omega)$ are interrelated as[45]

$$\begin{aligned} \theta(\omega) &= \frac{\omega}{\pi} \int_{-\infty}^{\infty} \frac{a(\Omega)}{\Omega^2 - \omega^2}\, d\Omega \\ a(\omega) &= a(0) - \frac{\omega^2}{\pi} \int_{-\infty}^{\infty} \frac{\theta(\Omega)}{\Omega(\Omega^2 - \omega^2)}\, d\Omega \end{aligned} \tag{1.17.2}$$

The a and θ cannot be specified independently. When $a(\omega)$ is specified, $\theta(\omega)$ is determined, and vice versa. The *group delay function* $\tau(\omega)$ is sometimes used to describe $H(\omega)$ rather than phase $\theta(\omega)$. Phase and group delay are related as

$$\tau(\omega) = -\frac{d\theta(\omega)}{d\omega}, \qquad \theta(\omega) = -\int_{-\infty}^{\omega} \tau(\Omega)\, d\Omega \tag{1.17.3}$$

Eq. 1.17.2 can be manipulated to show that $\tau(\omega)$ is related to $a(\omega)$ as[46]

$$\tau(\omega) = 2 \int_{-\infty}^{\infty} \frac{da(\Omega)}{d\Omega} \, \frac{1}{\omega - \Omega}\, d\Omega \tag{1.17.4}$$

Eqs. 1.17.2 and 1.17.4 are called *Hilbert transforms*. We now illustrate their use with an example.

EXAMPLE 1.17.1 Determine the phase function for the ideal low-pass filter having the gain response shown in Fig. 1.5.2a assuming it is minimum phase. The gain function was given by Eq. 1.5.8a, where for generality, we shall specify that $|H_1| = \epsilon$ for $|\omega| > \omega_o$.

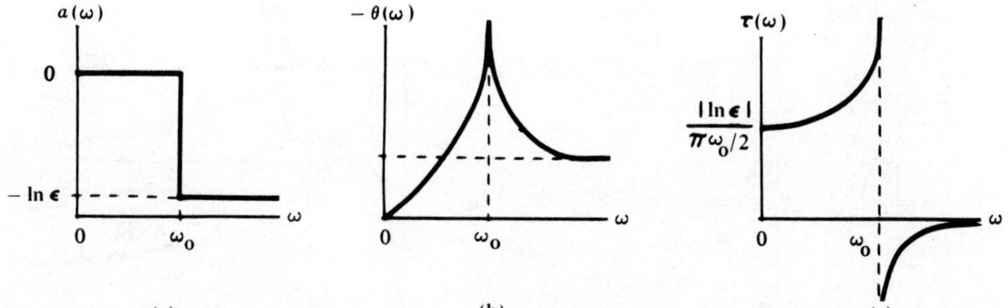

Fig. 1.17.1 (a) Attenuation, (b) phase, and (c) delay responses of ideal minimum-phase low-pass filter.

Solution We first determine the attenuation function $a(\omega)$ from Eq. 1.17.1 as

$$a(\omega) = 0, \quad |\omega| < \omega_o \qquad \text{and} \qquad -\ln \epsilon, \quad |\omega| > \omega_o \tag{1.17.5}$$

Substituting Eq. 1.17.5 into Eq. 1.17.2a, the phase function equals

$$\theta(\omega) = -\frac{2\omega}{\pi}\int_{\omega_o}^{\infty} \frac{\ln \epsilon}{\Omega^2 - \omega^2}\, d\Omega = \frac{\ln \epsilon}{\pi} \ln\left|\frac{\omega - \omega_o}{\omega + \omega_o}\right| \tag{1.17.6}$$

From Eq. 1.17.3, the group delay therefore equals

$$\tau(\omega) = -\frac{d\theta(\omega)}{d\omega} = \frac{\ln \epsilon}{\pi/2} \frac{\omega_o}{\omega^2 - \omega_o^2} \tag{1.17.7}$$

The attenuation, phase, and delay responses are shown in Fig. 1.17.1.

It can also be shown $H(j\omega)$ is uniquely determined if $a(\omega)$ and $\theta(\omega)$ are specified in complementary parts of the $j\omega$-axis.[47] When a is given for $|\omega| < \omega_o$ and θ is given for $|\omega| > \omega_o$, we solve

$$\frac{2\omega}{\pi}\int_0^{\omega_o} \frac{a(\Omega)}{\sqrt{\omega_o^2 - \Omega^2}\,(\Omega^2 - \omega^2)}\, d\Omega + \frac{2\omega}{\pi}\int_{\omega_o}^{\infty} \frac{\theta(\Omega)}{\sqrt{\Omega^2 - \omega_o^2}\,(\Omega^2 - \omega^2)}\, d\Omega$$
$$= \theta(\omega)/\sqrt{\omega_o^2 - \omega^2}, \quad 0 < \omega < \omega_o; \quad -a(\omega)/\sqrt{\omega^2 - \omega_o^2}, \quad \omega > \omega_o \tag{1.17.8}$$

for a and θ. When θ is given for $|\omega| < \omega_o$ and a is given for $|\omega| > \omega_o$, we solve

$$\frac{2\omega}{\pi}\int_0^{\omega_o} \frac{-\Omega\theta(\Omega)}{\sqrt{\omega_o^2 - \Omega^2}\,(\Omega^2 - \omega^2)}\, d\Omega + \frac{2\omega}{\pi}\int_{\omega_o}^{\infty} \frac{\Omega a(\Omega)}{\sqrt{\Omega^2 - \omega_o^2}\,(\Omega^2 - \omega^2)}\, d\Omega$$
$$= \omega a(\omega)/\sqrt{\omega_o^2 - \omega^2}, \quad 0 < \omega < \omega_o; \quad \omega\theta(\omega)/\sqrt{\omega^2 - \omega_o^2}, \quad \omega > \omega_o \tag{1.17.9}$$

for a and θ.

PROBLEMS

1.1 Derive the voltage-current equations which describe linear inductors and capacitors using $\lambda = LI$, $Q = CV$, Lenz's law, and the definition of current flow. What simplifications result when L and C are time-invariant?

1.2 Thermistors are temperature-sensitive resistors which can be used for temperature compensation.

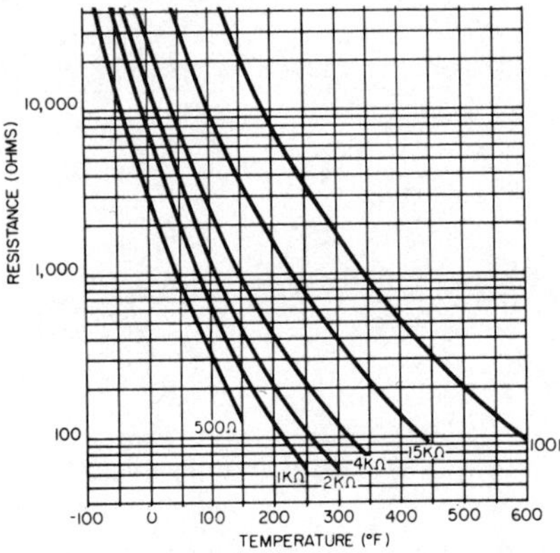

Fig. P1.2 (Courtesy of Fenwal Electronics[48])

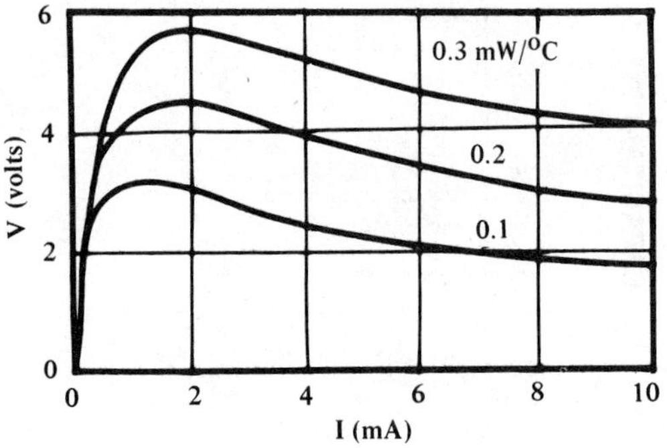

Fig. P1.3

Their resistances equal $R_o \exp \beta(1/T - 1/T_o)$ where R_o and T_o are the reference resistance and temperature of the thermistor and β is a parameter. Determine the small-signal equivalent circuit for a 1 K thermistor which operates at room temperature (77°F) and has the temperature characteristics shown in Fig. P1.2.

1.3 The V-I characteristics of a thermistor at a fixed ambient temperature, are shown in Fig. P1.3 for different thermal resistances θ of the case.[49] Determine the small-signal equivalent circuit for the thermistor for $\theta = 0.2$ mW/°C and a bias current of 5 mA.

1.4 A low-leakage diode has the typical I-V and capacitance characteristics shown in Fig. P1.4. Relate the small-signal resistance and capacitance of the diode to the curves. Draw the ac equivalent circuit for the diode when the forward bias current equals (a) 10 mA, (b) –0.2 nA.

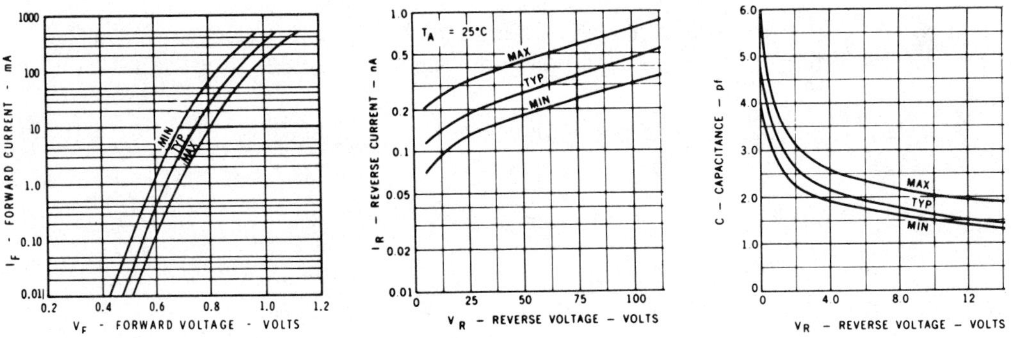

Fig. P1.4 (Courtesy of Fairchild Semiconductor[50])

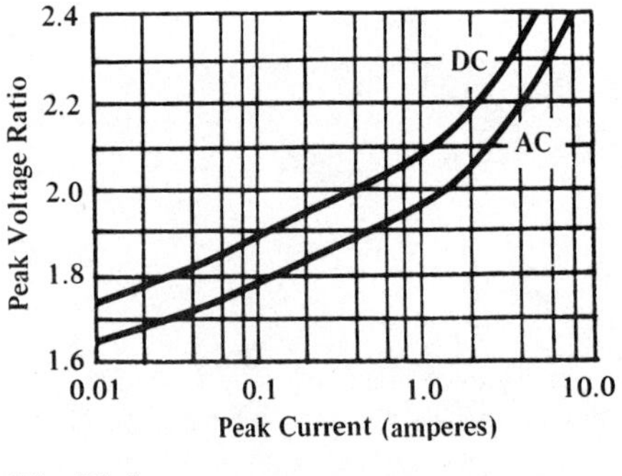

Fig. P1.5

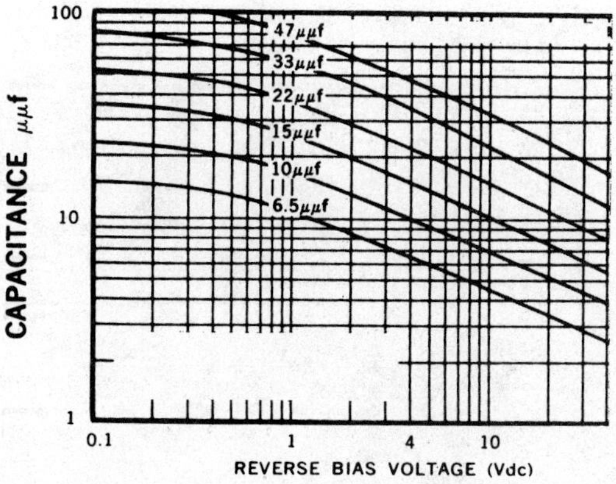

Fig. P1.6 (Courtesy of Crystalonics[53])

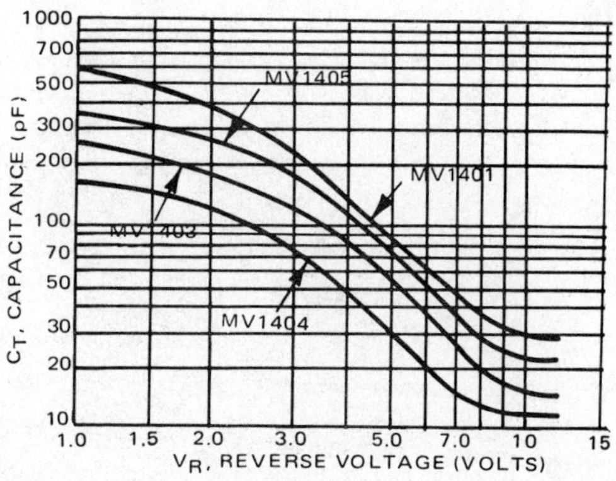

Fig. P1.7 (Courtesy of Motorola[54])

1.5 Varistors are voltage-dependent, symmetrical resistors which perform as back-to-back zener diodes. Their V-I characteristics follow power laws where $I = KV^n$. They provide circuit protection from high-voltage transients by fast clamping when their impedance changes from a very high standby value to a very low conducting value.[51] Discuss dc and ac resistance based on the power-law relation. A typical V-I characteristic is shown in Fig. P1.5.[52] Relate the dc curve to the power-law equation.

1.6 Varactors are voltage-controlled capacitors used for HF tuning of oscillators, VCO's, filters, and detectors. Varactors have the typical ac capacitance characteristics shown in Fig. P1.6. Determine the ac models of the varactor having C = 47 pF (at −4 V) for reverse bias voltages of 0.1, 1, and 10 V. Relate ac and dc capacitances.

1.7 Varactors typically have three states–the high state, the transitional state, and the low state. Their typical ac capacitance curves are shown in Fig. P1.7. Draw the ac models of the varactor having C = 600 pF (at −1 V) for reverse bias voltages of 1, 5, and 15 V. Determine its Q-V equation.

1.8 Photodiodes are used as light detectors in some active filter applications. The small-signal model of the photodiode is shown in Fig. P1.8 where the parameters I_o = reverse saturation current (dark current in nA), I_λ = photocurrent (nA or mA), R = diode series loss (Ω), G = diode junction loss (Ω^{-1}), and C = diode junction capacitance (pF). The photocurrent $I_\lambda = \eta kAH$ where k = conversion constant, A = active

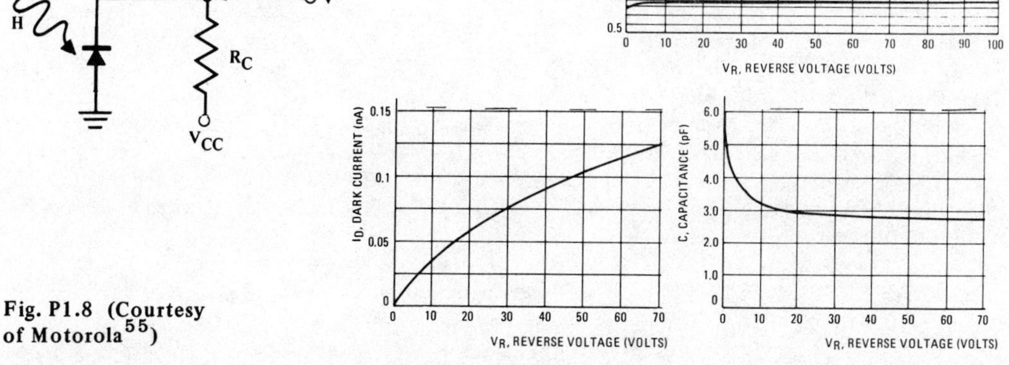

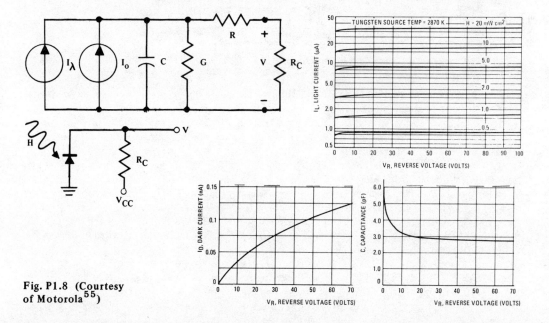

Fig. P1.8 (Courtesy of Motorola[55])

area (cm^2), η = quantum efficiency (ratio of current carriers to incident photons) dependent upon wavelength, and H = normal radiation intensity (watts/cm^2). Find the ac equivalent circuit for the photo-diode which has the characteristics shown in Fig. P1.8 assuming V_{CC} = 20 V and R_C = 1 M.

1.9 Phototransistors are used as light detectors in some active filter applications. The small-signal model of the phototransistor is shown in Prob. 1.8. Find the ac equivalent circuit for the phototransistor which has the characteristics shown in Fig. P1.9 assuming V_{CC} = 10 V and R_C = 1 K.

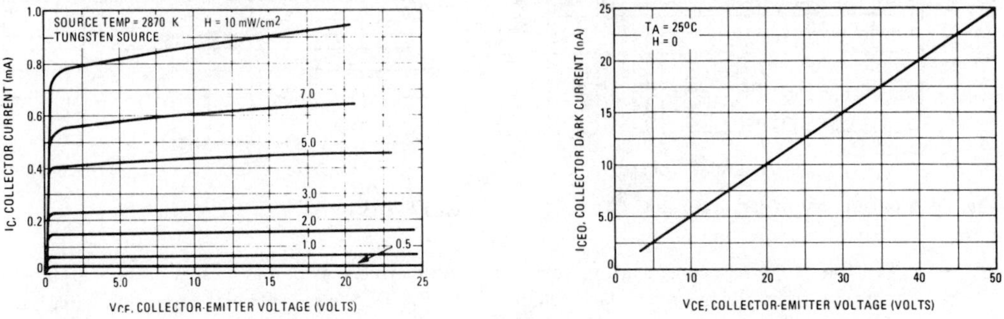

Fig. P1.9 (Courtesy of Motorola[56])

1.10 A transistor has the typical dc current gain h_{FE} variation with collector current I_c shown in Fig. P1.10. Determine how the ac current gain varies with collector bias current at room temperature.

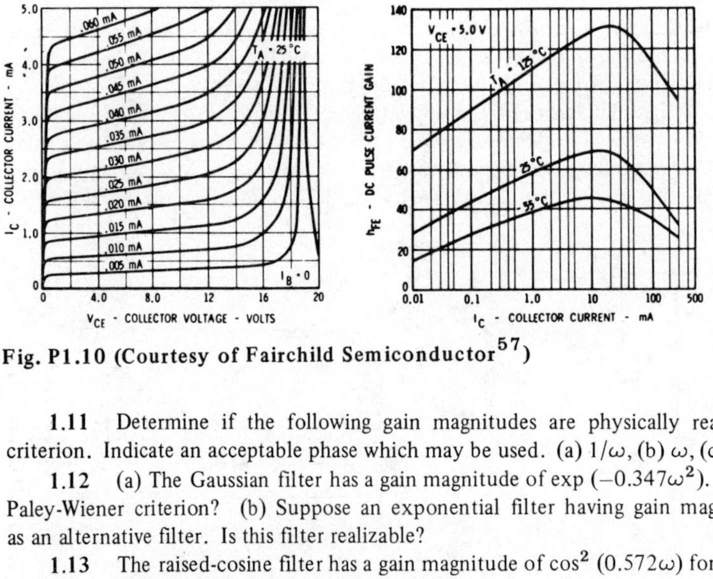

Fig. P1.10 (Courtesy of Fairchild Semiconductor[57])

1.11 Determine if the following gain magnitudes are physically realizable using the Paley-Wiener criterion. Indicate an acceptable phase which may be used. (a) $1/\omega$, (b) ω, (c) 1.

1.12 (a) The Gaussian filter has a gain magnitude of $\exp(-0.347\omega^2)$. Is the filter realizable using the Paley-Wiener criterion? (b) Suppose an exponential filter having gain magnitude $\exp(-|\omega|)$ is proposed as an alternative filter. Is this filter realizable?

1.13 The raised-cosine filter has a gain magnitude of $\cos^2(0.572\omega)$ for $|\omega| < 2.75$ and zero elsewhere. Is the filter realizable using the Paley-Wiener criterion?

1.14 An approximate ideal low-pass filter has a gain magnitude of 1 for $|\omega| \leq 1$ and ϵ for $|\omega| > 1$. Is the filter realizable using the Paley-Wiener criterion?

1.15 The waveforms shown in Fig. 1.6.1 were tested for stability (and causality) in the time domain. Now test for stability in the frequency domain using Eq. 1.6.1 and the transforms tabulated in Tables 1.8.1 and 1.9.1. (Hint: Is Fig. 1.8.3 helpful?)

1.16 Using only $\mathcal{L}[U_{-1}(t)] = 1/s$ for Re $s > 0$, show that the general properties of Laplace transforms listed in Table 1.8.2 can be used to prove the following transforms in Table 1.8.1: numbers (a) 5–9, (b) 10–14, (c) 15–18.

1.17 Prove the following properties of Laplace transforms listed in Table 1.8.2: (a) linearity, (b) scaling, (c) shifting, (d) time differentiation, (e) time integration, (f) frequency differentiation, (g) frequency integration, (h) initial value, (i) initial slope, (j) final value. (Hint: Manipulate the basic definition of the Laplace transform).

1.18 From among the following Laplace transforms listed in Table 1.8.1, determine which have Fourier transforms: numbers (a) 1–4, (b) 5–9, (c) 10–14, (d) 15–19. Verify your results from the Fourier transform table (Table 1.9.1).

1.19 Sketch the spectrums of the following signals listed in Table 1.9.1: numbers (a) 1–4, (b) 5–9, (c) 10–14, (d) 15–20, (e) 21–23.

1.20 Show how the following Fourier transform properties of Table 1.9.2 can be obtained from the Laplace transform properties listed in Table 1.8.2: (a) linearity, (b) symmetry, (c) scaling, (d) shifting, (e) periodicity, (f) convolution, (g) time differentiation, (h) time integration, (i) frequency differentiation, (j) frequency integration, (k) initial value, (l) initial slope, (m) final value.

1.21 (a) A one volt pulse of duration T centered at t = 0 has a Fourier transform $F(j\omega) = T(\sin\phi/\phi)$ where $\phi = \omega T/2$. Sketch its spectrum and label completely. (b) Over what bandwidth does the bulk of the energy lie? What is its asymptotic rolloff? (c) A triangular pulse of the same duration has a spectrum $F(j\omega) = (T/2)(\sin\phi/\phi)^2$ where $\phi = \omega T/4$. Sketch its spectrum and label completely. (d) Which pulse has the greater bandwidth? Which pulse has the greater asymptotic rolloff? Verify using the listings in Table 1.9.3. (e) Which pulse is more likely to pass unaltered through a low-pass filter with 3 dB bandwidth B = 2/T?

1.22 A second-order low-pass filter is shown in Fig. P1.22. Calculate $Z^{(0)}$, T_s, and T_∞ to use in Blackman's impedance relation. Then calculate the input impedance $Z^{(k)}$. Sketch the pole/zero pattern and magnitude of $Z^{(k)}$. (Hint: The gain expression H(s) is involved in $Z^{(k)}$ where $s_n = RCs$ and $K = K_1K_2$.)

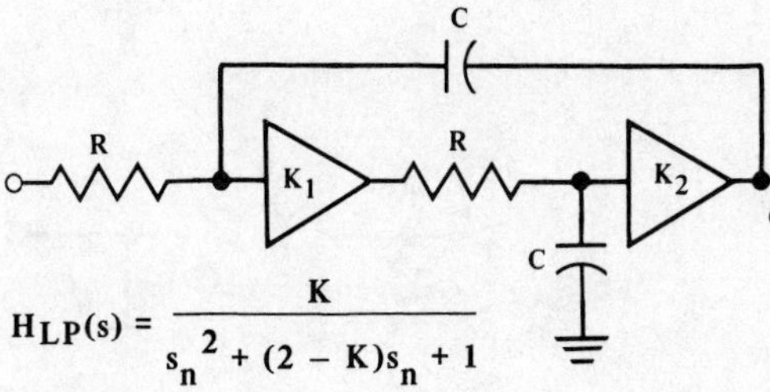

$$H_{LP}(s) = \frac{K}{s_n^2 + (2-K)s_n + 1}$$

Fig. P1.22

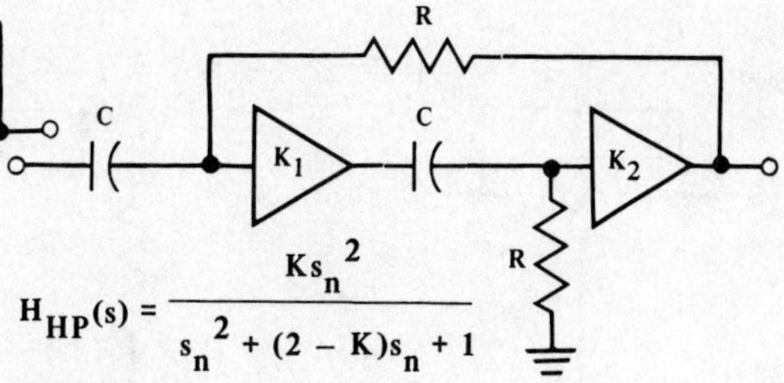

$$H_{HP}(s) = \frac{Ks_n^2}{s_n^2 + (2-K)s_n + 1}$$

Fig. P1.23

1.23 Repeat Prob. 1.22 for the second-order high-pass filter shown in Fig. P1.23.

1.24 Repeat Prob. 1.22 for the second-order band-pass filter shown in Fig. P1.24.

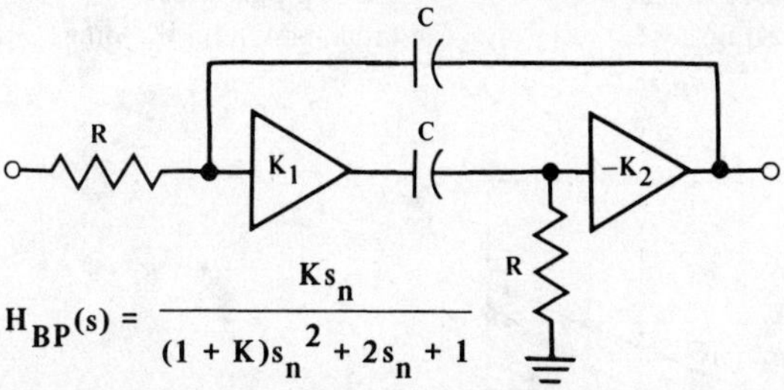

$$H_{BP}(s) = \frac{Ks_n}{(1+K)s_n^2 + 2s_n + 1}$$

Fig. P1.24

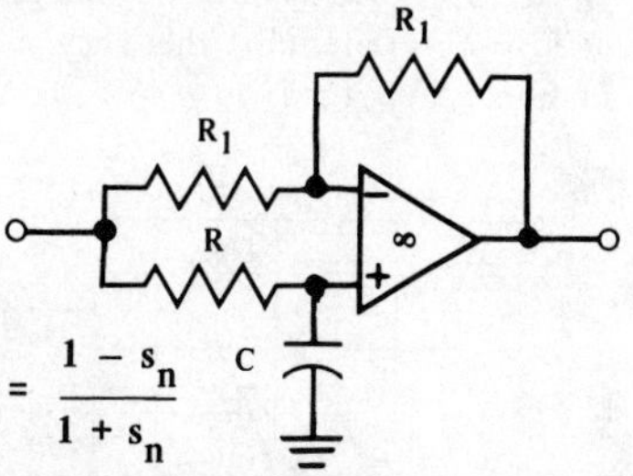

$$H_{AP}(s) = \frac{1 - s_n}{1 + s_n}$$

Fig. P1.25

1.25 Repeat Prob. 1.22 for the first-order all-pass filter shown in Fig. P1.25.

1.26 The z-parameters were interpreted in Eq. 1.11.4 as the open-circuit impedance parameters. Now interpret the meaning of the remaining two-port parameters.

1.27 The small-signal low-frequency characteristics of a high-speed transistor are listed in Table P1.27 (f = 1 KHz and V_{CB} = 10 V).[58] Interpret these results and draw the most convenient two-port equivalent

Symbol	Characteristic	Min.	Max.	Units	I_C (mA)
h_{ie}	Input Resistance	2.0	8.0	KΩ	1.0
		0.25	1.25	KΩ	10
h_{oe}	Output Conductance	5.0	35	μmhos	1.0
		25	200	μmhos	10
h_{re}	Voltage Feedback Ratio		800	$\times 10^{-6}$	1.0
			400	$\times 10^{-6}$	10
h_{fe}	Current Transfer Ratio	50	300		1.0
		75	375		10

Table P1.27

circuit under worst-case impedance and gain conditions. Assume the collector bias current equals 1 mA.

1.28 The impedance parameters for a uniform transmission line of length d are $z_{11} = z_{22} = Z_o \coth \gamma d$ and $z_{12} = z_{21} = Z_o \operatorname{csch} \gamma d$ where Z_o is its characteristic impedance and γ is its propagation function.[59] Find the admittance and inverse chain matrices for the transmission line.

1.29 The ideal transformer is described by $V_1 I_1 = -V_2 I_2$. The output power is equal to the input power so there is zero power loss within the ideal transformer itself. Determine the input impedance if the transformer turns ratio is n and the load impedance is Z_L.

1.30 Calculate Z_i, Z_o, A_v, and A_i for the transistor in Prob. 1.27 assuming that $Z_S = 0$ and $Z_L = \infty$.

1.31 Two distributed notch filters are shown in Fig. P1.31. Determine their open-circuit voltage transfer functions using the z-parameters listed in Prob. 1.28.

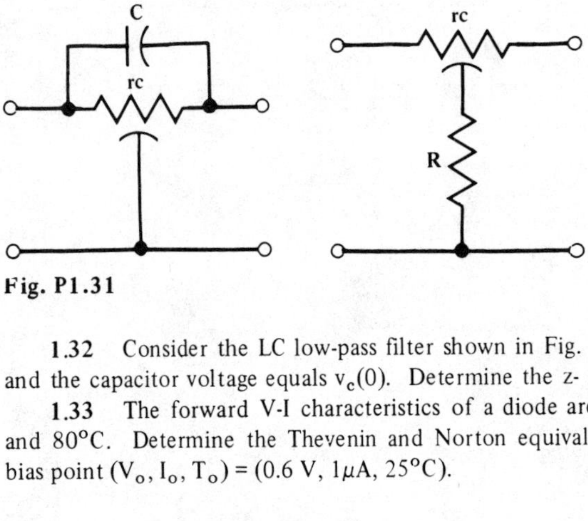

Fig. P1.31

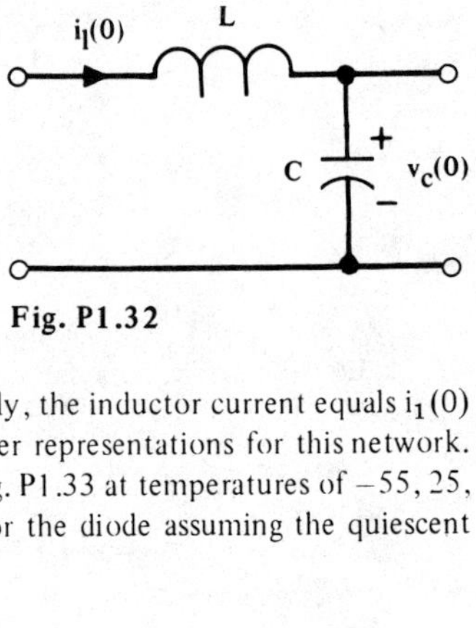

Fig. P1.32

1.32 Consider the LC low-pass filter shown in Fig. P1.32. Initially, the inductor current equals $i_1(0)$ and the capacitor voltage equals $v_c(0)$. Determine the z- and g-parameter representations for this network.

1.33 The forward V-I characteristics of a diode are shown in Fig. P1.33 at temperatures of −55, 25, and 80°C. Determine the Thevenin and Norton equivalent circuits for the diode assuming the quiescent bias point $(V_o, I_o, T_o) = (0.6\text{ V}, 1\mu\text{A}, 25°\text{C})$.

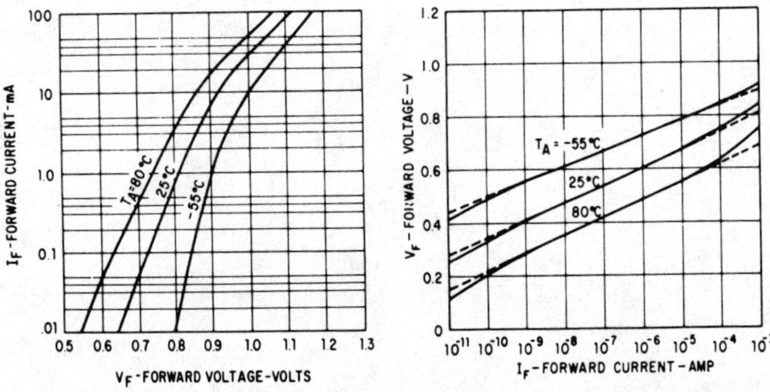

Fig. P1.33 (Courtesy of Fairchild Semiconductor[50])

1.34 We are interested in utilizing Llewellyn's criteria to investigate several useful networks. (a) Show that for unilateral networks, only Eq. 1.13.18 need be satisfied. (b) Show that for reciprocal networks, Eq. 1.13.17 reduces to $\text{Re } z_{11} \text{ Re } z_{22} = [\text{Re } z_{12}]^2$.

1.35 Draw the flow graph description for the z-parameters and describe how they can be determined experimentally.

1.36 Convert the z-representation of a two-port to the y-representation using signal flow graph manipulations.

1.37 Find the input impedance to the loaded two-port of Fig. 1.14.3 using its flow graph description and Blackman's impedance relation.

1.38 An *n*th-order canonical flow graph is one which describes a system having n controlled sources. The general gain expression can be easily expressed in matrix form as[61]

$$H(s) = T_{12} + \mathbf{T}_{42}^T[\mathbf{I} - \mathbf{KT}_{43}]^{-1}\mathbf{KT}_{13}$$

where **K** = diagonal matrix of amplifier gains, $\mathbf{T}_{13}$ = column matrix of gains of branches connecting filter input to amplifier inputs, $\mathbf{T}_{42}$ = column matrix of gains of branches connecting amplifier outputs to filter output, $\mathbf{T}_{43}$ = square matrix of local feedback and cross-coupling gains of branches connecting amplifier outputs to an amplifier input, and **I** = identity matrix. Apply this gain expression to the second-order canonical flow graph of Fig. 7.1.5 and show that it yields the same gain as that obtained by using Eq. 1.14.1.

1.39 A second-order low-pass filter is shown in Fig. P1.39. Its flow graph has the form of Fig. 7.1.1. Calculate the voltage transfer functions T_{13} and T_{43} using the ladder analysis technique shown in Fig. 1.14.7. Then calculate the overall transfer function V_2/V_1.

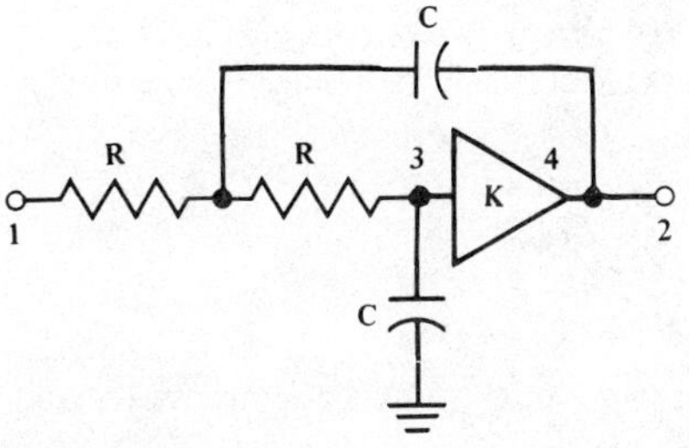

Fig. P1.39

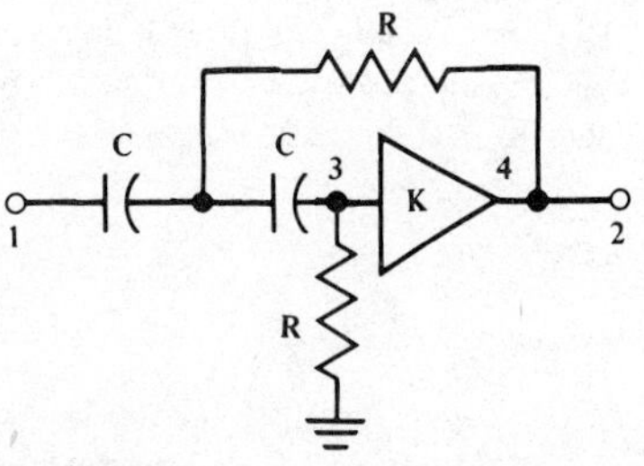

Fig. P1.40

1.40 Repeat Prob. 1.39 for the second-order high-pass filter shown in Fig. P1.40.

1.41 A number of useful sensitivity relations were listed in Table 1.15.1. Prove the relations involving: (a) a single variable y in column one, (b) two variables y and z in column two.

1.42 The resistor attenuator of Example 1.15.2 is redesigned using a potentiometer in place of the two resistors. One end of the pot is grounded and input signal is applied to the other end. The output signal is taken from the wiper. The open-circuit voltage gain H(s) = k where k is the percentage of the full scale pot setting. Determine the gain tolerance over a 100°C temperature range if the pot has a ± 10% resistance tolerance and a temperature coefficient of ± 50 PPM/°C.

1.43 The general determinant of a second-order active filter can be expressed as

$$\Delta(s) = s^2 + (a_1 + a_2)s + a_1 a_2 - K(\beta_2 s^2 + \beta_1 s + \beta_0)$$

(a) Show that the root locus of Δ for variable K is a circle with center σ_c and radius R where[62]

$$\sigma_c = -\frac{\beta_0 - \beta_2 a_1 a_2}{\beta_1 - \beta_2(a_1 + a_2)}, \qquad R = \sqrt{(\sigma_c + a_1)(\sigma_c + a_2)}$$

(b) Show that σ_c can be anywhere on the real axis except in the interval $-a_2 \leqslant \sigma_c \leqslant -a_1$. (c) Show that the root locus must always intersect the real axis between $-a_1$ and $-a_2$.

1.44 Some types of active filters have transfer functions with the denominators listed below. Draw the root locus for the filter poles. (Hint: Is Prob. 1.43 useful?) (a) $\Delta(s) = (s + a_1)(s + a_2) - Ks(s + a_3)$, (b) $\Delta(s) = (s + a_1)(s + a_2) - K(s + a_3)$, (c) $\Delta(s) = (s + a_1)(s + a_2) - K(s^2 + a_3^2)$.

1.45 A shunt-peaked gain function equals

$$H(s) = \frac{s_n + 1/m}{s_n^2 + s_n/m + 1/m}$$

where $s_n = s/\omega_o$ and m is the parameter of interest. Determine the root locus for the function.

1.46 Show that the transfer function for an rcg transmission line or "cable" terminated in a resistive load Y_L equals[63]

$$A_v^{-1} = \cosh \gamma d + Y_L rd \frac{\sinh \gamma d}{\gamma d}$$

where the propagation function $\gamma = \sqrt{r(g + sc)}$. Draw the root locus for the system poles as Y_L varies from 0 to ∞. (Hint: Use the following product expansions.)

$$\cosh f = \prod_{n=1}^{\infty} \left[1 + \frac{4f^2}{(2n-1)^2\pi^2}\right], \qquad \frac{\sinh f}{f} = \prod_{n=1}^{\infty} \left[1 + \frac{4f^2}{(2n)^2\pi^2}\right]$$

1.47 The gain of a distributed notch filter was derived in Prob. 1.31. Determine the root locus for the poles and zeros of the gain function A_v where[63]

$$A_v = \frac{1 + k\theta \sinh \theta}{\cosh \theta + k\theta \sinh \theta}$$

where $k = C/dc$, $\theta = \gamma d$, and $\gamma = \sqrt{src}$. (Hint: Use the product expansions of Prob. 1.46.)

1.48 A low-pass filter having an ideal magnitude response was analyzed in Example 1.17.1. Determine the magnitude and delay and sketch the responses of:[47] (a) an ideal linear phase or constant delay filter having a phase function $\theta = -t_o\omega$, (b) an approximate ideal filter having a phase function $\theta = -t_o\omega$, $|\omega| < \omega_o$ and $-t_o\omega_o$, $|\omega| > \omega_o$.

1.49 A low-pass filter has α and θ defined on complementary parts of the $j\omega$-axis as:[47] (a) $\alpha = 0$, $|\omega| < \omega_o$ and $\theta = -t_o\omega_o$, $|\omega| > \omega_o$, (b) $\theta = -t_o\omega$, $|\omega| < \omega_o$ and $\alpha = \epsilon$, $|\omega| > \omega_o$. Determine the magnitude and delay and sketch the responses of the resulting low-pass filters.

REFERENCES

1. Frymoyer, E. M., R. A. Johnson, and F. H. Schindelbeck, "Passive filters: today's offerings and tomorrow's promises," EDN Magazine, pp. 22–30, Oct 5, 1973.
2. Lindquist, C. S., "Large-signal and small-signal models and their utilization in computer-aided analysis," Tech. Rep. WP-2213, Collins Radio Group of Rockwell International, Newport Beach, CA, Aug., 1969.
3. Ghausi, M. S., *Principles and Design of Linear Active Circuits,* Chap. 7, McGraw-Hill, NY, 1965.
4. Panter, P. F., *Modulation, Noise, and Spectral Analysis*, Chap. 2, McGraw-Hill, NY, 1965.
   Schwartz, M., *Information Transmission, Modulation, and Noise,* 2nd ed., Chap. 2, McGraw-Hill, NY, 1970.
5. Paley, R. E. A. C., and N. Wiener, "Fourier transforms in the complex domain," Am. Math. Soc. Colloq. Publ., vol. 19, Chap. I, pp. 16–17, 1934.
6. Dirac, P. A. M., *The Principles of Quantum Mechanics,* Oxford Univ. Press, 1930.
   Schwartz, L., *Theorie des Distributions*, vols. I and II, Hermann et Cie, Paris, 1950 and 1951.
   Temple, G, "The theory of generalized functions," Proc. Royal Soc., A, vol. 228, pp. 175–190, 1955.
   Lighthill, M. J., *Fourier Analysis and Generalized Functions,* Cambridge Univ. Press, 1955.
7. Rehberg, C. F., "Theory of generalized functions for electrical engineers," Tech. Rep. 400-442, New York Univ., Aug., 1961.
8. Ley, B. J., S. G. Lutz, and C. F. Rehberg, *Linear Circuit Analysis,* Chap. 8, McGraw-Hill, NY, 1959.
9. Tuttle, D. F., Jr., *Network Synthesis,* vol. 1, Chap. 3, Wiley, NY, 1958.
10. Close, C. M., *The Analysis of Linear Circuits*, Chap. 10, Harcourt, Brace and World, NY, 1966.
11. Papoulis, A., *The Fourier Integral and Its Application*, Chap. 2, McGraw-Hill, NY, 1962.
12. Bennett, W. R., and J. R. Davey, *Data Transmission*, pp. 50–52, McGraw-Hill, NY, 1965.
13. Papoulis, A., *Probability, Random Variables, and Stochastic Processes*, Chaps. 9 and 10, McGraw-Hill, NY, 1965.
14. Skilling, H. H., *Electrical Engineering Circuits*, 2nd ed., Chap. 8, Wiley, NY, 1965.
15. Ref. 10, Chap. 11.

16. Blackman, R. B., "Effect of feedback on impedance," Bell System Tech. J., vol. 22, pp. 269–277, Oct., 1943.
17. Mulligan, J. H., Jr., "Feedback amplifiers and control systems," T34.1401 class notes, New York Univ., 1965.
18. Mulligan, J. H., Jr., "Signal transmission in nonreciprocal systems," Proc. of Symp. on Active Networks and Feedback Systems, pp. 125–153, Poly. Tech. Inst. of Brooklyn, April 19–21, 1960.
19. Larky, A. I., "Negative-impedance converters," IRE Trans. Circuit Theory, vol. CT-4, pp. 124–131, Sept., 1957.
20. Ref. 3, Chap. 3.
Potter, J. I., and S. Fich, *Theory of Networks and Lines,* Chap. 1, Prentice-Hall, NJ, 1963.
21. Schilling, D. L., and C. Belove, *Electronic Circuits: Discrete and Integrated*, Chap. 8.1, McGraw-Hill, NY, 1968.
22. Van Valkenburg, M. E., *Introduction to Modern Network Synthesis*, Chap. 11, Wiley, NY, 1960.
23. Lindquist, C. S., "Analysis and synthesis of active transmission lines," Chap. 2, Ph.D. Dissertation, Oregon State Univ., June, 1969.
24. Moad, M. F., "Two-port networks with independent sources," Proc. IEEE, vol. 54, pp. 1008–1009, July, 1966.
———, "Addendum: Two-port networks with independent sources," Proc. IEEE, vol. 54, pp. 1963–1964, Dec., 1966.
25. Huber, W. R., "Two-port equivalent noise generators," Proc. IEEE, vol. 58, pp. 807–809, May, 1970.
26. Linvill, J. G., and J. E. Gibbons, *Transistors and Active Circuits*, Chap. 17.2, McGraw-Hill, NY, 1961.
27. van Nie, A. G., "Representation of linear passive noisy 1-ports by two correlated noise sources," Proc. IEEE, vol. 60, pp. 751–753, June, 1972.
28. Brune, O., "Synthesis of a finite two-terminal network whose driving-point impedance is a prescribed function of frequency," J. Mathematics and Physics, vol. 10, pp. 191–236, Oct., 1931.
29. Ref. 23, Chap. 3.
30. Churchill, R. V., *Complex Variables and Applications*, 2nd ed., Sec. 54, McGraw-Hill, NY, 1960.
31. Reza, F. M., "A bound for the derivative of positive real functions," SIAM Rev., vol. 4, pp. 40–42, Jan., 1962.
Schneider, A. J., "A necessary condition on coefficients of a positive real function," Proc. IEEE, vol. 53, p. 1659, Oct., 1965.
32. Raisbeck, G., "A definition of passive linear networks in terms of time and energy," J. Appl. Phys., vol. 25, pp. 1510–1514, Dec., 1954.
Resh, R. A., "A note concerning the n-port passivity condition," IEEE Trans. Circuit Theory, vol. CT-13, pp. 238–239, June, 1966.
33. Ku, W. H., "A simple derivation for the stability criterion of linear active two-ports," Proc. IEEE, vol. 53, pp. 310–311, March, 1965.
34. Ref. 30, Sec. 34.
35. Llewellyn, F. B., "Some fundamental properties of transmission systems," Proc. IRE, vol. 40, pp. 271–283, March, 1952.
36. Mason, S. J., "Feedback theory–some properties of signal flow graphs," Proc. IRE, vol. 41, pp. 1142–1156, Sept., 1953.
———, "Feedback theory–further properties of signal flow graphs," Proc. IRE, vol. 44, pp. 920–926, July, 1956.
37. Higgins, W. H., and D. R. Entwisle, *Introductory Systems and Design*, Chaps. 1 and 2, Blaisdell, MA, 1968.
38. Truxal, J. G., *Control System Synthesis*, Chap. 2, McGraw-Hill, NY, 1955.
39. Wing, O., "Ladder network analysis by signal-flow graph–application to computer programming," IRE Trans. Circuit Theory, vol. CT-3, pp. 289–294, Dec., 1956.
40. Williamson, R. E., R. H. Crowell, and H. F. Trotter, *Calculus of Vector Functions*, 2nd ed., Chap. 3.3, Prentice-Hall, NJ, 1968.
Lasdon, L. S., and A. D. Waren, "Mathematical programming for optimal design," Electro-Technology, pp. 55–70, Nov., 1967.
41. Gorski-Popiel, J., "Classical sensitivity–A collection of formulas," IEEE Trans. Circuit Theory, vol. CT-10, pp. 300–302, June, 1963.

Geffe, P. R., "RC-amplifier resonators for active filters," IEEE Trans. Circuit Theory, vol. CT-15, pp. 415–419, Dec., 1968.

42. Balaban, P., and J. J. Golembeski, "Statistical analysis for practical circuit design," IEEE Trans. Circuits and Systems, vol. CAS-22, pp. 100–108, Feb., 1975.
43. Ref. 38, Chap. 4.
    D'Azzo, J. J., and C. H. Houpis, *Control System Analysis and Synthesis*, Chap. 7, McGraw-Hill, NY, 1960.
44. Nash, G., "Phase-locked loop design principles," Appl. Note AN-535, Motorola, Phoenix, AZ, 10-70.
    Viterbi, A. J., *Principles of Coherent Communications*, Chap. 2, McGraw-Hill, NY, 1966.
45. Bode, H. W., *Network Analysis and Feedback Amplifier Design*, Chap. 14, D. Van Nostrand, NY, 1945.
46. Liou, M. L., and C. F. Kurth, "Computation of group delay from attenuation characteristics via Hilbert transformation and spline function and its application to filter design," IEEE Trans. Circuits and Systems, vol. CAS-22, pp. 729–734, Sept., 1975.
47. Ref. 11, Chap. 10.
48. Iso-Curve Thermistors, Bull. L-2A, 5M-5-473-WP, p. 3, Fenwal Electronics, Framington, MA, 4/73.
    High-Reliability Thermistors, Tech. Bull. V1142A, p. 2, VECO, Springfield, NJ, 11/66.
49. Sapoff, M., and R. M. Oppenheim, "Theory and application of self-heated thermistors," Proc. IEEE, vol. 51, pp. 1292–1305, Oct., 1963.
    Bock, D. H., and R. A. Dunklin, "Comment on thermistor circuit design," Proc. IEEE, vol. 52, pp. 973–974, Aug., 1964.
50. Fairchild Discrete Products Databook, 2011-12-0001-023/65M, p. 5–9, Fairchild Semiconductor, Mt. View, CA, 1973.
51. "General characteristics of varistors," Appl. Data, Sec. 9703, NL Industries, Highstown, NJ.
52. Transient Voltage Suppression Manual, 108 p., General Electric Semiconductor Products Department, Syracuse, NY, 1976.
    Metal Oxide Varistor, Data Sheet 180.66, 1 p., General Electric Semiconductor Products Department, Syracuse, NY, 12/72.
53. 1975 Varactor Catalog, Model VA107-173, Crystalonics, Cambridge, MA, 1975.
54. Epicap Tuning and Hot Carrier Diodes, Publ. SG27, Motorola, Phoenix, AZ, 10-70.
55. MRD 500/510, Data Sheet DS2608, 2 p., Motorola, Phoenix, AZ, 9-69.
56. MRD 100/150, Data Sheet DS2605, 2 p., Motorola, Phoenix, AZ, 6-69.
57. Fairchild Semiconductor Transistor and Diode Data Catalog, BR-BR-0015-29, p. 2–112, Fairchild Semiconductor, Mt. View, CA, 1970.
58. Ref. 57, p. 2–103.
59. Ghausi, M. S., and J. J. Kelly, *Introduction to Distributed-Parameter Networks,* Chap. 1, Holt, Rinehart and Winston, NY, 1968.
60. Ref. 57, p. 5–125.
61. Sandberg, I. W., "On the theory of multiloop feedback systems," Bell System Tech. J., vol. 42, pp. 352–383, March, 1963.
62. Soderstrand, M. A., and S. K. Mitra, "Design of active RC filters with zero gain-sensitivity product," IEEE Trans. Circuit Theory, vol. CT-20, pp. 441–445, July, 1973.
63. Ref. 59, Chap. 5.

2 FREQUENCY DOMAIN ANALYSIS

A journey of a thousand miles began with a single step
Oriental Proverb

Frequency and time domain characteristics are of prime importance to the engineer in designing filters and assessing filter performance. This chapter is concerned with frequency domain behavior while the following chapter is concerned with the corresponding time domain behavior. The object of this chapter is to develop frequency domain analysis techniques, to apply them to filter analysis, to present a number of standard curves, and to apply these results to a myriad of practical filter design examples. To facilitate rapid filter analysis, useful approximations are also introduced. Engineers will find this chapter to be a useful compendium of frequency domain results.

First, we shall introduce the concept of ac steady-state performance and Bode plots. General Bode plot construction is discussed. Since we are primarily interested in filters, we shall utilize Bode plots for characterizing low-pass, high-pass, band-pass, band-stop, and all-pass filters. A number of standard transfer functions are tabulated and discussed. Next, we shall introduce dominant pole-zero analysis to simplify frequency domain (and later time domain) analysis. A number of often-encountered transfer functions are considered as examples. Finally, the important concept of delay is derived and examined. The results are applied to all-pass filters. Since this chapter and the next form the foundations for much of our later work, the engineer should strive to master this material.

Filters are characterized by their transfer functions. The *transfer function* H(s) of a linear, time-invariant (lumped and finite) filter having zero initial conditions is the ratio of the Laplace transformation of the filter's output to its input, and has the form

$$H(s) = \frac{a_m s^m + a_{m-1} s^{m-1} + \ldots + a_0}{b_n s^n + b_{n-1} s^{n-1} + \ldots + b_0} = \frac{\sum_{j=0}^{m} a_j s^j}{\sum_{i=0}^{n} b_i s^i} = \frac{a_m}{b_n} \frac{\prod_{j=1}^{m} (s + z_j)}{\prod_{i=1}^{n} (s + p_i)} \tag{2.0.1}$$

where $s = \sigma + j\omega$ is the complex frequency variable. The $-z_j$ are the *zeros* of the filter and the $-p_i$ are the *poles*. Generally, stable causal filters must have Re $p_i \leqslant 0$ for $i = 1, \ldots, n$ and all $j\omega$-axis poles must be simple (first-order). Since the filter response in real time must be real, all complex poles and zeros must exist in complex conjugate pairs. In practical filters, $m < n$ since the response must be zero at infinite frequency. However, in filters modelled mathematically (i.e., ideal filters), this condition need not be satisfied. For example, the ideal differentiator has a gain H(s) = as for Re $s > 0$. However, we know in practice that there are high-frequency poles which dominate the response causing $H(s) \to 0$ as $s \to \infty$. Therefore, when these high-frequency poles are included in the ideal model, $n > m$ in H(s).

The *order* of the filter is often a measure of filter complexity. A filter is said to be of order k where k is equal to the number of finite poles or zeros, whichever is greater. Mathematically, k = max (n, m) and in most situations where n > m, the filter order k = n. In this chapter, we shall be working primarily with first-, second-, and third-order filters. However, in Chaps. 4 and 5 which are concerned with classical and optimum filters, respectively, we shall consider some filters having orders greater than 20.

Sometimes two filters will have transfer function H_1 and H_2 whose product or sum is unity. Such filters are given special names. Filters are said to be *inverse* filters if

$$H_2(s) = 1/H_1(s) \tag{2.0.2}$$

and *complementary* filters if

$$H_2(s) = 1 - H_1(s) \tag{2.0.3}$$

We shall encounter several such filters in this chapter.

2.1 AC STEADY-STATE CHARACTERISTICS

The *frequency response* of a filter is a plot of its transfer function as a function of frequency in ac steady-state. Mathematically, it is a plot of H(s) for s = jω from ω = 0 to +∞. Recall that H(jω) is a complex number at any given frequency ω (rad/sec) where

$$H(j\omega) = H(s)\,\big|_{s=j\omega} = |H(j\omega)|\, e^{j \arg H(j\omega)} = \text{Re}\, H(j\omega) + j\, \text{Im}\, H(j\omega) \tag{2.1.1}$$

Thus, we must specify both its magnitude and phase, or alternatively, its real and imaginary parts at every frequency in the range from 0 to ∞ to completely characterize H. The first form is the polar representation for H while the second is its rectangular representation. Considering H to be an impedance Z, then the polar form gives the impedance magnitude and angle, while the rectangular form gives the resistive and reactive portions of the impedance. The application determines the most desirable form of expression.

The engineer is concerned with expressing H(jω) in the most illustrative manner to enhance his understanding. Several different forms have classically been used including (1) Bode plots, (2) polar plots (Nyquist plots), and (3) log magnitude-phase plots (on which Nichol's plots are based).[1] Although polar plots and log magnitude-phase plots often yield great insight into system performance, their construction requires that the magnitude and phase of H(jω) first be *calculated* at a large number of points. However, Bode plots can be easily constructed with only a few calculations. Thus, Bode plots are the most popular means for displaying ac steady-state behavior.

In filter applications, filters are classified by the form of their magnitude characteristics |H(jω)|. The filter classifications are:

1. *Low-pass filters:* Pass low frequencies and reject (attenuate) high frequencies.
2. *High-pass filters:* Pass high frequencies and reject (attenuate) low frequencies.
3. *Band-pass filters:* Pass a prescribed band (range) of frequencies and reject all other frequencies.
4. *Band-stop (band-reject, band-elimination, or notch) filters:* Reject a prescribed band of frequencies and pass all other frequencies.
5. *All-pass filters:* Pass all frequencies equally but modify their phases.

Their ideal magnitude characteristics are shown in Fig. 2.1.1 with some typical time domain responses. This terminology is very useful in generically classifying the type of filter being discussed. Many examples of these filters will be presented later in the chapter. Entire chapters (Chaps. 8, 9, 10, 11, and 12, respectively) will later be devoted to actually designing these filters.

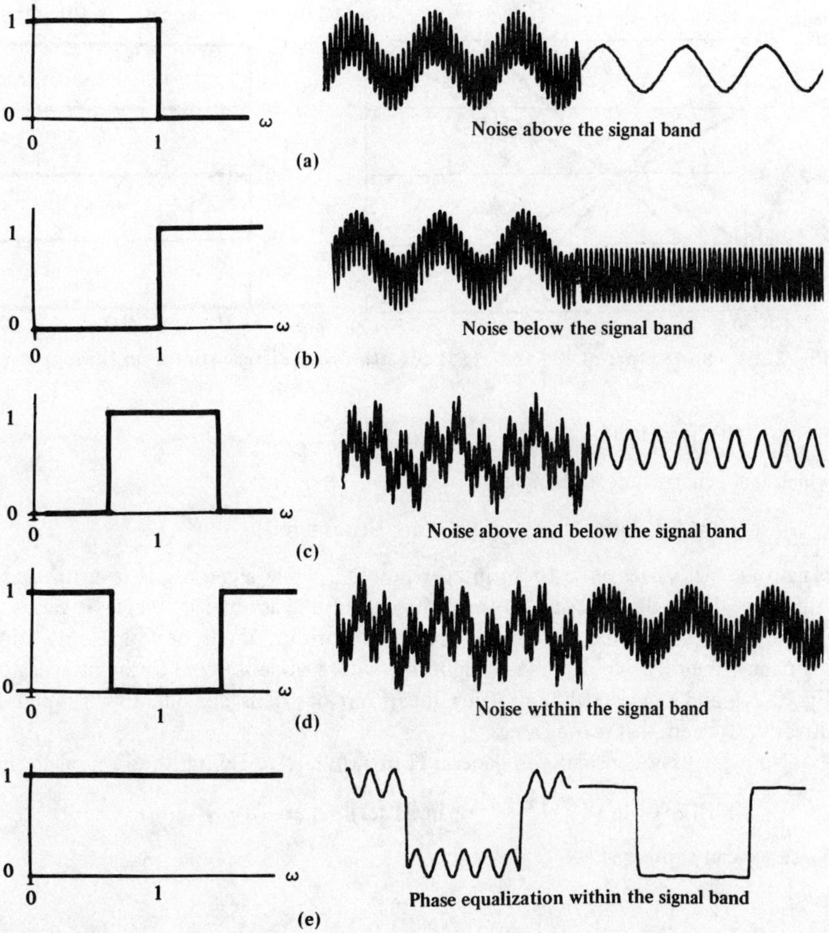

Fig. 2.1.1 Magnitude characteristics and time domain responses[2] of (a) low-pass, (b) high-pass, (c) band-pass, (d) band-stop, and (e) all-pass filters.

2.2 BODE PLOTS

Bode plots are plots of |H| and arg H as a function of frequency ω. Since the ac steady-state gain of a filter having the H(s) given by Eq. 2.0.1 equals

$$H(j\omega) = \frac{a_m}{b_n} \frac{\prod_{j=1}^{m} (z_j + j\omega)}{\prod_{i=1}^{n} (p_i + j\omega)} \tag{2.2.1}$$

$H(j\omega)$ is a complex number and its functional form may be complicated. Usually its frequency behavior is not obvious except at $\omega = 0$ and $\omega = \infty$ where

$$\begin{aligned} H(0) &= H(j\omega)\big|_{\omega=0} = H(s)\big|_{s=0} = \text{filter gain at dc or zero frequency} \\ H(\infty) &= H(j\omega)\big|_{\omega=\infty} = H(s)\big|_{s=\infty} = \text{filter gain at infinite frequency} \end{aligned} \tag{2.2.2}$$

For example, consider the gain function $H(s) = s^n$ where n is an integer (positive or negative). This is a system of n cascaded differentiators (n positive) or integrators (n negative). In ac steady-state, the gain equals

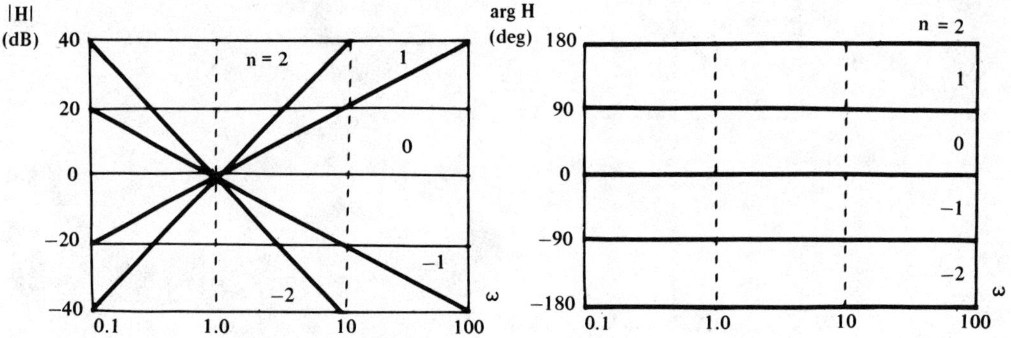

Fig. 2.2.1 Bode plots of |H| and arg H for nth-order differentiator and integrator.

$$H(j\omega) = H(s)\,\big|_{s=j\omega} = s^n\,\big|_{s=j\omega} = \omega^n e^{jn\pi/2}, \qquad \omega \geqslant 0 \tag{2.2.3}$$

which has a magnitude and angle of

$$|H| = |H(j\omega)| = \omega^n, \qquad \arg H = \arg H(j\omega) = n\pi/2 \tag{2.2.4}$$

Magnitude $|H|$ varies as ω to an integer power n while angle arg H is an integer multiple of $\pi/2$. Although the angle is easily plotted, the magnitude is difficult since it varies as a power of ω.

Note, however, that if we considered the logarithm of $|H|$, or equivalently plotted $|H|$ on semi-log paper, then $|H|$ would be a straight line whose slope is equal to the integer n. This is shown in Fig. 2.2.1 and suggests that plotting logarithm of $|H|$ is considerably simpler than plotting $|H|$ directly. Indeed, this is the case.

Now let us reconsider the general H in Eq. 2.1.1. Taking the natural logarithm of H yields

$$\ln H(j\omega) = \ln\left(|H|\, e^{j \arg H}\right) = \ln |H(j\omega)| + j \arg H(j\omega) \tag{2.2.5}$$

Since we can express H as

$$H(j\omega) = \frac{a_m \prod_{j=1}^{m} (z_j + j\omega)}{b_n \prod_{i=1}^{n} (p_i + j\omega)} = \frac{a_m \prod_{j=1}^{m} c_j}{b_n \prod_{i=1}^{n} d_i}\, e^{j\left(\sum_{j=1}^{m} \theta_j - \sum_{i=1}^{n} \phi_i\right)} \tag{2.2.6}$$

where[3]

$$c_j = (z_j^2 + \omega^2)^{1/2}, \qquad d_i = (p_i^2 + \omega^2)^{1/2}, \qquad \theta_j = \tan^{-1}\frac{\omega}{z_j}, \qquad \phi_i = \tan^{-1}\frac{\omega}{p_i} \tag{2.2.7}$$

Then the real and imaginary parts of ln H equal

$$\ln |H| = \ln a_m + \sum_{j=1}^{m} \ln c_j - \left(\ln b_n + \sum_{i=1}^{n} \ln d_i\right), \qquad \arg H = \sum_{j=1}^{m} \theta_j - \sum_{i=1}^{n} \phi_i \tag{2.2.8}$$

Thus, we see from Eq. 2.2.8 that not only does the logarithm operation convert *n*th-power curves to straight lines in magnitude plots, but it also converts the multiplication operation of individual pole and zero terms into a simple summation operation for the magnitude and angle of H. It is these two simplifications that facilitate plotting $H(j\omega)$.[4]

Note that the magnitude plot is in terms of dB (decibels) where

$$|H|_{dB} = \text{Lm } H = 20 \log_{10} |H(j\omega)| \tag{2.2.9}$$

The dB definition is used rather than ln $|H|$ since it has become a measurement standard in electrical engineering. To facilitate relating $|H|_{dB}$ and $|H|$, Table 2.2.1 is extremely useful. It provides

Table 2.2.1 dB and numeric equivalences.

Number	dB
10^{-6}	−120
10^{-5}	−100
10^{-4}	−80
10^{-3}	−60
10^{-2}	−40
10^{-1}	−20
1	0
10^{1}	+20
10^{2}	+40
10^{3}	+60
10^{4}	+80
10^{5}	+100
10^{6}	+120

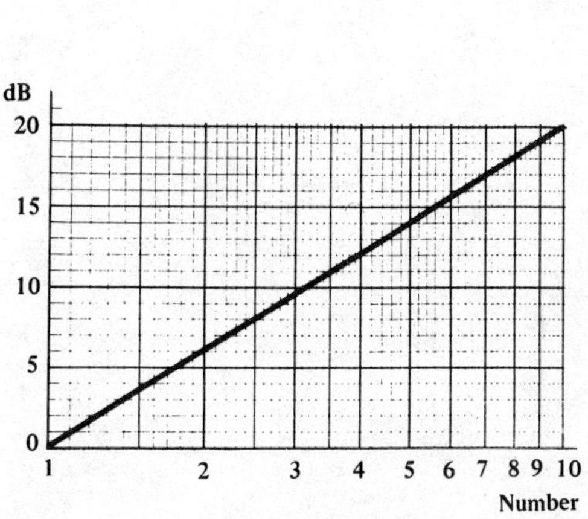

an especially simple graphical means for converting numbers to dB form and visa versa. Numbers in the 1–10 range have dB equivalents in the 0–20 dB range from Eq. 2.2.9. The correspondences are determined from the figure. The dB are listed on the ordinate scale and the numbers on the abcissa scale. For example, the number 6 is equivalent to 16 dB. This is found by entering 6 on the abcissa and determining the ordinate value of 16 dB from the curve. Conversely, 6 dB is equivalent to the number 2 as we see the entering 6 dB on the ordinate and reading off the abcissa value of 2.

Numbers outside the 1–10 range or 0–20 dB range are just as easily determined by observing the following. Suppose that two filters having gains H_1 and H_2 are cascaded, and that the overall gain is H. Denoting |H| in terms of dB as $|H|_{dB}$, etc.,

$$|H| = |H_1|\,|H_2|, \qquad |H|_{dB} = |H_1|_{dB} + |H_2|_{dB} \tag{2.2.10}$$

Thus, *numeric* values are *multiplied* while *dB* values (logarithmic values) are *added*.

EXAMPLE 2.2.1 Express the following numbers in dB using Table 2.2.1: 12, 250, and −250.
Solution Since $12 = 1.2 \times 10$, then $(12)_{dB} = (1.2)_{dB} + (10)_{dB} = 1.6 + 20 = 21.6$ dB. Likewise, since $250 = 2.5 \times 100$, then $(250)_{dB} = 8 + 40 = 48$ dB. Finally, −250 has a *magnitude* of 250 and a phase of ±180°. Thus, its dB equivalent is 48 dB.

EXAMPLE 2.2.2 Determine the numbers having the following dB values: 250 and −250.
Solution Since 250 dB = (10 + 12 × 20) dB, then 250 dB = 3.16×10^{12}. Since negative dB values are reciprocals of positive dB values, −250 dB = $1/3.16 \times 10^{12} = 0.316 \times 10^{-12}$

We shall often be referring to Table 2.2.1 in later work, so the engineer should thoroughly understand it and be proficient in its use.

Returning to Eq. 2.2.5, the two basic product term forms encountered in rational gains are

$$\begin{aligned} s + a\,\big|_{s=j\omega} &= a + j\omega \\ (s + p_n)(s + p_n^*)\,\big|_{s=j\omega} &= s^2 + 2\zeta\omega_n s + \omega_n^2\,\big|_{s=j\omega} = (\omega_n^2 - \omega^2) + j2\zeta\omega_n\omega \end{aligned} \tag{2.2.11}$$

The first corresponds to a real pole or zero on the σ-axis of the s-plane. The second corresponds to a pair of complex poles or zeros (for $|\zeta| < 1$) in the s-plane. This is shown in the root loci of Fig.

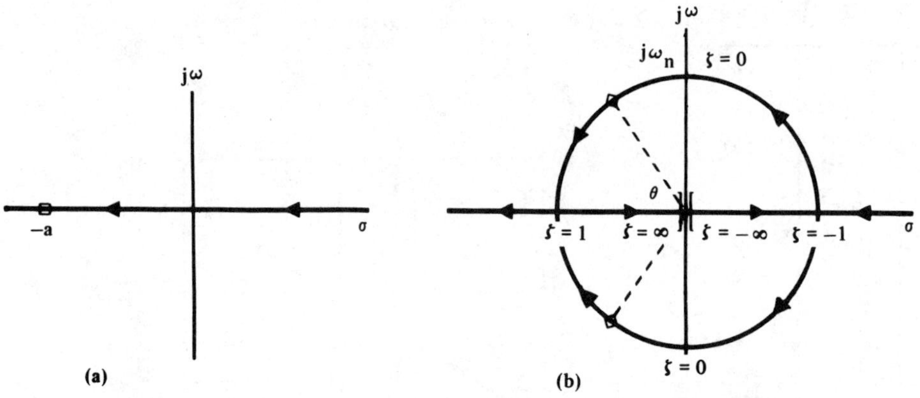

Fig. 2.2.2 Root locus showing the pole or zero location for (a) a real critical frequency and (b) complex critical frequencies having damping factor ζ and resonant frequency ω_n.

2.2.2. A root locus is simply the locus or path which the critical frequencies follow as some parameter varies from −∞ to ∞ as discussed in Sec. 1.16. In the real root case, the critical frequency lies in the left-half-plane for $a > 0$, the origin for $a = 0$, and the right-half-plane for $a < 0$. Complex poles and zeros are described using the following terminology:

ω_n = resonant frequency (corner or critical frequency)
$\theta = \cos^{-1}\zeta$ = angle of critical frequency location from $-\sigma$-axis
$\zeta = \cos\theta$ = damping factor of critical frequency
$\sigma = \zeta\omega_n$ = real part of critical frequency
$\beta = (1-\zeta^2)^{1/2}\omega_n$ = imaginary part of critical frequency.

Note that for $\zeta > 0$, the critical frequencies lie in the left-half-plane; when $\zeta < 0$, they lie in the right-half-plane; when $\zeta = 0$, they lie on the $j\omega$-axis. For $|\zeta| < 1$, the critical frequencies are complex, while for $|\zeta| \geq 1$, they are real. By convention, $\theta = 0$ for $|\zeta| \geq 1$ since $\cos^{-1}\zeta$ is undefined.

2.3 FIRST-ORDER POLES AND ZEROS

Let us now consider the Bode plots for these basic first-order and second-order product term forms. The first-order product terms equal

$$s + \omega_n \big|_{s=j\omega} = \omega_n + j\omega = (\omega_n^2 + \omega^2)^{1/2} e^{j\tan^{-1}(\omega/\omega_n)} \tag{2.3.1}$$

and often occur in the numerator or denominator of H(s). This corresponds to a first-order zero or pole, respectively, at $-\omega_n$. Consider the normalized case (normalized in magnitude to 0 dB and in frequency to a corner frequency of 1 rad/sec) for a simple pole where

$$H(j\omega) = 1/(1 + j\omega) = (1 + \omega^2)^{-1/2} e^{-j\tan^{-1}\omega} \tag{2.3.2}$$

whose logarithm equals

$$\ln H(j\omega) = \ln(1 + j\omega)^{-1} = -\ln(1 + \omega^2)^{1/2} - j\tan^{-1}\omega \tag{2.3.3}$$

Thus, we may write

$$|H(j\omega)| = (1 + \omega^2)^{-1/2}, \qquad \arg H(j\omega) = -\tan^{-1}\omega,$$
$$\ln|H(j\omega)| = -\tfrac{1}{2}\ln(1 + \omega^2), \qquad 20\log|H(j\omega)| = -10\log(1 + \omega^2) \tag{2.3.4}$$

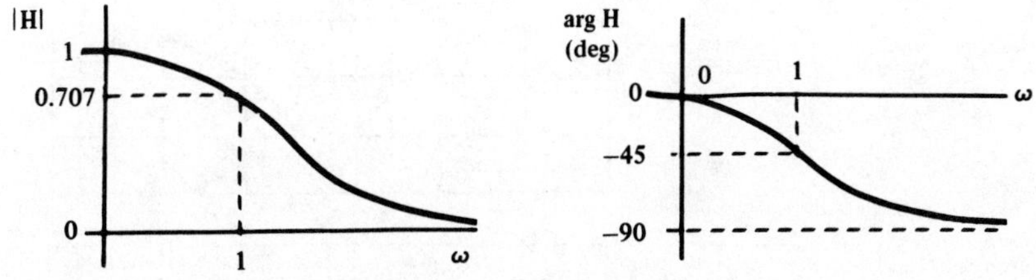

Fig. 2.3.1 Plots of |H| and arg H for first-order pole.

The magnitude and phase plots of H are shown in Fig. 2.3.1 while the log plots are shown in Fig. 2.3.2. Referring to Fig. 2.1.1, this is a first-order low-pass filter. Comparing the plots of Figs. 2.3.1 and 2.3.2, we see that the logarithmic plotting has led to curves which can be closely approximated by linear asymptotes while the arithmetic plots cannot be so conveniently approximated.

Two asymptotes to the exact curve can be established from Eq. 2.3.4 as

$$|H(j\omega)|_{dB} = 20 \log_{10} |H(j\omega)| \cong 20 \log_{10} 1 = 0 \quad \text{for} \quad \omega \ll 1$$
$$\cong -20 \log_{10} \omega \quad \text{for} \quad \omega \gg 1 \tag{2.3.5}$$

The two asymptotes intersect (i.e., are equal) at $\omega = 1$ which is called the *break* or *corner frequency*. The slope of the low-frequency asymptote of $|H|_{dB}$ equals zero while the slope of the high-frequency asymptote equals

$$\frac{d\,|H|_{dB}}{d \log_{10} \omega} = -20 \text{ dB/dec} \quad \text{or} \quad \frac{d\,|H|_{dB}}{d \log_2 \omega} = -6 \text{ dB/oct}, \quad \omega \gg 1 \tag{2.3.6}$$

The terms *decade* and *octave* refer to frequency ratios where, by convention, one decade equals 10 and one octave equals 2. If we consider the separation between two frequencies ω_1 and ω_2, then

$$\log_{10} (\omega_2/\omega_1), \quad \log_2 (\omega_2/\omega_1) = \text{the decade and octave separation between } \omega_2 \text{ and } \omega_1\text{, respectively} \tag{2.3.7}$$

Considering now the phase curve and its linear approximation of Fig. 2.3.2, note that the asymptotic value are established from Eq. 2.3.4 as

$$\arg H(j\omega) = -\tan^{-1} \omega \cong 0^\circ \text{ for } \omega \ll 1, \quad = -45^\circ \text{ at } \omega = 1, \quad \cong -90^\circ \text{ for } \omega \gg 1 \tag{2.3.8}$$

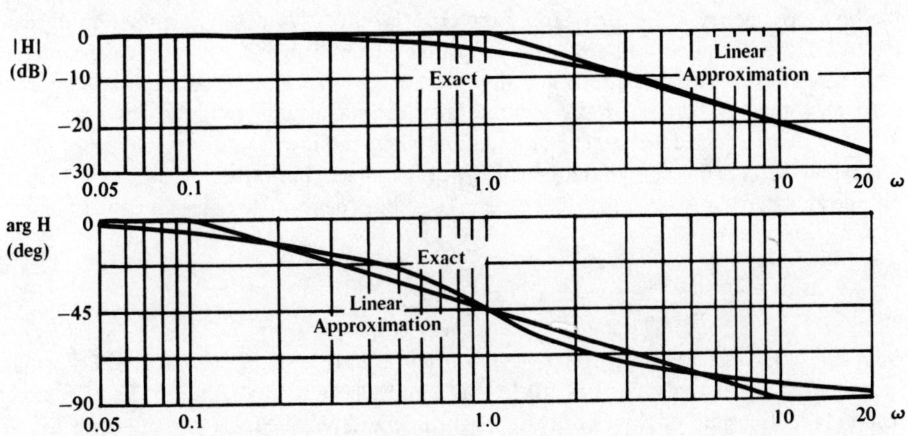

Fig. 2.3.2 Bode plots of |H| and arg H for first-order pole.

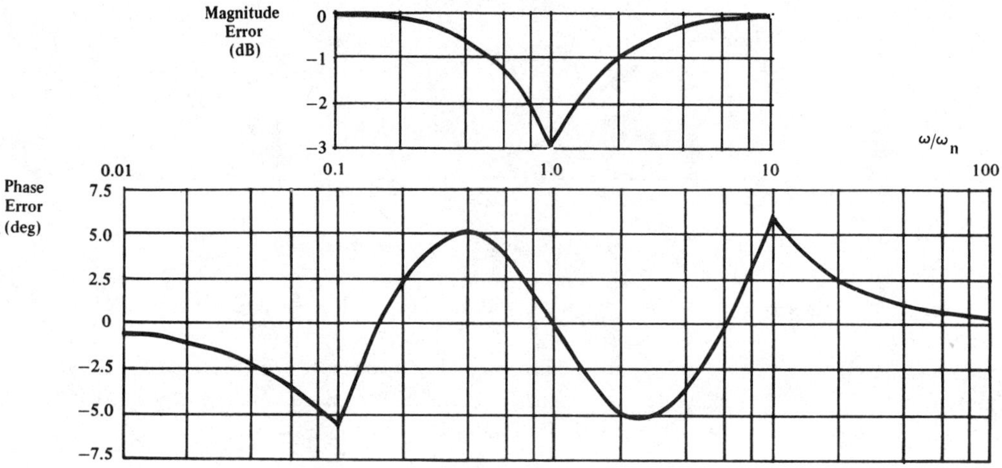

Fig. 2.3.3 Magnitude and phase approximation errors for first-order pole.

The phase slope at $\omega = 1$ equals

$$d \arg H(j\omega)/d\omega \,|_{\omega=1} = -\tfrac{1}{2} \text{ rad/rad/sec} \tag{2.3.9}$$

or

$$d \arg H/d \log_{10} \omega \,|_{\omega=1} = -1/2 \log_{10} e = -1.15 \text{ rad/dec} = -66.0\ ^\circ/\text{dec} \tag{2.3.10}$$

A more convenient slope to use which gives a better phase approximation over the entire frequency range is

$$d \arg H/d \log_{10} \omega = -45\ ^\circ/\text{dec} \quad \text{or} \quad d \arg H/d \log_2 \omega = -13.5\ ^\circ/\text{oct} \tag{2.3.11}$$

Thus, the approximate phase curve equals 0° from dc to $\omega = 0.1$ (one decade below the break frequency), decreases as −45 °/dec to $\omega = 10$ (one decade above the break frequency) passing through − 45° at $\omega = 1$, and equals − 90° beyond $\omega = 10$.

The difference between the actual curve and the asymptotic curve is the *error*. The magnitude and phase errors are plotted in Fig. 2.3.3. The errors are symmetrical about the corner frequency. Note that the magnitude error is maximum and equals − 3 dB at the break frequency. One octave away from the break frequency (a factor of two) the error is − 1 dB, while two octaves away from the break frequency (a factor of four) the error is only −1/4 dB. The numeric values corresponding to various dB values can easily be determined from Table 2.2.1. We see the phase errors are smaller. The maximum error is less than ±6° at $\omega = 0.1$ and 10 so the phase approximation is extremely good; in fact, it is more accurate than the magnitude approximation.

Now let us consider the general situation when the low-frequency gain is not unity (or 0 dB) but rather K, and the corner frequency is not 1 rad/sec, but rather ω_n rad/sec. This is called amplitude and frequency scaling, respectively. Here the "denormalized" gain equals

$$H(s) = \frac{K\omega_n}{s + \omega_n} = \frac{K}{1 + s/\omega_n} = \frac{K}{1 + s_n} \tag{2.3.12}$$

from Eq. 2.3.2. Clearly, the effect of *magnitude scaling* is simply to shift the Bode magnitude response from 0 dB to $20 \log_{10} K$ dB in Fig. 2.3.2. Phase is unaffected. The effect of *frequency scaling* is to translate or shift both the magnitude and phase curves to the left for $\omega_n < 1$ or right for $\omega_n > 1$ by $\log_{10} \omega_n$ decades. This is illustrated in Fig. 2.3.4. We see from Eq. 2.3.12 that

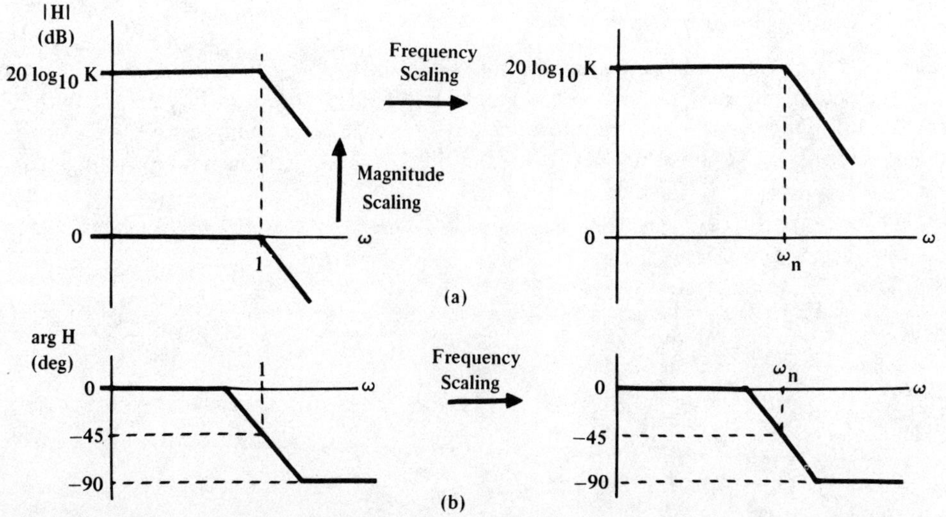

Fig. 2.3.4 Effect of (a) magnitude and (b) frequency scaling on magnitude and phase.

writing gain equations using normalized frequency s_n considerably simplifies their appearance. We shall frequently utilize this normalization.

A useful design parameter of a filter is its 3 dB bandwidth. We shall always denote bandwidth using B. The 3 dB *bandwidth* B equals the frequency range over which the gain is within 3 dB of its maximum value. All frequencies which enter the filter and fall within its 3 dB bandwidth pass through the filter with little or no attenuation. However, frequencies which fall outside the 3 dB bandwidth are attenuated in accordance with the gain characteristic. Thus, the filter bandwidth is a measure of its frequency selectivity. Setting $|H(jB)|^2 = ½$ in Eq. 2.3.12 and solving for B shows that the first-order low-pass filter has a 3 dB bandwidth $B = \omega_n$.

Now consider the filter which is characterized by a first-order zero, rather than a first-order pole, and whose normalized gain function equals

$$H(s) = s + 1 \tag{2.3.13}$$

Then the ac steady-state gain characteristic equals

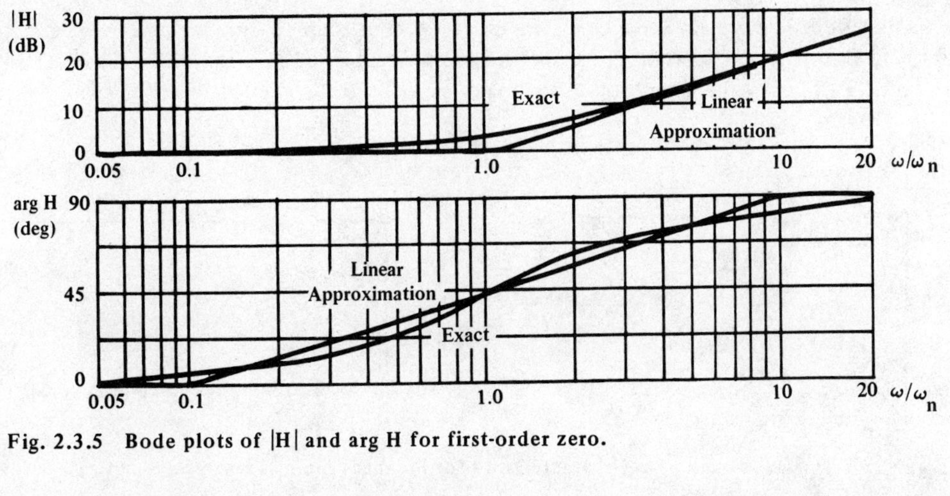

Fig. 2.3.5 Bode plots of |H| and arg H for first-order zero.

$$H(j\omega) = (1 + \omega^2)^{1/2} e^{j \tan^{-1} \omega} \tag{2.3.14}$$

from Eq. 2.3.2. Since this gain is the inverse of the single-pole gain of Eq. 2.3.1, the magnitude and phase characteristics are easily drawn from Eq. 2.3.2 as shown in Fig. 2.3.5. Both dc gains equal 0 dB, but the magnitude and phase slopes have their signs changed to +20 dB/dec and +45 °/dec, respectively. Comparing Figs. 2.3.5 and 2.2.1, we see that this is a type of high-pass filter.

EXAMPLE 2.3.1 Draw the Bode magnitude and phase characteristics of two cascaded first-order filters having total gain

$$H(s) = 2\left(\frac{10}{s + 10}\right)^2 \tag{2.3.15}$$

Solution Since the ac steady-state gain equals

$$H(j\omega) = 2\left(\frac{10}{10 + j\omega}\right)^2 \tag{2.3.16}$$

then the magnitude and phase equal

$$|H(j\omega)| = \frac{2}{1 + (\omega/10)^2}, \qquad \arg H(j\omega) = -2 \tan^{-1} (\omega/10) \tag{2.3.17}$$

Using the normalized Bode plot of Fig. 2.3.2 and denormalizing as shown in Fig. 2.3.4, then the resulting Bode plots are shown in Fig. 2.3.6. The dc gain equals 6 dB. The high-frequency magnitude asymptote has slope −40 dB/dec (the gain decreases as $1/\omega^2$). The phase slope doubles to −90 °/dec, so phase varies from 0° to −180°. This is a second-order low-pass filter.

EXAMPLE 2.3.2 Draw the Bode plots for

$$H(s) = \frac{s + 1}{s(s + 10)} \tag{2.3.18}$$

Solution The ac steady-state characteristics equal

$$|H(j\omega)| = \frac{1}{10}\frac{\sqrt{1 + \omega^2}}{\omega\sqrt{1 + (\omega/10)^2}}, \qquad \arg H(j\omega) = -\pi/2 + \tan^{-1} \omega - \tan^{-1} (\omega/10) \tag{2.3.19}$$

The Bode plots of Fig. 2.3.7 can be immediately drawn by combining Figs. 2.3.2 and 2.3.5 with proper magnitude and frequency denormalization. Note that the magnitude and phase slopes cancel in the frequency range from 1 to 10 rad/sec.

Magnitude denormalization can sometimes be confusing to the engineer inexperienced in forming Bode plots. To find the proper magnitude factor, $|H(j\omega)|$ can be evaluated at any frequency ω by using the asymptotic gain expression for the region in which ω falls. Note that

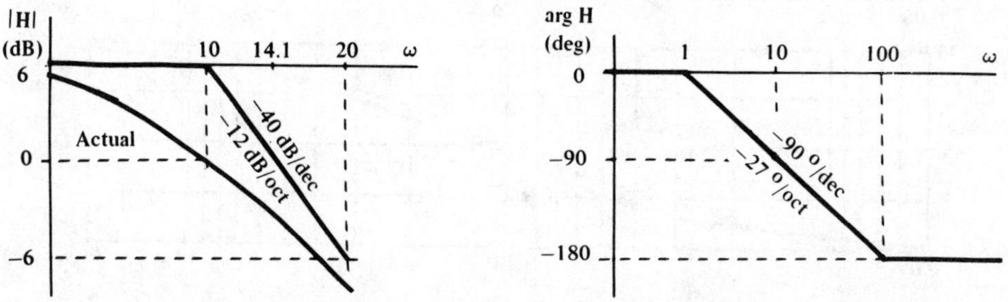

Fig. 2.3.6 Magnitude and phase characteristics for low-pass filter of Example 2.3.1.

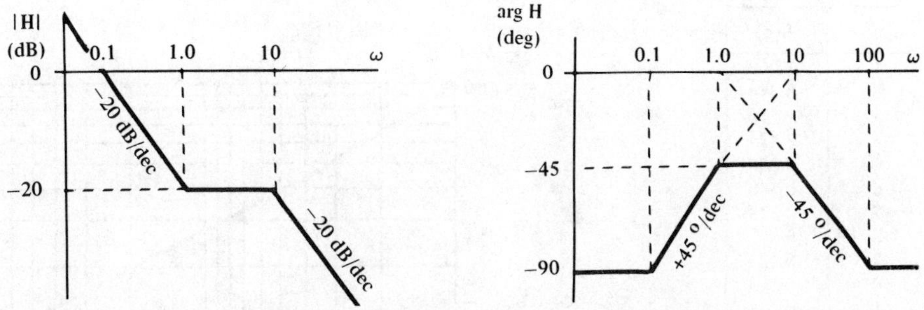

Fig. 2.3.7 Magnitude and phase characteristics for filter of Example 2.3.2.

the *asymptotic* gain expressions of Eq. 2.3.18 equal

$$H(s) = 1/10s, \quad |s| \leq 1 \tag{2.3.20}$$
$$= 1/10, \quad 1 \leq |s| \leq 10 \tag{2.3.21}$$
$$= 1/s, \quad |s| \geq 10 \tag{2.3.22}$$

Evaluating |H| at various frequencies gives

$$\begin{aligned} |H(j0.1)| &= 1 &&= 0 \text{ dB using Eq. 2.3.20} \\ |H(j1)| &= 0.1 &&= -20 \text{ dB using Eqs. 2.3.20 or 2.3.21} \\ |H(j10)| &= 0.1 &&= -20 \text{ dB using Eqs. 2.3.21 or 2.3.22} \\ |H(j100)| &= 0.01 &&= -40 \text{ dB using Eq. 2.3.22} \\ |H(j200)| &= 0.005 &&= -46 \text{ dB using Eq. 2.3.22} \end{aligned} \tag{2.3.23}$$

Thus, any one of these equations give the proper magnitude normalization or "positioning" values. At both low and high frequencies, the filter is an integrator with gains 1/10 and 1, respectively. An integrator is a type of low-pass filter having infinite dc gain.

This example shows that for any H(s) gain function given by Eq. 2.0.1, a very convenient form of re-expression for Bode plot analysis is

$$H(s) = K \frac{\prod_{j=1}^{m} (1 + s/z_j)}{\prod_{i=1}^{n} (1 + s/p_i)} \tag{2.3.24}$$

The low-frequency gain then equals K. The individual terms are neglected for $\omega < z_j$ or $\omega < p_i$. They become effective only when $\omega > z_j$ or $\omega > p_i$ when determining magnitude. When determining phase, they become effective one decade below the critical frequencies, i.e., $\omega > 0.1z_j$ or $\omega > 0.1p_i$. They become ineffective one decade above the critical frequencies, i.e., $\omega > 10z_j$ or $\omega > 10p_i$.

EXAMPLE 2.3.3 Consider an *n*th-order low-pass filter having gain

$$H(s) = (1 + s/\omega_o)^{-n} \tag{2.3.25}$$

Determine the 3 dB bandwidth of the filter. Sketch the magnitude characteristics of the filter for various n adjusting ω_o so that the bandwidth B remains unity.

Solution Since the gain magnitude equals

$$|H(jB)| = [1 + (B/\omega_o)^2]^{-n/2} = 2^{-1/2} \tag{2.3.26}$$

at the 3 dB frequency, then the filter bandwidth B must equal

$$B/\omega_o = S(n) = \sqrt{2^{1/n} - 1} \tag{2.3.27}$$

n	S(n)
1	1.000
2	0.644
3	0.510
4	0.435
5	0.386
6	0.350
7	0.323
8	0.301
9	0.283
10	0.268
11	0.255
12	0.244
13	0.234
14	0.225
15	0.217

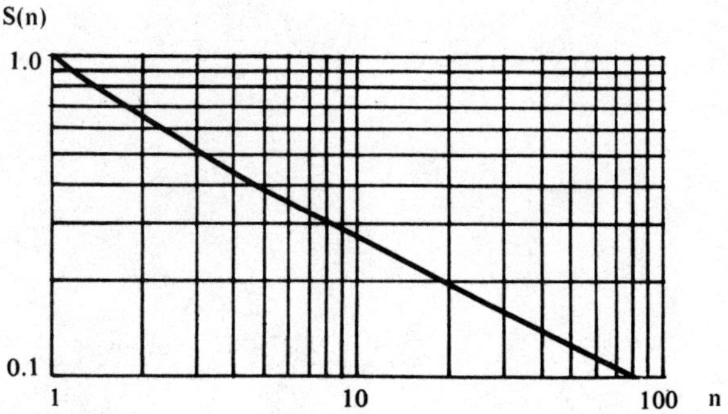

Fig. 2.3.8 Shrinkage factors S(n) for synchronously-tuned filters composed of first-order stages.

Since the Maclaurin series representation for $2^{1/n}$ equals[5]

$$2^{1/n} = 1 + \ln 2/n + (\ln 2/n)^2/2! + \ldots \cong 1 + \ln 2/n \tag{2.3.28}$$

then the approximate filter bandwidth is

$$B/\omega_0 \cong \sqrt{\ln 2/n} = 1/1.2\sqrt{n} \tag{2.3.29}$$

Therefore, to maintain B = 1, then we must adjust ω_o to satisfy Eq. 2.3.29. The approximate expression is accurate within 5% for n = 4 and improves with increasing n. For example, for n = 10 then $\omega_o \cong 3.8$. The magnitude characteristics are drawn in Fig. 4.13.1. The passband gain is almost independent of n; the 3 dB bandwidth has been maintained at unity; the asymptotic rolloffs are −20n dB/dec. Since the poles are identical, this is called a *synchronously-tuned filter*. It is a classical filter which will be discussed extensively in Chap. 4.

It is important to re-emphasize that when identical filters are cascaded, bandwidth shrinkage occurs. The *shrinkage factor* S(n) is defined as

$$S(n) = \frac{\text{Overall bandwidth of n identical stages}}{\text{Bandwidth of single stage}} \tag{2.3.30}$$

whose value is given by Eq. 2.3.27 and which is plotted in Fig. 2.3.8. We should also note that when other types of identical filters are cascaded, different shrinkage factors usually result. Shrinkage factors depend upon the form of the stage being used.[6] Eq. 2.3.27 describes only the shrinkage factor of synchronously-tuned filters having real poles.

One commonly encountered filter is the first-order *lead-lag* or *doublet* filter which has a transfer function

$$H(s) = \frac{1 + s/z}{1 + s/p} \tag{2.3.31}$$

The term lead-lag refers to the ac steady-state leading or lagging phase characteristics of H which we shall soon determine. The term doublet refers to the pair of critical frequencies (one pole/zero pair on the negative real axis) which characterize the filter. The ac steady-state gain equals

$$H(j\omega) = \left(\frac{1 + (\omega/z)^2}{1 + (\omega/p)^2}\right)^{1/2} \exp\left(j[\tan^{-1}(\omega/z) - \tan^{-1}(\omega/p)]\right) \tag{2.3.32}$$

The approximate magnitude and phase of the network are shown in Fig. 2.3.9. When $p < z$ (the pole is closest to the s-plane origin). The magnitude has a dc gain of 0 dB, a high-frequency gain of

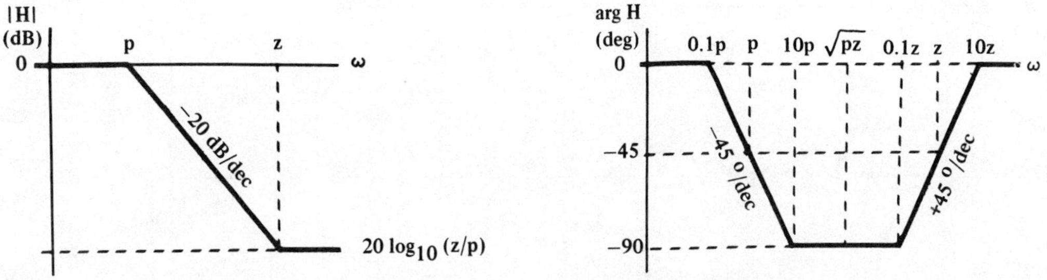

Fig. 2.3.9 Bode plots of |H| and arg H for first-order lag filters.

$20 \log_{10}$ (p/z) and an intermediate slope of −20 dB/dec. It is a type of low-pass filter. The phase characteristic is close to 0° at high and low frequencies and is symmetrical about $\omega = \sqrt{pz}$. As frequency approaches $\sqrt{pz}$, the phase decreases to a minimum value (not exceeding −90°) of

$$\theta_{min} = \tan^{-1} (p/z)^{1/2} - \tan^{-1} (z/p)^{1/2} = -\tan^{-1} \frac{z-p}{2\sqrt{zp}} = -\sin^{-1} \frac{z-p}{z+p} \tag{2.3.33}$$

Since the phase is always negative, these are sometimes called *lag* filters.

Suppose the zero is closer to the s-plane origin than the pole so $z < p$. The gain can still be described by the Bode plots of Fig. 2.3.9 if we let z = 1 and change the signs of the plots. Alternatively stated, the plots are turned over or rotated about their horizontal axis. Since the angle is positive in this situation, these are sometimes called *lead* filters. They are a type of high-pass filter. It is very convenient that the same curves can be used for analyzing both filters.

2.4 SECOND-ORDER POLES AND ZEROS

The second product term of interest in the general gain expression of Eq. 2.2.1 is

$$(s + \cos\theta + j\sin\theta)(s + \cos\theta - j\sin\theta)\big|_{s=j\omega} = s^2 + 2\zeta s + 1\big|_{s=j\omega} = (1-\omega^2) + j2\zeta\omega \tag{2.4.1}$$

This term is characterized by complex roots (rather than the real roots of the last section). The root locus showing the root location in the s-plane was shown in Fig. 2.2.2a. Note we have frequency normalized Eq. 2.4.1 so that $\omega_n = 1$ (see Eq. 2.2.11). The critical frequencies lie on a circle of unity radius at angle $\theta = \cos^{-1}\zeta$ from the negative real axis. We first consider $0 < \zeta < 1$ and will then generalize for other values. We shall use the basic gain term

$$H(j\omega) = \frac{1}{s^2 + 2\zeta s + 1}\bigg|_{s=j\omega} = \frac{1}{(1-\omega^2) + j2\zeta\omega} \tag{2.4.2}$$

The gain magnitude and phase therefore equal

$$|H(j\omega)| = [(1-\omega^2)^2 + (2\zeta\omega)^2]^{-1/2}, \qquad \arg H(j\omega) = -\tan^{-1} [2\zeta\omega/(1-\omega^2)] \tag{2.4.3}$$

We see that the asymptotic gain values equal

$$H(j\omega) = 1 \text{ for } \omega \ll 1, \qquad 1/j2\zeta \text{ at } \omega = 1, \qquad -1/\omega^2 \text{ for } \omega \gg 1 \tag{2.4.4}$$

From Eq. 2.4.4b, we anticipate a peaked response for small ζ. This is indeed the case as seen from the Bode plots which are drawn in Fig. 2.4.1 for the second-order low-pass filter.

The magnitude characteristics are established from Eq. 2.4.4 as

$$\begin{aligned} |H(j\omega)|_{dB} &= 20 \log_{10} |H(j\omega)| = 20 \log_{10} 1 = 0 \quad \text{for } \omega \ll 1 \\ &= -20 \log_{10} 2\zeta \quad \text{at } \omega = 1 \qquad = -40 \log_{10} \omega \quad \text{for } \omega \gg 1 \end{aligned} \tag{2.4.5}$$

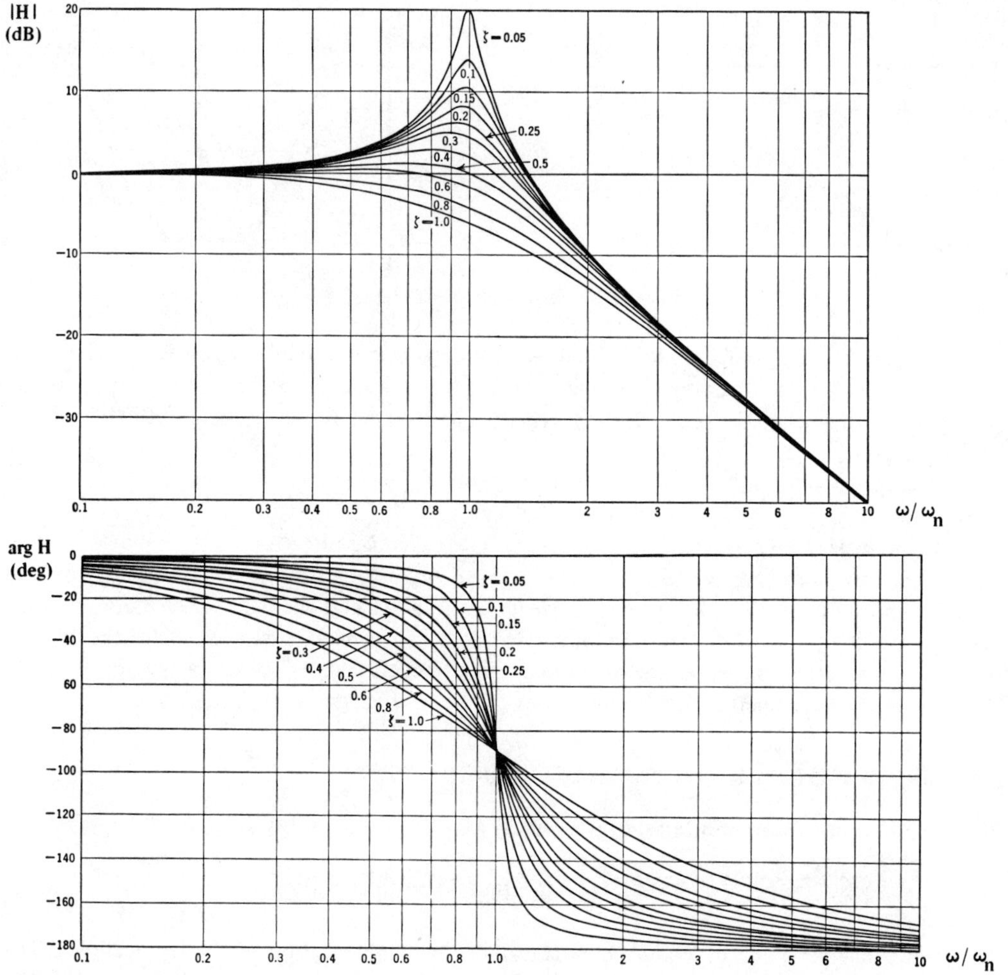

Fig. 2.4.1 Bode plots of |H| and arg H for second-order poles. (From H. Chestnut and R. W. Mayer, "Servomechanism and Regulating System Design," 2nd ed., vol. 1, Chap. 11, Wiley, NY, 1959.)

The low-frequency and high-frequency asymptotes intersect at $\omega = 1$ which is called the *break* or *corner* frequency. The asymptotic slopes of the magnitude characteristic equal

$$\frac{d\,|H|_{dB}}{d\log_{10}\omega} = 0 \text{ dB/dec}, \qquad \omega \ll 1$$

$$\frac{d\,|H|_{dB}}{d\log_{10}\omega} = -40 \text{ dB/dec} \quad \text{or} \quad \frac{d\,|H|_{dB}}{d\log_{2}\omega} = -12 \text{ dB/oct}, \qquad \omega \gg 1 \tag{2.4.6}$$

Therefore, the low-frequency slope is zero and the high-frequency slope is –40 dB/dec, or equivalently, –12 dB/oct.

The magnitude characteristic exhibits peaking near the corner frequency for small damping factors. The magnitude response equals $1/2\zeta$ at $\omega = 1$ so peaking occurs for $\zeta < 0.5$, at least (actually, we shall prove for $\zeta < 0.707$). To determine the maximum ζ for peaking and the peaking frequency ω_p, we differentiate Eq. 2.4.3a with respect to ω and set the result equal to zero.

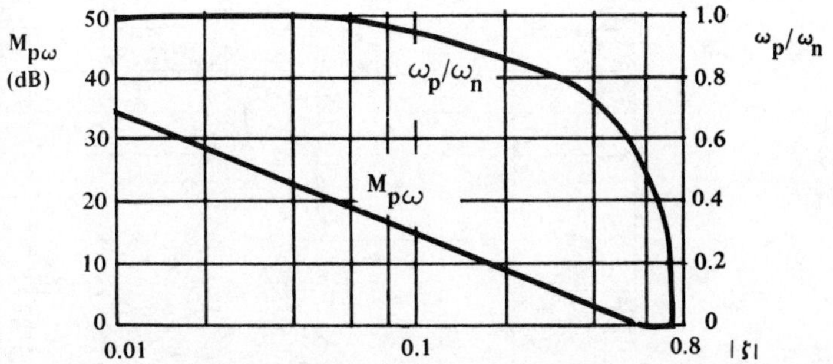

Fig. 2.4.2 Maximum response and normalized peaking frequency.

Solving this equation for ω_p, we find that the peak response occurs at a normalized frequency of

$$\omega_p/\omega_n = \sqrt{1 - 2\zeta^2}, \qquad |\zeta| < 0.707 \tag{2.4.7}$$

Substituting this frequency into Eq. 2.4.3 gives the peak response value, denoted as $M_{p\omega}$, as

$$M_{p\omega} = 1/2|\zeta|\sqrt{1 - \zeta^2}, \qquad |\zeta| < 0.707 \tag{2.4.8}$$

Note that ω_p/ω_n and $M_{p\omega}$ are the same for positive and negative ζ which shall be useful later. For $|\zeta| > 0.707$, the magnitude response is monotonically nonincreasing so no peaking occurs. We will see in the next chapter that for this type of gain function, $\zeta = 0.707$ corresponds to critical damping which is the demarcation between underdamped ($\zeta < 0.707$) and overdamped ($\zeta > 0.707$) unit step response. ω_p/ω_n and $M_{p\omega}$ are plotted in Fig. 2.4.2 over a useful $|\zeta|$ range. From Fig. 2.4.2, we see that there is no peaking for $|\zeta| = 0.707$ (the peak value equals 0 dB and the peaking frequency equals dc). As $|\zeta| \to 0$, the peak value approaches infinity and the peaking frequency approaches the corner frequency.

Clearly, one must use caution in establishing the Bode plots for second-order poles or zeros because of this peaking. This is emphasized in Fig. 2.4.3 which shows the error between the actual and approximate responses as a function of $|\zeta|$. We see that the magnitude approximation is less than 2 dB in error for $0.5 < |\zeta| < 0.6$. In forming Bode diagrams for second-order terms, the actual magnitude curve of Fig. 2.4.1 is generally used.

The phase characteristic is seen from Fig. 2.4.1 to be a monotonically nonincreasing function of ω. Phase decreases from 0° at dc to −180° at high-frequencies; it passes through −90° at $\omega = 1$ (see Eq. 2.4.4), where the phase slope increases towards $-\infty$ as $\zeta \to 0$. Differentiating the phase of H given by Eq. 2.4.3b, it is easy to show that the phase slope at $\omega = 1$ equals

$$d \arg H/d\omega \,|_{\omega=1} = -1/\zeta \text{ rad/rad/sec} \tag{2.4.9}$$

Alternatively expressed, the phase slope at $\omega = 1$ equals

$$d \arg H/d \log_{10} \omega \,|_{\omega=1} = -1/\zeta \log_{10} e = -2.31/\zeta \text{ rad/dec} = -135/\zeta \text{ °/dec} \tag{2.4.10}$$

A more convenient slope to use which gives a better approximation to phase over the entire frequency range is

$$d \arg H/ d \log_{10} \omega \cong -90/\zeta \text{ °/dec} = -27/\zeta \text{ °/oct} \tag{2.4.11}$$

The phase error between the actual and approximate phase responses is shown in Fig. 2.4.3. The maximum phase error is dependent on ζ and is always less than ±25°. The approximate phase curve is almost always used in practice since it is accurate to within at least ± 14%.

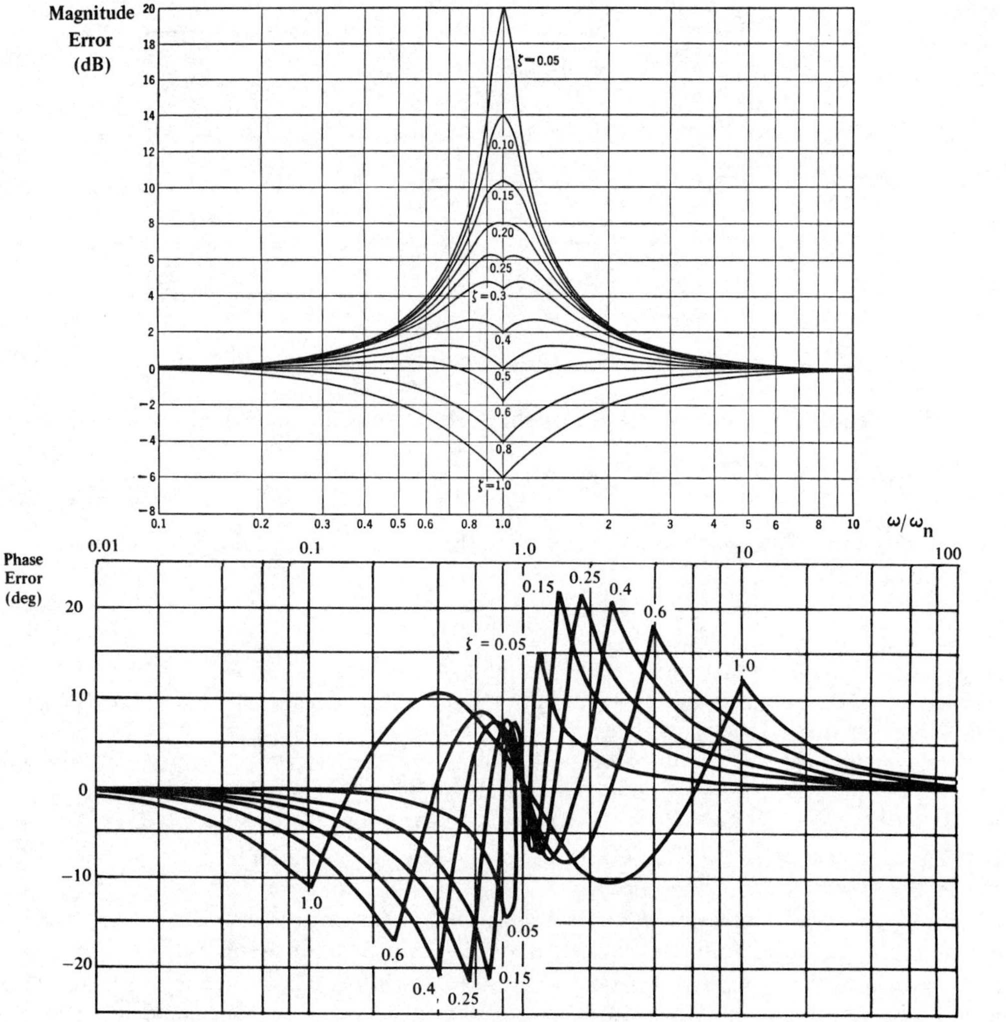

Fig. 2.4.3 Magnitude and phase approximation errors for second-order poles. (Magnitude error from H. Chestnut and R. W. Mayer, "Servomechanism and Regulating System Design," 2nd ed., vol. 1, Chap. 11, Wiley, NY, 1959.)

Since the phase approximation makes its transition from 0° to −180° with a slope of $-90/\zeta$ °/dec, we must determine the two break or corner frequencies for the *phase* approximation. In other words, we must determine the frequencies where the phase approximation begins and ends its linear transition. The transition occurs over a frequency interval D of

$$D = \Delta\theta/m = -180/(-90/\zeta) = 2\zeta \text{ decades} \tag{2.4.12}$$

Since the phase always equals −90° at ω_n, the phase transition begins at 0° at ζ decade below ω_n and terminates ζ decade above ω_n. The frequency ratio R corresponding to ζ decade equals

$$R = 10^{D/2} = 10^{\zeta} \tag{2.4.13}$$

This is very convenient as we shall see.

The 3 dB bandwidth B of the magnitude response second-order filter shown in Fig. 2.4.1 is often a necessary design parameter. Setting $|H(jB)|^2 = ½$ using Eq. 2.4.3 and solving for the 3

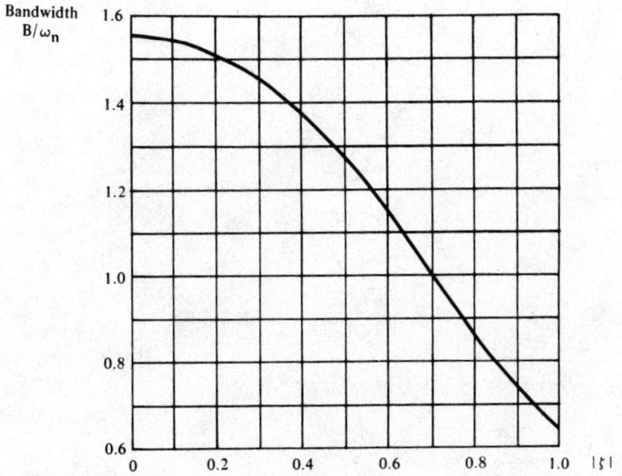

$\lvert\zeta\rvert$	B/ω_n
0.00	1.554
0.05	1.551
0.10	1.543
0.15	1.529
0.20	1.510
0.25	1.485
0.30	1.454
0.35	1.417
0.40	1.375
0.45	1.326
0.50	1.272
0.55	1.213
0.60	1.148
0.65	1.080
0.70	1.010
0.75	0.940
0.80	0.871
0.85	0.806
0.90	0.746
0.95	0.692
1.00	0.644

Fig. 2.4.4 Normalized bandwidth of second-order low-pass filters.

dB frequency B gives

$$B/\omega_n = \sqrt{1 - 2\zeta^2 + \sqrt{2 - 4\zeta^2 + 4\zeta^4}} \tag{2.4.14}$$

which is plotted in Fig. 2.4.4. The normalized bandwidth B/ω_n equals 1.554 for $\zeta = 0$ and decreases as $\zeta \to \infty$. Note that it equals unity when $\zeta = 0.707$.

Before solving examples, we should note the effect of negative ζ. Negative ζ produces two critical frequencies lying in the right-half of the s-plane as shown by the root locus of Fig. 2.2.2b. From Eq. 2.4.3, we see negative ζ effects the Bode phase plot but *not* the Bode magnitude plot. For right-half-plane poles, the phase is positive rather than negative in Fig. 2.4.1, and the phase slope is positive in Eqs. 2.4.9, 2.4.10, and 2.4.11. The magnitude plot of Fig. 2.4.1 is unaffected by negative ζ. Therefore, we can make the observation that complex *right-half-plane zeros* have the same ac steady-state phase characteristics (but inverse gain characteristics) as complex *left-half-plane poles* (and visa versa). This extremely useful fact is utilized in all-pass filters which are discussed later in the chapter.

EXAMPLE 2.4.1 Determine the gain function for a low-pass filter having a dc gain of 40 dB, a 3 dB bandwidth of 1 KHz, and a –40 dB/dec asymptotic rolloff. It must have as rapid a cutoff as possible with not more than 20% peaking. Phase is arbitrary. Plot the resulting gain and phase characteristics.

Solution We can express an acceptable low-pass filter function as

$$H(s) = \frac{100\omega_n^2}{s^2 + 2\zeta\omega_n s + \omega_n^2} \tag{2.4.15}$$

where the dc gain $H(0) = 100 = 40$ dB. ζ must first be chosen to obtain as rapid a cutoff as possible (where $M_{p\omega} \leqslant 1.2 = 1.6$ dB) and then ω_n is chosen to obtain the required bandwidth. From Fig. 2.4.2, $\zeta \geqslant 0.45$. Increasing ζ beyond the minimum value decreases the cutoff rate as seen in Fig. 2.4.1. Thus, we choose $\zeta = 0.45$. From Fig. 2.4.4, $B/\omega_n = 1.33$ for this ζ. Thus, $\omega_n = B/1.33 = 2\pi(10^3/1.33) = 4.72 \times 10^3$. The resulting gain and phase characteristics are shown in Fig. 2.4.5. Note that the phase slope equals $-90/0.45 = -200$ °/dec from Eq. 2.4.11. The phase transition occurs over $D = 180/200 = 0.9$ decade $= 10^{0.9} = 8$ from Eq. 2.4.12. Since $R = 10^{0.45} \cong \sqrt{8}$ from Eq. 2.4.13, the phase transition begins at $\omega_n/\sqrt{8}$ and ends at $\sqrt{8}\omega_n$.

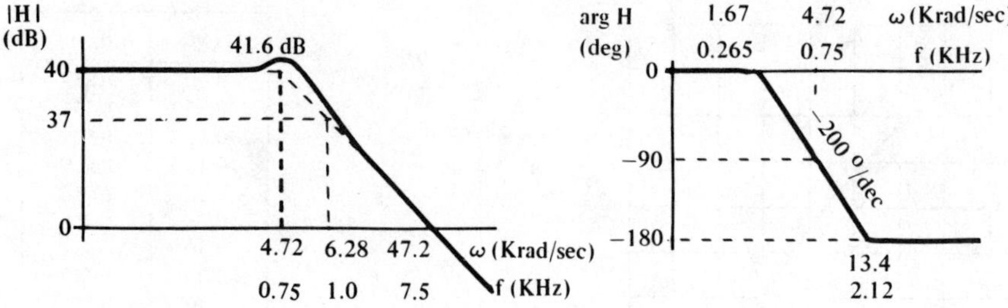

Fig. 2.4.5 Magnitude and phase characteristics for low-pass filter of Example 2.4.1.

EXAMPLE 2.4.2 Draw the gain and phase characteristics for the filters having gains

$$H_1(s) = \frac{1}{(s+1)(s^2+s+1)}, \qquad H_2(s) = \frac{(0.3)(0.9^2)}{(s+0.3)(s^2+2(0.17)(0.9)s+0.9^2)} \tag{2.4.16}$$

Compare the characteristics for gain and phase slopes, bandwidth, ripple, etc.

Solution H_1 has $\zeta = 0.5$ and $\omega_n = 1$ while H_2 has $\zeta = 0.17$ and $\omega_n = 0.9$. The pole-zero distributions differ as shown in Fig. 2.4.6. H_1 has a 1 dB peaking contribution from the second-order poles. Thus, H_1 has a monotonic nonincreasing gain response, but H_2 has a passband ripple of 3 dB. These low-pass characteristics are drawn in Fig. 2.4.7. Both have the same bandwidth of 1 rad/sec. H_2 has a steeper phase characteristic than H_1. We will see in Chap. 4 that H_1 is the gain of a third-order Butterworth filter and H_2 is the gain of a third-order Chebyshev filter with 3 dB ripple. The Chebyshev filter makes a more rapid transition from its passband to its stopband than the Butterworth filter as we shall discuss in depth in Chap. 4.

EXAMPLE 2.4.3 The input signal to a sonar processing system is provided by a hydrophone. The hydrophone has a second-order low-pass gain characteristic with a 30 Hz cutoff frequency; it must be compensated with an input filter to emphasize the frequencies above 30 Hz which are attenuated by the hydrophone. Equalization must be maintained to 300 Hz. The input filter must cut off sharply at 400 Hz to reject background noise picked up by the hydrophone. The required input filter characteristic must fall within the unshaded areas shown in Fig. 2.4.8. The shaded areas represent the forbidden regions in which the filter response must *not* fall.

Solution For convenience, we shall partition the input filter into separate pre-emphasis and band-limiting filters as shown in Fig. 2.4.9. To obtain the +40 dB/dec in-band gain slope, we use a second-order pre-emphasis filter. To maintain small ripple and variation from the approximate response, we use a damping factor of 0.55. The ripple will then not exceed ±0.75 dB as seen from Fig. 2.4.3. Therefore, the pre-emphasis filter gain H_1 equals

$$H_1(s) = K\frac{1+(0.55)(s/2\pi30)+(s/2\pi30)^2}{1+(0.55)(s/2\pi300)+(s/2\pi300)^2} \tag{2.4.17}$$

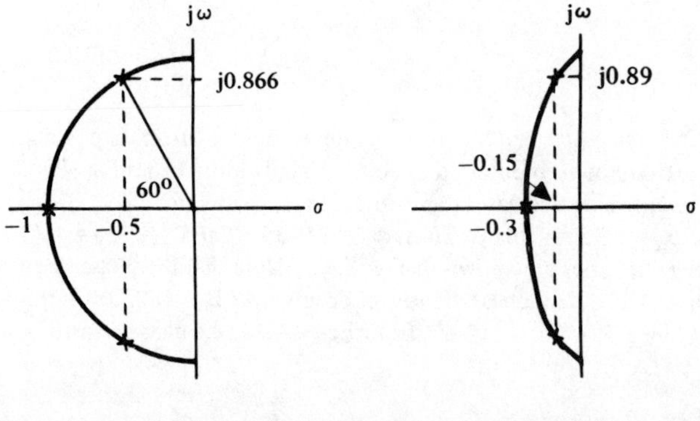

Fig. 2.4.6 Pole-zero distributions for H_1 and H_2 of Example 2.4.2.

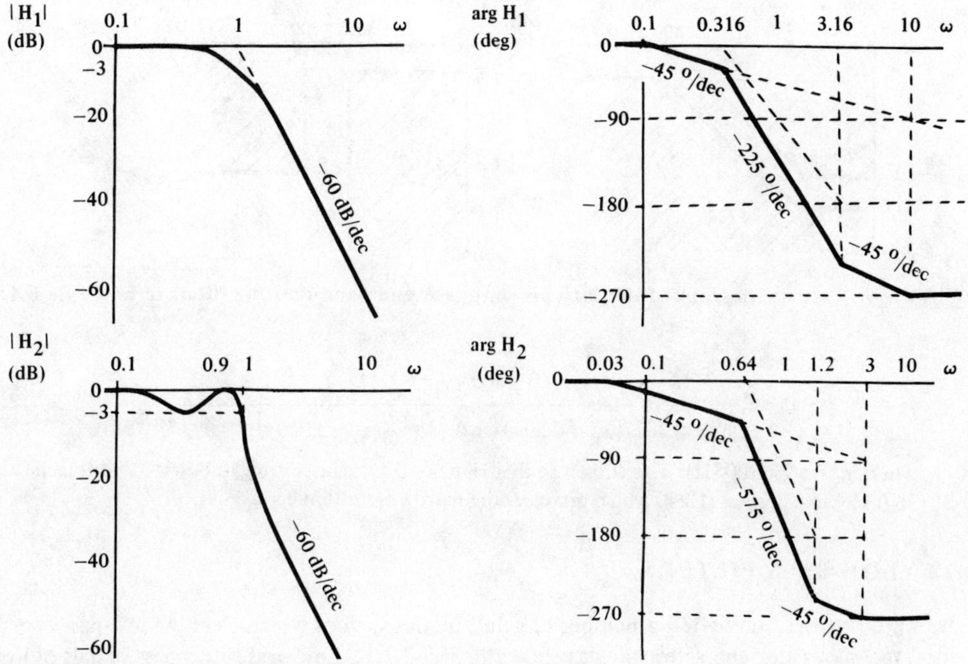

Fig. 2.4.7 Magnitude and phase characteristics for low-pass filters of Example 2.4.2.

where $K = H_1(0) = -(40 + 41.5)/2 = -40.75$ dB $= 1/109$ from Table 2.3.1. Thus, H_1 is a second-order doublet or lead network.

The band-limiting (low-pass) filter requirement is too stringent for us to determine by trial-and-error methods due to its narrow transition band. If we attempt to use the synchronously-tuned filter of Fig. 4.13.1, it is obvious that we cannot reach −40 dB attenuation at a normalized frequency of 400/300 = 1.33 (relative to the −1.5 dB frequency) regardless of how large we make n. In Chaps. 4 and 5, we shall introduce several filters which can satisfy this requirement. For example, we will find that we could use a fifteenth-order Butterworth, an eighth-order Chebyshev, or a fifth-order elliptic filter. The elliptic filter gain function would equal

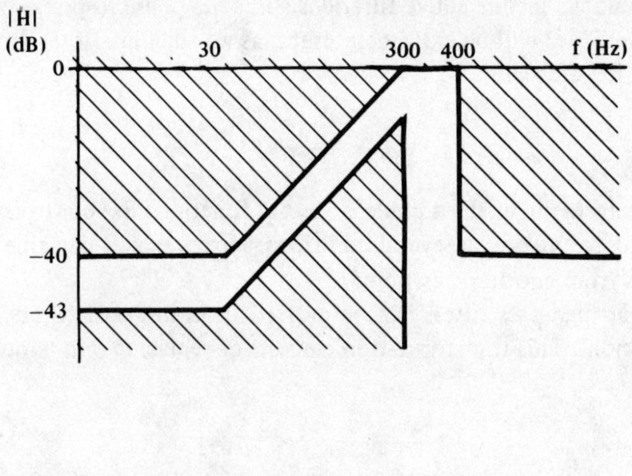

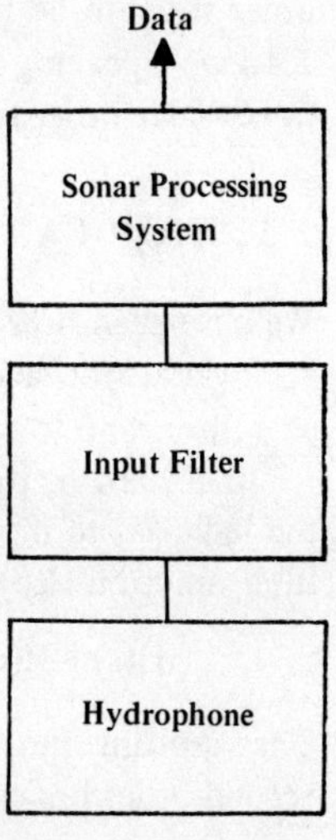

Fig. 2.4.8 Sonar processing system and the required input filter characteristic of Example 2.4.3.

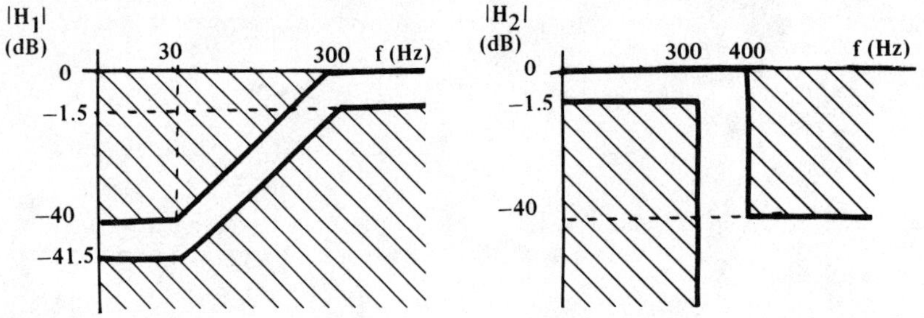

Fig. 2.4.9 Partitioning input filter into pre-emphasis and band-limiting filters in Example 2.4.3.

$$H_2(s) = K\frac{(s_n{}^2 + 1.240^2)(s_n{}^2 + 1.737^2)}{(s_n + 0.357)[(s_n + 0.201)^2 + 0.738^2]\,[(s_n + 0.045)^2 + 0.993^2]} \qquad (2.4.18)$$

where $s_n = s/2\pi(300\ \text{Hz})$. K is chosen so that $H_2(0) = 1$. It is interesting to observe that it is the zero of $H_2(s)$ located at $s_n = \pm j1.240$ which produces the narrow transition band required.

2.5 LOW-PASS FILTERS

We have thus far considered a number of gain functions, all of which were the low-pass type. The ideal low-pass filter characteristic was shown in Fig. 2.1.1. Low-pass filters pass signals of low frequencies and attenuate signals of high frequencies.

The first-order low-pass filter had the magnitude and phase characteristics of Fig. 2.3.2. When n identical first-order filters were cascaded, the so-called synchronously-tuned filter resulted having the magnitude characteristic of Fig. 4.13.1. The lead-lag filter of Fig. 2.3.9 was another example of a low-pass filter. Such a filter is often said to be a quasi-low-pass type since its high-frequency gain is nonzero. In filter applications, the term *quasi-* is used to denote a filter which fails to have the proper asymptotic behavior. We shall not use this more precise terminology until Chap. 7 when we classify active filters. At that time, the *quasi-* term will be required.

Second-order low-pass filters had the magnitude and phase characteristics shown in Fig. 2.4.1. This is another very commonly used filter. In the later work of Chaps. 4 and 5, we will view *n*th-order low-pass filters as the cascade of n/2 second-order filters for n even, or (n − 1)/2 for n odd where one stage is first-order. Thus, we shall find the second-order filter and the simpler first-order filter to be the basic building blocks in our active filter designs. The phase response of Fig. 2.4.1 and peaking information of Fig. 2.4.2 will be extremely useful as we shall later see. Now let us consider other filter types.

2.6 HIGH-PASS FILTERS

We have seen how the pole-zero arrangement in the s-plane of a gain function H(s) controls its ac steady-state behavior. We now want to introduce several additional curves which describe high-pass filters and to describe Bode plots from another viewpoint.

In Chap. 6, it will be shown that high-pass filters can be derived from low-pass filters using the low-pass to high-pass transformation. This transformation consists of replacing p in a low-pass filter function H(p) by 1/s as

$$H(s) = H(p)\,\big|_{p=1/s} \qquad (2.6.1)$$

The resulting function H(s) describes the gain of a high-pass filter. For example, the first- and second-order low-pass filters had transfer functions given by Eqs. 2.3.2 and 2.4.2 as

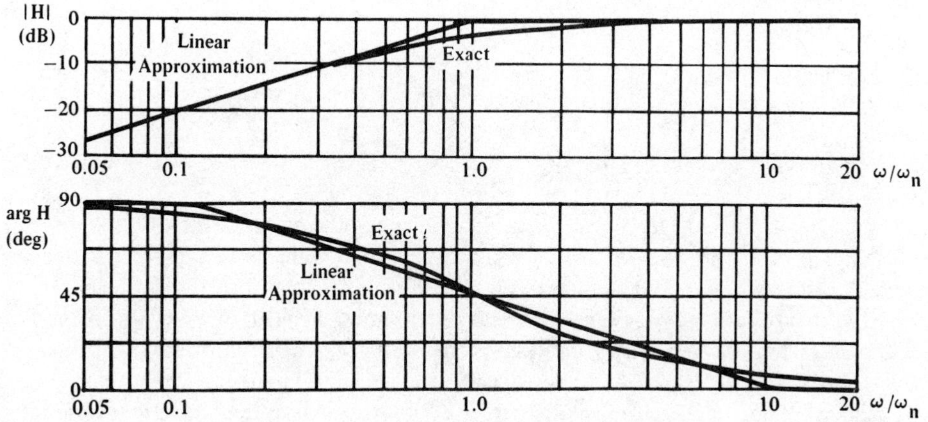

Fig. 2.6.1 Bode plots of |H| and arg H for first-order high-pass filters.

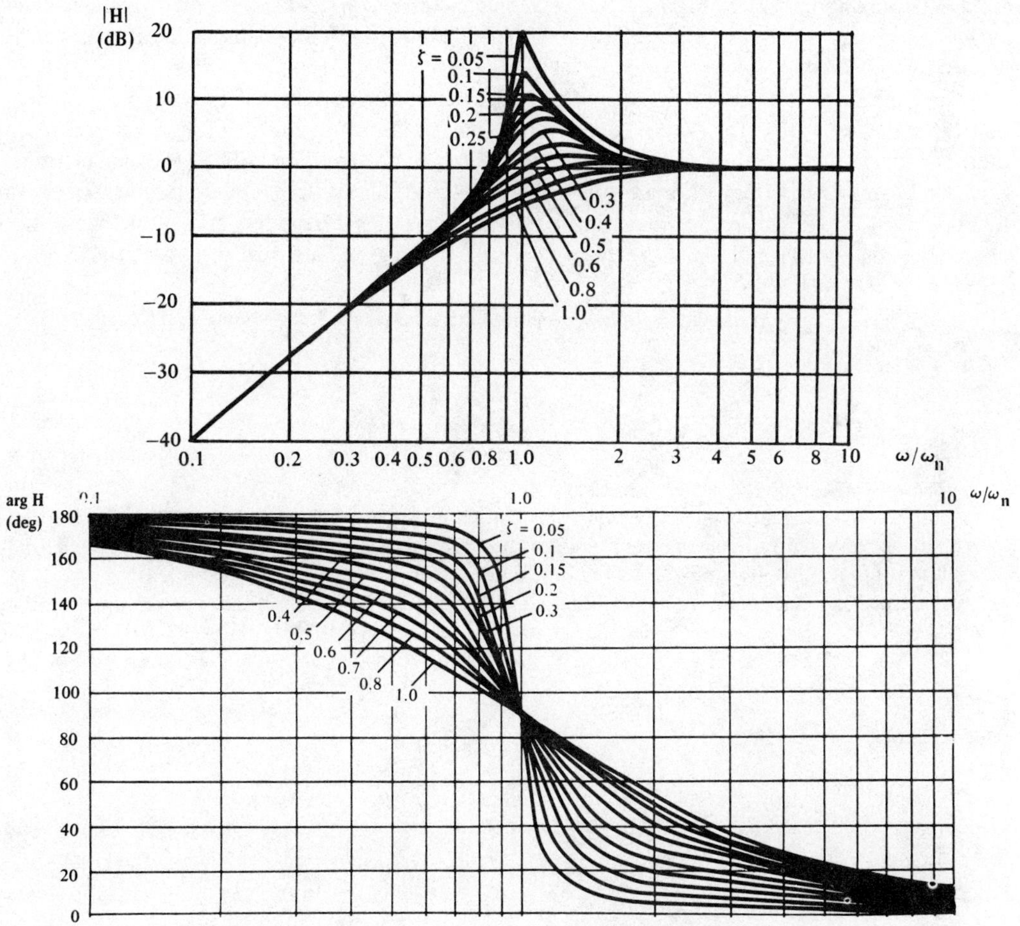

Fig. 2.6.2 Bode plots of |H| and arg H for second-order high-pass filters.

$$H_1(p) = \frac{1}{1+p}, \qquad H_2(p) = \frac{1}{1 + 2\zeta p + p^2} \tag{2.6.2}$$

Making the required low-pass to high-pass substitution p = 1/s, then

$$H_1(s) = \frac{s}{1+s}, \qquad H_2(s) = \frac{s^2}{1 + 2\zeta s + s^2} \tag{2.6.3}$$

The poles remain unchanged but zeros are introduced at the origin of the s-plane. Thus, if the low-pass filter is nth-order, the corresponding high-pass filter will also be nth-order with n zeros at the origin. The effect of these n zeros is to produce constant gain at high frequencies.

The first-order high-pass gain characteristic is shown in Fig. 2.6.1, and the second-order characteristic in Fig. 2.6.2. These are easily constructed by modifying Figs. 2.3.2 and 2.4.1. The transformation p = 1/s has the effect of inverting negative frequency (i.e., $v = -1/\omega$). Inverting frequency rotates the magnitude characteristic about $\omega = 1$ so that the asymptotic rolloff occurs at low frequencies rather than high frequencies. The asymptotic slope is positive rather than negative. The phase characteristic is also rotated about $\omega = 1$ and made negative, or more simply, augmented by 90n°. It is still monotonically nonincreasing, i.e., it has zero or negative slope. The error and peaking curves of Figs. 2.3.3, 2.4.2, and 2.4.3 remain valid where the normalized frequency axis becomes ω_n/ω. The reciprocal stopband bandwidth (i.e., reciprocal 3 dB bandwidth) is given by Fig. 2.4.4.

The concept of frequency transformations is tremendously useful to filter designers. We mention it here to show that for evey low-pass filter, there is an analogous high-pass filter and when the Bode diagram is constructed for a low-pass filter, it can be easily modified (rotate magnitude, augment phase) to describe the analogous high-pass filter. This viewpoint adds another dimension to Bode plots which the reader may find useful for enlarging his understanding of them. The transformation details will be thoroughly discussed in Chap. 6 and shall not concem us now.

EXAMPLE 2.6.1 Plot the magnitude and phase characteristics of the second-order high-pass filter having a gain of

$$H(s) = \frac{10 s_n^2}{s_n^2 + 2(0.2)s_n + 1} \tag{2.6.4}$$

where $s_n = s/2\pi(1000\text{ Hz})$. Label completely.

Solution The high-frequency gain equals 20 dB and the corner frequency equals 1000 Hz. The magnitude exhibits 8 dB of peaking (from Fig. 2.4.2) and the normalized 3 dB frequency or stopband bandwidth $B/f_n = 1/1.510$ (from Fig. 2.4.4) so B = 662 Hz.

The phase varies from 180° to 0° and equals 90° at 1000 Hz. The phase slope in the transition region equals –90/0.2 = –490 °/dec. The phase transition begins at $10^{-0.2}(1000) = 631$ Hz and ends at $10^{0.2}(1000) = 1585$ Hz. The magnitude and phase characteristics are shown in Fig. 2.6.3.

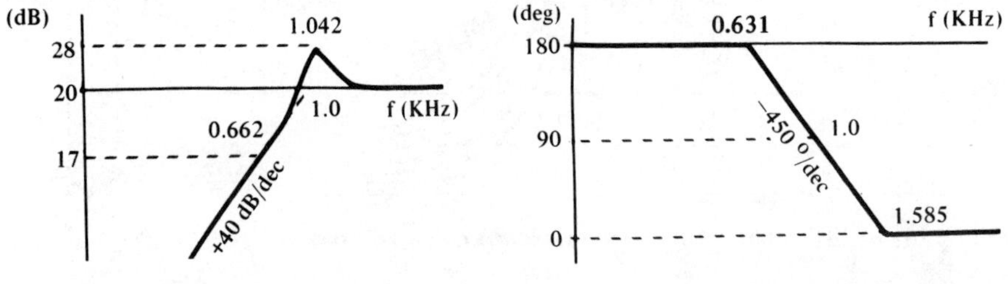

Fig. 2.6.3 Magnitude and phase characteristics for high-pass filter of Example 2.6.1.

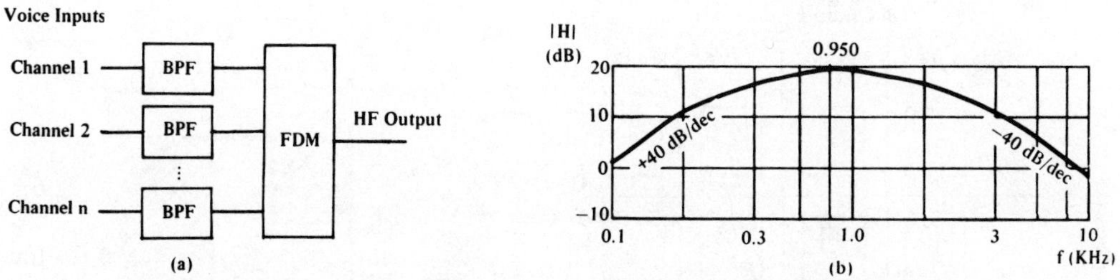

Fig. 2.6.4 (a) FDM system and (b) band-pass filter specification of Example 2.6.2.

EXAMPLE 2.6.2 Frequency-division multiplexing (FDM) systems combine a number of input channels for transmission over a common transmission channel. Each input channel is assigned a specific frequency band within the transmission channel bandwidth. A band-pass filter is to be designed for each input voice channel as shown in Fig. 2.6.4.[7] A cascaded low-pass and high-pass filter will be used. The filter specifications are: (1) midband gain = 20 dB, (2) 3 dB frequencies = 300 and 3000 Hz, (3) asymptotic rolloffs = ±40 dB/dec, (4) band-edge slopes (selectivity) = maximum, (5) gain peaking = none, and (6) phase = arbitrary. Write the gain expression for the low-pass and high-pass filters. Assign filter parameters to meet the specifications and show the cascaded gain blocks which are required.

Solution The required cascaded high-pass and low-pass stages are shown in Fig. 2.6.5. Since the asymptotic rolloffs are ±40 dB/dec, second-order stages must be used. If their corner frequencies are separated by more than three octaves, there will be almost no interaction of stopband behavior between the two stages. Thus, if there is to be no peaking, then $\zeta \geq 0.707$ from Fig. 2.4.2. To obtain maximum band-edge selectivity or slope at the 3 dB frequencies, the minimum ζ must be used; therefore, $\zeta = 0.707$. The normalized 3 dB cutoff frequency equals 1 from Fig. 2.4.4; therefore, the corner frequencies of the stages must be 300 and 3000 Hz. The midband gain of 20 dB is divided equally between the two stages. This design information is summarized in the blocks of Fig. 2.6.5. We shall find a different (and more precise) realization form for this filter in Example 2.7.3 using a different approach. In later chapters, we will design active filters to realize each stage.

EXAMPLE 2.6.3 Touch-Tone telephones simultaneously transmit two audio frequencies when a digit is depressed. One frequency is from the high group and the other frequency is from the low group as shown in Fig. 2.6.6. At the central office where these signals are decoded, two band-splitting filters are used to separate the high group and low group frequencies (see Fig. 2.7.3). Determine the parameters of a second-order high-pass and low-pass filter to obtain maximum stopband rejection, consistent with the frequency responses shown in Fig. 2.6.6. What is the minimum stopband rejection, and are second-order filters adequate in this application?

Solution To obtain maximum rejection, we want to use the minimum damping factor allowable. Since the maximum in-band magnitude ripple is 3 dB, we choose $\zeta = 0.38$ from Fig. 2.4.2 for both high-pass and low-pass filters. To determine the resonant frequency of the high-pass filter, we note that the reciprocal normalized (stopband) bandwidth $f_n/B = 1.39$ from Fig. 2.4.4. Since $B = 1209$ Hz, then

$$f_{n1} = 1.39B = 1680 \text{ Hz} \tag{2.6.5}$$

Analogously, the low-pass filter has a normalized bandwidth of $B/f_n = 1.39$. Since $B = 941$ Hz then

$$f_{n2} = B/1.39 = 677 \text{ Hz} \tag{2.6.6}$$

Setting the high-frequency gain of the high-pass filter equal to −3 dB and the low-frequency gain of the low-pass filter equal to −3 dB, the designs are completed. The minimum stopband rejection of both

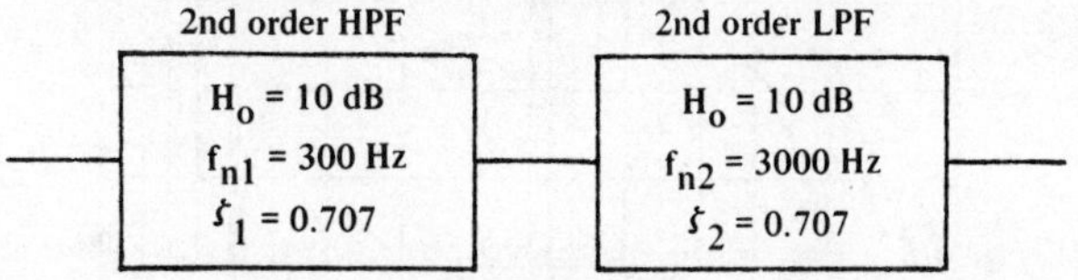

Fig. 2.6.5 Band-pass filter realization of Example 2.6.2.

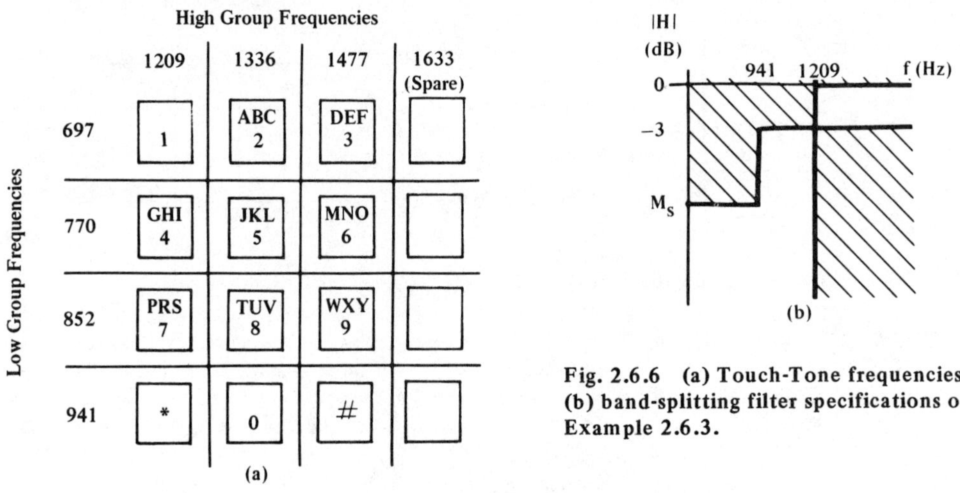

Fig. 2.6.6 (a) Touch-Tone frequencies and (b) band-splitting filter specifications of Example 2.6.3.

filters is easily determined from the gain function, Eq. 2.4.3, as

$$
\begin{aligned}
M_s &= |H(j(2\pi(1209\text{ Hz}))|^{-1} = ([1 - (1209/677)^2]^2 + [2(0.38)(1209/677)]^2)^{1/2} \\
&= (2.19^2 + 1.36^2)^{1/2} = 2.58 = 8.2\text{ dB} \qquad (2.6.7)
\end{aligned}
$$

Unfortunately, only 8.2 dB of rejection is obtained which is inadequate. A higher order filter is required. We will see in Chap. 4 that a third-order elliptic filter or a fifth-order Chebyshev filter will provide 20 dB of rejection, and a fifth-order elliptic filter can provide 40 dB of rejection.

EXAMPLE 2.6.4 Noise in telephone circuits which is heard or felt by subscribers is objectionable. Noise measuring instruments must have frequency responses which match those of the average subscriber's ear, and also take into account the psychological effects of the noise the subscriber perceives. The instrument must also account for the frequency response of the telephone equipment used including the telephone receiver (i.e., the handset). Passing the telephone circuit noise through the proper filter subjectively "weights" the objectionable portion of the telephone circuit noise.[8]

The telephone system uses standard input filters in noise measurement equipment. Such input filters have standard magnitude characteristics which are shown in Fig. 2.6.7. The 144-line weighting was used for the deskstand telephone sets of the 1920's and 30's; F1A-line weighting was used for the Model 302 handset; and the C-message weighting is used in the present Model 500 handset.

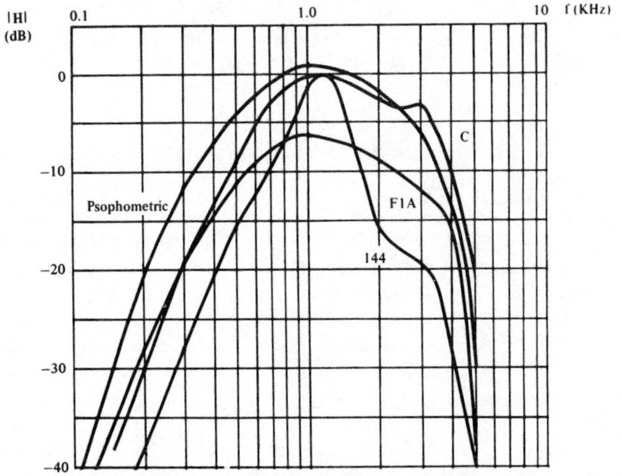

Fig. 2.6.7 Standard noise weighting filters for telephone noise measurement of Example 2.6.4.

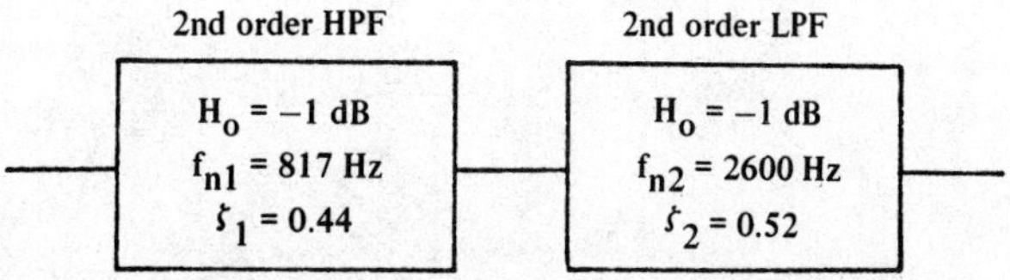

Fig. 2.6.8 Band-pass filter realization of Example 2.6.4.

Approximate the C-weighting curve as closely as possible using, at most, a fourth-order filter. Draw the completed design in block diagram form and label completely. Phase is arbitrary.

Solution We shall design the filter by cascading a second-order high-pass and low-pass filter and choose their parameters to match the C-weighting characteristic. For the high-pass filter stage, we require approximately that

$$M_{p\omega} = 2\text{ dB}, \qquad B_{3\text{ dB}} = 610\text{ Hz} \tag{2.6.8}$$

From Fig. 2.4.2, we use $\zeta = 0.44$. Then since $B/f_n = 1/1.34$ from Fig. 2.4.4, the corner frequency of the high-pass filter equals

$$f_{n1} = 1.34B = 1.34(610) = 817\text{ Hz} \tag{2.6.9}$$

For the low-pass stage, we require approximately that

$$M_{p\omega} = 1\text{ dB}, \qquad B_{3\text{ dB}} = 3250\text{ Hz} \tag{2.6.10}$$

Therefore, from Fig. 2.4.2, we use $\zeta = 0.52$. Then since $B/f_n = 1.25$ from Fig. 2.4.4, the corner frequency of the low-pass filter equals

$$f_{n2} = B/1.25 = 3250/1.25 = 2600\text{ Hz} \tag{2.6.11}$$

Since the overall midband gain equals $H_{o1}H_{o2} = -2\text{ dB} = 0.79$, then we set $H_{o1} = H_{o2} = -1\text{ dB} = 0.89$. The completed design is shown in Fig. 2.6.8. In Chap. 5 where optimum filters are considered, we shall discuss optimization methods for determining such filter parameters.

2.7 BAND-PASS FILTERS

Just as high-pass filters can be derived from low-pass filters, band-pass filters can also be derived from low-pass filters. This is accomplished using the low-pass to band-pass transformation $p = s + 1/s$. Thus, if the low-pass filter has gain $H(p)$, then the corresponding band-pass filter has gain

$$H(s) = H(p)\,\Big|_{p = s + 1/s = \frac{s^2+1}{s}} \tag{2.7.1}$$

For example, the first-order low-pass filter with bandwidth 2ζ has a gain

$$H_1(p) = \frac{1}{1 + p/2\zeta} \tag{2.7.2}$$

Therefore, the analogous band-pass filter has a gain

$$H_1(s) = \left(1 + \frac{1}{2\zeta}\frac{s^2+1}{s}\right)^{-1} = \frac{2\zeta s}{s^2 + 2\zeta s + 1} \tag{2.7.3}$$

The poles are complex with damping factor ζ. Their relation to the low-pass filter pole will be discussed in Chap. 6.

The Bode plots of the magnitude and phase of the band-pass gain characteristic are shown in Fig. 2.7.1 and can be easily obtained by modifying Fig. 2.4.1. Since

$$H(j\omega) = \frac{j2\zeta\omega}{j2\zeta\omega + 1 - \omega^2} = \left(1 + j\frac{\omega^2 - 1}{2\zeta\omega}\right)^{-1} = \left(1 + j\frac{\omega - 1/\omega}{2\zeta}\right)^{-1} \tag{2.7.4}$$

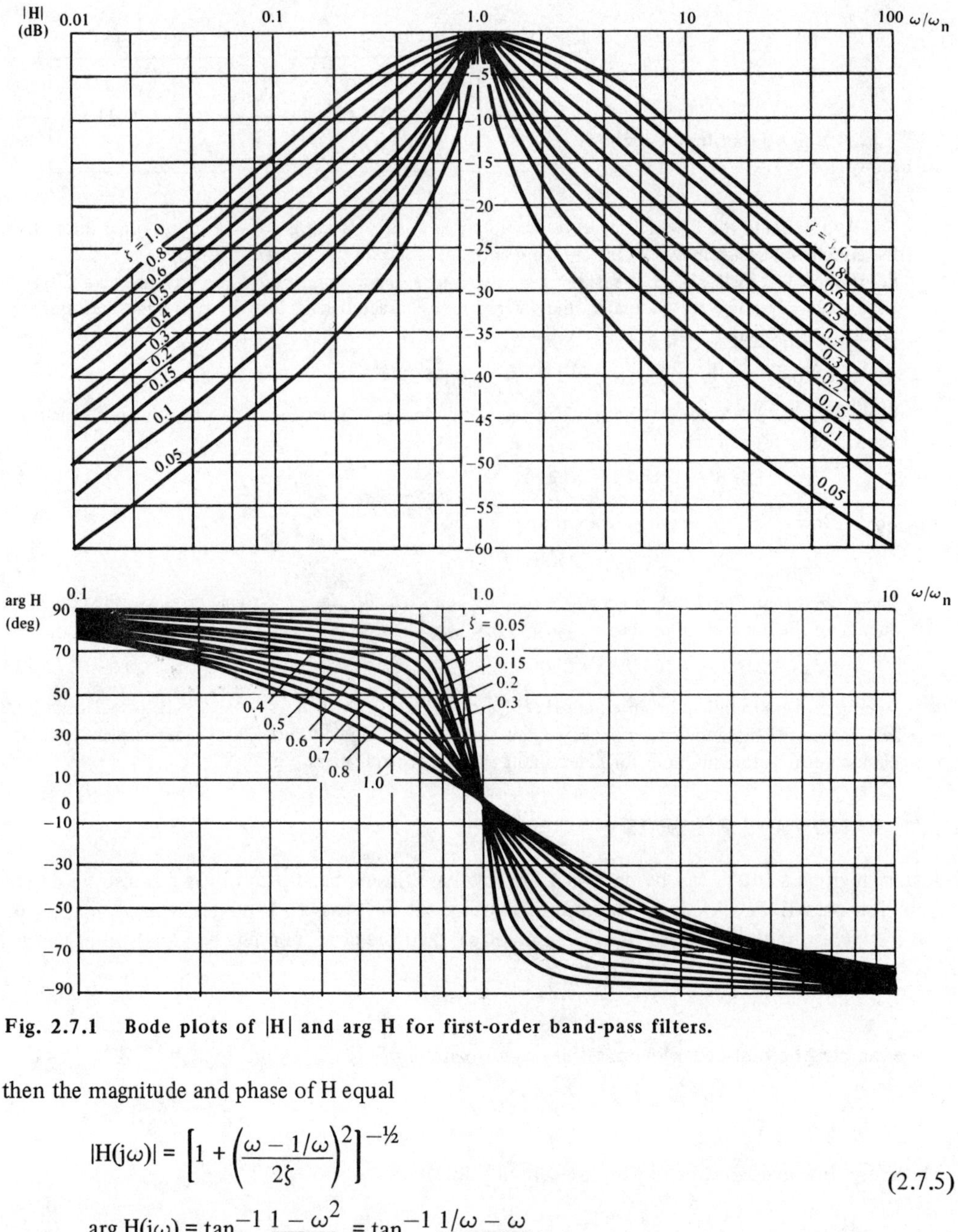

Fig. 2.7.1 **Bode plots of |H| and arg H for first-order band-pass filters.**

then the magnitude and phase of H equal

$$|H(j\omega)| = \left[1 + \left(\frac{\omega - 1/\omega}{2\zeta}\right)^2\right]^{-1/2}$$
$$\arg H(j\omega) = \tan^{-1}\frac{1-\omega^2}{2\zeta\omega} = \tan^{-1}\frac{1/\omega - \omega}{2\zeta} \qquad (2.7.5)$$

Both |H| and arg H have geometric symmetry about the center frequency $\omega = 1$. The midband gain equals 0 dB. Since the asymptotic rolloff is ±20 dB/dec, the band-pass filter is referred to as first-order. In a more general context, however, the band-pass filter is first-order since it is derived from a first-order low-pass filter. However, when we consider only the denominator, we say it is a second-order filter. Appreciation of the distinction between the two terms is of great importance since we shall use them both.

The 3 dB bandwidth of the band-pass filter is very important in design. Setting $|H|^2 = ½$ in

Eq. 2.7.5 and solving for normalized 3 dB frequencies gives

$$\omega_{3\ dB}/\omega_n = [\zeta^2 + 1]^{1/2} \pm \zeta \tag{2.7.6}$$

Thus, the normalized 3 dB bandwidth B equals

$$B/\omega_n = (\omega_{3\ dB\ upper} - \omega_{3\ dB\ lower})/\omega_n = 2\zeta = 1/Q \tag{2.7.7}$$

where Q is often referred to as the "Q" of the band-pass filter. Thus, for first-order band-pass filters, specifying the normalized filter bandwidth determines the required Q or damping factor ζ for the filter. The bandwidth for both low-pass and band-pass filters is $2\zeta\omega_n$. We shall see in Chap. 6 that the low-pass to band-pass transformation preserves bandwidth which is very useful.

Since band-pass filters are used to attenuate signals having frequencies lying in their stopbands, it is of interest to obtain a figure of merit regarding the steepness of the magnitude characteristic or the narrowness of the transition band separating the passband and the stopband. One such standard parameter is the 3–20 dB shaping factor which is the ratio of the 20 dB bandwidth to the 3 dB bandwidth. The normalized 20 dB frequencies and the 20 dB bandwidth can easily be shown to equal

$$\omega_{20\ dB}/\omega_n = [(9.95\zeta)^2 + 1]^{1/2} \pm 9.95\zeta, \qquad B_{20\ dB}/\omega_n = 19.9\zeta \tag{2.7.8}$$

from Eq. 2.7.5. The 3–20 dB shaping factor therefore equals

$$S_{3\ dB}^{20\ dB} = B_{20\ dB}/B_{3\ dB} = 19.9\zeta/2\zeta = 9.95 \cong 10 \tag{2.7.9}$$

which is independent of the filter Q or damping factor. Thus, the signal rejection ratio at these two frequencies is not improved by increasing filter Q as one might first imagine.

The phase characteristic in Fig. 2.7.1 decreases monotonically from 90° at dc to –90° at high frequencies with a slope of $-90/\zeta$ °/dec. Phase passes through 0° at $\omega = 1$, and is identical to that for the second-order low-pass filter except for the 90° offset due to the zero at the origin. Often the phase characteristics in the immediate vicinity of the center frequency are important. We saw earlier in Eq. 2.4.10 that the exact center frequency slope equals

$$d \arg H/d \log_{10} \omega \big|_{\omega=1} = -2.31/\zeta \text{ rad/dec} \cong -135/\zeta\ ^\circ/\text{dec} = -41/\zeta\ ^\circ/\text{oct} \tag{2.7.10}$$

Thus, the approximate phase transition occurs over a frequency interval of D beginning at $\omega = \omega_n/R$ and ending at $\omega = R\omega_n$ where D and R equal

$$D = \pi/(2.31/\zeta) = 1.36\zeta \text{ decade}, \qquad R = 10^{D/2} = 10^{0.68\zeta} \tag{2.7.11}$$

Suppose we now consider n identical first-order band-pass filters each having a Q = ½ which are cascaded together. Their overall gain equals

$$H(s) = \left(\frac{s/Q}{s^2 + s/Q + 1}\right)^n \tag{2.7.12}$$

Since the bandwidths are maintained under the low-pass to band-pass transformation, so are the bandwidth shrinkage factors.[9] Thus, S(n) for the overall band-pass filter must equal

$$S(n) = \frac{\text{Bandwidth of n synchronously-tuned stages}}{\text{Bandwidth of each individual stage}} = \sqrt{2^{1/n} - 1} \tag{2.7.13}$$

from Eq. 2.3.27. The shrinkage factor is plotted in Fig. 2.3.8.

EXAMPLE 2.7.1 Draw the approximate magnitude and phase characteristics of a first-order band-pass filter having gain

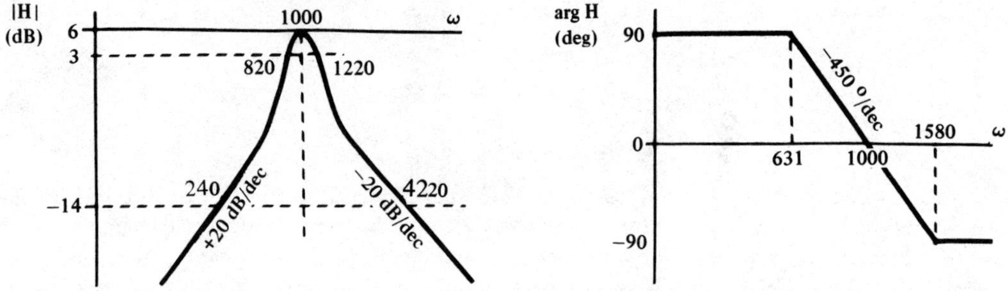

Fig. 2.7.2 Magnitude and phase characteristics for band-pass filter of Example 2.7.1.

$$H(s) = 2\frac{2(0.2)(s/1000)}{(s/1000)^2 + 2(0.2)(s/1000) + 1} \tag{2.7.14}$$

Solution The gain of the first-order band-pass filter is in the standard form of Eq. 2.7.3 where the midband gain $H_o = 2 = 6$ dB, $\zeta = 0.2$ so $Q = 1/2(0.2) = 2.5$, and normalized frequency $s_n = s/1000$ so the center frequency $\omega_n = 1000$. Thus, the magnitude characteristic is easily plotted in Fig. 2.7.2. The normalized 3 dB frequencies equal

$$\omega_{3\text{ dB}}/\omega_n = \sqrt{1.04} \pm 0.2 = 0.82, \quad 1.22 \tag{2.7.15}$$

from Eq. 2.7.6 while from Eq. 2.7.8, the normalized 20 dB frequencies equal

$$\omega_{20\text{ dB}}/\omega_n = \sqrt{(9.95\zeta)^2 + 1} \pm 9.95\zeta = 0.24, \quad 4.22 \tag{2.7.16}$$

The phase characteristic varies from +90° to −90° with a phase slope of −90/0.2 = −450 °/dec using the "wideband" approximation of Eq. 2.4.11. The transition occurs over D = 2(0.2) = 0.4 decade and the frequency ratio $R = 10^{0.4/2} = 1.58$ using Eqs. 2.4.12 and 2.4.13. Thus, the transition begins at 1000/1.58 = 631 rad/sec and ends at 1.58(1000) = 1580 rad/sec. The phase characteristic is also plotted in Fig. 2.7.2.

EXAMPLE 2.7.2 As discussed in Example 2.6.3, depressing any one of the buttons on the Touch-Tone telephone set causes two frequencies (one low and one high) from 697 to 1633 Hz to be generated. These two frequencies are transmitted over the telephone line to the switching office where they are decoded by eight *tone detection filters* as shown in Fig. 2.7.3a. Are the band-pass filters constant bandwidth B or constant Q filters? Draw the magnitude responses for all band-pass filters assuming they are first-order; their midband gain is 0 dB, and their gains cross-over at their −20 dB frequencies. What must their Q's equal?

Solution Testing the center frequencies f_n, constant bandwidth filters would satisfy $\Delta f = f_n - f_{n-1}$ while constant Q filters would satisfy $r = f_n/f_{n-1}$ where Δf and r are constants. In this case, we find that the filters have center frequencies spaced geometrically where r = 1.1. Thus, the band-pass filters are constant Q types. To determine Q, we note from Eq. 2.7.10 that since the 3–20 dB shaping factor equals 9.95 for first-order band-pass filters, then Q can be expressed as $Q = \omega_n/B_{3dB} = 9.95\omega_n/B_{20dB}$ from Eq. 2.7.7. Since we can find B_{20dB}/ω_n, we can determine Q.

The normalized frequency response of the band-pass filters are shown in Fig. 2.7.3b. Since the responses intersect or *crossover* at their −20 dB values and the center frequencies are close together, then the normalized −20 dB frequencies equal

$$\begin{aligned} \omega_{20\text{ dB}} &\cong \sqrt{\omega_n\omega_{n+1}} = \sqrt{1(1.1)} = 1.05 \quad \text{(upper)} \\ &\cong \sqrt{\omega_n\omega_{n-1}} = \sqrt{1(0.9)} = 0.95 \quad \text{(lower)} \end{aligned} \tag{2.7.17}$$

so that the normalized 20 dB bandwidth $B_{20dB} = 1.05 - 0.95 = 0.1$. Therefore, the required Q of the band-pass filter equals

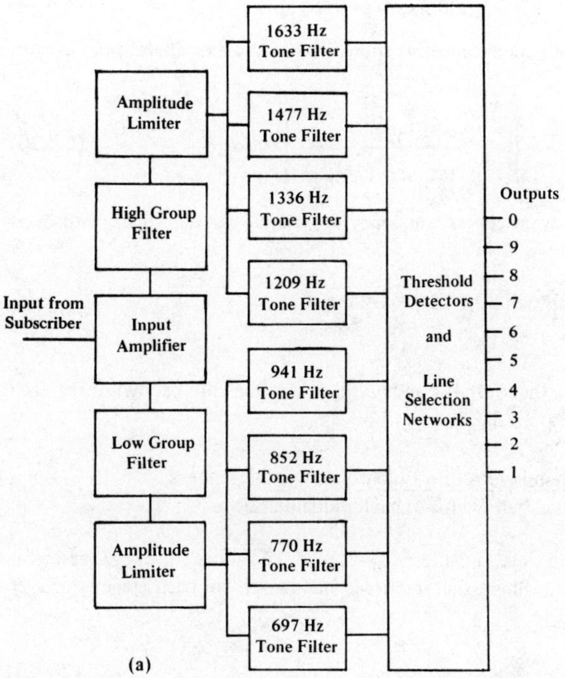

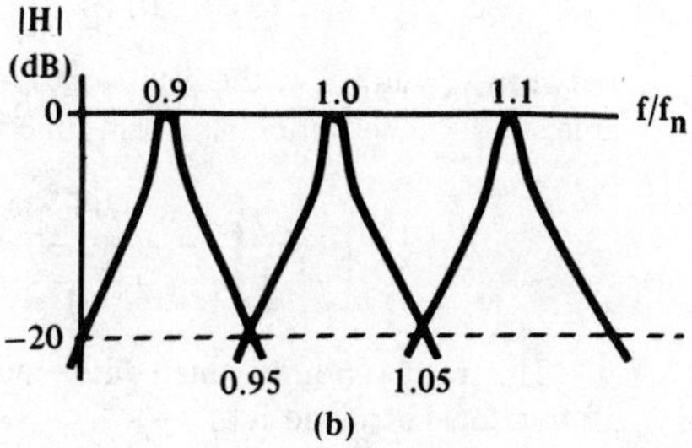

Fig. 2.7.3 (a) Touch-Tone decoder and (b) normalized frequency response of band-pass filters of Example 2.7.2.

$$Q = 9.95\omega_n/B_{20\ dB} = 9.95/0.1 \cong 100 \tag{2.7.18}$$

or $\zeta = 1/2(100) \cong 0.005$. Thus, each band-pass filter has the same Q or ζ. The center frequencies are given in Fig. 2.7.3 and the midband gain $H_o = 1$. In practice, filters having lower Q's (25–50) are used; of course, they also have higher gain crossover values.

EXAMPLE 2.7.3 Obtain parameters for a second-order band-pass filter to satisfy the following specifications: (1) midband gain = 10, (2) center frequency = 1800 Hz, (3) 3 dB frequencies = 600 and 3000 Hz, and (4) asymptotic rolloffs = ± 12dB/oct.

Solution In general, either two *synchronously-tuned* stages (having identical pole-zero configurations) or two *stagger-tuned* stages (having different pole-zero configurations), where each stage is a first-order band-pass filter, can be used. Let us design one filter of each type. The two magnitude characteristics to be used are shown in Fig. 2.7.4.

For the stagger-tuned design, let us choose $\zeta = 0.5$ so the magnitude approximation is almost identical to the actual characteristic. Then by proper "staggering" or spacing of the two filter center frequencies, we can obtain the desired overall characteristic. Since the slopes equal ±12 dB/oct, the corner frequencies are ¼ octave = $2^{1/4}$ = 1.19 away from the 3 dB frequencies. Thus, the corner frequencies equal

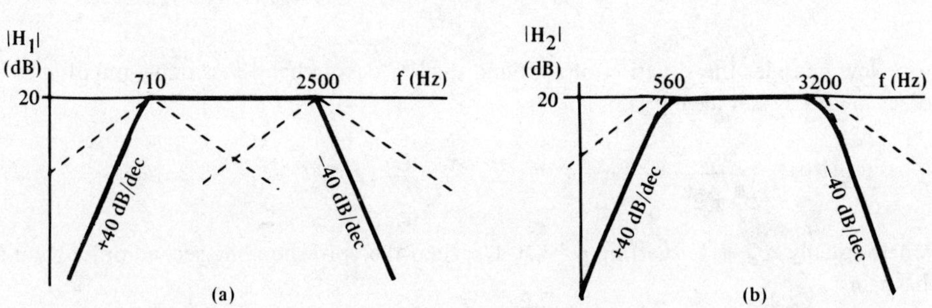

Fig. 2.7.4 Magnitude characteristics for (a) stagger-tuned and (b) synchronously-tuned filters of Example 2.7.3.

$$f_{n1} = 600(1.19) \cong 710 \text{ Hz} \quad \text{and} \quad f_{n2} = 3000/1.19 \cong 2500 \text{ Hz} \tag{2.7.19}$$

Between f_{n1} and f_{n2}, the gain slopes of each stage cancel as shown in Fig. 2.7.4a. Therefore, one suitable stagger-tuned filter has a gain function

$$H_1(s) = 10\,\frac{f_{n2}}{f_{n1}}\left[\frac{2\pi f_{n1}s}{s^2 + 2\pi f_{n1}s + (2\pi f_{n1})^2}\right]\left[\frac{2\pi f_{n2}s}{s^2 + 2\pi f_{n2}s + (2\pi f_{n2})^2}\right] \tag{2.7.20}$$

The synchronously-tuned filter must have a center frequency f_n, overall bandwidth B_o, and overall fractional bandwidth of

$$f_n = \sqrt{600(3000)} = 1340 \text{ Hz}, \qquad B_o = 3000 - 600 = 2400 \text{ Hz}, \qquad B_o/f_n = 2400/1340 = 1.79 \tag{2.7.21}$$

respectively. Due to bandwidth shrinkage, the overall bandwidth is less than the bandwidth of each stage. Since the shrinkage factor, given by Eq. 2.7.13, equals

$$S(n) = \frac{B_o}{B} = \frac{B_o/f_n}{B/f_n} = \frac{\text{Fractional bandwidth of n synchronously-tuned stages}}{\text{Fractional bandwidth of each individual stage}} \tag{2.7.22}$$

the fractional bandwidth for each first-order stage satisfies $B/f_n = (B_o/f_n)/S_n$. The shrinkage factor for two stages is $S(2) = 0.644$ from Fig. 2.3.8. Since the fractional bandwidth for each stage equals 2ζ from Eq. 2.7.7, then from Eq. 2.7.22,

$$2\zeta = \frac{1}{0.644}\frac{B_o}{f_n} = \frac{1.79}{0.644} = 2.80 \tag{2.7.23}$$

Therefore, each stage requires a damping factor $\zeta = 1.4$ and a center frequency $f_n = 1340$ Hz. Since $\zeta \geqslant 1$, the roots are real. They must nevertheless have geometric symmetry about f_n. The denominator of the individual gain functions can be expressed as

$$(s + k\omega_n)(s + \omega_n/k) = s^2 + \omega_n(k + 1/k)s + \omega_n^2 = s^2 + 2\zeta\omega_n s + \omega_n^2 \tag{2.7.24}$$

where the pole placement factor k must satisfy $\zeta = (k + 1/k)/2 = (k^2 + 1)/2k$. Therefore, k must equal

$$k = \zeta \pm \sqrt{\zeta^2 - 1} \tag{2.7.25}$$

Since the damping factor equals 1.4, then

$$k = 1.4 \pm \sqrt{1.96 - 1} = 1.40 \pm 0.98 = 0.42, \quad 2.38 \tag{2.7.26}$$

Thus, the synchronously-tuned filter has double real poles located at $s = -0.42\,\omega_n$ and $s = -\omega_n/0.42 = -2.38\omega_n$. Therefore, each band-pass stage has corner frequencies at 560 Hz and 3200 Hz. The gain function of the synchronously-tuned filter equals

$$H(s) = 10\left[\frac{2(1.4)(2\pi 1340)s}{(s + 2\pi 560)(s + 2\pi 3200)}\right]^2 = 10\left[\frac{2(1.4)(2\pi 1340)s}{s^2 + 2(1.4)(2\pi 1340)s + (2\pi 1340)^2}\right]^2 \tag{2.7.27}$$

Now consider the situation of applying the low-pass to band-pass transformation to a second-order low-pass filter having gain

$$H(p) = \frac{\omega_o^2}{p^2 + 2\zeta\omega_o p + \omega_o^2} \tag{2.7.28}$$

where usually $\omega_o \leqslant 1$. Letting $p = s + 1/s$, then the corresponding second-order band-pass filter has gain

$$H(s) = \frac{\omega_o^2 s^2}{s^4 + 2\zeta\omega_o s^3 + (2 + \omega_o^2)s^2 + 2\zeta\omega_o s + 1} \tag{2.7.29}$$

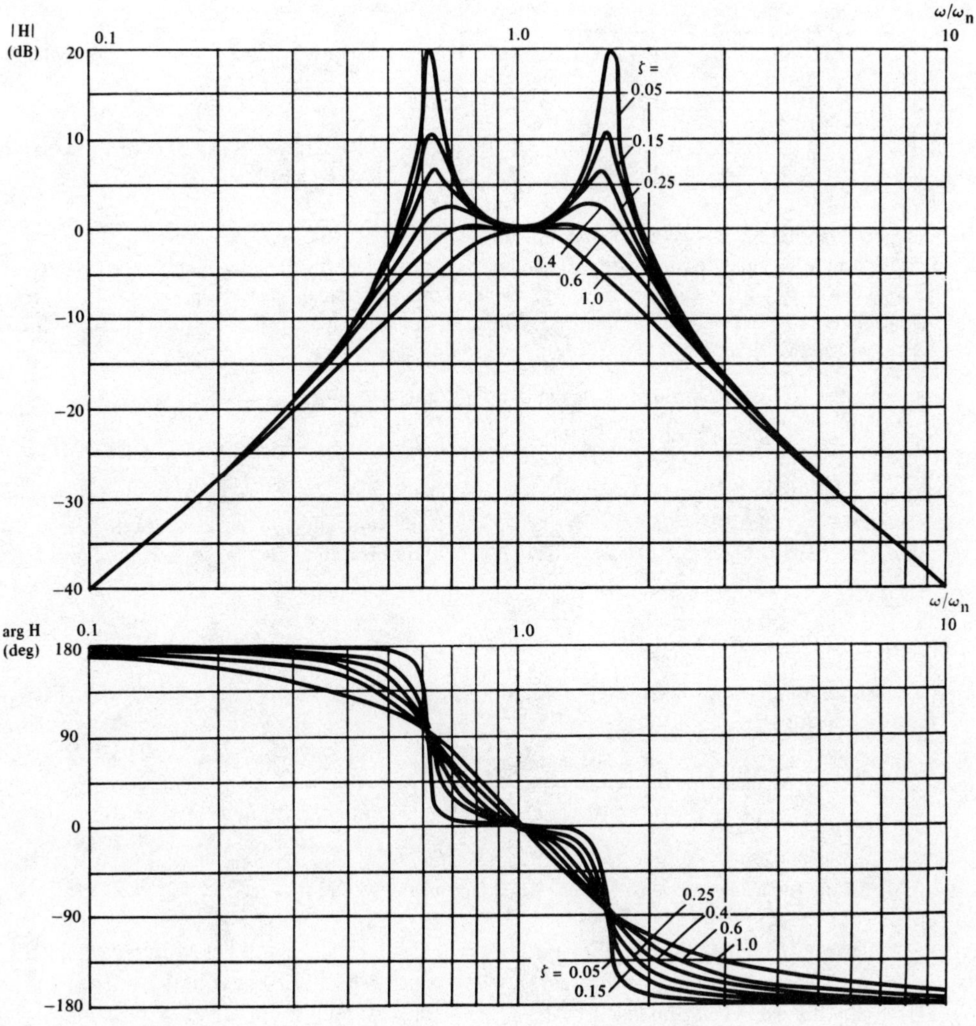

Fig. 2.7.5 Bode plots of |H| and arg H for second-order band-pass filters.

The pole locations will be fully investigated in Chap. 6. The Bode plot for the gain can be easily drawn by combining the second-order low-pass and high-pass characteristics of Figs. 2.4.1 and 2.6.2, or the first-order band-pass characteristics of Fig. 2.7.1. In either case, the Bode plots for the magnitude and phase are shown in Fig. 2.7.5. The magnitude has geometric symmetry about $\omega_o = 1$ and rolls off at ±40 dB/dec. Sometimes this is referred to as a *double-tuned* filter and has found great use in the past as an interstage coupling network.[10]

We shall see that the shape of the magnitude curves is preserved under the transformation. Thus, the error, peaking, and bandwidth curves of Figs. 2.3.3, 2.4.2, 2.4.3, and 2.4.4 can still be used when frequency is interpreted as offset frequency relative to center frequency. We shall now present an example to illustrate this result.

EXAMPLE 2.7.4 We determined the parameters of a band-pass filter in Example 2.6.2 using a cascaded second-order low-pass and high-pass filter. Determine the cascaded band-pass filters which can be used instead to meet the same specifications.

Solution Since the asymptotic rolloff equals ±40 dB/dec, a second-order band-pass filter is required

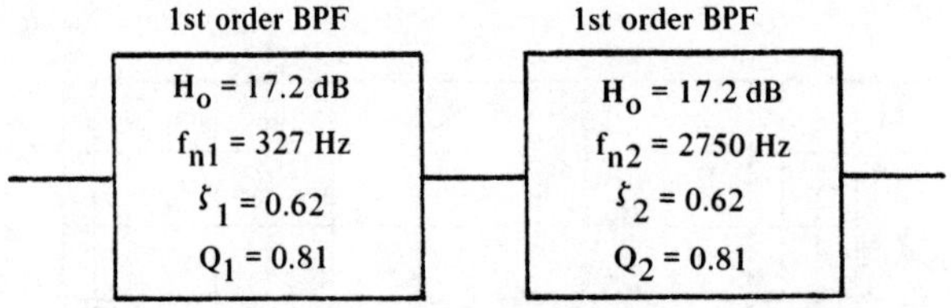

Fig. 2.7.6 Band-pass filter realization of Example 2.7.4.

which will consist of two cascaded first-order band-pass filters. Its gain is given by Eq. 2.7.29. To obtain maximum band-edge slope with no peaking, we must select the damping factor appropriately. The analogous low-pass filter requires $\zeta = 0.707$ to meet this requirement as seen in Fig. 2.4.1. It remains only to determine the frequencies involved. The band-pass filter has a center frequency, bandwidth, and fractional bandwidth of

$$f_n = \sqrt{300(3000)} = 949 \text{ Hz}, \qquad B = 3000 - 300 = 2700 \text{ Hz}, \qquad B/f_n = 2700/949 = 2.85 \tag{2.7.30}$$

The analogous low-pass filter has the same absolute bandwidth. Since $\zeta = 0.707$, its normalized corner frequency f_o satisfies $B/f_o = 1$ from Fig. 2.4.4. Therefore, combining this result with Eq. 2.7.30c shows that f_o is related to f_n as $f_o/f_n = 2.85$. Thus, the required transfer function for the band-pass filter is

$$H(s) = 10\frac{2.85^2 s_n^{\,2}}{s_n^{\,4} + 1.414(2.85)s_n^{\,3} + (2 + 2.85^2)s_n^{\,2} + 1.414(2.85)s_n + 1} \tag{2.7.31}$$

by substituting the various parameters above into Eq. 2.7.29 and letting $s_n = s/2\pi(949 \text{ Hz})$. Factoring the denominator yields

$$H(s) = 52.8\left[\frac{2(0.62)(s_n/2.90)}{(s_n/2.90)^2 + 2(0.62)(s_n/2.90) + 1}\right]\left[\frac{2(0.62)(2.90s_n)}{(2.90s_n)^2 + 2(0.62)(2.90)s_n + 1}\right] \tag{2.7.32}$$

Thus, the band-pass filter is composed of two first-order band-pass stages each having $\zeta = 0.62$ as shown in Fig. 2.7.6. The first is tuned to $f_n/2.90 = 327$ Hz and the second is tuned to $2.90f_n = 2750$ Hz.

It is useful to recognize that a second-order (or *n*th-order) band-pass filter can always be realized using a second-order (or *n*th-order) low-pass/high-pass filter combination. This is shown by rearranging the gain equation given by Eq. 2.7.29 (as was done in Eq. 2.7.32) so that

$$\begin{aligned} H(s) &= \frac{H_{o1}2\zeta_1\omega_{n1}s}{s^2 + 2\zeta_1\omega_{n1}s + \omega_{n1}^{\,2}}\,\frac{H_{o2}2\zeta_2\omega_{n2}s}{s^2 + 2\zeta_2\omega_{n2}s + \omega_{n2}^{\,2}} \\ &= 4H_{o1}H_{o2}\zeta_1\zeta_2\frac{\omega_{n2}}{\omega_{n1}}\,\frac{\omega_{n1}^{\,2}}{s^2 + 2\zeta_1\omega_{n1}s + \omega_{n1}^{\,2}}\,\frac{s^2}{s^2 + 2\zeta_2\omega_{n2}s + \omega_{n2}^{\,2}} \end{aligned} \tag{2.7.33}$$

which is the product of a second-order low-pass and high-pass filter function. Their gain product equals $H_o^{\,2} = 4H_{o1}H_{o2}\zeta_1\zeta_2\omega_{n2}/\omega_{n1}$.

The alert engineer will ask why the results of Fig. 2.7.6 disagree with those shown in Fig. 2.6.5 when the two filters satisfy the same specifications. Since we can redistribute the s^2 numerator term of the high-pass gain block into s numerator terms in each gain block (and scale gain accordingly) which would result in Fig. 2.7.6, this is indeed a valid question. The answer is that the band-pass filter in Fig. 2.7.6 was derived exactly from equations using transformations, while that in Fig. 2.6.5 was derived approximately by inspection. Thus, although visual inspection of Fig. 2.4.1 indicated that $\zeta = 0.707$ would yield maximum steepness at the 3 dB frequencies with no peaking, the mathematics show that this is not quite the case. Although using $\zeta = 0.707$

introduces no peaking (see Fig. 2.4.2) for a pole pair, the gain tends to be slightly lower due to other pole pairs located one decade away. Using instead $\zeta = 0.62$ compensates for this error by introducing slight peaking (about 3%).

2.8 BAND-STOP FILTERS

Band-stop, notch, band-reject, or band-elimination filters can also be derived from low-pass filters using the low-pass to band-stop transformation $p = (s + 1/s)^{-1}$. Alternatively, they can be derived from high-pass filters using the low-pass to band-pass transformation. This will be extensively discussed in Chap. 6. If the low-pass filter has gain H(p), then the notch filter has gain

$$H(s) = H(p)\Big|_{p = \frac{1}{s+1/s} = \frac{s}{s^2+1}} \tag{2.8.1}$$

For example, the first-order low-pass filter of 3 dB bandwidth 2ζ has a gain of

$$H(p) = \frac{1}{1 + p/2\zeta} \tag{2.8.2}$$

Thus, the corresponding notch filter has gain

$$H_1(s) = \left(1 + \frac{1}{2\zeta}\frac{s}{s^2+1}\right)^{-1} = \frac{s^2+1}{s^2 + s/2\zeta + 1} = \frac{s^2+1}{s^2 + 2\gamma s + 1} \tag{2.8.3}$$

The poles are complex with damping factor $\gamma = 1/4\zeta$. The zeros are pure imaginary and are located at $s = \pm j1$. The Bode magnitude and phase plots can be easily obtained by modifying Fig. 2.4.1 and are shown in Fig. 2.8.1. Since

$$H(j\omega) = \frac{1-\omega^2}{1 - \omega^2 + j\omega/2\zeta} \tag{2.8.4}$$

then the magnitude and phase of H equal

$$|H(j\omega)| = \frac{[(1-\omega^2)^2]^{1/2}}{[(1-\omega^2)^2 + (\omega/2\zeta)^2]^{1/2}}$$

$$\arg H(j\omega) = -\tan^{-1}\frac{1}{2\zeta}\frac{\omega}{1-\omega^2}, \qquad |\omega| < 1 \tag{2.8.5}$$

$$= \pi - \tan^{-1}\frac{1}{2\zeta}\frac{\omega}{1-\omega^2}, \qquad |\omega| > 1$$

Both |H| and arg H have geometric symmetry about the notch frequency, $\omega = 1$. The midband gain is zero and the phase makes an abrupt $-180°$ transition at the notch frequency. Notice that the magnitude approaches an asymptotic rolloff slope equalling infinity at the notch frequency. This is a first-order notch filter since it is derived from a first-order low-pass filter. The zeros are called *zeros of transmission* since the gain equals zero at the frequency where the zeros are located.[11] The 3 dB notch bandwidth B of the band-stop filter is very important in design. Since reciprocal bandwidth is preserved under the low-pass to band-stop transformation, then the normalized 3 dB (stopband) bandwidth of the notch filter equals

$$B/\omega_n = 1/2\zeta = 2\gamma = 1/Q \tag{2.8.6}$$

where Q is referred to as the "Q" of the notch filter. Therefore, specifying the fractional bandwidth of the notch determines the required damping factor γ or the Q of the notch filter. The reciprocal 3–20 dB shaping factor of the notch filter is invariant under the transformation. Thus,

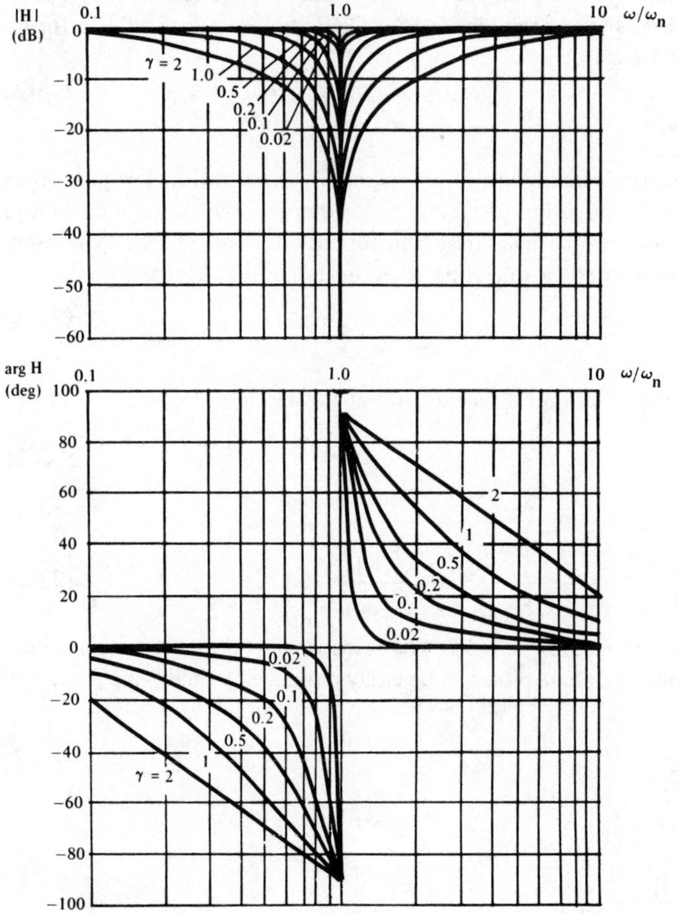

Fig. 2.8.1 Bode plots of |H| and arg H for first-order band-stop filters.

$$S_{3\text{ dB}}^{20\text{ dB}} = B_{3\text{ dB}}/B_{20\text{ dB}} = 9.95 \cong 10 \tag{2.8.7}$$

where $B_{20dB}/\omega_n = 1/19.9\zeta = \gamma/4.975 = 1/9.95Q$ by analogy with the band-pass filter results of Eqs. 2.7.8 and 2.7.9. Thus, the signal rejection ratio at these two frequencies is not improved by increasing filter Q as one might first think.

The phase characteristics decrease monotonically from 0° to –90° as ω increases from 0 to 1, jumps +180° at $\omega = 1$ to +90°, and then decreases from +90° to 0° as $\omega \to \infty$. In the immediate vicinity of the notch frequency, the exact phase slope equals

$$d \arg H/d \log_{10} \omega \,|_{\omega=1} = -2.31/\gamma \text{ rad/sec} \cong -135/\gamma\ ^\circ/\text{dec} = -27/\gamma\ ^\circ/\text{oct} \tag{2.8.8}$$

As in the band-pass filter case, the approximate phase transition takes place over a frequency interval D beginning at $\omega = \omega_n/R$ and ending at $\omega = R\omega_n$ where D and R equal

$$D = 1.36\gamma \text{ decade}, \qquad R = 10^{D/2} = 10^{0.68\gamma} \tag{2.8.9}$$

Recall that these phase results use the exact phase slope at the notch frequency.

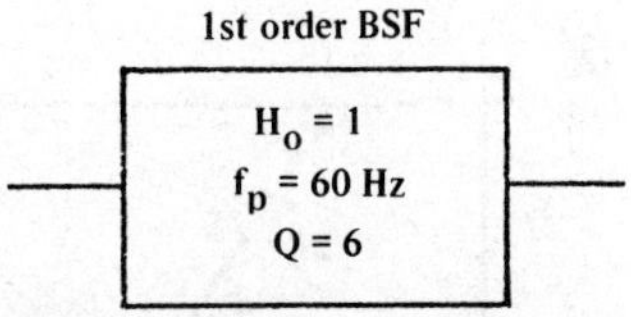

Fig. 2.8.2 Band-stop filter realization of Example 2.8.1.

EXAMPLE 2.8.1 60 Hz band-stop filters are often required in medical electronics systems where the signal levels are very low and 60 Hz pickup tends to obscure physiological data. To minimize the data lost in the vicinity of the notch frequency, we wish to design a high-Q filter. The 20 dB bandwidth should equal 1 Hz to allow for temperature drift in the center frequency of the filter. Low-frequency and high-frequency gains should equal unity.

Solution The center frequency of the notch filter must equal 60 Hz. Since the normalized 20 dB bandwidth of the stopband must equal 1 Hz, then

$$B_{20\,dB}/f_n = 1\text{ Hz}/60\text{ Hz} = \gamma/4.975 \tag{2.8.10}$$

from Eq. 2.8.7. Solving for the damping factor of the notch, $\gamma = 4.975/60 = 0.083$. From Eq. 2.8.6, this is equivalent to a $Q = 1/2(0.083) = 6$. The 3 dB bandwidth $B_{3dB} = \omega_n/Q = 9.95B_{20dB} = 10$ Hz from Eq. 2.8.6 so little data is lost in the vicinity of the notch frequency. The block diagram realization for the filter is shown in Fig. 2.8.2. If we had been more stringent and required a 40 dB bandwidth of 1 Hz, then since $B_{40dB} = 10B_{20dB}$, Eq. 2.8.7 gives

$$B_{40\,dB}/f_n = 1\text{ Hz}/60\text{ Hz} = \gamma/0.4975 \tag{2.8.11}$$

so that $\gamma = 0.0083$ or $Q = 60$.

EXAMPLE 2.8.2 Most avionic (airborne) electronic systems are designed to operate off 400 Hz power sources. This frequency (and its harmonics) can be particularly troublesome in terms of interference for electronic equipment. Notch filters are sometimes used to reduce this form of interference. Determine the parameters of a first-order notch filter which will reduce a 400 Hz signal of 1 volt to less than 1 mV assuming that the power sources can drift ± 10% in frequency.

Solution The required attenuation of the notch filter equals

$$|H(jf)| \leqslant -60\text{ dB} \qquad \text{for} \qquad 0.90(400) \leqslant f \leqslant 1.1(400) \tag{2.8.12}$$

The required notch frequency equals

$$f_o = 400\sqrt{0.9(1.1)} = 0.995(400\text{ Hz}) = 398\text{ Hz} \tag{2.8.13}$$

The 60 dB bandwidth equals 400(1.1 – 0.9) = 0.2(400) = 80 Hz. Rather than using the bandwidth equations, let us find the solution graphically. The notch filter gain function can be expressed as

$$H(s) = \frac{s^2 + \omega_o^2}{s^2 + 2\gamma\omega_o s + \omega_o^2} = \left[\frac{\omega_o^2}{s^2 + 2\gamma\omega_o s + \omega_o^2}\right]\left[\frac{s^2 + \omega_o^2}{\omega_o^2}\right] \tag{2.8.14}$$

which is the product of a low-pass and a type of high-pass transfer function. The low-pass filter characteristic is given in Fig. 2.4.1. The high-pass filter has an inverse characteristic where $\zeta = 0$ and provides a rejection of

$$|H_{HP}(j0.905)| = 1 - 0.905^2 = 0.182 \cong -15\text{ dB} \tag{2.8.15}$$

at a frequency of 360 or 440 Hz, or at a normalized frequency $\omega_n = \omega/\omega_o = 0.905$ or 1.106. Therefore, the low-pass filter must provide an additional 45 dB of rejection at the same frequency so

$$|H_{LP}(j0.905)| = -45\text{ dB} = 10^{-3}/0.182 = 5.49 \times 10^{-3} \tag{2.8.16}$$

to obtain a total rejection of 60 dB. From Fig. 2.4.1, it is clear that the poles of the low-pass filter are real with $\zeta \gg 1$ rather than complex. Using Eq. 2.8.16 and the dominant pole approximation to be discussed in the next section, the normalized low-pass poles must be located at $s_{p1} = -5.49 \times 10^{-3}$ and $s_{p2} = 1/s_{p1} = -182$. This can be simply verified by constructing a sample $H_{LP}(j\omega/\omega_n)$ having $\zeta \gg 1$

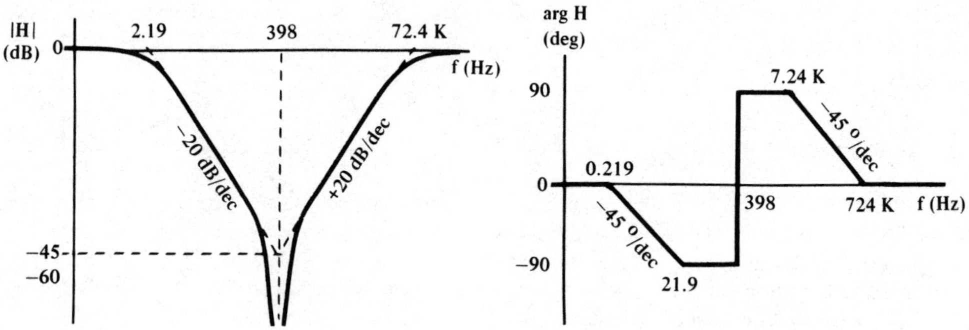

Fig. 2.8.3 Magnitude and phase characteristics for band-stop filter of Example 2.8.2.

where $\omega_n = 1$. Thus, the required damping factor of the notch filter equals

$$\gamma = -(s_{p1} + s_{p2})/2\sqrt{s_{p1}s_{p2}} = 182/2(1.0) = 91 \gg 1 \tag{2.8.17}$$

The transfer function of the notch equals

$$H(s) = \frac{s_n^{\ 2} + 1}{s_n^{\ 2} + 182s_n + 1} \tag{2.8.18}$$

where $s_n = s/2\pi(398\text{ Hz})$. The filter characteristic is drawn in Fig. 2.8.3. Although the curves of Fig. 2.4.1 were used to gain insight into the problem, the construction is perhaps more easily seen by re-expressing the notch filter gain of Eq. 2.8.14 as

$$H(s) = \left[\frac{2\gamma\omega_o s}{s^2 + 2\gamma\omega_o s + \omega_o^{\ 2}}\right]\left[\frac{s^2 + \omega_o^{\ 2}}{2\gamma\omega_o s}\right] \tag{2.8.19}$$

which is the product of a band-pass gain function and an inverse band-pass gain function. These were plotted in Fig. 2.7.1. Properly manipulating them yields the results shown in Fig. 2.8.3. Although this filter characteristic is mathematically suitable for such power line filtering applications, it would not be used in general applications due to the wide 3 dB bandwidth. Notch filters having much higher selectivity (i.e., smaller shaping factors) are required. Many possibilities will be discussed in Chaps. 4–6 and 11.

2.9 DOMINANT POLE-ZERO ANALYSIS

In this chapter, we have been considering the frequency response of various gain functions. When approximate behavior is adequate, dominant pole-zero analysis can be used to advantage to simplify the analysis and gain insight into the key parameters which determine frequency response. Dominant pole/zero simplifications allow rapid prediction of filter performance to be made, usually with minimum investment of time. This is an especially convenient technique for approximating time domain behavior. Although the great value of dominant pole-zero analysis may not be completely evident until Chaps. 3 and 6, the analysis requires bandwidth and phase calculations which we have been investigating in this chapter. Thus, we wish now to introduce this topic along with a variety of often encountered functions which we shall be considering in Chap. 3.

Dominant pole-zero analysis can be used for analysis of all types of low-pass, high-pass, band-pass, band-stop, and all-pass filters. However, it is usually applied to low-pass filters which gives the simplest results. We shall here consider low-pass and high-pass filters and reserve discussion of the other types for Chap. 6.

A dominant pole-zero analysis considers only first-order effects due to the so-called dominant poles and zeros of the response function. Nondominant poles and zeros give rise to second-order magnitude effects and are neglected. However, the second-order phase effects are included in analysis by using a so-called excess phase factor. Low-pass gain functions which exhibit *no magnitude peaking* are approximated using a single pole. Thus, the approximate gain equals

$$H(s) = \frac{e^{-\tau_0 s}}{1 + s/B} \tag{2.9.1}$$

The *dominant pole* is set equal to the 3 dB frequency B. Then the phase is calculated at the 3 dB frequency. Any phase in excess of that contributed by the dominant pole (–45°) is accounted for by an *excess phase factor* $e^{-j\omega\tau_0}$. τ_0 is called the *delay* of the filter whose significance we shall discuss in the next chapter. We shall now consider two examples which illustrate the calculation of these factors.

EXAMPLE 2.9.1 A lead-lag filter has a gain given by Eq. 2.3.31. Determine the dominant pole approximation for H assuming z > p. Draw and compare the Bode magnitude and phase curves for H and its approximation. Find the dominant pole gain expression when p = 1 and z = 4.

Solution The dominant pole expression is given by Eq. 2.9.1. We first determine the 3 dB bandwidth of the filter by solving

$$|H(jB)|^2 = \left|\frac{1 + jB/z}{1 + jB/p}\right|^2 = \frac{1 + (B/z)^2}{1 + (B/p)^2} = ½ \tag{2.9.2}$$

for B. Cross-multiplying the equation and solving for B/p gives the normalized bandwidth as

$$B/p = [1 - 2(p/z)^2]^{-½} \cong 1 + (p/z)^2, \qquad |p/z| \ll 1 \tag{2.9.3}$$

where the radical is eliminated by use of the binomial theorem which is[12]

$$(1 + x)^n = 1 + nx + n(n-1)x^2/2! + \ldots \cong 1 + nx, \qquad |x| < 1 \tag{2.9.4}$$

This result is accurate to about 1% for $z/p \geq 4$. Now the delay τ_0 is chosen so that the excess phase $-B\tau_0$ equals the excess phase over and above the –45° contributed by the dominant pole at s = jB. Since the phase of the filter equals

$$\arg H(jB) = \tan^{-1}(B/z) - \tan^{-1}(B/p) = -\tan^{-1}\frac{B(z-p)}{zp + B^2} = -\tau_0 B - \pi/4 \tag{2.9.5}$$

at the 3 dB frequency B, solving for the delay gives

$$\tau_0 = -[\pi/4 + \tan^{-1}(B/z) - \tan^{-1}(B/p)]/B \tag{2.9.6}$$

Since we can express a tangent function as

$$\tan(\pi/4 + \theta) \cong 1 + 2\tan\theta, \qquad |\theta| \ll 1 \tag{2.9.7}$$

then the inverse tangent function equals

$$\tan^{-1}(1 + 2\tan\theta) \cong \pi/4 + \theta, \qquad |\theta| \ll 1 \tag{2.9.8}$$

Therefore, we can re-express the last term of Eq. 2.9.6 as

$$\tan^{-1}(B/p) = \tan^{-1}[1 + (p/z)^2] \cong \pi/4 + \tan^{-1}[½(p/z)^2] \cong \pi/4 + ½(p/z)^2 \tag{2.9.9}$$

We expand the second term of Eq. 2.9.6 using the Maclaurin series for the $\tan^{-1}x$ function which is[13]

$$\tan^{-1}x = x - x^3/3 + x^5/5 - \ldots \cong x, \qquad |x| < 1 \tag{2.9.10}$$

Thus, the delay given by Eq. 2.9.6 reduces to

$$\tau_0 = -[\pi/4 + B/z - \pi/4 - ½(p/z)^2]/B \cong -[1 - ½(p/z)]/z \tag{2.9.11}$$

which is accurate to within 20% for $p/z \geq 4$. The actual response of the lead-lag filter and its dominant pole approximation is shown in Fig. 2.9.1.

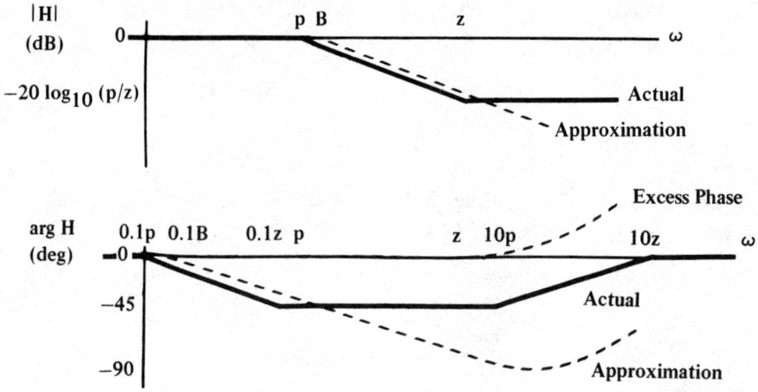

Fig. 2.9.1 Magnitude and phase characteristics for lead-lag filter of Example 2.9.1.

In the case where p = 1 and z = 4, the normalized bandwidth of the lead-lag filter equals $B/p = 1 + (1/4)^2 = 1.063$ from Eq. 2.9.3 and the delay $\tau_0 = -[1 - (1/4)(1/2)]/4 = -0.875/4 = -0.22$ from Eq. 2.9.11. Thus, the dominant pole approximation becomes

$$H(s) = \frac{1 + s/4}{1 + s} \cong \frac{e^{0.22s}}{1 + s/1.063}, \qquad |s| \ll 4 \tag{2.9.12}$$

EXAMPLE 2.9.2 Calculate the approximate frequency response for an *n*th-order synchronously-tuned filter having a gain given by Eq. 2.3.25 using a single dominant pole. Compare the approximate and exact filter responses. Determine the dominant pole approximation for n = 10 and unity bandwidth.

Solution We approximate H(s) using a single dominant pole as

$$H(s) = \frac{p_o^n}{(s + p_o)^n} \cong \frac{e^{-s\tau_0}}{1 + s/p_1}, \qquad |s| \ll p_o \tag{2.9.13}$$

The dominant pole p_1 must equal the 3 dB frequency of $H(j\omega)$. Thus, from Eqs. 2.3.27 and 2.3.29

$$p_1 = p_o\sqrt{2^{1/n} - 1} = 0.83 p_o/\sqrt{n} \tag{2.9.14}$$

The excess phase $\omega\tau_0$ at 3 dB frequency, p_1 equals the difference between the phase of $H(jp_1)$ and that of the dominant pole approximation (−45°). Therefore, the excess phase equals

$$-p_1\tau_0 = -n \arg(1 + jp_1/p_o) + \pi/4 = -n \tan^{-1}(p_1/p_o) + \pi/4 \tag{2.9.15}$$

Solving for the delay τ_0 gives

$$\tau_0 = \frac{n}{p_1}\tan^{-1}\frac{p_1}{p_o} - \frac{\pi}{4}\frac{1}{p_1} \tag{2.9.16}$$

If $n \gg 1$ so $p_1 \ll p_o$, then the $\tan^{-1}x$ term can be approximated using the series of Eq. 2.9.10 so that the delay equals

$$\tau_0 = \frac{n}{p_1}\frac{p_1}{p_o} - \frac{\pi}{4}\frac{1}{p_1} = \frac{1}{p_o}\left(n - \frac{\pi}{4}\frac{p_o}{p_1}\right) \cong \frac{n}{p_o}\left(1 - \frac{1}{1.06\sqrt{n}}\right), \qquad n \gg 1 \tag{2.9.17}$$

Therefore, the dominant pole approximation for the gain H(s) equals

$$H(s) = (1 + s/p_o)^{-n} \cong \left(1 + s\Big/\frac{0.83}{\sqrt{n}}p_o\right)^{-1}\exp\left[-s\frac{n}{p_o}\left(1 - \frac{1}{1.06\sqrt{n}}\right)\right], \qquad |s| \ll p_o \tag{2.9.18}$$

The two gain functions are compared in Fig. 2.9.1 Their 3 dB frequencies are equal but their asymptotic rolloffs differ by factor n. At frequency p_1, their phases differ by the excess phase $p_1\tau_0$. Although the gain using the dominant pole fails to approximate the high-frequency behavior of magnitude

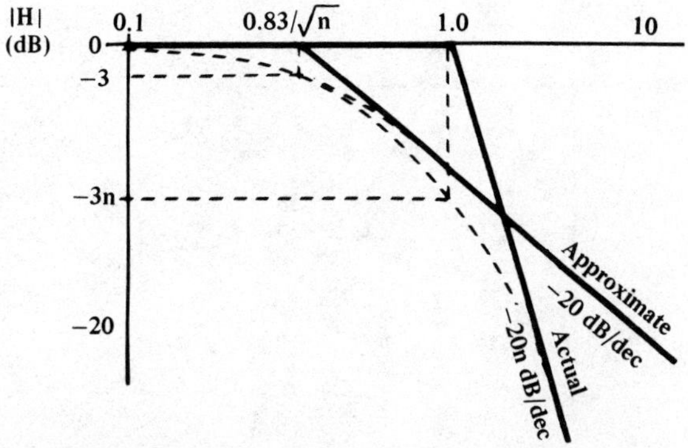

Fig. 2.9.2 Magnitude characteristics for nth-order synchronously-tuned low-pass filter of Example 2.9.2.

and phase, it is nevertheless a very useful approximation for low-frequency behavior. We shall see that the approximate time domain response can be easily written from the dominant pole expression.

In the case where $n = 10$ and the bandwidth $p_1 = 1$, the delay equals

$$\tau_o \cong (0.83\sqrt{n} - \pi/4)/p_1 = 0.83\sqrt{10} - 0.78 = 1.84 \tag{2.9.19}$$

combining Eqs. 2.9.14 and 2.9.16. Thus, the dominant pole expression becomes

$$H(s) = \frac{1}{(1 + s/p_o)^n} \cong \frac{e^{-1.84s}}{1 + s} \tag{2.9.20}$$

where $p_o \cong 1.2\sqrt{10} = 3.8$.

As long as there is negligible peaking in the magnitude characteristic of a gain function, a first-order dominant pole-zero gain approximation is used. However, when there is *peaking in the magnitude characteristic*, then second-order dominant pole-zero approximations become necessary as given by Eq. 2.9.24. They are also useful when the gain expressions themselves are more complicated than second-order. In these approximations, the damping factor is first chosen to produce the same magnitude peaking; the resonant frequency is next chosen to produce the proper bandwidth; and finally, the excess phase factor is calculated to maintain phase at the 3 dB frequency. We now consider these approximations in greater detail.

An often encountered gain is the third-order function

$$H(s) = \frac{p\omega_n^2}{(s + p)(s^2 + 2\zeta\omega_n s + \omega_n^2)} \tag{2.9.21}$$

The ac steady-state gain magnitude and phase equal

$$|H(j\omega)| = \frac{p\omega_n^2}{[p^2 + \omega^2]^{1/2}[(\omega_n^2 - \omega^2)^2 + (2\zeta\omega\omega_n)^2]^{1/2}}$$
$$\arg H(j\omega) = -\tan^{-1}\frac{\omega}{p} - \tan^{-1}\frac{2\zeta\omega\omega_n}{\omega_n^2 - \omega^2} \tag{2.9.22}$$

The Bode characteristics are shown in Fig. 2.9.3. When $p \gg \omega_n$, p is often said to be a parasitic pole. Then the complex pole pair dominate and Eq. 2.9.22 reduces to

$$|H(j\omega)| \cong \frac{\omega_n^2}{[(\omega_n^2 - \omega^2)^2 + (2\zeta\omega\omega_n)^2]^{1/2}}, \qquad |\omega/p| \ll 1 \tag{2.9.23a}$$

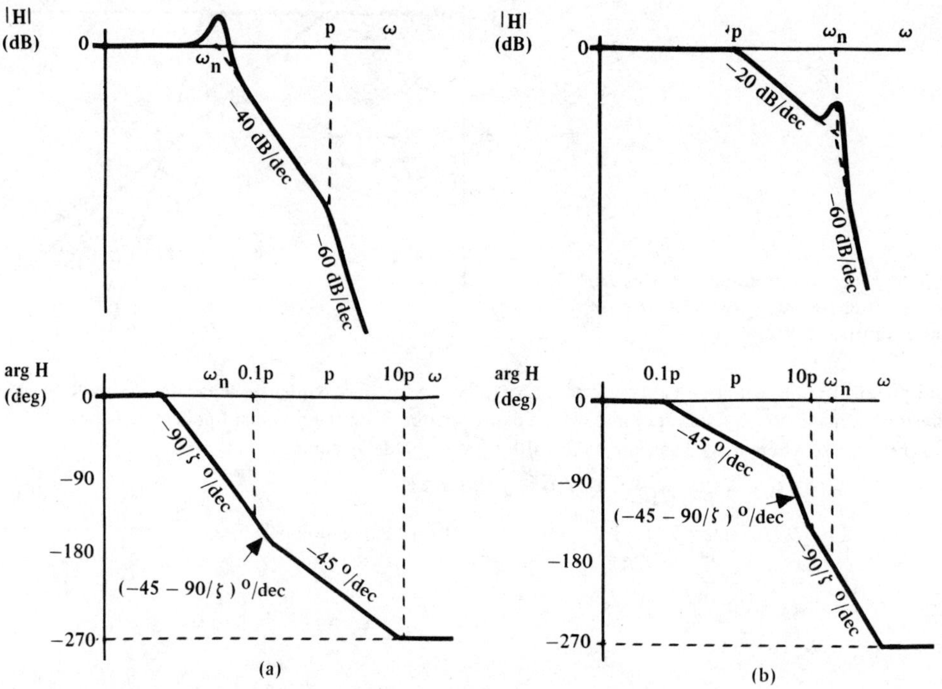

Fig. 2.9.3 Magnitude and phase characteristics for third-order gain function of Eq. 2.9.21.

$$\arg H(j\omega) \cong -\tan^{-1} \frac{2\zeta\omega\omega_n}{\omega_n^2 - \omega^2} - \frac{\omega}{p}, \qquad |\omega/p| \ll 1 \tag{2.9.23b}$$

Thus, the dominant pole approximation is

$$H(s) \cong \frac{\omega_n^2 e^{-s/p}}{s^2 + 2\zeta\omega_n s + \omega_n^2}, \qquad |s| \ll p \tag{2.9.24}$$

The second-order dominant pole approximation must be used to obtain the peaking and increased phase slope characteristics. The complex poles are dominant for $p \geqslant 10\alpha = 10\zeta\omega_n$.[14] However, when $p \ll \omega_n$, the real pole dominates the response and the complex poles are nondominant if ζ is not too small. In this case, Eq. 2.9.22 reduces to

$$|H(j\omega)| \cong \frac{p}{[p^2 + \omega^2]^{1/2}}$$

$$\arg H(j\omega) \cong -\frac{2\zeta\omega\omega_n}{\omega_n^2 - \omega^2} - \tan^{-1}\frac{\omega}{p} \cong -\frac{2\zeta\omega}{\omega_n} - \tan^{-1}\frac{\omega}{p} \qquad |\omega| \ll \omega_n \tag{2.9.25}$$

Then the dominant pole approximation is

$$H(s) \cong \frac{pe^{-2\zeta s/\omega_n}}{s + p}, \qquad |s| \ll \omega_n \tag{2.9.26}$$

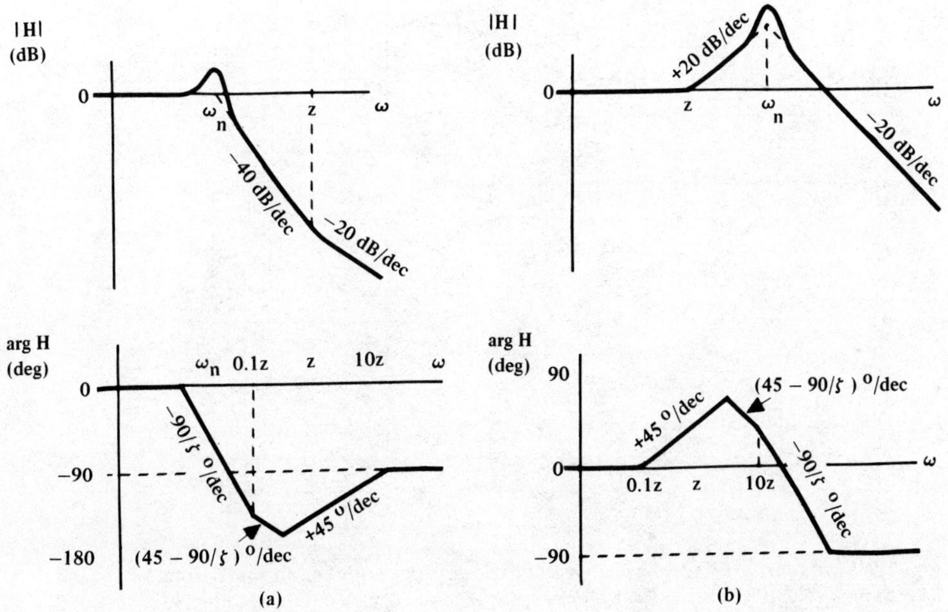

Fig. 2.9.4 Magnitude and phase characteristics for second-order gain function of Eq. 2.9.27.

Another common gain function is

$$H(s) = \frac{\omega_n^2}{z}\,\frac{s+z}{s^2 + 2\zeta\omega_n s + \omega_n^2} \tag{2.9.27}$$

which differs from the previous gain function (Eq. 2.9.22) in that H(s) has a real zero rather than real pole. This gain function is often encountered in control systems and phase-locked loop designs.[15] When used in electronic designs, it describes the gain of a so-called *shunt-peaked* stage.[16] The magnitude and phase of the gain equal

$$\begin{aligned} |H(j\omega)| &= \frac{\omega_n^2}{z}\,\frac{[z^2+\omega^2]^{1/2}}{[(\omega_n^2-\omega^2)^2 + (2\zeta\omega\omega_n)^2]^{1/2}} \\ \arg H(j\omega) &= -\tan^{-1}\frac{2\zeta\omega\omega_n}{\omega_n^2-\omega^2} + \tan^{-1}\frac{\omega}{z} \end{aligned} \tag{2.9.28}$$

The Bode characteristic are shown in Fig. 2.9.4. In the situation where $z \gg \omega_n$, Eq. 2.9.28 reduces to

$$\begin{aligned} |H(j\omega)| &\cong \frac{\omega_n^2}{[(\omega_n-\omega)^2 + (2\zeta\omega\omega_n)^2]^{1/2}} \qquad |\omega/z| \ll 1 \\ \arg H(j\omega) &\cong -\tan^{-1}\frac{2\zeta\omega}{\omega_n^2-\omega^2} + \frac{\omega}{z} \end{aligned} \tag{2.9.29}$$

Therefore, the dominant pole approximation is

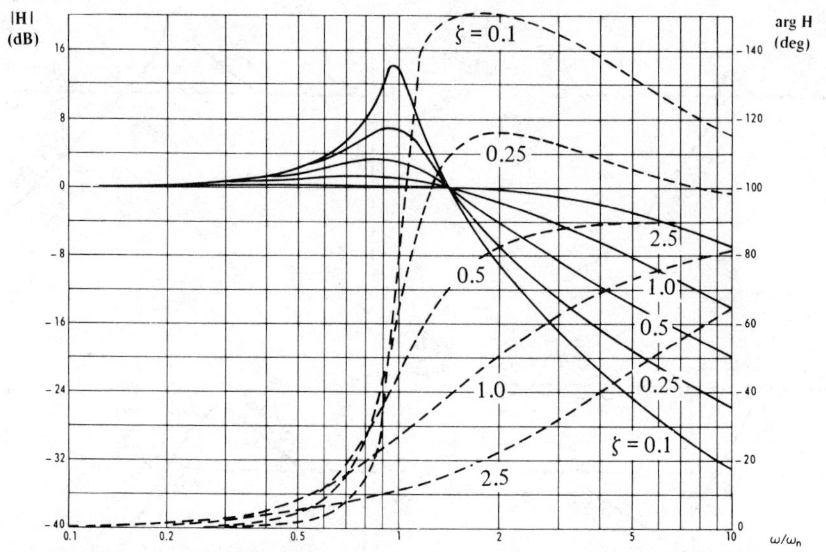

Fig. 2.9.5 Magnitude and phase-characteristics of phase-locked loop. (From J. Klapper and J. T. Frankle, "Phase-locked and Frequency Feedback Systems," p. 88, Fig. 5.5, Academic Press, NY, 1972.)

$$H(s) \cong \frac{\omega_n^2 e^{s/z}}{s^2 + 2\zeta\omega_n s + \omega_n^2}, \qquad |s| \ll z \tag{2.9.30}$$

A type 2 second-order phase-locked loop (PLL) was considered in Examples 1.16.3 and 1.16.4. Its gain H(s) is given by Eq. 1.16.16 which we see has the same form as Eq. 2.9.27. The gain characteristic of the PLL is shown in Fig. 2.9.5 for various ζ. The root locus of the gain function was described in Example 1.16.4 which the engineer should now review. For small ζ, the zero $z \gg \omega_n$ which corresponds to the situation shown in Fig. 2.9.4a. As $\zeta \to \infty$, the poles become real and the one closest the origin cancels the zero. The other pole is located at $s \cong -2\zeta$ and H(s) behaves as a single-pole system. Thus, at low-frequencies, the responses in Fig. 2.9.5 lie between those of the second-order low-pass filter in Fig. 2.4.1 ($\zeta \cong 0$) and the first-order low-pass filter in Fig. 2.3.2 ($\zeta \gg 1$). It is useful to note that the normalized 3 dB bandwidth equals

$$B/\omega_n = \sqrt{1 + 2\zeta^2 + \sqrt{2 + 4\zeta^2 + 4\zeta^4}} \tag{2.9.31}$$

which is plotted in Fig. 2.9.6. We see that bandwidth is a monotonically increasing function of ζ and varies as 2ζ for large ζ. With no finite zero, the bandwidth would be described by Fig. 2.4.4.

EXAMPLE 2.9.3 The phase-locked loop of Example 1.16.4 is designed to meet the following damping factor, bandwidth, and phase error requirements: $\zeta = 0.50$, $B = 2\pi(1000\text{ Hz})$ and $\theta(jB) = -81°$ (corresponds to the ζ value). Determine the second-order dominant pole approximation for the PLL.

Solution The second-order approximation will be obtained when the peaking, 3 dB bandwidth, and 3 dB phase of the gain approximation match those of the PLL. Expressing the approximation as

$$H_a(s) = \frac{e^{-s\tau_o}}{(s/\omega_n')^2 + 2\zeta'(s/\omega_n') + 1} \tag{2.9.32}$$

then ω_n', ζ', and τ_o must be determined.

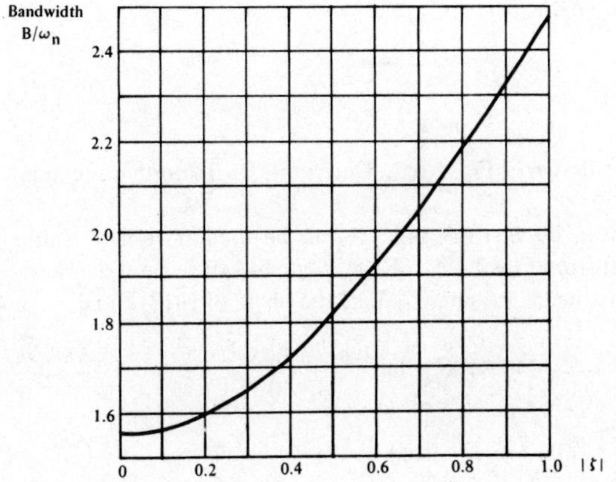

$\lvert\zeta\rvert$	B/ω_n
0.00	1.554
0.05	1.557
0.10	1.565
0.15	1.578
0.20	1.597
0.25	1.622
0.30	1.651
0.35	1.686
0.40	1.725
0.45	1.769
0.50	1.817
0.55	1.870
0.60	1.926
0.65	1.986
0.70	2.049
0.75	2.115
0.80	2.184
0.85	2.255
0.90	2.329
0.95	2.405
1.00	2.482

Fig. 2.9.6 Normalized bandwidth of phase-locked loop.

ζ' is chosen so that $|H_a|$ exhibits the same peaking as the PLL. The PLL has $M_{p\omega} \cong 3.4$ dB since $\zeta = 0.50$ from Fig. 2.9.5. Then from Fig. 2.4.2, the dominant pole approximation must have $\zeta' = 0.35$. Having determined the damping factor, we now find $\omega_n{}'$.

The critical frequency $\omega_n{}'$ is found from ζ' and the PLL bandwidth B. We know from Fig. 2.4.4 that $B/\omega_n{}' = 1.42$ since $\zeta' = 0.35$. Therefore, $\omega_n{}' = B/1.42 = 2\pi(1000\text{ Hz})/1.42 = 2\pi(704\text{ Hz})$.

Finally, the delay τ_0 must be determined for the excess phase factor which accounts for the phase error between H and H_a at the 3 dB frequency B. Thus,

$$-B\tau_0 = \frac{\pi}{180}\left\{-81 + \tan^{-1}\left(\frac{2\zeta'(B/\omega_n{}')}{1-(B/\omega_n{}')^2}\right)\right\} = \frac{\pi}{180}\left\{-81 + \tan^{-1}\left(\frac{2(0.35)(1.42)}{1-1.42^2}\right)\right\}$$

$$= [-81 + \tan^{-1}(-1)]\,\pi/180 = [180 - (81+45)]\,\pi/180 = 55\pi/180 = 0.96\text{ rad} \qquad (2.9.33)$$

Therefore, the delay $\tau_0 = -0.96/2\pi(1000) = -0.15$ msec so negative delay must be added in H_a to maintain the PLL phase requirement.

The dominant pole-zero approximation for a high-pass filter is analogous to that of a low-pass filter so we shall discuss it only briefly. When the high-pass filter magnitude characteristic exhibits no peaking, a first-order approximation is used. When peaking is present, a second-order approximation is used. The two dominant pole approximations equal

$$H_1(s) = \frac{se^{-\tau_0/s}}{1+s}, \qquad H_2(s) = \frac{s^2e^{-\tau_0/s}}{1+2\zeta s+s^2} \qquad (2.9.34)$$

In low-pass filters, we used the dominant pole-zero approximation to represent their low-frequency behavior. However, in high-pass filters, we approximate the high-frequency behavior. The high-pass filter dominant pole-zero approximation follows directly from Eqs. 2.9.1 and 2.9.24 using the low-pass to high-pass transformation of Eq. 2.6.1. It is important to recognize that the excess phase term is $c^{-\tau_o/s}$ for the high-pass filter. In the low-pass filter, the excess phase term equalled $e^{-\tau_0 s}$. These terms produce quite different effects in the time domain as we shall discuss in Chap. 6.

EXAMPLE 2.9.4 A second-order high-pass filter has a gain of

$$H(s) = 10\frac{s^2}{s^2 + 2(0.6)s + 1} \cong \frac{10}{B}\frac{se^{-\tau_0/s}}{1 + s/B} \tag{2.9.35}$$

whose magnitude and phase characteristics were drawn in Fig. 2.6.2. Determine its first-order dominant pole-zero approximation.

Solution The first-order approximation is given by Eq. 2.9.34a. It can be used since $|H|$ exhibits negligible peaking. The bandwidth is determined from Fig. 2.4.4 as $B/\omega_n = 1/1.148$ since $\zeta = 0.6$. Therefore, $B = 0.871$ when $\omega_n = 1$. We now determine the excess phase. Since the phase of $H(jB)$ equals

$$\arg H(jB) = 180 - \arg \frac{1}{1 - 0.871^2 + j1.2(0.871)} = 180 - \tan^{-1} \frac{1.045}{1 - 0.76}$$

$$= 180 - \tan^{-1}(1.045/0.24) = 180 - 77.1 = 102.9^{\circ} \tag{2.9.36}$$

at the 3 dB corner frequency, then the excess phase term equals

$$-\tau_0/B = [102.9 - (90 - 45)]\,\pi/180 = 57.9\pi/180 = 1.01 \text{ rad} \tag{2.9.37}$$

The delay $\tau_0 = -1.01B = -0.88$. Therefore, the dominant pole approximation equals

$$H(s) = \frac{10se^{0.88/s}}{s + 0.871} \tag{2.9.38}$$

2.10 DELAY ANALYSIS

We have been considering gain functions having the general form

$$H(j\omega) = \prod_{i=1}^{n} H_i(j\omega), \qquad \theta(j\omega) = \arg H(j\omega) = \sum_{i=1}^{n} \arg H_i(j\omega) \tag{2.10.1}$$

where the H_i can be considered as the "elementary" gain functions described by the first- and second-order normalized curves of Figs. 2.3.2 and 2.4.1.

Now, assume a narrowband signal of approximate frequency ω is inputted to a filter having gain H. This narrowband signal will propagate through the filter with some delay. The *envelope* enclosing the narrowband output signal will be delayed by $\tau(j\omega)$ seconds where τ is the group delay (or equivalently, envelope delay) of the gain H. The *group delay* (in seconds) is related to the *phase* (in radians) of H as

$$\tau(j\omega) = -d\theta(j\omega)/d\omega, \qquad \theta(j\omega) = -\int_{-\infty}^{\omega} \tau(j\Omega)\, d\Omega \tag{2.10.2}$$

Therefore, group delay is the negative derivative of phase, and phase is the negative integral of group delay. Group delay is a function of frequency. In many applications such as communication and radar systems, group delay characteristics are as important as magnitude and/or phase characteristics. Group delay will be fully investigated and interpreted in Chaps. 3–5 and 12. We here want to lay the foundations for the general group delay analysis of filters. We will usually refer to group delay simply as delay for brevity.

To begin, note that the group delay of H in Eq. 2.10.1 can be expressed as[18]

$$\tau(j\omega) = -d \arg H(j\omega)/d\omega = -\sum_{i=1}^{n} d \arg H_i(j\omega)/d\omega = \sum_{i=1}^{n} \tau_i(j\omega) \tag{2.10.3}$$

τ is always an even function since arg H is always an odd function. τ_i is the group delay arising from the H_i term in the gain expression. We see that group delay is *additive*. General delay analysis is facilitated by choosing, when possible, a product expansion of elementary gain func-

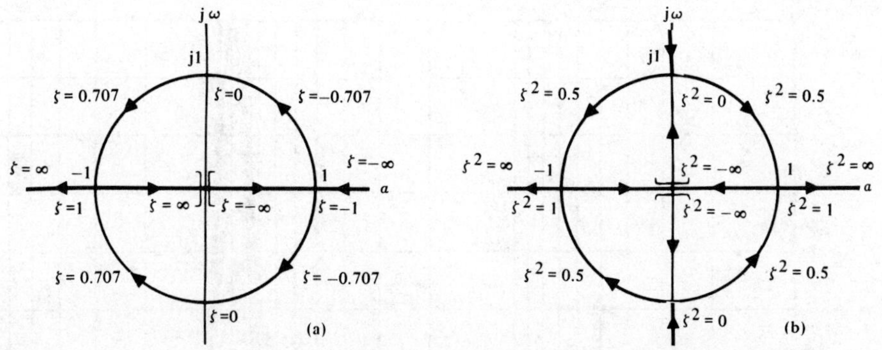

Fig. 2.10.1 Root locus for denominator of (a) gain H(s) and (b) delay $\tau(s)$.

tions H_i having readily described delay characteristics. Let us first determine the delay of the second-order low-pass gain function

$$H(s) = \frac{1}{s^2 + 2\zeta s + 1} \tag{2.10.4}$$

Using Eq. 2.10.3, the delay is equal to

$$\tau(j\omega) = -\frac{d}{d\omega}\tan^{-1}\frac{2\zeta\omega}{1-\omega^2} = 2\zeta\frac{1+\omega^2}{1+(2\zeta^2-1)2\omega^2+\omega^4} \tag{2.10.5}$$

Since

$$\tau(j0) = 2\zeta \tag{2.10.6}$$

delay has a value of 2ζ at dc (or $2\zeta/\omega_n$ when the break frequency equals ω_n) and a value of zero at $\omega = \infty$. However, the form of $\tau(j\omega)$ from $\omega = 0$ to ∞ is by no means obvious. To gain insight into the form of τ, let us first find the Laplace transform $\tau(s)$, and then sketch its Bode magnitude characteristic to give the delay $\tau(j\omega)$. Since τ is an even function, it is always real. Thus, its sign is either positive (indicating envelope retardation) or negative (indicating envelope advancement). We shall discuss the significance of these terms in Chap. 3.

The Laplace transform of delay $\tau(s)$ is obtained by setting $\omega = s/j$ (called analytic continuation[19]) in Eq. 2.10.5. This gives

$$\tau(s) = -2\zeta\frac{s^2-1}{s^4-(2\zeta^2-1)2s^2+1} \tag{2.10.7}$$

The zeros of $\tau(s)$ are real and equal ± 1. The poles of $\tau(s)$ are a function of the damping factor squared ζ^2 (or equivalently, $|\zeta|$), and are easily located by considering the root locus of the denominator of $\tau(s)$. The denominator can be expressed in the root locus form as

$$1 + k\frac{s^2}{s^4+1} = 0 \tag{2.10.8}$$

where $k = -2(2\zeta^2 - 1)$. Since $\zeta^2 \geqslant 0$ for real physical systems, then k lies in the range $(-\infty, 2]$. The root locus of both H and τ is shown in Fig. 2.10.1.

The poles of $\tau(s)$ originate at the origin and infinity, travel along the $j\omega$-axis, break onto and travel around a circle of unity radius, and break onto the σ-axis where they travel to the origin and infinity. Since $\zeta^2 \geqslant 0$, the $j\omega$-axis of the root locus is shown only for mathematical complete-

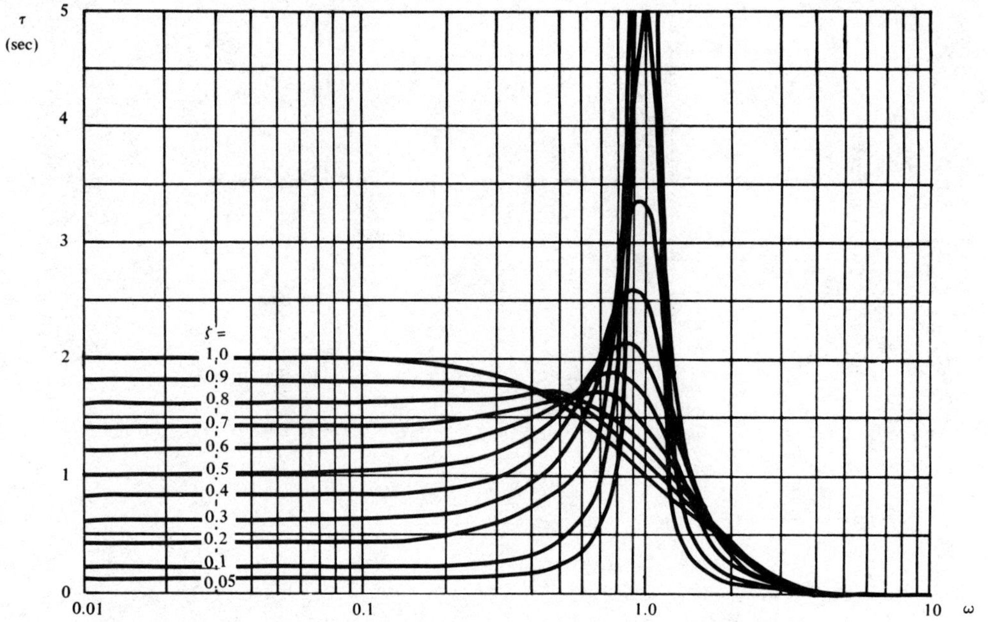

Fig. 2.10.2 Delay characteristic for various damping factors.

ness. Denoting $H(s) = N(s)/D(s)$ and calculating the product $D(s)\,D(-s)$ gives

$$D(s)D(-s) = (s^2 + 1 + 2\zeta s)(s^2 + 1 - 2\zeta s) = (s^2 + 1)^2 - 4\zeta^2 s^2$$
$$= s^4 - (2\zeta^2 - 1)2s^2 + 1 = \text{Den}\ [\tau(s)] \qquad (2.10.9)$$

Thus, the two poles of the gain function and the two left-half-plane poles of the delay function have the same location. The two right-half-plane poles of τ are right-half-plane images of its left-half-plane poles. Therefore, only the two zeros at $s = \pm 1$ and the right-half-plane image poles need be added to the pole distribution of H to obtain the pole-zero distribution of τ. The plot of delay versus frequency is shown in Fig. 2.10.2.

Normalizing the delay to a unity dc value as

$$\tau_n(j\omega) = \frac{\tau(j\omega)}{2\zeta} = \frac{1 + \omega^2}{1 + (2\zeta^2 - 1)2\omega^2 + \omega^4} \qquad (2.10.10)$$

forms a convenient reference function. It is drawn in Fig. 2.10.3 for various $|\zeta|$ in the range (0, 1). For $|\zeta| > 1$, Bode magnitude approximations are used which will soon be discussed. The frequency at which peaking occurs in τ_n is found by setting $d\tau_n/d\omega = 0$ to yield

$$(3 - 4\zeta^2) - 2\omega_p^2 - \omega_p^4 = 0 \qquad (2.10.11)$$

Solving Eq. 2.10.11 for the peaking frequency ω_p gives

$$\omega_p = \sqrt{2\sqrt{1 - \zeta^2} - 1}, \qquad |\zeta| < 0.866 \qquad (2.10.12)$$

For $|\zeta| \geqslant 0.866$, the delay is monotonically nonincreasing. A maximally-flat delay characteristic is obtained for $|\zeta| = 0.866$.

The maximum delay equals

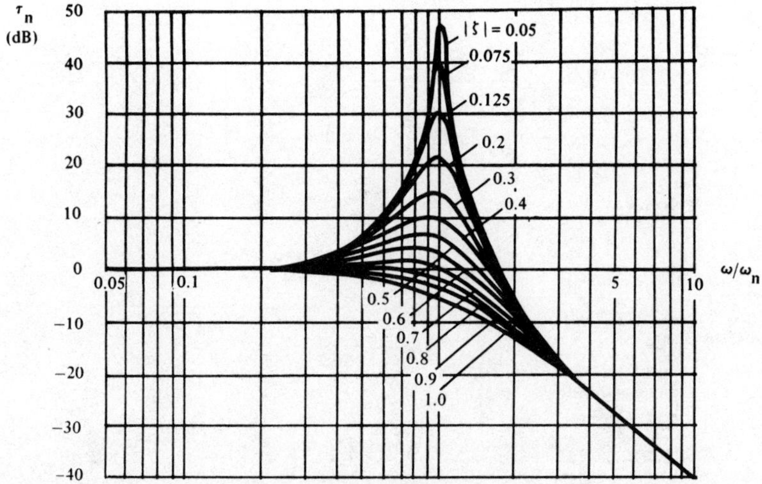

Fig. 2.10.3 Normalized delay characteristic for various damping factors.

$$\tau_p = \tau(j\omega_p) = \frac{\zeta}{2} \frac{1}{(1-\zeta^2)^{1/2}\,[1-(1-\zeta^2)^{1/2}]} = \frac{1}{2\zeta}[1 + (1-\zeta^2)^{-1/2}], \qquad |\zeta| < 0.866 \tag{2.10.13}$$

Normalizing the maximum delay against its dc value gives

$$\tau_{np} = \tau_p/2\zeta = \frac{1}{4\zeta^2}\,[1 + (1-\zeta^2)^{-1/2}], \qquad |\zeta| < 0.866 \tag{2.10.14}$$

There is no peaking for $|\zeta| > 0.866$. The normalized delay varies as $1/2\zeta^2$ for small $|\zeta|$. A detailed peaking plot is given in Fig. 2.10.4. A design requirement giving the maximum allowable peaking determines the minimum allowable $|\zeta|$.

Now let us determine the delay of the first-order low-pass gain function

$$H_1(s) = \frac{1}{s+1} \tag{2.10.15}$$

Noting that we can express

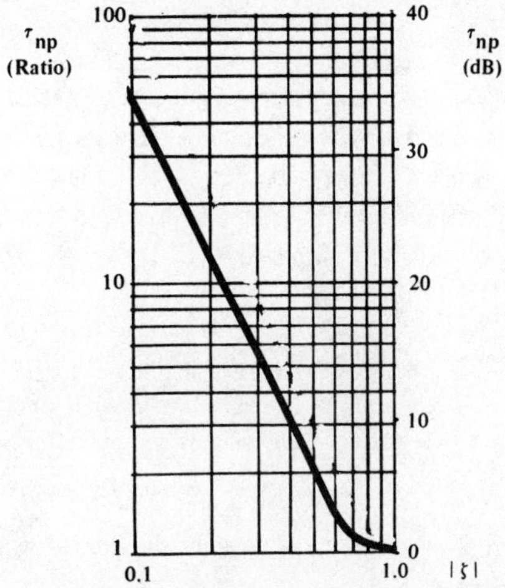

Fig. 2.10.4 Normalized delay peaking as a function of damping factor.

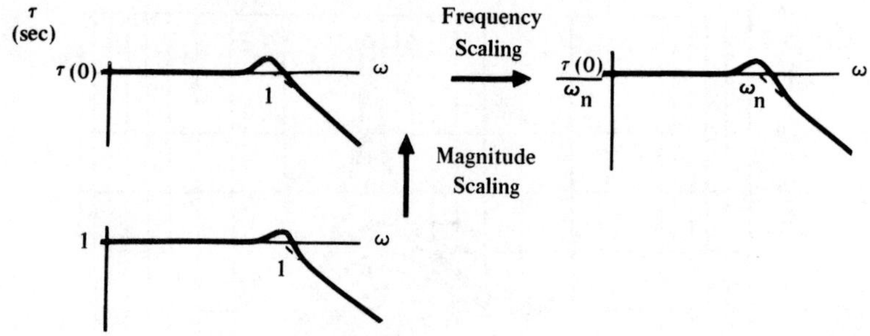

Fig. 2.10.5 Effect of magnitude and frequency scaling on delay.

$$H_1(s)^2 = \frac{1}{(s+1)^2} = \left.\frac{1}{s^2+2\zeta s+1}\right|_{\zeta=1} = H(s) \tag{2.10.16}$$

where H was given by Eq. 2.10.4 and recalling that delay is additive, then

$$\tau_1(j\omega) = ½\,\tau(j\omega) \tag{2.10.17}$$

The delay τ_1 of the first-order gain H_1 is exactly *half* that for the second-order gain H where $\zeta = 1$. Thus, the normalized delay characteristic for τ_1 is also given by Fig. 2.10.3. The dc delay value is therefore half of 2ζ for $\zeta = 1$, or 1 second (or $1/\omega_n$ second for an ω_n cutoff frequency). The asymptotic slopes are –40 dB/dec for both first- and second-order poles. The pole-zero pattern for delay consists simply of single poles located at $s = \pm 1$ (note there is pole-zero cancellation when $\zeta = 1$ from Fig. 2.10.1). Thus, only right-half-plane image poles need be added to the pole distribution of a gain H having only real poles to obtain the pole-zero distribution for its delay.

We found frequency and magnitude normalization to be useful in previous Bode plot analysis. The same is true of delay analysis. Let us denote the frequency-normalized delay as $\tau_n(j\omega/\omega_n)$ and the frequency-denormalized delay as $\tau(j\omega)$. Since τ_n can be expressed in terms of τ as

$$\tau_n(j\omega/\omega_n) = \frac{d \arg H(j\omega/\omega_n)}{d\,(\omega/\omega_n)} = \omega_n \frac{d \arg H(j\omega)}{d\omega} = \omega_n \tau(j\omega) \tag{2.10.18}$$

by a change of variables, then

$$\tau(j\omega) = \frac{1}{\omega_n}\tau_n(j\omega/\omega_n) \tag{2.10.19}$$

Thus, frequency-normalized delay is *divided* by ω_n to obtain frequency-denormalized delay. We found that a second-order filter having $\omega_n = 1$ had a dc delay of 2ζ seconds. Thus, if instead $\omega_n = 10^3$, its dc delay would equal 2ζ msec. We can also magnitude normalize $\tau(j\omega/\omega_n)$ for convenience. For example, we magnitude-normalized the second-order filter delay function by 2ζ seconds so its dc delay equalled 1 second. These normalizations are shown in Fig. 2.10.5 and should be compared with those discussed in Fig. 2.3.4. Note that scaling a filter's gain does *not* effect its delay.

EXAMPLE 2.10.1 Calculate the delay of the two cascaded first-order low-pass filters analyzed in Example 2.3.1 whose gain equalled $H(s) = 2/(1 + s/10)^2$ as given by Eq. 2.3.15.

Solution The ac steady-state filter phase equals

$$-\arg H(j\omega) = 2 \tan^{-1} (\omega/10) \tag{2.10.20}$$

Therefore, the delay of the filter equals

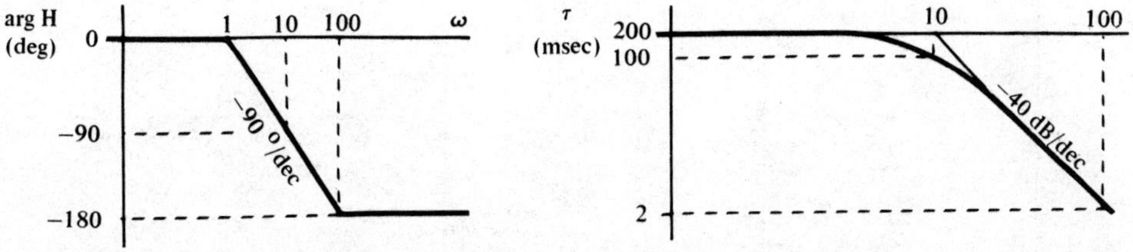

Fig. 2.10.6 Phase and delay characteristics for two cascaded first-order low-pass filters of Example 2.10.1.

$$\tau(j\omega) = -\frac{d \arg H}{d\omega} = \frac{2}{10}\,\frac{1 + (\omega/10)^2}{1 + 2(\omega/10)^2 + (\omega/10)^4} \tag{2.10.21}$$

using Eqs. 2.10.10 and 2.10.20 and summing the individual delays of each stage. The dc delay equals

$$\tau(0) = 2(0.1) = 0.2 \text{ sec} \tag{2.10.22}$$

since each stage has 0.1 second dc delay.

The delay characteristic is shown in Fig. 2.10.6. It has an asymptotic rolloff of –40 dB/dec with a corner frequency of 10 rad/sec. It is drawn using Fig. 2.10.3 for $\zeta = 1$. Fig. 2.10.3 forms the basis for all such delay plots. The low-frequency and high-frequency filter delay behavior can alternatively be established using asymptotic phase approximations. Note that

$$\begin{aligned} \arg H(j\omega) &= -2\tan^{-1}(\omega/10) \cong -\omega/5, \quad |\omega/10| \ll 1 \\ &\cong \pi/2 - 10/\omega, \quad |\omega/10| \gg 1 \end{aligned} \tag{2.10.23}$$

using the Maclaurin series for $\tan^{-1}x$ as[13]

$$\begin{aligned} \tan^{-1} x &= x - x^3/3 + x^5/5 - \ldots, \quad x^2 < 1 \\ &= \pi/2 - 1/x + 1/3x^3 - \ldots, \quad x^2 > 1 \end{aligned} \tag{2.10.24}$$

Therefore, the approximate delay equals

$$\tau(j\omega) = -d \arg H(j\omega)/d\omega \cong 1/5, \quad |\omega/10| \ll 1 \quad \text{and} \quad 10/\omega^2, \quad |\omega/10| \gg 1 \tag{2.10.25}$$

which agrees with Eq. 2.10.21 and Fig. 2.10.6. In general, however, we shall not verify our delay characteristic using such series.

EXAMPLE 2.10.2 Draw the phase and delay characteristics for the second-order low-pass filter having gain

$$H(s) = \frac{1}{(s/1000)^2 + 2(0.3)(s/1000) + 1} \tag{2.10.26}$$

Solution The low-pass filter has a corner frequency of 1000 and a damping factor of 0.3. The phase slope equals $-90/0.3 = 300$ °/dec so it requires $180/300 = 2(0.3) = 0.6$ decade to make the 180° phase transition. Since $R = 10^{0.3} = 2$, the phase transition begins at 1000/2 and ends at 2(1000). The dc delay value equals $2\zeta/\omega_n = 0.6$ msec. The delay has 15 dB of peaking from Fig. 2.10.4, a –40 dB/dec rolloff, and a corner frequency of 1000. The phase and delay characteristics are shown in Fig. 2.10.7.

From the delay results of first- and second-order poles, we saw that *left-half-plane (LHP) poles contribute positive delay* (i.e., envelope retardation). We can easily extend these results to first- and second-order zeros. Since the phase of LHP zeros differs from that of LHP poles of identical location in sign only (i.e., LHP poles have negative phase and LHP zeros have positive phase), *LHP zeros contribute negative delay* (i.e., envelope advancement). Therefore, in calculating the total delay due to both zeros and poles, the sign must be carefully assigned. The delay of LHP poles and zeros tend to cancel which reduces the delay magnitude due to either poles or

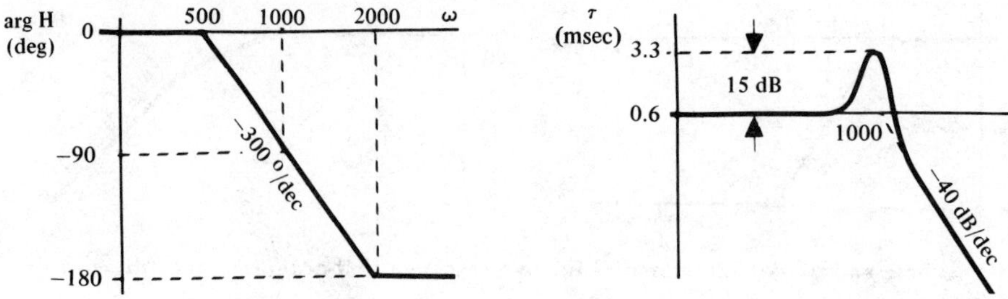

Fig. 2.10.7 Phase and delay characteristics for low-pass filter of Example 2.10.2.

zeros acting alone.

To show the change of sign mathematically, suppose the filter gain H having only LHP poles equals

$$H_1(s) = \frac{1}{D(s)} = \frac{1}{\text{Ev}\,(D) + \text{Od}\,(D)} \tag{2.10.27}$$

where Ev(D) and Od(D) denote the even and odd parts of D, respectively. The ac steady-state phase and delay of H_1 then equal

$$\arg H_1(j\omega) = -\tan^{-1}\,[\text{Od}\,D(s)/\text{Ev}\,D(s)]_{s=j\omega}, \qquad \tau_1(j\omega) = -d\arg H_1(j\omega)/d\omega \tag{2.10.28}$$

Now assume the filter has LHP zeros which are images of the LHP poles. Its gain, therefore, equals $H_2(s) = D(s)$ so its phase and delay equal

$$\begin{aligned} \arg H_2(j\omega) &= \tan^{-1}\,[\text{Od}\,D(s)/\text{Ev}\,D(s)]_{s=j\omega} = -\arg H_1(j\omega) \\ \tau_2(j\omega) &= -d\arg H_2(j\omega)/d\omega = -\tau_1(j\omega) \end{aligned} \tag{2.10.29}$$

whose signs are negative. Thus, only their signs differ. It is important to note that the delay pole-zero patterns are *identical* for both filters.

Now consider right-half-plane (RHP) poles and zeros. For RHP poles which are images of LHP poles, then the filter gain equals $H_3(s) = 1/D(-s)$. The filter phase and delay equal

$$\begin{aligned} \arg H_3(j\omega) &= -\tan^{-1}\,[\text{Od}\,D(-s)/\text{Ev}\,D(-s)]_{s=j\omega} \\ &= \tan^{-1}\,[\text{Od}\,D(s)/\text{Ev}\,D(s)]_{s=j\omega} = -\arg H_1(j\omega) \\ \tau_3(j\omega) &= -d\arg H_3(j\omega)/d\omega = -\tau_1(j\omega) \end{aligned} \tag{2.10.30}$$

Thus, *RHP image poles have identical (negative) delay to LHP poles.* In similiar fashion, RHP zeros which are images of LHP poles have H(s) = D(–s) so

$$\begin{aligned} \arg H_4(j\omega) &= \tan^{-1}\,[\text{Od}\,D(-s)/\text{Ev}\,D(-s)]_{s=j\omega} \\ &= -\tan^{-1}\,[\text{Od}\,D(s)/\text{Ev}\,D(s)]_{s=j\omega} = \arg H_1(j\omega) \\ \tau_4(j\omega) &= -d\arg H_4(j\omega)/d\omega = \tau_1(j\omega) \end{aligned} \tag{2.10.31}$$

Therefore, *RHP image zeros have identical (positive) delay to LHP poles.* As before, RHP poles and zeros of identical location have the same delay pole-zero pattern. In general then, poles and zeros having identical locations (anywhere in the s-plane) or image locations all have identical pole-zero patterns for delay. Only their signs differ. This is an extremely useful fact.

The engineer may wonder why we are interested in RHP poles and zeros. In Sec. 1.6, we saw that stable causal systems were required to possess only LHP poles or simple poles on the jω-axis.

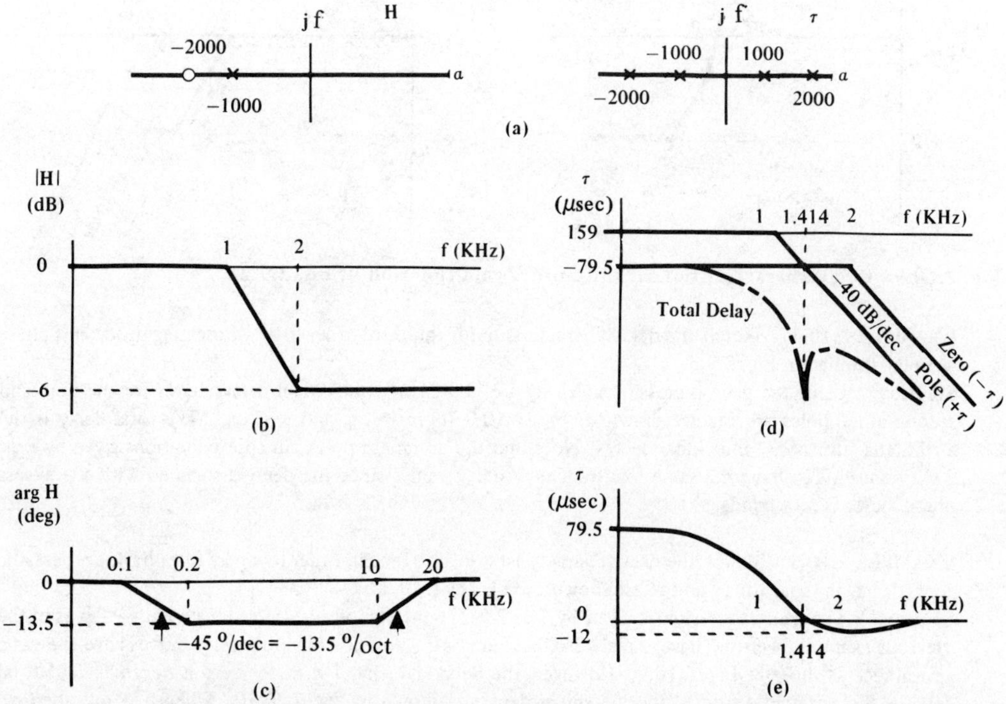

Fig. 2.10.8 (a) Pole-zero patterns for gain and delay, (b) magnitude, (c) phase; (d) and (e) delay characteristics for lead-lag filter of Example 2.10.3.

Since we generally wish to analyze stable systems, RHP poles are of little use. However, we also saw that the zeros could be anywhere in the s-plane. From Sec. 1.17, systems having RHP zeros (and poles) were said to be of *nonminimum-phase* type. Such systems are very useful as delay equalizers or all-pass filters which we shall introduce in the next section and study extensively in Chap. 12. They often arise in optimum filters to be discussed in Chap. 5. Thus, we shall later utilize the RHP zero results.

EXAMPLE 2.10.3 Determine the pole-zero pattern for the delay τ of a first-order lead-lag filter having a gain given by Eq. 2.3.31 where the break frequencies are 1000 Hz (pole) and 2000 Hz (zero), respectively. Draw the magnitude, phase, and delay characteristics for the filter.

Solution The pole-zero pattern for τ is easily constructed as shown in Fig. 2.10.8a. The poles of τ are identical to the poles and zeros of H and their images. Recall that τ has no zeros when H has only real poles and zeros (see Eq. 2.10.16). The magnitude and phase characteristics are easily drawn in Fig. 2.10.8b and c. The delay characteristics are constructed in Fig. 2.10.8d. We find the delay characteristics of the pole and zero terms individually and then sum them to find the total delay of the filter. The dc delay values equal

$$\tau_p(0) = 1/2\pi(1000) = 159\ \mu\text{sec}, \qquad \tau_z(0) = -1/2\pi(2000) = -79.5\ \mu\text{sec} \tag{2.10.32}$$

from Eqs. 2.10.6 and 2.10.17. Recall that the real poles and zeros have dc delay magnitudes of $1/\omega_n$. Their break frequencies are 1 and 2 KHz, respectively. Both have asymptotic rolloffs of −40 dB/dec.

The total delay is the *arithmetic sum* of the individual delays using Eq. 2.10.3. Remembering the LHP pole has positive delay and the LHP zero has negative delay, the composite delay curve is easily constructed by taking the delay *difference*. There is zero delay at 1414 Hz (i.e., $\sqrt{2} \times 1000$ Hz). When $f < 1414$ Hz, delay is positive; when $f > 1414$ Hz, delay is negative. In such situations where delay is both positive and negative over various frequency ranges, an *arithmetic plot* of delay is often useful to emphasize the sign changes. This is shown in Fig. 2.10.8e.

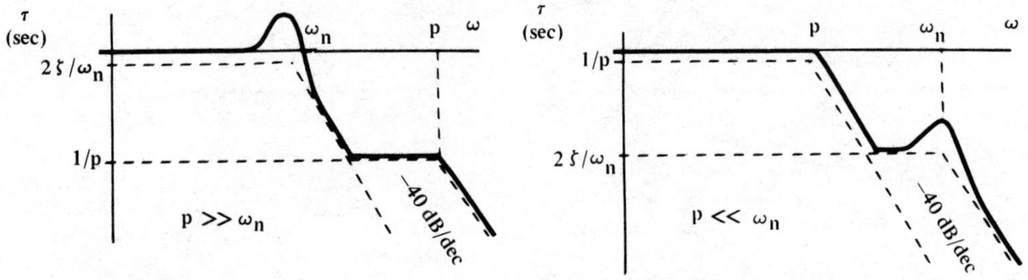

Fig. 2.10.9 Delay characteristics for third-order gain function of Eq. 2.9.21.

EXAMPLE 2.10.4 Sketch the delay characteristic for the third-order filter whose magnitude and phase were determined in Fig. 2.9.3.

Solution Using the gain expression given by Eq. 2.9.21, the individual delay curves for the first- and second-order poles are readily drawn in Fig. 2.10.9 for $p \gg \omega_n$ and $p \ll \omega_n$. The total delay is the arithmetic sum of the individual delays. Note that the dominant pole gain approximations given by Eqs. 2.9.24 and 2.9.26 have the same low-frequency delay values since the delay associated with the excess phase factor is τ_o seconds.

EXAMPLE 2.10.5 Sketch the delay characteristic for the second-order low-pass filter having a parasitic zero. It has the magnitude and phase shown in Fig. 2.9.4.

Solution The gain expression is given by Eq. 2.9.27. Instead of a real pole located at $s = -p$ as in the previous example, we now have a real zero located at $s = -z$. The individual delay curves have the same appearance as those in Fig. 2.10.9. However, the delay associated with the zero is *negative*. The total delay is the arithmetic sum of the individual delays as shown in Fig. 2.10.10. When $p \gg \omega_n$, the low-frequency delay is positive and the high-frequency delay is negative. When $\omega_n \gg p$, the situation is reversed. The delay is zero where the delays due to the poles and zero cancel. This corresponds to the frequency when the phase slope is zero in Fig. 2.9.4.

These examples illustrate the simplicity of using Bode plot techniques for analyzing delay. We have seen that the dc value, peaking, and asymptotic rolloff of delay are simply depicted using Bode plots. It is very convenient that a single normalized delay curve can be used for delay analysis of all systems having rational gain functions. However, composite delay plots require *arithmetic summing* of individual delay curves which must be exercised with caution. We have also seen that the information derived from the Bode delay plot is sometimes more illuminating if it is transferred onto an arithmetic delay plot. Delay is always an even function of frequency.

Another useful result concerns the low- and high-frequency delays of a filter. If we express its gain in the summation form given by Eq. 2.0.1, then when $s \to 0$, H(s) can be expressed as

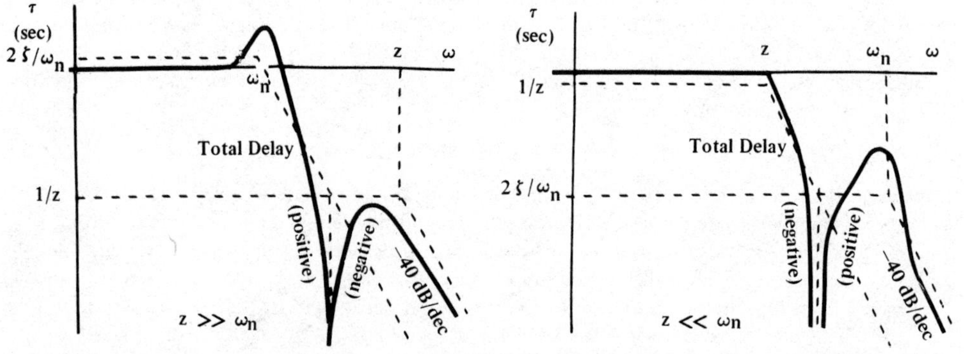

Fig. 2.10.10 Delay characteristics for second-order gain function of Eq. 2.9.27.

$$H(s) \cong \frac{a_0 + a_1 s}{b_0 + b_1 s}, \qquad s \to 0 \tag{2.10.33}$$

Therefore, the low-frequency phase and delay equal

$$\begin{aligned} \arg H(j\omega) &\cong \tan^{-1}(a_1\omega/a_0) - \tan^{-1}(b_1\omega/b_0) \\ \tau(j\omega) &\cong (b_1/b_0) - (a_1/a_0) \end{aligned} \qquad \omega \to 0 \tag{2.10.34}$$

The delay is obtained from the phase using the $\tan^{-1}x$ series of Eq. 2.10.24a. When $s \to \infty$, then H(s) can be expressed as

$$H(s) \cong \frac{a_{m-1}s^{m-1} + a_m s^m}{b_{n-1}s^{n-1} + b_n s^n} = s^{m-n}\,\frac{a_{m-1} + a_m s}{b_{n-1} + b_n s}, \qquad s \to \infty \tag{2.10.35}$$

Therefore, the high-frequency phase and delay equal

$$\begin{aligned} \arg H(j\omega) &\cong (m-n)\pi/2 + \tan^{-1}(a_m\omega/a_{m-1}) - \tan^{-1}(b_n\omega/b_{n-1}) \\ \tau(j\omega) &\cong (b_{n-1}/b_n - a_{m-1}/a_m)/\omega^2 \end{aligned} \qquad \omega \to \infty \tag{2.10.36}$$

The delay is obtained from the phase using the $\tan^{-1}x$ series of Eq. 2.10.24b. Thus, the low-frequency delay of a filter depends only upon the coefficients of the first two lowest-degree terms in the numerator and denominator of its gain equation. Its high-frequency delay characteristics depend only upon the coefficients of the last two highest-degree terms. If the filter has no finite zeros, as is the case in many low-pass filters, then $a_0 = 1$ and $a_1 = 0$. The asymptotic delay expressions then reduce to

$$\tau(j\omega) = b_1/b_0, \qquad \omega \to 0 \qquad \text{and} \qquad (b_{n-1}/b_n)/\omega^2, \qquad \omega \to \infty \tag{2.10.37}$$

These are extremely convenient results as we shall see in later chapters.

It is important to note the difference between the dc delay of a filter $\tau(0)$, and its delay τ_o in a dominant pole-zero sense. $\tau(0)$ is equal to the total dc delay of the gain of the filter. τ_o is equal to the dc delay of only the excess phase factor in the dominant pole-zero gain expression of the filter. Thus, they differ by the low-frequency delay of the dominant pole-zero term itself. This distinction will be considered fully in the next chapter.

Now let us consider the effect of poles or zeros located at the s-plane origin. Returning to the general gain function which describes integrators and differentiators, their gain equalled $H(s) = s^n$ from Eq. 2.2.3. We found the ac steady-state phase equalled $n\pi/2$ for $\omega > 0$ and $-n\pi/2$ for $\omega < 0$ in Eq. 2.2.4b. We may express the phase as

$$\arg H(j\omega) = (n\pi/2)[2U_{-1}(\omega) - 1] \tag{2.10.38}$$

where $U_{-1}(\omega)$ is a unit step function extensively discussed in Sec. 1.7. Recall from Eq. 1.7.1 that $U_{-1}(\omega)$ is defined to equal zero for $\omega < 0$ and unity for $\omega > 0$ which simply makes a one unit transition at $\omega = 0$. The delay τ equals

$$\tau(j\omega) = -\,d \arg H/d\omega = -n\pi U_0(\omega) \tag{2.10.39}$$

where $U_0(\omega)$ is the unit impulse located at $\omega = 0$ having area $-n\pi$ and zero value elsewhere.

The phase and delay characteristics of H are shown in Fig. 2.10.11. We see that since phase equals the negative integral of delay, the delay impulses of area $-n\pi$ allow the phase to make an abrupt $n\pi$ radian transition at $\omega = 0$. Thus, poles and zeros at the origin in a general gain function introduce only delay impulses at $\omega = 0$. In other words, they contribute no delay *except* at $\omega = 0$.

In this chapter, we have considered a variety of gain functions. Many of these gain functions

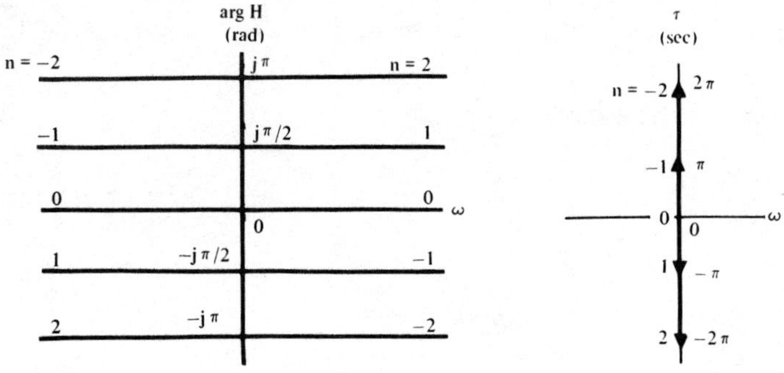

Fig. 2.10.11 Phase and delay characteristics of nth-order differentiator and integrator.

differ only in their number of zeros or poles at the origin. For example, the first-order low-pass and high-pass filters had gains $H_{LP} = 1/(s+1)$ and $H_{HP} = s/(s+1)$. H_{HP} differs from H_{LP} only in that it has a zero at the origin. Therefore, the delay of the high-pass filter equals

$$\tau_{HP}(j\omega) = \tau_{LP}(j\omega) - \pi U_0(\omega) \tag{2.10.40}$$

from Eq. 2.10.39, where τ_{LP} is the delay of the low-pass filter. Thus, H_{HP} and H_{LP} have identical delays except at $\omega = 0$.

Now consider the second-order low-pass, high-pass, band-pass, and band-stop filters having $H_{LP} = 1/D(s)$, $H_{HP} = s^2/D(s)$, $H_{BP} = s/D(s)$, and $H_{BS} = (s^2 + \omega_o{}^2)/D(s)$ where $D(s) = s^2 + 2\zeta s + 1$. Since H_{LP}, H_{HP}, and H_{BP} differ only in their number of zeros at the origin, they all have the same delay characteristics for a given ζ, except at $\omega = 0$. The delays of the high-pass and band-pass filters equal

$$\tau_{HP}(j\omega) = \tau_{LP}(j\omega) - 2\pi U_0(\omega), \qquad \tau_{BP}(j\omega) = \tau_{LP}(j\omega) - \pi U_0(\omega) \tag{2.10.41}$$

Recall that the notch filter has transmission zeros at $s = \pm j1$. These zeros cause the phase to make a $+180°$ transition at $\omega = \pm 1$ as seen from Eq. 2.8.5b. This causes delay impulses of area $-\pi$ to occur at $\omega = \pm 1$. Thus, the delay of the notch filter equals

$$\tau_{BS}(j\omega) = \tau_{LP}(j\omega) - \pi U_0(\omega - 1) - \pi U_0(\omega + 1) \tag{2.10.42}$$

and differs from the delay of H_{LP} only at $\omega = \pm 1$ where the impulses occur. These examples show that in general, although introducing poles and zeros on the $j\omega$-axis contribute constant phase, they only modify delay by introducing delay impulses where phase transitions occur (of course they modify the magnitude characteristic of the filter).

EXAMPLE 2.10.6 Determine the delay characteristic for the stagger-tuned band-pass filter of Example 2.7.3. The filter consisted of two cascaded first-order band-pass filters having $\zeta = 0.5$ and center frequencies of 710 Hz and 2500 Hz.

Solution Let us first determine the delay characteristics of each stage and then sum the individual delays to obtain the total delay. From Eq. 2.10.6, the dc delays equal

$$\tau_1(0) = \frac{2\zeta_1}{\omega_{n1}} = \frac{1}{2\pi(710)} = 0.224 \text{ msec}, \qquad \tau_2(0) = \frac{2\zeta_2}{\omega_{n2}} = \frac{1}{2\pi(2500)} = 0.064 \text{ msec}$$
$$\tau(0) = \tau_1(0) + \tau_2(0) = 0.29 \text{ msec} \tag{2.10.43}$$

From Fig. 2.10.4, the normalized delay peaking equals

$$\tau_{n1_{max}} = \tau_{n2_{max}} = 2 = 6 \text{ dB} \tag{2.10.44}$$

Using the normalized curve of Fig. 2.10.3, we draw τ_1 and τ_2 in Fig. 2.10.12. Arithmetically summing

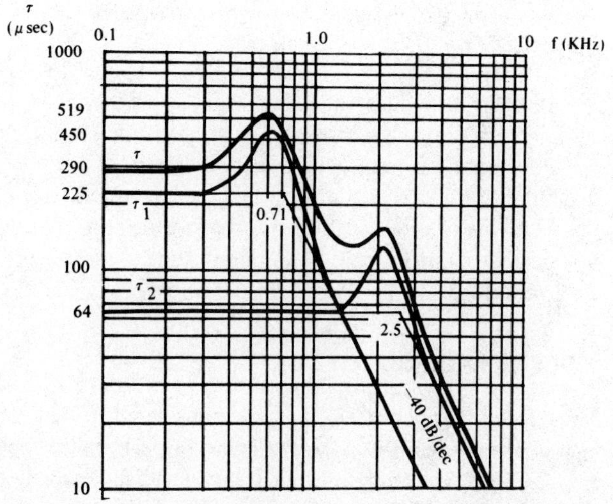

Fig. 2.10.12 Delay characteristic for band-pass filter of Example 2.10.6.

the two curves gives the total delay as shown. The average passband delay τ_{av} between 600 and 3000 Hz is about $(\tau_{max} + \tau_{min})/2 = (0.52 + 0.06)/2 = 0.29$ msec. We note that the maximum delay variation $\Delta\tau$ is about $\pm(\tau_{max} - \tau_{min})/2 = \pm(0.52 - 0.06)/2 = \pm 0.23$ msec through the filter passband. In some systems, this is considered excessive *delay distortion* (which is defined to be in-band delay variation). Since the filter center frequency is 1340 Hz, the cycle period is 1/1340 Hz = 0.75 msec. Thus, passband signal frequencies can be advanced or retarded by about ±0.23 msec or about ± 30% of a cycle. The absolute delay value is not of importance in most systems. However, the absolute delay variation is generally of great interest.

EXAMPLE 2.10.7 Determine the delay characteristic for the synchronously-tuned band-pass filter of Example 2.7.3. The filter consisted of two identical cascaded first-order band-pass filters having $\zeta = 1.4$ and center frequencies of 1340 Hz (these correspond to real poles at 560 and 3200 Hz). Is the delay characteristic better than that of the stagger-tuned design in Example 2.10.6?

Solution The dc delay of the stages equals

$$\tau_1(0) = \tau_2(0) = 2(1.4)/2\pi(1340) = 0.333 \text{ msec}, \qquad \tau(0) = 2\tau_1(0) = 0.666 \text{ msec} \tag{2.10.45}$$

There is no delay peaking since the poles are real. The delay characteristic is shown in Fig. 2.10.13. In this case, the passband delay variation is about $\pm(0.360 - 0.07)/2 = \pm 0.145$ msec. This is only about

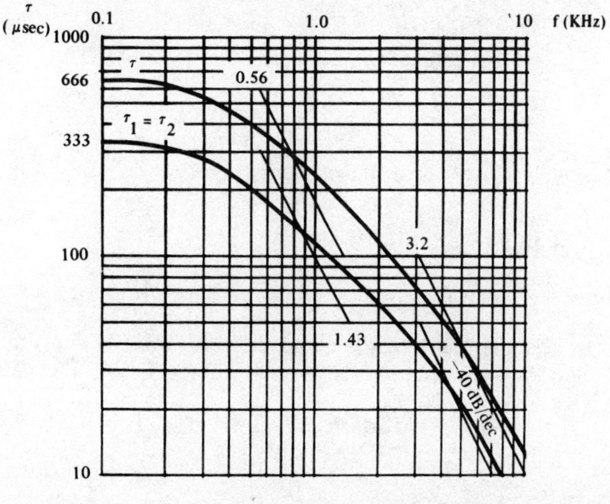

Fig. 2.10.13 Delay characteristic for band-pass filter of Example 2.10.7.

60% of that in Example 2.10.6 so the delay characteristic is improved. The average passband delay is (0.360 + 0.07)/2 = 0.215 msec.

In order to reduce the delay variation through the filter passband, these examples show that it is necessary to use a lower Q first-stage (tuned in the vicinity of the lower cutoff frequency and a higher Q second-stage (tuned in the vicinity of the upper cutoff frequency). This will introduce magnitude variation in the passband (which is defined to be *amplitude distortion*) but will reduce the delay distortion, and thereby improve delay. Often when both small amplitude and delay distortions are required, the desired amplitude characteristic is obtained using the proper filter. It is then followed by a delay equalizer (i.e., all-pass filter) to reduce delay variation in the passband.

2.11 ALL-PASS FILTERS

Thus far in this chapter, we have considered a variety of filters including low-pass, high-pass, band-pass, and band-stop types. These filters have the ideal characteristics shown in Fig. 2.1.1 and are classified according to the frequency bands which they pass and those which they reject. Another very interesting and useful filter is the all-pass filter. This filter passes all frequencies and rejects none as shown in Fig. 2.1.1e. Although its magnitude characteristic is flat (i.e., constant) over all frequencies from zero to infinity, it shifts the phase of the various frequencies in accordance with its phase characteristic. All-pass filters are often called *delay equalizers* for reasons which we shall see. We first derive the general gain expressions which describe all-pass filters.

Suppose the all-pass filter has the gain function, H(s), where

$$H(s) = kN(s)/D(s) \tag{2.11.1}$$

If the filter is to be an all-pass type, then its ac steady-state magnitude characteristic |H| must be constant over all frequencies and satisfy

$$|H(j\omega)|^2 = H(s)H(-s)\Big|_{s=j\omega} = \frac{N(s)N(-s)}{D(s)D(-s)}\Big|_{s=j\omega} = k^2 \tag{2.11.2}$$

Then the numerator and denominator of an all-pass filter are related as

$$N(s) = kD(-s) \tag{2.11.3}$$

so that the zeros are the *images* of the poles. That is, if H(s) has a pole at $s = s_p$, then it *must* also have an image zero at $s = -s_p = s_p e^{j\pi}$. Thus, image zeros lie diagonally opposite their respective poles in the s-plane.

The ac steady-state phase characteristic of the all-pass filter can be easily determined. From Eq. 2.11.1, its phase equals

$$\arg H(j\omega) = \arg N(j\omega) - \arg D(j\omega) \tag{2.11.4}$$

Since

$$\arg N(j\omega) = \arg D(-j\omega) = -\arg D(j\omega) \tag{2.11.5}$$

from Eq. 2.11.3, then

$$\arg H(j\omega) = -2 \arg D(j\omega) = 2 \arg H_{LP}(j\omega) \tag{2.11.6}$$

so that the phase of the all-pass filter is *double* that due to the poles acting alone (i.e., its associated low-pass filter having gain $H_{LP}(s) = k/D(s)$). The delay of the all-pass filter equals

$$\tau(j\omega) = -d \arg H(j\omega)/d\omega = 2\, d \arg D(j\omega)/d\omega = 2\tau_{LP}(j\omega) \tag{2.11.7}$$

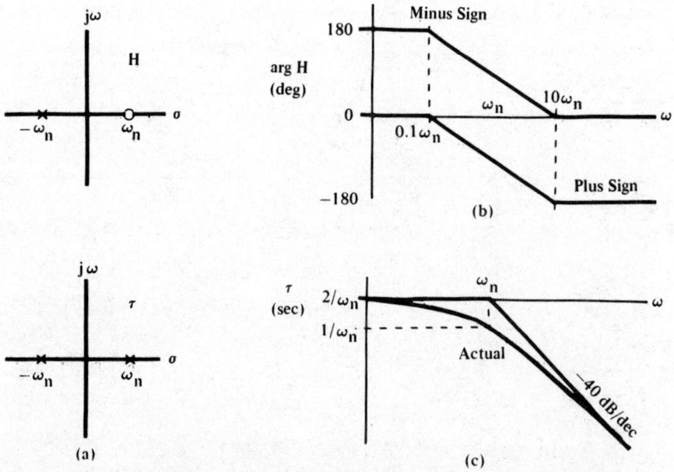

Fig. 2.11.1 (a) Pole-zero pattern for gain and delay, (b) phase, and (c) delay characteristics for all-pass filter of Example 2.11.1.

which is double the delay of its associated low-pass filter.

Note that we could also have chosen N(s) = kD(s) as a second solution to Eq. 2.11.2. However, in this case, the gain H(s) would equal k so that the phase would either be 0° or 180° and the delay would equal zero. Since such filters would provide only gain, they would be useless as delay equalizers which modify delay. Hence, we consider this to be a trivial solution.

Now let us interrelate the poles and zeros of all-pass filters. We know that stable causal systems can have no RHP poles and only simple jω-axis poles. Their zeros can lie anywhere in the s-plane and have any multiplicity. Complex poles and zeros always exist in conjugate pairs. General stable causal all-pass filters have the additional constraints that N(s) = kD(−s) from Eq. 2.11.3. Since the zeros are images of the poles, we can conclude the following facts about stable, causal all-pass filters (the usual case of interest):

1. All zeros must lie in right-half-plane. Any LHP zero would have to have an RHP image pole which would produce instability.
2. Therefore, all poles must lie in the left-half plane and have image zeros in the right-half-plane for stability.
3. No poles or zeros can lie on the jω-axis because the image zeros or poles would produce pole-zero cancellation.
4. All-pass filters can only introduce positive delay (i.e., envelope retardation) and never negative delay (i.e., envelope advancement). Their delay characteristic is always *twice* that of their associated low-pass filters having gain H(s) = k/D(s). This follows from Eqs. 2.10.3, 2.10.5, 2.10.6, and 2.11.7.
5. Thus, the phase characteristics of all-pass filters must always be monotonically non-increasing functions.

Now let us consider several examples to illustrate these results.

EXAMPLE 2.11.1 Determine the delay characteristic for the first-order all-pass filter having gain

$$H(s) = k\frac{s-\omega_n}{s+\omega_n} = -k\frac{\omega_n - s}{\omega_n + s} \tag{2.11.8}$$

Determine and sketch its delay characteristics.

Solution Since N(s) = kD(−s) the filter is indeed an all-pass type. The gain |H(jω)| = k and the phase equals (for $\omega \geqslant 0$)

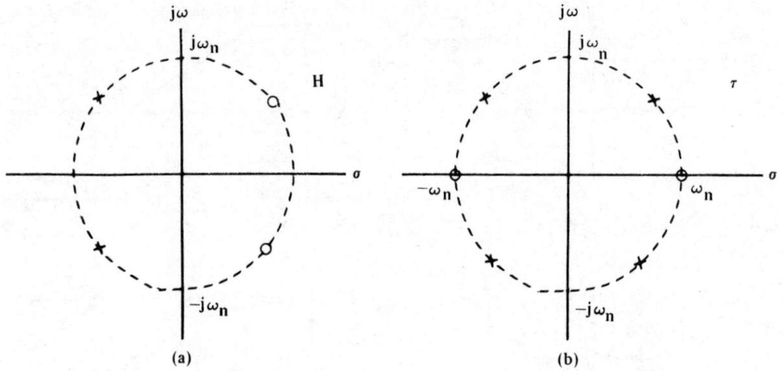

Fig. 2.11.2 Pole-zero patterns for (a) gain and (b) delay for all-pass filter of Example 2.11.2.

$$\arg H(j\omega) = \pi - 2\tan^{-1}(\omega/\omega_n), \ (k>0) \quad \text{or} \quad -2\tan^{-1}(\omega/\omega_n), \ (k<0) \tag{2.11.9}$$

The delay characteristic is double that of a low-pass filter having gain $H(s) = 1/(s + \omega_n)$ and equals

$$\tau(j\omega) = 2\frac{d[\tan^{-1}(\omega/\omega_n)]}{d\omega} = \frac{2}{\omega_n}\frac{1}{1+(\omega/\omega_n)^2} \tag{2.11.10}$$

from Eq. 2.10.5 for $\zeta = 1$. The normalized delay plot is given by Fig. 2.10.3. The pole-zero pattern, phase characteristics, and delay characteristic for the first-order all-pass filter are shown in Fig. 2.11.1. Notice that the phase characteristics are monotonically nonincreasing as required of all delay equalizers. The delay characteristic exhibits no peaking.

EXAMPLE 2.11.2 Now consider the second-order all-pass filter having complex poles and gain

$$H(s) = k\frac{s^2 - 2\zeta\omega_n s + \omega_n^2}{s^2 + 2\zeta\omega_n s + \omega_n^2} \tag{2.11.11}$$

Determine the delay and sketch its pole-zero pattern.

Solution The zeros are images of the poles. Since the poles and zeros of H(s) lie on a circle of radius ω_n, so do the poles of delay as shown in Fig. 2.11.2. Note that the RHP zeros of H(s) have the same delay poles as the LHP poles of H(s). Delay zeros lie at $s = \pm\omega_n$. The ac steady-state gain $|H(j\omega)| = k$ and the phase and delay equal

$$\arg H(j\omega) = -2\tan^{-1}\frac{2\zeta\omega_n\omega}{\omega_n^2 - \omega^2}, \qquad \tau(j\omega) = \frac{4\zeta}{\omega_n}\frac{1+(\omega/\omega_n)^2}{1+(2\zeta^2-1)2(\omega/\omega_n)^2 + (\omega/\omega_n)^4} \tag{2.11.12}$$

from Eqs. 2.10.4, 2.10.5, and 2.11.7. The dc delay equals

$$\tau(0) = 2(2\zeta/\omega_n) = 4\zeta/\omega_n \tag{2.11.13}$$

from Eq. 2.10.6. When $|\zeta| < 0.866$, delay peaking occurs at frequency ω_p given by Eq. 2.10.12. The maximum delay equals

$$\tau_{max}(j\omega_p) = \frac{1}{2\zeta\omega_n}\left[1 + \frac{1}{\sqrt{1-\zeta^2}}\right] \tag{2.11.14}$$

from Eq. 2.10.13. The normalized delay characteristic is shown in Fig. 2.10.3.

EXAMPLE 2.11.3 Determine the delay characteristic for a second-order all-pass filter having a gain given by Eq. 2.11.11 where $\zeta = 1.5$. Draw the pole-zero pattern for both gain and delay.

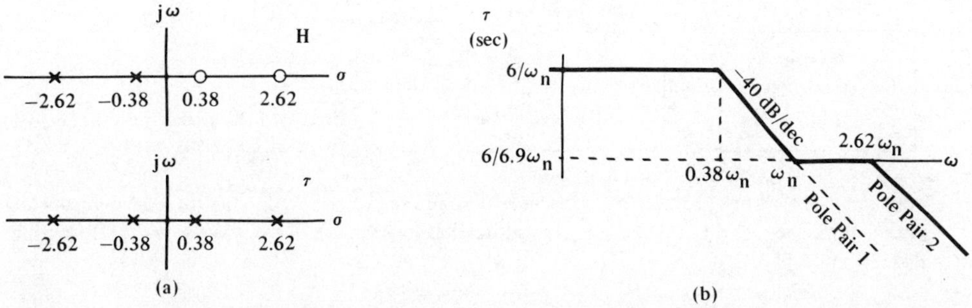

Fig. 2.11.3 **(a) Normalized pole-zero patterns for gain and delay and (b) delay characteristics for all-pass filter of Example 2.11.3.**

Solution The filter is an all-pass type since N(s) = kD(−s). The gain $|H(j\omega)| = k$ and the phase and delay are given by Eq. 2.11.12. Since $\zeta = 1.5$, the gain poles are real rather than complex and the delay response must be monotonically nonincreasing. From Eq. 2.7.25, the normalized poles are located at

$$s/\omega_n = -\zeta \mp \sqrt{\zeta^2 - 1} = -1.5 \mp \sqrt{1.5^2 - 1} = -1.5 \mp 1.12 = -0.38, \quad -2.62 \tag{2.11.15}$$

The normalized pole-zero patterns for gain H(s) and delay $\tau(s)$ are shown in Fig. 2.11.3a. Recall that half of the delay poles are always identical to the gain poles (and zeros) and every delay pole has an associated image pole. In addition, delay has zeros at $s = \pm 1$ for every complex pole (or zero) pair. This is not the case here. The dc delay of the all-pass filter $\tau(0) = 4(1.5)/\omega_n = 6/\omega_n$ from Eq. 2.11.13. The delay characteristic is shown in Fig. 2.11.3b.

These examples show that the delay characteristic can be modified by proper selection of the damping factor ζ and corner frequency ω_n. When all-pass filters are cascaded with other filters or systems for the purpose of shaping the overall delay characteristic into some desired form, such all-pass filters are called *delay equalizers*. These are in contrast to *amplitude equalizers* which are used to shape a magnitude characteristic without modifying its phase or delay. As a practical matter, amplitude equalizers do affect phase and delay and are cascaded with delay equalizers in critical applications to obtain the proper overall magnitude and delay characteristics. Analytical methods for determining the pole-zero configurations for delay and amplitude equalizers are considered in Chap. 5 when we discuss optimum filters.

EXAMPLE 2.11.4 Determine the second-order delay equalizer which, when cascaded with the low-pass filter of Example 2.10.2 as shown in Fig. 2.11.4, will reduce the in-band delay variation. Draw the total delay characteristic of the equalized low-pass filter.

Solution Without the optimization techniques of Chap. 5, delay equalization requires trial-and-error solution. The delay characteristic of the low-pass filter is drawn in Fig. 2.11.5. We must now determine ω_n and ζ of the delay equalizer so that its delay characteristic shown in Fig. 2.10.2, when added to that of the low-pass filter, will reduce the delay variation. It is clear from Fig. 2.10.2 that we should use a fairly large ζ and a ω_n somewhat less than 1000 rad/sec to reduce the delay peaking. For convenience, let us select $\zeta = 0.87$ so that the actual delay curve of the equalizer falls approximately upon its asymptotic approximation. The dc delay of the equalizer equals

$$\tau(0) = 4\zeta/\omega_n = 3.5/\omega_n \tag{2.11.16}$$

from Eq. 2.11.13. Its stopband delay approximately equals

$$\tau(j\omega) \cong \frac{4\zeta}{\omega_n}\left(\frac{\omega_n}{\omega}\right)^2 = \frac{3.5}{\omega_n}\left(\frac{\omega_n}{\omega}\right)^2, \qquad |\omega| \gg \omega_n \tag{2.11.17}$$

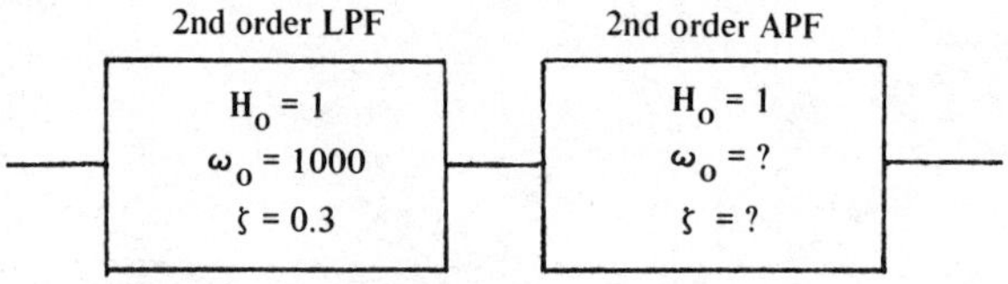

Fig. 2.11.4 Delay-equalized low-pass filter of Example 2.11.4.

from Eqs. 2.11.12 or 2.10.27. We determine the required ω_n by setting the total delay of the low-pass filter and delay equalizer at dc equal to their total delay at $\omega = 1000$, and solve for ω_n. Thus, using Eqs. 2.11.16 and 2.11.17,

$$\frac{3.5}{\omega_n} + \frac{0.6}{1000} = \frac{3.5}{\omega_n}\left(\frac{\omega_n}{1000}\right)^2 + \frac{3.3}{1000} \tag{2.11.18}$$

Rearranging the equation and dividing by 3.5 gives

$$(\omega_n/1000)^2 + 0.77(\omega_n/1000) - 1 = 0 \tag{2.11.19}$$

Solving Eq. 2.11.19 for ω_n gives

$$\frac{\omega_n}{1000} = \frac{-0.77 \pm \sqrt{0.77^2 + 4}}{2} = \frac{-0.77 \pm 2.14}{2} = 1.37/2 = 0.69 \tag{2.11.20}$$

so $\omega_n = 690$ rad/sec. The delay of the equalizer and the total delay are sketched in Fig. 2.11.5.

Let us now evaluate the improvement in the delay variation. Originally, the average delay τ_{av} of the low-pass filter in the passband ($\omega \leqslant 1450$ rad/sec) equalled $(3.3 + 0.6)/2 = 1.95$ msec while the delay variation $\Delta\tau$ equalled $\pm(3.3 - 0.6)/2 = \pm 1.35$ msec. Now by incorporating the delay equalizer, the overall average delay τ_{av} (for $\omega \leqslant 1000$ rad/sec) equals $(5.75 + 5.0)/2 = 5.4$ msec, and the delay variation $\Delta\tau$ equals $\pm(5.75 - 5.0)/2 = \pm 0.4$ msec. Thus, we have reduced the delay variation by a factor of three which is a great improvement. It is important to remember that generally we are not interested in either the average delay or the percentage variation. Since the 3 dB bandwidth extends to 1450 rad/sec, another delay equalizer stage would be required to equalize delay in the region of the band-edge ($1000 < \omega < 1450$). This example shows that a computer is indispensible for the design of delay equalizers.

EXAMPLE 2.11.5 The delay characteristic of a 500 mile length of telephone line is shown in Fig. 2.11.6. A delay equalizer must be designed which will compensate or augment the telephone line delay to produce a constant overall delay and ideally, eliminate delay distortion. One possible delay equalizer characteristic is shown in Fig. 2.11.6a (an infinite number are possible). The normalized delay characteristic is shown in Fig. 2.11.6b. Determine the parameters of a fourth-order delay equalizer which will

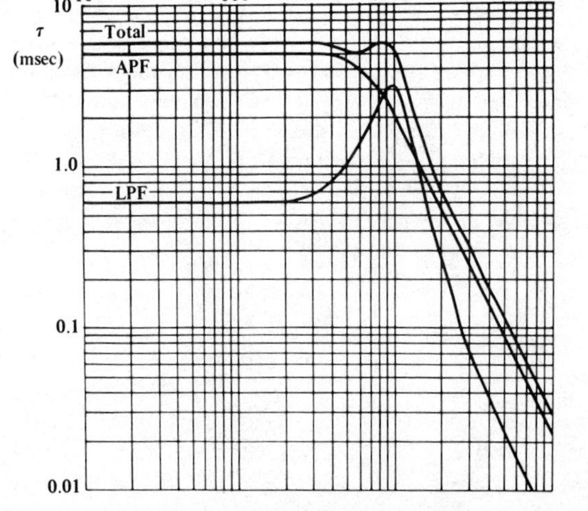

Fig. 2.11.5 Delay characteristics for low-pass filter and delay equalizer of Example 2.11.4.

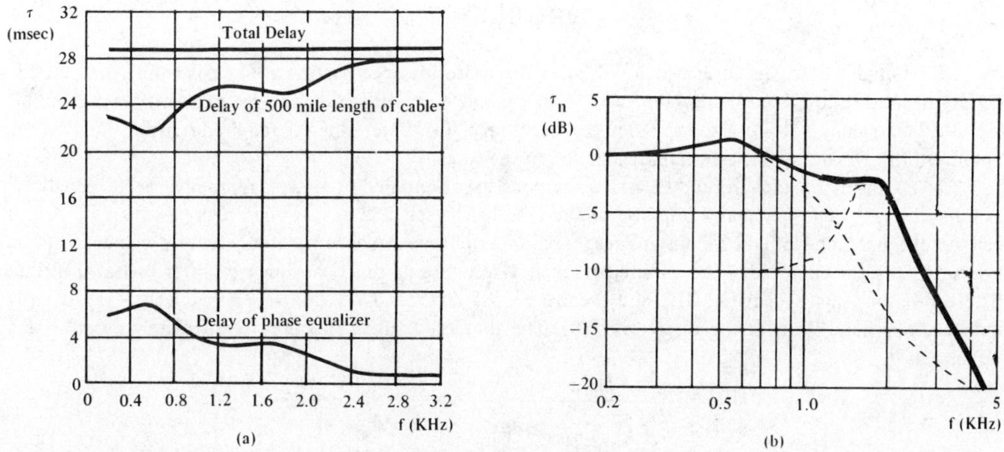

Fig. 2.11.6 (a) Delay to be equalized and (b) normalized delay characteristic required for Example 2.11.5.[20]

approximate this characteristic. Draw a block diagram of the delay equalizer showing the required parameters. How many stages must be cascaded to obtain the required delay characteristic?

Solution The normalized delay characteristic of Fig. 2.11.6b is obtained from that in Fig. 2.11.6a after dividing by the dc delay $\tau(0)$ = 5.3 msec. An infinite number of designs are possible, although they employ one of the two approaches shown in Fig. 2.11.7. One approach consists of cascading a number of stagger-tuned high-Q stages (a high-Q stage gives large τ_{max} values but narrow bandwidth). The other approach consists of cascading a number of synchronously-tuned low-Q stages (a low-Q stage gives wide bandwidth but small τ_{max}). One such design to obtain the delay of Fig. 2.11.6b uses the following parameters:

$$\begin{aligned} &\zeta_1 = 0.75 \qquad \text{(gives 1 dB peaking)} \\ &\omega_{n1} = 2\pi(450/0.57) = 2\pi(790\text{ Hz}) \qquad \text{(produces peaking at } \omega_p = 2\pi(450\text{ Hz})) \\ &\zeta_2 = 0.5 \qquad \text{(gives 7 dB peaking)} \\ &\omega_{n2} = 2\pi(1600/0.86) = 2\pi(1860\text{ Hz}) \qquad \text{(produces peaking at } \omega_p = 2\pi(1600\text{ Hz})) \end{aligned} \tag{2.11.21}$$

This trial and error design method is unsuitable in all but the simplest situations. The design methods for optimum filters in Chap. 5 must be used. Note that the dc delay of this equalizer equals

$$\tau(0) = 2[\tau_1(0) + \tau_2(0)] = 2\left[\frac{2(0.75)}{2\pi(790)} + \frac{2(0.5)}{2\pi(1860)}\right] = 2(0.30 + 0.09) = 0.78\text{ msec} \tag{2.11.22}$$

Since the required dc delay equals 5.3 msec, then n = 5.3/0.78 ≅ 7 stages. Thus, 7 stages of this fourth-order delay equalizer must be used and a 28th-order filter results. A slightly lower-order delay equalizer would result if stagger-tuned high-Q stages were used instead. Delay equalizers shall be discussed at length in Chap. 12.

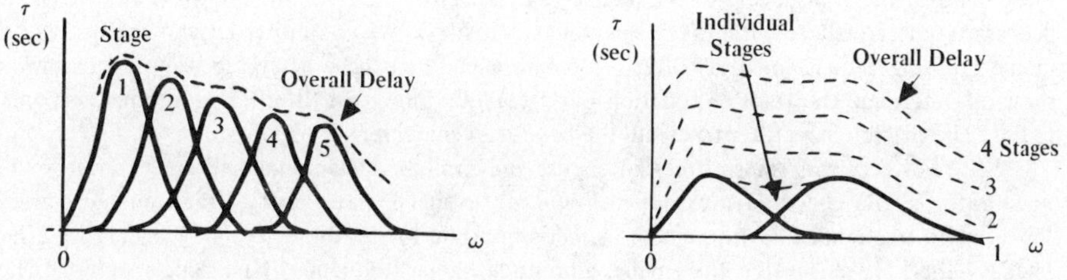

Fig. 2.11.7 Delay equalizer design approaches.

PROBLEMS

2.1 Design a low-pass filter which will meet the following specifications: (1) passband gain = 20 dB, (2) asymptotic rolloff = −40 dB/dec, (3) gain peaking ⩽ 1 dB, (4) band-edge selectivity = maximum, (5) 3 dB frequency = 1000 Hz, and (6) phase = arbitrary. (a) Determine the required transfer function for the filter. (b) Draw the block diagram realization of the filter.

2.2 A magnetic tape reproducing system consists essentially of a tape reproduce head, equalizer, and amplifier.[21] The frequency response of the tape head itself is that of a quasi-high-pass filter. To compensate the head and obtain a constant response, an amplitude equalizer is used. Its gain characteristic is inverse to that of the head. The required frequency response of this quasi-low-pass filter is shown in Fig. P2.2 for various tape speeds (A, B, C, and D equal 15, 7.5, 3.75, and 1.875 in/sec, respectively). (a) What is the transition band slope of the responses? (b) The simplest transfer function to adequately describe this response is

$$H(s) = \frac{s + \omega_{n1}}{s^2 + 2\zeta_1\omega_{n1}s + \omega_{n1}^2} \; \frac{s^2 + 2\zeta_2\omega_{n2}s + \omega_{n2}^2}{s + \omega_{n2}}$$

Determine the parameters of the four equalizers.

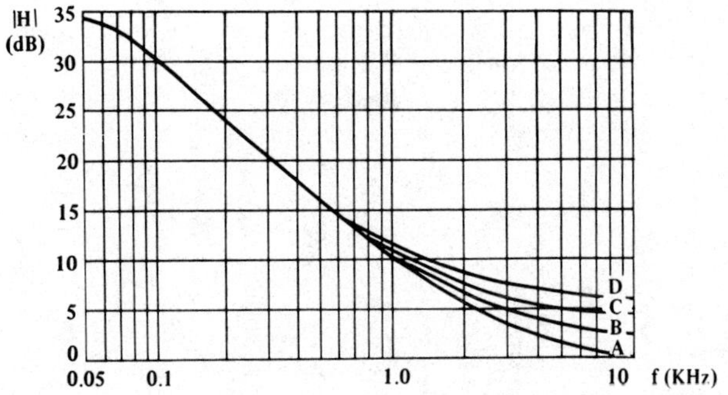

Fig. P2.2

2.3 Plot the magnitude and phase characteristics for the input admittance of an RC transmission line where $y_{11}(s) = d\sqrt{src}\coth d\sqrt{src}$. Show that the magnitude approaches a +10 dB/dec asymptote and the phase approaches +45° as ω approaches infinity. (Hint: Use the product expansions of Prob. 1.45.)

2.4 Plot the magnitude, phase, and delay characteristics of the second-order high-pass filter having unity high-frequency gain, a corner frequency of 100 Hz, and $\zeta = 0.9$. Label completely.

2.5 Plot the magnitude, phase, and delay characteristics of the second-order high-pass filter having unity high-frequency gain, a corner frequency of 1000 Hz, and $\zeta = 0.4$. Label completely.

2.6 Design a high-pass filter which will meet the specifications of Prob. 2.1 with the exception that asymptotic rolloff = +40 dB/dec.

2.7 Hydrophones and seismometers (or geophones) are transducers used to convert acoustical vibrations into electrical signals. At low frequencies, these transducers behave as high-pass filters with real poles. They have the gains shown in Fig. P2.7 where A and B represent operation in the velocity and displacement modes, respectively. In many applications, the frequency components of interest fall below the measurement band of the transducer. To equalize (or "flatten") the response below 0.1 Hz, we can utilize a cascaded amplitude equalizer with the proper characteristics. We can either extend the bandwidth of the seismometer using a quasi-low-pass filter, or create a band-pass characteristic using a quasi-low-pass filter as shown. Determine the transfer function of a: (a) quasi-low-pass filter to extend the seismometer responses to 0.01 Hz, (b) low-pass filter to create the band-pass characteristics shown.

2.8 FM receivers/transmitters often use pre-emphasis/de-emphasis filters to improve their signal-to-noise ratio (SNR) characteristics. Speech and music signals have most of their energy concentrated at the lower audio frequencies. Although the larger-amplitude lower-frequency (LF) signals are effectively modulated by the FM transmitter, the smaller-amplitude higher-frequency (HF) signals are not. Therefore, a pre-emphasis filter is used in the transmitter to emphasize the HF signals and de-emphasize the LF signals. In

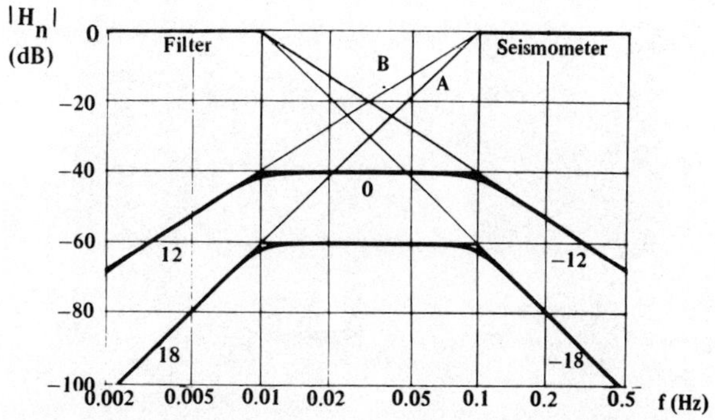

Fig. P2.7 (Courtesy of Rockland Systems Corp.[22])

the receiver, the inverse operation is performed using a de-emphasis filter to restore the original signal spectrum. The typical frequency characteristics of these two filters are shown in Fig. P2.8. Classify the filters by their type and determine their transfer functions.

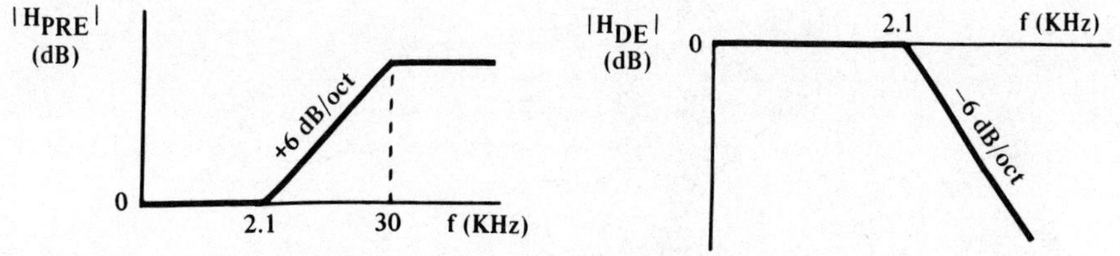

Fig. P2.8

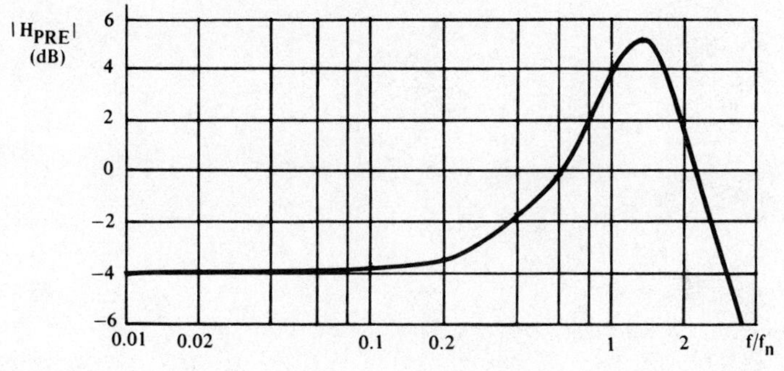

Fig. P2.9

2.9 FDM systems use pre-emphasis filters[23] having the magnitude response shown in Fig. P2.9. The de-emphasis filter has an inverse characteristic. The benefits derived using these filters are discussed in Prob. 2.8. Classify the pre-emphasis and de-emphasis filters by their type and determine their transfer functions.

2.10 The Dolby B noise reduction system, shown in Fig. P2.10, is used in commercial magnetic tape recording to improve signal-to-noise ratios. It is a variable rather than a fixed equalization scheme. In both schemes, high frequencies are pre-emphasized during recording and de-emphasized during playback. In fixed equalization, the filter corner frequencies are fixed. However, in the Dolby B system, a tunable high-pass filter is used whose corner frequency is controlled by the incoming signal. This approach makes more efficient use of the recording medium. When recording, the system provides high-frequency "boost" by addition; during playback, it provides high-frequency "cut" by subtraction (using a complementary characteristic). The magnitude characteristic of the variable high-pass filter is also shown in Fig. P2.10. Determine the transfer function of the tunable high-pass filter.

2.11 Audio equalization is different than recording head equalization in magnetic tape recording systems. Audio equalization must also be matched inversely to the response of the ear (see Fig. P2.20).[25] The equalization characteristics for both record and reproduce filters (at 15 in/sec) are shown in Fig. P2.11. In this country, NAB compensation is generally used. Design the filters in block diagram form. (a) NAB filter (National Association of Broadcasters), (b) CCIR filter (Consultant Committee for International

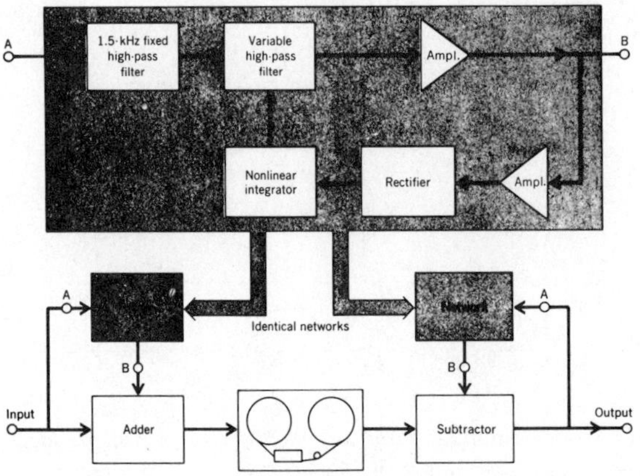

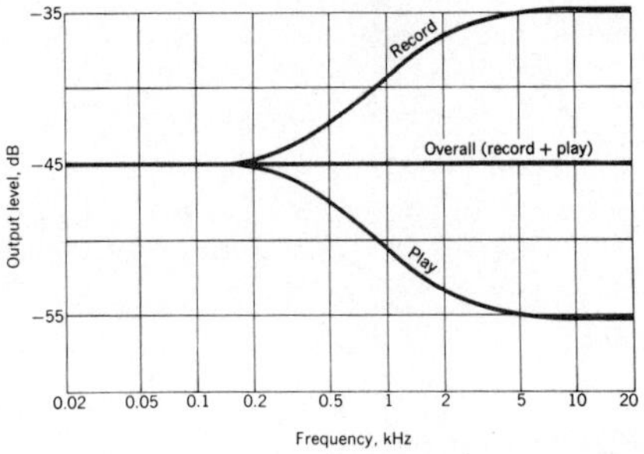

Fig. P2.10 (Courtesy of IEEE Spectrum[24])

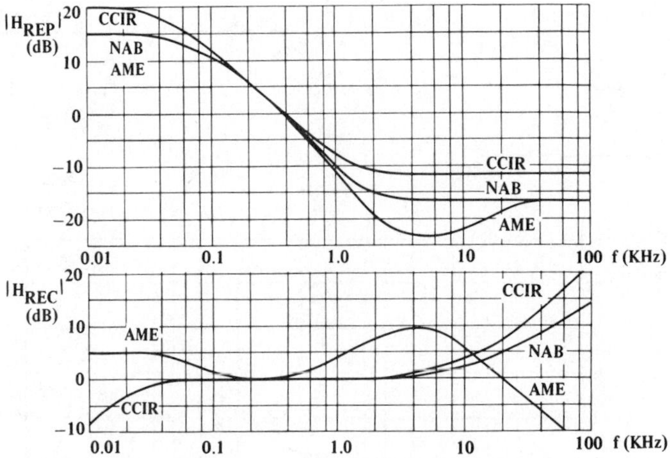

Fig. P2.11

Radio), (c) AME filter (Ampex Mastering Equalization).

2.12 A stereo phonograph recording system consists basically of microphones, equalizers, amplifiers, and cutters.[26] The cutter has a low-pass filter characteristic which requires inverse high-frequency compensation by the equalizer. The standard RIAA (Record Industry of America) compensation characteristic is shown in Fig. P2.12. Determine the required transfer function.

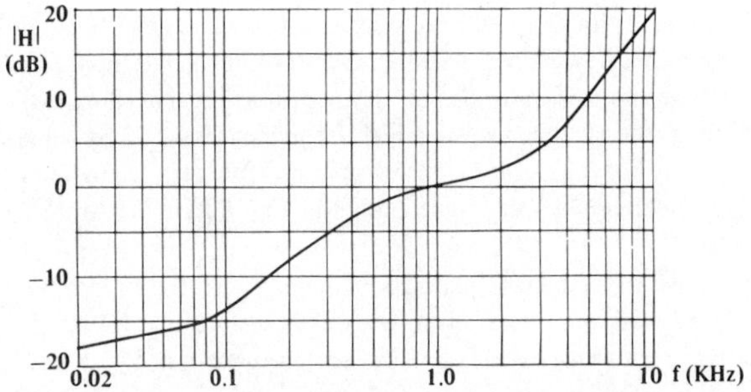

Fig. P2.12

2.13 Plot the magnitude, phase, and delay characteristics of the first-order band-pass filter having a midband gain of 10, a center frequency of 1000 Hz, and $\zeta = 0.4$. Label completely.

2.14 Design a band-pass filter which will meet the following specifications (see Fig. P2.14): (1) midband gain = 10, (2) asymptotic rolloff = ±40 dB/dec, (3) gain peaking ⩽ 2 dB, (4) band-edge selectivity = maximum, (5) 3 dB frequencies = 600, 3000 Hz; and (6) phase = arbitrary. Justify the parameters you choose. (Hint: Cascade a low-pass and high-pass filter).

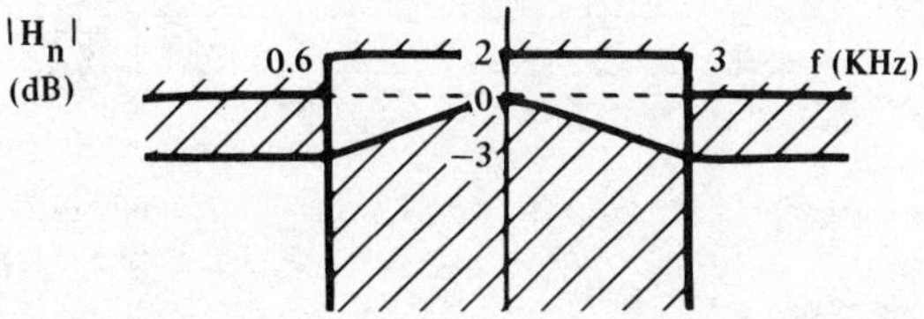

Fig. P2.14

2.15 Design a band-pass filter which will meet the specifications of Prob. 2.14 with the exception that gain peaking ⩽ 3 dB.

2.16 Redesign the band-pass filter of Example 2.6.2 using the approaches of Example 2.7.4: (a) synchronous-tuning, (b) stagger-tuning.

2.17 (a) Show that the frequencies at which a first-order band-pass filter has a gain |H| equal $\omega = (1 + K^2\zeta^2)^{1/2} \pm K\zeta$ where $K = (|H|^{-2} - 1)^{-1/2}$. (b) Show that the bandwidth equals $B = 2\zeta K$. (c) Show that the general shaping factors corresponding to gains of $|H_1|$ and $|H_2|$ must therefore equal K_1/K_2.

2.18 As discussed in Example 2.6.4, noise in telephone circuits heard or felt by subscribers is objectionable. Different weighting characteristics are shown in Fig. 2.6.7. Approximate the following curves as closely as possible using, at most, a fourth-order filter. Draw the completed design in block form. (a) F1A filter, (b) 144 filter, (c) psophometric filter. (Hint: Cascade a low-pass and a high-pass filter.)

2.19 Audiometers are used to measure the acuity of hearing. Their general construction is shown in Fig. P2.19; the attenuator is calibrated in dB above a reference threshold sound pressure. Three standard reference threshold curves are also shown in Fig. P2.19. Most audiometers use the ANSI characteristic and test tones of 0.125, 0.25, 0.5, 1, 1.5, 2, 3, 4, 6, and 8 KHz. The subject adjusts the attenuator until he can just hear the tone (one ear at a time). For a reading of 0 dB relative to the ANSI threshold at any frequency, there is no hearing loss. Any hearing threshold above this curve constitutes the hearing loss in dB. Typically, a hearing handicap is considered to exist for an average loss of 25 dB at 500, 1000, and 2000 Hz.[27]

The attenuator/amplifier can be replaced by a filter having inverse characteristics to those shown. Then, any hearing threshold above 0 dB constitutes the hearing loss in dB directly which simplifies the measurements. Design the filter in block diagram form. Use a maximum midband gain of 0 dB for convenience. (a) ANSI filter (American National Standards Institute), (b) ISO filter (International Standards Organization), (c) ASA filter (American Standards Association). (Hint: Cascade a low-pass and a high-pass filter.)

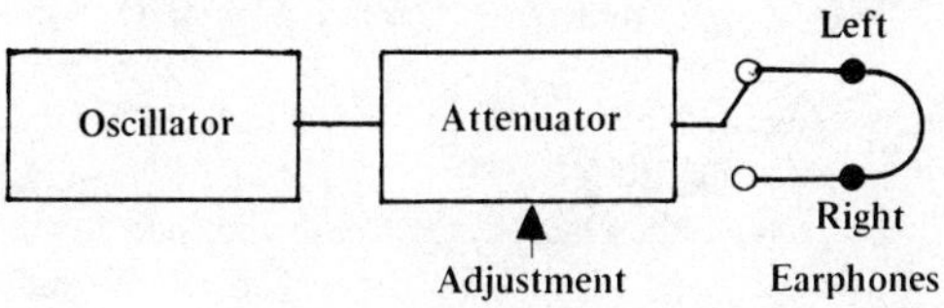

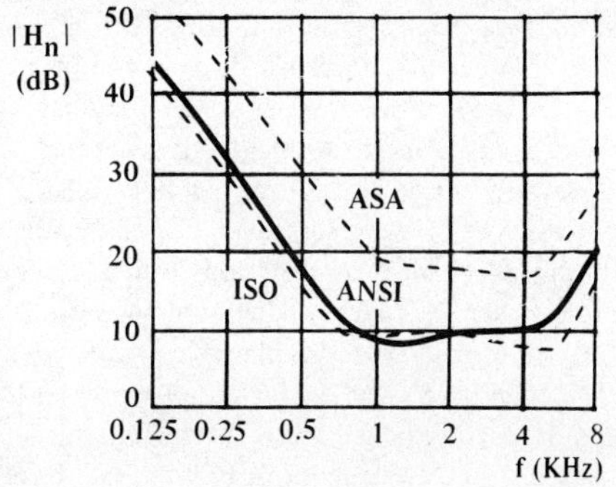

Fig. P2.19

2.20 Sound level meters are used for sound analysis in offices, factories, auditoriums, etc. These meters use standard A, B, C, or D weighting filters when making measurements.[28] Their characteristics are

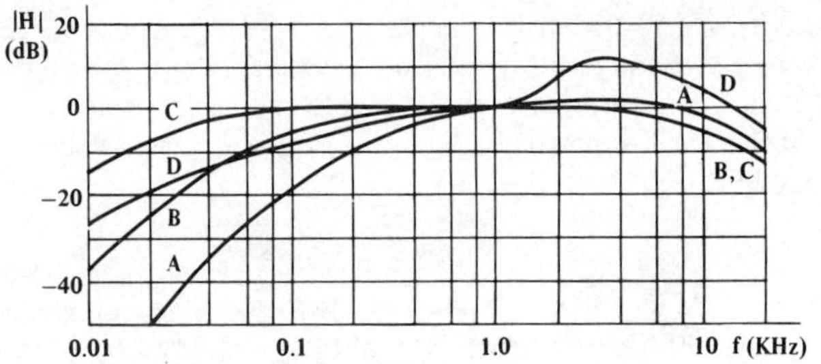

Fig. P2.20

shown in Fig. P2.20. The A weighting filter simulates the response of human hearing. Determine the proper transfer function for the: (a) A filter, (b) B filter, (c) C filter, (d) D filter. (Hint: Cascade a low-pass and a high-pass filter.)

2.21 In voice analysis, audio spectrometers utilize comb filters (i.e., a bank of identical filters in parallel) to analyze frequency content. Octave-bandwidth and one-third octave-bandwidth filters are usually used. Octave-bandwidth (one-third octave-bandwidth) filters have upper and lower 3 dB frequencies (f_2 and f_1, respectively) which differ by one (one-third) octave. Mathematically, $f_2 = 2f_1 = 2^{1/2} f_o$ (octave filters) and $f_2 = 2^{1/3} f_1 = 2^{1/6} f_o$ (one-third octave filters) where f_o is the center frequency. International standards fix the center frequencies as listed in Table P2.21.[29] The exact shape and selectivity of the filters differ between manufacturers. However, they usually exhibit about 40 dB of rejection at frequencies removed one octave from their center frequency. (a) Show how to arrange an array of octave filters for voice analysis. (b) Are the band-pass filters constant bandwidth or constant Q? (c) Assign the design parameters to the block diagram. (d) Plot the magnitude responses (note that figuratively speaking, they resemble the fingers of a comb).

Octave-bandwidth Filter (Hz)

16	1000
31.5	2000
63	4000
125	8000
250	16K
500	31.5K

One-third Octave-bandwidth Filter (Hz)

12.5	50	200	800	3150	12,500
16	63	250	1000	4000	16,000
20	80	315	1250	5000	20,000
25	100	400	1600	6300	25,000
31.5	125	500	2000	8000	31,500
40	160	630	2500	10,000	40,000

Table P2.21

2.22 A patient monitoring system requires that biological signals of the patient (EKG, etc.) be amplified, transmitted, conditioned, and recorded. The conditioning consists of filtering to best obtain the data from the transducer signals. One such system uses cascaded second-order low-pass and high-pass filters having $\zeta = 0.707$ and variable corner frequencies.[30] The low-pass filter has selectable corner frequencies of 5, 25, 50, 100, 200, 400, 800, 2500, and 10,000 Hz. The high-pass filter has selectable corner frequencies of dc, 0.1, 0.5, 25, 50, 100, 200, 400, and 800 Hz. What is the widest and narrowest bandwidth band-pass filter that can be obtained? Explain and plot their responses.

2.23 Electroencephalography studies electrical signals generated by the brain (the so-called "brain waves" or EEG). A normal adult generates an EEG spectrum extending from 0.5 Hz to 30 Hz. This range is commonly divided into four bands each identified by a Greek letter. Each band is related to and indicative of the states of awareness, attention, and consciousness. (1) Delta rhythm (0–3 Hz): deep sleep; (2) Theta rhythm (4–7 Hz): unconscious or near unconscious states and appears as one drifts towards unawareness or drowsiness; conducive to creative process and assimilation of new information; (3) Alpha rhythm (8–13 Hz): internally focused state; a non-drowsy state with an apparent enhancement of recall; not externally focused nor engaged in logical processes; (4) Beta rhythm (14–26 Hz): active thought, alertness, visual scanning, externally focused attention, and problem solving.[31] Assume that the filters are required to have the characteristics shown in Fig. P2.23. Determine the design data of the filters for type, order, center frequency, bandwidth, etc.

2.24 The telephone system uses multi-frequency (MF) pulsing as one means of conveying information between central dial offices and among toll switching centers. Each digit from 0 to 9 is assigned two out of

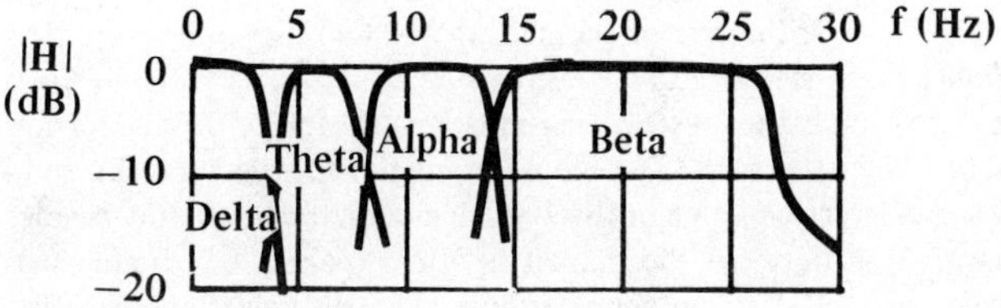

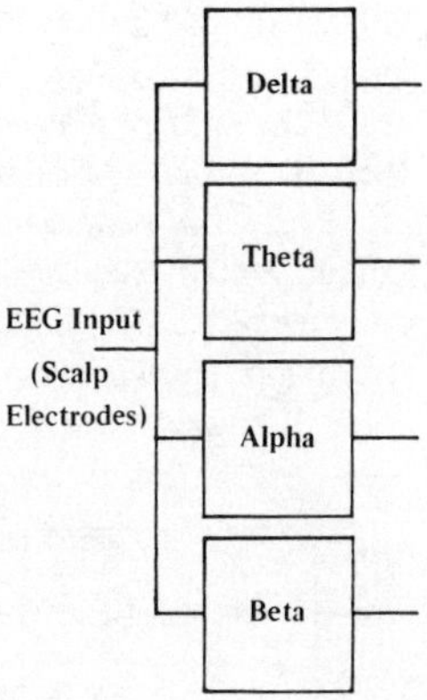

Fig. P2.23

five possible frequencies from 700 to 1500 Hz as shown in Fig. P2.24. A sixth frequency of 1700 Hz is used with the other frequencies to provide additional signals for supervision, control, and other functions.[32] These two frequencies are transmitted over telephone lines between offices after which they are decoded by six band-pass filters as shown in Fig. 2.7.3 (but tuned to different frequencies). (a) Are they constant bandwidth or constant Q filters? (b) What is the frequency spacing and is it arithmetic or geometric? (c) What must the Q's equal? (d) Plot the magnitude responses for all six filters assuming that they are first-order, their midband gain is 0 dB, and their gains crossover at their 20 dB frequencies. (e) Design the filters in the block diagram form.

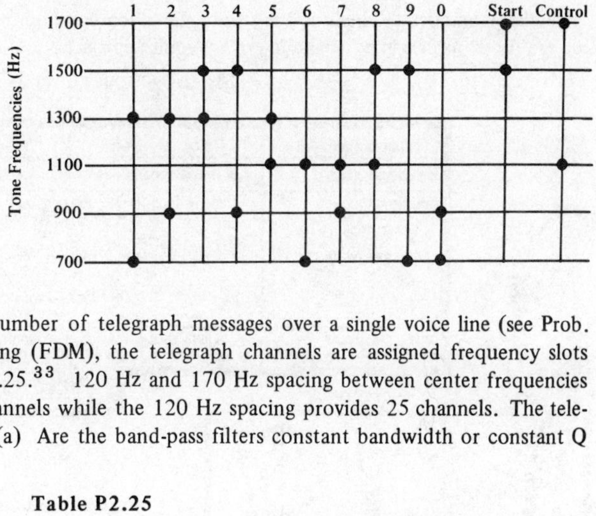

Fig. P2.24

2.25 Telegraph systems transmit a number of telegraph messages over a single voice line (see Prob. 2.27). Using frequency-division multiplexing (FDM), the telegraph channels are assigned frequency slots across the voice band as listed in Table P2.25.[33] 120 Hz and 170 Hz spacing between center frequencies is standard; 170 Hz spacing provides 18 channels while the 120 Hz spacing provides 25 channels. The telegraph data rate is usually about 50 Bps. (a) Are the band-pass filters constant bandwidth or constant Q

Table P2.25

120 HZ SPACING		170 HZ SPACING	
TRANSMIT	RECEIVE	TRANSMIT	RECEIVE
±35 Hz = less than 1.5 dB	±32 Hz = less than 2.5 dB	±50 Hz = less than 1.5 dB	±45 Hz = less than 2.5 dB
Crossover = approx. 7 dB	Crossover = approx. 16 dB	Crossover = approx. 7 dB	Crossover = approx. 16 dB
±88 Hz = at least 16 dB	±92 Hz = at least 35 dB	±125 Hz = at least 16 dB	±130 Hz = at least 35 dB

120 Hz Spacing Frequencies (Hz)

420	1020	1620	2220	2820
540	1140	1740	2340	2940
660	1260	1860	2460	3060
780	1380	1980	2580	3180
900	1500	2100	2700	3300

170 Hz Spacing Frequencies (Hz)

425	1275	2125	2975
595	1445	2295	3145
765	1615	2465	3315
935	1785	2635	
1105	1955	2805	

filters? (b) What is the frequency spacing and is it arithmetic or geometric? (c) Can first-order band-pass filters be used to obtain the magnitude response data listed in Table P2.25?

2.26 A frequency-shift-keying (FSK) communication system transmits 950 Hz for a "0" of data and 1050 Hz for a "1" of data. The digital data rate is 100 Bps. The block diagram of the system is shown in Fig. P2.26. A band-pass filter is used as a pre-detection filter in the FSK demodulator to eliminate noise and unwanted frequencies. If the phase variation between the mark ("1") and space ("0") frequencies cannot exceed 20°, design a first-order band-pass filter to obtain maximum stopband rejection. Plot the resulting magnitude response.

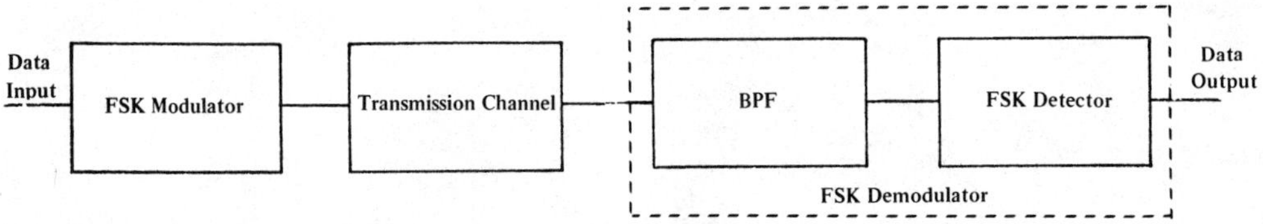

Fig. P2.26

2.27 Standard telephone lines, often referred to as voice lines, are used to transmit digital data in modulated form. The maximum data rate is about 1200 Bps. To achieve higher data rates to about 10 KBps, telephone lines are leased (or "dedicated") and then "conditioned" to achieve more uniform attenuation and delay characteristics. In the United States, AT & T's standard conditioning is referred to as C1, C2, C4, and C5. The basic leased line without conditioning is described by Schedule 3002. The distortion limits for these (except C5) and another type are listed in Fig. P2.27. The higher the conditioning number, the narrower the limits.[34] (a) The C2 characteristic is drawn in the figure. Redraw the limits on the magnitude characteristics to include the stopband response bounds. (b) Using the slopes listed, what filter orders are required? Is design by trial-and-error a good approach?

Bell Schedule	3002	C1	C2	C4	DCS-S3
INSERTION LOSS	16±1db @ 1000Hz	16±1db @ 1000Hz	16±1db @ 1000Hz	16±1db @ 1000Hz	16±1db @ 1000Hz
ATTENUATION CHARACTERISTIC (Ref. 1000Hz)	300 to 3000 Hz −3 to +12db	300 to 2700 Hz −2 to +6dB	300 to 3000 Hz −2 to +6dB	300 to 3200 Hz −2 to +6dB	300 to 3000 Hz −1 to +3dB
VARIATION IN dB	500 to 2500Hz −2 to +8db	1000 to 2400Hz −1 to +3dB	500 to 2800Hz −1 to +3dB	500 to 3000Hz −2 to +3dB	500 to 2800Hz −0.5 to +1.5dB
		2700 to 3000Hz +3 to +12dB			
ENVELOPE DELAY DISTORTION (max. μsec.)	800 to 2600 Hz 1750 μsec.	1000 to 2400Hz 1000 μsec.	1000 to 2600Hz 500 μsec.	1000 to 2600Hz 300 μsec.	1000 to 2600Hz 100 μsec.
		800 to 2600Hz 1750 μsec.	600 to 2600Hz 1500 μsec.	800 to 2800Hz 500 μsec.	600 to 2600Hz 300 μsec.
			500 to 2800Hz 3000 μsec.	600 to 3000Hz 1500 μsec.	500 to 2800Hz 600 μsec.
				500 to 3000Hz 3000 μsec.	

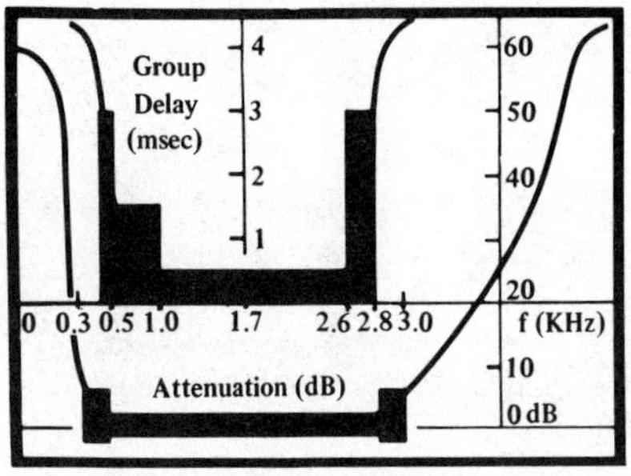

Out-of-band Characteristics
Above Band: 80dB/octave roll-off to 50dB holding to 10kHz
Below Band: 24dB/octave roll-off to 150Hz holding to DC
Delay: 3000 μ sec. minimum at band edges
DCS = Defense Communication System

Fig. P2.27 (Courtesy of SEG Electronics[35])

2.28 The standard conditioning limits for voice lines were listed in Prob. 2.27. High-order filters are required to meet the out-of-band gain characteristics. Suppose we wish only to obtain the in-band gain characteristics. (a) Design a first-order band-pass filter which will meet the 4 dB bandwidth requirements of 500 and 2800 Hz. (Hint: Remember the maximum in-band gain is 1 dB.) (b) Design a second-order band-pass filter to meet the same requirements. Use the procedure of Example 2.7.4. Verify the results using a low-pass/high-pass filter. (c) Plot the delay characteristics for the two band-pass filters of parts (a) and (b). (d) Design a first- or second-order delay equalizer which will improve the delay characteristic of part (b).

2.29 Band-pass and band-stop filters can be obtained using low-pass and high-pass filters. To construct band-pass filters, we cascade the low-pass and high-pass filters. To construct band-stop filters, we parallel the low-pass and high-pass filters. Assume the low-pass and high-pass filters are second-order having $\zeta = 0.707$ and independently controlled corner frequencies. (a) Discuss the magnitude response form of the band-pass filters. (b) Derive the transfer function of the band-stop filters. (c) How do ω_1 and ω_2 control the center frequency, bandwidth, and Q of notch in part (b)? (Hint: Let $s = j\omega$ to find $\omega_o = \sqrt{\omega_1\omega_2}$, etc.) (d) The band-stop filter operates in the following way: "Null operation is obtained by setting the high cutoff a factor of approximately two above the desired null frequency and the low cutoff a factor of approximately two below it, then moving both cutoffs very slightly up and down until phase cancellation produces the desired null. . . Null operation can be attained anywhere between approximately twice the lower limit and one-half the upper tuning limit."[36] Do the results of part (c) substantiate this? Justify.

2.30 The telephone system uses holding tones and test tones in measuring impulse noise, gain hits, phase hits, phase jitter, and crosstalk in transmission channels. Generally, the tone frequencies are 1010 Hz and 2805 Hz. Notch filters are often used to eliminate these tones when telephone lines are being monitored for other purposes. Assume that the passband gain of the notch filter equals 0 dB and that their other specifications are: (1) 3 dB frequencies = 838, 1182 Hz and 50 dB frequencies = 995, 1025 Hz; (2) 3 dB frequencies = 2650, 2960 Hz and 50 dB frequencies = 2795, 2815 Hz. (a) Plot their approximate frequency responses. (b) Is the symmetry arithmetic or geometric? (c) Can the notch filters be realized with a single first-order stage? Justify your answer.

2.31 Filters must often be "tuned" to obtain their required parameters. Tuning consists of adjusting the ω_n and ζ of each block in the design to equal the theoretical values. Consider a second-order low-pass filter block having a gain given by Eq. 2.4.2. (a) Describe how phase shift measurements can be used to determine and adjust ω_n. (b) Describe how gain measurements can be used to determine and adjust ζ.[37]

2.32 Repeat Prob. 2.31 and explain how to tune (a) second-order high-pass and (b) first-order band-pass filters having the transfer functions given by Eqs. 2.6.3 and 2.7.3, respectively.

2.33 Filters having zeros of transmission are more difficult to tune than those having no finite zeros. Tuning consists of adjusting ω_{np}, ζ_p, and ω_{nz} of each block in the design to equal the theoretical values. Consider a band-stop filter block having gain

$$H(s) = H_o \frac{\omega_{np}^2}{\omega_{nz}^2} \frac{s^2 + \omega_{nz}^2}{s^2 + 2\zeta_p\omega_{np}s + \omega_{np}^2}$$

(a) Describe how gain measurements can be used to determine and adjust ω_{nz}. (b) Describe how phase shift measurements can be used to determine and adjust ζ_p. (c) Describe how gain measurements can be used to determine and adjust ω_{np}.

2.34 A modified lag filter has a transfer function $H(s) = (1 + s/z)/[(1 + s)(1 + s/2z)]$ where $z = 2$. (a) Plot the magnitude, phase, and delay responses for H(s). (b) Determine the first-order dominant pole approximation for H(s).

2.35 (a) Plot the magnitude, phase, and delay responses of the modified lead-lag filter having the gain given in Prob. 2.34 where $z = \frac{1}{4}$. (b) Determine second-order dominant pole approximation for H(s).

2.36 Determine the first-order dominant pole approximation for a second-order low-pass filter having gains H(s) of (a) $1/(s^2 + 1.8s + 1)$, (b) $1/(s^2 + 1.6s + 1)$.

2.37 Determine the first-order dominant pole approximation for a second-order synchronously-tuned low-pass filter having gain $H(s) = 100/(s^2 + 20s + 100)$.

2.38 Determine the dominant pole-zero approximations for the magnitude responses of the ANSI, ISO, and ASA filters used in audiometers and discussed in Prob. 2.19. Note that the excess phase term cannot be evaluated since the phase characteristics of the filters are not given.

2.39 Repeat Prob. 2.38 for the A, B, C, and D weighting filters used in sound level meters and discussed in Prob. 2.20.

2.40 Determine the dominant pole approximation for the phase-locked loop of Example 2.9.3 when $\zeta = 0.3$ and $B = 2\pi(1000\text{ Hz})$.

2.41 Determine the general delay characteristics of the lead-lag filter having a gain given by Eq. 2.3.31.

Plot its delay response.

2.42 Plot the delay characteristic of the phase-locked loop of Example 2.9.3 where $\zeta = 0.5$ and $B = 2\pi(1000\text{ Hz})$.

2.43 Repeat Prob. 2.4 2 when $\zeta = 0.3$.

2.44 Plot the delay characteristics of the filters determined in Prob. 2.16 using the approach of Example 2.10.8.

2.45 (a) Write the transfer function for a second-order low-pass filter having $\zeta = 0.707$ and $\omega_n = 1$. Accurately plot its delay characteristic. (This produces a Butterworth filter as we shall see in Chap. 4.) (b) What is the dc delay and the maximum delay? (c) The delay peaking must be reduced by use of a delay equalizer. Using a first-order all-pass filter, determine its parameters so that the in-band delay variation of the overall filter is reduced as much as possible. (Hint: Equate dc and maximum delay values.) (d) Plot the overall delay characteristic. Has the low-pass filter been effectively delay equalized?

2.46 A delay equalizer is designed to equalize the band-pass filter delay of Example 2.10.6. Its parameters are shown in Fig. P2.46. (a) Calculate the dc and maximum delays for the delay equalizer. (b) Plot its delay characteristic and the overall characteristic using Fig. 2.10.12. (c) Has the band-pass filter been effectively delay equalized?

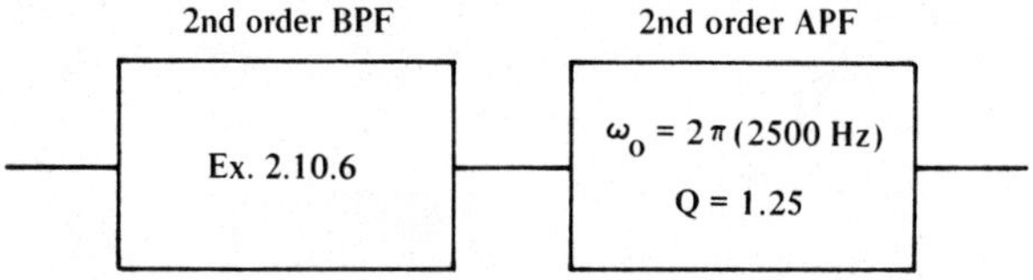

Fig. P2.46

2.47 The magnitude and phase of a third-order Butterworth and Chebyshev filter were determined in Example 2.4.2. Now plot their delay characteristics.

2.48 As we shall see in Chap. 4, the delay characteristics of fourth-order (a) Butterworth and (b) 0.5 dB Chebyshev filters having unity 3dB bandwidths are shown in Figs. 4.3.2 and 4.4.6. Both filters exhibit delay peaking which results in delay distortion. The delay distortion can be reduced by cascading a delay equalizer with either of these filters. Repeat parts (b)–(d) of Prob. 2.45.

2.49 Plot the delay characteristic for the third-order elliptic low-pass filter having the transfer function

$$H(s) = 0.2\,\frac{s^2 + 1.47^2}{(s + 0.463)[(s + 0.129)^2 + 0.962^2]}$$

and a magnitude characteristic like that shown in Fig. 4.8.1 where $M_p = 2$ dB, $M_s = 25$ dB, and $\Omega_s = 1.33$.

REFERENCES

1. D'Azzo, J. J., and C. H. Houpis, *Control System Analysis and Synthesis*, Chaps. 8–10, McGraw-Hill, NY, 1960.
2. 1974 Catalog, p. 2, Krohn-Hite Corp., Cambridge, MA, 1974.
3. Churchill, R. V., *Complex Variables and Applications*, 2nd ed., Chap. 3, McGraw-Hill, NY, 1960.
4. Bode, H. W., *Network Analysis and Feedback Amplifier Design*, Chaps. 13–15, D. Van Nostrand, NY, 1945.
5. Selby, S. M. (ed.), *Standard Mathematical Tables*, 21st ed., p. 472, Chemical Rubber Co., Cleveland, OH, 1973.
6. Valley, G. E., Jr., and H. Wallman, *Vacuum Tube Amplifiers*, Chap. 7, McGraw-Hill, NY, 1948.
7. Elder, M. A., R. L. Tucker, and J. D. Winter, "Higher order multiplexing equipment," Telecommunications, pp. 32–41, Jan., 1971.
   Libby, P. T., "Time division multiplexing," Telecommunications, pp. 55–81, June, 1972.
8. "Filters for telephone message circuit noise measurement," Feedback, vol. 1, no. 3, pp. 8–9, KTI, Santa Clara, CA, Dec., 1973.

Beckman, U. L., "Voice channel noise measurements at line frequency on carrier frequency communications systems," Telecommunications, pp. 21–24, March, 1971.
9. Dutta Roy, S. C., "On the Q of cascaded identical resonators," Proc. IEEE, vol. 61, p. 790, June, 1973.
10. Ref. 6, Chap. 5.
Docherty, I. S., and J. L. Casse, "The design of maximally flat wideband amplifiers with double-tuned interstage coupling," Proc. IEEE, vol. 55, pp. 513–522, April, 1967.
11. Van Valkenburg, M. E., *Introduction to Modern Network Synthesis*, Chap. 10, Wiley, NY, 1960.
12. Ref. 5, p. 470.
13. Ref. 5, p. 473.
14. Clement, P. R., "A note on third-order linear systems," IRE Trans. on Automatic Control, vol. AC-5, p. 151, June, 1960.
15. Viterbi, A. J., *Principles of Coherent Communication*, Chap. 2, McGraw-Hill, NY, 1966.
Klapper, J., and J. T. Frankle, *Phase-Locked and Frequency Feedback Systems*, pp. 62–63, Academic Press, NY, 1972.
16. Ghausi, M. S., *Principles and Design of Linear Active Circuits*, Chap. 12, McGraw-Hill, NY, 1965.
Millman, J., and H. Taub, *Pulse, Digital, and Switching Waveforms*, Chap. 5, McGraw-Hill, NY, 1965.
17. Gardner, F. M., *Phaselock Techniques*, Chap. 2, Wiley, NY, 1966.
18. Lindquist, C. S., "Delay characteristics of second-order bandpass filters," Proc. IEEE, vol. 58, pp. 826–828, May, 1970.
19. Ref. 3, Chap. 12.
Tuttle, D. F., Jr., *Network Synthesis*, vol. 1, Chaps. 3 and 8, Wiley, NY, 1958.
20. Lane, C. E., "Phase distortion in telephone apparatus," Bell System Tech. J., vol. 9, pp. 493–521, July, 1930.
21. Olson, H. F., *Modern Sound Reproduction*, Chap. 8, Van Nostrand Reinhold, NY, 1972.
22. Series 1000, Appl. Note AN–12, 4 p., Rockland Systems Corp., West Nyack, NY, 1970.
23. Oliver, W., Marconi Instruments Ltd., "White noise loading of multi-channel communications systems," Sept., 1964.
24. Mennie, D., "What's new in consumer electronics circuits," IEEE Spectrum, vol. 10, pp. 26–35, Dec., 1973.
25. Lowman, C. E., *Magnetic Recording*, Chap. 7, McGraw-Hill, NY, 1972.
26. Ref. 21, Chap. 9.
27. Ref. 21, Chap. 13.
Grove, A. C., "International standardization–interface with the future," IEEE Spectrum, vol. 3, pp. 91–101, Aug., 1966.
28. SC301-24 Data Sheet, 1 p., Spectral Dynamics Corp. of San Diego, San Diego, CA, 10/72.
Starr, E. A., "Measuring noise pollution," IEEE Spectrum, vol. 9, pp. 18–25, June, 1972.
29. Starr, E. A., Ref. 28.
30. Koerner, H., and E. F. Furst, "Electrically isolated instrumentation for cardiac catherization laboratory," Conf. Rec., pp. 706–710, 7th Asilomar Conf. on Circuits, Systems, and Computers, Nov., 1973.
31. "Filters for EEG analysis and feedback," Feedback, vol. 1, no. 2, pp. 4–7, KTI, Santa Clara, CA, July, 1973.
32. Talley, D., *Basic Telephone Switching Systems*, Chap. 4, Hayden, NJ, 1969.
33. Catalog, 4 p., BG Electronics, Inc., Mt. Vernon, NY.
34. Martin, J., *Systems Analysis for Data Transmission*, Chap. 17, Prentice-Hall, NJ, 1972.
35. Standard Telephone Data Line Simulators, Data Sheet 348SM873, 1 p., SEG Electronics, Richmond Hill, NY, 8/73.
36. Ref. 2, p. 9.
37. Luttropp, D., "Measure phase instead of amplitude," Electronic Design, pp. 72–74, April 13, 1972, copyright Hayden Publishing, 1972.

3 TIME DOMAIN ANALYSIS

Two arrows in the quiver are better than one, and three are better still

In the previous chapter, we studied the ac steady-state frequency domain behavior of various filters. This chapter is concerned with studying their corresponding time domain behavior. We know that the time domain and frequency domain are interrelated by the Fourier transform and, more generally, the Laplace transform. We discussed these transforms at great length in Chap. 1. Unfortunately, there is no more *direct* relationship between the time domain behavior of a filter and its ac steady-state behavior. In general, exact analysis requires that the time domain behavior be determined from the frequency domain behavior. For complex systems, this is a tedious operation where little insight is gained into time domain performance. However, an exact analysis becomes feasible for simple systems, and the results can be used to give insight into the general behavior of the more complicated systems. Thus, this analysis will be carried out for a number of the commonly encountered filters discussed in the previous chapter.

Fortunately, several useful approximations exist which allow time domain behavior to be estimated, and design tradeoffs to be made directly between the frequency and time domains. These analysis aids make use of Elmore's results, Valley and Wallman's relation, and the dominant pole-zero approximations investigated in the last chapter. These approximations will be fully developed and the results compared with those obtained using exact analysis. By using these analysis aids, we can extrapolate the exact results describing simple systems to approximate results describing more complex systems. The engineer will find this chapter to be a useful collection of time domain information and an invaluable complement to the frequency domain results of the previous chapter.

3.1 RELATION BETWEEN TIME AND FREQUENCY DOMAINS

In the previous chapter, we studied the transfer function H(s) of various filters where

$$H(s) = \frac{\sum_{j=0}^{m} a_j s^j}{\sum_{i=0}^{n} b_i s^i} = \frac{a_m}{b_n}\frac{\prod_{j=1}^{m}(s+z_j)}{\prod_{i=1}^{n}(s+p_i)}, \qquad \operatorname{Re} s \in R \tag{3.1.1}$$

from Eq. 2.0.1. The transfer function H(s) is equal to the ratio of the Laplace-transformed output Y(s) of the filter and its Laplace-transformed input X(s), where the filter has zero initial conditions (i.e., zero initial stored energy). Therefore, the output Y(s) in the frequency domain equals

$$Y(s) = H(s)X(s) \tag{3.1.2}$$

The output y(t) in the time domain equals

$$y(t) = h(t)*x(t) \tag{3.1.3}$$

using the time convolution theorem of Table 1.8.2.

When the filter input is an impulse so that $x(t) = U_0(t)$, then $X(s) = 1$ and the filter output equals $Y(s) = H(s)$. The impulse response h(t) of the filter equals the inverse Laplace transform of H(s) where

$$h(t) = \mathcal{L}^{-1}[H(s)] = \frac{1}{2\pi j}\int_{c-j\infty}^{c+j\infty} H(s)e^{st}\,ds, \qquad c \in R \tag{3.1.4}$$

Therefore, H(s) equals the Laplace transform of h(t) where

$$H(s) = \mathcal{L}[h(t)] = \int_{-\infty}^{\infty} h(t)e^{-st}\,dt, \qquad \text{Re } s \in R \tag{3.1.5}$$

Thus, once the impulse response h(t) is known, the system response to any arbitrary input x(t) can be found. This means that the behavior of the filter is completely determined by its H(s) or h(t). In the last chapter, we discussed the frequency domain behavior of H(s). Now we want to find the corresponding time domain behavior. The engineer may find it useful to reread Sec. 1.8 and review Laplace transformations before proceeding further.

3.2 PARTIAL FRACTION EXPANSIONS

To determine h(t), we must find the inverse Laplace transform of H(s). This is facilitated by expressing H(s) in a partial fraction expansion which is[1]

$$H(s) = \sum_{i=1}^{n} \frac{K_i}{s + p_i} \tag{3.2.1}$$

K_i is the residue of H(s) evaluated at the pole $s = -p_i$. Such an expansion or representation is valid for any rational H(s) having: (1) $n > m$ (denominator order > numerator order) and (2) only simple or first-order poles. The expansion is valid for all values of s. In a moment, we will consider the modifications required in the expansion when these two restrictions are removed.

The residue K_i is obtained by multiplying H(s) by $(s + p_i)$ and evaluating the product at $s = -p_i$ as

$$K_i = (s + p_i)H(s)\big|_{s=-p_i} = K_i + \sum_{\substack{q=1 \\ q\neq i}}^{n} \frac{(s + p_i)K_i}{s + p_q}\Bigg|_{s=-p_i} = K_i \tag{3.2.2}$$

All the terms within the summation equal zero since $p_q \neq p_i$. Notice also that if we express $H(s) = N(s)/D(s)$, then K_i can be expressed as

$$K_i = \lim_{s\to -p_i} (s + p_i)\frac{N(s)}{D(s)} = \lim_{s\to -p_i} \frac{N(s)}{D(s)/(s + p_i)} = \frac{N(s)}{dD(s)/ds}\bigg|_{s=-p_i} \tag{3.2.3}$$

which is a useful form in many situations. The residue is a measure of the contribution to the filter response due to the pole at $s = -p_i$. A pole close to the other poles but far-removed from the zeros have large residues, and visa versa.

The residue has the well-known graphical interpretation shown in Fig. 3.2.1. From Eq. 3.2.2, K_i is a complex number equal to

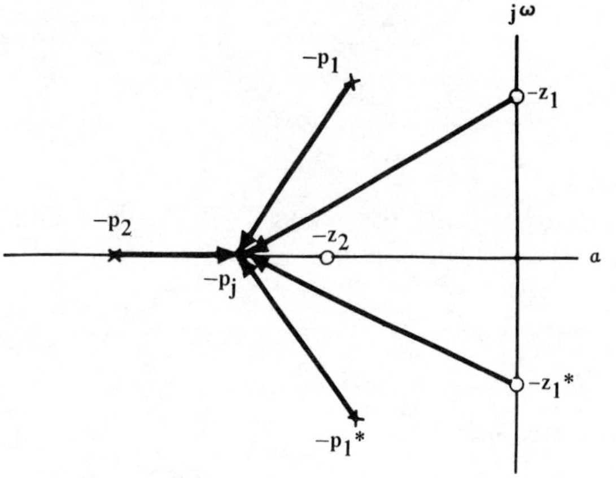

Fig. 3.2.1 Graphical interpretation for residue K_i.

$$K_i = (s+p_i)H(s)\big|_{s=-p_i} = \frac{a_m \prod_{j=1}^{m} (z_j - p_i)}{b_n \prod_{\substack{q=1\\ q\neq i}}^{n} (p_q - p_i)} = \frac{a_m \prod_{j=1}^{m} M_j \exp j\theta_j}{b_n \prod_{\substack{q=1\\ q\neq i}}^{n} N_q \exp j\phi_q} = |K_i| e^{j \arg K_i} \tag{3.2.4}$$

whose magnitude and angle equal

$$|K_i| = (a_m/b_n) \prod_{j=1}^{m} M_j \Big/ \prod_{\substack{q=1\\ q\neq i}}^{n} N_q, \qquad \arg K_i = \sum_{j=1}^{m} \theta_j - \sum_{\substack{q=1\\ q\neq i}}^{n} \theta_q \tag{3.2.5}$$

The magnitude of K_i is equal to the product of a_m and the "zero" vectors divided by the product of b_n and the "pole" vectors. The "zero" vectors originate at each zero and extend to the test pole $s = -p_i$; the "pole" vectors originate at each pole and extend to $s = -p_i$ except, of course, the test pole itself. The phase of K_i is equal to the sum of "zero" vector angles minus the "pole" vector angles. Since the polynomials in the numerator and denominator of H(s) have real coefficients, all poles and zeros exist in complex conjugate pairs when complex. Thus, the net angle contribution from a complex pole or zero pair must be zero when $-p_i$ is real and, therefore, all real poles have positive or negative real residues. The residues for a complex pole pair must be complex conjugates so that the two terms in the partial fraction expansion arising from these poles can be re-expressed as

$$\frac{K}{s+a+j\omega} + \frac{K^*}{s+a-j\omega} = 2\,\frac{(s+a)\,\mathrm{Re}\,K + \omega\,\mathrm{Im}\,K}{(s+a)^2+\omega^2} \tag{3.2.6}$$

Thus, the partial fractional expansion form for an H(s) having only n simple poles (of which p pairs are complex) and $n > m$ is

$$H(s) = \sum_{i=p+1}^{n} \frac{K_i}{s+p_i} + \sum_{i=1}^{p} \frac{(s+a_{2i-1})\,\mathrm{Re}\,K_{2i-1} + \omega_{2i-1}\,\mathrm{Im}\,K_{2i-1}}{(s+a_{2i-1})^2 + \omega_{2i-1}^{\ 2}} \tag{3.2.7}$$

where the K_i are given by Eq. 3.2.3. It is useful to notice that if H(s) fails to have a pole at some s value where the residue is evaluated, then $K_i = 0$ at that point. This situation arises, for instance, when there is a pole-zero cancellation in H(s) which is not recognized. It is encouraging to see that residue evaluation is so forgiving. Now let us consider the more general situation.

First, suppose that H(s) has a pole of order k. Then H(s) equals

$$H(s) = \frac{a_m}{b_n} \frac{\prod_{j=1}^{m} (s + z_j)}{(s + p_1)^k \prod_{i=k+1}^{n} (s + p_i)} \tag{3.2.8}$$

where $n > m$. Then the partial fraction expansion of H(s) equals

$$H(s) = \sum_{i=1}^{k} \frac{K_{1,i}}{(s + p_1)^i} + \sum_{i=k+1}^{n} \frac{K_i}{s + p_i} \tag{3.2.9}$$

Thus, the portion of the partial fraction expansion of H(s) corresponding to the *k*th-order term equals

$$\sum_{i=1}^{k} \frac{K_{1,i}}{(s + p_1)^i} = \frac{K_{1,k}}{(s + p_1)^k} + \frac{K_{1,k-1}}{(s + p_1)^{k-1}} + \ldots + \frac{K_{1,1}}{s + p_1} \tag{3.2.10}$$

The residue $K_{q,i}$ is subscripted so that q equals the pole number, and i equals the order of pole begin considered. Note that if the pole is simple, then $k = 1$ and all the $K_{1,i} = 0$ except $K_{1,1}$. The residue $K_{1,i}$ equals

$$K_{1,i} = \frac{1}{(k - i)!} \frac{d^{k-i}}{ds^{k-i}} [(s + p_1)^k H(s)] \Big|_{s=-p_i}, \qquad i = 1, 2, \ldots, k \tag{3.2.11}$$

using the same reasoning as that resulting in Eq. 3.2.2. As before, this equation is true for both real and complex multiple-order poles. Thus, for every multiple-order pole in H(s), we must add the summation terms given by Eq. 3.2.10 to the partial fraction expansion for H(s).[2]

Now suppose that H(s) has at least as many zeros as poles so that $n \leq m$. Then additional terms must be included in the partial fraction expansion of H(s) given by Eq. 3.2.9. The partial fraction expansion becomes

$$H(s) = \sum_{i=0}^{m-n} K_{-i} s^i + R(s) \tag{3.2.12}$$

where R(s) is given by Eq. 3.2.9. The terms in ascending powers of s from s^0 to s^{m-n} arise when the degree of the numerator is equal to or greater than the degree of the denominator. The residues of these terms equal

$$K_{-i} = \frac{1}{(m - n - i)!} \frac{d^{m-n-i}}{d(1/s)^{m-n-i}} [H(s)/s^{m-n}] \Big|_{|s|=\infty}, \qquad i = 0, 1, \ldots, m - n \tag{3.2.13}$$

using the same reasoning as that used to obtain Eq. 3.2.11 and recalling that $R(s) \to 0$ as $|s| \to \infty$. Alternatively, if we express H(s) in the summation form of Eq. 3.1.1, then we can express H(s) in its Laurent series about $|s| = \infty$ as

$$H(s) = \frac{a_m}{b_n} s^{m-n} + \frac{a_{m-1}b_n - a_m b_{n-1}}{b_n^2} s^{m-n-1} + \ldots + c_0 s^0 + \sum_{i=1}^{\infty} c_i/s^i \tag{3.2.14}$$

This series is obtained by dividing the denominator of H(s) into its numerator. The remainder function (given by the summation) which is left after long division has no poles at infinity and approaches zero as $|s| \to \infty$. It can be expressed in the form of Eq. 3.2.9. Notice that the residues of the finite poles can be evaluated using H(s) or simply the remainder R(s) and the residue equations (Eqs. 3.2.2, 3.2.3, or 3.2.11). Thus, this flexibility should be used to advantage.[3]

3.3 IMPULSE RESPONSE

We see from this discussion that the partial fraction expansion for a rational H(s), given by Eq. 3.1.1 for Re s > max Re $(p_i, \ldots, p_n)$, equals

$$H(s) = \sum_{i=p+1}^{n} \frac{K_i}{s + p_i} + \sum_{i=1}^{p} \frac{(s + a_{2i-1}) \operatorname{Re} K_{2i-1} + \omega_{2i-1} \operatorname{Im} K_{2i-1}}{(s + a_{2i-1})^2 + \omega_{2i-1}^2} \tag{3.3.1}$$

when H(s) has n > m and only first-order poles. The unit impulse response h(t) of the system may now be easily determined by finding the inverse Laplace transform of H(s) given by Eq. 3.1.4. Since the Laplace transform and its inverse are linear operators as shown in Table 1.8.2, h(t) is equal to the sum of responses due to each individual term in the partial fraction expansion of H(s). Using the transform pairs listed in Table 1.8.1 as

$$\mathcal{L}^{-1}\left(\frac{1}{s + p}\right) = e^{-pt}\, U_{-1}(t)$$
$$\mathcal{L}^{-1}\left(\frac{s + a}{(s + a)^2 + \omega^2}\right) = e^{-at} \cos \omega t\, U_{-1}(t), \qquad \mathcal{L}^{-1}\left(\frac{\omega}{(s + a)^2 + \omega^2}\right) = e^{-at} \sin \omega t\, U_{-1}(t) \tag{3.3.2}$$

then we can determine h(t) from its partial fraction expansion, given by Eq. 3.3.1, as

$$\begin{aligned} h(t) = \mathcal{L}^{-1}[H(s)] &= \sum_{i=p+1}^{n} K_i e^{-p_i t} + 2 \sum_{i=1}^{p} e^{-a_{2i-1} t} [\operatorname{Re} K_{2i-1} \cos \omega_{2i-1} t \\ &\qquad + \operatorname{Im} K_{2i-1} \sin \omega_{2i-1} t]\, U_{-1}(t) \\ &= \sum_{i=p+1}^{n} K_i e^{-p_i t} + 2 \sum_{i=1}^{p} |K_{2i-1}|\, e^{-a_{2i-1} t} \cos(\omega_{2i-1} t - \arg K_{2i-1})\, U_{-1}(t) \end{aligned} \tag{3.3.3}$$

The response form of h(t) depends upon the pole locations as shown in Fig. 3.3.1. A simple real-axis pole gives rise to an exponential response whose time constant depends upon its location on the real axis. The root locus for this type of term was shown in Fig. 2.2.2a. Left-half-plane locations give rise to exponentially decreasing responses (stable responses); right-half-plane locations to exponentially increasing responses (unstable responses); and origin locations to a constant

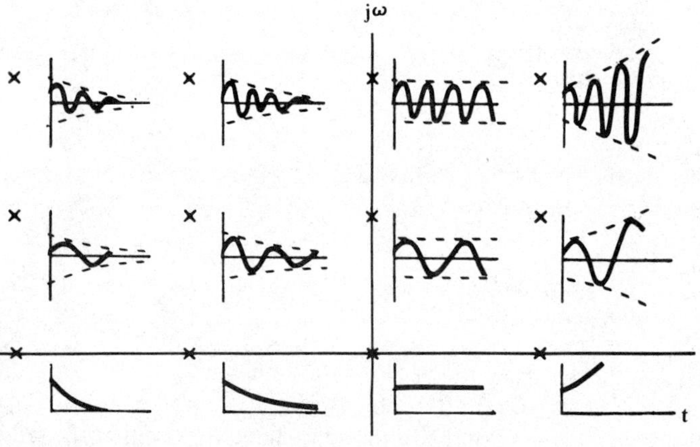

Fig. 3.3.1 Impulse response for first-order poles having various s-plane locations. (The conjugate poles are not shown.)

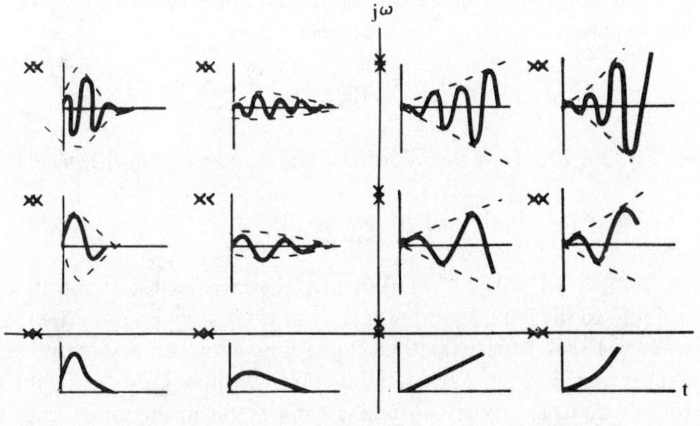

Fig. 3.3.2 Impulse response for second-order poles having various s-plane locations. (The conjugate poles are not shown.)

response (conditionally stable response). The closer the pole is to the origin, the larger the time constant and the slower the response.

Complex poles give rise to oscillating responses. Their root locus was shown in Fig. 2.2.2b. The frequency of oscillation is equal to the imaginary part of the pole; it equals zero for poles on the real axis and increases as the imaginary part of the poles increases. The amplitude of the response is bounded positively and negatively by exponential envelopes. The positive exponential envelope corresponds to the exponential response of a real-axis pole whose real part is equal to that of the complex pole being considered; the negative exponential envelope is the negative of the positive exponential envelope. All pole pairs on a vertical line in Fig. 3.3.1 have the same real part and, therefore, have the same exponential response bounds (assuming their residues have the same value). Left-half-plane poles give rise to oscillating responses with exponentially-decreasing bounds (stable); right-half-plane poles to oscillating responses with exponentially-increasing bounds (unstable); and jω-axis poles to oscillating responses with constant bounds (conditionally stable).

Now let us consider the effects that multiple-order poles have upon the impulse response. If H(s) contains a pole p_1 of order k, then the additional terms in the partial fraction expansion of H(s) given by Eq. 3.3.1 are

$$H_1(s) = \sum_{i=1}^{k} \frac{K_{1,i}}{(s+p_1)^i}, \qquad \operatorname{Re} s > \operatorname{Re} p_1 \tag{3.3.4}$$

using Eq. 3.2.10. Then the additional terms in the impulse response are

$$h_1(t) = \mathcal{L}^{-1}[H_1(s)] = \sum_{i=1}^{k} \frac{|K_{1,i}|}{(i-1)!} t^{i-1} e^{-a_1 t} U_{-1}(t) \tag{3.3.5}$$

from Table 1.8.1 assuming the poles are real. If they are complex where $p_1 = a_1 + j\omega_1$, then the response becomes

$$h_1(t) = 2 \sum_{i=1}^{k} \frac{|K_{1,i}|}{(i-1)!} t^{i-1} e^{-a_1 t} \cos(\omega_1 t + \arg K_{1,i}) \; U_{-1}(t) \tag{3.3.6}$$

In either case, the response decays to zero for Re $p_1 > 0$, but rises to infinity for Re $p_1 \leq 0$. Thus, multiple-poles on the jω-axis cause the system to be unstable. Therefore, stable causal systems can have only first-order (simple) poles on the jω-axis. The impulse response for second-order poles having different s-plane locations is shown in Fig. 3.3.2.

When the numerator of H(s) is of equal or greater degree than the denominator, the partial action expansion of H(s) must be augmented by

$$H_2(s) = \sum_{i=0}^{m-n} K_{-i} s^i, \qquad \text{Re } s = 0 \tag{3.3.7}$$

from Eq. 3.2.12. Then the additional terms appearing in the partial fraction expansion of H(s) are

$$h_2(t) = \mathcal{L}^{-1}[H_2(s)] = \sum_{i=0}^{m-n} K_{-i} U_i(t) \tag{3.3.8}$$

from Table 1.8.1. These terms involve the impulse $U_0(t)$ and its derivatives. Since these terms contribute to the impulse response only at t = 0, they do not affect system stability.

We see that partial fraction expansions allow us to determine the impulse response of any system having a rational transfer function. Although this is a conceptually simple process, it can become tedious and time consuming for systems having more than several poles. In practice, the engineer will want to utilize complete transform tables where the partial fraction expansions have already been tabulated.[4] Nevertheless, the residue and partial fraction expansion viewpoint is necessary and useful for justifying and interpreting the tabulated results.

EXAMPLE 3.3.1 Determine the impulse response of the first-order low-pass filter having the transfer function given by Eq. 2.3.12 as

$$H(s) = \frac{K\omega_n}{s + \omega_n}, \qquad \text{Re } s > -\omega_n \tag{3.3.9}$$

Solution The impulse response h(t) of the filter equals

$$h(t) = \mathcal{L}^{-1}[H(s)] = [K\omega_n e^{-\omega_n t}]U_{-1}(t) \tag{3.3.10}$$

using Table 1.8.1. The normalized response is shown in Fig. 3.3.3. Increasing the bandwidth ω_n of the filter decreases the time constant $T = 1/\omega_n$ of the impulse response and increases its magnitude. Increasing the filter gain increases the magnitude of the impulse response but does not affect its time constant.

EXAMPLE 3.3.2 Determine the impulse response for the general second-order low-pass filter having a transfer function given by Eq. 2.9.27 as

$$H(s) = \frac{as + b}{s^2 + 2\zeta s + 1}, \qquad \text{Re } s > -\zeta \tag{3.3.11}$$

and normalized poles $s = -\zeta \pm j(1 - \zeta^2)^{1/2}$.

Solution We shall find the impulse response using three different methods. First, let us simply manipulate the transfer function into a form where the Laplace transform table (Table 1.8.1) may be used directly. If H(s) is rewritten as

$$H(s) = \frac{a(s + \zeta) + \dfrac{b - a\zeta}{\sqrt{1 - \zeta^2}}\sqrt{1 - \zeta^2}}{(s + \zeta)^2 + (\sqrt{1 - \zeta^2})^2} \tag{3.3.12}$$

then h(t) can be written by inspection as

$$\begin{aligned} h(t) = \mathcal{L}^{-1}[H(s)] &= e^{-\zeta t}\left[a \cos \sqrt{1 - \zeta^2}\, t + \frac{b - a\zeta}{\sqrt{1 - \zeta^2}} \sin \sqrt{1 - \zeta^2}\, t\right] U_{-1}(t) \\ &= \sqrt{a^2 + \frac{(b - a\zeta)^2}{1 - \zeta^2}}\; e^{-\zeta t} \cos\left[\sqrt{1 - \zeta^2}\, t - \tan^{-1} \frac{b/a - \zeta}{\sqrt{1 - \zeta^2}}\right] U_{-1}(t) \end{aligned} \tag{3.3.13}$$

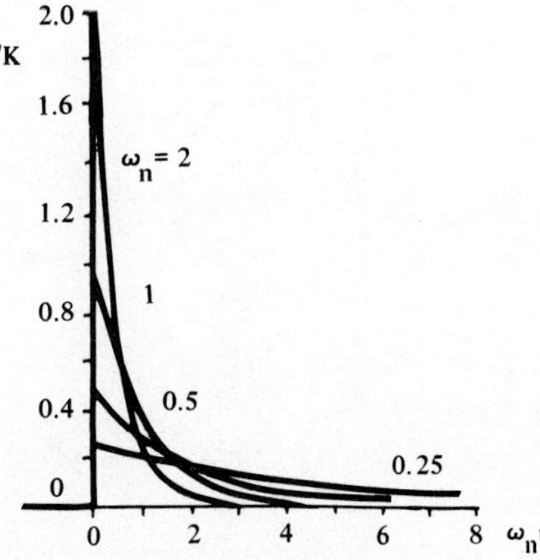

Fig. 3.3.3 Impulse response of first-order low-pass filter.

Thus, if $b/a = \zeta$, then h(t) becomes a cosine wave; when a = 0, then h(t) becomes a sine wave.

Now let us use the residue approach and Eq. 3.2.6. Here, the residue of the pole at $s = -\zeta + j(1 - \zeta^2)^{1/2}$ equals

$$K = (s + \zeta - j\sqrt{1-\zeta^2})H(s)\big|_{s=-\zeta+j\sqrt{1-\zeta^2}}$$

$$= \frac{b + a(-\zeta + j\sqrt{1-\zeta^2})}{-\zeta + j\sqrt{1-\zeta^2} + \zeta + j\sqrt{1-\zeta^2}} = \frac{b - a\zeta + ja\sqrt{1-\zeta^2}}{2j\sqrt{1-\zeta^2}} = \tfrac{1}{2}\left(a - j\frac{b - a\zeta}{\sqrt{1-\zeta^2}}\right) \tag{3.3.14}$$

The conjugate pole has a residue of value K*. Then the impulse response equals

$$h(t) = 2|K|e^{-\zeta t}\cos(\sqrt{1-\zeta^2}\,t - \arg K)\,U_{-1}(t) \tag{3.3.15}$$

which agrees with h(t) given by Eq. 3.3.13.

Lastly, let us use the derivative form given by Eq. 3.2.3. Here

$$K = \frac{\text{Num } H(s)}{d\,\text{Den } H(s)/ds}\bigg|_{s=-p_i} = \frac{b + as}{2(s+\zeta)}\bigg|_{s=-\zeta+j\sqrt{1-\zeta^2}} = \frac{b - a(\zeta - j\sqrt{1-\zeta^2})}{j2\sqrt{1-\zeta^2}}$$

$$= \tfrac{1}{2}\left(a - j\frac{b - a\zeta}{\sqrt{1-\zeta^2}}\right) \tag{3.3.16}$$

which agrees with the residue given by Eq. 3.3.14. Thus, the impulse response is also the same. In general analysis, many residue evaluation methods may be used, but the easiest depends upon the problem being solved. As Kipling said, "There are nine and sixty ways of constructing tribal lays, and–every–single–one–of–them–is–right!"

EXAMPLE 3.3.3 Determine the partial fraction expansion for the transformed step response R(s) of the *n*th-order synchronously-tuned low-pass filter. Its transfer function H(s) was given by Eq. 2.3.25 so that R(s) equals

$$R(s) = \frac{H(s)}{s} = \frac{p_o^n}{s(s+p_o)^n} = \sum_{i=1}^{n} \frac{K_{o,i}}{(s+p_o)^i} + \frac{K_1}{s} \tag{3.3.17}$$

Solution Here is a case involving multiple-order poles. Using Eq. 3.2.11, the various residues equal

$$K_{o,n} = (1/0!)\,[(s+p_o)^n R(s)]_{s=-p_o} = p_o^n[1/s]_{s=-p_o} = -p_o^{n-1}$$

$$K_{o,n-1} = (p_o^n/1!)\,d[1/s]/ds\big|_{s=-p_o} = -p_o^{n-2} \tag{3.3.18a, b}$$

$$K_{0,n-2} = (p_o{}^n/2!)\, d[-1/s^2]/ds\,\big|_{s=-p_o} = \tfrac{1}{2}[2/s^3]_{s=-p_o} = -p_o{}^{n-3}$$

$$\vdots \qquad (3.3.18c, d)$$

$$K_{0,1} = (p_o{}^n/(n-1)!)\, d^{n-1}[1/s]/ds^{n-1}\,\big|_{s=-p_o} = -1$$

From Eq. 3.2.2, the K_1 residue equals

$$K_1 = \frac{p_o{}^n}{(s+p_o)^n}\bigg|_{s=0} = 1 \qquad (3.3.19)$$

Therefore, the partial fraction expansion of R(s) equals

$$R(s) = \frac{1}{s} - \sum_{i=1}^{n} \frac{p_o{}^{i-1}}{(s+p_o)^i} = \frac{1}{s} - \sum_{i=1}^{n} \frac{1/p_o}{(1+s/p_o)^i} \qquad (3.3.20)$$

EXAMPLE 3.3.4 Determine the impulse response of a lead-lag filter having a transfer function given by Eq. 2.3.31 as

$$H(s) = \frac{1+s/z}{1+s/p} \qquad (3.3.21)$$

Solution Here we encounter the situation where the numerator of H(s) is *not* of lower degree than the denominator. Thus, we must use the partial fraction expansion form given by Eq. 3.2.12. Dividing the numerator of H(s) by its denominator, we obtain

$$H(s) = p/z + p(1 - p/z)\frac{1}{s} + \ldots = p/z + \frac{1 - p/z}{1 + s/p} + \ldots \qquad (3.3.22)$$

The first equation is the Laurent expansion for H(s) about $|s| = \infty$, while the second equation is the entire partial fraction expansion for H(s) using the remainder form. The first term equals

$$K_0 = (1/0!)\, H(s)\,\big|_{|s|=\infty} = p/z \qquad (3.3.23)$$

which is the residue of the zero-order term s^0 using Eq. 3.2.13. Therefore, the impulse response of the lead-lag filter equals

$$h(t) = \mathcal{L}^{-1}[H(s)] = (p/z)U_0(t) + p(1 - p/z)e^{-pt}U_{-1}(t) \qquad (3.3.24)$$

using Table 1.8.1. Note that when p = z, pole-zero cancellation occurs so H(s) = 1 and $h(t) = U_0(t)$.

3.4 STEP RESPONSE

In measuring filter response, it is often more convenient to use a step input rather than an impulse input. Thus, we shall often be analyzing step responses rather than impulse responses. Therefore, let us now establish the relationship between these two responses.

The unit step response r(t) and unit impulse response h(t) are related as

$$h(t) = \frac{dr(t)}{dt}, \qquad r(t) = \int_{-\infty}^{t} h(\tau)\, d\tau \qquad (3.4.1)$$

To show this, let us consider Fig. 3.4.1a. The unit impulse response of H(s) is h(t) where the unit impulse is obtained by differentiating a unit step. Since the differentiator is a linear network, it may be interchanged with h(t) and the same output will be obtained. Denoting the unit step response of H(s) as r(t) in Fig. 3.4.1b, we see that h(t) is integrated to obtain r(t). Therefore, we may characterize a filter by its step response just as well as its impulse response. For that matter, any singularity function may be used.

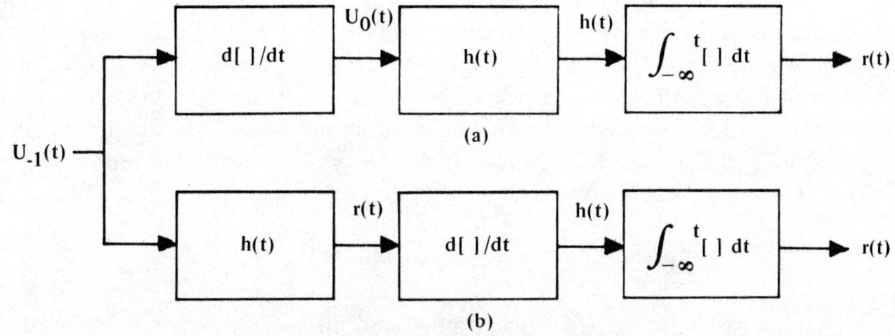

Fig. 3.4.1 Relation between impulse and step responses.

In quantitively describing step responses, standard terminology is used. The normalized response of a low-pass filter to a unit step input is shown in Fig. 3.4.2. It is characterized by several parameters:

1. *Rise Time* t_R: Time required for unit step response to rise from 10 to 90% of its final steady-state value.
2. *Rise Time* t_{R1}: Time required for unit step response to rise from 0 to (first) 100% of its final steady-state value.
3. *Delay Time* t_D: Time required for unit step response to rise from 0 to 50% of its final steady-state value.
4. *Peak Time* T_p: Time required for unit step response to rise from 0 to peak value.
5. *Settling Time* T_s: Time required for unit step response to settle within δ percent of its final steady-state value.
6. *Peak Response* M_{pt}: Peak value of unit step response relative to final steady-state value.
7. *Percent Overshoot* γ: Difference between peak response and final steady-state value expressed as a percentage of final value.

In some actual filters, nonlinearities produce asymmetrical step responses. In such cases, analogous terms are used for the filter response to a negative step (i.e., falling edge), where "fall time" replaces "rise time", "storage time" replaces "delay time", and "undershoot" replaces "overshoot". Since we shall consider only linear systems, the responses will be symmetrical and the analogous times equal. We should note that high-pass, band-pass, band-stop, and all-pass filters have different response forms as $t \to \infty$. Additional terms are used to describe these responses as we shall discuss later.

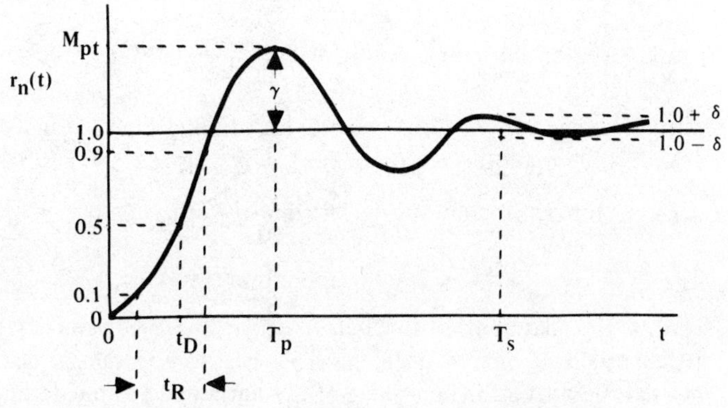

Fig. 3.4.2 Normalized step response of low-pass filter.

The calculations required to obtain these parameters are usually quite tedious and involved. Momentarily, we shall introduce approximations for several of these parameters which will considerably simplify our later work. These approximations will give us insight into the parameters that primarily determine filter performance. Let us first consider the initial and final behavior of the step response. Immediately we can make several statements about the step response r(t) of any H(s). These are based upon the initial value, initial slopes, and final value theorems of Table 1.8.2. The initial value theorem allows us to determine r(0) directly from H(s) using

$$r(0) = \lim_{s \to \infty} sR(s) = \lim_{s \to \infty} sH(s)/s = \lim_{s \to \infty} H(s) \tag{3.4.2}$$

Thus, the initial value of r(t) depends only upon the *high-frequency* behavior of the transfer function H(s). Expressing H(s) in the summation form given by Eq. 3.1.1, then the initial value of the step response equals

$$r(0) = \lim_{s \to \infty} H(s) = \lim_{s \to \infty} a_m s^m / b_n s^n = \lim_{s \to \infty} s^{m-n} a_m / b_n$$

$$= 0,\ n > m; \qquad a_n/b_m,\ n = m; \qquad \infty,\ n < m \tag{3.4.3}$$

When the high-frequency gain is zero, the initial response must be zero since no high-frequency signal components are transmitted through the filter. When the high-frequency gain is constant, the step response makes an instantaneous jump to that gain value. When the high-frequency gain approaches infinity, impulses appear at t = 0 so that r(0) = ∞.

The initial slope theorem says that

$$d^p r(0)/dt^p = \lim_{s \to \infty} s^{p+1} R(s) = \lim_{s \to \infty} s^p H(s) \tag{3.4.4}$$

Thus, if the high-frequency gain varies as $a_m s^{m-n}/b_n$ from Eq. 3.1.1, then the *p*th derivative of r(t) at t = 0 equals

$$d^p r(0)/dt^p = \lim_{s \to \infty} s^{m-n+p} a_m / b_n$$

$$= 0,\ n > m + p; \qquad a_m/b_n,\ n = m + p; \qquad \infty,\ n < m + p \tag{3.4.5}$$

For every initial derivative of r(0) which must be nonzero, an additional finite zero must be added to H(s). Since zeros emphasize high-frequency behavior and allow more high-frequency energy to be transmitted through the filter, addition of zeros can force the initial response slopes to be nonzero. From another viewpoint, since (m – n) equals the number of excess (finite) poles over zeros, the first (m – n – 1) derivatives of the step response will initially equal zero.

Lastly, the final value theorem allows us to determine r(∞) as

$$r(\infty) = \lim_{s \to 0} sR(s) = \lim_{s \to 0} sH(s)/s = \lim_{s \to 0} H(s) \tag{3.4.6}$$

when H(s) has only left-half-plane poles or poles at the origin. Therefore, the final value of r(t) depends only upon the dc gain of H(s), which equals

$$\lim_{s \to 0} H(s) = \lim_{s \to 0} a_j s^j / b_i s^i = \lim_{s \to 0} s^{j-i} a_j / b_i$$

$$= 0,\ j > i; \qquad a_i/b_i,\ \min(i = j); \qquad \infty,\ j < i \tag{3.4.7}$$

Thus, if H(s) has zeros at the s-plane origin, the final value r(∞) equals zero. When H(s) has poles at the origin, r(∞) = ∞ since the filter has infinite gain at dc. When H(s) has neither poles nor zeros at the origin, the final value of the output equals the dc filter gain.

Although these results are useful in determining the initial and final behavior of the step response of a filter, they do not give us any indications of the response parameters shown in Fig. 3.4.2. These are the parameters in which we are primarily interested for evaluating response. Now let us investigate how to find their approximate values.

3.5 TIME DOMAIN APPROXIMATIONS USING ELMORE'S RESULTS

One useful method for deriving the approximate rise and delay times for filters having monotonic (nondecreasing) step response was introduced by Elmore.[5] He observed that when the normalized step response $r_n(t)$ was monotonic and approached a value of unity at $t \to \infty$, then $r_n(t)$ could be viewed as a probability distribution function in time t. Correspondingly, $h_n(t)$ could be viewed as its associated probability density function.

Consider the impulse response $h_n(t)$ and the step response $r_n(t)$ shown in Fig. 3.5.1. As discussed in Sec. 1.9, two common statistics used for describing $h_n(t)$ are its mean and variance which equal[6]

$$E(t) = \int_{-\infty}^{\infty} th_n(t)\,dt, \quad \text{var}(t) = \int_{-\infty}^{\infty} [t - E(t)]^2 h_n(t)\,dt = \int_{-\infty}^{\infty} t^2 h_n(t)\,dt - E^2(t) \tag{3.5.1}$$

Another useful statistic is the median of $h_n(t)$ which equals the value of t when $r_n(t) = 0.5$. Thus, the median of $h_n(t)$ is equal to the delay time of $r_n(t)$. When $h_n(t)$ is symmetrical, then its mean and median are equal, in which case the delay time equals

$$t_d = E(t) \tag{3.5.2}$$

The rise time t_r of $r_n(t)$ is equal to the time difference $(t_2 - t_1)$ between which $r_n(t_2) = 0.9$ and $r_n(t_1) = 0.1$. When $h_n(t)$ is a Gaussian pulse (see Eq. 1.5.9b), then

$$t_r = \sqrt{2\pi\,\text{var}(t)} \tag{3.5.3}$$

Although the impulse response of only a Gaussian filter is truly Gaussian, many filters have responses which tend to be Gaussian so this forms a very useful and practical approximation.[7]

To relate the time and frequency domain behaviors of a filter, recall that its transfer function H(s) is related to its impulse response h(t) by Eq. 3.1.5. Expanding e^{-st} in its Maclaurin series, then H(s) may be expressed as

$$\begin{aligned} H(s) = \mathcal{L}[h(t)] &= \int_{-\infty}^{\infty} h(t)e^{-st}\,dt = \int_{-\infty}^{\infty} h(t)\,[1 - st + (st)^2/2! - \dots]\,dt \\ &= \int_{-\infty}^{\infty} h(t)\,dt - s\int_{-\infty}^{\infty} th(t)\,dt + (s^2/2!)\int_{-\infty}^{\infty} t^2h(t)\,dt + \dots \\ &= H(0) + sH'(0) + s^2H''(0)/2! + \dots \end{aligned} \tag{3.5.4}$$

Dividing H(s) by its dc value H(0) yields the normalized transfer function which equals

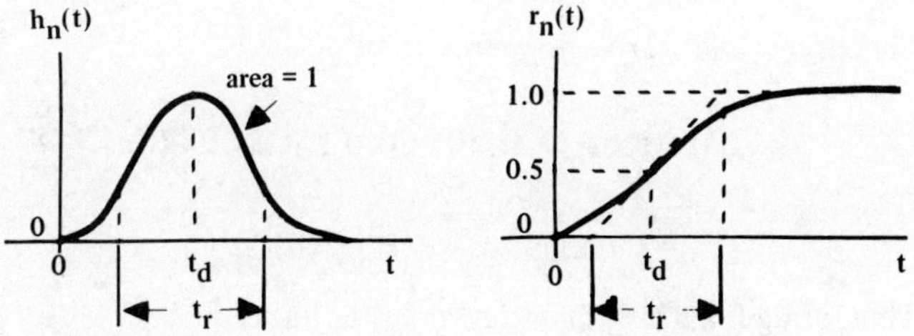

Fig. 3.5.1 Normalized impulse and step responses of low-pass filter.

$$H_n(s) = H(s)/H(0) = \mathcal{L}[h_n(t)] = \int_{-\infty}^{\infty} h_n(t)\,dt - s\int_{-\infty}^{\infty} th_n(t)\,dt$$

$$+ (s^2/2!)\int_{-\infty}^{\infty} t^2h_n(t)\,dt + \ldots = 1 - sE(t) + s^2E(t^2)/2! - \ldots \quad (3.5.5)$$

We see that since the normalized dc gain equals unity (i.e., $H_n(0) = 1$), then $r_n(t)$ is a probability distribution function. The general normalized transfer function of Eq. 3.1.1 equals

$$H_n(s) = \frac{1 + a_1s + a_2s^2 + \ldots + a_ms^m}{1 + b_1s + b_2s^2 + \ldots + b_ns^n} = 1 - (b_1 - a_1)s + (b_1^2 - a_1b_1 + a_2 - b_2)s^2 + \ldots \quad (3.5.6)$$

Equating coefficients in Eqs. 3.5.5 and 3.5.6, solving for $E(t)$ and $E(t^2)$, and substituting the results into Eqs. 3.5.2 and 3.5.3, the delay and rise times of a filter are found to equal

$$t_d = E(t) = b_1 - a_1$$

$$t_r = \sqrt{2\pi\,\mathrm{var}\,(t)} = \sqrt{2\pi}\sqrt{E(t^2) - E^2(t)} \quad (3.5.7)$$

$$= 2.51\,[b_1^2 - a_1^2 + 2(a_2 - b_2)]^{1/2} = 2.51\ [t_d(b_1 + a_1) + 2(a_2 - b_2)]^{1/2}$$

assuming that $h_n(t)$ is both symmetrical and Gaussian. Therefore, we can approximate the delay and rise times of the normalized step response of a filter by considering only the first several terms in its gain expression. In terms of the frequency response, Eq. 3.5.7 can be re-expressed as

$$t_d = -H_n'(0) = -H'(0)/H(0)$$

$$t_r = \sqrt{2\pi}\ [H_n''(0) - H_n'^2(0)]^{1/2} = \sqrt{2\pi}\ [H''(0)/H(0) - (H'(0)/H(0))^2]^{1/2} \quad (3.5.8)$$

Note that we shall use the lower case subscripts "d" and "r" on "t" to show these are delay and rise time *approximations*, and "n" to remind us that dc normalized gains must be used.

Elmore also found the delay and rise times for n cascaded filter stages. If each stage has a normalized transfer function $H_i(s)$ where

$$H_i(s) = \sum_{k=0}^{\infty} \frac{s^k}{k!}\frac{d^kH_i(0)}{ds^k} = 1 + sH_i'(0) + s^2H_i''(0)/2! + \ldots \quad (3.5.9)$$

then the overall normalized transfer function H(s) equals

$$H_{no}(s) = \prod_{i=1}^{n} H_i(s) = \prod_{i=1}^{n}\left(\sum_{k=0}^{\infty} \frac{s^k}{k!}\frac{d^kH_i(0)}{ds^k}\right) \quad (3.5.10)$$

Simplifying and rearranging terms gives

$$H_{no}(s) = 1 + s\sum_{i=1}^{n} H_i'(0) + (s^2/2!)\left(\sum_{i=1}^{n} H_i''(0) + 2\sum_{i=1}^{n}\sum_{j=i+1}^{n} H_i'(0)H_j'(0)\right) + \ldots$$

$$= 1 + sH_{no}'(0) + s^2H_{no}''(0)/2! + \ldots \quad (3.5.11)$$

Thus, using Eq. 3.5.8, the delay and rise times equal

$$t_d = -H_{no}'(0) = \sum_{i=1}^{n} t_{d_i}$$

$$t_r = \sqrt{2\pi}\,[H_{no}''(0) - H_{no}'^2(0)]^{1/2} = [\sum_{i=1}^{n} t_{r_i}^2]^{1/2} \tag{3.5.12}$$

The total delay equals the sum of individual delays; the total rise time squared equals the sum of individual rise times squared.[8] It is important to remember that *every* stage must have a monotonically nondecreasing step response to utilize these results. Therefore, if any stage exhibits step response peaking, then Elmore's results cannot be used.

Another convenient approximation for rise time is obtained using the bandwidth-rise time product. An empirical relationship between bandwidth and rise time was observed by Valley and Wallman to be[9]

$$f_{3\,dB}t_r = 0.35 \text{ (to 0.45)}, \qquad \omega_{3\,dB}t_r = 2.2 \text{ (to 2.8)} \tag{3.5.13}$$

(f_{3dB} in Hertz, ω_{3dB} in rad/sec, and t_r in seconds) when the step response overshoot is not excessive. In essence, the filter's bandwidth dictates its step response rise time. These relations demonstrate the rise time-bandwidth tradeoff and show that the two parameters cannot be independently specified. In general, however, there is no direct relation between the bandwidth and rise time. We will usually use the lower limits in Eq. 3.5.13.

3.6 TIME DOMAIN APPROXIMATIONS USING DOMINANT POLES-ZEROS

An alternative method can be used for obtaining the step response parameters. This method makes use of the dominant pole-zero analysis discussed in Sec. 2.9. Recall that we approximated the normalized (quasi-) low-pass transfer function

$$H_n(s) = \frac{1 + a_1 s + a_2 s^2 + \ldots + a_m s^m}{1 + b_1 s + b_2 s^2 + \ldots + b_n s^n}, \qquad n \geqslant m \tag{3.6.1}$$

with a first-order transfer function

$$H_n(s) \cong H_1(s) = \frac{e^{-\tau_o s}}{1 + s/p}, \qquad |s| < k_1 \tag{3.6.2}$$

or a second-order transfer function

$$H_n(s) \cong H_2(s) = \frac{e^{-\tau_o s}}{1 + 2\zeta(s/\omega_n) + (s/\omega_n)^2}, \qquad |s| < k_2 \tag{3.6.3}$$

Then the exact normalized step response

$$r_n(t) = \mathcal{L}^{-1}[H_n(s)/s] \tag{3.6.4}$$

is approximated by the step response of the dominant pole approximation. We shall soon see that these responses are given by

$$r_1(t) = \mathcal{L}^{-1}[R_1(s)] = [1 - e^{-p(t - \tau_o)}]\,U_{-1}(t - \tau_o) \tag{3.6.5}$$

or

$$r_2(t) = \mathcal{L}^{-1}[R_2(s)]$$
$$= \left(1 - \frac{1}{\sqrt{1-\zeta^2}} e^{-\zeta\omega_n(t-\tau_0)} \sin[\sqrt{1-\zeta^2}\,\omega_n(t-\tau_0) + \theta]\right) U_{-1}(t-\tau_0) \quad (3.6.6)$$

where $\theta = \cos^{-1}\zeta$. The characteristics of $r_1(t)$ and $r_2(t)$ will be discussed in the next two sections.

Notice that the delay τ_0 in the excess phase factor introduces an actual delay of τ_0 seconds in the step responses. Thus, the total delay is equal to the sum of τ_0 and the actual delay time of the approximate step response.

Also note that the low-frequency phase of $H_n(j\omega)$ equals

$$\arg H_n(j\omega) \cong \arg \frac{1 + ja_1\omega}{1 + jb_1\omega} = -\tan^{-1} b_1\omega + \tan^{-1} a_1\omega, \qquad \omega \cong 0 \quad (3.6.7)$$

Using the Maclaurin series expansion for $\tan^{-1} x$ as

$$\tan^{-1} x = x - x^3/3 + \ldots, \qquad |x| < 1 \quad (3.6.8)$$

then the dc delay of H_n equals

$$\tau(0) = -\,d \arg H_n(j\omega)/d\omega = b_1 - a_1 \quad (3.6.9)$$

which corresponds to the delay time given by Elmore. Since τ_0 in the excess phase factor is chosen to maintain the phase of the dominant pole approximation at the 3 dB frequency and therefore the low-frequency phase, we anticipate that τ_0 will be very close to the dc delay $\tau(0)$.

3.7 LOW-PASS FILTER RESPONSE–REAL POLES

The low-pass filter having a simple pole had a normalized transfer function

$$H(s) = \frac{1}{1+s} \quad (3.7.1)$$

as given by Eq. 2.3.2. The step response of this first-order filter equals

$$r(t) = \mathcal{L}^{-1}[H(s)/s] = \mathcal{L}^{-1}\left[\frac{1}{s} - \frac{1}{s+1}\right] = (1 - e^{-t})\,U_{-1}(t) \quad (3.7.2)$$

which is found by expressing H(s)/s in a partial fraction expansion and using Table 1.8.1. If the pole was located at $s = -p_o$ rather than -1, then by the frequency scaling theorem of Table 1.8.2,

$$H(s) = \frac{1}{1 + s/p_o} \quad (3.7.3)$$

and

$$r(t) = (1 - e^{-p_o t})\,U_{-1}(t) \quad (3.7.4)$$

This response is shown in Fig. 3.7.1 for n = 1. It rises exponentially from zero to unity with a time constant of $1/p_o$. Since the 3 dB bandwidth of the low-pass filter equals p_o, the time constant is equal to the reciprocal of the bandwidth. Increasing filter bandwidth decreases its time constant and visa versa.

Now let us determine the step response of the *n*th-order synchronously-tuned low-pass filter having an overall gain of

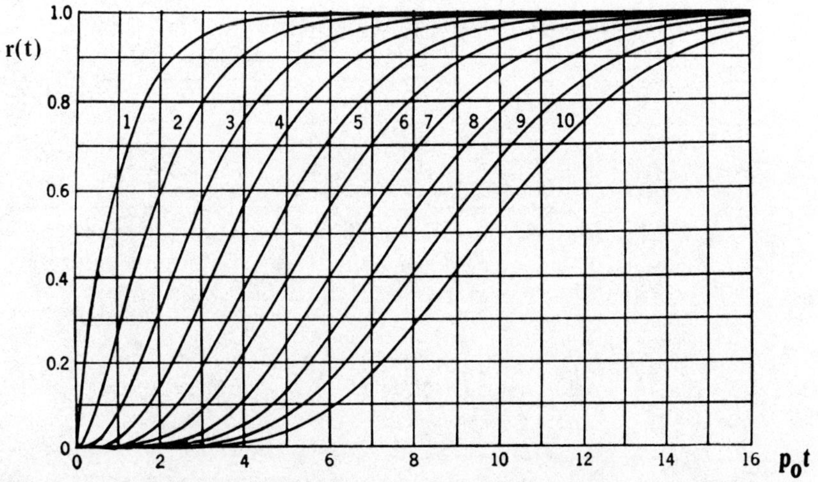

Fig. 3.7.1 Normalized step responses of nth-order synchronously-tuned low-pass filter. (From G. E. Valley, Jr. and H. Wallman, "Vacuum Tube Amplifiers," p. 66, Fig. 1–25, McGraw-Hill, NY, 1948.)

$$H(s) = \frac{1}{(1 + s/p_o)^n} \tag{3.7.5}$$

Recall that this filter was analyzed in Example 2.3.3. Its transformed step response equals

$$R(s) = \frac{1}{s(1 + s/p_o)^n} = \frac{1}{s} - \sum_{k=1}^{n} \frac{1/p_o}{(1 + s/p_o)^k} \tag{3.7.6}$$

whose partial fraction expansion was found in Example 3.3.3. Since

$$\mathcal{L}^{-1}[1/s^n] = \frac{t^{k-1}}{(k-1)!} U_{-1}(t) \tag{3.7.7}$$

from Table 1.8.1, then we can write

$$\mathcal{L}^{-1}\left[\frac{1/p_o}{(1 + s/p_o)^k}\right] = \frac{(p_o t)^{k-1}}{(k-1)!} e^{-p_o t} U_{-1}(t) \tag{3.7.8}$$

using the frequency scaling and shifting theorems of Table 1.8.2. Thus, the step response of the *n*th-order synchronously-tuned filter equals

$$r(t) = \mathcal{L}^{-1}[R(s)] = [1 - e^{-p_o t} \sum_{k=0}^{n} (p_o t)^k/k!]\ U_{-1}(t) \tag{3.7.9}$$

which is also plotted in Fig. 3.7.1. The step response monotonically increases towards unity with increasing delay and rise times.

For the first-order low-pass filter, the delay time equals

$$t_D = 0.69/p_o \tag{3.7.10}$$

which is found by setting $r(t_D) = 0.5$ and solving for t_D in Eq. 3.7.4. The rise time equals

$$t_R = 2.3/p_o - 0.1/p_o = 2.2/p_o \tag{3.7.11}$$

Table 3.7.1 Exact and approximate normalized rise times for nth-order synchronously-tuned filter.

$t_R p_o$	1	2	3	4	5	6	7	8	9	10
Exact (Fig. 3.7.1)	2.2	3.3	4.2	4.9	5.5	6.2	6.6	7.3	7.6	7.9
Elmore (Eq. 3.7.15b)	2.5	3.5	4.3	5.0	5.6	6.1	6.6	7.1	7.5	7.8
Dominant Pole (Eq. 3.7.23)	2.2	3.4	4.3	5.1	5.7	6.3	6.8	7.3	7.8	8.2

which is determined by setting $r(t_1) = 0.1$ and $r(t_2) = 0.9$ and finding $t_R = t_2 - t_1$. For higher order filters, the delay time is calculated using the empirical expression[8]

$$t_D = (n - 0.3)/p_o \tag{3.7.12}$$

The rise times t_R are determined from Eq. 3.7.9 using iterative techniques. They are listed in Table 3.7.1.

EXAMPLE 3.7.1 Determine the delay and rise times of the step response of six cascaded single-pole low-pass filters each having a 3 dB bandwidth of 1000 Hz. Determine the overall 3 dB bandwidth.

Solution The overall transfer function is given by Eq. 3.7.5 for n = 6 and $p_o = 2\pi(10^3)$. From Table 3.7.1 and Eq. 3.7.12, the rise and delay times equal

$$t_R = 6.1/2\pi(10^3) = 0.97 \text{ msec}, \qquad t_D = (6.0 - 0.3)/2\pi(10^3) = 0.91 \text{ msec} \tag{3.7.13}$$

Both are about equal to 1 msec. The normalized step response is shown in Fig. 3.7.1 for n = 6. The overall bandwidth is equal to the bandwidth of the individual stage reduced by the bandwidth shrinkage factor S(n). Since n = 6, then S(6) = 0.350 from Fig. 2.3.8 so that the overall bandwidth is 350 Hz. Instead, using the empirical result that the bandwidth-rise time product equals 0.35 from Eq. 3.5.13, then the approximate rise time $t_r = 0.35/350 = 1$ msec which is in good agreement with the exact results.

Let us now obtain the approximate delay and rise times of synchronously-tuned filters utilizing Elmore's results. To apply the results, the step response must be monotonic and have a final value of unity which is indeed the case. Then since the gain can be expressed as

$$H(s) = (1 + s/p_o)^{-n} = [1 + n(s/p_o) + n(n-1)(s/p_o)^2/2! + \ldots + (s/p_o)^n]^{-1} \tag{3.7.14}$$

we can write the approximate delay and rise times by inspection. From Eq. 3.5.7, Elmore's approximations give

$$t_d = n/p_o, \qquad t_r = 2.51[n^2 - 2n(n-1)/2]^{1/2}/p_o = 2.51\sqrt{n}/p_o \tag{3.7.15}$$

The delay time agrees closely with the empirical value given by Eq. 3.7.12. The rise times are listed in Table 3.7.1 and show close agreement with the exact values for $n \geqslant 3$. Recall that Elmore's results are very good when r(t) and h(t) are symmetrical (about the median) and Gaussian. We see from Fig. 3.7.1 that this is the case for $n \geqslant 3$.

These results are important for they emphasize that the delay time increases as n while the rise time increases only as $\sqrt{n}$ when the bandwidth p_o of each *individual* stage is fixed. Recall that in Example 2.3.3, we determined the overall 3 dB bandwidth of the synchronously-tuned filter to equal

$$B/p_o = (2^{1/n} - 1)^{1/2} \cong 1/1.2\sqrt{n} \tag{3.7.16}$$

Combining Eqs. 3.7.15b and 3.7.16, the Elmore bandwidth-rise time product equals 2.51/1.2 = 2.1 which closely agrees with the empirical relation of Valley and Wallman in Eq. 3.5.13.

Now let us consider the time domain effects of maintaining the *overall* bandwidth of the synchronously-tuned filter constant at B for various n. Then the individual stages must have their bandwidths p_o adjusted to satisfy

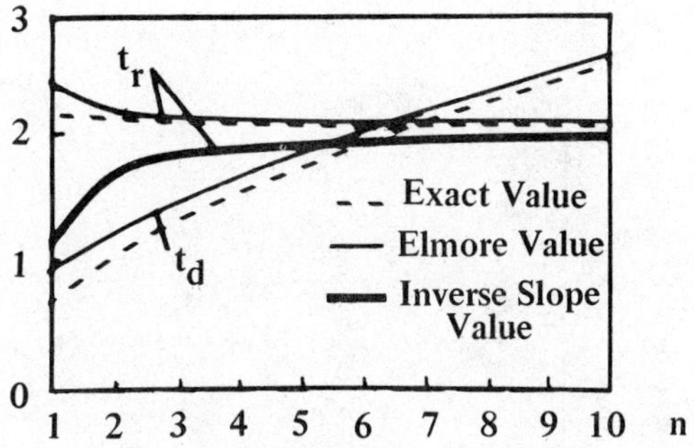

Fig. 3.7.2 Normalized delay and rise times of nth-order synchronously-tuned filter. (From S. C. Dutta Roy, "On the transient response of all-pole low-pass filters," IEEE Trans. Circuit Theory, vol. CT-15, pp. 485–488, Dec., 1968.)

$$p_o = B/(2^{1/n} - 1)^{1/2} \cong 1.2\sqrt{n}\, B \tag{3.7.17}$$

from Eq. 3.7.16. Substituting this result into Eq. 3.7.15, the delay and rise times of this filter equal

$$t_d = n/p_o = n/[B/(2^{1/n} - 1)^{1/2}] \cong \sqrt{n}/1.2B, \qquad t_r = 2.51\sqrt{n}/[B/(2^{1/n} - 1)^{1/2}] \cong 2.1/B \tag{3.7.18}$$

Thus, the delay time varies as $\sqrt{n}$ while the rise time remains constant. Elmore's values are compared with the exact values in Fig. 3.7.2 which shows them to be in close agreement. The step response of a synchronously-tuned filter having a unity 3 dB bandwidth is shown in Fig. 4.13.3. These results show that when the order of the fixed-bandwidth synchronously-tuned filter is increased to obtain greater asymptotic rolloff (i.e., greater out-of-band rejection as shown in Fig. 4.13.1), only the delay time is increased. In many filter applications, this is a small price to pay for the improved frequency response.

Now let us determine the approximate step response of synchronously-tuned filters based upon the dominant pole approximation. We found in Example 2.9.2 that the approximate gain of the *n*th-order synchronously-tuned filter equals

$$H(s) = \frac{1}{(1 + s/p_o)^n} \cong \frac{e^{-\tau_o s}}{1 + s/p_1}, \qquad |s| \ll p_o \tag{3.7.19}$$

where

$$p_1 \cong 0.83 p_o/\sqrt{n}, \qquad \tau_o \cong n(1 - 1/1.06\sqrt{n})/p_o \tag{3.7.20}$$

equal the dominant pole value and delay, respectively. Therefore, we can write the approximate step response as

$$r(t) = [1 - e^{-p_1(t - \tau_o)}]\, U_{-1}(t - \tau_o) \tag{3.7.21}$$

using Eq. 3.7.4 and the time shifting theorem of Table 1.8.2. The delay time equals

$$t_d = 0.69/p_1 + \tau_o \cong [n - 0.095/(0.83/\sqrt{n})]/p_o \cong n(1 - 0.11/\sqrt{n})/p_o \cong n/p_o \tag{3.7.22}$$

from Eq. 3.7.10, while the rise time equals

$$t_r = 2.2/p_1 \cong 2.2/(0.83\, p_o/\sqrt{n}) \cong 2.65\sqrt{n}/p_o \tag{3.7.23}$$

from Eq. 3.7.11. Comparing Eqs. 3.7.12, 3.7.15a, and 3.7.22, the delay time is closer to the exact value than that obtained using Elmore's results. The situation is reversed ($n \geq 4$) for the rise time, which is listed in Table 3.7.1. The reason for the poor results for large n will be discussed now.

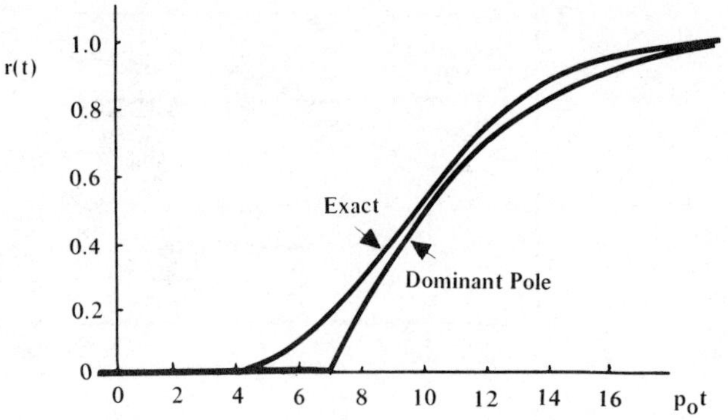

Fig. 3.7.3 Exact and approximate step responses of tenth-order synchronously-tuned low-pass filter.

EXAMPLE 3.7.2 Calculate the step response for a tenth-order synchronously-tuned filter using a dominant pole approximation. Compare the exact and approximate responses.
Solution The dominant pole value and delay equal

$$p_i \cong 0.83p_o/\sqrt{10} = 0.262p_o, \qquad \tau_o \cong 10(1 - 1/1.06\sqrt{10})/p_o \cong 7/p_o \tag{3.7.24}$$

from Eq. 3.7.20. Therefore, the approximate step response equals

$$r(t) = (1 - \exp[-0.262(p_o t - 7)])U_{-1}(p_o t - 7) \tag{3.7.25}$$

which is plotted in Fig. 3.7.3 with the exact response. The responses are in fairly close agreement for $t > \tau_o$. From Eq. 3.7.22, $p_o t_d = 9.7$ which is almost exact; but $p_o t_r = 8.2$ from Table 3.7.1 which is somewhat in error. The rise time discrepancy is due to the gain approximation which is shown in Fig. 2.9.2. The approximate gain has more high-frequency content than the actual gain. Hence, its approximate step response exhibits a slightly faster rise time.

Before considering other types of low-pass filters having real poles, we make two useful observations related to what we have just discussed. First, another approximation is sometimes used to estimate rise time. Here the approximate rise time is equal to the inverse of the maximum slope of the step response, or

$$t_r = 1/|h_n(t)|_{max} = [|dr_n(t)/dt|_{max}]^{-1} \tag{3.7.26}$$

Dutta Roy shows that for synchronously-tuned filters,[10]

$$t_r = \frac{(n-1)!\,(2^{1/n}-1)^{1/2}}{(n-1)^{n-1}\,e^{-(n-1)}} \cong [2\pi n(2^{1/n}-1)]^{1/2}, \qquad n \gg 1 \tag{3.7.27}$$

which agrees with Elmore's result. The exact value of t_r is also plotted in Fig. 3.7.2. We see that Elmore's result provides a better approximation than the inverse slope approximation for small n. Since the inverse slope definition requires as much computation as that required for calculating t_R directly, this approximation is not widely used. The engineer may find it of interest to review alternative rise and delay time approximations.[11]

Second, it is often of interest to obtain a minimum rise time and/or minimum delay time step response for a given order filter of constant bandwidth. Consider a unity-bandwidth low-pass filter having no finite zeros and only real poles p_i. Dutta Roy shows that to obtain minimum rise and delay times, all the p_i must be identical and must equal p_o as given by Eq. 3.7.17.[10] Thus, an *n*th-order synchronously-tuned filter has the minimum rise time and delay time of all *n*th-order filters having negative real poles. Elmore found the same result to minimize rise time.[5]

Another low-pass filter of interest is the lead-lag filter having a gain

$$H(s) = \frac{1 + s/z}{1 + s/p} \tag{3.7.28}$$

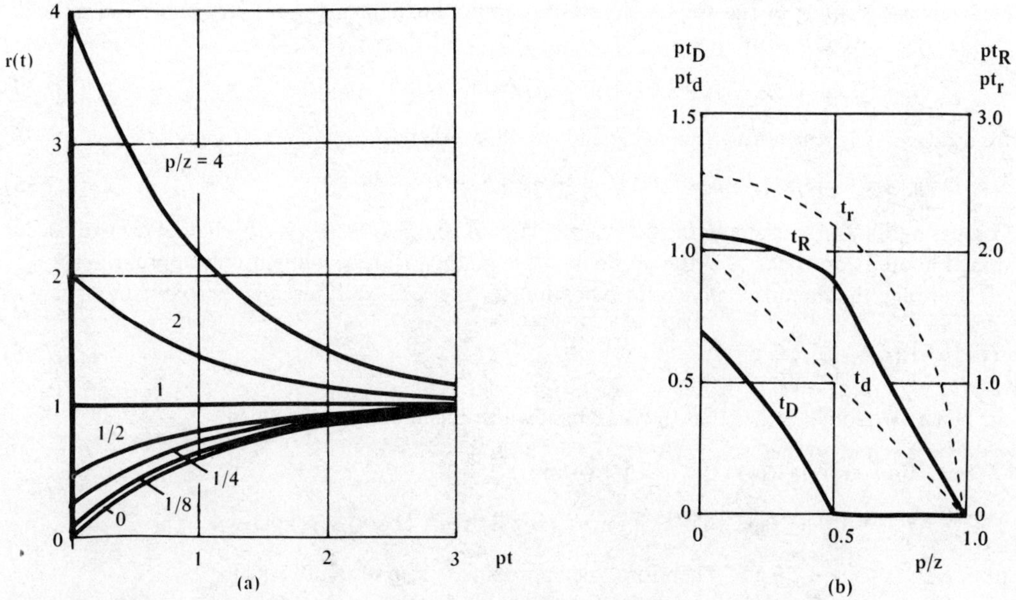

Fig. 3.7.4 (a) Step response and (b) exact and Elmore's normalized rise and delay times of lead-lag filter.

from Eq. 2.3.31. Its magnitude and phase characteristics were shown in Fig. 2.3.9 and its delay characteristic was shown in Fig. 2.10.8. Now let us determine its step response. The transformed step response can be expressed in a partial fraction expansion as

$$R(s) = H(s)/s = p\,\frac{1 + s/z}{s(s+p)} = \frac{1}{s} - \frac{1 - p/z}{s+p} \tag{3.7.29}$$

Therefore, the step response equals

$$r(t) = \mathcal{L}^{-1}[R(s)] = [1 - (1 - p/z)e^{-pt}]\,U_{-1}(t) \tag{3.7.30}$$

from Table 1.8.1. The response is exponential and is plotted in Fig. 3.7.4a. Using Eqs. 3.4.3 and 3.4.7, the initial and final values equal

$$r(0) = \lim_{s\to\infty} H(s) = p/z, \qquad r(\infty) = \lim_{s\to 0} H(s) = 1 \tag{3.7.31}$$

The response is monotonically nondecreasing as long as $p/z \leqslant 1$ ($p/z > 1$ corresponds to a high-pass filter to be discussed later). The normalized delay time equals

$$pt_D = 0.694 + \ln(1 - p/z), \quad 0 \leqslant p/z < 0.5; \quad = 0, \quad 0.5 \leqslant p/z \leqslant 1.0 \tag{3.7.32}$$

while the normalized rise time equals

$$\begin{aligned} pt_R &= 2.2, \quad 0 \leqslant p/z < 0.1 \\ &= 2.2 + \ln(1 - p/z), \quad 0.1 \leqslant p/z < 0.9 \\ &= 0, \quad 0.9 \leqslant p/z \leqslant 1.0 \end{aligned} \tag{3.7.33}$$

Delay and rise times can become zero since the filter is quasi-low-pass and has finite gain as $|s| \to \infty$. This allows the step response to make an instantaneous transition at $t = 0$. These times are plotted in Fig. 3.7.4b.

Let us consider Elmore's delay and rise time approximations. Due to the large asymmetry and non-Gaussian shaping of the step response, this approximation method is very poor. Since the dc gain $H(0) = 1$, we can write that

$$t_d = 1/p - 1/z, \qquad t_r = 2.51(1/p^2 - 1/z^2)^{1/2} \tag{3.7.34}$$

from Eq. 3.7.28. The normalized delay and rise times, therefore, equal

$$pt_d = 1 - p/z, \qquad pt_r = 2.51[1 - (p/z)^2]^{1/2} \tag{3.7.35}$$

Comparing Elmore's results with the exact results in Fig. 3.7.4b, we verify that large errors occur using Elmore's approach. A better approximation method is the dominant pole approach.

Forming the dominant pole approximation for the lead-lag filter, we approximate its gain as

$$H(s) = \frac{1 + s/z}{1 + s/p} \cong \frac{e^{-\tau_0 s}}{1 + s/B} \tag{3.7.36}$$

for $z > p$. We found earlier that the 3 dB bandwidth B and delay τ_0 equalled

$$\begin{aligned} B/p &= [1 - 2(p/z)^2]^{-1/2} \cong 1 + (p/z)^2 \cong 1 \\ \tau_0 &= -[\pi/4 + \tan^{-1}(B/z) - \tan^{-1}(B/p)]/B \cong -[1 - 0.5(p/z)]/z \cong -1/z \end{aligned} \tag{3.7.37}$$

from Eqs. 2.9.3 and 2.9.11. Therefore, the approximate step response equals

$$r(t) \cong [1 - e^{-p(t + 1/z)}]U_{-1}(t + 1/z) \cong [1 - (1 - p/z)e^{-pt}]U_{-1}(t + 1/z) \tag{3.7.38}$$

Comparing the dominant pole response with the exact response, we see that there is almost perfect agreement for $t \geqslant 0$. Note that the time advance of $1/z$ seconds permits the approximate response to better fit the exact response for positive t.

EXAMPLE 3.7.3 The frequency response of a lead-lag filter having a gain given by Eq. 3.7.36 and break frequencies of 1 KHz (pole) and 2 KHz (zero), respectively, was plotted in Example 2.10.3. Determine its corresponding step response. Compare the dominant pole response with the exact response.

Solution Its normalized step response is shown in Fig. 3.7.4a for $p/z = 1/2$. The dominant pole response can also be easily determined. Since p and z are relatively close together, let us use the exact relations for B and τ_0. From Eq. 3.7.37,

$$\begin{aligned} B/p &= [1 - 2(1/2)^2]^{-1/2} = 1/2^{-1/2} = 2^{1/2} = 1.414 \\ \tau_0 &= -[\pi/4 - \tan^{-1} 2^{1/2} + \tan^{-1}(2^{1/2}/2)]/B = -[\pi/4 - \pi(54.7 - 35.3)/180]/B = -0.447/B \\ p\tau_0 &= -0.447p/B = -0.316 \end{aligned} \tag{3.7.39}$$

where $p = 2\pi(1\text{ KHz})$. Therefore, the approximate step response equals

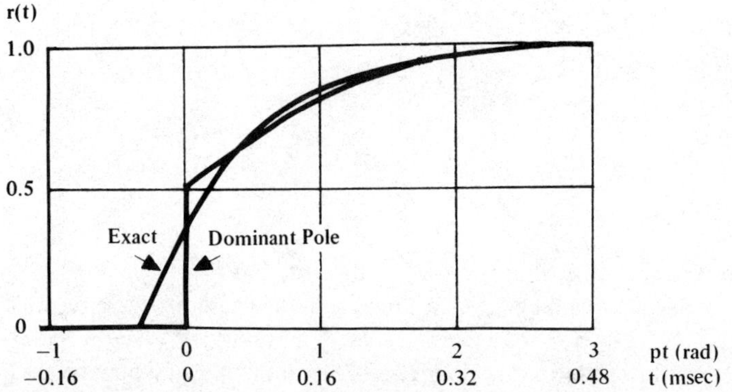

Fig. 3.7.5 Normalized step response for lead-lag filter of Example 3.7.3.

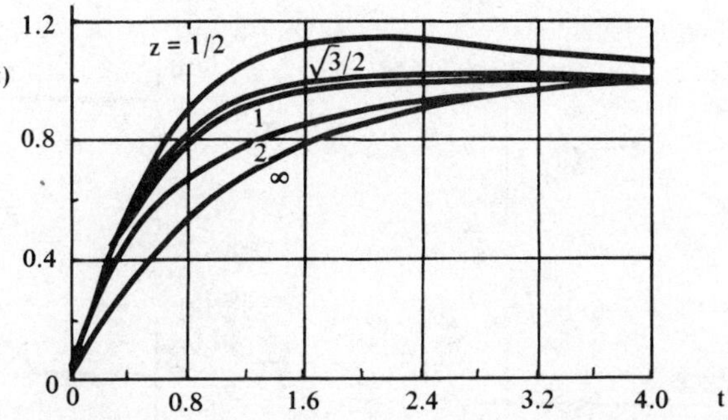

Fig. 3.7.6 Normalized step response of low-pass filter cascaded with lead-lag filter.

$$r(t) \cong (1 - \exp[-2^{1/2}(pt + 0.316)])U_{-1}(pt + 0.316) \tag{3.7.40}$$

which is drawn in Fig. 3.7.5. There is reasonably close agreement for $t > 0$. If we use the approximate results given by Eq. 3.7.37, then $B/p = 1.25$, $\tau_o = -0.25/p$, and $p\tau_o = -0.25$ which are very close to the exact values because we included second-order terms in their expressions.

In Chap. 2, we considered the effects that a closely-spaced pole-zero pair or doublet had upon the frequency response of a filter (e.g., see Fig. 2.9.4). Now let us investigate the effects they have on the time domain response. Consider a first-order low-pass filter followed by a first-order lead-lag filter; the overall normalized gain equals

$$H(s) = \frac{1}{1+s}\,\frac{1+s/z}{1+s/p} = \frac{1+s/z}{1+s(1+1/p)+s^2/p} \tag{3.7.41}$$

so that the transformed step response of the filter equals

$$R(s) = H(s)/s = \frac{1}{s(1+s)}\,\frac{1+s/z}{1+s/p} = \frac{K_0}{s} + \frac{K_1}{1+s} + \frac{K_2}{1+s/p} \tag{3.7.42}$$

The residues of the poles at $s = 0, -1$, and $-p$ equal

$$K_0 = sR(s)\big|_{s=0} = 1, \qquad K_1 = (1+s)R(s)\big|_{s=-1} = -\frac{1-1/z}{1-1/p}$$
$$K_2 = (1+s/p)R(s)\Big|_{s=-p} = -\frac{1}{p}\,\frac{1-p/z}{1-p} = \frac{1/p-1/z}{1-1/p} \tag{3.7.43}$$

Thus, the step response equals

$$r(t) = \mathcal{L}^{-1}[R(s)] = \left\{1 - \frac{1}{1-1/p}\left[(1-1/z)e^{-t} - (1/p-1/z)e^{-pt}\right]\right\}U_{-1}(t) \tag{3.7.44}$$

The shape of the response depends basically upon the location of the pole relative to unity, and the pole-zero separation ratio p/z. If $p = z$, the doublet disappears and the response is simply that of the real pole at $s = -1$. If $p \cong z$ and $z > 1$, the real pole at $s = -1$ dominates the response. However if $z < 1$, the doublet dominates the response. For example, let us assume that $p = 2z$. The step response is plotted in Fig. 3.7.6 as a function of the zero z. As z is decreased, the step response becomes faster. Using Elmore's relations and Eq. 3.7.41, we can write that the approximate delay and rise times equal

$$t_d = 1 + (1/p - 1/z), \qquad t_r = 2.51(1 + 1/p^2 - 1/z^2)^{1/2} \tag{3.7.45}$$

Note that the total delay is the sum of the individual delays of the low-pass filter and lead-lag filter. The total rise time squared is the sum of the individual rise times squared. For the case in Fig. 3.7.6 where $p = 2z$, then $t_d = 1 - 1/2z$ and $t_r = 2.51(1 - 0.75/z^2)^{1/2}$. Since the step response

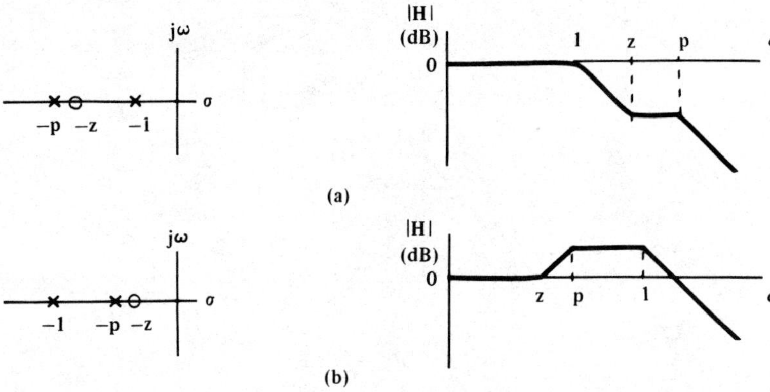

Fig. 3.7.7 Frequency responses for low-pass and lead-lag filter combination.

is asymmetrical and non-Gaussian, we shall not expect Elmore's results to be too accurate.

Now let us interpret these results from a dominant pole-zero standpoint. The pole-zero diagram for the filter is shown in Fig. 3.7.7 where $p \cong z$, and $z \gg 1$ or $z \ll 1$. In the first case, the overall bandwidth is increased due to the presence of the zero. In the second case, the overall bandwidth is increased even more and in-band magnitude peaking is produced. In general, B continues to increase for decreasing z. Thus, the rise time decreases. Since the zero also reduces low-frequency phase, the delay is also decreased. These results agree with the trend seen in Fig. 3.7.6.

3.8 LOW-PASS FILTER RESPONSE—COMPLEX POLES

Now let us consider the time domain response of a low-pass filter having complex poles. The normalized low-pass filter having a complex pole pair was considered in Eq. 2.4.2 and had a gain

$$H(s) = \frac{1}{1 + 2\zeta s + s^2} \tag{3.8.1}$$

Its transformed step response equals

$$R(s) = \frac{1}{s(s^2 + 2\zeta s + 1)} = \frac{1}{s} - \frac{s + 2\zeta}{s^2 + 2\zeta s + 1} = \frac{1}{s} - \frac{(s+\zeta) + \zeta}{(s+\zeta)^2 + (1-\zeta^2)} \tag{3.8.2}$$

From Table 1.8.1, the step response must therefore be

$$r(t) = [1 - e^{-\zeta t}(\cos\sqrt{1-\zeta^2}\,t + \frac{\zeta}{\sqrt{1-\zeta^2}} \sin\sqrt{1-\zeta^2}\,t)]\,U_{-1}(t) \tag{3.8.3}$$

If the frequency is scaled by ω_n so that

$$H(s) = \frac{1}{1 + 2\zeta(s/\omega_n) + (s/\omega_n)^2} \tag{3.8.4}$$

then

$$r(t) = [1 - e^{-\zeta\omega_n t}(\cos\sqrt{1-\zeta^2}\,\omega_n t + \frac{\zeta}{\sqrt{1-\zeta^2}} \sin\sqrt{1-\zeta^2}\,\omega_n t)]\,U_{-1}(t) \tag{3.8.5}$$

Denoting the real and imaginary pole parts as

$$a = \zeta\omega_n, \quad \beta = \sqrt{1-\zeta^2}\,\omega_n \tag{3.8.6}$$

then the step response may be rewritten as

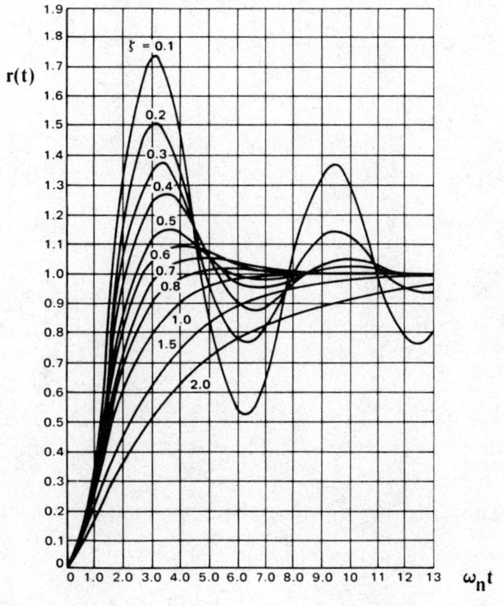

Fig. 3.8.1 Normalized step response of second-order low-pass filter. (From G. Nash, "Phase-locked loop design fundamentals," Appl. Note AN-535, Motorola, Phoenix, AZ, April, 1971.)

$$r(t) = \left[1 - \frac{1}{\sqrt{1-\zeta^2}} e^{-at} \sin(\beta t + \theta)\right] U_{-1}(t) \tag{3.8.7}$$

where $\theta = \tan^{-1} \beta/a = \cos^{-1} \zeta$. The step response is plotted in Fig. 3.8.1 as a function of normalized time $\omega_n t$. The response begins at zero and increases to a final value of unity. The overshoot increases for decreasing damping factor $\zeta = \cos\theta$ where θ is the pole angle from the negative-real axis (see the root locus of Fig. 2.2.2b). The frequency of oscillation β is shown in Fig. 3.8.2a and increases for decreasing ζ.

By differentiating r(t) and setting the result equal to zero, the time of the peak response T_p is found to depend only upon β as

$$T_p = \pi/\beta = \pi/\omega_n\sqrt{1-\zeta^2} \tag{3.8.8}$$

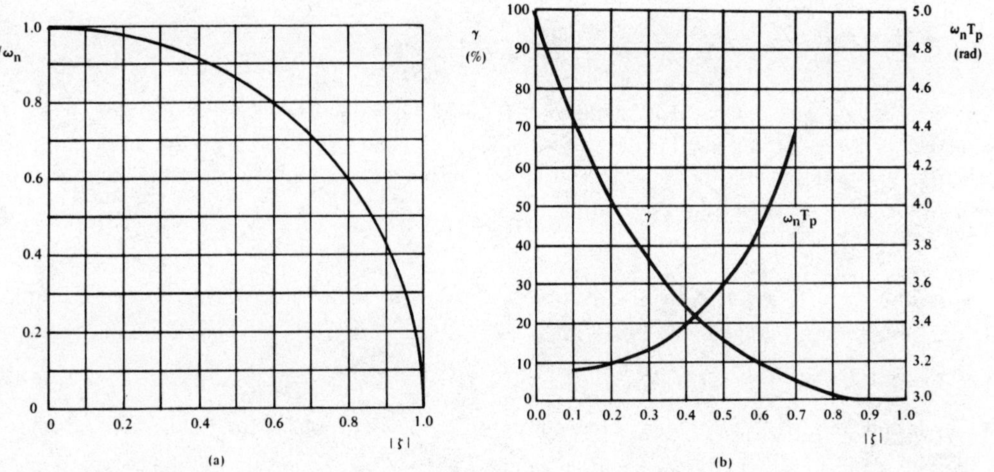

Fig. 3.8.2 (a) Normalized frequency of oscillation and (b) percentage overshoot and peak time for second-order low-pass filter.

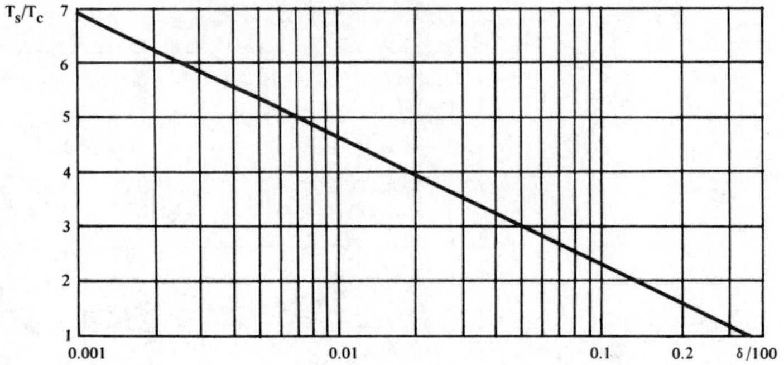

Fig. 3.8.3 Normalized settling time for second-order low-pass filter.

Evaluating $r(T_p)$, we find that the peak value M_{pt} of the step response equals

$$M_{pt} = 1 + \exp(-\zeta\pi/\sqrt{1-\zeta^2}) = 1 + \exp(-\alpha\pi/\beta) \tag{3.8.9}$$

Thus, the percentage overshoot γ equals

$$\gamma = 100 \exp(-\zeta\pi/\sqrt{1-\zeta^2}) = 100 \exp(-\alpha\pi/\beta) \tag{3.8.10}$$

These results are plotted in Fig. 3.8.2b. They show that the amount of peaking, normalized peaking time, and overshoot are controlled entirely by ζ.

The normalized delay and rise times must be calculated from Eq. 3.8.7 using iterative techniques. When $\zeta > 1.0$, the step response is monotonically nondecreasing and Elmore's results can be applied so

$$\omega_n t_d = 2\zeta, \qquad \omega_n t_r = [2\pi(4\zeta^2 - 2)]^{1/2} = 3.54(2\zeta^2 - 1)^{1/2} \tag{3.8.11}$$

The approximations improve somewhat with increasing ζ; however, due to the asymmetry and non-Gaussian shaping of the response, we cannot expect good results. Note that rise time is undefined for $\zeta < 0.707$.

The settling time T_s is a measure of the filter's damping of sustained oscillations. It is equal to the time required for the step response to settle and remain within δ percent of its final value. This was shown in Fig. 3.4.2. From Eq. 3.8.7, the error between the step response and its final value equal

$$e(t) = r(t) - 1 = \frac{1}{\sqrt{1-\zeta^2}} e^{-\alpha t} \sin(\beta t + \theta), \qquad t > 0 \tag{3.8.12}$$

The error is given by Fig. 3.8.1 after the plot is translated downward by one unit. By differentiating e(t) and setting the result equal to zero, it is easy to show that e(t) is maximum or minimum when $\beta t = n\pi$ for any integer n. Substituting this result into Eq. 3.8.12, then the maximum (or worst case) absolute error must be less than

$$|e(t)| \leqslant \exp(-\alpha t) \tag{3.8.13}$$

The settling time T_s required for the maximum absolute error to settle within ±δ percent of final value is found by rearranging Eq. 3.8.13 as

$$\delta/100 = \exp(-\alpha T_s) = \exp(-T_s/T_c) \tag{3.8.14}$$

which is controlled by α. Defining a time constant $T_c = 1/\alpha$ and solving for T_s, the normalized settling time equals

$$\omega_n T_s/\omega_n T_c = \ln(100/\delta) \tag{3.8.15}$$

which is plotted in Fig. 3.8.3. Three time constants are required for the response to be within 5%, and four time constants to be within 2% of the final value. To further interpret this result, let us consider the root locus of the filter poles when they are constrained to have a constant real part. Their root locus was drawn in Fig. 1.16.2a as a function of ζ; when $|\zeta| > 1$, the root locus describes the poles of a second-order low-pass filter having a fixed time constant T_c. It should be remembered that T_s may be less than the value calculated in Eq. 3.8.15 since the actual error varies sinusoidally (see Eq. 3.8.12).

Summarizing these results from a design standpoint, the procedure for designing a second-order low-pass filter in the time domain often begins by selecting the permissible overshoot and, therefore, the damping factor (Eq. 3.8.10); a compromise is then made between the peak response time T_p (or β in Eq. 3.8.8) and settling time T_s (Eq. 3.8.15 or α in Fig. 3.8.3) such that $\tan^{-1} \beta/\alpha = \cos^{-1} \zeta$.

EXAMPLE 3.8.1 A second-order low-pass noise suppression filter processing a 1000 Bps data stream must meet the time domain specifications shown in Fig. 3.8.4a where: (1) overshoot $\gamma \leqslant 20\%$, (2) peak time $T_p \leqslant 0.1$ msec, and (3) settling time $T_s \leqslant 0.5$ msec for error $\delta \leqslant \pm 5\%$. Determine and draw the s-plane restrictions required to meet these conditions.

Solution From (1) and Fig. 3.8.2, $\zeta \geqslant 0.45$ so that the pole angle cannot exceed

$$\theta \leqslant \cos^{-1} 0.45 = 63^{\circ} \tag{3.8.16}$$

From (2) and Eq. 3.8.8, the imaginary part of the pole β can be no less than

$$\beta = \pi/T_p \geqslant \pi \times 10^4 \tag{3.8.17}$$

From (3), $1/T_s \geqslant 2 \times 10^3$ and $100/\delta \geqslant 20$ so that from Eq. 3.8.15,

$$\alpha = \ln (100/\delta)/T_s \geqslant (\ln 20)(2 \times 10^3) = 3(2 \times 10^3) = 6 \times 10^3 \tag{3.8.18}$$

The permissible pole locations are shown in Fig. 3.8.4b.

EXAMPLE 3.8.2 We determined the limiting values for α, β, and ζ of the second-order noise suppression filter in Example 3.8.1 from the time domain specifications. Let us now complete the design so that the filter meets the following frequency domain specifications: (1) low-frequency gain = 20 dB, (2) 3 dB frequency = minimum (must satisfy time domain specifications), (3) asymptotic rolloff = –40 dB/dec, (4) band-edge slopes = maximum, and (5) gain peaking = arbitrary (must satisfy time domain specifications). Considering the spectrum of a single 1 msec data pulse and the filter bandwidth, will this design produce good noise suppression?

Solution The transfer function of the second-order low-pass filter equals

$$H(s) = \frac{H(0)}{(s/\omega_n)^2 + 2\zeta(s/\omega_n) + 1} \tag{3.8.19}$$

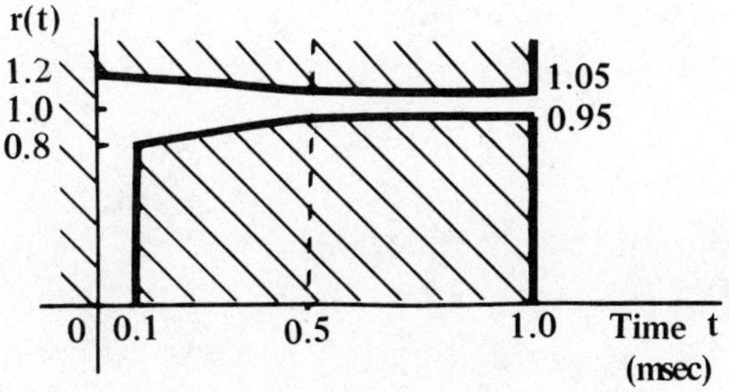

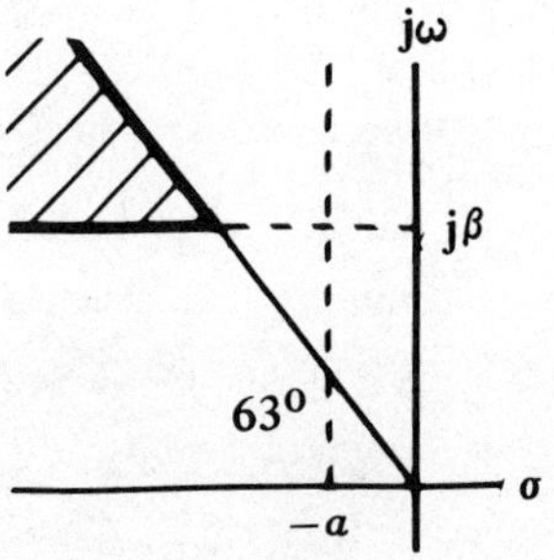

Fig. 3.8.4 (a) Data pulse restrictions and (b) resulting s-plane restrictions (lower half plane not shown) for noise suppression filter of Example 3.8.1.

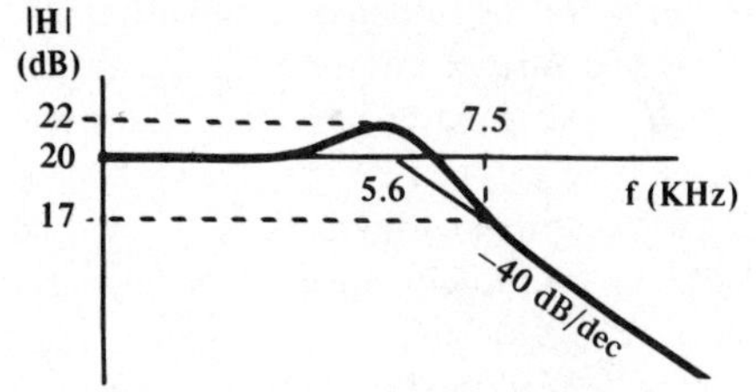

Fig. 3.8.5 Frequency response of noise suppression filter of Example 3.8.2.

The dc gain must equal 20 dB so H(0) = 10. To obtain the maximum band-edge slope (i.e., sharpest cutoff), we must use the smallest allowable ζ, so $\zeta = 0.45$. To obtain the minimum bandwidth, we must use the smallest allowable ω_n, so

$$\omega_n = \pi \times 10^4/\sin 63^o = 3.53 \times 10^4, \qquad f_n = \omega_n/2\pi = 5.6 \text{ KHz} \tag{3.8.20}$$

from Fig. 3.8.4b. Thus, the bandwidth must equal

$$B = 1.33\omega_n = 47 \times 10^3 \text{ rad/sec} = 7.5 \text{ KHz} \tag{3.8.21}$$

from Fig. 2.4.4. The gain characteristic is drawn in Fig. 3.8.5. To assess the filter's noise suppression qualities, let us determine the spectrum of a single 1000 Bps data pulse. We shall then compare its bandwidth to that of the filter. The data pulse is shown in Fig. 1.9.4a. Its spectrum was discussed in Example 1.9.5 and was found to equal

$$F(j\omega) = 10^{-3}\,\frac{\sin 0.5 \times 10^{-3}\omega}{0.5 \times 10^{-3}\omega} \tag{3.8.22}$$

It has a sin x/x characteristic so that the spectrum rolls off asymptotically at $1/\omega = -20$ dB/dec. The zero-crossings occur at integer multiples of

$$\omega_o = \pi/0.5 \times 10^{-3} = 2\pi \times 10^3 \text{ rad/sec}, \qquad f_o = 1 \text{ KHz} \tag{3.8.23}$$

The bulk of the signal energy is contained at frequencies below 1 KHz. Using 2 KHz for extra measure, the filter bandwidth is about 3.8 times more than required. Thus, this extra bandwidth will allow additional noise to pass through the filter with little additional signal. Thus, this design will produce good noise suppression for frequencies above 7.5 KHz, but none below 7.5 KHz. From the information spectrum viewpoint, we obtain poor noise suppression. To improve this suppression, we must relax our time domain specifications on γ, T_p, and T_s.

EXAMPLE 3.8.3 A low-pass filter having no finite zeros has a monotonic step response with t_D = 10 μsec and t_R = 5 μsec. Using Elmore's results, determine the approximate second-order filter having this step response, and locate the filter poles.

Solution The approximate transfer function equals

$$H(s) = \frac{1}{1 + b_1 s + b_2 s^2} = \frac{1}{1 + 2\zeta(s/\omega_n) + (s/\omega_n)^2} \tag{3.8.24}$$

Using Elmore's results, then

$$t_d = b_1 = 10\ \mu\text{sec}, \qquad t_r = 2.51(b_1^{\,2} - 2b_2)^{1/2} = 5\ \mu\text{sec} \tag{3.8.25}$$

Combining these equations and solving for b_2 gives

$$b_2 = 0.5[10^2 - (5/2.51)^2]\,10^{-12} = 0.5(100 - 4)10^{-12} = 48 \times 10^{-12} \tag{3.8.26}$$

Let us determine the ω_n, f_n, and ζ of the filter. Here

$$\begin{aligned} \omega_n &= b_2^{\,-1/2} = 10^6/48^{1/2} = 0.144 \times 10^6 \text{ rad/sec}, \qquad f_n = \omega_n/2\pi = 23.0 \text{ KHz} \\ \zeta &= b_1/2b_2^{\,1/2} = 0.5(10 \times 10^{-6})(0.144 \times 10^6) = 0.72 \end{aligned} \tag{3.8.27}$$

The approximate step response is shown in Fig. 3.8.1 where $\zeta = 0.72$.

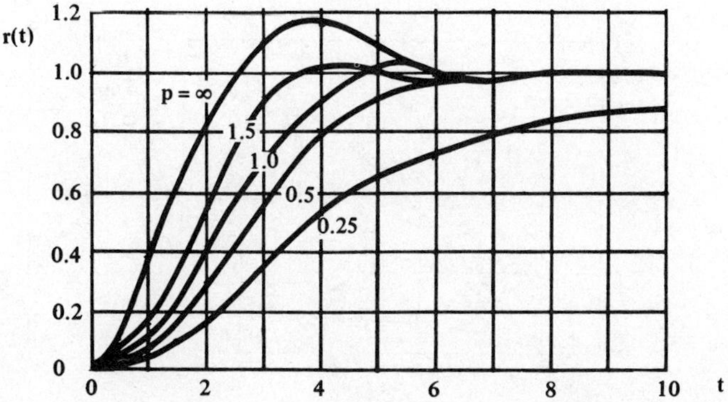

Fig. 3.8.6 Effect of parasitic pole on step response of second-order low-pass filter having $\zeta = 0.5$.[13]

Now let us consider the effects of adding a parasitic pole to the second-order filter. A third-order filter results having gain

$$H(s) = \frac{p\omega_n^2}{(s+p)(s^2 + 2\zeta\omega_n s + \omega_n^2)} \tag{3.8.28}$$

The step response is tedious to determine, but can be written directly from any complete Laplace transform table as[12]

$$r(t) = \left[1 + \frac{p/d}{\sqrt{1-\zeta^2}} e^{-\zeta\omega_n t} \sin\left(\sqrt{1-\zeta^2}\,\omega_n t + \phi_1 - \phi_2\right) - \left(\frac{\omega_n}{d}\right)^2 e^{-pt}\right] U_{-1}(t) \tag{3.8.29}$$

The constants equal

$$d = |a \pm j\omega_n - p| = [(a-p)^2 + \omega_n^2]^{1/2}, \qquad \phi_1 = \tan^{-1}[(1-\zeta^2)^{1/2}/\zeta] = \cos^{-1}\zeta$$
$$\phi_2 = \tan^{-1}[\omega_n(1-\zeta^2)^{1/2}/(p-a)] = \tan^{-1}[(1-\zeta^2)^{1/2}/\zeta(1-\zeta\omega_n/p)] \tag{3.8.30}$$

where d equals the distance between the real and either complex pole and ϕ_2 is the angle of the complex poles relative to the real pole. Introducing the parasitic pole modifies the step response of the second-order filter in two ways. First, it introduces an exponential term which is small when $d \gg \omega_n$ and which dies out quickly when $p \gg \zeta\omega_n$. Second, it reduces the amplitude of the oscillatory component by p/d and reduces phase by ϕ_2 (note that the complex pole residue is reduced by $pe^{-\phi_2}/d$ due to the parasitic pole).

To gain a greater insight into the step response, consider the dominant pole results of Fig. 2.9.3 for fixed ζ and ω_n. When $p \gg \omega_n$, the parasitic pole reduces bandwidth slightly and adds phase. Reducing bandwidth will slightly increase rise time; increasing phase will add slight delay. As p passes through ω_n and approaches zero, the bandwidth, as well as the phase, continues to decrease. The pole also reduces any gain peaking. Thus, the effect of a parasitic pole is to make the step response more sluggish.

This is illustrated in Fig. 3.8.6 for $\omega_n = 1$ and $\zeta = 0.5$. The response of the second-order filter corresponds to $p = \infty$. As the parasitic pole approaches zero, the rise time and delay time increase; the overshoot disappears and the response becomes exponential with time constant 1/p.

The percentage overshoot and normalized rise time of the step response are shown in Fig. 3.8.7. For fixed ζ and ω_n, we see that decreasing p decreases the overshoot and increases rise time as we have just discussed. For example, the overshoot and rise time of the step response shown in Fig. 3.8.6 can be easily determined from these curves. Recalling that $\zeta = 0.5$ and ω_n =

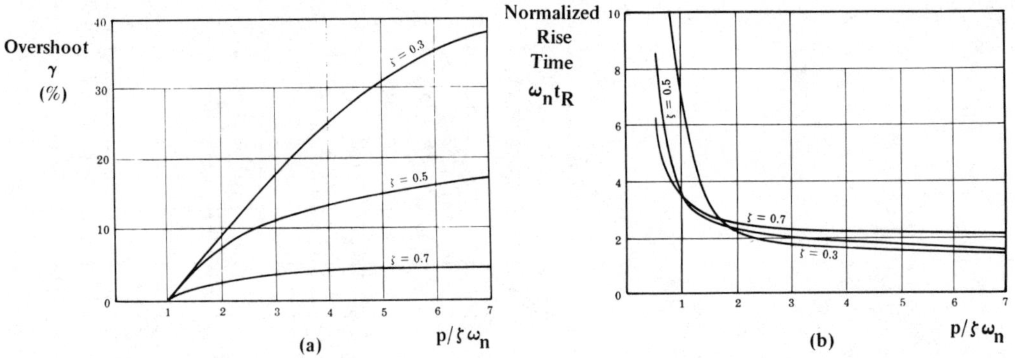

Fig. 3.8.7 **(a) Percentage overshoot and (b) normalized rise time of third-order low-pass filter. (From J. J. DiStefano, A. R. Stubberud, and I. J. Williams, "Feedback and Control Systems," Schaum's Outline Series, p. 264, Figs. 14-8 and 14-9, McGraw-Hill, NY, 1967.)**

1, parameter $p/\zeta\omega_n = 2p$ in Fig. 3.8.7. When $p = 0.5$, then $p/\zeta\omega_n = 1$ so $\gamma = 0\%$ and $t_R = 3.7$ sec; for $p = 1.5$, then $p/\zeta\omega_n = 3$ so $\gamma = 12\%$ and $t_R = 2$ sec. These values agree with those of the step response in Fig 3.8.6.

Now let us investigate Elmore's approximations for delay and rise times. Re-expressing the gain in Eq. 3.8.28 as

$$H(s) = [1 + (2\zeta + \omega_n/p)s + (1 + 2\zeta\omega_n/p)s_n^2 + (\omega_n/p)s_n^3]^{-1} \tag{3.8.31}$$

where $s_n = s/\omega_n$, then the approximate normalized delay and rise times equal

$$\begin{aligned} \omega_n t_d &= 2\zeta + \omega_n/p \\ \omega_n t_r &= 2.51\,[(2\zeta + \omega_n/p)^2 - 2(1 + 2\zeta\omega_n/p)]^{1/2} = 2.51\,[4\zeta^2 - 2 + (\omega_n/p)^2]^{1/2} \end{aligned} \tag{3.8.32}$$

The total delay is the sum of individual delays and the total rise time squared is the sum of individual rise times squared. The step response has overshoot for $p \gg a = \zeta\omega_n$ and small ζ so that Elmore's results must be used with caution. When $p \gg a$, then the complex poles dominate the step response where $\omega_n t_d \cong 2\zeta$ and $\omega_n t_r \cong 3.54(2\zeta^2 - 1)^{1/2}$. This is indicated by the curves approaching horizontal asymptotes in Fig. 3.8.7b. For $p \ll a$, the real pole dominates the step response so there is no overshoot and $t_d \cong 1/p$ and $t_r \cong 2.51/p$. This is confirmed by the t_R curves approaching k/p shapes for small p.

Let us apply Elmore's results to the step response shown in Fig. 3.8.6. Since it is fairly symmetrical and Gaussian, we expect good results when there is negligible peaking. When $p = 0.5$, then Elmore's results give $t_d = 3.0$ and $t_r = 4.3$ while the exact values are $t_D = 3.8$ and $t_R = 3.7$. When $p = 1.5$, then $t_d = 1.7$ and t_r is undefined (ζ is too small) where the exact values are $t_D = 1.9$ and $t_R = 2.0$. Thus, we see there is relatively close agreement.

A slightly different viewpoint can be gained by considering the response of the third-order filter under a constant bandwidth condition.[14] Consider the special case in Eq. 3.8.28 where $p = a$ so that the real parts of the three poles are equal. Under this condition, unity bandwidth requires that the real and imaginary parts of the complex poles (a, β) satisfy

$$\beta = \left(\frac{\pm a[2(2a^2 - 1)(a^2 + 1)]^{1/2} - (a^4 + 1)}{a^2 - 1}\right)^{1/2} \tag{3.8.33}$$

Since β is real, a must always exceed 0.707. For $a < 1.0$, two β values are possible; these are de-

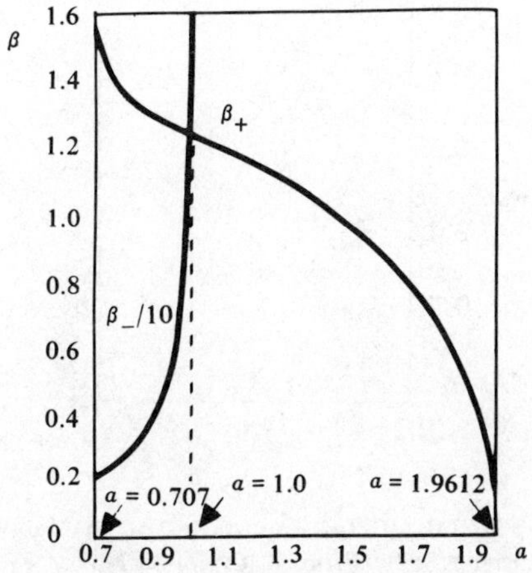

Fig. 3.8.8 Pole locations (α, $j\beta$) required to maintain unity bandwidth of third-order low-pass filter. (From S. C. Dutta Roy, "Transient response characteristics of a third-order filter," IEEE Trans. Circuit Theory, vol. CT-15, pp. 69–71, March, 1968.)

noted as β^+ and β^- which corresponds with the sign in Eq. 3.8.33. For $1.0 \leqslant \alpha \leqslant 1.961$, only β^+ can be used. No solution exists for higher β. The β^+ and β^- values are plotted versus α in Fig. 3.8.8 for $0.707 \leqslant \alpha \leqslant 1.961$.

The step response of the filter depends upon these pole locations. Five different pole combinations selected from Fig. 3.8.8 are shown in Fig. 3.8.9 along with their associated step responses. Also tabulated is the exact rise time t_R, delay time t_D, and dc delay $\tau(0)$. In general, the delay time decreases for each successive filter listed. We see that the rise time is always about 2.1 seconds. We anticipate this result from the Valley-Wallman relation, given by Eq. 3.5.13, since the bandwidth is maintained at unity. Thus, decreasing delay time is obtained at the expense of creating inflection points in the step response. This stairstep-type response becomes oscillatory for large β values.

Now let us correlate the time domain behavior with the frequency domain behavior. The magnitude and delay responses for the five filters just discussed are drawn in Fig. 3.8.10. They all have unity bandwidth since α and β were properly chosen as dictated by Fig. 3.8.8. The frequency domain responses differ primarily in their stopband characteristics. Essentially, the complex pole pairs move out further in frequency ω_n with the necessary decrease in ζ (and corresponding increase in peaking $M_{p\omega}$) to maintain bandwidth. The decrease in ζ produces greater variation in the delay responses. This variation produces delay variation in the spectrum of the unit step input. This results in the stairstep, and more generally the oscillatory, response shape.

Filter	α	β	t_R (sec)	t_D (sec)	$\tau(0)$ (sec)
A	0.707	1.580	2.150	1.515	1.885
B	1.961	0.000	2.150	1.360	1.530
C	0.740	1.939	2.040	1.420	1.695
D	0.920	4.556	2.030	0.770	1.174
E	0.960	6.775	2.120	0.620	1.083

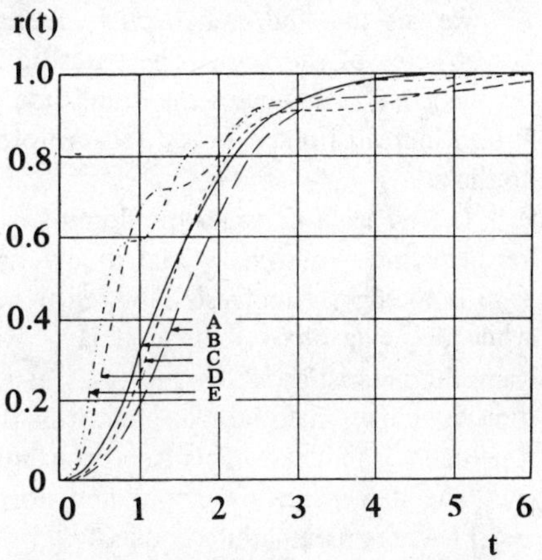

Fig. 3.8.9 Step responses for five different unity-bandwidth third-order low-pass filters. (From S. C. Dutta Roy, "Transient response characteristics of a third-order filter," IEEE Trans. Circuit Theory, vol. CT-15, pp. 69–71, March, 1968.)

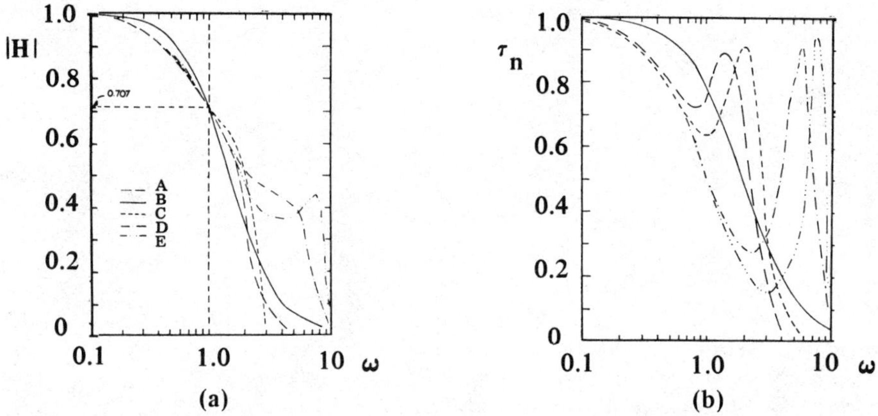

Fig. 3.8.10 (a) Magnitude and (b) delay responses for the low-pass filters listed in Fig. 3.8.9. (From S. C. Dutta Roy, "Transient response characteristics of a third-order filter," IEEE Trans. Circuit Theory, vol. CT-15, pp. 69–71, March, 1968.)

Now that we have determined the effects of adding a parasitic pole to a second-order filter, let us instead add a parasitic zero. The filter is still second-order and has gain

$$H(s) = \frac{\omega_n^2}{z} \frac{s + z}{s^2 + 2\zeta\omega_n s + \omega_n^2} \tag{3.8.34}$$

The step response is[15]

$$r(t) = \left[1 - \frac{d/z}{\sqrt{1-\zeta^2}} e^{-\zeta\omega_n t} \sin\left(\sqrt{1-\zeta^2}\,\omega_n t + \phi_1 + \phi_2\right)\right] U_{-1}(t) \tag{3.8.35}$$

where the constants equal

$$\begin{aligned} &d = |a \pm j\beta - z| = [(a - z)^2 + \beta^2]^{1/2}, \qquad \phi_1 = \tan^{-1}[(1-\zeta^2)^{1/2}/\zeta] = \cos^{-1}\zeta \\ &\phi_2 = \tan^{-1}[(1-\zeta^2)^{1/2}\omega_n/(z-a)] = \tan^{-1}[(1-\zeta^2)^{1/2}/\zeta(z/\zeta\omega_n - 1)] \end{aligned} \tag{3.8.36}$$

d equals the distance between the zero and either pole. ϕ_1 equals the angle of the complex poles from the negative-real axis, while ϕ_2 equals the angle of the complex poles relative to the zero.

We see that the oscillation frequency and exponential time constant are the same as that in the absence of the zero. The parasitic zero does modify the second-order filter response in two ways. First, it decreases the amplitude of the oscillatory component by the d/z factor. Second, it also increases phase by ϕ_2 (again note that the complex pole residue is increased by de^{ϕ_2}/z due to the zero).

Let us again consider the dominant pole-zero results of Fig. 2.9.4 to gain more insight into filter behavior. For fixed ζ and ω_n, we will reduce z from infinity. When $z \gg \omega_n$, the effect of the zero is to slightly increase bandwidth and reduce phase. Increasing bandwidth decreases rise time while reducing phase reduces delay. Reducing z so that $s \cong \omega_n$ produces more peaking in the gain characteristic, which increases as $z \to 0$, and increases bandwidth. This further reduces rise time and may introduce overshoot in the step response. The low-frequency phase is reduced so that delay is reduced. This trend continues as $z \to 0$.

The percentage overshoot and normalized rise time of the step response are shown in Fig. 3.8.11 where parameter a equals

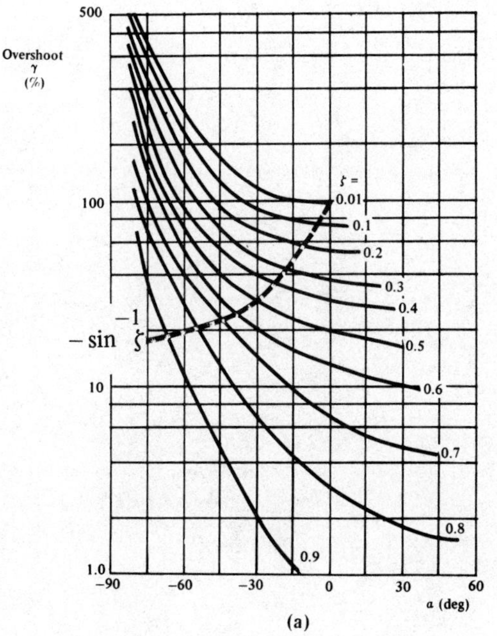

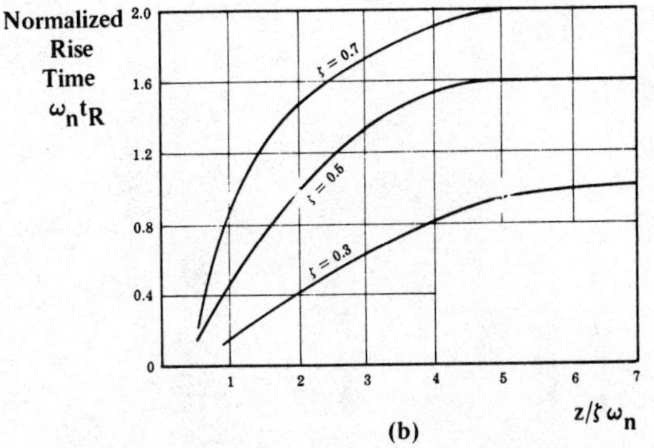

Fig. 3.8.11 (a) Percentage overshoot[16] and (b) normalized rise time of second-order low-pass filter having parasitic zero. ((b) from J. J. DiStefano, A. R. Stubberud, and I. J. Williams, "Feedback and Control Systems," Schaum's Outline Series, p. 264, Fig. 14-8, McGraw-Hill, NY, 1967.)

$$a = \pi/2 - (\phi_1 + \phi_2) = \tan^{-1}\,[\zeta(1 - \omega_n/\zeta z)/(1 - \zeta^2)^{1/2}] \tag{3.8.37}$$

For fixed ζ and ω_n, we verify that decreasing z increases the overshoot and decreases rise time. (Note that decreasing z between $(\infty, 0)$ results in decreasing a between $(\sin^{-1}\zeta, -90^\circ)$.)

Elmore's results are not useful here unless $z > \omega_n$ and $\zeta > 0.7$ because of the peaking the zero produces in the frequency response. This will lead to an oscillatory step response. However, Elmore's results do show the general effects of a finite zero. Since we can rewrite the gain given by Eq. 3.8.34 as

$$H(s) = \frac{1 + (\omega_n/z)(s/\omega_n)}{1 + 2\zeta(s/\omega_n) + (s/\omega_n)^2} \tag{3.8.38}$$

then by Elmore's results, the approximate normalized delay and rise times equal

$$\omega_n t_d = 2\zeta - \omega_n/z, \qquad \omega_n t_r = 2.51\,[(2\zeta)^2 - (\omega_n/z)^2 - 2]^{1/2} \tag{3.8.39}$$

This shows that the presence of the finite zero reduces the normalized delay and rise times. This result is substantiated from the dominant pole-zero viewpoint.

One example of a system having a second-order gain with a finite zero is the phase-locked loop of Example 2.9.3 where

$$H(s) = 2\zeta\omega_n \frac{s + \omega_n/2\zeta}{s^2 + 2\zeta\omega_n s + \omega_n^2} \tag{3.8.40}$$

Using Eq. 3.8.35, its step response therefore equals

$$r(t) = [1 - \frac{1}{\sqrt{1 - \zeta^2}}\, e^{-\zeta\omega_n t} \sin(\sqrt{1 - \zeta^2}\,\omega_n t + \phi_1 + \phi_2)]\, U_{-1}(t) \tag{3.8.41}$$

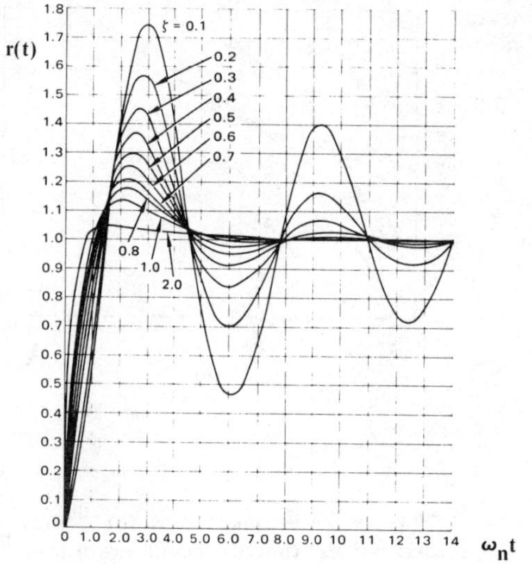

Fig. 3.8.12 Step response of phase-locked loop. (From G. Nash, "Phase-locked loop design fundamentals," Appl. Note AN-535, Motorola, Phoenix, AZ, April, 1971.)

where d/z = 1 and

$$\phi_1 = \cos^{-1}\zeta, \qquad \phi_2 = \tan^{-1}[2\zeta(1-\zeta^2)^{1/2}/(1-2\zeta^2)] \tag{3.8.42}$$

from Eq. 3.8.36. The step response is shown in Fig. 3.8.12. To interpret this response, reconsider the root locus of the system poles and zero that was discussed in Example 1.16.4. For small ζ, the poles are complex with damping factor ζ and the zero is at infinity. Thus, the magnitude response is similar to that shown in Fig. 2.9.4a. The step response should correspond to that for the second-order filter. Comparing Figs. 3.8.12 and 3.8.1, we see that this is the case. However, as ζ passes through unity and becomes larger, the zero travels inward to the origin trailed by a pole. Thus, the magnitude response exhibits less peaking as shown in Fig. 3.7.7, but the bandwidth continues to increase (and will about equal the value of the second pole). Thus, we obtain a faster step response with less overshoot. It approaches an exponential response of time constant $1/2\zeta\omega_n$ as $\zeta \to \infty$. We see this trend developing in Fig. 3.8.12. The percentage overshoot and normalized rise time can be obtained from Fig. 3.8.11. From Eq. 3.8.37, $a = -\sin^{-1}\zeta$ so a is simply equal to the negative of 90° minus the pole angle.

Elmore's results should not be used because of the peaking in the magnitude response except for large $\zeta \to \infty$. This observation is substantiated by the asymmetrical, non-Gaussian, and peaked step response. Evaluating the delay and rise time using Elmore's results, we see that

$$t_d = 2\zeta - 2\zeta = 0, \qquad t_r = \sqrt{2\pi(-2)} = \text{undefined} \tag{3.8.43}$$

which would appear frustrating had we not found their use to be inappropriate.

EXAMPLE 3.8.4 The dominant pole approximation of a phase-locked loop having $\zeta = 0.5$, $\omega_n = 2\pi(550\text{ Hz})$, and $B = 2\pi(1000\text{ Hz})$ was determined in Example 2.9.3. Using the approximation, determine the step response of the PLL. Compare this with the exact response given in Fig. 3.8.12.

Solution The exact PLL response is shown in Fig. 3.8.13. By inspection, we see that $\gamma = 30\%$ and $\omega_n T_p = 2.5$. The second-order dominant pole approximation was given by Eq. 2.9.32 and had parameters $\zeta' = 0.35$, $\omega_n' = 2\pi(704\text{ Hz})$, and $\tau_o = -0.15$ msec. Using the step response of Fig. 3.8.1, we can easily draw the approximate response as shown in Fig. 3.8.13. Note that the response is advanced due to negative delay by $\omega_n\tau_o = 2\pi(550\text{ Hz})(0.15\text{ msec}) = 0.52$ which produces a better approximation. The response has $\gamma = 31\%$ and a normalized peaking time $\omega_n T_p = 3.35(550/704) - 0.52 = 2.1$ using Fig. 3.8.2b. It shows reasonably good agreement with the exact response.

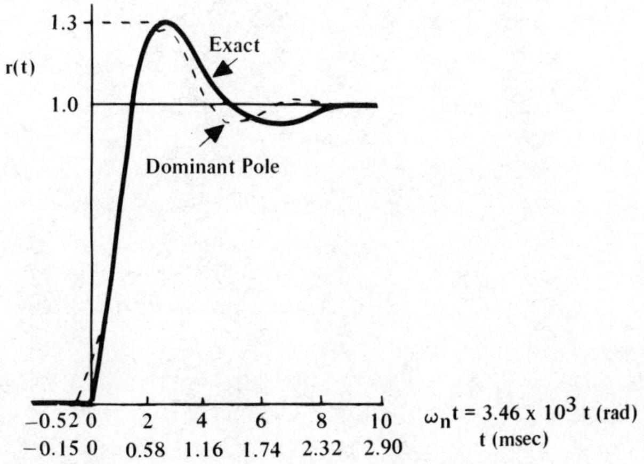

Fig. 3.8.13 Approximate and exact step response of phase-locked loop of Example 3.8.4.

A single zero in the transfer function of Eq. 3.8.34 tends to increase the overshoot and settling time while reducing the delay and rise times of the step response. However, a *pair* of complex zeros can also be used to reduce the overshoot and settling time.[17] Depending upon their location, rise time may increase or decrease. To show this, suppose that the step response of a filter with a gain H(s) can be approximated as

$$r(t) \cong 1 + ke^{-\alpha t} \sin \beta t, \; t \geqslant T \tag{3.8.44}$$

We wish to eliminate the oscillatory term by forming a corrected or compensated response as

$$c(t) = r(t) + a_1 r'(t) + a_2 r''(t), \qquad t \geqslant T$$
$$\cong 1 + ke^{-\alpha t} \; [1 - a_1\alpha + a_2(\alpha^2 - \beta^2)] \sin \beta t + [\beta(a_1 - 2a_2\alpha)] \cos \beta t \tag{3.8.45}$$

by properly choosing a_1 and a_2. The oscillatory terms can be removed by setting

$$1 - a_1\alpha + a_2(\alpha^2 - \beta^2) = 0, \qquad a_1 - 2a_2\alpha = 0 \tag{3.8.46}$$

Solving Eq. 3.8.46 for a_1 and a_2 gives

$$a_1 = 2\alpha/(\alpha^2 - \beta^2) = 2\zeta/\omega_n, \qquad a_2 = 1/(\alpha^2 + \beta^2) = 1/\omega_n^2 \tag{3.8.47}$$

Using these values in Eq. 3.8.45, then the response $c(t) \cong 1$ for $t \geqslant T$. Therefore, by adding small fractions of the first and second derivatives of the step response to the step response itself, the overshoot and ringing can be greatly reduced.

The compensated filter has a step response related to that of the original filter as

$$R_c(s) = R(s)[1 + a_1 s + a_2 s^2] \tag{3.8.48}$$

from Eq. 3.8.45 so their gains are related as

$$H_c(s) = H(s)[1 + a_1 s + a_2 s^2] \tag{3.8.49}$$

Thus, the compensated filter with gain $H_c(s)$ has two additional zeros located at

$$z_1, z_1^* = [-a_1 \pm (a_1^2 - 4a_2)^{1/2}]/2a_2 = -\alpha \pm j\beta \tag{3.8.50}$$

The required α and β are determined from the step response of the original filter.

For example, consider the step response of a filter shown in Fig. 3.8.14. (It happens to be a tenth-order Butterworth filter to be discussed in the next chapter which is unimportant here.) α equals the reciprocal of the envelope time constant and β equals the ringing frequency. Inspection

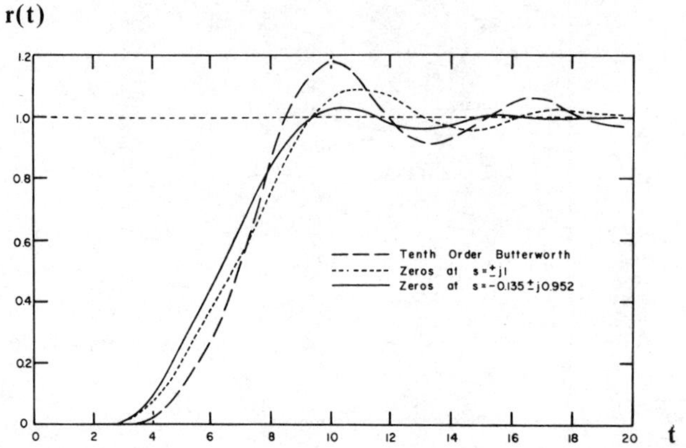

Fig. 3.8.14 Step response of tenth-order Butterworth filter and zero-compensated filters. (From S. C. Dutta Roy, "Reducing overshoot and ringing in filters," Proc. IEEE, vol. 54, pp. 1189–1190, Sept., 1966.)

of Fig. 3.8.14 shows that $\alpha = 0.135$ and $\beta = 0.952$. Using Eq. 3.8.50, the zeros are located at

$$z_1, z_1^* = -0.135 \pm j0.952 \qquad (3.8.51)$$

and constants $a_1 = 0.292$ and $a_2 = 1.08$ from Eq. 3.8.47. The step response of the compensated filters having these zeros (and also zeros at $s = \pm j1$) are also shown in the Fig. 3.8.14. Clearly, the overshoot and ringing are reduced. The delay is decreased but the rise time is increased. This is consistent with Elmore's results given by Eq. 3.5.7, where we anticipated that addition of zeros would decrease t_d but increase t_r (assuming $2a_2 \geqslant a_1^2$ or $\zeta \leqslant 1$ which is usually the case). From the bandwidth-rise time result of Eq. 3.5.13, since t_r must increase, the bandwidth of the compensated filter must decrease. The frequency responses of the original and compensated filters are shown in Fig. 3.8.15 for various pure imaginary zero locations. We see that the bandwidth does indeed decrease.

So far in this chapter, we have discussed many types of low-pass filters and have utilized Elmore's, Valley and Wallman's and dominant pole-zero approximations to estimate their parameters. In so doing, we have established several general relationships between the time and frequency domain behaviors of low-pass filters. They are:

1. Rise time-bandwidth: $f_{3dB}t_r = 0.35$ (to 0.45)
2. Delay time: $t_d = \tau(0) = -d \arg H(j0)/d\omega$
3. Settling time: $f_{3dB}T_s = 0.5M_{p\omega} \ln(100/\delta)$
4. Percentage overshoot: $\gamma = 100 \exp(-\pi/2M_{p\omega})$
5. In-band frequency response: Primarily controls shape of step response after delay time (e.g., delay time, rise time, overshoot, settling time, etc.)

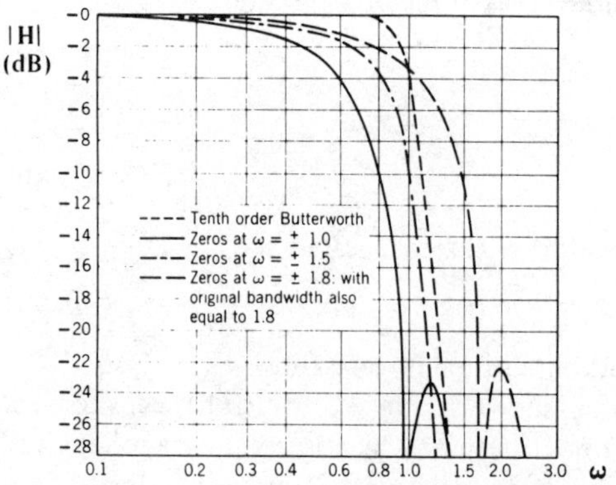

Fig. 3.8.15 Magnitude characteristic of tenth-order Butterworth filter and zero-compensated filters. (From. F. F. Kuo, "Network Analysis and Synthesis," 2nd ed., Chap. 13, Wiley, NY, 1966. Reprinted by permission of John Wiley & Sons, Inc.)

6. Stopband frequency response: Primarily controls shape of step response before delay time (e.g., monotonic, stairstep, or oscillating).

These general relations and observations prove to be of immense value to the engineer in quickly assessing filter behavior. This will become especially clear when we discuss classical and optimum filter response (Chaps. 4 and 5, respectively).

3.9 HIGH-PASS FILTER RESPONSE

Now that we have considered low-pass filter response in great detail, we wish to briefly review the response of the other filter types. We shall reserve their detailed discussion for Chap. 6.

High-pass filters have step and impulse responses which are different from those of low-pass filters. The step response of a high-pass filter is shown in Fig. 3.9.1. Its response parameters are defined in the same way as those for the low-pass filter shown in Fig. 3.4.2. Note that in high-pass filters, the initial value is nonzero since the high-frequency filter response is nonzero. The final value is zero since the low-frequency response is zero. In low-pass filters, the situation is reversed.

High-pass filters are obtained from low-pass filters using the low-pass to high-pass transformation given by Eq. 2.6.1 where p is replaced by 1/s. The high-pass filter of first-order has a gain

$$H(s) = \frac{s}{s+1} \tag{3.9.1}$$

while a second-order high-pass filter has a gain

$$H(s) = \frac{s^2}{s^2 + 2\zeta s + 1} \tag{3.9.2}$$

An *n*th-order synchronously-tuned high-pass filter has a gain

$$H(s) = \left(\frac{s}{s+1}\right)^n \tag{3.9.3}$$

The step response of the synchronously-tuned filter equals

$$r(t) = \mathcal{L}^{-1}\left[\frac{1}{s}\left(\frac{s}{s+1}\right)^n\right] = \mathcal{L}^{-1}\left(s^n \frac{1}{s(s+1)^n}\right) \tag{3.9.4}$$

Since

$$r(t) = \mathcal{L}^{-1}\left[\frac{1}{s(s+1)^n}\right] = \left(1 - e^{-t} \sum_{k=0}^{n-1} \frac{t^k}{k!}\right) U_{-1}(t) \tag{3.9.5}$$

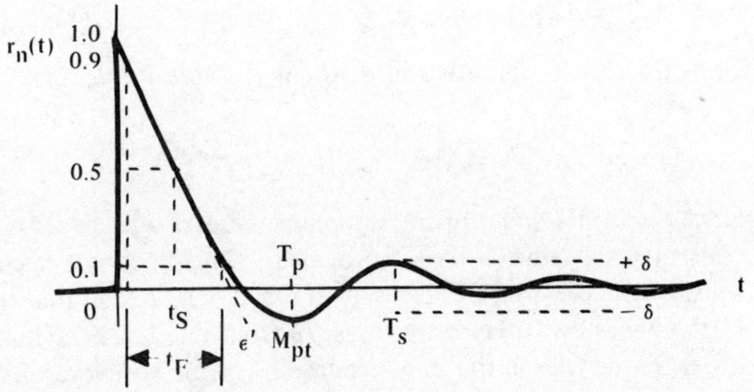

Fig. 3.9.1 Normalized step response of high-pass filter.

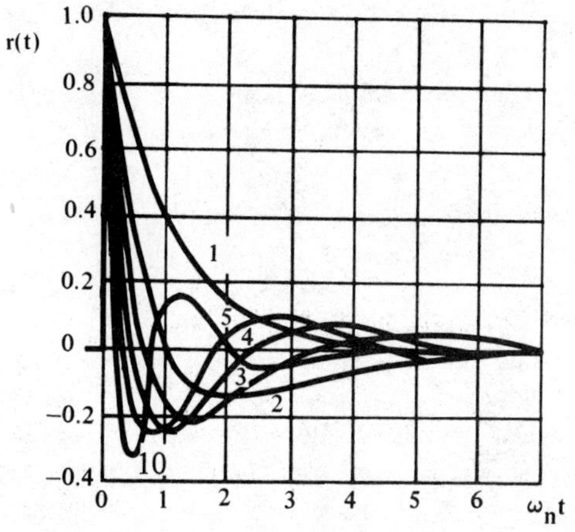

Fig. 3.9.2 Step response of nth-order synchronously-tuned high-pass filter.

from Eq. 3.7.9, then using the time differentiation theorem of Table 1.8.2, the step response equals

$$r(t) = d^n r(t)/dt^n = \frac{d^{n-1}}{dt^{n-1}} \frac{t^{n-1} e^{-t}}{(n-1)!} U_{-1}(t) = e^{-t} L_{n-1}(t) \tag{3.9.6}$$

where L_n is the *n*th-order Laguerre function.[18] The step response is shown in Fig. 3.9.2. The first three responses equal

$$r_1(t) = e^{-t} U_{-1}(t), \qquad r_2(t) = e^{-t}(1-t)U_{-1}(t), \qquad r_3(t) = e^{-t}(1 - 2t + t^2/2!)U_{-1}(t) \tag{3.9.7}$$

The initial and final values of the step response are easily derived using the initial and final value theorems of Eqs. 3.4.3 and 3.4.7 where

$$r(0) = \lim_{s\to\infty} H(s) = 1, \qquad r(\infty) = \lim_{s\to 0} H(0) = 0 \tag{3.9.8}$$

Another parameter used to describe high-pass filter step response is *sag* or *tilt* which equals

$$\epsilon(t) = 1 - r(t) \tag{3.9.9}$$

Sag depends upon the time t at which it is measured and is generally expressed in percent. If r(t) is fairly linear over the time range considered, then expressing r(t) in a Maclaurin series and retaining only the first-order term gives

$$\epsilon = -t\, dr(0)/dt = -tr'(0) \tag{3.9.10}$$

The initial sag slope therefore equals

$$\epsilon' = -r'(0) \ \ \%/\text{sec} \tag{3.9.11}$$

Using the time differentiation theorem of Table 1.8.2, then

$$\epsilon' = -r'(0) = -\lim_{s\to\infty} [sR(s) - 1] = -\lim_{s\to\infty} [H(s) - 1] = n \tag{3.9.12}$$

Since the initial slopes of the responses increase with order n, their storage times and effective time constants are reduced by a factor of n. The responses become faster for increasing order unlike those of the low-pass filter shown in Fig. 3.7.1. Recall that the 3 dB bandwidths (of the stopband) of the high-pass filters increase as $\sqrt{n}$ from Eq. 2.3.29. Thus, increasing order serves to reduce the lower frequencies in the step response spectrum which results in increasing speed.

Note that the step responses exhibit undershoot and ringing. The ringing is damped within (roughly) the envelope of the first-order filter. Meyer has shown that any high-pass filter having *more* than one zero at the origin (i.e., more than +6 dB/oct or +20 dB/dec low-frequency rolloff in its magnitude characteristic) must always have step response overshoot.[19] We will show in Chap. 6 that high-pass filters which result from low-pass filters using the standard low-pass to high-pass transformation p = 1/s invariably become more oscillatory. This is due to the transform since

$$r_{HP}(t) = \int_0^\infty J_0(2\sqrt{t\tau})h_{LP}(\tau)\, d\tau\, U_{-1}(t) \tag{3.9.13}$$

where J_o is the zero-order Bessel function of the first kind (J_o is an oscillatory function as shown in Fig. 6.3.12). Therefore, although the low-pass filter impulse response h_{LP} may be non-negative (i.e., r_{LP} is a monotonic response), J_o can easily cause r_{HP} to oscillate.

We will also show in Chap. 6 that when we want to preserve the low-pass filter step response parameters in the high-pass filter so that

$$r_{HP}(t) = 1 - r_{LP}(t) \tag{3.9.14}$$

it is necessary to use the so-called low-transient or complementary low-pass to high-pass transformation which equals

$$H_{HP}(s) = 1 - H_{LP}(s) \tag{3.9.15}$$

Thus, in this transform we take a difference of gains rather than inverting frequency as before where p = 1/s. For example, the gain of the second-order complementary high-pass filter equals

$$H_{HP}(s) = 1 - \frac{1}{s^2 + 2\zeta s + 1} = \frac{s(s + 2\zeta)}{s^2 + 2\zeta s + 1} \tag{3.9.16}$$

Observing that its step response is equal to one minus the step response of the second-order low-pass filter using Eq. 3.9.14, the same performance indices describing the low-pass filter can be used including, for example, the frequency of oscillation (Fig. 3.8.2a), undershoot and peaking time (Fig. 3.8.2b), storage and fall times and settling time (Fig. 3.8.3).

We can also utilize this result to determine the step response of the second-order high-pass filter whose gain is given by Eq. 3.9.2. Using Eq. 3.9.15, the complementary low-pass filter has a gain

$$H_{LP}(s) = 1 - \frac{s^2}{s^2 + 2\zeta s + 1} = \frac{2\zeta s + 1}{s^2 + 2\zeta s + 1} \tag{3.9.17}$$

which is identical to Eq. 3.8.40. Thus, the step response of the second-order high-pass filter is one minus the step response of the low-pass filter which is shown in Fig. 3.8.12. Therefore, the undershoot and fall time are shown in Fig. 3.8.11 and the initial sag is 2ζ. These two examples illustrate the great usefulness of the complementary low-pass to high-pass transformation.

EXAMPLE 3.9.1 A cascade of up to 40 wideband amplifiers is often used in cable transmission systems such as cable television (CATV) and data transmission.[20] Many of the amplifiers incorporate automatic gain control (AGC) to maintain signal levels. Often a carrier is amplitude-modulated which is then demodulated by the amplifier to control its gain. AGC performance shows progressive deteriora-

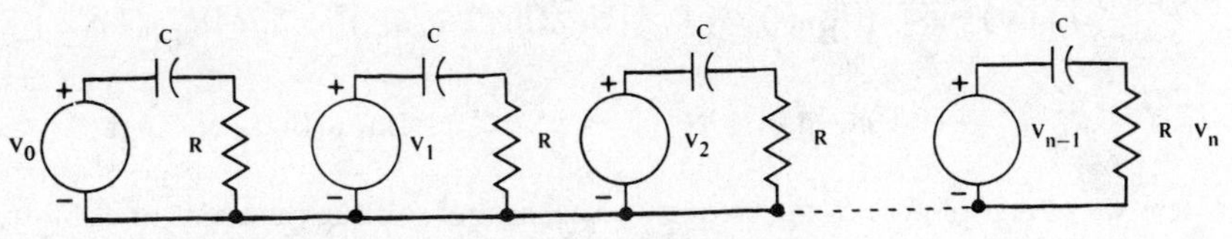

Fig. 3.9.3 Cascaded high-pass filters in Example 3.9.1.

Table 3.9.1 Normalized and denormalized storage and fall times of high-pass filters of Example 3.9.1.

n	1	5	10	n	1	5	10
$\omega_n T_s$ (rad)	0.69	0.2	0.15	T_s (msec)	110	32	24
$\omega_n T_F$ (rad)	2.2	0.075	0.05	T_F (msec)	350	12	8.0

tion with increasing cascade length. For AGC analysis, assume that the amplifier can be represented as shown in Fig. 3.9.3. Plot the step responses of the first, fifth, and tenth amplifiers as the step propagates through the chain, assuming that the 3 dB corner frequency of each amplifier is 1 Hz. What are the storage and fall times of the responses?

Solution Assuming that each stage is tuned to the same lower corner frequency $\omega_n = 1/RC$, the amplifiers are synchronously-tuned and the overall gain is given by Eq. 3.9.3 where $s_n = s/\omega_n$. The step responses of the various stages are shown in Fig. 3.9.2; since $f_n = 1$ Hz, then time is denormalized by $1/\omega_n = 0.159$. The storage and fall times of the responses are easily written by inspection of Fig. 3.9.1 and are listed in Table 3.9.1.

3.10 BAND-PASS FILTER RESPONSE

Low-pass and high-pass filters are characterized by their unit step response. Band-pass, band-stop, and sometimes all-pass filters are characterized by their unit cosine step response where the input equals $\cos \omega_o t\, U_{-1}(t)$. ω_o is equal to the center frequency of the filter.

The band-pass filter response depends upon the Q of the filter where $Q = \omega_o/B$ and B is its bandwidth. Since the generalized low-pass to band-pass transformation equals

$$p = Q(s/\omega_o + \omega_o/s) \tag{3.10.1}$$

from Eq. 2.7.1, then solving Eq. 3.10.1 for s yields

$$s/\omega_o = p/2Q \pm \sqrt{(p/2Q)^2 - 1} \tag{3.10.2}$$

Every pole and zero of the low-pass filter transforms into a *pair* of poles and zeros for the band-pass filter. The location of these critical frequencies depends upon p and Q. When $|p/2Q| \ll 1$, then s equals

$$s/\omega_o = p/2Q \pm j1 \qquad \text{or} \qquad s = Bp/2 \pm j\omega_o \tag{3.10.3}$$

Thus, in high-Q band-pass filters, the poles and zeros are obtained by scaling the low-pass filter poles and zeros by B/2 and then translating them vertically to $\pm j\omega_o$.

The impulse response of high-Q or narrowband band-pass filters can be easily written. The gain of the band-pass filter can be expressed as

$$H_{BP}(s) \cong H_{LP}(p)\,|_{p=p_1(s)} + H_{LP}(p)\,|_{p=p_2(s)} \tag{3.10.4}$$

where p_1 and p_2 are the pole/zero patterns just discussed. In the high-Q case, the impulse response equals

$$\begin{aligned} h_{BP}(t) &= \mathcal{L}^{-1}[H_{BP}(s)] \cong \mathcal{L}^{-1}[H_{LP}(Bp/2 - j\omega_o)] + \mathcal{L}^{-1}[H_{LP}(Bp/2 + j\omega_o)] \\ &= (B/2)h_{LP}(Bt/2)(e^{j\omega_o t} + e^{-j\omega_o t}) = Bh_{LP}(Bt/2)\cos \omega_o t \end{aligned} \tag{3.10.5}$$

Here we have made use of the frequency scaling and shifting theorems of Table 1.8.2. In like manner, the unit cosine step response of a high-Q band-pass filter is also easily determined to be

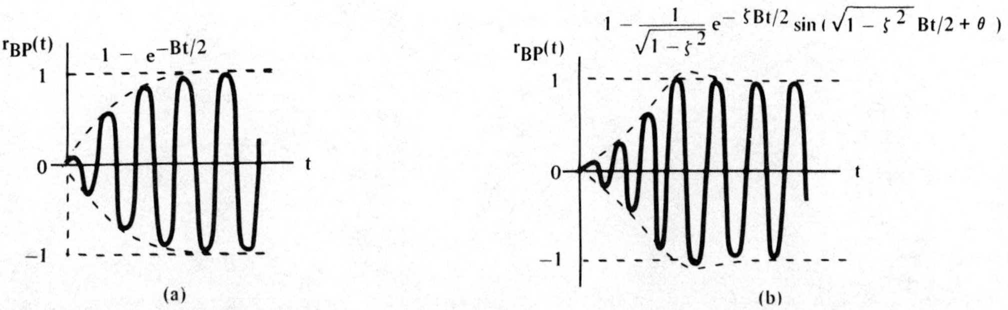

Fig. 3.10.1 Cosine step response of (a) first- and (b) second-order narrowband band-pass filters.

$$r_{BP}(t) = r_{LP}(Bt/2) \cos \omega_o t \tag{3.10.6}$$

This shows that the step (or impulse) response of a band-pass filter is a cosine step whose frequency is that of the filter, and whose envelope corresponds to the step (or impulse) response of its associated low-pass filter. Thus, we can easily determine the response of narrowband band-pass filters by using the responses of their associated low-pass filters. Of course, we must be careful to scale time by B/2. This is especially convenient since the envelope will have the same performance parameters (e.g., rise time, overshoot, and settling time) as the low-pass filter responses. Thus, we can use the low-pass filter results of the earlier sections in calculating the response of high-Q band-pass filters. Unfortunately, this is not true for intermediate- and low-Q filters whose response must be calculated explicitly. The cosine step responses for the first- and second-order (high-Q) band-pass filters of Sec. 2.7 are shown in Fig. 3.10.1. It is important to remember that band-pass filters of the same type having identical bandwidths but different center frequencies have identical envelope responses but different frequencies of oscillation, and visa versa.

EXAMPLE 3.10.1 Touch-Tone systems use band-pass filters to decode two frequencies as discussed in Example 2.7.2. Using a Q of 100 and the center frequencies listed in Fig. 2.7.3, plot the cosine step responses of the first-order band-pass filters.

Solution Since there are high-Q filters, we can use the narrowband response given by Eq. 3.10.6. Therefore, the envelope of the cosine step response of the first-order band-pass filter is given by the step response of its associated first-order low-pass filter. Using the step response of Fig. 3.7.1 for n = 1, we can easily sketch the cosine step responses for the 697 and 1477 Hz filters as shown in Fig. 3.10.1a. The 3 dB bandwidths B equal 6.97 and 14.77 Hz, respectively, since Q = 100. This sets the response time of the envelopes. For example, the rise time $t_R = 0.7/B$ from Eq. 3.5.13. Then the rise times become 50 and 24 msec, respectively, for the two filters. Ot course, the frequencies of oscillation of the signals within the envelopes correspond to the center frequencies of the filters which are 697 and 1477 Hz.

3.11 BAND-STOP FILTER RESPONSE

The unit cosine step response of narrowband band-stop filters can also be easily determined. Their response is related to that of high-pass filters as the band-pass filter response is related to that of low-pass filters. This is shown by recalling from Eq. 2.8.1 that the low-pass to band-stop transformation equals

$$1/p = Q(s/\omega_o + \omega_o/s) \tag{3.11.1}$$

This transformation may alternatively be viewed as a sequence of two LP—HP and LP—BP transformations. Therefore, the gain of narrowband or high-Q band-stop filter can be expressed as

$$H_{BS}(s) = H_{HP}(p)\,|_{p=p_1(s)} + H_{HP}(p)\,|_{p=p_2(s)} \tag{3.11.2}$$

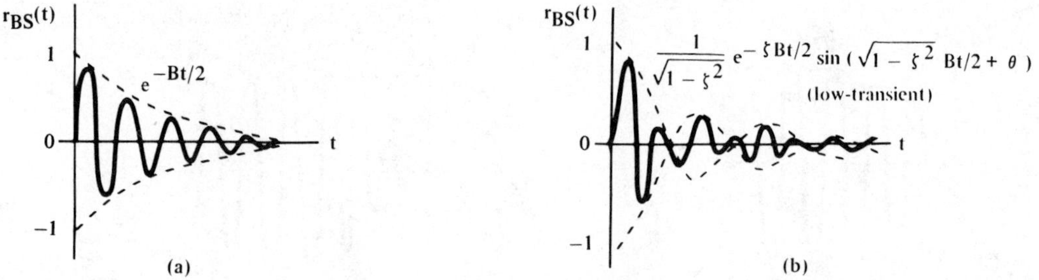

Fig. 3.11.1 Cosine step response of (a) first- and (b) second-order narrowband band-stop filters.

where the high-pass filters are first obtained from the low-pass filters using frequency inversion. Therefore, by analogy with Eqs. 3.10.5 and 3.10.6, the unit cosine step and impulse responses of narrowband band-stop filters equal

$$r_{BS}(t) = r_{HP}(Bt/2) \cos \omega_o t, \qquad h_{BS}(t) = Bh_{HP}(Bt/2) \cos \omega_o t \tag{3.11.3}$$

The step (or impulse) response of a band-stop filter is a cosine step whose frequency is that of the filter, and whose envelope corresponds to the step (or impulse) response of its associated high-pass filter. The unit cosine step response of first- and second-order (high-Q) band-stop filters are shown in Fig. 3.11.1. Again the time domain performance parameters of the high-pass filter correspond to those of the band-stop filter. Thus, the high-pass filter results of Sec. 3.9 can be used in calculating the response of high-Q band-stop filters. Again, this is not true for intermediate- and low-Q filters whose response must be calculated explicitly. As with band-pass filters, it is important to remember that band-stop filters of the same type having identical bandwidths but different center frequencies, have identical envelope responses but different frequencies of oscillation, and visa versa.

EXAMPLE 3.11.1 A 60 Hz first-order band-stop filter having a Q of 60 was designed in Example 2.8.1 for a medical electronics application. Plot the cosine step response of the filter.

Solution Since this is a high-Q application, we can use the narrowband response given by Eq. 3.11.3. Therefore, the envelope of the cosine step response of the first-order band-stop filter is given by the step response of its associated first-order high-pass filter. Using the step response of Fig. 3.9.1, the cosine step response of the band-stop filter is easily drawn as shown in Fig. 3.11.1a. Since its center frequency is 60 Hz, the frequency of oscillation is 60 Hz. Since its bandwidth B = 60 Hz/60 = 1 Hz, the envelope has a fall time $t_F = 0.35/B = 0.35$ second.

3.12 ALL-PASS FILTER RESPONSE

All-pass filters have gains given by

$$H(s) = D(-s)/D(s) \tag{3.12.1}$$

where D(s) is any polynomial. Unfortunately, although their gain function is perhaps the simplest of all the filter types to express, their unit step or cosine step response must be calculated explicitly. For simplicity, let us only consider their step response. All-pass filters have step responses with initial values of

$$r(0) = \lim_{s\to\infty} H(s) = +1, \text{ n even} \quad \text{and} \quad -1, \text{ n odd} \tag{3.12.2}$$

and final values of

$$r(\infty) = \lim_{s\to 0} H(s) = 1 \tag{3.12.3}$$

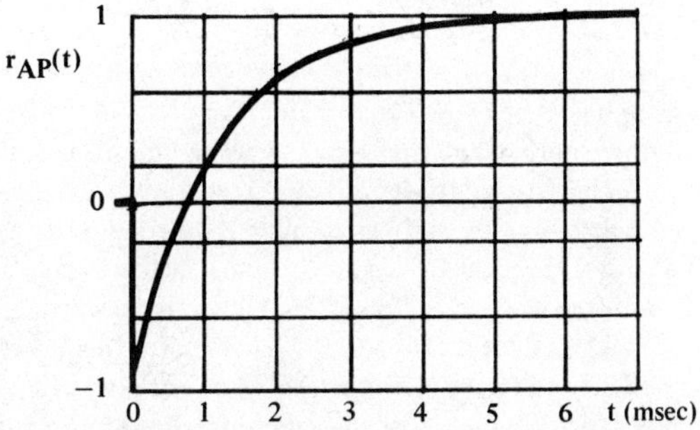

Fig. 3.12.1 Step response of first-order all-pass filter.

Thus, they have both initial and final values of ±1. Note that band-stop filters have this same property with values of +1. The first-order all-pass filter has gain

$$H_1(s) = \frac{1-s}{1+s} \tag{3.12.4}$$

Its step response equals

$$r_1(t) = \mathcal{L}^{-1}\left[\frac{1-s}{s(1+s)}\right] = \mathcal{L}^{-1}\left[\frac{1}{s} - \frac{2}{1+s}\right] = (1-2e^{-t})U_{-1}(t) \tag{3.12.5}$$

which is plotted in Fig. 3.12.1. The response begins at −1 and increased exponentially to +1. Its performance parameters are the same as the first-order low-pass filter.

PROBLEMS

3.1 A second-order low-pass filter having real poles has gain $H(s) = 1/[(1+ks)(1+s/k)]$. Determine (a) its exact step response and (b) its approximate step response using a dominant pole approximation for H(s). (c) Plot the two responses. Show that the approximate response approaches the exact response for $t \gg 1/k$ and $k \gg 1$.

3.2 The dominant pole approximation for the lead-lag filter is given by Eq. 3.7.36. (a) Derive B/p using the binomial theorem. (b) Derive τ_o using the Maclaurin series for $\tan^{-1} x$ and $\log_{10} x$. (c) Verify that the approximate step response is given by Eq. 3.7.38.

3.3 A lag filter has a gain given by Eq. 3.7.28. If z = 3p, determine (a) its exact step response and (b) its approximate step response using a dominant pole approximation for H(s). (c) Plot the two responses and compare their parameters.

3.4 Determine the approximate rise and delay times in Example 3.7.3 using Elmore's results. Compare them with the exact values given by Eqs. 3.7.32 and 3.7.33.

3.5 Magnetic tape reproducing systems use standard A, B, C, and D filters as discussed in Prob. 2.2. Their characteristics are very close to those of a lag filter whose gain H(s) is given by Eq. 3.7.28. (a) Find p, z, and H_o in Eq. 3.7.28 for each of the four filters. (b) Determine their step responses. (c) Find the dominant pole approximation for each gain H(s). (d) Determine their approximate step responses based on the results of part (c). (e) Plot the step responses and compare their exact and approximate rise and delay times.

3.6 Sound level meters use standard A, B, C, and D weighting filters as discussed in Prob. 2.20. (a) Determine the dominant pole approximation for each of the filters. Why can't the excess phase term be determined? (Hint: Treat them as cascaded high-pass and low-pass filters.) (b) Plot their apuroximate step responses by neglecting the low-frequency rolloff and treating them as low-pass filters.

3.7 A lead filter has a parasitic pole p_o. Its gain is given by Eq. 3.7.41 except that (1 + s) is replaced by $(1 + s/p_o)$. Assume that $p > z$ and $p_o \gg p$. (a) Determine its general dominant pole approximation. (b) Determine the gain approximation for z = 1, p = 2, and p_o = 10. (c) Determine the step response for part (b). (d) Plot the step response and compare it with Fig. 3.7.6.

3.8 Repeat Prob. 3.7 for a lead filter having z = 1, p = 2, and p_o = 4.

3.9 The open-circuit voltage gain of an rcg transmission line was found in Prob. 1.46 to equal H(s) = $1/\cosh \gamma d$ where $\gamma = d\sqrt{r(g + sc)}$. The cosh function can be expanded in a Maclaurin series as

$$\cosh d\sqrt{r(g+sc)} = \cosh d\sqrt{rg}\,[1 + \frac{T \tanh b}{2b} s + \frac{T^2(b - \tanh b)}{3b^2} s^2 + \ldots]$$

where $b = d\sqrt{rg}$ is the conductance factor and $T = d\sqrt{rc}$ is a time constant. Determine the approximate delay and rise times of the step response using Elmore's results.[22]

3.10 An *n*th-order all-pole low-pass filter has a step response with less than 5% overshoot, rise time t_r, and delay time t_d. (a) Determine its second-order gain approximation based upon Elmore's results. Relate its corner frequency ω_n and damping factor ζ to t_r and t_d. What is ω_n and ζ if (b) $t_d = t_r = 5$ msec, or (c) $t_d = 10$ msec and $t_r = 5$ msec? (d) Plot the magnitude and step responses of the filter.

3.11 Repeat Prob. 3.10 when (a) $t_d = t_r = 5$ msec, and (b) $t_r = 10$ μsec and $t_d = 5$ μsec.

3.12 Determine the rise time of the first-order low-pass filter having a gain given by Eq. 3.3.9 based upon the (a) Valley-Wallman relation and (b) inverse slope approximation. (Hint: See Fig. 3.3.3.) (c) Compare these values with the exact value.

3.13 (a) Using Elmore's results, determine the optimum normalized pole positions of a second-order low-pass filter to obtain minimum rise time. (b) What is the resulting delay time? Interpret the results using Fig. 3.8.1.

3.14 A low-pass filter has a dc gain of 10, $\omega_n = 2\pi(100$ KHz), and $\zeta = 0.2$. Plot its step response. What are the approximate delay, rise, and 5% settling times?

3.15 A low-pass filter has a dc gain of 10, $\omega_n = 2\pi(10$ KHz), and $\zeta = 0.4$. Repeat Prob. 3.14.

3.16 Accelerometers are transducers which produce electrical outputs proportional to their acceleration. Their sensitivity is measured in mV/g (or sometimes pC/g). The accelerometer behaves as a low-pass filter above 10 Hz. Plot the step response and determine the delay, rise, and 5% settling times when:[23] (a) $f_o = 75$ KHz, $\zeta = 0.025$, and $H_o = 1.2$; (b) $f_o = 1.4$ KHz, $\zeta = 0.55$, and $H_o = 10$.

3.17 The frequency response ot the second-order filter, based upon the time domain specifications of Example 3.8.1 and the frequency domain specifications of Example 3.8.2, is plotted in Fig. 3.8.5. Its 3 dB bandwidth equalled 7.5 KHz while the bulk of the data pulse spectrum conservatively occupied only 2 KHz. Thus, the filter bandwidth was 3.8 more than required. (a) Reduce the filter bandwidth to 1 KHz and discuss the changes this requires in the time domain specifications. (b) List a new set of specifications which will allow a better frequency response to be obtained. (Hint: From a data recovery standpoint, $\gamma \leqslant 50\%$ and $T_s \leqslant 0.5$ msec for $\delta \leqslant 5\%$. See Fig. P3.17.)

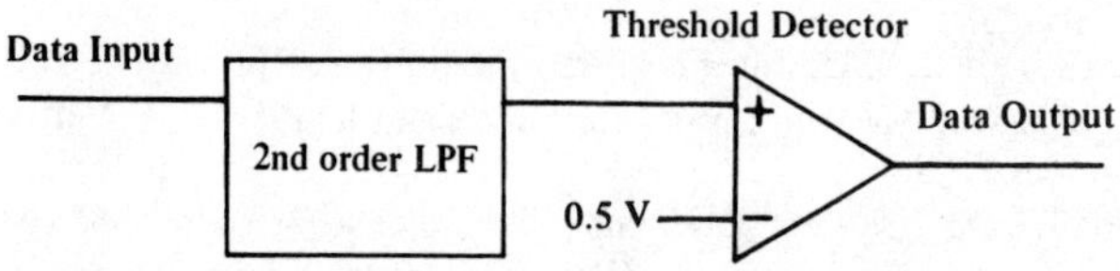

Fig. P3.17

3.18 (a) Determine the first-order dominant pole approximation for a second-order low-pass filter having gain $H(s) = 1/(s^2 + 1.6s + 1)$. (b) Determine its approximate step response. (c) Plot this response and compare it with the exact step response shown in Fig. 3.8.1.

3.19 Repeat Prob. 3.18 when $H(s) = 1/(s^2 + 1.8s + 1)$.

3.20 A third-order low-pass filter has a gain given by Eq. 3.8.28 where $\omega_n = 1$ and $\zeta = 0.5$, and the step response shown in Fig. 3.8.6. (a) What conditions must be satisfied for the percentage overshoot to be independent of ζ? (Hint: Use Fig. 2.9.3.) (b) What is the limiting condition in part (a) using Fig. 3.8.7a? (c) Determine the approximate delay and rise times when $p \gg 0.5$. (d) Repeat part (c) for $p = 0.1$.

3.21 A third-order low-pass filter has gain $H(s) = 1/[(s+1)(s^2 + 0.6s + 1)]$. Determine the gain of the second-order low-pass filter which has approximately the same step response.

3.22 The step response of a unity-bandwidth third-order low-pass filter is shown in Fig. 3.8.9 for different (α, β) where $p = \alpha$. (a) Plot the various pole locations in the s-plane. Discuss their locus as t_D decreases from 1.515 to 0.620. (b) Justify the magnitude and delay responses shown in Fig. 3.8.10 from the results of part (a).

3.23 The approximate overshoot and settling time of a low-pass filter can be obtained from dominant pole-zero analysis. (a) Show that the maximum magnitude response $M_{p\omega}$ determines the damping factor as $\zeta = 1/2M_{p\omega}$ for $\zeta < 0.5$. (b) Show that ζ determines the percentage overshoot γ as $\gamma = 100 \exp(-\pi/2M_{p\omega})$. (c) Show that ζ determines the normalized 3 dB bandwidth as $B/\omega_n \cong 1.55(1 - 0.71\zeta^2)$

for $\zeta < 0.5$. (d) Show that $\omega_n T_s \cong 2M_{p\omega} \ln(100/\delta)$, and that $f_{3dB} T_s \cong 0.5 M_{p\omega} \ln(100/\delta)$.

3.24 The phase-locked loop (PLL) of Example 2.9.3 has a step response given by Eq. 3.8.41. If the step response has 20% overshoot and a 5% settling time of 1 msec, determine the parameters of the PLL. Plot the pole-zero pattern of the gain function and its step response.

3.25 Repeat Prob. 3.24 when the step response has 30% overshoot.

3.26 The dominant pole approximation of a phase-locked loop having $\zeta = 0.3$ and $B = 2\pi(1000\text{ Hz})$ was determined in Prob. 2.40 to equal

$$H_a(s) = \frac{e^{0.12 \times 10^{-3} s}}{s^2 + 2(0.25)\omega_n' s + \omega_n'^2}, \qquad \omega_n' = 4.23 \times 10^3$$

Determine the approximate step response. Plot this response and compare it with the exact step response shown in Fig. 3.8.12.

3.27 The gain of a shunt-peaked filter was given in Prob. 1.45. Suppose that its step response has 10% overshoot and a rise time of 1 msec. (a) Determine the parameters m and ω_n of the filter. (b) How is the damping factor ζ of the filter related to parameter m?

3.28 (a) Determine the sag of a general high-pass filter having a gain given by Eq. 3.1.1 where $a_m = b_n = 1$. (Hint: Expand H(s) in a power series in 1/s.) (b) Sag compensation is obtained by setting as many coefficients in the power series equal to zero as possible. Discuss what this means in the frequency domain with an example. (c) Show that for cascaded high-pass filters, the total sag is the sum of the individual sags.

3.29 A lead-lag filter can be used for sag compensation. When used with a first-order high-pass filter, the overall gain equals $H(s) = s(s + \gamma)/[(s + \alpha)(s + \delta)]$ where γ and δ must be properly chosen. (a) Determine the expression for the step response of the network. (b) How must γ and δ be chosen to produce zero sag? Show that this satisfies the condition of Prob. 3.28. (c) Show how the lead-lag filter modifies the frequency response of the high-pass filter. How should γ and δ be chosen to minimize changes in the response? Is this consistent with part (b)?

3.30 Plot the step response of the second-order high-pass filter of Example 2.6.1. Determine its storage, fall, and 5% settling times.

3.31 The band-pass filter of Example 2.6.2 was realized as the cascade of a high-pass and a low-pass filter. Plot the step response of the high-pass filter section. Determine its storage, fall, and 5% settling times.

3.32 Band-splitting filters used in telephone systems were analyzed in Example 2.6.3. Plot the step responses of both the high-pass and the low-pass filters. Compare their step response parameters.

3.33 Repeat Prob. 3.31 for the band-pass filter of Example 2.6.4.

3.34 A complementary high-pass filter has gain

$$H(s) = 10[1 - 1/(s_n^2 + 2(0.4)s_n + 1)]$$

where $s_n = s/2\pi(10\text{ KHz})$. Plot its step response. What are the storage, fall, and 5% settling times?

3.35 One-third octave- bandwidth filters have the standard 3 dB bandwidth B and center frequency f_o specifications listed in Prob. 2.21. Assume that first-order band-pass filters are used. (a) Show that $f_o = 4.3B$. (b) Plot the cosine step responses of the band-pass filters having center frequencies of 12.5 Hz, 1 KHz, and 40 KHz. (c) What are the approximate delay, rise, and 5% settling times of the envelope responses?

3.36 MF filters used in telephone systems were analyzed in Prob. 2.24. Assume that first-order band-pass filters having 3 dB bandwidths of 50 Hz are used. Plot the cosine step responses of the band-pass filters having center frequencies of 700 Hz and 1700 Hz. What are the approximate delay, rise, and 5% settling times of the envelope responses?

3.37 Telegraph systems use constant-bandwidth band-pass filters to decode one of many frequencies as discussed in Prob. 2.25. Plot the cosine step responses of the Receive band-pass filters having 3 dB bandwidths of about 65 Hz and 90 Hz. What are the approximate delay, rise, and 5% settling times of the envelope responses?

3.38 The FSK communication system analyzed in Prob. 2.26 requires a first-order band-pass filter having a center frequency of 1000 Hz and Q = 2.5. Treating it as a narrowband filter, plot its cosine step response. What are the approximate delay, rise, and 5% settling times of the envelope response?

3.39 Notch filters having the 3 dB bandwidth and center frequency specifications listed in Prob. 2.30, are used to eliminate test tones from telephone line measurements. Assume that first-order notch filters are used. Plot the cosine step responses of the two notch filters. What are the approximate delay, rise, and 5%

settling times of the envelope responses?

3.40 A 400 Hz first-order notch filter was designed in Example 2.8.2 to eliminate interference. Plot the cosine step response of the filter. What are the approximate delay, rise, and 5% settling times of the envelope response?

REFERENCES

1. Close, C. M., *The Analysis of Linear Circuits*, Chap. 10, Harcourt, Brace and World, NY, 1966.
2. Karni, S., "Easy partial fraction expansion with multiple poles," Proc. IEEE, vol. 57, pp. 231–232, Feb., 1969.
   Moad, M. F., "On partial fraction expansions with multiple poles through derivatives," Proc. IEEE, vol. 57, pp. 2056–2057, Nov., 1969.
3. Moad, M. F., "On rational function expansion," Proc. IEEE, vol. 54, pp. 899–900, June, 1966.
4. Selby, S. M. (ed.), *Standard Mathematical Tables*, 21st ed., Chemical Rubber Co., Cleveland, OH, 1973.
   Doetsch, G., *Guide to the Applications of Laplace and Z-Transforms*, 2nd ed., Van Nostrand Reinhold, NY, 1972.
   Nixon, F. E., *Handbook of Laplace Transformation*, Prentice-Hall, NJ, 1960.
5. Elmore, W. C., "The transient response of damped linear network with particular regard to wideband amplifiers," J. of Applied Physics, vol. 19, pp. 55–63, Jan., 1948.
6. Parzen, E., *Modern Probability Theory and Its Applications*, Chap. 5, Wiley, NY, 1960.
7. Papoulis, A., *Probability, Random Variables, and Stochastic Processes*, Chaps. 3 and 8, McGraw-Hill, NY, 1965.
   Schwartz, M., *Information Transmission, Modulation, and Noise*, 2nd ed., Chap. 6, McGraw-Hill, NY, 1970.
8. Millman, J., and H. Taub, *Pulse, Digital, and Switching Waveforms*, Chap. 4, Sec. 11, McGraw-Hill, NY, 1965.
9. Valley, G. E., Jr., and H. Wallman, *Vacuum Tube Amplifiers*, p. 80, McGraw-Hill, NY, 1948.
10. Dutta Roy, S. C., "On the transient response of all-pole low-pass filters," IEEE Trans. Circuit Theory, vol. CT-15, pp. 485–488, Dec., 1968.
11. Su, K. L., "The nominal delay and rise times of lumped delay networks," IEEE Trans. Circuit Theory, vol. CT-16, pp. 574–577, Nov., 1969.
    Rochelle, J. M., "An approximation for transfer functions having only infinite zeros and negative real poles," IEEE Trans. Circuit Theory, vol. CT-16, pp. 410–411, Aug., 1969.
12. Nixon, F. E., Ref. 4, p. 72.
13. Truxal, J. G., *Control System Synthesis*, p. 41, McGraw-Hill, NY, 1955.
14. Dutta Roy, S. C., "Transient response characteristics of a third-order filter," IEEE Trans. Circuit Theory, vol. CT-15, pp. 69–71, March, 1968.
15. Nixon, F. E., Ref. 4, p. 87.
16. Sancedo, R., and E. L. Schiring, *Introduction to Continuous and Digital Control Systems*, p. 274, Macmillan, NY, 1968.
17. Kuo, F. F., "A method to reduce overshoot in filters," IRE Trans. Circuit Theory, vol. CT-9, pp. 413–414, Dec., 1962.
    Dutta Roy, S. C., "Reducing overshoot and ringing in filters," Proc. IEEE, vol. 54, pp. 1189–1190, Sept., 1966.
18. Karni, S., R. D. Kelly, and B. J. Smith, "Laguerre functions and rc cascaded networks," Proc. IEEE, vol. 54, p. 1230, Sept., 1966.
19. Meyer, E. R., "A note on the step response of high-pass filters," IEEE Trans. Circuit Theory, vol. CT-15, pp. 481–482, Dec., 1968.
20. Zelenz, M. L., "On AGC transient-response behavior in cascaded amplifiers," Proc. IEEE, vol. 58, pp. 1130–1131, July, 1970.
21. Rainville, E. D., *Infinite Series*, Macmillan, NY, 1967.
22. Dutta Roy, S. C., and B. A. Shenoi, "Transient and frequency response of the distributed rcg network," Electronics Letters, vol. 2, pp. 60–61, Feb., 1966.
23. Vibration Transducers Product Data, Catalog 11-219, pp. 3–4, B and K Instruments, Inc., Cleveland, OH.

4 CLASSICAL FILTER RESPONSE

It is good to rub and polish our minds against those of others

In Chap. 2, we considered frequency domain approximations and performed some preliminary filter designs. In Chap. 3, we designed filters on the basis of time domain approximations. The quality of the designs depended largely on our engineering knowledge, intuition, and experience. We now want to obtain filter designs using systematic design procedures. In this chapter, we consider classical transfer functions which have been derived and their frequency and time domain behavior. In the next chapter, we consider optimum transfer functions which have been created to meet certain optimization criteria. In these two chapters we will be considering only low-pass filters. The transformations to be discussed in Chap. 6 allow high-pass, band-pass, band-stop, and all-pass filters to be similarly designed using these results.

We begin by considering the ideal low-pass filter. Since we will see it is nonrealizable, we can only design filters which approximate the ideal behavior. A wide variety of filters have been developed which approximate the ideal frequency response either in magnitude or delay (i.e., phase). Some filters attempt to realize both magnitude and delay responses simultaneously and are called transitional types. The filters considered in this chapter are *classical filters*. By this we mean that their gain expressions are directly related to well-known classical polynomials or curves. A wide variety of classical filters will be investigated. Their magnitude, delay, and step responses will be tabulated. In addition, a series of nomographs will be introduced which facilitate the rapid determination of the required filter order to meet arbitrary frequency domain requirements. This chapter will forge an indispensable link in the chain of understanding for the engineer. It will also give him a wide variety of standard filter response forms. From these, he may select the one best suited to meet his particular requirements.

4.1 IDEAL LOW-PASS FILTERS

The magnitude response of a general low-pass filter has the form shown in Fig. 4.1.1. In quantitatively describing magnitude responses, the following terminology is often used:

1. *Passband*: Frequencies over which response is within M_p dB of its maximum value ($\omega \leqslant \omega_p$).
2. *Stopband*: Frequencies over which response is attenuated at least M_s dB from its maximum value ($\omega \geqslant \omega_s$).
3. *Transition Band*: Intermediate frequencies lying between passband and stopband ($\omega_p < \omega < \omega_s$).
4. *Band-edge Frequency* (Cutoff Frequency): Frequency ω_p marking edge of passband.
5. *Stopband Frequency*: Frequency ω_s marking edge of stopband.
6. *M_p Bandwidth*: Equals band-edge frequency.

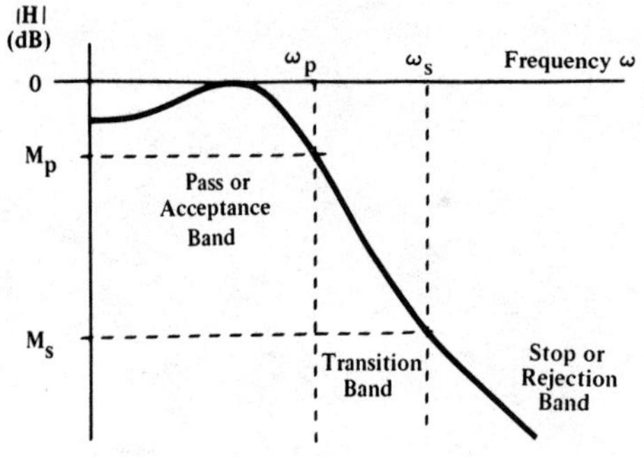

Fig. 4.1.1 Magnitude response of low-pass filter.

7. *3 dB Bandwidth* (3 dB Frequency): Maximum frequency at which response is down 3 dB from its maximum value ($\omega = \omega_{3dB} = B$).

An ideal low-pass filter would have intinite rejection in its stopband, a transition band of zero width, and constant gain in its passband. The ideal low-pass filter response having unity gain and unity bandwidth is shown in Fig. 1.5.2a. It is assumed to have linear phase of slope $-\tau_o$ (i.e., constant delay) through the passband. Thus, the gain equals

$$H(j\omega) = e^{-j\omega\tau_o}, \quad |\omega| \leqslant 1 \qquad \text{and} \qquad 0, \quad |\omega| > 1 \tag{4.1.1}$$

No ratio of finite degree polynomials (i.e., a rational function) will realize the filter gain magnitude exactly. In general, however, the higher the degree of the gain function, the better will be the approximation. This chapter shall be concerned with the various approaches for approximating the ideal low-pass filter.

4.2 MAXIMALLY FLAT MAGNITUDE FILTERS

Suppose that we approximate the squared magnitude of the ideal filter by the ratio of two polynomials of finite degree where

$$|H(j\omega)|^2 = \frac{1 + a_1\omega^2 + a_2\omega^4 + \ldots + a_m\omega^{2m}}{1 + b_1\omega^2 + b_2\omega^4 + \ldots + b_n\omega^{2n}} \tag{4.2.1}$$

Since the magnitude function is always even, the two polynomials must also be even. Since gain $|H|$ approaches zero as ω approaches infinity, then order $m < n$. To obtain as "square" a magnitude characteristic as possible, we want to choose the a_i and b_j coefficients so as many derivatives of $|H|^2$ equal zero at $\omega = 0$ as possible. Expanding $|H|^2$ in a Maclaurin series gives

$$|H(j\omega)|^2 = G(0) + G'(0)\omega + G''(0)\omega^2/2! + G'''(0)\omega^3/3! + \ldots \tag{4.2.2}$$

where the derivatives equal

$$G^{(n)}(0) = d^n|H(j\omega)|^2/d\omega^n \,\big|_{\omega=0} \tag{4.2.3}$$

Therefore, we obtain a maximally flat magnitude (MFM) characteristic by setting $G^{(n)}(0) = 0$ starting with $n = 1$ and following with as many consecutive terms as possible. By long division of $|H|^2$ given by Eq. 4.2.1, then

$$|H(j\omega)|^2 = 1 + (a_1 - b_1)\omega^2 + [(a_2 - b_2) - b_2(a_1 - b_1)]\,\omega^4 + \ldots \tag{4.2.4}$$

Equating coefficients in Eqs. 4.2.2 and 4.2.5, $(n - 1)$ terms may be set equal to zero. Thus, we set

$$a_i = b_i,\ i = 1, 2, \ldots, m; \quad b_i = 0,\ i = m+1, \ldots, n-1; \quad \text{and} \quad b_n \neq 0 \tag{4.2.5}$$

Therefore, the denominator polynomial of $|H|^2$ equals the numerator polynomial plus the term $b_n\omega^{2n}$ for an MFM characteristic.

EXAMPLE 4.2.1 Determine the coefficients so that

$$H(s) = \frac{1}{1 + b_1 s + b_2 s^2} \tag{4.2.6}$$

is an MFM gain function with a 3 dB corner frequency of 1 rad/sec.

Solution Since the squared magnitude of the gain function equals

$$|H(j\omega)|^2 = \frac{1}{(1 - b_2\omega^2)^2 + b_1{}^2\omega^2} = \frac{1}{1 + (b_1{}^2 - 2b_2)\omega^2 + b_2{}^2\omega^4} \tag{4.2.7}$$

we set

$$b_1 = \sqrt{2b_2}, \quad b_2 \neq 0 \tag{4.2.8}$$

b_2 must be chosen so that the 3 dB corner frequency is unity. Setting $|H(j1)|^2 = ½$ requires $b_2 = 1$ so $b_1 = \sqrt{2}$. Thus, the poles lie on a circle of unity radius and have a $\zeta = 0.707$ or a $\pm 45°$ angle from the negative-real axis. This result is substantiated by inspection of Fig. 2.4.1.

EXAMPLE 4.2.2 Determine the coefficients so that

$$H(s) = \frac{1 + a_1 s}{1 + b_1 s + b_2 s^2} \tag{4.2.9}$$

is an MFM gain function with a 3 dB corner frequency of 1 rad/sec.

Solution Since the squared magnitude of the gain function equals

$$|H(j\omega)|^2 = \frac{1 + a_1{}^2\omega^2}{1 + (b_1{}^2 - 2b_2)\omega^2 + b_2{}^2\omega^4} \tag{4.2.10}$$

for an MFM gain, we set

$$b_1{}^2 - 2b_2 = a_1{}^2, \quad b_2 \neq 0 \tag{4.2.11}$$

Normalizing the 3 dB frequency to unity requires

$$b_2{}^2\omega^4/(1 + a_1{}^2\omega^2)\ |_{\omega=1} = 1 \quad \text{or} \quad a_1{}^2 = b_2{}^2 - 1 \tag{4.2.12}$$

Thus, we have obtained two equations (Eqs. 4.2.11 and 4.2.12) in three unknowns (a_1, b_1 and b_2). Therefore, we can specify one of these parameters independently. Root locus analysis shows that the primary difference in these combinations is the form of their transition band responses.

4.3 BUTTERWORTH FILTERS

Butterworth filters[1] are the class of MFM filters which have all of their transmission zeros at infinity. From Eq. 4.2.5, this requires

$$a_1 = a_2 = \ldots = a_m = 0, \quad b_{m+1} = b_{m+2} = \ldots = b_{n-1} = 0, \quad \text{and} \quad b_n \neq 0 \tag{4.3.1}$$

Therefore, the Butterworth filter has a gain with a squared magnitude of

$$|H(j\omega)|^2 = \frac{1}{1 + \omega^{2n}} \tag{4.3.2}$$

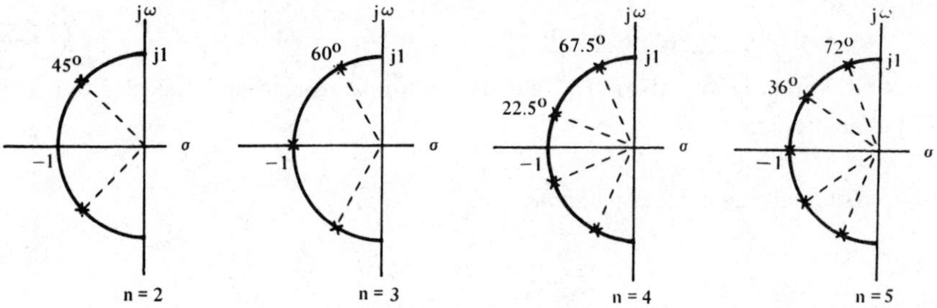

Fig. 4.3.1 Butterworth filter pole locations for second- through fifth-order filters.

where the 3 dB frequency is normalized to unity by setting $b_n = 1$. Sometimes $|H|^2$ is called a Butterworth function. The denominator polynomials which are derived from it are called the Butterworth polynomials; thus, its network realizations or implementations are called Butterworth filters. The pole locations for H(s) are determined using analytic continuation.[2] This consists of noting that the squared magnitude function equals

$$H(s)H(-s) = |H(s)|^2 \big|_{s=j\omega} = |H(j\omega)|^2 \big|_{\omega = s/j = -js} \tag{4.3.3}$$

Therefore, we find the product by analytic continuation and select the left-half-plane pole pattern for H(s); the right-half-plane poles constitute H(−s). From Eq. 4.3.2, then

$$H(s)H(-s) = \frac{1}{1 + (-js)^{2n}} = \frac{1}{1 + (-1)^n s^{2n}} \tag{4.3.4}$$

Thus, the poles of H(s)H(−s) satisfy $s_k{}^{2n} = -1$ for n even and +1 for n odd. The poles have magnitudes $|s_k| = 1$ and angles of[3]

$$\left.\begin{aligned} \arg s_k &= (1 \pm 2k)\pi/2n, && n \text{ even} \\ &= \pm 2k\pi/2n, && n \text{ odd} \end{aligned}\right\} \quad \text{for } k = 0, 2, \ldots 2n \tag{4.3.5}$$

They are symmetrically distributed around a unit circle with a separation of π/n radians. The first pole is located $\pi/2n$ radians from the real axis for n even, and on the real axis for n odd. The left-half-plane pole locations for n = 2, 3, 4, and 5 are shown in Fig. 4.3.1. The transfer function for the Butterworth filter equals

$$H(s) = \frac{1}{1 + b_1 s + b_2 s^2 + \ldots + b_{n-1} s^{n-1} + b_n s^n} \tag{4.3.6}$$

where the denominator D(s) equals the product of the pole terms so

$$D(s) = \prod_{k=1}^{n/2} (s^2 + 2\cos\theta_k\, s + 1),\ n \text{ even}; \qquad (s+1) \prod_{k=1}^{½(n-1)} (s^2 + 2\cos\theta_k\, s + 1),\ n \text{ odd} \tag{4.3.7}$$

where the θ_k's are given by Eq. 4.3.5. The denominator polynomials for Butterworth filters of various orders are listed in Table 4.3.1. For simplicity, these are often called Butterworth polynomials. When the order of the filter is specified, the required polynomial is simply taken from the table. Both factored and nonfactored forms are listed for later computational convenience.

Since the Butterworth filter has a gain of

$$|H(j\omega)| = \frac{1}{\sqrt{1 + \omega^{2n}}} \tag{4.3.8}$$

Table 4.3.1 Butterworth filter poles.

$D_1 = s + 1$

$D_2 = s^2 + 1.4142s + 1 = (s + 0.7071)^2 + 0.7071^2$

$D_3 = s^3 + 2.0000s^2 + 2.0000s + 1 = (s + 1.0000)[(s + 0.5000)^2 + 0.8660^2]$

$D_4 = s^4 + 2.6131s^3 + 3.4142s^2 + 2.6131s + 1 = [(s + 0.3827)^2 + 0.9239^2][(s + 0.9239)^2 + 0.3827^2]$

$D_5 = s^5 + 3.2361s^4 + 5.2361s^3 + 5.2361s^2 + 3.2361s + 1$
$= (s + 1.0000)[(s + 0.3090)^2 + 0.9511^2][(s + 0.8090)^2 + 0.5878^2]$

$D_6 = s^6 + 3.8637s^5 + 7.4641s^4 + 9.1416s^3 + 7.4641s^2 + 3.8637s + 1$
$= [(s + 0.2588)^2 + 0.9659^2][(s + 0.7071)^2 + 0.7071^2][(s + 0.9659)^2 + 0.2588^2]$

$D_7 = s^7 + 4.4940s^6 + 10.0978s^5 + 14.5918s^4 + 14.5918s^3 + 10.0978s^2 + 4.4940s + 1$
$= (s + 1.0000)[(s + 0.2225)^2 + 0.9749^2][(s + 0.6235)^2 + 0.7818^2][(s + 0.9010)^2 + 0.4339^2]$

$D_8 = s^8 + 5.1258s^7 + 13.1371s^6 + 21.8462s^5 + 25.6884s^4 + 21.8462s^3 + 13.1371s^2 + 5.1258s + 1$
$= [(s + 0.1951)^2 + 0.9808^2][s + 0.5556)^2 + 0.8315^2][(s + 0.8315)^2 + 0.5556^2]$
$\times [(s + 0.9808)^2 + 0.1951^2]$

$D_9 = s^9 + 5.7588s^8 + 16.5817s^7 + 31.1634s^6 + 41.9864s^5 + 41.9864s^4 + 31.1634s^3 + 16.5817s^2$
$+ 5.7588s + 1$
$= (s + 1.0000)[(s + 0.1737)^2 + 0.9848^2][(s + 0.5000)^2 + 0.8660^2][(s + 0.7660)^2 + 0.6428^2]$
$\times [(s + 0.9397)^2 + 0.3420^2]$

$D_{10} = s^{10} + 6.3925s^9 + 20.4317s^8 + 42.8021s^7 + 64.8824s^6 + 74.2334s^5 + 64.8824s^4 + 42.8021s^3$
$+ 20.4317s^2 + 6.3925s + 1$
$= [(s + 0.1564)^2 + 0.9877^2][(s + 0.4540)^2 + 0.8910^2][(s + 0.7071)^2 + 0.7071^2]$
$\times [(s + 0.8910)^2 + 0.4540^2][(s + 0.9877)^2 + 0.1564^2]$

from Eq. 4.3.2, the magnitude characteristics may be easily plotted as shown in Fig. 4.3.2. Note that all the filters have a 3 dB bandwidth of unity as required. As the filter order increases, the magnitude approximation approaches the ideal magnitude response of Fig. 1.5.2a. Ideally, the response makes an abrupt transition from unity gain to zero gain at $\omega = 1$. However, the approximation has only finite slope at $\omega = 1$. A measure of the "skirt" steepness is the *filter selectivity* or *cutoff rate* which, by definition, equals the negative of the gain slope at the band-edge. Thus, the ideal low-pass filter has a band-edge selectivity of infinity. Butterworth filters have band-edge selectivities which equal

$$-d|H|/d\omega\,\big|_{\omega=1} = n/2\sqrt{2} = 0.354n \tag{4.3.9}$$

which is easily calculated from Eq. 4.3.8. Thus, they have slopes which vary directly with order.

Another useful figure of merit is the *shaping factor* S. The shaping factor equals the ratio of bandwidths at which the magnitude response is at specified attenuation levels. Attenuation levels of 6 dB and 60 dB have become industrial standards. Thus, the 6–60 dB shaping factor equals

$$S_{6\text{ dB}}^{60\text{ dB}} = B_{60\text{ dB}}/B_{6\text{ dB}} \tag{4.3.10}$$

where $S \geqslant 1$. The smaller the shaping factor ratio, the steeper is the magnitude slope in the transition band; therefore, the narrower is the transition band. Ideal low-pass filters have shaping factors of unity. The 6–60 shaping factor for Butterworth filters is easily shown to equal

$$S_{6\text{ dB}}^{60\text{ dB}} = \left(\frac{10^{6/m} - 1}{4^{1/m} - 1}\right)^{1/2n} \tag{4.3.11}$$

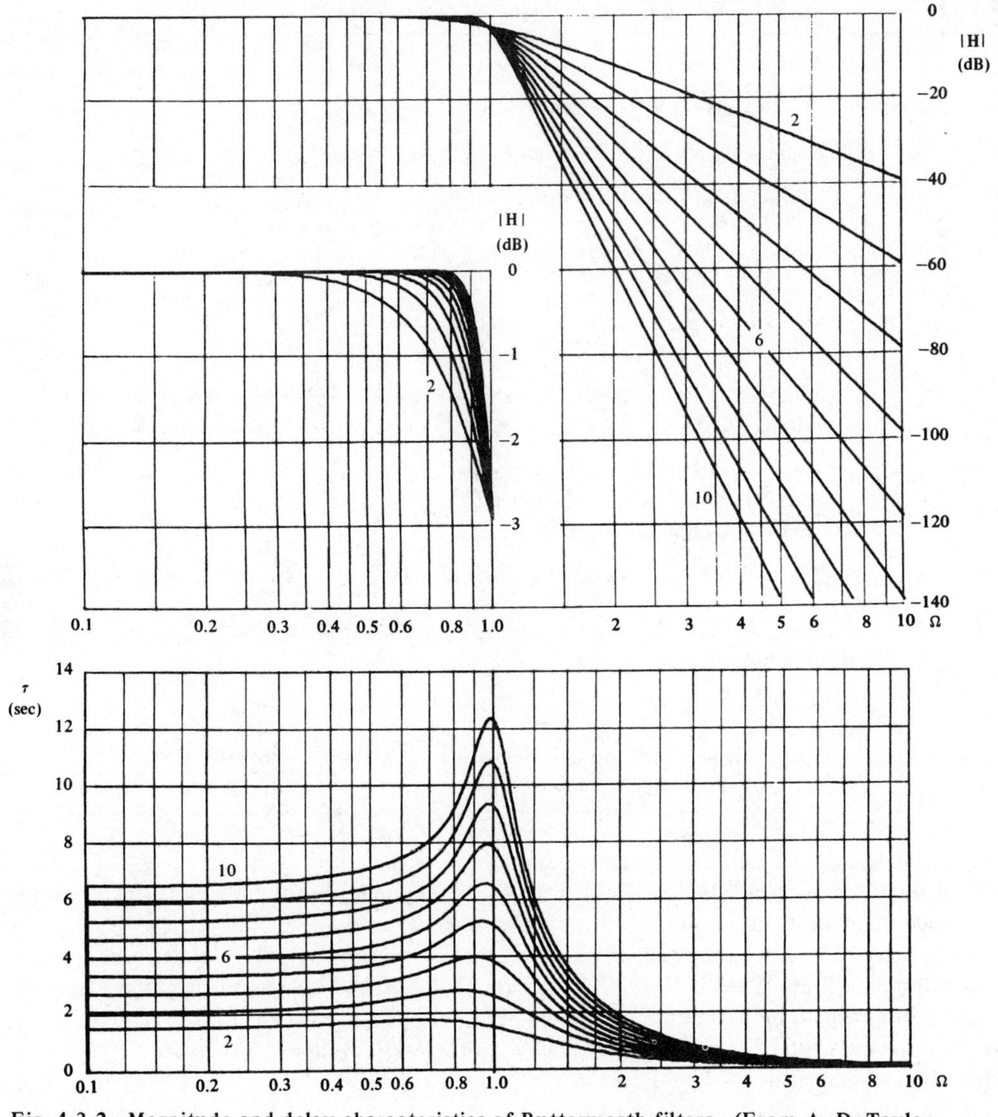

Fig. 4.3.2 Magnitude and delay characteristics of Butterworth filters. (From A. D. Taylor, "A study of transitional filters," M.S.E.E. Directed Research, California State Univ., Long Beach, Aug., 1975.)

where m = 1. When m stages of an *n*th-order Butterworth filter are cascaded together, the shaping factor is given by the same equation. The product nm is equal to the total number of filter poles, which in turn, is directly related to filter complexity as we shall later see. The shaping factor is reduced, and therefore, out-of-band rejection is improved by using a single *nm*th-order Butterworth filter rather than nm first-order Butterworth filters of m *n*th-order Butterworth filters.[4]

The order of the Butterworth filter is determined by the required attenuation or rejection at one or more specified stopband frequencies. To determine order, let us express the squared magnitude gain as

$$|H(j\omega)|^2 = \frac{1}{1 + \epsilon^2 S_n^{\ 2}(\omega)} \tag{4.3.12}$$

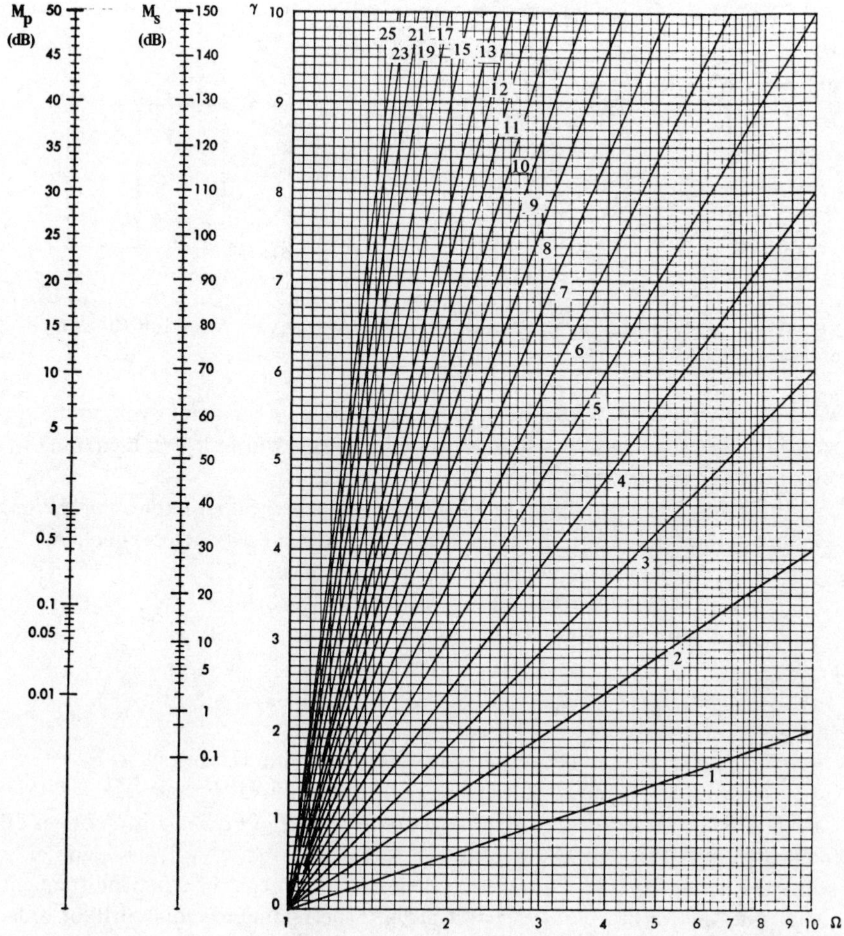

Fig. 4.3.3 Nomograph for Butterworth filters. (From J. N. Hallberg, "Filters and nomographs," M.S.E.E. Directed Research, California State Univ., Long Beach, Jan., 1974.)

which is a standard form for most filters. $S_n(\omega)$ is some well-known classical *n*th-order polynomial, and ϵ is related to the passband ripple. Then $S_n(\omega) = \omega^n$ for the Butterworth filter. If the gain magnitude equals $|H_1|$ at ω_1 and $|H_2|$ at ω_2, then Eq. 4.3.12 can be manipulated to yield the minimum n required as

$$n \geqslant \frac{\log\left[(|H_2|^{-2} - 1)^{1/2}/(|H_1|^{-2} - 1)^{1/2} \right]}{\log(\omega_2/\omega_1)} = \frac{\ln(\epsilon_2/\epsilon_1)}{\ln(\omega_2/\omega_1)} \tag{4.3.13}$$

The *smallest integer* n satisfying this relation is chosen. If k frequencies and attenuations are specified, then Eq. 4.3.13 is evaluated at each of the k frequencies and the *largest* n is chosen from among the k values so obtained.

Generally, more insight can be gained in filter order by using a nomograph (i.e., a graphical aid) rather than an equation (in the Butterworth case, Eq. 4.3.13). Nomographs derive their name from the Greek words nomos (law) and graphein (to write). They are literally graphical representations of equations and were introduced in 1891 by d'Ocagne and recently applied to filters by Kawakami.[5] They form marvelous design aids as we shall soon see. The nomograph for Butter-

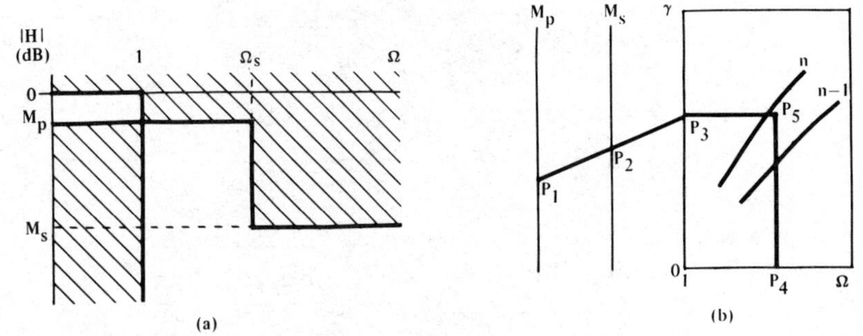

Fig. 4.3.4 (a) General magnitude specification for low-pass filter and (b) entry of data onto nomograph.

worth filters is shown in Fig. 4.3.3. A momograph on nomographs will not be presented here, but we shall utilize their results. The interested engineer will find it enlightening to review the theoretical basis of nomographs.[6]

The procedure for determining filter order begins by first expressing the required frequency response in the form shown in Fig. 4.3.4a. The pertinent parameters equal:

M_p = maximum attenuation in (dB) in the passband
M_s = minimum attenuation in (dB) in the stopband
Ω_s = normalized stopband frequency

where

$$\Omega_s = f_s/f_p = \omega_s/\omega_p \tag{4.3.14}$$

and

f_p (or ω_p) = band-edge frequency of passband in Hz (or rad/sec)
f_s (or ω_s) = band-edge frequency of stopband in Hz (or rad/sec)

This data is then entered on the nomograph as shown in Fig. 4.3.4b. A line is drawn through M_p (point P_1) and M_s (point P_2) until it intersects the graph at P_3. A horizontal line is then drawn across the graph from P_3. A vertical line is drawn through the stopband frequency Ω_s. The horizontal line and vertical lines intersect at P_5. The minimum required filter order is given by the first curve lying *above* P_5. After practice, this procedure will become second-nature to the engineer. Let us now consider several examples to demonstrate the usefulness of nomographs.

EXAMPLE 4.3.1 Determine the order required for a Butterworth filter to meet the specification shown in Fig. 4.3.5a using the Butterworth nomograph. Here 40 dB and 60 dB of rejection is required at frequencies of twice and three times the 1.25 dB bandwidth, respectively.

Solution To use the nomograph, we first write that

$$\begin{aligned} &M_p = 1.25 \text{ dB} \quad (\text{at } f = 1 \text{ KHz}) \\ &M_{s1} = 40 \text{ dB} \quad (\text{at } f = 2 \text{ KHz}), \qquad \Omega_{s1} = 2 \text{ KHz}/1 \text{ KHz} = 2 \\ &M_{s2} = 60 \text{ dB} \quad (\text{at } f = 3 \text{ KHz}), \qquad \Omega_{s2} = 3 \text{ KHz}/1 \text{ KHz} = 3 \end{aligned} \tag{4.3.15}$$

Entering this data on the nomograph as shown in Fig. 4.3.4b, we find $n_1 \geqslant 8$ and $n_2 \geqslant 7$. Thus, an eighth-order Butterworth filter is required.

EXAMPLE 4.3.2 A low-pass filter having the gain characteristics shown in Fig. 4.3.5a must be realized. However, the band-edge frequencies are f_p = 2 KHz, f_{s1} = 3 KHz, and f_{s2} = 4 KHz. Size and cost considerations limit the filter order $n \leqslant 8$. Can a Butterworth filter be used?

Solution Since M_p = 1.25 dB and

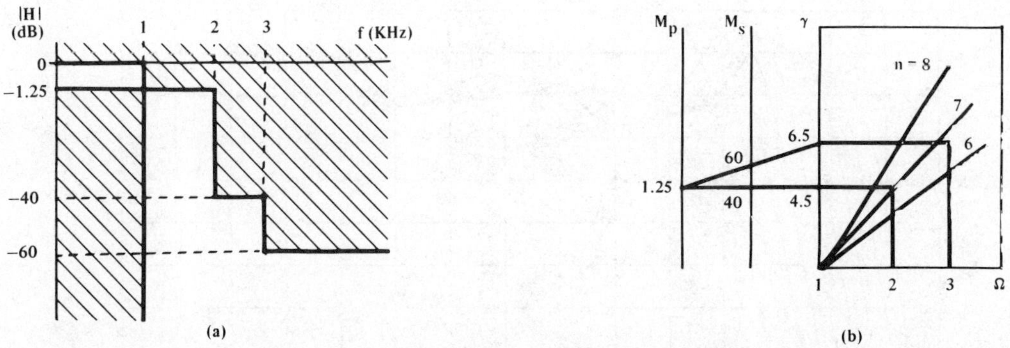

Fig. 4.3.5 (a) Filter specification for Example 4.3.1 and (b) entry of data onto nomograph.

$$\begin{aligned} M_{s1} &= 40\text{ dB} \quad \text{at} \quad \Omega_{s1} = 3\text{ KHz}/2\text{ KHz} = 1.5 \\ M_{s2} &= 60\text{ dB} \quad \text{at} \quad \Omega_{s2} = 4\text{ KHz}/2\text{ KHz} = 2 \end{aligned} \tag{4.3.16}$$

using the Butterworth filter nomograph, we find $n_1 \geqslant 13$ and $n_2 \geqslant 11$. Therefore, $n \geqslant 13$ and a Butterworth filter cannot be designed to meet the maximum order requirement of 8.

Sometimes filter specifications are drawn differently in the frequency domain than we have thus far shown. One such commonly encountered form is shown in Fig. P4.27. Rather than having a stairstep rolloff, it has a ramp rolloff. This type of specification insures a minimum rate of attenuation rolloff into the stopband. Thus, it is more stringent than that in Fig. 4.3.4. Very often, we *assume* that the filters being considered have rapid enough rolloffs so that the specification form of Fig. 4.3.4 is adequate. However, when required it is wise to be more explicit and use the form of Fig. P4.27 to eliminate misunderstanding. The filter nomographs are still used to analyze such situations. The only difference is that the ramp requires several data points to be entered on the nomograph.

We mentioned earlier that another benefit of nomographs, in addition to their ease and speed to use, was the great insight they gave to the properties of the filter. Returning to Fig. 4.3.4 for a moment, we see that the nomograph graphically depicts the interrelation between M_p, M_s, Ω_s, and n. Mathematically, this means that any three of the parameters may be independently specified, and the fourth parameter is thereby fixed or determined. Thus, rather than specifying M_p, M_s, and Ω_s and determining n as in the previous examples, we could instead specify a different combination. For example, we could specify M_p and n, and look at the M_s and Ω_s values which result. This is illustrated in the following example.

EXAMPLE 4.3.3 Determine the order required for a Butterworth filter to meet the general specifications: (1) in-band ripple = 0.5 dB for $\omega \leqslant 1$, and (2) 3 dB corner frequency = 1.1. Determine the frequencies at which 20 dB and 60 dB attenuations are obtained.
Solution Using $M_p = 0.5$ dB and $M_s = 3$ dB at $\Omega_s = 1.1/1 = 1.1$, we find that $n \geqslant 11$. We can now determine the frequencies at which we obtain the specified attenuations. For example, using n = 11 and $M_p = 0.5$, then from the nomograph, the 20 dB rejection frequency $\Omega_{s1} = 1.36$ when $M_s = 20$ dB. For $M_s = 60$ dB, then the 60 dB rejection frequency $\Omega_{s2} = 2.05$.

The delay characteristic of the Butterworth filter is shown in Fig. 4.3.2. The mathematical expressions for delay are complicated[7] and can only be easily evaluated by use of a computer. Thus, we shall not write the delay expressions for filters. We can, however, interpret and predict the delay using the filter pole locations given in Table 4.3.1 and the delay results of Sec. 2.10. Using these results, we anticipate that all Butterworth filters will exhibit peaking except for n = 1

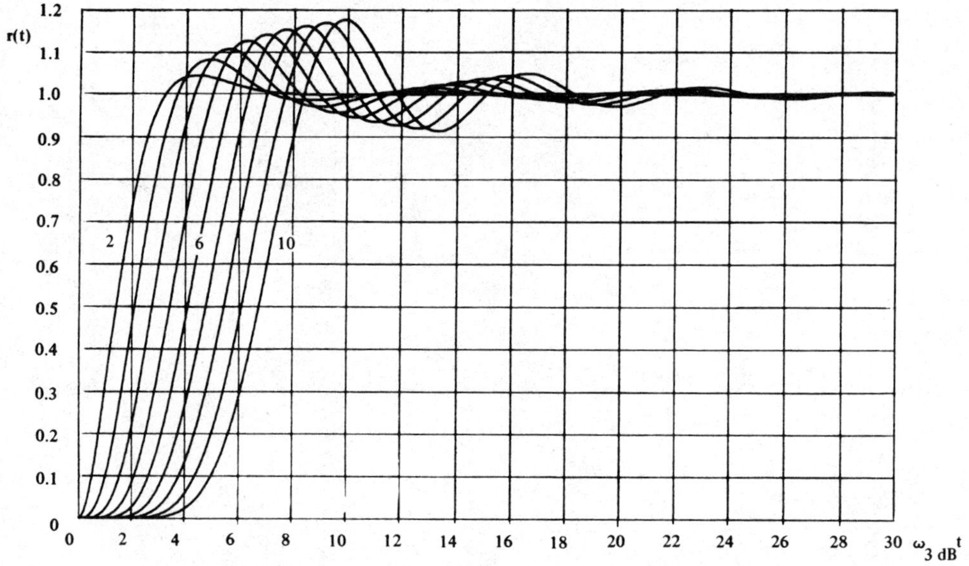

Fig. 4.3.6 Step response of Butterworth filters. (From A. D. Taylor, loc. cit.)

which is indeed the case. We see that the delay variation increases with filter order in the passband. For n = 3, the delay variation is about 1 second (or 50%); for n = 9, the delay variation is almost 6 seconds (or 100%). Even with this amount of delay variation, the Butterworth filter has better delay characteristics than most of the other filters (having fairly narrow transition bands) which we will consider. It is important to remember that the absolute delay value is not of importance in most filters, but rather the delay variation.

It is useful to recall from Sec. 2.10 that when the gain of a filter is expressed in the form of Eq. 2.0.1, then the low-frequency delay is given by Eq. 2.10.34 and the high-frequency is given by Eq. 2.10.36. If the filter has no finite zeros, as is the case in almost all the low-pass filters we will consider, then these delays reduce to

$$\tau(j0) = b_1/b_0; \qquad \tau(j\omega) = b_{n-1}/b_n\omega^2, \quad \omega \to \infty \tag{4.3.17}$$

The b_i coefficients are the coefficients of the filter polynomial given by Eq. 4.3.6. The Butterworth filter polynomials were listed in Table 4.3.1. Thus, we can easily substantiate the low- and high-frequency behaviors of delay in Fig. 4.3.2. For example, when n = 10, then $\tau(j0) = 6.3925$ seconds while $\tau(j\omega) = 6.3925/\omega^2$ seconds as $\omega \to \infty$. These values verify these two asymptotic values in Fig. 4.3.2 (note that $\tau(j2) = 6.3925/2^2 = 1.6 \approx 1.8$). Since Butterworth filters always have $b_o = b_n$ and $b_1 = b_{n-1}$, the asymptotic delay strengths are always equal. Also note that the asymptotic phase of every all-pole filter approaches $-n\pi/2$ radians or $-90n^\circ$ as $\omega \to \infty$.

We can also observe that it is the pole pair having minimum damping factor or maximum Q that primarily determines the maximum delay value (this assumes all have the same ω_n). From Eq. 2.10.13, we recall that the maximum delay contributed by a pole pair with damping factor ζ and resonant frequency ω_n equals approximately

$$\tau_{max} \cong 1/\zeta\omega_n = 1/a, \qquad |\zeta| \ll 1 \tag{4.3.18}$$

which occurs at frequency ω_n. Thus, using the poles listed in Table 4.3.1, we see $\tau_{max} \cong 1/(0.1564)(1) = 6.39$ seconds at $\omega = 1$ for n = 10. We see that the actual delay is about 12 seconds. The discrepancy is due to the fact that the other Butterworth poles add appreciable delay because their ζ's do not increase rapidly and their ω_n's are equal. In filters we shall study later, the poles will be distributed on more elliptical or parabolic curvatures rather than circles. This will result in ζ's which do increase rapidly with decreasing ω_n. Then this approximation for τ_{max} will yield better results.

The unit step response of the Butterworth filter is shown in Fig. 4.3.6. It is composed of gated sinusoids, each having a frequency equal to the imaginary part of the pole, and an attenuation constant equal to the real part of the pole. It may be calculated from Eqs. 4.3.6 and 4.3.7 using a partial fraction expansion as discussed in Sec. 3.2. Generally, however, no insight is gained by writing this equation and a computer is required for plotting the result. It is important to note that the step response is plotted as a function of normalized time $\omega_{3dB}t$ (in radians). Normalized time is used since the step response was calculated using the poles of Table 4.3.1 where ω_{3dB} was unity. Using the time scaling theorem of Table 1.8.2, if the poles are scaled by any nonunity ω_{3dB}, then the time domain responses (in seconds) are scaled in time by ω_{3dB}.

We see that the step responses exhibit more overshoot as n increases. This is due to the damping factors which decrease with increasing order. The delay time increases with filter order, but rise time remains approximately constant. The rise time result agrees with the empirical relation of Valley and Wallman given by Eq. 3.5.13 where $t_r \cong 2.2/\omega_{3dB} = 2.2$ seconds since all filters have a normalized bandwidth of 1 rad/sec. Notice that the delay value corresponds closely with the low-frequency value of the delay curves. We anticipated this result in Eq. 3.6.9.

EXAMPLE 4.3.4 Determine if a Butterworth filter can be designed to meet the frequency and time requirements shown in Fig. 4.3.7. Design for minimum filter order and draw the block diagram of the filter if it can be realized.

Solution We begin by determining the required filter order from the frequency response. Since $M_p = 3$ dB, $M_{s1} = 10$ dB at $\Omega_{s1} = 2$, and $M_{s2} = 40$ dB at $\Omega_{s2} = 4$, we see from the Butterworth filter nomograph that $n_1 \geqslant 2$ and $n_2 \geqslant 4$. Thus, at least a fourth-order filter is required.

Now we sketch the step response of the filter noting n = 4. Since the bandwidth $\omega_{3dB} = 2\pi(2$ KHz), we must denormalize time by ω_{3dB} in Fig. 4.3.7. We now transfer the normalized step response of Fig. 4.3.6 onto Fig. 4.3.7. We see that we have easily met the time domain requirements. Noting the time differences

$$\Delta t_1 = 5 - 2.3 = 2.7 \text{ sec} \quad (r = 0.5), \quad \Delta t_2 = 7.5 - 3.5 = 4.0 \text{ sec} \quad (r = 0.8), \quad \Delta t_3 = 10 - 7.3 = 2.7 \text{ sec} \quad (r = 1.05) \tag{4.3.19}$$

we see that we may reduce the time domain specification by $\Delta t = \min(\Delta t_1, \Delta t_2, \Delta t_3) = 2.7$ seconds, if we so desire. Alternatively, we could consider expanding the bandwidth—however, here we require the 2 KHz bandwidth shown. The transfer function of the filter equals

$$H(s) = \frac{1}{(s_n^2 + 0.765s_n + 1)(s_n^2 + 1.848s_n + 1)} \tag{4.3.20}$$

where $s_n = s/2\pi(2$ KHz) using Table 4.3.1. The block diagram realization of the filter is shown in Fig. 4.3.8.

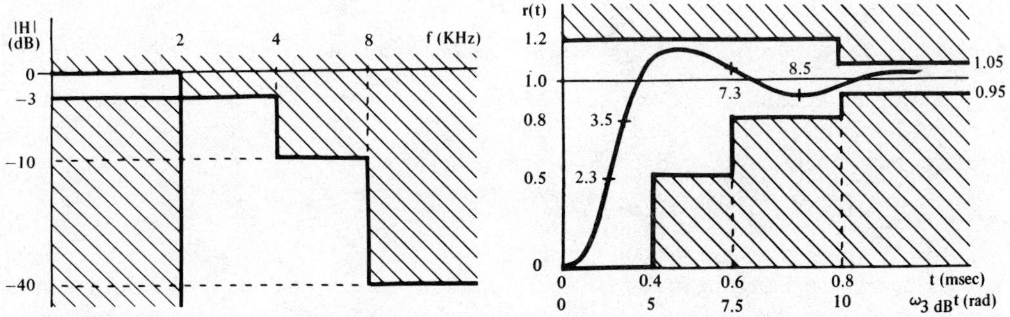

Fig. 4.3.7 Filter specifications for Example 4.3.4.

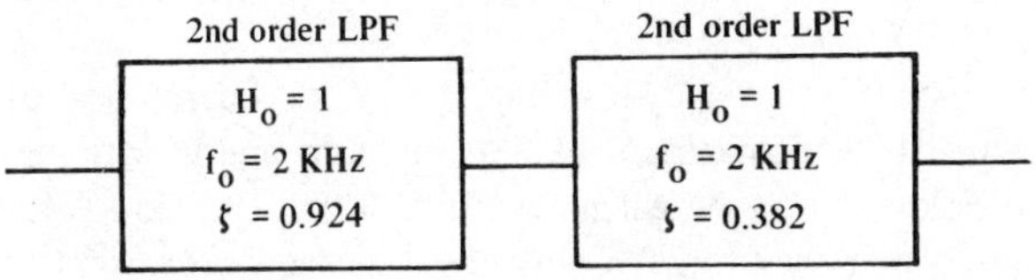

Fig. 4.3.8 Block diagram of Butterworth filter of Example 4.3.4.

We now see the great ease in utilizing classical filter results since we merely need to rewrite the tabulated transfer function. The bulk of the work involves determining the acceptable type of filter (e.g., Butterworth) and its required order. The transfer functions can *always* be easily expressed using the *frequency normalized form* involving s_n. The engineer will find that using denormalized forms involving s appear more complicated and will obscure the pertinent information involving the ω_n and ζ of each pole pair. It is also important to remember that each design block must be explicitly labelled with (1) order and type, (2) dc gain H_o, (3) resonant frequency of pole (ω_n or f_n), and (4) damping factor of pole (ζ). In Chap. 8, we shall utilize such block diagrams in the design of low-pass filters.

One other comment should be made. We shall usually realize *n*th-order filters by cascading n/2 (for n even) or (n + 1)/2 (for n odd) second-order stages. The primary advantage of cascade design is the ease of both tuning and temperature compensation.

Now that we have analyzed Butterworth filters in great detail, we proceed to consider a variety of other types. Since the development of each filter type follows the same pattern as that of the Butterworth filter, we shall be briefer (but no less complete) in our discussions.

4.4 CHEBYSHEV FILTERS

The Butterworth filter has a monotonically decreasing passband and stopband response. In contrast, the Chebyshev filter, sometimes called the equal-ripple or equiripple filter, has a response which ripples throughout the passband between 1 and $(1 + \epsilon^2)^{-1/2}$ as shown in Fig. 4.4.1. It has a narrower transition band (i.e., faster cutoff) than the Butterworth filter but increased passband delay variation. Of course, both filters have the same asymptotic slope for a given order. Chebyshev filters also exhibit more step response overshoot.

The Chebyshev filter[8] has a magnitude function

$$|H(j\omega)|^2 = \frac{1}{1 + \epsilon^2 T_n^{\,2}(\omega)} \tag{4.4.1}$$

where T_n is the *n*th-order Chebyshev (sometimes spelled Tschebyscheff) polynomial[9] and $\epsilon < 1$ is the parameter which determines the ripple magnitude. The *n*th-order Chebyshev polynomial (of the first-kind) equals

$$T_n(\omega) = \cos(n \cos^{-1} \omega),\ 0 \leqslant \omega \leqslant 1 \qquad \text{and} \qquad \cosh(n \cosh^{-1} \omega),\ \omega > 1 \tag{4.4.2}$$

T_n is an even function for n odd and an odd function for n even. The polynomials oscillate between ± 1 in the frequency interval $[-1, 1]$ so $|T_n| \leqslant 1$ for $|\omega| \leqslant 1$. Beyond this region, T_n increases monotonically and asymptotically approaches

$$T_n(\omega) \cong 2^{n-1}\omega^n, \qquad |\omega| \gg 1 \tag{4.4.3}$$

Since the T_n polynomials can take on negative as well as positive values for $|\omega| < 1$, they cannot be used directly to generate gain functions. Thus, we use the square of T_n which will always be non-negative. Since it is also easy to show from Eq. 4.4.2 that $T_n^{\,2} = (T_{2n} + 1)/2$, we could just as well use Chebyshev polynomials of order 2n. The parameter ϵ^2 is used to limit the in-band varia-

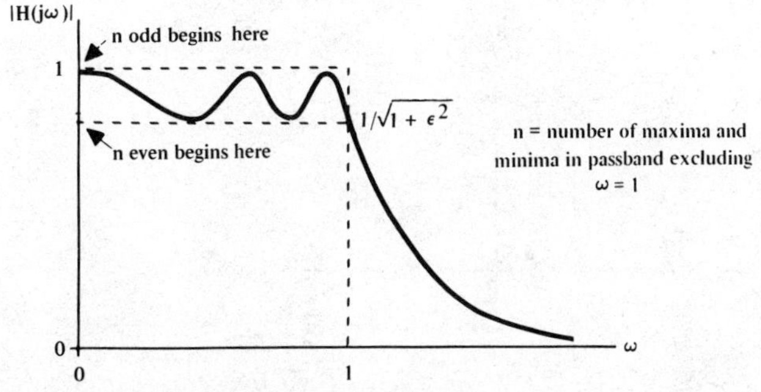

Fig. 4.4.1 Chebyshev filter magnitude characteristic.

tion of T_n^2 in Eq. 4.4.1. Note from Fig. 4.4.1 that the ripple width equals

$$\text{Ripple} = 1 - (1+\epsilon^2)^{-1/2} \cong 1 - (1 - \epsilon^2/2) = \epsilon^2/2, \qquad \epsilon \ll 1 \tag{4.4.4}$$

The ripple width is usually specified in dB where ripple (dB) $\cong 4.34\epsilon^2$ so that specifying the maximum amount of ripple determines parameter ϵ. Ripples of 0.5, 1, 2, and 3 dB have corresponding ϵ's of 0.35, 0.51, 0.76, and 1, respectively.

The poles of the Chebyshev filter are determined by first finding the poles of s_k of T(s)T(–s). We then discard those poles lying in the right-half-plane. The poles of T(s)T(–s) must satisfy $1 + \epsilon^2 T_n^2(s_k/j) = 0$ from Eq. 4.4.1 using analytic continuation. Solving for T_n^2 gives

$$T_n(s_k/j) = \cos\,[n \cos^{-1}(s_k/j)] = \pm j/\epsilon \tag{4.4.5}$$

Defining the term $p_k = u_k + jv_k = \cos^{-1} s_k/j$, then we can re-express Eq. 4.4.5 as

$$\cos np_k = \cos nu_k \cosh nv_k - j \sin nu_k \sinh nv_k = \pm j/\epsilon \tag{4.4.6}$$

where we have expanded the cosine of a complex argument.[10] The real and imaginary parts of p_k must therefore satisfy

$$\cos nu_k \cosh nv_k = 0, \qquad \sin nu_k \sinh nv_k = \pm 1/\epsilon \tag{4.4.7}$$

Since $\cosh nv_k$ is positive and nonzero for real v_k, then $\cos nu_k$ must equal zero so $u_k = (2k-1) \times \pi/2n$ for $k = 1, 2, \ldots, 2n$. From the second equation, then v_k must satisfy

$$v_k = v = (1/n) \sinh^{-1}(1/\epsilon) \tag{4.4.8}$$

which is a constant dependent upon order n and ripple factor ϵ. Therefore, the poles s_k equal

$$s_k = \sigma_k + j\omega_k = j \cos p_k = j \cos(u_k + jv) = \sin u_k \sinh v + j \cos u_k \cosh v \tag{4.4.9}$$

Squaring σ_k and ω_k, dividing by their respective hyperbolic terms, and adding these two equations gives

$$\frac{\sigma_k^2}{\sinh^2 v} + \frac{\omega_k^2}{\cosh^2 v} = 1 \tag{4.4.10}$$

which is the standard equation for an ellipse. Thus, the poles lie on an ellipse having its axis coinciding with the s-plane axis. The semi-major axis has value cosh v, the semi-minor axis has value sinh v, and the foci are located at $\omega = \pm 1$.

The Chebyshev filter poles are easily constructed from the Butterworth filter poles based on Eq. 4.4.10. A vertical ellipse having a semi-minor axis value of tanh v and a semi-major axis value of unity is drawn inside the unit circle. Horizontal lines are drawn through the Butterworth poles. The Chebyshev poles are given by the intersection of these poles with the ellipse as shown in Fig.

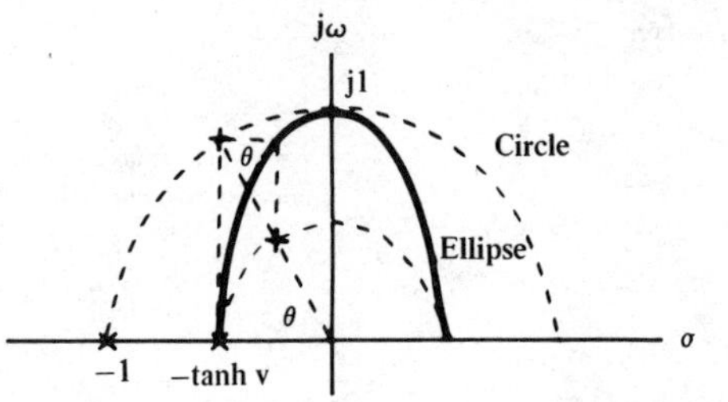

Fig. 4.4.2 Chebyshev pole construction using Butterworth poles. (The conjugate poles are not shown.)

4.4.2. Alternatively, Weinberg noted that an inner circle of radius $[\sinh^{-1}(1/\epsilon)]/n$ could be used to locate the poles in place of the ellipse.[7] Using this approach, each Chebyshev pole is located at the intersection of a vertical line drawn from each inner circle pole and a horizontal line drawn from each outer circle pole (see Fig. 4.4.2). Note that Chebyshev poles approach Butterworth poles in the limiting case where the in-band ripple approaches zero since $\tanh v \to 1$ as $\epsilon \to 0$.

In practice, it is more convenient to utilize tables of Chebyshev filter poles rather than to generate them. The pole locations for Chebyshev filters having in-band ripples of 0.5, 1, 2, and 3 dB are listed in Table 4.4.1 (for other ripples, see Ref. 11). It is important to note that the frequency has been normalized so that the cutoff frequency of 1 rad/sec corresponds to the point where the gain is reduced by the *amount of ripple* (rather than 3 dB as for the Butterworth filter).

The Chebyshev filter has a gain

$$|H(j\omega)| = \frac{1}{\sqrt{1+\epsilon^2 T_n^{\,2}(\omega)}} \tag{4.4.11}$$

Chebyshev filters having in-band ripples of 0.1 and 1 dB have the magnitude characteristics shown in Fig. 4.4.3 (for other ripples, see Refs. 12 and 13). Note that the magnitude characteristics have been drawn so they all have a 3 dB cutoff frequency of 1 rad/sec. We see that the Chebyshev filter has a more rapid cutoff than the Butterworth filter. In fact, the Chebyshev filter is optimum in the sense that there is no other low-pass filter, with all of its zeros of transmission at infinity and an in-band ripple not exceeding a maximum value, having a faster cutoff rate outside its passband.[7] The price paid for this rapid cutoff rate is delay having large variations within the filter passband as we shall see.

We can determine the 3 dB bandwidth of Chebyshev filters having unity ripple bandwidth from Eq. 4.4.1. Since $|H|^2 = ½$ at the 3 dB frequency, the Chebyshev polynomial must equal $T_n(\omega_{3dB}) = 1/\epsilon$. Solving for ω_{3dB}, we find

$$\omega_{3\,dB} = \cosh\,[(1/n)\cosh^{-1}(1/\epsilon)] \tag{4.4.12}$$

Since the band-edge frequency is unity (for ripples $\leqslant$ 3 dB), this equation relates the ratio of the 3 dB and band-edge frequencies. Notice that $\cosh^{-1}x$ and $\sinh^{-1}x$ are about equal for $x \geqslant 2$ (or $\epsilon \leqslant ½$). Thus, from Eq. 4.4.12, the 3 dB bandwidth of the Chebyshev filter is approximately cosh v.[14] Another useful approximation for ω_{3dB} is obtained by substituting a Maclaurin series for $\cosh^{-1}x$ into Eq. 4.4.12 which yields

$$\omega_{3\,dB} \cong (2/\epsilon)^{1/n}/2, \qquad \epsilon \ll 1 \tag{4.4.13}$$

Thus, for fixed ripple parameter ϵ, then the 3 dB bandwidths vary as the *n*th root of a constant.

We should make one comment concerning the additional rejection provided by Chebyshev filters over Butterworth filters. If we compare their stopband responses when both have unity ripple bandwidths (where their gains equal $(1+\epsilon^2)^{-½}$), Eqs. 4.3.2 and 4.4.3 can be used to show that the Chebyshev filter provides an additional 6(n − 1) dB of rejection over the Butterworth

Table 4.4.1 Chebyshev filter poles.

n	0.5 dB Ripple		1 dB Ripple		2 dB Ripple		3 dB Ripple	
	a	β	a	β	a	β	a	β
1	2.8628	0	1.9652	0	1.3076	0	1.0024	0
2	0.7128	1.0040	0.5489	0.8951	0.4019	0.8133	0.3224	0.7772
3	0.3132	1.0219	0.2471	0.9660	0.1845	0.9231	0.1493	0.9038
	0.6265	0	0.4942	0	0.3689	0	0.2986	0
4	0.1754	1.0163	0.1395	0.9834	0.1049	0.9580	0.0852	0.9465
	0.4233	0.4209	0.3369	0.4073	0.2532	0.3968	0.2056	0.3920
5	0.1120	1.0116	0.0895	0.9901	0.0675	0.9735	0.0549	0.9659
	0.2931	0.6252	0.2342	0.6119	0.1766	0.6016	0.1436	0.5970
	0.3623	0	0.2895	0	0.2183	0	0.1775	0
6	0.0777	1.0085	0.0622	0.9934	0.0470	0.9817	0.0382	0.9764
	0.2121	0.7382	0.1699	0.7272	0.1283	0.7187	0.1044	0.7148
	0.2898	0.2702	0.2321	0.2662	0.1753	0.2630	0.1427	0.2616
7	0.0570	1.0064	0.0457	0.9953	0.0346	0.9866	0.0281	0.9827
	0.1597	0.8071	0.1281	0.7982	0.0969	0.7912	0.0789	0.7881
	0.2308	0.4479	0.1851	0.4429	0.1400	0.4391	0.1140	0.4373
	0.2562	0	0.2054	0	0.1553	0	0.1265	0
8	0.0436	1.0050	0.0350	0.9965	0.0625	0.9898	0.0216	0.9868
	0.1242	0.8520	0.0997	0.5448	0.0754	0.8391	0.0614	0.8365
	0.1859	0.5693	0.1492	0.5644	0.1129	0.5607	0.0920	0.5590
	0.2193	0.1999	0.1760	0.1982	0.1332	0.1969	0.1055	0.1962
9	0.0345	1.0040	0.0277	0.9972	0.0209	0.9919	0.0171	0.9896
	0.0992	0.8829	0.0797	0.8769	0.0603	0.8723	0.0491	0.8702
	0.1520	0.6553	0.1221	0.6509	0.0924	0.6474	0.0753	0.6459
	0.1864	0.3487	0.1497	0.3463	0.1134	0.3445	0.0923	0.3437
	0.1984	0	0.1593	0	0.1206	0	0.0983	0
10	0.0279	1.0033	0.0224	0.9978	0.0170	0.9935	0.0138	0.9915
	0.0810	0.9051	0.1013	0.7143	0.0767	0.7113	0.0401	0.8945
	0.1261	0.7183	0.0650	0.9001	0.0493	0.8962	0.0625	0.7099
	0.1589	0.4612	0.1277	0.4586	0.0967	0.4567	0.0788	0.4558
	0.1761	0.1589	0.1415	0.1580	0.1072	0.1574	0.0873	0.1570

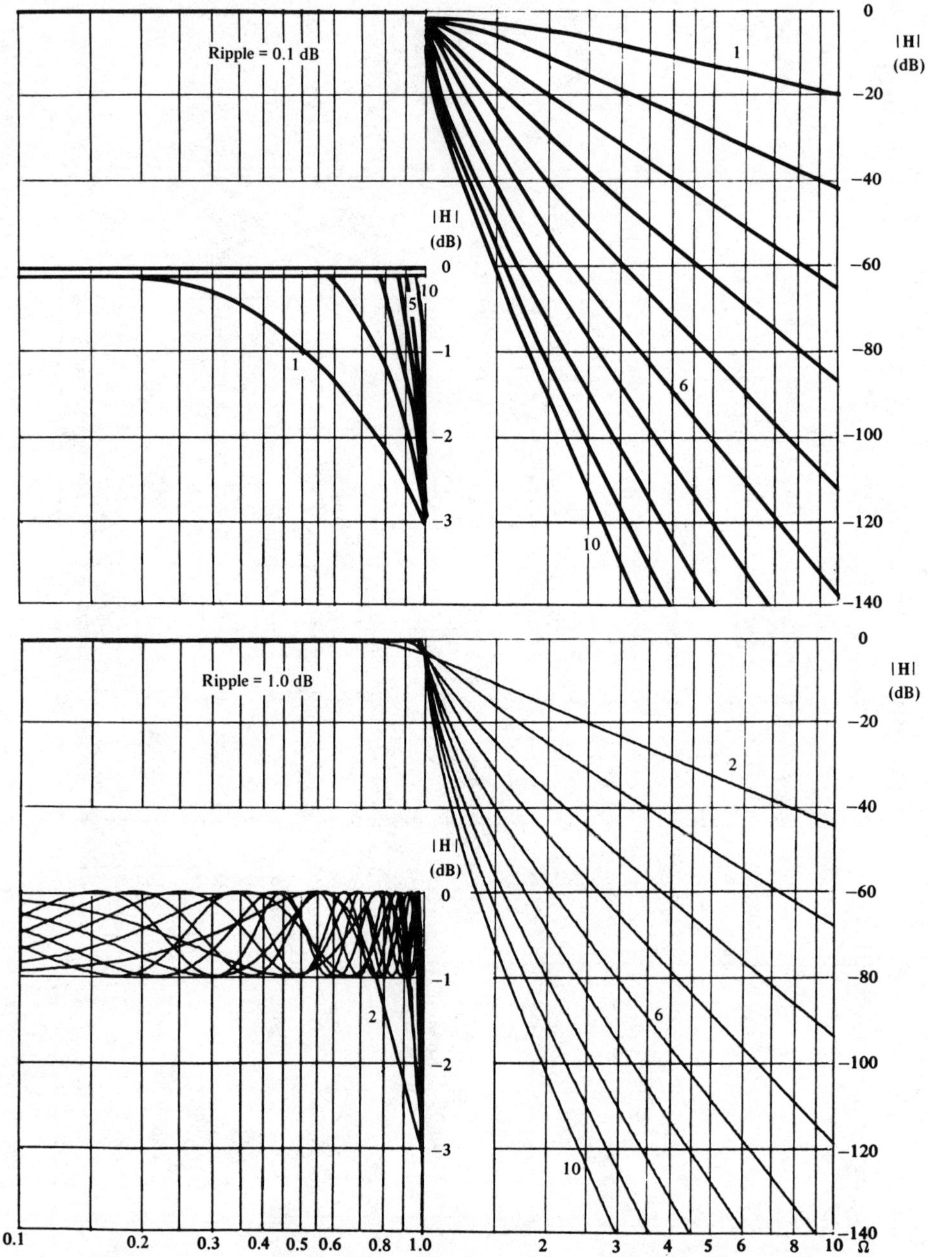

Fig. 4.4.3 Magnitude characteristics of Chebyshev filters having 0.1 and 1 dB ripples and unity 3 dB bandwidths. (1 dB ripple characteristics from A. D. Taylor, loc. cit.)

filter. If we instead normalize their 3 dB bandwidths to unity (rather than $(1 + \epsilon^2)^{-1/2}$), their responses become those shown in Fig. 4.4.4. This demonstrates that little is gained by using a Chebyshev filter with small in-band ripple when the 3 dB bandwidth is fixed.

The Chebyshev filter has a band-edge selectivity of[15]

$$-d|H|/d\omega \,\Big|_{\omega=1} = \frac{\epsilon^2 T_n T_n'}{(1+\epsilon^2 T_n^2)^{3/2}}\Bigg|_{\omega=1} = \frac{\epsilon^2 n^2}{(1+\epsilon^2)^{3/2}} \tag{4.4.14}$$

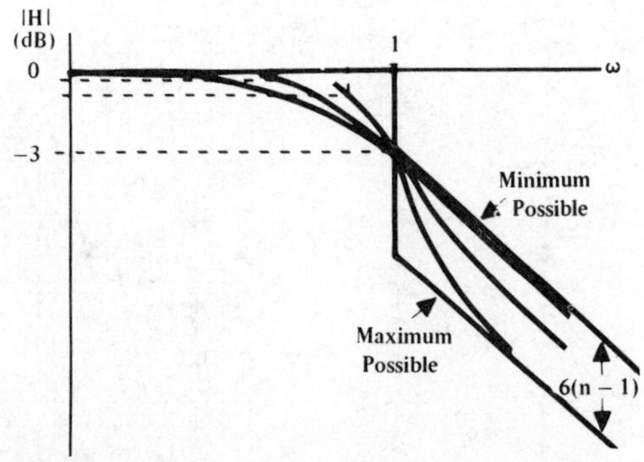

Fig. 4.4.4 Rejection characteristics of Butterworth and Chebyshev filters having unity 3 dB bandwidths.

from Eq. 4.4.1 where $T_n(1)T_n'(1) = n^2$. Note that this is the selectivity at the ripple cutoff frequency and *not* the 3 dB frequency. It may, of course, be evaluated at other frequencies but the calculation becomes more involved. Comparing the 3 dB ripple results with the Butterworth slopes in Eq. 4.3.9, we verify that the Chebyshev filter has a cutoff which is n times larger.

We saw in Eq. 4.4.4 that specifying the maximum amount of ripple determines parameter ϵ. The asymptotic slope or required rejection at a specified stopband frequency determines the required filter order n. Expressing the gain as $|H_1|$ at ω_1 and $|H_2|$ at ω_2, then solving for the filter order n using Eq. 4.4.2 gives (assuming $\omega_1 = 1$)

$$n \geqslant \frac{\cosh^{-1}(\epsilon_2/\epsilon_1)}{\cosh^{-1}\omega_2} = \frac{\ln(2\epsilon_2/\epsilon_1)}{\sqrt{2(\omega_2 - 1)}} \tag{4.4.15}$$

The analogous Butterworth equation was derived in Eq. 4.3.13. The smallest integer satisfying this equation is chosen. This is an inconvenient equation to apply in practice, and much greater insight may be gained by using the nomograph shown in Fig. 4.4.5. The same low-pass filter specifications and data entry format are used as for the Butterworth nomograph.

EXAMPLE 4.4.1 Determine the order of the Chebyshev filter required and meet the specifications of Example 4.3.1 where $M_p = 1.25$ dB, $M_{s1} = 40$ dB at $\Omega_{s1} = 2$, and $M_{s2} = 60$ dB at $\Omega_{s2} = 3$.
Solution The minimum order filter results when we let $M_p = 1.25$ dB rather than some lesser value. Entering this data on Fig. 4.4.5 yields $n_1 \geqslant 5$ and $n_2 \geqslant 5$. Thus, a fifth-order Chebyshev filter having an in-band ripple of 1.25 dB can be used. Since we found that an eighth-order Butterworth filter was required, we can reduce the order by three (almost half) using a Chebyshev filter. We should point out that all the nomographs in this chapter have been constructed so they have the same M_p, M_s, Ω_s, and γ-axes. Thus, once we have obtained the (γ, Ω_s) combinations, they can be used on all the nomographs which helps to simplify the use of nomographs even further. For example, the two data points (γ, Ω_s) from Example 4.3.1 are (4.5, 2) and (6.5, 3).

EXAMPLE 4.4.2 A low-pass filter having the rejection of the last example but different stopband frequencies was analyzed in Example 4.3.2 where size and cost limitations required the filter order $n \leqslant 8$. Can a Chebyshev filter meet these requirements?
Solution Since $\Omega_{s1} = 1.5$ and $\Omega_{s2} = 2$, then we find $n_1 \geqslant 7$ and $n_2 \geqslant 7$ from the Chebyshev filter nomograph. Thus, a seventh-order Chebyshev filter can be used to meet the requirement. Since a thirteenth-order Butterworth filter was required, we have again reduced the filter order by about half.

The delay characteristics of the Chebyshev filter are shown in Fig. 4.4.6 (for other ripples, see Refs. 12, 13, and 16). For small in-band ripple (i.e., small ϵ), they do not differ greatly from the Butterworth characteristics. However, for large ϵ and large ripple, the delay peaking and variation do increase greatly. For only 0.5 dB ripple, the delay variation is about 2 seconds (or 100%) for n = 3; for n = 9, the delay variation is 30 seconds (or 400%). This is due to the fact that the

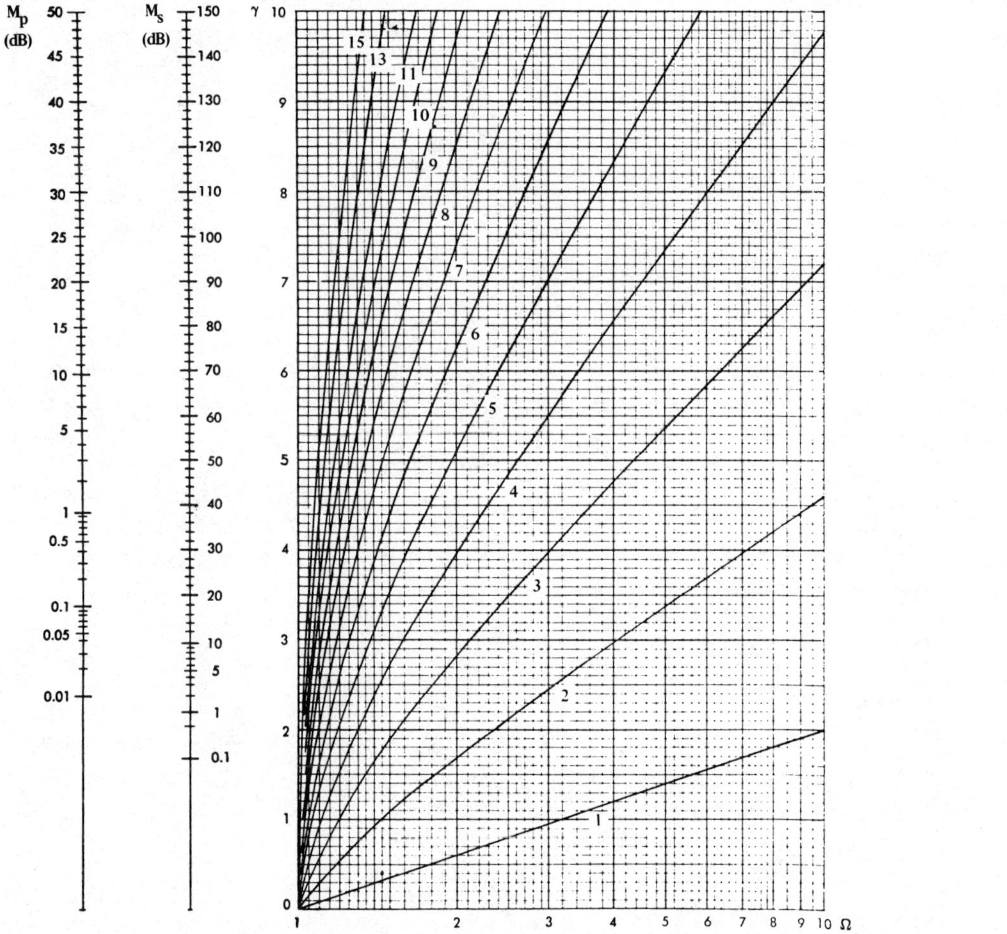

Fig. 4.4.5 Nomograph for Chebyshev filters. (From J. N. Hallberg, loc. cit.)

Butterworth poles have real parts reduced by tanh v. This is much less than unity for large ϵ and n. Thus, the Chebyshev poles have a smaller damping factor than the Butterworth poles and the maximum peaking varies as $1/\zeta\omega_n$ from Eq. 4.3.18.

The unit step responses of the Chebyshev filter for ripples of 0.5, 1, 2, and 3 are shown in Fig. 4.4.7. These responses are based on filters having ripple (not 3 dB) band-edge frequencies of unity. Thus, on a normalized 3 dB bandwidth basis, the time must be *increased* by ω_{3dB} given by Eq. 4.4.12. Due to the higher-Q poles, overshoot increases with increasing filter order n. The delay and overshoot increase with filter order, but not significantly with increasing ripple. The rise time remains approximately constant which agrees with the empirical result of Valley and Wallman when all filters have a normalized 3 dB bandwidth of 1 rad/sec. It is important to note that even-order filters exhibit more percentage overshoot than odd-order filters. This difference is accentuated for large ripple values. Also even-order filters tend to "pull-down" to their final values while odd-order filters tend to "pull-up."[17]

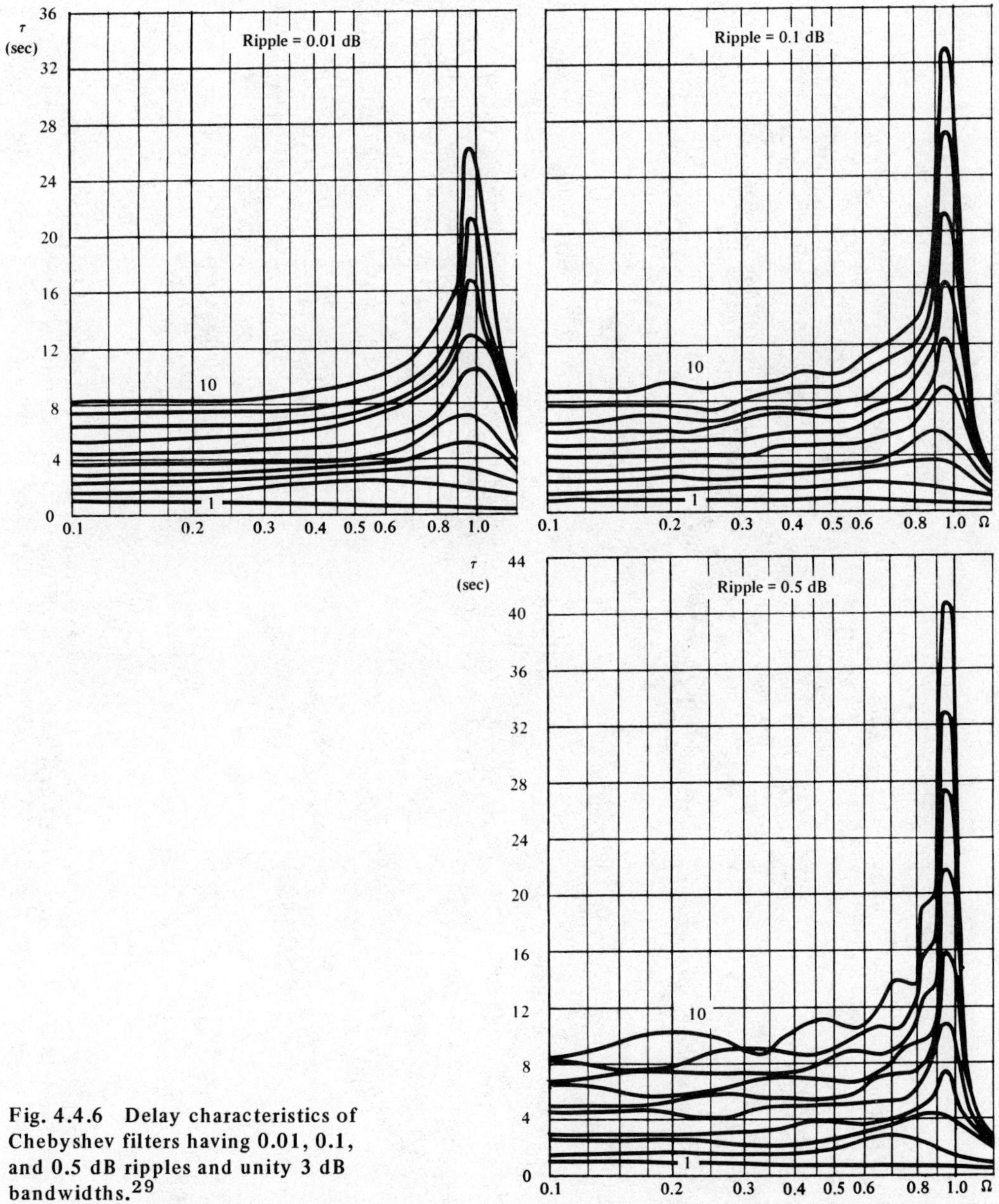

Fig. 4.4.6 Delay characteristics of Chebyshev filters having 0.01, 0.1, and 0.5 dB ripples and unity 3 dB bandwidths.[29]

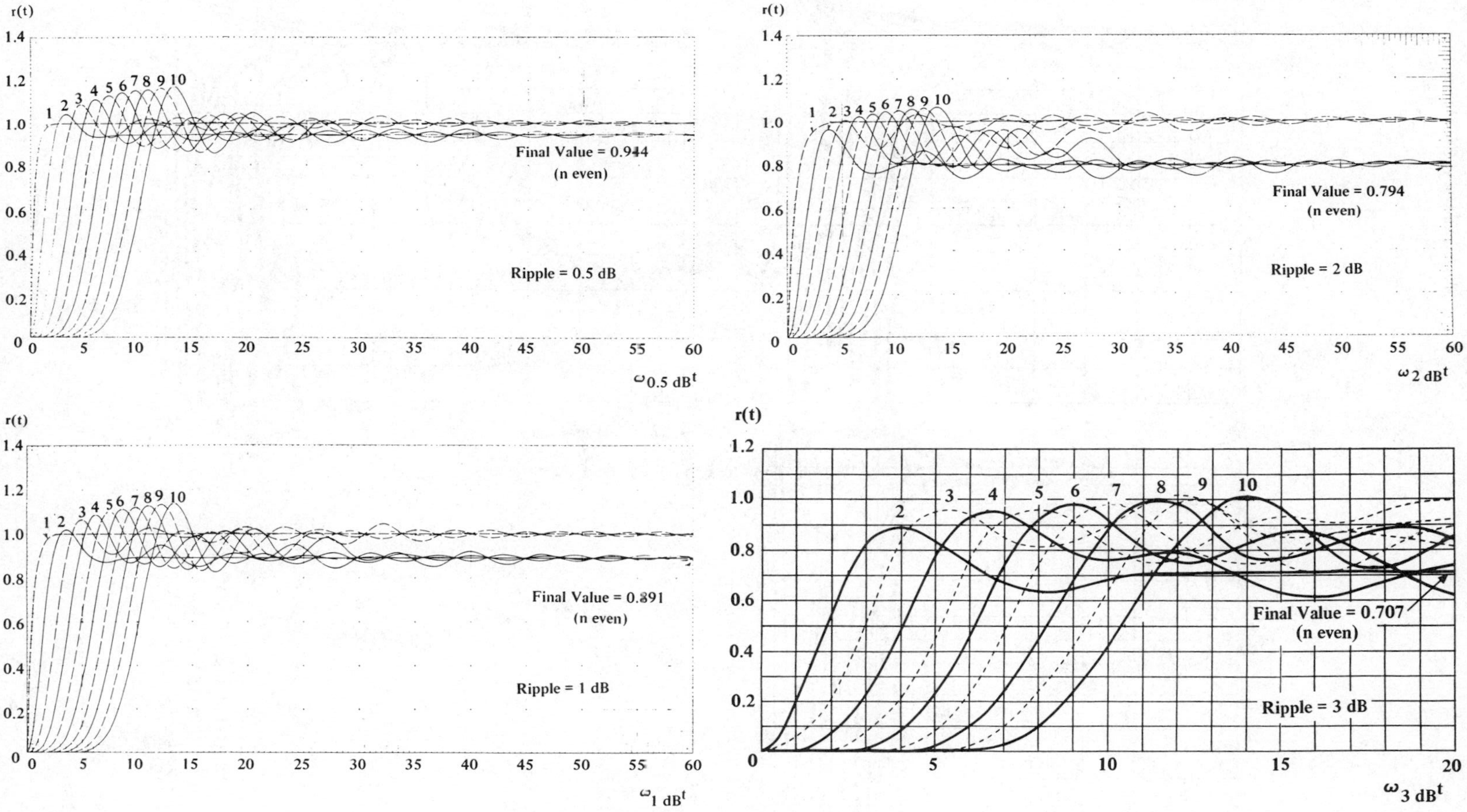

Fig. 4.4.7 Step responses of Chebyshev filter having ripples of 0.5, 1, 2, and 3 dB and unity ripple bandwidths. (From K. W. Henderson and W. H. Kautz, "Transient responses of conventional filters," IRE Trans. Circuit Theory, vol. CT-5, pp. 333–347, Dec., 1958. (Excluding 3 dB ripple responses.))

4.5 ULTRASPHERICAL AND LEGENDRE FILTERS

Ultraspherical filters were introduced by Johnson and Johnson[15] as a more general form of (and alternative to) Butterworth and Chebyshev filters. Ultraspherical filters can be used to obtain faster cutoff than Chebyshev filters, but have corresponding degradation in their delay and step responses. They have in-band ripple which is not equiripple.

In designing filters, we are interested in controlling the passband ripple, band-edge selectivity (or the width of the transition band), and the stopband rejection of the frequency response. Butterworth filters had only a single parameter, n (i.e., order), with which to design. Hence, only one of these three frequency response characteristics can be selected. Chebyshev filters were more flexible since they had two parameters, n and ϵ, with which to design. Ultraspherical filters are more flexible yet in that they have three parameters, n, ϵ, and a, to utilize in design. Thus, all three frequency response characteristics can be obtained simultaneously using ultraspherical filters. Alternatively, more latitude or flexibility is available in obtaining the desired magnitude, delay, and step response characteristics. Ultraspherical filters are also *conceptually useful* since so many other classes of filters are subclasses of this type and can be derived from them.

The ultraspherical filter has a gain magnitude

$$|H(j\omega)|^2 = \frac{1}{1+\epsilon^2[F_n{}^a(\omega)]^2} = \frac{1}{1+\epsilon^2[a_n C_n{}^{a+\frac{1}{2}}(\omega)]^2} \tag{4.5.1}$$

where $F_n{}^a$ (or $C_n{}^a$) is a normalized (or unnormalized) *n*th-order ultraspherical (or Gegenbauer) polynomial. Parameter a determines the cutoff rate, and ϵ determines the passband ripple.

Ultraspherical polynomials are special cases of Jacobi polynomials (when $a = \beta$) which, in turn, are special cases of hypergeometric polynomials as shown in Fig. 4.5.1. Since Jacobian polynomials satisfy

$$P_n{}^{(a,\beta)}(-\omega) = (-1)^n P_n{}^{(\beta,a)}(\omega) \tag{4.5.2}$$

and any polynomial $P_n{}^2$ used in the gain expression Eq. 4.5.1 must make $|H|^2$ even, then $a = \beta$. Thus, ultraspherical polynomials must be used. In order that $T_n{}^a$ have its zeros within $|\omega| < 1$ and $|T_n{}^a|$ increase monotonically for $|\omega| \geqslant 1$, parameter $a > -1$. a can, therefore, assume any integer or noninteger value in the range $-1 < a < \infty$. Butterworth and Chebyshev filters are spec-

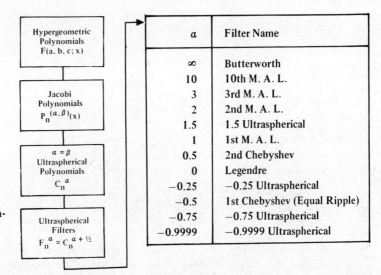

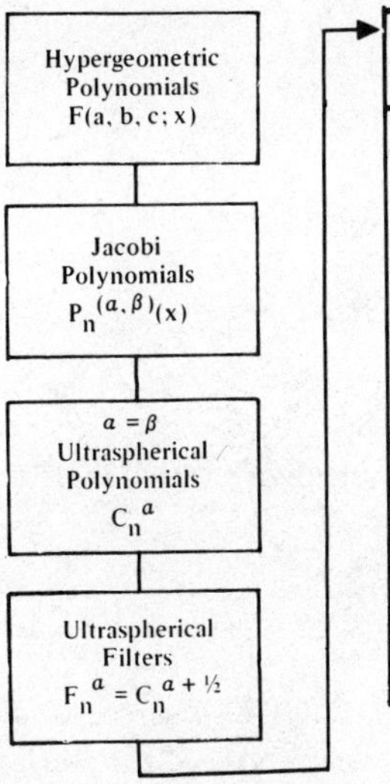

a	Filter Name
∞	Butterworth
10	10th M. A. L.
3	3rd M. A. L.
2	2nd M. A. L.
1.5	1.5 Ultraspherical
1	1st M. A. L.
0.5	2nd Chebyshev
0	Legendre
−0.25	−0.25 Ultraspherical
−0.5	1st Chebyshev (Equal Ripple)
−0.75	−0.75 Ultraspherical
−0.9999	−0.9999 Ultraspherical

Fig. 4.5.1 Source of ultrasperical polynomials and the filters derived from them. (From J. N. Hallberg, loc. cit.)

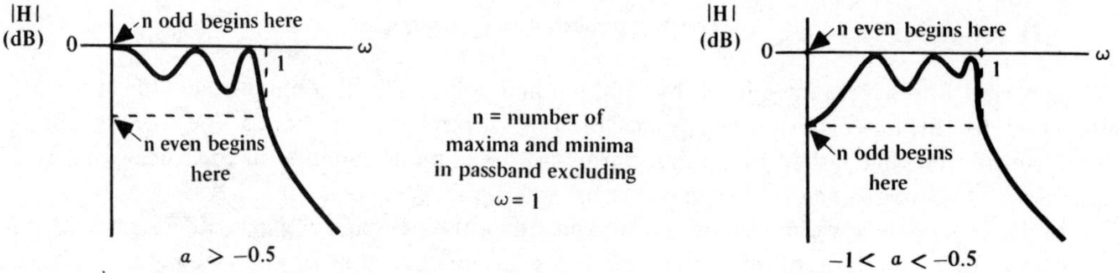

Fig. 4.5.2 Ultraspherical filter magnitude characteristics.

ial classes of ultraspherical filters where $a = \infty$ and $a = -½$, respectively. Before 1966 when Johnson and Johnson introduced ultraspherical filters, several other special cases had been investigated and given names. These were the Legendre and modified associated Legendre filters introduced by Ku and Drubin.[18] The Legendre filter results when $a = 0$ and the mth modified associated Legendre filters result when $a = m$ where m is any integer greater than 0 (i.e., 1, 2, 3, . . .). Since these filters fall in the entire continuum of ultraspherical filters and exhibit the same properties, we have chosen not to treat them as a separate class of filter.

Ultraspherical filters are non-equiripple filters and have the general behavior shown in Fig. 4.5.2. When $a > -0.5$, the response has an increasing ripple through the passband. For $-1 < a < -0.5$, it has decreasing ripple through the passband. The Chebyshev filter (of the first kind) having $a = -0.5$ separates these two response forms. Important filter parameters can be derived by observing that $F_n{}^a(\omega)$ has the following properties:

$$F_n{}^a(0) = 0, \ \text{n odd} \quad \text{and} \quad (-1)^{n/2}\binom{n/2 + a}{a}\binom{n + 2a}{n}^{-1}, \ \text{n even}$$
$$F_n{}^a(1) = 1 \tag{4.5.3}$$

For $|\omega| \leqslant F_n{}^a$ is bounded by

$$\left.\begin{aligned} |F_n{}^a(\omega)| &\leqslant 1, \quad a \geqslant ½ \\ &\leqslant |F_n(0)|, \quad -1 < a < -½ \end{aligned}\right\} \qquad |\omega| \leqslant 1 \tag{4.5.4}$$

while for $|\omega| \gg 1$,

$$|F_n{}^a(\omega)| = \frac{(2a + n + 1)_n}{2^n(1 + a)_n}|\omega|^n \tag{4.5.5}$$

The slope of $|F_n{}^a|$ at $\omega = 1$ equals

$$d|F_n{}^a|/d\omega\,\Big|_{\omega=1} = \frac{n(2a + n + 1)}{2(a + 1)} \tag{4.5.6}$$

The slope is maximum at the cutoff frequency for $a > -½$. For $-1 < a < -½$, the absolute maximum slope occurs inside the passband.

The ultraspherical filter has a band-edge selectivity which equals

$$-d|H|/d\omega\,\Big|_{\omega=1} = \frac{\epsilon^2 n(2a + n + 1)}{2(1 + a)(1 + \epsilon^2)^{3/2}} = \frac{\epsilon^2 n}{(1 + \epsilon^2)^{3/2}}\left[1 + \frac{n - 1}{2(a + 1)}\right] \tag{4.5.7}$$

which is an increasing function for decreasing a. Thus, we see that intermediate selectivities can be obtained for $-0.5 < a < \infty$ which lie between those of the Butterworth and Chebyshev filters.

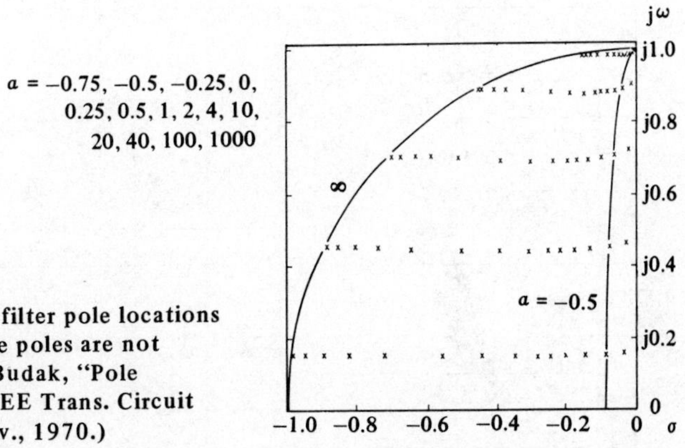

Fig. 4.5.3 Tenth-order ultraspherical filter pole locations for 3 dB ripple ($\epsilon = 1$). (The conjugate poles are not shown.) (From D. M. Petrela and A. Budak, "Pole locations for ultraspherical filters," IEEE Trans. Circuit Theory, vol. CT-17, pp. 668–670, Nov., 1970.)

The selectivity exceeds that of the Chebyshev filter for $-1 < a < -\frac{1}{2}$, but the ripple is increased.

The in-band ripple equals

$$\begin{aligned} \text{Ripple} &\leq 1 - (1 + \epsilon^2)^{-\frac{1}{2}} \cong \epsilon^2/2, \qquad a \geq -\tfrac{1}{2} \\ &= \binom{n/2 + a}{a}\binom{n + 2a}{n}^{-1} \geq 1 - (1 + \epsilon^2)^{-\frac{1}{2}}, \qquad -1 < a < -\tfrac{1}{2} \end{aligned} \tag{4.5.8}$$

The ripple is maximum at the ripple cutoff frequency $\omega = 1$ for $a \geq -\frac{1}{2}$. The 3 dB bandwidth ω_{3dB} is determined by computerized solution to $F_n^a(\omega_{3dB}) = \pm 1/\epsilon$. When $\epsilon = 1$ for 3 dB ripple, then ω_{3dB} equals unity.

The ultraspherical filter poles are determined by analytic continuation from Eq. 4.5.1 using Eq. 4.3.4 and retaining only left-half-plane poles. A computer must be used to determine these roots (for various poles, see Refs. 12 and 19). To gain insight into the relation between these poles and those of the Butterworth ($a = \infty$) and Chebyshev filters ($a = -0.5$), the pole locations for a tenth-order ultraspherical filter are drawn in Fig. 4.5.3. The heavy lines indicate the Butterworth and Chebyshev filter bounds. We see that for $-0.5 < a < \infty$, the poles still lie on ellipses. Their imaginary parts remain about constant, but their real parts approach unity as $a \to \infty$.

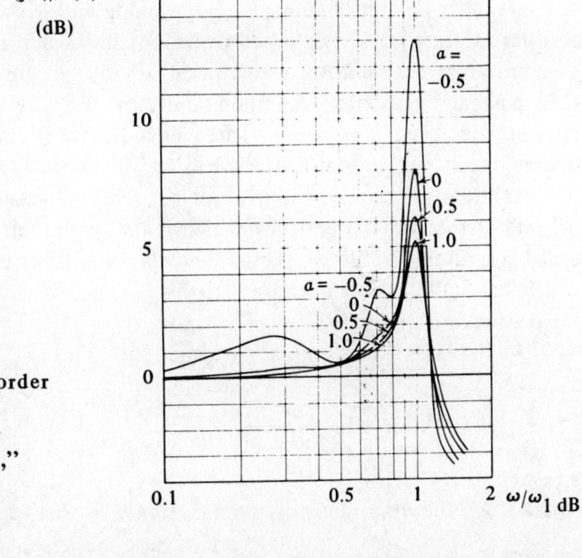

Fig. 4.5.4 Delay characteristics of sixth-order ultraspherical filters having 1 dB ripple. (From J. Vlach, "Computerized Approximation and Synthesis of Linear Networks," Chap. 8, Wiley, NY, 1969. Reprinted by permission of John Wiley & Sons, Inc.)

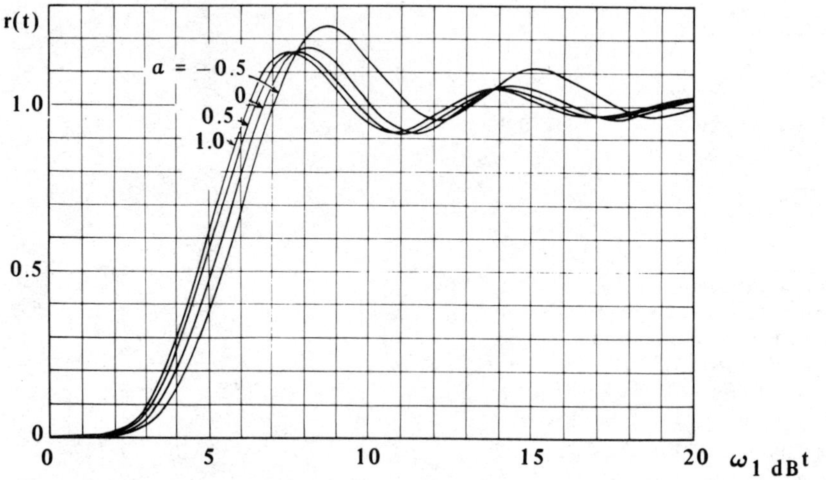

Fig. 4.5.5 Step response of sixth-order ultraspherical filter having 1 dB ripple and unity dc gain. (From J. Vlach, "Computerized Approximation and Synthesis of Linear Networks," Chap. 8, Wiley, NY, 1969. Reprinted by permission of John Wiley & Sons, Inc.)

The required order of ultraspherical filters can be easily determined using nomographs. Nomographs are available for the a values listed in Fig. 4.5.1.[6] The delay characteristics of ultraspherical filters lie between those for Butterworth and Chebyshev filters for $-0.5 < a < \infty$. They exceed the Chebyshev filter delay characteristics for $-1 < a < -0.5$. The delay characteristics for a sixth-order ultraspherical filter having $\epsilon = 0.5$ (about 1 dB ripple) and $a = -0.5, 0, 0.5$, and 1 are shown in Fig. 4.5.4. These results show that we can interpolate Butterworth and Chebyshev delay characteristics to obtain the delay for ultraspherical filters.

The unit step response characteristics of ultraspherical filters also lie between those for Butterworth and Chebyshev filters for $-0.5 < a < \infty$ as shown in Fig. 4.5.5 (for 1 dB bandwidths of unity). We can again interpolate such results as delay time, rise time, settling time, etc.

4.6 PAPOULIS (MONOTONIC-L) FILTERS

The Chebyshev filter cuts off more rapidly than the Butterworth filter. Chebyshev filter delay characteristics exhibit large band-edge peaking and in-band delay variation. The Chebyshev filter also has increased delay time and overshoot in its step response. The ultraspherical filters afford a compromise between Butterworth and Chebyshev filter behavior; however, they have ripple in their passband response. Another family of filters having monotonic (i.e., ripple-free) passband response has been developed. These include the Papoulis filters and others which combine the desirable characteristics of Butterworth and Chebyshev filters.

Papoulis filters have a magnitude response which is monotonically nonincreasing and a cutoff rate at the corner frequency which is the maximum possible. Originally, Papoulis filters were called monotonic-L filters. Unfortunately, this filter is often confused with the Legendre filter which has quite different characteristics. Thus, we shall call it the Papoulis filter to eliminate any confusion.

The Papoulis filter[20] has a magnitude function

$$|H(j\omega)|^2 = \frac{1}{1 + \epsilon^2 L_n(\omega^2)} \tag{4.6.1}$$

where L_n is the nth-order polymonial *related to* the Legendre polynomial and ϵ is the parameter

Table 4.6.1 Papoulis filter poles.

n	Poles ω_n	Poles ζ	n	Poles ω_n	Poles ζ
2	1.0000	0.7071	6	0.9847	0.1170
				0.7635	0.4047
3	0.9647	0.3578		0.5002	0.8774
	0.6203	real			
			7	0.9881	0.0872
4	0.9735	0.2380		0.8137	0.2918
	0.6563	0.8376		0.5532	0.6313
				0.3821	real
5	0.9803	0.1567			
	0.7051	0.5505	8	0.9904	0.0696
	0.4681	real		0.8473	0.2293
				0.6188	0.4853
				0.4093	0.8971

which determines the attenuation at the cutoff frequency $\omega = 1$. L_n had the convenient properties that[15]

$$L_n(0) = 0, \quad L_n(1) = 1, \quad dL_n/d\omega \leqslant 0 \text{ (monotonically nonincreasing)}$$
$$dL_n/d\omega\,|_{\omega=1} = (n+1)^2/2, \text{ n odd} \quad \text{and} \quad n(n+2)/2, \text{ n even} \quad \text{(maximum possible)} \tag{4.6.2}$$

For $|\omega| < 1$, L_n is bounded by $|L_n| \leqslant 1$ while for $|\omega| \gg 1$, L_n increases monotonically as

$$|L_n(\omega^2)|^{1/2} \cong [n(n+2)^{1/2}/4(n-1)!]\,[(n/2-1)!]^2/\omega_n, \quad \text{n odd}$$
$$\cong [(n+1)n^{1/2}/2n!]\,[((n-1)/2)!]^2/\omega_n, \quad \text{n even} \tag{4.6.3}$$

Although this is a complicated result, we will find it is very useful for later comparisons.

The Papoulis filter poles are determined by analytic continuation from Eq. 4.6.1 using Eq. 4.3.4 and retaining only left-half-plane poles. The poles obtained by this procedure are listed in Table 4.6.1 where ϵ has been set equal to unity to yield a 3 dB bandwidth of unity. All poles are located within the Butterworth unit circle.

The gain function has the form of Eq. 4.3.6. Its denominator is found by using the Papoulis filter polynomials listed in Table 4.6.1. The magnitude and delay characteristics are plotted in Fig. 4.6.1. The magnitude characteristics are monotonically nonincreasing with faster cutoff at the band-edge compared to the Butterworth characteristic of Fig. 4.3.2. Although a 3 dB ripple Chebyshev filter has a more rapid cutoff, its in-band ripple is not monotonic. The selectivity of the Papoulis filter at its band-edge equals

$$-d|H|/d\omega\,|_{\omega=1} = L_n'/2(1+L_n)^{3/2} = 0.0884(n+1)^2, \quad \text{n odd}$$
$$= 0.0884n(n+2), \quad \text{n even} \tag{4.6.4}$$

from Eqs. 4.6.1 and 4.6.2. Note that these slopes vary as n^2 while Butterworth filter slopes vary only as n (from Eq. 4.3.9) so Papoulis filters have faster cutoffs. Chebyshev slopes also vary as n^2 but have larger values for any n. The order of the Papoulis filter is easily determined using the nomograph of Fig. 4.6.2.

EXAMPLE 4.6.1 A Papoulis filter must be designed to meet the specifications of Example 4.3.2 and must also have a minimum high-frequency rolloff of –60 dB/dec. Determine the required filter order. Compare this result with these two earlier examples.

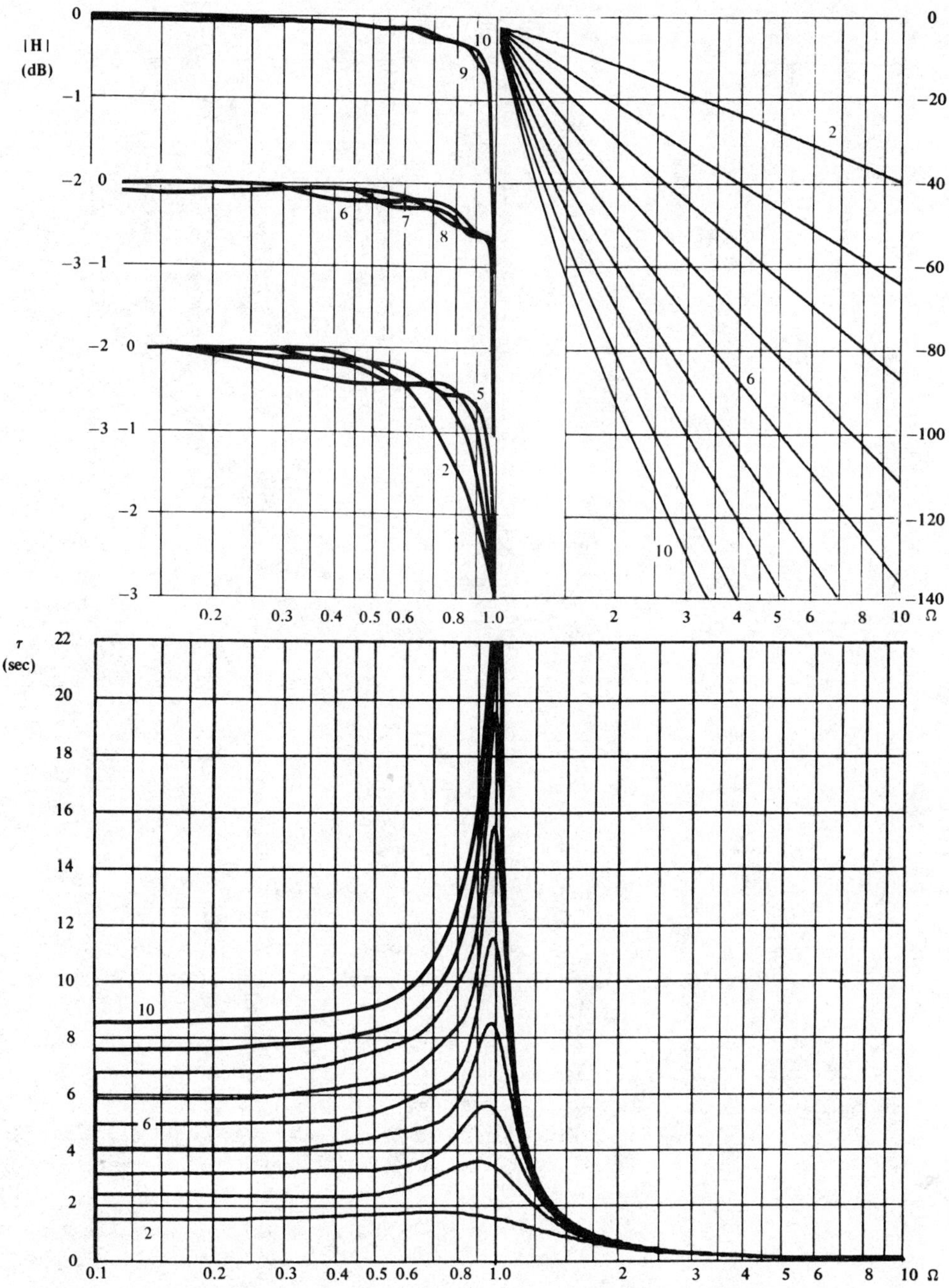

Fig. 4.6.1 Magnitude and delay characteristics of Papoulis filters. (From A. D. Taylor, loc. cit.)

Solution The high-frequency rolloff requirement dictates a minimum filter order of $n \geq -60/-20 = 3$. Since $M_p = 1.25$ dB, $M_{s1} = 40$ dB at $\Omega_{s1} = 1.5$, and $M_{s2} = 60$ dB at $\Omega_{s2} = 2$, we find $n_1 \geq 8$ and $n_2 \geq 8$ from the Papoulis filter nomograph. Thus, an eighth-order filter will be sufficient to meet all the requirements. We found earlier in Examples 4.3.2 and 4.4.2 that a thirteenth-order Butterworth filter or a seventh-order Chebyshev filter was required to meet the same requirements, respectively (note they will also meet the slope specification of this example). Thus, if a monotonic response is more desirable

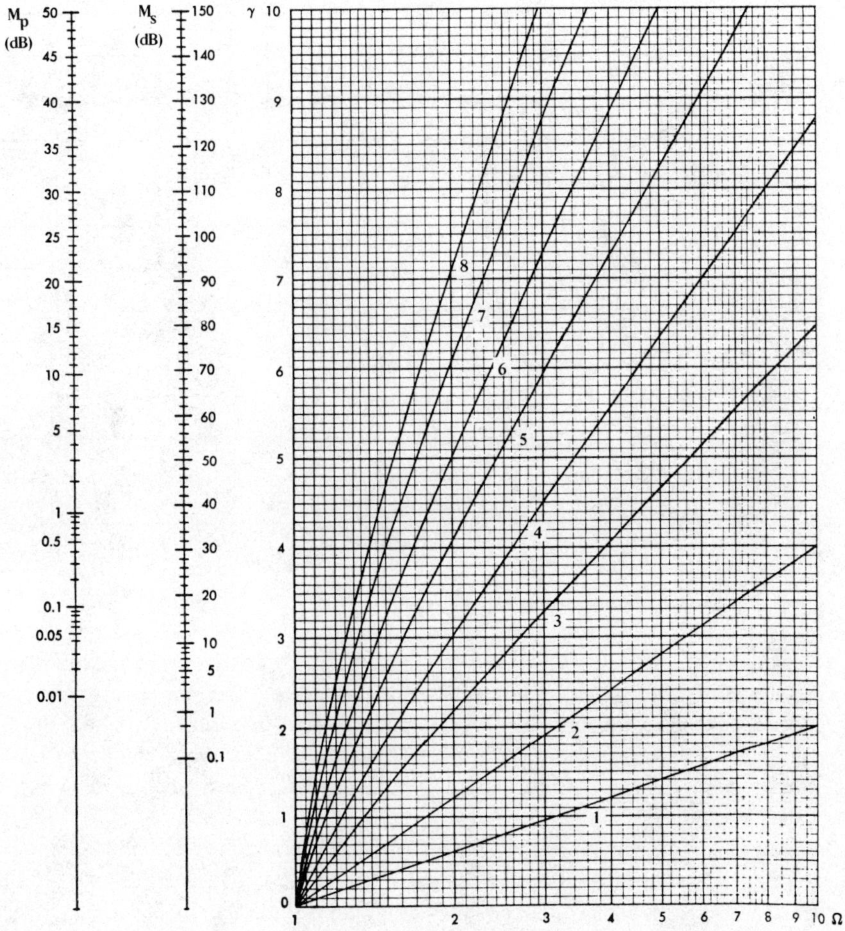

Fig. 4.6.2 Nomograph for Papoulis filters. (From J. N. Hallberg, loc. cit.)

for this application, an eighth-order Papoulis filter can be used in place of the thirteenth-order Butterworth filter. This represents a savings of five poles and thus reduces the complexity (i.e., size) of the filter.

The delay characteristic of the Papoulis filter is shown in Fig. 4.6.1. The delay is more peaked than the Butterworth filter due to its poles having slightly decreased damping factors. The peak delay is about doubled while the dc delay values are increased slightly. For $n = 3$, the delay variation is less than 2 seconds (100%); for $n = 9$, the variation is about 17 seconds (300%). The delay characteristics are very close to those of the Chebyshev filter with 0.01 dB ripple. The Papoulis filter has less delay than Chebyshev filters having larger ripple values.

The unit step response of the Papoulis filter is shown in Fig. 4.6.3. There is little difference between the step response of the Papoulis, Butterworth, and small-ripple Chebyshev filters except for their delay times.

Halpern developed a filter which has very similar characteristics to the Papoulis filter.[21] The Papoulis filter was designed to have maximum band-edge selectivity with monotonic response. The Halpern filter was designed to have maximum asymptotic rejection with monotonic response. The magnitude function of the Halpern filter is given by Eq. 4.6.1 where L_n is the nth-order polynomial *related* to the nth-order Jacobi polynomial. The Halpern filter provides a stopband

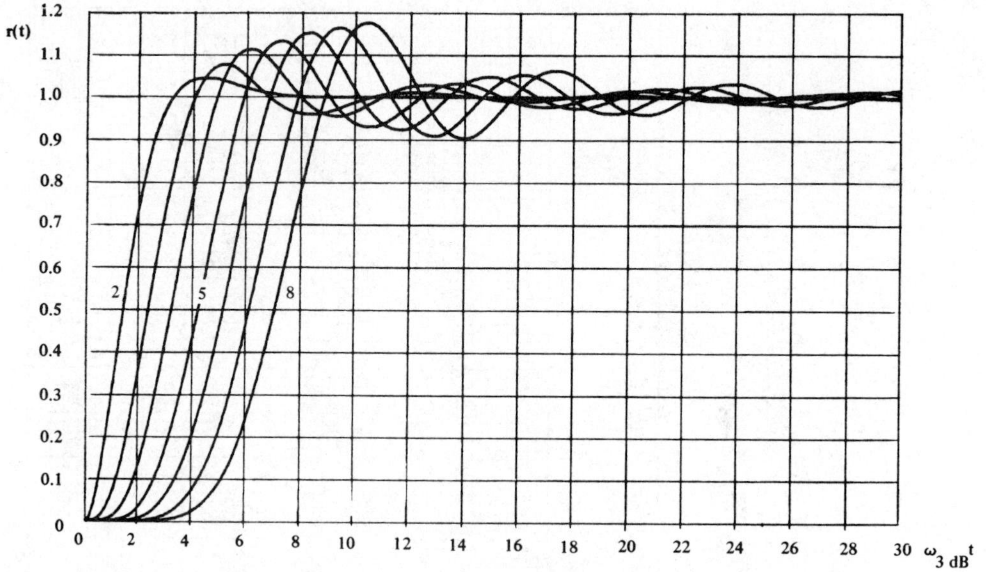

Fig. 4.6.3 Step response of Papoulis filters. (From A. D. Taylor, loc. cit.)

rejection which is about $0.5\sqrt{n}$ greater than that provided by the Papoulis filter. Thus, a sixth-order Halpern filter provides only 3 dB more rejection. The nomograph for the Halpern filter is almost identical to the Papoulis filter nomograph. Therefore, the filters have almost identical magnitude characteristics in the stopband. Their step response characteristics are very similar. Another closely-related monotonic response filter has been investigated, but this shall not be pursued further.[22]

Another interesting filter which has monotonic response for odd orders was introduced by Aronhime and Budak[23] (for response data, see Ref. 24). It is an all-pole filter whose magnitude characteristic is maximally flat beyond the origin (MFMBO). Its passband characteristics are similar to a third-order Halpern filter for odd orders, and a second-order Chebyshev filter for even orders. It provides slightly more stopband rejection than the Papoulis filter, but not as much as the Halpern filter for odd orders. For even orders, its stopband rejection is unlike that of any of our previous filters. Aronhime and Budak show that the band-edge selectivity of the MFMBO filter is equal to (for n odd) or twice that (for n even) of the Butterworth filter.

4.7 INVERSE CHEBYSHEV FILTERS

In this chapter, we have thus far considered so-called all-pole filters which have all their transmission zeros at infinity. Now we want to consider the effects of introducing finite zeros of transmission. Very often, these zeros allow the filter to possess a narrower transition band than it would otherwise have.

One such filter having finite zeros of transmission is the inverse Chebyshev filter. This filter has magnitude characteristics which complement (or are inverse to) those of the Chebyshev filter as shown in Fig. 4.7.1. The relation between the two responses can be seen from the gain function of the inverse Chebyshev filter gain function[7]

$$|H(j\omega)|^2 = \frac{\epsilon^2 T_n^{\,2}(1/\omega)}{1 + \epsilon^2 T_n^{\,2}(1/\omega)} = \left(1 + \frac{1}{\epsilon^2 T_n^{\,2}(1/\omega)}\right)^{-1} \tag{4.7.1}$$

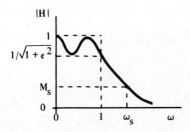

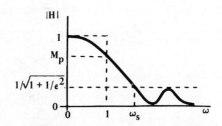

Fig. 4.7.1 Magnitude characteristics for third-order Chebyshev and inverse Chebyshev filters.

While the Chebyshev filter is equiripple in the passband and MFM in the stopband, the inverse Chebyshev filter is MFM in the passband and equiripple in the stopband. This inversion in performance is obtained by inverting both frequency in $T_n(\omega)$, and $T_n(1/\omega)$ itself. The MFM property follows because Eq. 4.7.1 satisfies the MFM conditions of Eq. 4.2.5.

Inverse Chebyshev filters of odd-order have high-frequency magnitude responses which decrease as $1/\omega$ while even-order filters have a response which approaches a constant. We see from Fig. 4.7.1 that $\omega = 1$ marks the edge of the *stopband* rather than the passband. The maximum stopband ripple occurs at frequencies where $T_n(1/\omega) = \pm 1/\epsilon$. The transmission zeros occur at frequencies where $T_n(1/\omega) = 0$. Since T_n is given by Eq. 4.4.2, the transmission zeros equal

$$n \cos^{-1}(1/\omega_z) = (2k+1)\pi/2 \qquad \text{or} \qquad \omega_z = \sec\,[(2k+1)\pi/2n] \tag{4.7.2}$$

for $k = 0, 1, \ldots, n$. The maximum stopband ripple occurs at frequencies equalling $\sec(k\pi/n)$.

The poles and zeros are easily determined. The zeros of H(s) are equal to $s = \pm j\omega_z$. The poles of H(s) are determined by considering Eq. 4.7.1. Since the denominator is identical for that of the Chebyshev filter (see Eq. 4.4.1) except that frequency ω is replaced by $1/\omega$, the poles are equal to the reciprocal values of the Chebyshev poles. Thus, by expressing the poles listed in Table 4.4.1 in polar form and taking their reciprocals, the poles of the inverse Chebyshev filter are easily determined (or see Ref. 11). If the Chebyshev filter pole is given by $s_k = r_k \exp(\pm j\theta_k)$, then the inverse Chebyshev filter pole becomes $s_k = (1/r_k)\exp(\pm j\theta_k)$. Thus, the angle remains unchanged, but the radius is inverted. Henderson and Kautz show that these poles lie on a curve that looks similar to an ellipse as shown in Fig. 4.7.2a. A peculiar shape occurs when the Chebyshev curve intersects the unit circle as shown in Fig. 4.7.2b. It must be remembered that the ripple parameter which must be used when first obtaining the Chebyshev poles must be calculated from the required stopband rejection M_s. Since the inverse Chebyshev filter in Fig. 4.7.1b has a gain of $M_s = (1 + 1/\epsilon^2)^{-1/2}$ at the edge of the stopband using Eq. 4.7.1, then ϵ equals

Fig. 4.7.2 Transformation of Chebyshev poles into inverse Chebyshev poles. (The conjugate poles are not shown.) (From K. W. Henderson, and W. H. Kautz, "Transient responses of conventional filters," IRE Trans. Circuit Theory, vol. CT-5, pp. 333–347, Dec. 1958.)

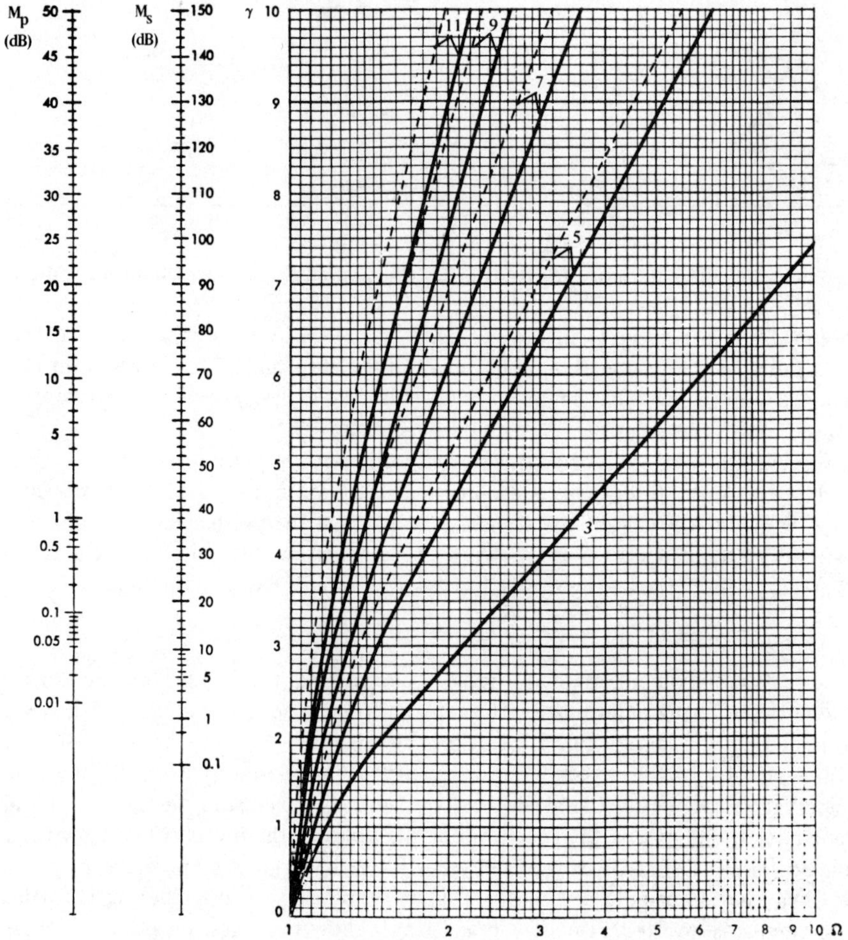

Fig. 4.7.3 Nomograph for generalized inverse Chebyshev filter having one (solid lines) or two (dotted lines) zeros of transmission.

$$\epsilon = M_s(1 - M_s^2)^{-1/2} \cong M_s \quad \text{for} \quad M_s \cong 0 \tag{4.7.3}$$

This approximation is less than 1% in error for a stopband rejection M_s of about 20 dB or more. Thus, for a stopband rejection of 40 dB, M_s = –40 dB = 10^{-2} so $\epsilon = 0.01$. When we wish to use the Chebyshev pole results, then the analogous ripple value which must be used equals $4.34M_s^2$ dB from Eq. 4.4.4. Thus for M_s = –40 dB, then the analogous Chebyshev filter has a ripple of $4.34(10^{-2}) = 0.043$ dB.

The required inverse Chebyshev filter order can be determined from Eq. 4.7.1. Expressing the gain as

$$|H(j\omega_1)|^2 = [1 + 1/\epsilon^2 T_n^2(\omega_1)]^{-1} = [1 + 1/\epsilon_1^2]^{-1} \tag{4.7.4}$$

then for a specified ϵ_1 and ω_1, solving for the filter order yields

$$n \geqslant [\cosh^{-1}(\epsilon/\epsilon_1)]/[\cosh^{-1}(1/\omega_1)] \tag{4.7.5}$$

which is identical to Eq. 4.4.15. Thus, inverse Chebyshev filters and Chebyshev filters of the same order will satisfy identical magnitude specifications. Therefore, the nomograph of Fig. 4.4.5

describes inverse Chebyshev filters as well as Chebyshev filters.

Since the *n*th-order inverse Chebyshev filter requires n zeros (for n even) or (n – 1) zeros (for n odd) in addition to the n poles required for the Chebyshev filter, it is more complex. Since filter complexity is usually proportional to the total number of poles and zeros, inverse Chebyshev filters are about twice as complex as Chebyshev filters. Since they provide no improvement in reducing the width of the transition band but yet are more complex, they are seldom used in practical applications. However, they are important in illustrating the use of zeros of transmission. By combining the Chebyshev passband characteristic with the inverse Chebyshev stopband characteristic to yield equiripple passband and stopband performance, the transition band *can* be significantly reduced. Such filters are called elliptic filters which we will consider in the next section.

Generalized inverse Chebyshev filters have been considered by Chang.[26] These are *n*th-order filters which have from 0 to n zeros of transmission. They are maximally flat at low frequencies with monotonic passband response. When there are no finite transmission zeros, they become Butterworth filters. When there are n zeros (for n even) or (n – 1) zeros (for n odd), they are inverse Chebyshev filters. For an intermediate number m of zeros, they are called generalized filters. These filters can be used to obtain more rapid asymptotic rolloff than inverse Chebyshev filters, and a narrower transition band than Butterworth filters. They are attractive when only one (m = 2) or perhaps two (m = 4) zeros of transmission are utilized. The nomograph for these number of zeros are shown in Fig. 4.7.3. Comparing this nomograph with the Chebyshev filter nomograph of Fig. 4.4.5, we see that m = 4 inverse filters are very close to Chebyshev filters in order. Generalized inverse Chebyshev filters form an attractive alternative to Chebyshev filters when monotonic passband response is desired.

4.8 ELLIPTIC FILTERS

The elliptic filter has an equal-ripple response in both its passband and its stopband. Permitting stopband ripple allows the transition band to be narrower. Elliptic filters have narrower transition bands than Chebyshev and inverse Chebyshev filters, and in fact, the narrowest transition band of all of the presently-known filters. They have finite zeros of transmission. The first zero pair is located just outside of the passband and forces the response to rapidly approach zero as ω frequency approaches Ω_s. The price paid for these improved gain characteristics is passband and stopband ripple, and asymptotic rolloffs of either –20 (n odd) or –40 dB/dec (n even). The magnitude response of a third-order elliptic filter having 0.1 dB in-band ripple and arbitrary stopband ripple is shown in Fig. 4.8.1 (for others, see Ref. 13). The response of a Butterworth filter having a 0.1 dB frequency of unity is also shown. The great improvement in reducing the width of the transition band is obvious.

The elliptic filter, sometimes called the Cauer or Cauer-Chebyshev filter, has a magnitude function

$$|H(j\omega)|^2 = \frac{1}{1 + \epsilon^2 Z_n^{\,2}(\omega)} \tag{4.8.1}$$

where Z_n is the *n*th-order elliptic function and ϵ is the parameter which determines the attenuation at the cutoff frequency $\omega = 1$. Elliptic functions have equal ripple in both the passband and stopband. Z_n has the property that $Z_n(1/\omega) = 1/Z_n(\omega)$ so that its value at a frequency $1/\omega$ is equal to the reciprocal of its value at a frequency ω.[7] Thus, the poles of Z_n are the reciprocals of its zeros. If the critical frequencies can be found where Z_n is equal-ripple in its passband, it will automatically be equal-ripple in its stopband. Z_n is obtained from[27]

$$Z_n(\omega) = \mathrm{sn}\ [n\ \mathrm{sn}^{-1}\ (\omega, 1/m) + c; m'] \tag{4.8.2}$$

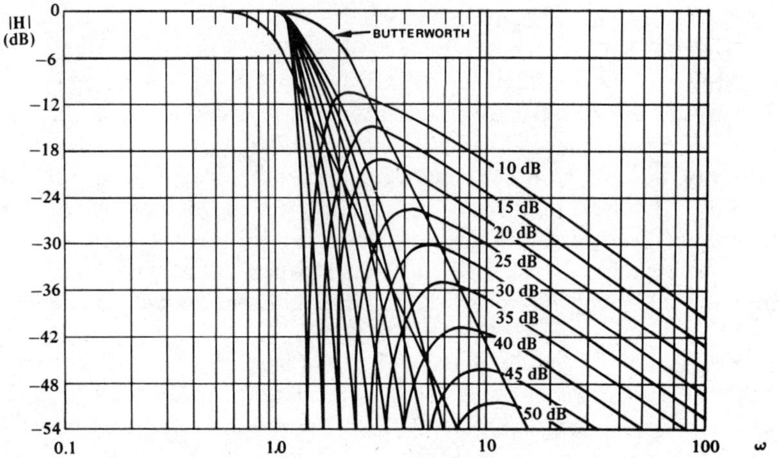

Fig. 4.8.1 Magnitude response of third-order elliptic filter having 0.1 dB in-band ripple. (From Feedback, vol. 1, no. 1, p. 8, KTI, Santa Clara, CA, April, 1973.)

where sn(ω; m′) is the elliptic sine of argument ω and parameter m′. Parameters m and m′ equal

$$m = 1/\Omega_s^2, \qquad m' = (\epsilon_1/\epsilon_2)^2 \tag{4.8.3}$$

where Ω_s is the corner frequency of the stopband and ϵ_1 and ϵ_2 are the passband and stopband ripple parameters respectively. Constant c is equal to

$$c = 0, \ n \text{ odd} \qquad \text{or} \qquad K(m'), \ n \text{ even} \tag{4.8.4}$$

K is the complete elliptic integral which equals

$$K(m) = u(\pi/2; m) = \int_0^{\pi/2} \frac{1}{\sqrt{1 - m\sin^2\theta}}\, d\theta \tag{4.8.5}$$

Evaluation requires a tabulation of the complete elliptic integrals.[28]

Calahan shows that the required order of an elliptic filter is given by[27]

$$n \geqslant \frac{K(m)K(m_1')}{K(m')K(m_1)} = \frac{K(1/\Omega_s)\, K([1 - (\epsilon_1/\epsilon_2)^2]^{1/2})}{K(\epsilon_1/\epsilon_2)\, K([1 - 1/\Omega_s^2]^{1/2})} \tag{4.8.6}$$

where $m_1 = 1 - m$. When $m \cong 1$ so $\Omega_s \cong 1$, then the filter order approximately equals

$$n \geqslant (2/\pi^2) \ln(4\epsilon_2/\epsilon_1) \ln(8/[\Omega_s - 1]) \tag{4.8.7}$$

which is still involved to calculate. Greater insight into the required filter order is gained from the nomograph of Fig. 4.8.2.

EXAMPLE 4.8.1 Determine the order of the elliptic filter required to meet the specification of Example 4.3.2 where M_p = 1.25 dB, M_{s1} = 40 dB at Ω_{s1} = 1.5, and M_{s2} = 60 dB at M_{s2} = 2.

Solution Entering the data on the elliptic filter nomograph, we see $n_1 \geqslant 4$ and $n_2 \geqslant 5$. Thus, only a fifth-order elliptic filter is required. Earlier in Examples 4.3.2, 4.4.2, and 4.6.1, we found that thirteenth-order Butterworth, eighth-order Papoulis, and seventh-order Chebyshev filters were needed. Thus, this represents a further savings in filter order. It should be noted, however, that a fifth-order elliptic filter requires two pairs of zeros of transmission which increases filter complexity. Therefore, although one filter stage is eliminated, there is little savings in the total parts count between the Chebyshev filter and the elliptic filter.

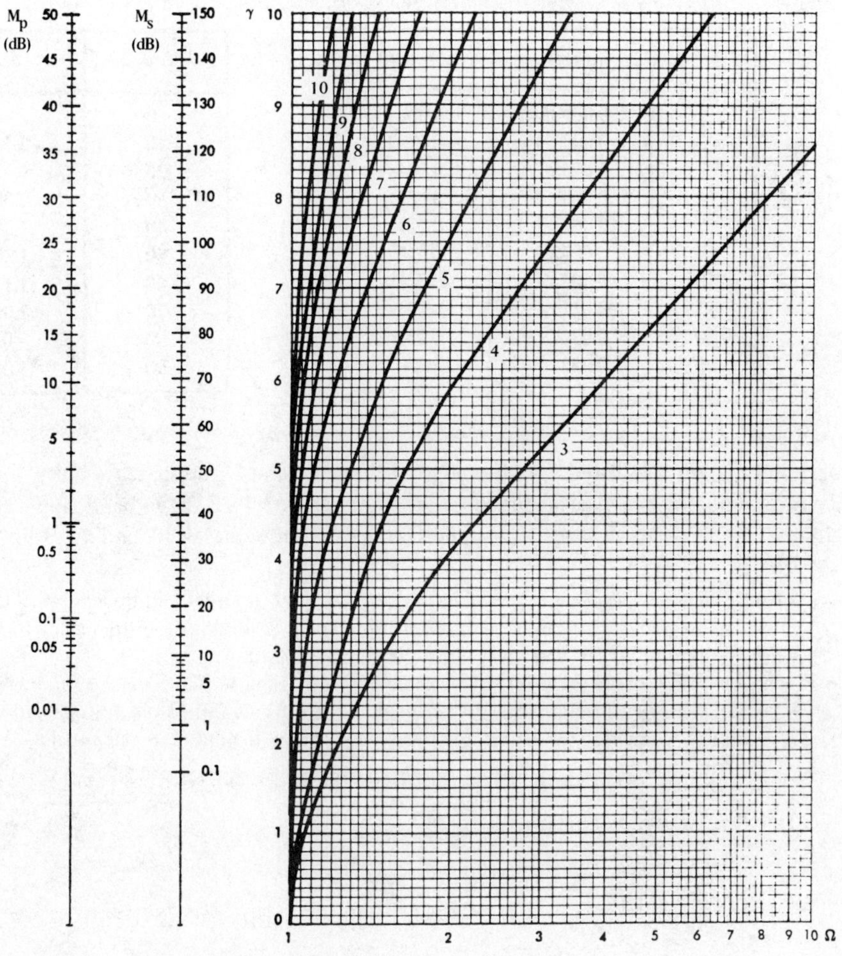

Fig. 4.8.2 Nomograph for elliptic filters.

The poles and zeros of elliptic filters are given by

$$z_k, z_k^* = \pm j/m^{1/2} \text{ sn } [kK(m)/n; m], \qquad p_k, p_k^* = j \text{ sn } [\pm kK(m)/n + jv_o; m] \tag{4.8.8}$$

where k = 0, 2, ... , n − 1 for n odd and k = 1, 3, ... , n − 1 for n even. Parameter v_o equals

$$v_o = \frac{K(m)}{nK(m')} \text{sc}^{-1} (1/\epsilon_1; m_1') \cong \frac{K(m)}{nK(m')} \sinh^{-1} (1/\epsilon_1), \qquad m' \cong 0 \tag{4.8.9}$$

where sc is the elliptic cosecant function. In practice, normalized design tables are used to determine the pole and zero locations. Zverev has tabulated design data for elliptic filters of orders two through seven in terms of parameters θ (degrees) and ρ (%).[29] The angle θ equals

$$\theta = \sin^{-1} (1/\Omega_s), \qquad \Omega_s = 1/\sin\theta = \csc\theta \tag{4.8.10}$$

and the reflection coefficient ρ equals

$$\rho = [1 - \exp(-2m_p)]^{1/2} \tag{4.8.11}$$

where m_p (nepers) = M_p (dB)/8.69 = 0.115M_p (dB).

A convenient reference listing relating ρ, m_p, and M_p is given in Table 4.8.1. Several values

Table 4.8.1 Relations between (a) ρ, m_p, and M_p, and (b) θ and Ω_s.[29]

ρ (%)	m_p (Np)	M_p (dB)
1	0.00005	0.00043
2	0.0002	0.0017
3	0.0005	0.004
4	0.0008	0.007
5	0.0013	0.011
8	0.0032	0.028
10	0.005	0.044
15	0.0113	0.098
20	0.0207	0.18
25	0.032	0.28
50	0.14	1.25

θ (degrees)	Ω_s
0	∞
10	5.759
20	2.924
30	2.000
40	1.556
50	1.305
60	1.155
70	1.064
80	1.015
90	1.000

of θ and Ω_s are also listed. As the edge of the stopband Ω_s approaches unity, θ approaches 90°. Zverev's data for the typical industrial requirement of 1.25 dB in-band ripple (about 1 dB) for elliptic filters of orders three, four, and five is listed in Tables 4.8.2 and 4.8.3 for ready reference.

EXAMPLE 4.8.2 Write the transfer function for a fourth-order elliptic low-pass filter having a maximum low-frequency gain of 10, an in-band ripple of 1.25 dB, a corner frequency of 1 KHz, and a stopband rejection of 60 dB. Draw the block diagram for the filter.

Solution The design data for fourth-order filters is listed in Table 4.8.2. Although we are not given θ or Ω_s, the M_s values are already listed in the third column. Thus, no calculation of θ, Ω_s, or M_s is necessary. Using $M_s = 59.87$ dB, the two pole pairs and the one zero pair equal

$$p_1, p_1^* = -0.317 \pm j0.422, \qquad p_2, p_2^* = -0.119 \pm j0.978, \qquad z_1, z_1^* = \pm j2.577 \tag{4.8.12}$$

Thus, the transfer function equals

$$H(s) = \frac{10}{1.15}\,\frac{[\omega_{o1}^2\omega_{o2}^2/\omega_{oz}^2]\,[s_n^2 + 2.577^2]}{[(s_n + 0.317)^2 + 0.422^2]\,[(s_n + 0.119)^2 + 0.978^2]} \tag{4.8.13}$$

where $s_n = s/2\pi(1\text{ KHz})$. Note the normalization constant is selected so that $H(0) = -1.25\text{ dB} = 1/1.15$. The filter can be realized as the cascade of a low-pass and band-stop filter as shown in Fig. 4.8.3. Alternatively, we can interchange the pole parameters between the blocks for a different realization.

EXAMPLE 4.8.3 Determine the poles and zeros of an elliptic filter which has the following specifications: (1) passband ripple ≤ 2 dB, and (2) minimum stopband attenuation of 25 dB for $\omega \geq 1.33$.

Solution Since $n = 3$, we only need to calculate θ and ρ as

$$\theta = \sin^{-1}(1/1.33) = \sin^{-1} 0.75 = 49^\circ, \qquad \rho = [1 - e^{-0.23(2)}]^{1/2} = 0.369^{1/2} \cong 61\% \tag{4.8.14}$$

However, only reflection coefficients of 50% or less are tabulated. Thus, let us use $\rho = 50\%$ so the passband ripple is only 1.25 dB rather than 2 dB. The elliptic filter nomograph shows that we must increase the filter order to $n = 4$ to maintain at least 25 dB stopband rejection. Thus, our requirement becomes $n = 4$, $\rho = 50\%$, and $\theta = 49°$. We see from Table 4.8.2 that the normalized stopband frequency Ω_s

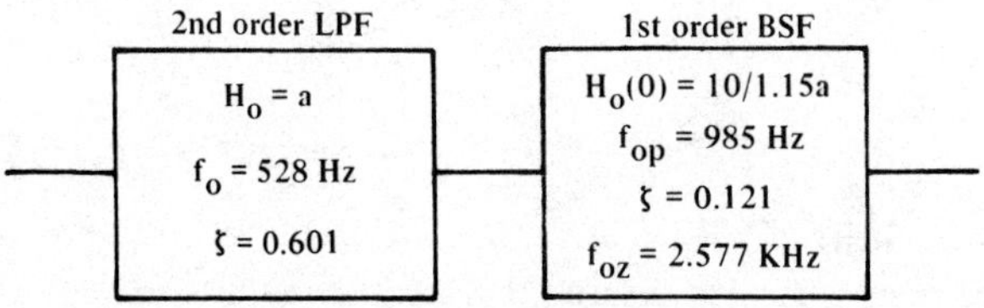

Fig. 4.8.3 Block diagram of fourth-order elliptic filter of Example 4.8.2.

Table 4.8.2 Poles and zeros of elliptic filters of third- and fourth-orders having 1.25 dB in-band ripple. (From A. I. Zverev, "Handbook of Filter Synthesis," Chap. 5, Wiley, NY, 1967. Reprinted by permission of John Wiley & Sons, Inc.)

θ	Ω_s	M_s	α_0	α_1	β_1	β_2
6.	9.5668	78.09	0.45472	0.22557	0.95147	11.0392
7.	8.2055	74.06	0.45526	0.22520	0.95170	9.4661
8.	7.1853	70.57	0.45589	0.22477	0.95197	8.2868
9.	6.3925	67.49	0.45661	0.22428	0.95228	7.3700
10.	5.7588	64.73	0.45741	0.22373	0.95262	6.6370
11.	5.2408	62.23	0.45830	0.22313	0.95299	6.0377
12.	4.8097	59.95	0.45928	0.22246	0.95340	5.5386
13.	4.4454	57.85	0.46035	0.22174	0.95385	5.1166
14.	4.1336	55.90	0.46151	0.22096	0.95433	4.7552
15.	3.8637	54.08	0.46276	0.22012	0.95484	4.4423
16.	3.6280	52.38	0.46411	0.21922	0.95539	4.1688
17.	3.4203	50.78	0.46555	0.21826	0.95597	3.9277
18.	3.2361	49.26	0.46708	0.21724	0.95659	3.7137
19.	3.0716	47.83	0.46871	0.21616	0.95724	3.5224
20.	2.9238	46.47	0.47045	0.21503	0.95791	3.3505
21.	2.7904	45.17	0.47228	0.21383	0.95863	3.1951
22.	2.6695	43.93	0.47422	0.21256	0.95937	3.0541
23.	2.5593	42.74	0.47627	0.21124	0.96014	2.9256
24.	2.4586	41.59	0.47842	0.20986	0.96095	2.8079
25.	2.3662	40.50	0.48069	0.20841	0.96178	2.6999
26.	2.2812	39.44	0.48307	0.20690	0.96264	2.6003
27.	2.2027	38.42	0.48556	0.20533	0.96353	2.5083
28.	2.1301	37.43	0.48818	0.20369	0.96445	2.4231
29.	2.0627	36.48	0.49092	0.20199	0.96539	2.3438
30.	2.0000	35.55	0.49379	0.20023	0.96636	2.2701
31.	1.9416	34.65	0.49678	0.19840	0.96736	2.2012
32.	1.8871	33.78	0.49991	0.19650	0.96838	2.1368
33.	1.8361	32.93	0.50318	0.19454	0.96942	2.0765
34.	1.7883	32.10	0.50660	0.19252	0.97049	2.0199
35.	1.7434	31.30	0.51016	0.19043	0.97158	1.9666
36.	1.7013	30.51	0.51387	0.18827	0.97268	1.9165
37.	1.6616	29.74	0.51774	0.18604	0.97381	1.8692
38.	1.6243	28.99	0.52178	0.18374	0.97495	1.8245
39.	1.5890	28.26	0.52598	0.18138	0.97611	1.7823
40.	1.5557	27.54	0.53036	0.17894	0.97729	1.7423
41.	1.5243	26.83	0.53493	0.17644	0.97848	1.7044
42.	1.4945	26.14	0.53968	0.17387	0.97968	1.6684
43.	1.4663	25.46	0.54464	0.17123	0.98089	1.6343
44.	1.4396	24.79	0.54980	0.16851	0.98211	1.6018
45.	1.4142	24.14	0.55518	0.16573	0.98334	1.5710
46.	1.3902	23.49	0.56078	0.16288	0.98457	1.5415
47.	1.3673	22.86	0.56662	0.15995	0.98581	1.5135
48.	1.3456	22.23	0.57270	0.15695	0.98705	1.4868
49.	1.3250	21.62	0.57904	0.15388	0.98828	1.4613
50.	1.3054	21.01	0.58565	0.15074	0.98951	1.4369
51.	1.2868	20.41	0.59255	0.14753	0.99074	1.4137
52.	1.2690	19.82	0.59974	0.14424	0.99196	1.3914
53.	1.2521	19.24	0.60725	0.14088	0.99317	1.3702
54.	1.2361	18.66	0.61509	0.13745	0.99436	1.3498
55.	1.2208	18.09	0.62327	0.13396	0.99554	1.3303

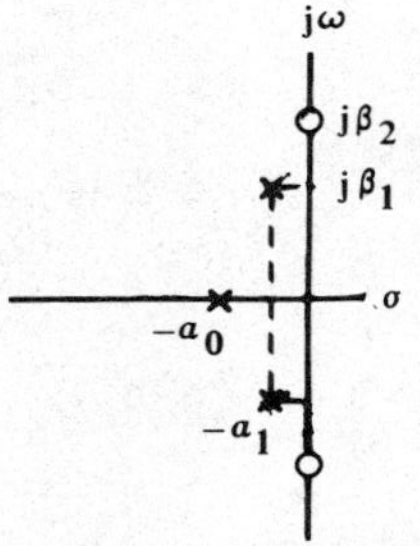

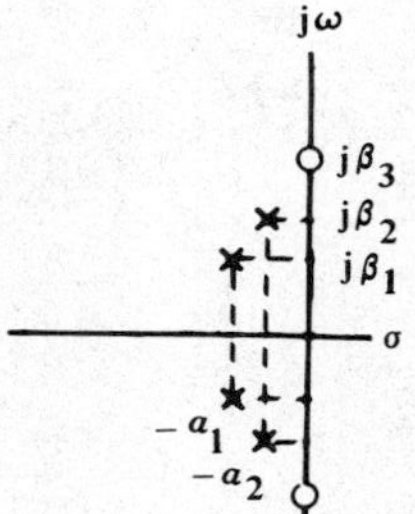

θ	Ω_s	M_s	α_1	α_2	β_1	β_2	β_3
11.	5.2408	91.38	0.3109331	0.1267466	0.4065895	0.9750421	6.215646
12.	4.8097	88.35	0.3111680	0.1264533	0.4071596	0.9751629	5.701423
13.	4.4454	85.55	0.3114238	0.1261341	0.4077808	0.9752944	5.266618
14.	4.1336	82.96	0.3117006	0.1257888	0.4084536	0.9754363	4.894214
15.	3.8637	80.55	0.3119984	0.1254174	0.4091783	0.9755889	4.571732
16.	3.6280	78.30	0.3123173	0.1250196	0.4099554	0.9757521	4.289813
17.	3.4203	76.17	0.3126576	0.1245955	0.4107855	0.9759259	4.041300
18.	3.2361	74.17	0.3130194	0.1241447	0.4116691	0.9761103	3.820626
19.	3.0716	72.27	0.3134027	0.1236672	0.4126068	0.9763054	3.623399
20.	2.9238	70.47	0.3138079	0.1231627	0.4135991	0.9765111	3.446101
21.	2.7904	68.75	0.3142349	0.1226312	0.4146468	0.9767275	3.285888
22.	2.6695	67.11	0.3146842	0.1220724	0.4157505	0.9769546	3.140431
23.	2.5593	65.55	0.3151557	0.1214861	0.4169111	0.9771923	3.007807
24.	2.4586	64.04	0.3156498	0.1208721	0.4181292	0.9774408	2.886413
25.	2.3662	62.60	0.3161667	0.1202301	0.4194058	0.9777000	2.774903
26.	2.2812	61.21	0.3167065	0.1195600	0.4207418	0.9779699	2.672139
27.	2.2027	59.87	0.3172697	0.1188615	0.4221381	0.9782505	2.577149
28.	2.1301	58.58	0.3178563	0.1181344	0.4235956	0.9785419	2.489103
29.	2.0627	57.33	0.3184668	0.1173783	0.4251155	0.9788440	2.407283
30.	2.0000	56.12	0.3191014	0.1165930	0.4266988	0.9791568	2.331070
31.	1.9416	54.94	0.3197604	0.1157782	0.4283468	0.9794804	2.259921
32.	1.8871	53.81	0.3204441	0.1149335	0.4300607	0.9798146	2.193363
33.	1.8361	52.70	0.3211529	0.1140587	0.4318418	0.9801596	2.130982
34.	1.7883	51.63	0.3218872	0.1131535	0.4336914	0.9805153	2.072410
35.	1.7434	50.58	0.3226474	0.1122174	0.4356110	0.9808816	2.017322
36.	1.7013	49.56	0.3234339	0.1112501	0.4376021	0.9812585	1.965429
37.	1.6616	48.57	0.3242470	0.1102513	0.4396664	0.9816461	1.916475
38.	1.6243	47.60	0.3250874	0.1092205	0.4418056	0.9820441	1.870229
39.	1.5890	46.65	0.3259554	0.1081573	0.4440213	0.9824527	1.826485
40.	1.5557	45.72	0.3268517	0.1070613	0.4463156	0.9828717	1.785057
41.	1.5243	44.82	0.3277767	0.1059321	0.4486904	0.9833010	1.745777
42.	1.4945	43.93	0.3287310	0.1047691	0.4511479	0.9837406	1.708493
43.	1.4663	43.06	0.3297153	0.1035720	0.4536901	0.9841904	1.673069
44.	1.4396	42.21	0.3307302	0.1023401	0.4563195	0.9846502	1.639380
45.	1.4142	41.37	0.3317765	0.1010731	0.4590386	0.9851199	1.607311
46.	1.3902	40.55	0.3328548	0.0997703	0.4618500	0.9855993	1.576760
47.	1.3673	39.74	0.3339660	0.0984313	0.4647564	0.9860884	1.547632
48.	1.3456	38.95	0.3351109	0.0970553	0.4677608	0.9865868	1.519839
49.	1.3250	38.17	0.3362905	0.0956419	0.4708662	0.9870944	1.493303
50.	1.3054	37.40	0.3375056	0.0941904	0.4740761	0.9876110	1.467949
51.	1.2868	36.65	0.3387575	0.0927002	0.4773939	0.9881361	1.443712
52.	1.2690	35.90	0.3400471	0.0911706	0.4808232	0.9886696	1.420528
53.	1.2521	35.17	0.3413756	0.0896009	0.4843682	0.9892111	1.398341
54.	1.2361	34.44	0.3427445	0.0879905	0.4880330	0.9897601	1.377098
55.	1.2208	33.73	0.3441551	0.0863385	0.4918221	0.9903164	1.356750

Table 4.8.3 Poles and zeros of elliptic filters of fifth-order having 1.25 dB in-band ripple. (From A. I. Zverev, "Handbook of filter synthesis," Chap. 5, Wiley, NY, 1967. Reprinted by permission of John Wiley & Sons, Inc.)

θ	Ω_S	M_S	α_0	α_1	α_2	β_1	β_2	β_3	β_4
11.0	5.2408	114.93	0.26910	0.21542	0.08089	0.61262	0.9847	5.5057	8.8625
12.0	4.8097	111.13	0.26961	0.21539	0.08062	0.61345	0.9847	5.0520	8.1241
13.0	4.4454	107.62	0.27016	0.21536	0.08032	0.61436	0.9848	4.6684	7.4993
14.0	4.1336	104.37	0.27077	0.21532	0.08000	0.61533	0.9849	4.3401	6.9638
15.0	3.8637	101.35	0.27142	0.21528	0.07965	0.61639	0.9851	4.0559	6.4997
16.0	3.6280	98.51	0.27212	0.21524	0.07928	0.61752	0.9852	3.8076	6.0936
17.0	3.4203	95.84	0.27286	0.21519	0.07889	0.61872	0.9853	3.5888	5.7353
18.0	3.2361	93.32	0.27366	0.21514	0.07847	0.62000	0.9854	3.3946	5.4168
19.0	3.0716	90.93	0.27451	0.21508	0.07803	0.62136	0.9856	3.2212	5.1318
20.0	2.9238	88.65	0.27541	0.21501	0.07757	0.62280	0.9857	3.0654	4.8753
21.0	2.7904	86.49	0.27636	0.21494	0.07708	0.62432	0.9859	2.9246	4.6433
22.0	2.6695	84.42	0.27736	0.21486	0.07657	0.62592	0.9860	2.7970	4.4323
23.0	2.5593	82.44	0.27842	0.21478	0.07603	0.62760	0.9862	2.6807	4.2397
24.0	2.4586	80.53	0.27953	0.21469	0.07547	0.62936	0.9864	2.5743	4.0631
25.0	2.3662	78.70	0.28070	0.21459	0.07489	0.63120	0.9865	2.4767	3.9007
26.0	2.2812	76.94	0.28193	0.21448	0.07428	0.63313	0.9867	2.3868	3.7507
27.0	2.2027	75.24	0.28321	0.21436	0.07365	0.63514	0.9869	2.3038	3.6119
28.0	2.1301	73.59	0.28456	0.21423	0.07300	0.63724	0.9871	2.2270	3.4829
29.0	2.0627	72.00	0.28597	0.21409	0.07232	0.63942	0.9873	2.1556	3.3629
30.0	2.0000	70.46	0.28744	0.21394	0.07162	0.64170	0.9875	2.0892	3.2508
31.0	1.9416	68.96	0.28897	0.21377	0.07089	0.64407	0.9878	2.0274	3.1460
32.0	1.8871	67.50	0.29058	0.21360	0.07014	0.64652	0.9880	1.9695	3.0476
33.0	1.8361	66.09	0.29225	0.21341	0.06937	0.64907	0.9882	1.9154	2.9553
34.0	1.7883	64.71	0.29399	0.21320	0.06857	0.65172	0.9884	1.8646	2.8683
35.0	1.7434	63.36	0.29581	0.21297	0.06775	0.65446	0.9887	1.8170	2.7864
36.0	1.7013	62.05	0.29770	0.21273	0.06691	0.65729	0.9889	1.7722	2.7089
37.0	1.6616	60.77	0.29967	0.21247	0.06604	0.66023	0.9892	1.7299	2.6356
38.0	1.6243	59.52	0.30172	0.21219	0.06515	0.66327	0.9894	1.6901	2.5662
39.0	1.5890	58.29	0.30386	0.21189	0.06424	0.66641	0.9897	1.6525	2.5003
40.0	1.5557	57.09	0.30608	0.21156	0.06330	0.66966	0.9899	1.6170	2.4377
41.0	1.5243	55.91	0.30839	0.21121	0.06234	0.67301	0.9902	1.5833	2.3781
42.0	1.4945	54.75	0.31079	0.21084	0.06136	0.67648	0.9905	1.5515	2.3213
43.0	1.4663	53.62	0.31330	0.21043	0.06036	0.68005	0.9908	1.5213	2.2672
44.0	1.4396	52.50	0.31590	0.21000	0.05933	0.68374	0.9910	1.4926	2.2154
45.0	1.4142	51.41	0.31860	0.20953	0.05828	0.68755	0.9913	1.4654	2.1660
46.0	1.3902	50.33	0.32142	0.20902	0.05721	0.69147	0.9916	1.4396	2.1187
47.0	1.3673	49.26	0.32435	0.20848	0.05611	0.69552	0.9919	1.4150	2.0733
48.0	1.3456	48.22	0.32740	0.20790	0.05499	0.69969	0.9922	1.3916	2.0299
49.0	1.3250	47.18	0.33058	0.20728	0.05386	0.70399	0.9925	1.3693	1.9881
50.0	1.3054	46.16	0.33389	0.20661	0.05270	0.70841	0.9928	1.3481	1.9480
51.0	1.2868	45.13	0.33734	0.20590	0.05151	0.71297	0.9931	1.3279	1.9095
52.0	1.2690	44.16	0.34093	0.20513	0.05031	0.71767	0.9934	1.3087	1.8724
53.0	1.2521	43.17	0.34468	0.20430	0.04809	0.72250	0.9937	1.2903	1.8366
54.0	1.2361	42.20	0.34859	0.20342	0.04784	0.72748	0.9940	1.2728	1.8021
55.0	1.2208	41.23	0.35267	0.20247	0.04658	0.73260	0.9943	1.2561	1.7689
56.0	1.2062	40.27	0.35693	0.20145	0.04529	0.73787	0.9946	1.2402	1.7368
57.0	1.1924	39.33	0.36138	0.20036	0.04399	0.74330	0.9949	1.2250	1.7057
58.0	1.1792	38.38	0.36604	0.19918	0.04267	0.74888	0.9952	1.2104	1.6757
59.0	1.1666	37.45	0.37091	0.19792	0.04133	0.75463	0.9955	1.1966	1.6467
60.0	1.1547	36.52	0.37602	0.19657	0.03997	0.76054	0.9957	1.1834	1.6185

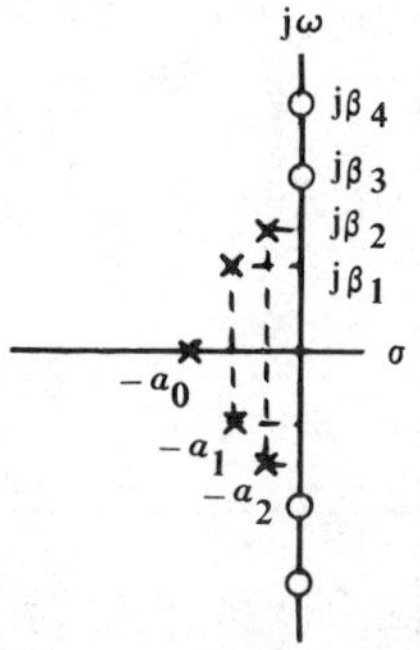

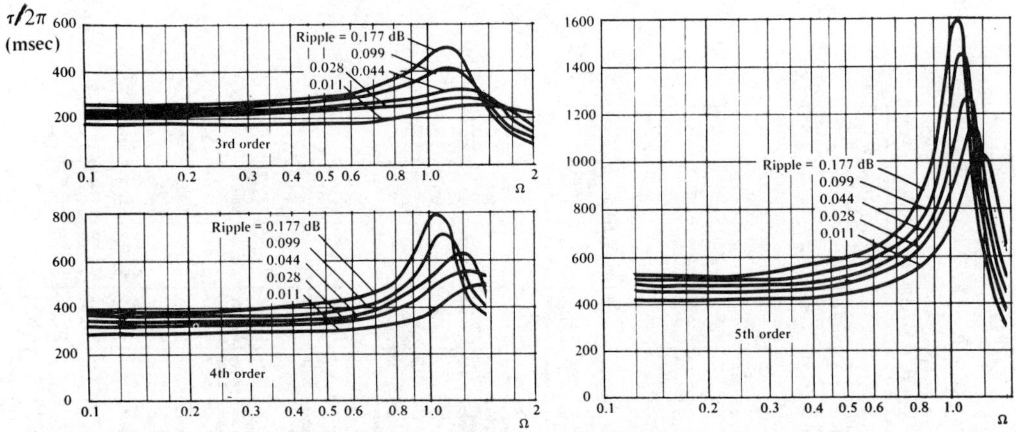

Fig. 4.8.4 Delay characteristics of third-, fourth-, and fifth-order elliptic filters having 60 dB stopband rejection.

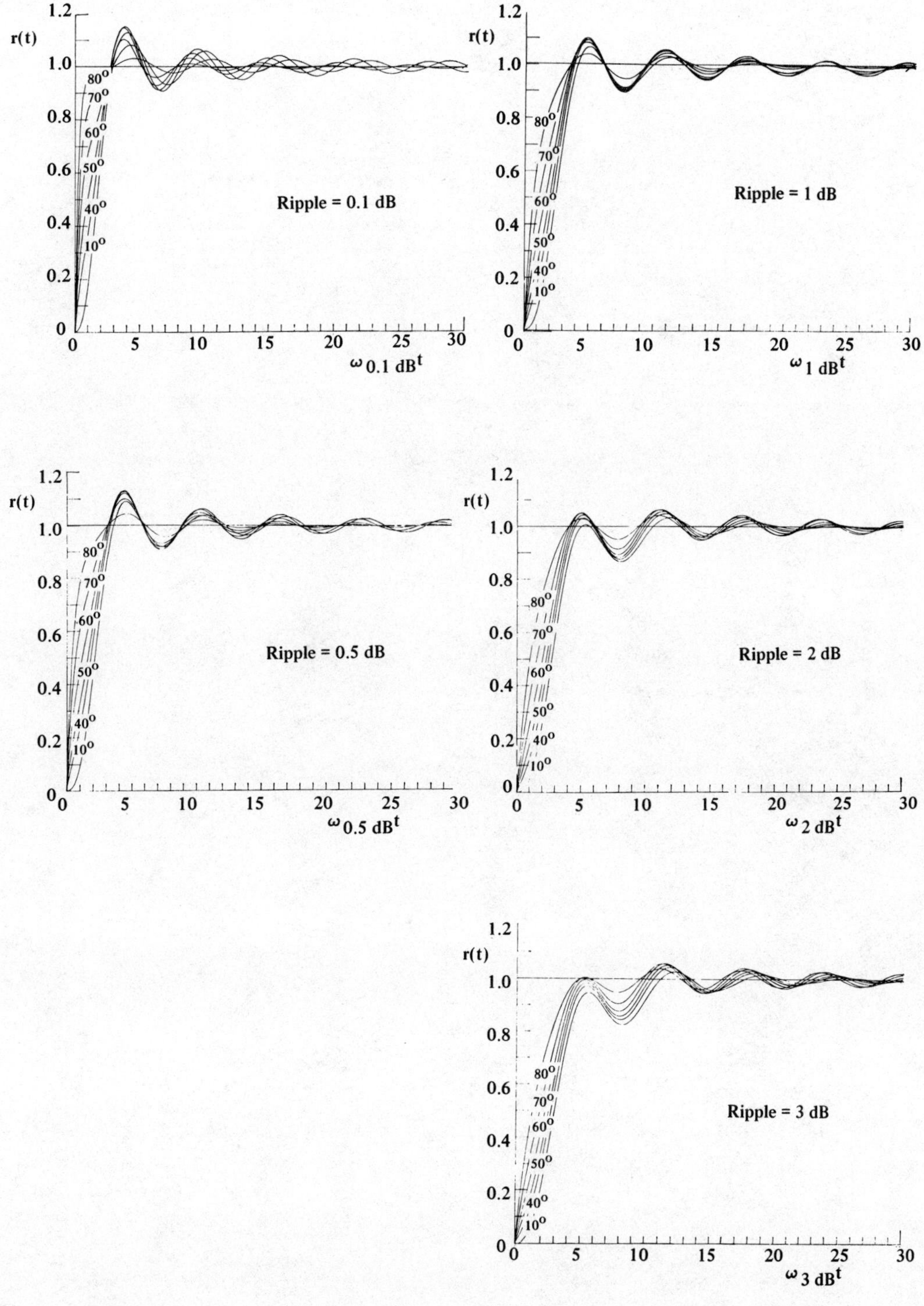

Fig. 4.8.5 Step responses of third-order elliptic filters. (From A. G. J. Holt, J. P. Gray, and J. K. Fidler, "Transient response of elliptic function filters," IEEE Trans. Circuit Theory, vol. CT-15, pp. 71–73, March, 1968.)

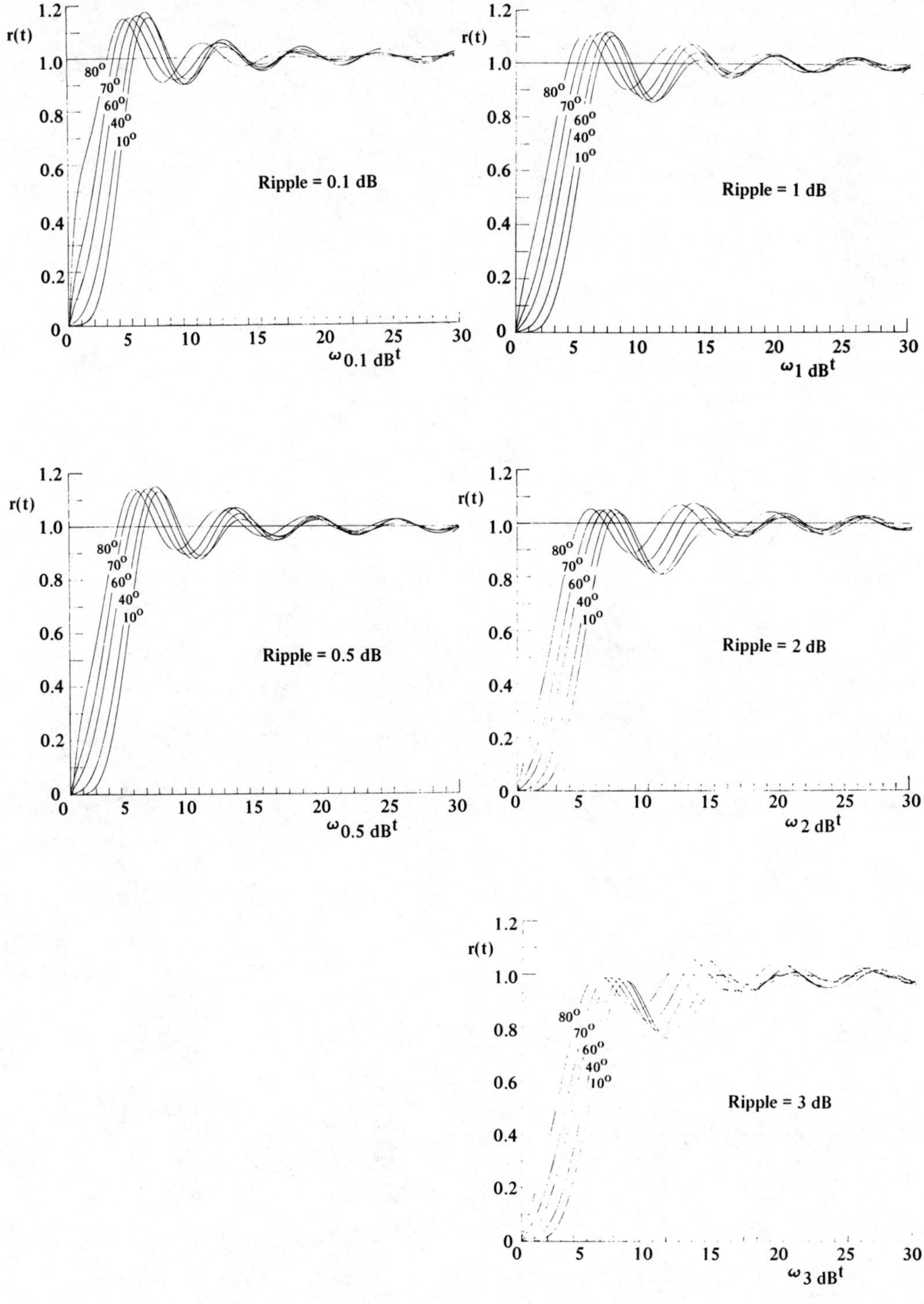

Fig. 4.8.6 Step responses of fifth-order elliptic filters. (From A. G. J. Holt, J. P. Gray, and J. K. Fidler, "Transient response of elliptic function filters," IEEE Trans. Circuit Theory, vol. CT-15, pp. 71–73, March, 1968.)

= 1.3965 and that the minimum stopband attenuation M_s = 38.17 dB. The poles and zeros equal

$$p_1, p_1^* = -0.0956 \pm j0.987, \quad p_2, p_2^* = -0.336 \pm j0.471, \quad z_1, z_1^* = \pm j1.493 \tag{4.8.15}$$

Thus, we exceed our minimum stopband attenuation by about 13 dB. Since we used the required θ = 49°, our 25 dB stopband frequency still equals 1.33. This is an important detail to remember. Note that the high-frequency asymptotic rolloff is –40 dB/dec. This example illustrates how design tradeoffs are sometimes required to use the tabulated data.

The delay characteristics of third-, fourth-, and fifth-order elliptic filters having 60 dB stopband rejection are shown in Fig. 4.8.4 (for others, see Ref. 13). Since the poles of elliptic filters almost fall on an ellipse, they are somewhat similar in form to Chebyshev delay curves. However, they exhibit less delay variation but more delay peaking. Delay increases with in-band ripple and filter order. Negative delay impulses of area $-\pi$ appear at the zero frequencies. Note if the zeros were not purely imaginary but lay off the $j\omega$-axis, this would produce negative delay peaking of non-zero bandwidth which would significantly change the delay curves near the band-edge.

The unit step responses for third- and fifth-order elliptic filters having various in-band ripples (0.1 – 3.0 dB) and angles (10° – 80°) are shown in Figs. 4.8.5 and 4.8.6. Note that for a constant in-band ripple, the step response depends on angle θ or, equivalently, the stopband frequency Ω_s. Increasing θ corresponds to decreasing Ω_s and to narrowing the transition band. The low-frequency delay and thus the delay time decreases as Ω_s decreases. The rise time remains relatively constant as long as the 3 dB bandwidth is about constant. The overshoot decreases as Ω_s decreases. The overshoot is determined primarily by the highest-Q complex pole pair of radius ω_n in H(s). As Ω_s decreases, these poles move closer to the imaginary zeros; this reduces the residue value for that pole and, therefore, the overshoot. For fixed θ or Ω_s, the overshoot increases with filter order. Also note that reducing θ is equivalent to increasing Ω_s, and the elliptic filter step response approaches that of the corresponding Chebyshev filter.

4.9 LINEAR PHASE (MAXIMALLY FLAT DELAY) FILTERS

So far in this chapter, we have considered a variety of filters. We began with Butterworth filters and found they had fairly good magnitude and delay characteristics. As we progressed into filters having more and more magnitude selectivity, we found that their delay characteristics exhibited increasing delay ripple and delay peaking. Ideally, their passband delay should be constant as we found in Eq. 4.1.1. Equivalently stated, the passband phase should be linear with a value of zero (i.e., zero intercept) at dc (ω = 0). Any deviation from constant delay is called *delay distortion*, and any deviation from linear phase (but not necessarily zero intercept) is called *phase distortion*. Thus, Butterworth filters have moderate delay and phase distortion; Chebyshev and elliptic filters have large delay and phase distortion.

Now we want to consider filters that have small delay and phase distortion. In general, such filters are called *linear phase*, or alternatively, *maximally flat delay* or *constant delay* filters. We will see they have fairly constant passband delay. Their step responses will exhibit less overshoot and ringing. However, their magnitude responses will be much less selective than the filters previously discussed. It is possible to reduce the passband delay variation and thereby equalize delay of a filter by use of a delay equalizer as discussed in Sec. 2.10. However, use of delay equalizers introduces more complexity and increases the size of a filter; thus, making specification compromises when possible is desirable. We began this chapter by considering maximally flat magnitude responses. Let us now apply this same approach to produce maximally flat delay response.

The general transfer function in ac steady-state of any filter can be expressed as

$$H(j\omega) = \frac{a(\omega^2) + j\omega b(\omega^2)}{c(\omega^2) + j\omega d(\omega^2)} \tag{4.9.1}$$

where a, b, c, and d are rational polynomials of ω^2. The phase of the filter function H equals

$$\theta(j\omega) = \arg H(j\omega) = \tan^{-1}[\omega b(\omega^2)/a(\omega^2)] - \tan^{-1}[\omega d(\omega^2)/c(\omega^2)] \tag{4.9.2}$$

Expanding $\tan^{-1}x$ in a Maclaurin series as

$$\tan^{-1}x = x - x^3/3 + x^5/5 - \ldots, \qquad |x| < 1 \tag{4.9.3}$$

gives

$$\theta(j\omega) = [(\omega b/a) - (\omega b/a)^3/3 + (\omega b/a)^5/5 - \ldots] - [(\omega d/c) - (\omega d/c)^3/3 + (\omega d/c)^5/5 - \ldots] \tag{4.9.4}$$

Combining coefficients of like powers of ω gives

$$\theta(j\omega) = \omega[(b/a) - (d/c)] - (\omega^3/3)[(b/a)^3 - (d/c)^3] + (\omega^5/5)[(b/a)^5 - (d/c)^5] - \ldots = -a_1\omega - a_3\omega^3 - a_5\omega^5 - \ldots \tag{4.9.5}$$

Since the delay equals

$$\tau(j\omega) = -d\theta(j\omega)/d\omega = a_1 + 3a_3\omega^2 + 5a_5\omega^4 + \ldots \tag{4.9.6}$$

linear phase or maximally flat delay (MFD) is obtained by setting as many consecutive derivatives of delay equal to zero as possible excluding the first derivative. Thus,

$$a_1 \neq 0, \qquad a_3 = a_5 = \ldots = 0 \tag{4.9.7}$$

for a MFD response. As many derivatives may be set to zero as there are degrees of freedom in τ. If we consider delay directly, the delay may be expressed as

$$\tau(\omega^2) = \tau(0)\frac{1 + k_2\omega^2 + k_4\omega^4 + \ldots}{1 + l_2\omega^2 + l_4\omega^4 + \ldots} \tag{4.9.8}$$

MFD response is obtained by setting as many coefficients equal as possible where

$$k_{2i} = l_{2i}, \qquad i = 1, 2, 3, \ldots \tag{4.9.9}$$

This is the same coefficient condition as that for the MFM filter discussed in Sec. 4.2.

EXAMPLE 4.9.1 For a second-order low-pass filter having a gain given by Eq. 4.2.6, determine the coefficient conditions for H(s) to be a maximally flat delay (MFD) filter.

Solution We first express the filter phase as

$$\theta(j\omega) = \arg H(j\omega) = -\tan^{-1}\frac{b_1\omega}{1 - b_2\omega^2} = -\left[\frac{b_1\omega}{1 - b_2\omega^2} - \frac{1}{3}\left(\frac{b_1\omega}{1 - b_2\omega^2}\right)^3 + \ldots\right] \tag{4.9.10}$$

Using the binomial expansion

$$(1 + x)^n = 1 + nx + n(n-1)x^2/2! + \ldots, \qquad |x| < 1 \tag{4.9.11}$$

then the first two phase terms in Eq. 4.9.10 equal

$$\begin{aligned} b_1\omega[1 - b_2\omega^2]^{-1} &= b_1\omega[1 + b_2\omega^2 + (b_2\omega^2)^2 + \ldots] \\ -(b_1^3\omega^3/3)[1 - b_2\omega^2]^{-3} &= -(b_1^3\omega^3/3)[1 + 3b_2\omega^2 + 6(b_2\omega^2)^2 + \ldots] \end{aligned} \tag{4.9.12}$$

Combining like powers of ω gives

$$-\theta(j\omega) = b_1\omega + b_1\omega^3[b_2 - b_1^2/3] + b_1b_2\omega^5[b_2 - b_1^2] + \ldots \tag{4.9.13}$$

Thus, to obtain MFD or linear phase, we set as many coefficients of ascending powers of ω equal to zero as possible where $b_1 \neq 0$. Since two degrees of freedom are available (i.e., b_1 and b_2), we may set two coefficients equal to zero as

$$b_2 - b_1^2/3 = 0, \qquad b_2 - b_1^2 = 0 \tag{4.9.14}$$

These last two equations require the trivial solution that $b_1 = b_2 = 0$ which contradicts $b_1 \neq 0$. Thus, we omit Eq. 4.9.15b and rewrite Eq. 4.9.15a as

$$b_1 = \sqrt{3b_2}, \qquad b_1 \neq 0 \tag{4.9.15}$$

This is in contrast to the MFM condition of Eq. 4.2.8. Choosing $b_1 = 1$, the second-order MFD gain function has $\omega_n = \sqrt{3}$ and $\zeta = \sqrt{3}/2 = 0.866$. This agrees with the result we obtained in Chap. 2 in Eq. 2.10.12. Recall that the second-order low-pass filter had no delay peaking for $\zeta \geqslant 0.866$. Note that had we determined the delay function as

$$\tau(\omega^2) = b_1 \frac{1 + b_2\omega^2}{1 + (b_1^2 - 2b_2)\omega^2 + b_2^2\omega^4} \tag{4.9.16}$$

from Eq. 2.5.5, then an MFD response is obtained by setting the polynomial coefficients of the numerator and denominator equal as

$$b_1^2 = 3b_2, \qquad b_2^2 = 0 \tag{4.9.17}$$

which is equivalent to Eq. 4.9.15 so the results agree.

EXAMPLE 4.9.2 Determine the coefficient conditions to force H(s) of Example 4.2.2 to have maximally flat delay (MFD) and a 3 dB bandwidth of 1 rad/sec. Is the solution unique (i.e., only a single a_1 value unlike Example 4.2.2)? Determine the coefficients if possible.

Solution Requiring $\omega_{3dB} = 1$ rad/sec in Eq. 4.2.9 constrains the gain as $|H(j1)|^2 = ½$. This requires

$$2a_1^2 = b_1^2 - 2b_2 + b_2^2 - 1 = (b_1 - b_2)^2 - 1 \tag{4.9.18}$$

Expressing the phase of H as

$$\theta(j\omega) = \arg H(j\omega) = \tan^{-1} a_1\omega - \tan^{-1} \frac{b_1\omega}{1 - b_2\omega^2} \tag{4.9.19}$$

we may expand $\tan^{-1}x$ in a Maclaurin series as before as

$$\theta(j\omega) = [a_1\omega - \frac{1}{3}(a_1\omega)^3 + \frac{1}{5}(a_1\omega)^5 - \ldots] - [\frac{b_1\omega}{1 - b_2\omega^2} - \frac{1}{3}\left(\frac{b_1\omega}{1 - b_2\omega^2}\right)^3 + \ldots]$$

$$= \omega[a_1 - b_1] + \omega^3[b_1^3/3 - b_1b_2 - a_1^3/3] + \omega^5[b_1^3b_2 - b_1b_2^2 + a_1^5/5] + \ldots \tag{4.9.20}$$

Since we have three degrees of freedom (i.e., a_1, b_1, and b_2) and have used one degree of freedom to obtain unity bandwidth, we may set two coefficients of ω^n to zero as

$$b_1^3/3 - b_1b_2 - a_1^3/3 = 0, \qquad b_1^3b_2 - b_1b_2^2 + a_1^5/5 = 0 \tag{4.9.21}$$

These three nonlinear equations in Eqs. 4.9.18 and 4.9.21 must be solved simultaneously for a_1, b_1, and b_2. A unique set of parameters will be obtained.

4.10 BESSEL (THOMSON) FILTERS

The Bessel or Thomson filter[30] is the class of linear phase (or MFD) filter having all of its zeros of transmission at infinity. It is analogous to the Butterworth MFM filter. Its transfer function equals

$$H(s) = \frac{a_0}{a_0 + a_1s + \ldots + a_ns^n} = \frac{P_n(0)}{P_n(s)} \tag{4.10.1}$$

Table 4.10.1 Bessel filter poles.

n	Poles		n	Poles	
	ω_n	ζ		ω_n	ζ
2	1.2723	0.8660	8	2.1914	0.4079
				1.9556	0.7034
3	1.4494	0.7235		1.8343	0.8935
	1.3243	real		1.7806	0.9882
4	1.6043	0.6207	9	2.3228	0.3782
	1.4310	0.9580		2.0808	0.6574
				1.9483	0.8483
5	1.7573	0.5456		1.8788	0.9621
	1.5581	0.8873		1.8570	real
	1.5040	real			
			10	2.4539	0.3533
6	1.9070	0.4886		2.2067	0.6174
	1.6911	0.8181		2.0650	0.8058
	1.6058	0.9798		1.9832	0.9301
				1.9453	0.9922
7	2.0529	0.4439			
	1.8254	0.7566			
	1.7192	0.9392			
	1.6871	real			

$P_n(s)$ are polynomials which are obtained from Bessel polynomials as

$$P_n(s) = s^n B_n(1/s) = \sum_{i=0}^{n} \frac{(2n-i)!}{2^{n-i}(n-i)!\,i!}\, s^i \tag{4.10.2}$$

where $B_n(s)$ is the *n*th-order Bessel polynomial of the first kind. Unfortunately, the $P_n(s)$ polynomials are often mistakenly called Bessel polynomials which leads to confusion. The poles of the Bessel filter are listed in Table 4.10.1 (for orders through 31, see Ref. 31). These poles have been frequency normalized to produce a 3 dB bandwidth of unity.

The Bessel filter transfer function is derived in the following manner. The transfer function of an ideal constant delay (or linear phase) filter equals

$$H(s) = \exp(-s\tau_0)\Big|_{\tau_0=1} = \frac{1}{e^s} = \frac{1}{\sinh s + \cosh s} \tag{4.10.3}$$

for one second delay. Storch suggested a procedure for obtaining the *n*th-order approximation of Eq. 4.10.3.[32] Utilizing the Maclaurin series expansion for sinh s and cosh s where

$$\sinh s = s + s^3/3! + s^5/5! + \dots, \qquad \cosh s = 1 + s^2/2! + s^4/4! + \dots \tag{4.10.4}$$

the continued fraction expansion of cosh s is determined as

$$\coth s = \frac{\cosh s}{\sinh s} = \frac{1}{s} + \cfrac{1}{\cfrac{3}{s} + \cfrac{1}{\cfrac{5}{s} + \cfrac{1}{\dots}}} = \frac{1}{s} + \frac{1|}{|3/s} + \frac{1|}{|5/s} + \dots \tag{4.10.5}$$

The *n*th-order approximation of e^s is obtained by truncating the continued fraction expansion at the $(2n-1)/s$ term as

$$\coth s = \frac{\cosh s}{\sinh s} \cong \frac{1}{s} + \frac{1|}{|3/s} + \dots + \frac{1|}{|(2n-1)/s} = \frac{L_n(1/s)}{M_n(1/s)} \tag{4.10.6}$$

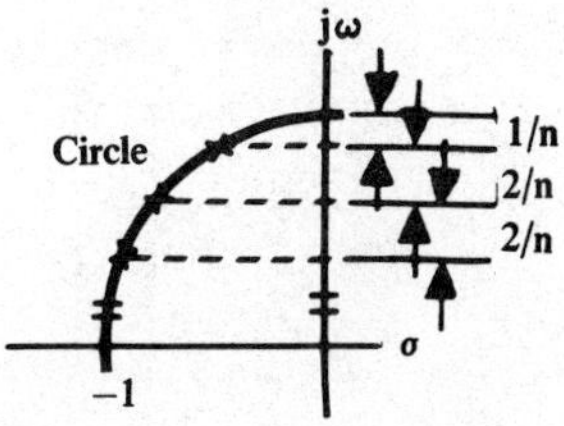

Fig. 4.10.1 Approximate pole locations for Bessel filters. (The conjugate poles are not shown.)

and summing numerator and denominator polynomials. For example, the third-order polynomial approximation is found from

$$\coth s = \frac{\cosh s}{\sinh s} = \frac{1}{s} + \frac{1|}{|3/s} + \frac{1|}{|5/s} = \frac{6s^2 + 15}{s^3 + 15s} = \frac{s^3}{s^3}\,\frac{6/s + 15/s^3}{1 + 15/s^2} \tag{4.10.7}$$

Therefore, from Eq. 4.10.7, the third-order Bessel filter has a transfer function

$$H(s) = \frac{15}{15 + 15s + 6s^2 + s^3} = \frac{P_3(0)}{P_3(s)} = \frac{s^3 B_3(\infty)}{s^3 B_3(1/s)} \tag{4.10.8}$$

which has an ideal delay of one second and a dc gain of unity.

Scanlan found a simple method for determining the approximate poles of a Bessel filter.[33] The approximate Bessel filter poles are located on the Butterworth unit circle. Their imaginary parts are separated by 2/n of the diameter beginning and ending with half this value as shown in Fig. 4.10.1. The magnitude and delay characteristics are shown in Fig. 4.10.2. The delay characteristics are maximally flat. The transfer function given by Eq. 4.10.1 can be expressed in a Maclaurin series as

$$H(s) = e^{-s}e^{\Gamma(s)} \tag{4.10.9}$$

where

$$\Gamma(s) = \gamma_2 s^2 + \gamma_4 s^4 + \ldots \tag{4.10.10}$$

The γ_n coefficients are given by

$$\gamma_n = \frac{1}{n}\sum_{k=1}^{n} p_k^{-n} \tag{4.10.11}$$

where the p_k are the poles of the Bessel filter.[32] Of special importance is γ_2 where $\gamma_2 = 1/2(2n - 1)$. Thus, truncating Γ at the s^2 term for small ω, then Eq. 4.10.9 becomes

$$H(j\omega) = \exp\left[-\omega^2/2(2n-1)\right] \exp\left[-j\omega\right] \tag{4.10.12}$$

It has a Gaussian magnitude as we will discuss later and a delay of one second. Thus, the magnitude for small ω equals

$$|H(j\omega)| \cong \exp\left[-\omega^2/2(2n-1)\right] = -10\omega^2/(2n-1)\ln 10 \quad \text{(dB)} \tag{4.10.13}$$

which improves with increasing n. Setting $|H|^2 = ½$, the approximate 3 dB bandwidth of the Bessel filter equals[30]

$$\omega_{3\text{ dB}} = \sqrt{(2n-1)\ln 2} \tag{4.10.14}$$

The approximation is accurate to within 6% for $n \geqslant 3$ and improves for increasing n. The exact bandwidths were used to frequency normalize the $P_n(s)$ polynomials of Eq. 4.10.1 to produce the poles listed in Table 4.10.1.

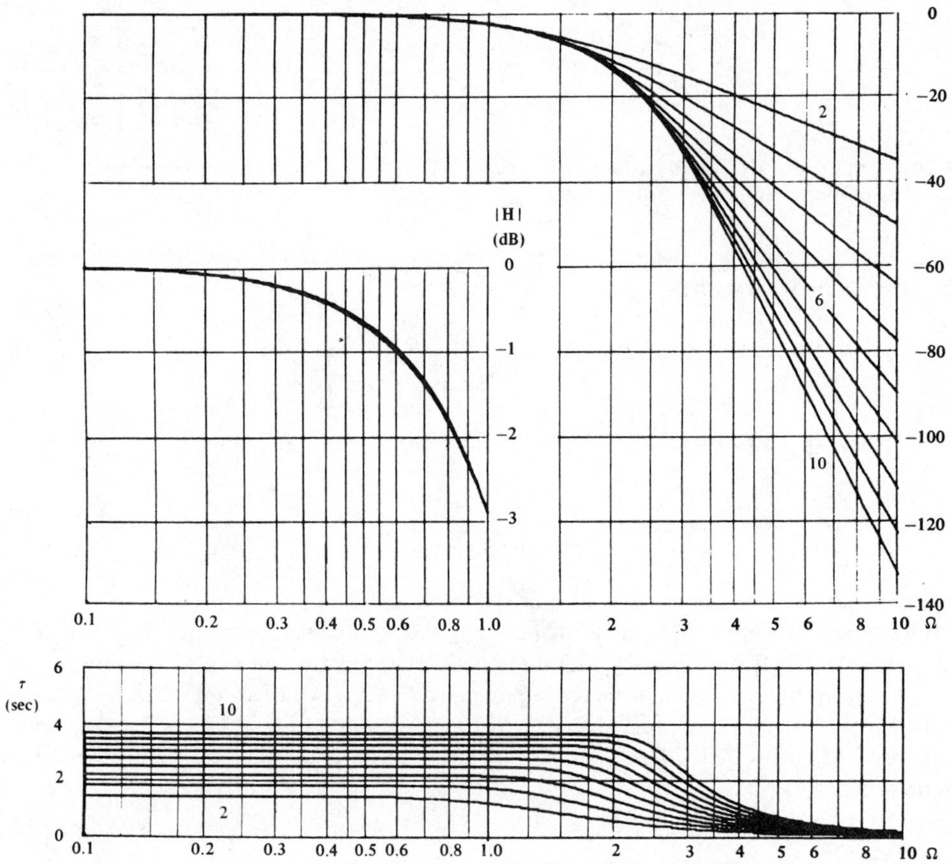

Fig. 4.10.2 Magnitude and delay characteristics of Bessel filters. (From A. D. Taylor, loc. cit.)

The filter selectivity at the band-edge equals

$$-d|H|/d\omega\,\Big|_{\omega=\omega_{3\,dB}} = P_n(0)P_n'/2P_n^{3/2}\,\Big|_{\omega=\omega_{3\,dB}} \to 0.491 \tag{4.10.15}$$

which is virtually independent of n for large n using Eqs. 4.10.13 and 4.10.14. The selectivity of the Bessel filter is less than that of a second-order Butterworth filter. Thus, Bessel filters have very poor selectivity compared with Chebyshev, Papoulis, elliptic, and other narrow transition band filters.

The order of a Bessel filter can be easily determined from the nomograph of Fig. 4.10.3. The very poor selectivity of the Bessel filter is obvious from the nomograph when it is compared with the earlier nomographs. In the stopband, the Bessel filter provides about $(0.4n)^{0.5n}$ less rejection than a Butterworth filter. As we will see later from the peculiar cross-over for n = 10 and 15, the nomograph confirms that the Bessel filter becomes Gaussian at small ω and large n.

EXAMPLE 4.10.1 Determine the order of a Bessel filter to meet the specification of Example 4.3.1 where $M_p = 1.25$ dB, $M_{s1} = 40$ dB at $\Omega_{s1} = 2$, and $M_{s2} = 60$ dB at $\Omega_{s2} = 3$.

Solution Entering the data on the Bessel filter nomograph, we see that it is impossible to meet this specification.

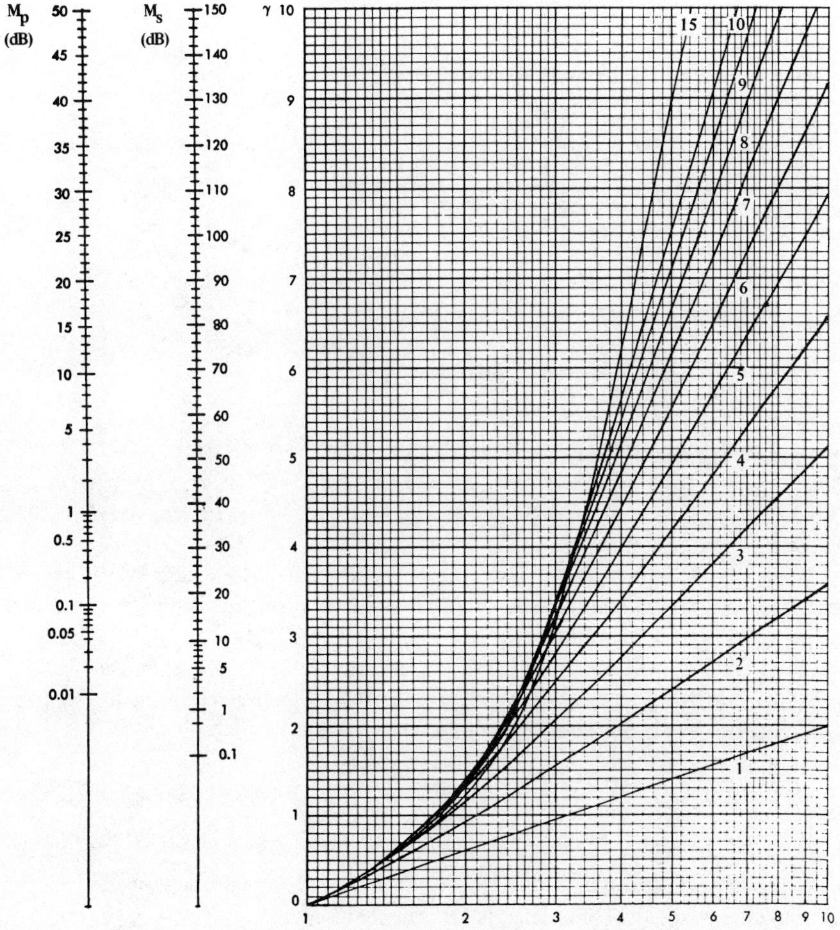

Fig. 4.10.3 Nomograph for Bessel filters. (From J. N. Hallberg, loc. cit.)

EXAMPLE 4.10.2 A low-pass Bessel filter must be designed to meet the following specifications: (1) low-frequency gain = 20 dB, (2) 3 dB frequency = 1000 Hz, (3) 20 dB frequency = 2700 Hz, (4) 60 dB frequency = 10 KHz, and (5) minimum high-frequency rolloff = –60 dB/dec. Determine the required order of the filter. Write its transfer function. Draw a cascaded block diagram showing the required design parameters for each stage.

Solution From the rolloff requirement, the order must be at least equal to $n \geqslant -60/-20 = 3$. From the nomograph, we find $n_1 \geqslant 4$ and $n_2 \geqslant 4$. The transfer function of the filter must, therefore, equal

$$H(s) = \frac{10[1.431^2]\,[1.604^2]}{[s_n{}^2 + 2(0.958)(1.431)s_n + 1.431^2]\,[s_n{}^2 + 2(0.621)(1.604)s_n + 1.604^2]} \tag{4.10.16}$$

where $s_n = s/2\pi(1\text{ KHz})$ from Table 4.10.1. The block diagram of the filter is easily drawn in Fig. 4.10.4.

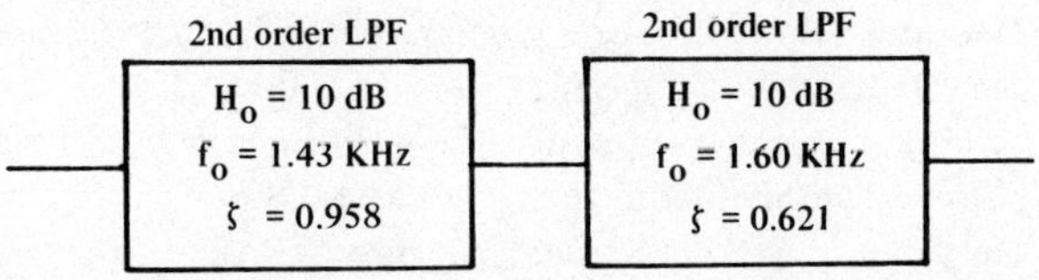

Fig. 4.10.4 Block diagram of Bessel filter of Example 4.10.2.

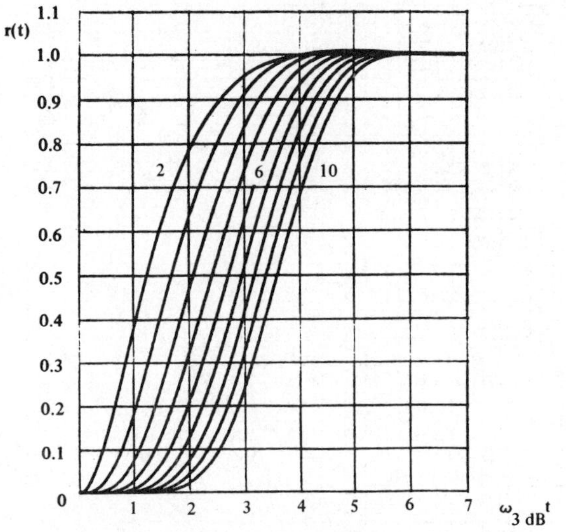

Fig. 4.10.5 Step response of Bessel filters. (From A. D. Taylor, loc. cit.)

Although the Bessel filter has poor selectivity, it has excellent delay characteristics (MFD) as seen in Fig. 4.10.2. The Bessel filter having the transfer function given by Eq. 4.10.1 has a one second dc delay (and a 3 dB bandwidth given by Eq. 4.10.14). When we normalize the 3 dB bandwidth to unity as was done for the poles listed in Table 4.10.1, then the dc delay is increased by ω_{3dB} so $\tau(0)$ has the value given by Eq. 4.10.14 which agrees with the figure. Storch showed that delay can be expressed as[32]

$$\tau(j\omega) = 1 - \frac{(2n)!}{2^n n!}\,\omega^{2n}\left(1 + [1/(2n-1)]\,\omega^2 + [2(n-2)/(2n-1)2(2n-3)]\,\omega^4 + \ldots\right) \tag{4.10.17}$$

Since the first n terms in $\omega^0, \omega^2, \ldots, \omega^{2n-2}$ are missing, we see that the first $(n-1)$ derivatives of τ are zero at $\omega = 0$. Thus, delay is MFD as required.

The unit step response of the Bessel filter having unity 3 dB bandwidth is shown in Fig. 4.10.5. The rise time is almost constant at two seconds, but the delay increases with filter order. Although overshoot is not apparent from Fig. 4.10.5, it does occur for $n \geqslant 2$ but is less than 1%.

4.11 EQUIRIPPLE DELAY FILTERS

The equiripple delay filter approximates an MFD response as the Chebyshev filter approximates an MFM response. The equiripple delay filter approximates constant delay over a wider frequency range than does the Bessel filter.

The equiripple delay filter has a delay function

$$\tau(\omega) = \frac{\tau_0}{1 + \epsilon T_{2n}(\omega)} \tag{4.11.1}$$

where parameter ϵ is the delay ripple parameter and T_{2n} is a $2n$th-order Chebyshev polynomial. The nominal low-frequency delay is τ_0 seconds. Since $|T_{2n}| \leqslant 1$ in $|\omega| \leqslant 1$, the low-frequency delay is bounded between $\tau_0/(1+\epsilon)$ and $\tau_0/(1-\epsilon)$ as shown in Fig. 4.11.1. The dc delay equals $\tau_0/(1+\epsilon)$ for n even and $\tau_0/(1-\epsilon)$ for n odd. The filter order n equals the number of delay maxima and minima in the filter passband $|\omega| \leqslant 1$ (excluding the minimum at $\omega = 1$). Recall that the delay, phase, and magnitude responses are interrelated as discussed in Sec. 1.17. Thus, the

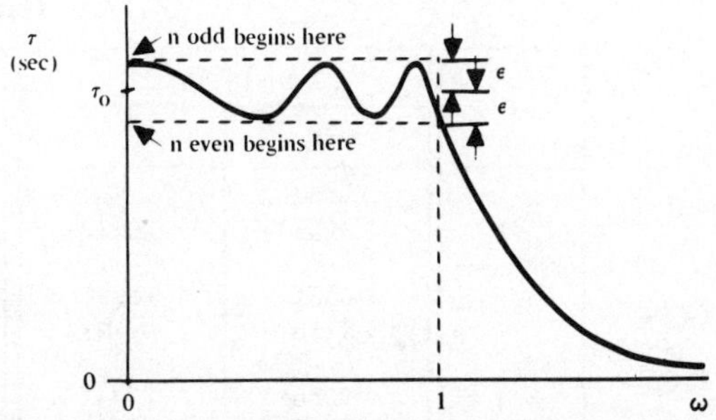

Fig. 4.11.1 Delay characteristic of equiripple delay filter.

magnitude function can be found from the phase or delay function. A closed form solution has not yet been found, but the poles have been determined by Ulbrich and Piloty[34] and later by Abele[35] using iterative procedures (also, see Refs. 36 and 37).

The frequency responses for these filters are not yet available (some data can be obtained from Ref. 38 and bandwidth information can be obtained from Ref. 36). As a practical matter, this presents little problem since the equiripple delay filter has almost identical characteristics to the equiripple phase and symmetrical delay filters which will be discussed in the next chapter. Therefore, these filters can be used in place of the equiripple delay filter.

The step response of equiripple delay filters is step-like in that the output approaches unity in a sequence of steps of decreasing size separated by approximately constant plateaus.[39] For n even, the plateaus alternate above and below unity. For n odd, the plateaus are all above unity. These plateaus are due to "echos" in the impulse response of the filter. The echos arise from the oscillatory delay of the filter.

4.12 GAUSSIAN FILTERS

Gaussian filters have characteristics very similar to those of Bessel filters. The magnitude function of the ideal Gaussian filter equals

$$|H(j\omega)| = e^{-0.347\omega^2} = 1/e^{0.347\omega^2} \tag{4.12.1}$$

where $|H(j1)|^2 = ½$. By analytic continuation, then

$$H(s)H(-s) = |H(j\omega)|^2 \Big|_{\omega=-js} = e^{0.694s^2} = 1/e^{-0.694s^2} \tag{4.12.2}$$

Expanding the exponential term in a Maclaurin series where

$$e^{ax^2} = 1 + ax^2 + a^2x^4/2! + a^3x^6/3! + \ldots \tag{4.12.3}$$

then

$$H(s)H(-s) = 1/[1 - 0.694s^2 + 0.241s^4 - \ldots] \tag{4.12.4}$$

Dishal truncated this series at the 2*n*th term to result in the so-called *n*th-order Gaussian filter.[40] Identifying the left-half-plane poles of $|H(s)|^2$ results in the poles of the *n*th-order Gaussian filter which are listed in Table 4.12.1. They are normalized so that the 3 dB bandwidth is unity.

The magnitude characteristics are shown in Fig. 4.12.1. It is clear that Gaussian and Bessel filters have magnitude characteristics which are very similar. Comparing Figs. 4.12.1 and 4.10.2, the Gaussian filter does not exhibit quite the stopband selectivity of the Bessel filter. For orders of 20 or more, the *n*th-order Gaussian filter magnitude response is essentially that of the ideal Gaussian filter (n = ∞).

Table 4.12.1 Gaussian filter poles.

n	Poles ω_n	Poles ζ
2	1.3908	0.9239
3	1.6661	0.8252
	1.5116	real
4	1.9086	0.7441
	1.6768	0.9720
5	2.1309	0.6795
	1.8498	0.9213
	1.7765	real
6	2.3373	0.6275
	2.0211	0.8688
	1.9022	0.9855
7	2.5394	0.5849
	2.1953	0.8200
	2.0436	0.9553
	1.9988	real
8	2.7240	0.5492
	2.3584	0.7761
	2.1821	0.9201
	2.1061	0.9911
9	2.9095	0.5189
	2.5249	0.7371
	2.3282	0.8843
	2.2284	0.9712
	2.1974	real
10	3.0783	0.4127
	2.4657	0.8499
	2.6787	0.7024
	2.3471	0.9462
	2.2931	0.9940

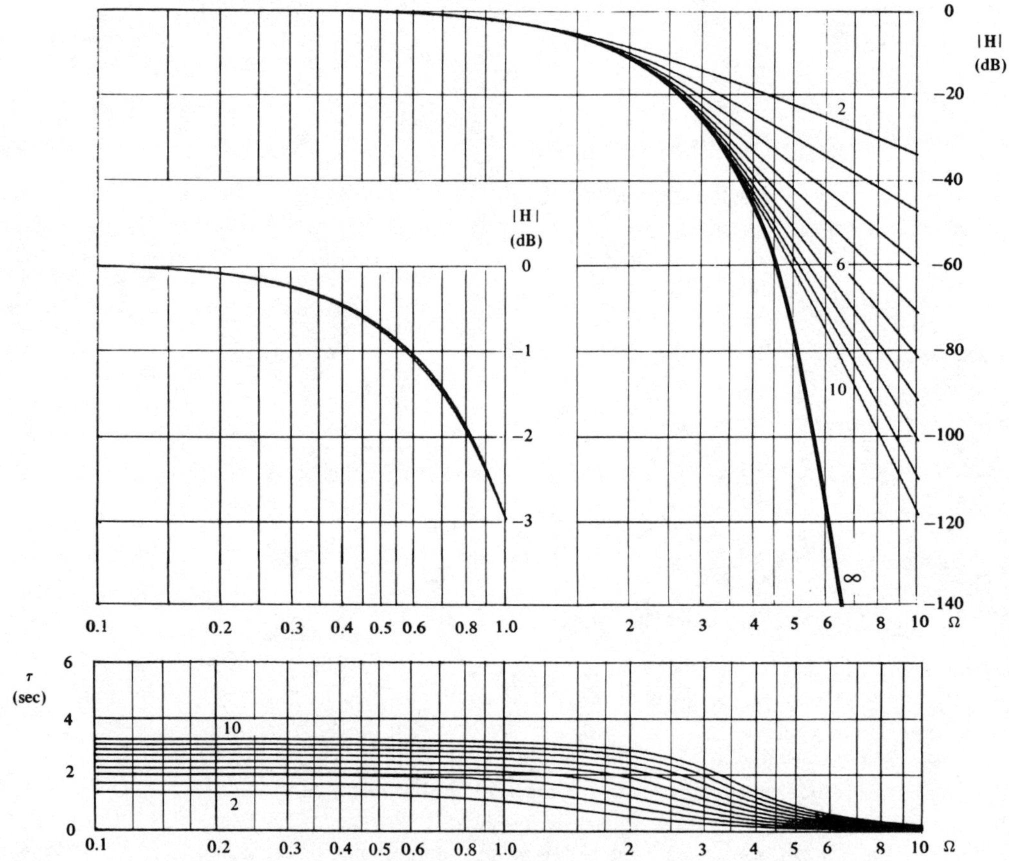

Fig. 4.12.1 Magnitude and delay characteristics of Gaussian. (From A. D. Taylor)

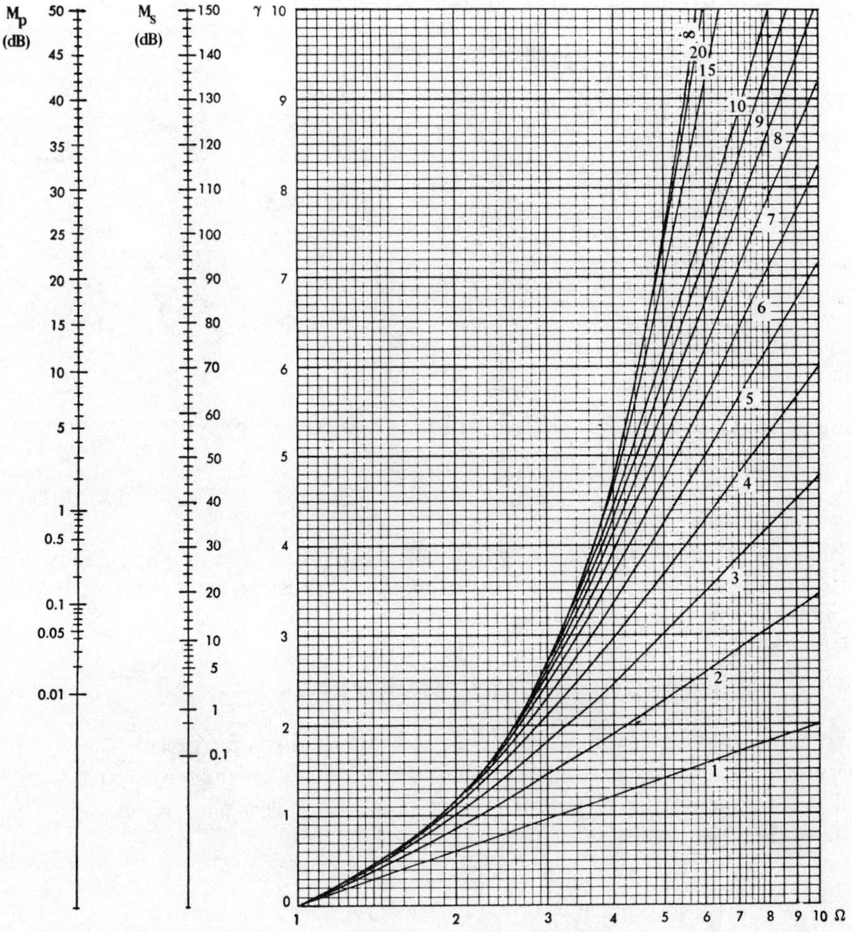

Fig. 4.12.2 Nomograph for Gaussian filters. (From J. N. Hallberg, loc. cit.)

The ideal Gaussian filter has a band-edge selectivity of

$$-d|H|/d\omega\,\big|_{\omega=1} = 0.491 \tag{4.12.5}$$

from Eq. 4.12.1. Thus, its value is less than that of a second-order Butterworth filter. We see from Fig. 4.12.1 that the band-edge selectivity is virtually independent of order. This is intuitively pleasing since increasing the degree of the approximation serves primarily to control the stopband magnitude shaping by adding higher-order terms.

The order of a Gaussian filter can be determined from the nomograph of Fig. 4.12.2. We confirm the earlier observation that Gaussian filters do not exhibit quite as much selectivity as Bessel filters by comparing their nomographs.

The delay characteristic of a Gaussian filter is shown in Fig. 4.12.1. Although it is monotonic, the Bessel filter exhibits a superior delay characteristic since it remains flatter (in fact, MFD) over a wider frequency range. In other words, the Bessel filter has a wider delay bandwidth.

The unit step response of the Gaussian filter having unity 3 dB bandwidth is shown in Fig. 4.12.3. It is monotonically nondecreasing and exhibits negligible overshoot. We see that its delay is less than that for the Bessel filter. In applications where the delay time is of no importance, the Gaussian filter is inferior to the Bessel filter because of its magnitude and delay response

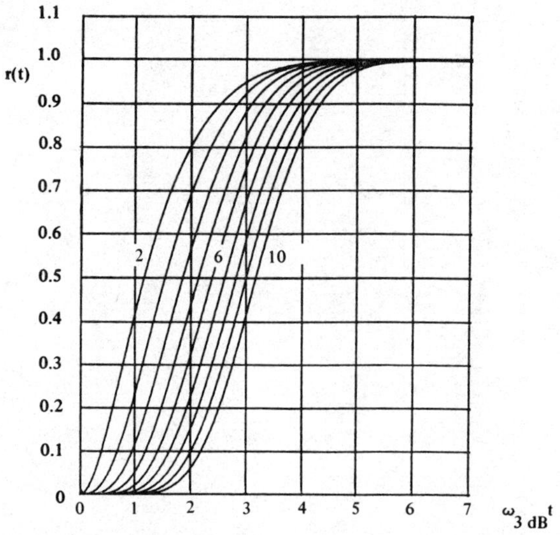

Fig. 4.12.3 Step response of Gaussian filters. (From A. D. Taylor)

(although its step response overshoot and rise time are almost equal). However classically, the ideal Gaussian filter has always been of interest. We calculated its step response in Example 1.5.2 and found that this filter was nonrealizable.

4.13 SYNCHRONOUSLY-TUNED FILTERS

Synchronously-tuned filters are the simplest of all the filter types. They consist of n identical cascaded filter stages each having a simple pole. They are easy to construct and tune. Although they have monotonic step response and delay, they have poor selectivity. The synchronously-tuned filter has a transfer function

$$H(s) = \frac{1}{(1 + s/p_o)^n} \tag{4.13.1}$$

Since the 3 dB bandwidth ω_{3dB} must equal unity for all n, and

$$\omega_{3\,dB} = p_o(2^{1/n} - 1)^{1/2} \tag{4.13.2}$$

then the pole value p_o must equal

$$p_o = (2^{1/n} - 1)^{-1/2} \cong 1.2\sqrt{n}, \qquad n \geqslant 3 \tag{4.13.3}$$

Synchronously-tuned filters have the magnitude and delay responses shown in Fig. 4.13.1. It is easy to show that synchronously-tuned filters become Gaussian as n approaches infinity. Therefore, the filter selectivity approaches that of a Gaussian filter (–0.491) for large n.

The order of the synchronously-tuned filter can be determined by using the nomograph of Fig. 4.13.2. Comparing this nomograph with that for the Bessel filter in Fig. 4.10.2, we see that the synchronously-tuned filter is inferior in both band-edge selectivity and stopband rejection.

The 6–60 dB shaping factor for an *m*th-order synchronously-tuned filter is given by Eq. 4.3.11 (let n = 1). The equation shows that synchronously-tuned filters have much wider transition bands than Butterworth filters of equal order.

The delay characteristic of the synchronously-tuned filter is shown in Fig. 4.13.1 and is monotonically nonincreasing. The delay expression is given by Eq. 2.10.10 (for $\zeta = 1$) when it is increased by n. The dc delay $\tau(0) = n/\omega_n$ from the discussions of Sec. 2.10. We see that synchronously-tuned filters have inferior delay characteristics when compared to those of Bessel filters.

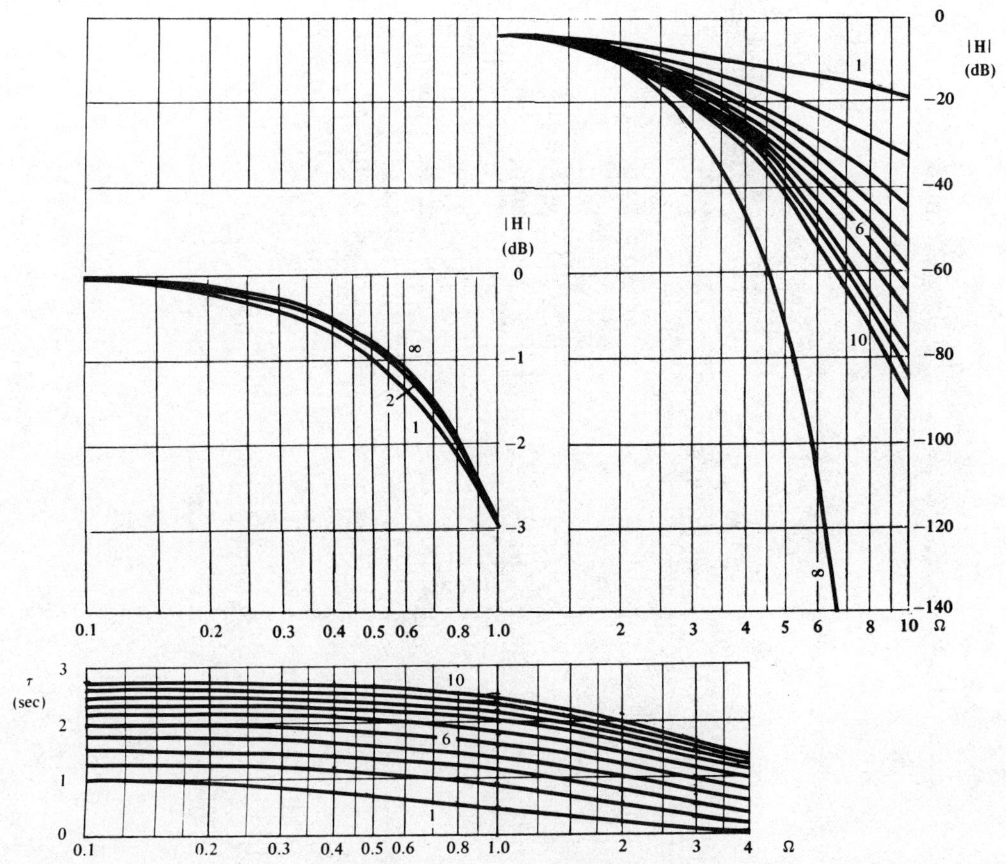

Fig. 4.13.1 Magnitude and delay characteristics of synchronously-tuned filters.

The unit step response of the synchronously-tuned filter having unity 3 dB bandwidth is shown in Fig. 4.13.3. It is a monotonically nondecreasing response. The rise time remains constant at about 2.1 seconds and delay time varies as the square root of filter order. It should be noted that there is no conflict between the step response of Fig. 4.13.3 and that of Fig. 3.7.1. Recall that Fig. 3.7.1 was based upon cascaded stages of each having unity 3 dB bandwidth and that bandwidth shrinkage occurred reducing the overall bandwidth. Rise time varied as $\sqrt{n}$ and delay time varied as n. However, Fig. 4.13.3 is the step response of n cascaded stages each having a 3 dB bandwidth of about $1.2\sqrt{n}$ which maintains the overall bandwidth at unity. Thus, rise time is constant and delay time varies as $\sqrt{n}$.

EXAMPLE 4.13.1 Determine the synchronously-tuned filter order to satisfy the filter requirements in Example 4.10.2.

Solution Entering the data onto the nomograph of Fig. 4.13.2, we find $n_1 \geqslant 20$ and $n_2 \geqslant 6$. From the slope requirement, $n \geqslant 3$. Thus, a twentieth-order synchronously-tuned filter is required due to its poor selectivity. Only a fourth-order Bessel filter was required in the same application.

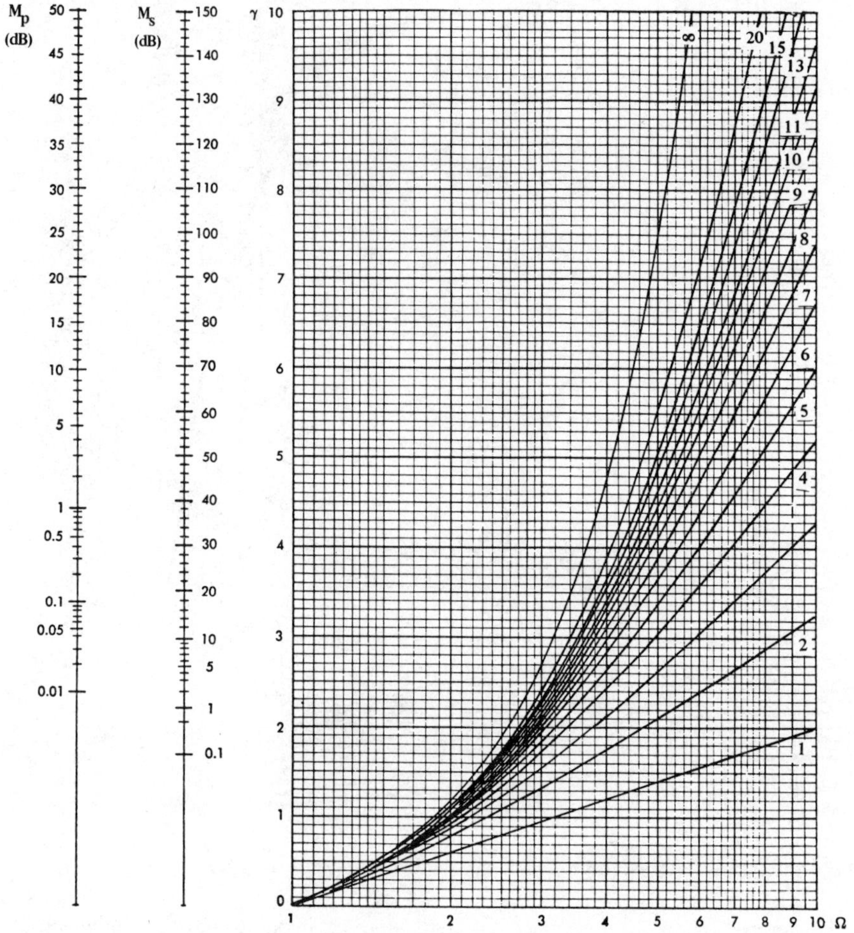

Fig. 4.13.2 Nomograph for synchronously-tuned filters. (From J. N. Hallberg, loc. cit.)

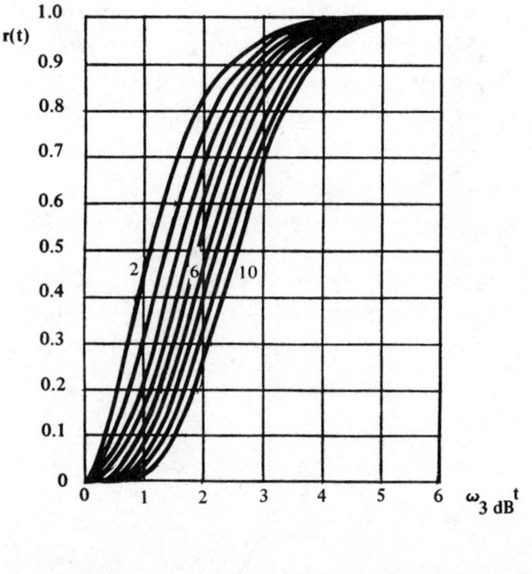

Fig. 4.13.3 Step response of synchronously-tuned filters.

4.14 PARABOLIC FILTERS

Parabolic filters were introduced by Mullick.[41] Their step response overshoot is lower than that of the Butterworth filter. Their delay times are less than those for Butterworth and even Bessel filters. However, their selectivity is very poor. The parabolic filter has a magnitude function tion

$$|H(j\omega)|^2 = \frac{P_n^{\,2}(0)}{P_n(j\omega)P_n(-j\omega)} \tag{4.14.1}$$

where P_n is the nth-order polynomial for the parabolic filter. The zeros of the polynomial are located on the parabola

$$4(b + 1)(\sigma_k + 1) = \omega_k^{\,2} \tag{4.14.2}$$

whose focus is on the positive real axis at s = b and whose vertex is located at s = –1. The zero location is given by the intersection of the parabola and a radial line having angle θ_k where θ_k is the Butterworth pole angle given by Eq. 4.3.5. This general construction is shown in Fig. 4.14.1 along with the pole distribution for a third-order parabolic filter having b = 1.25. The poles, therefore, equal $s_k = \sigma_k + j\omega_k$ whose real and imaginary parts are given by

$$\begin{aligned} \sigma_k &= -\cos\theta_k \\ \omega_k &= 2[(b + 1)(1 + \sigma_k)]^{1/2} = 2[(b + 1)(1 - \cos\theta_k)]^{1/2} = 2(b + 1)^{1/2}\sin(\theta_k/2) \end{aligned} \tag{4.14.3}$$

The poles for the parabolic filter are listed in Table 4.14.1 for parameter values b = 0, 1.25, and 3. It is important to note that these poles have been frequency normalized to yield unity 3 dB bandwidth. We will now see that b in the range from zero to three gives a useful set of responses.

The magnitude responses of parabolic filters are shown in Fig. 4.14.2. We see that although they are monotonic in shape, parabolic filters are not as selective as Butterworth filters. They are even less selective than Bessel filters. Parabolic filters tend to be Butterworth for $n \leqslant 3$ and become almost synchronously-tuned for larger n in the transition band. However, their gain tends to drop rapidly in the stopband. Selectivity decreases with increasing b. This is confirmed by the nomograph of Fig. 4.14.4.

The delay responses of parabolic filters are shown in Fig. 4.14.3. We see they have fairly flat response in the passband and exhibit slight peaking in the stopband. This peaking decreases for increasing b and moves further into the stopband. The bandwidth of the delay response is wider than that of Bessel filters and the dc delay is slightly less for $b > 0$.

The unit step responses of parabolic filters are shown in Fig. 4.14.5. In general, increasing b reduces the overshoot. Delay time decreases but rise time remains about constant. With the exception of delay time, we see that b controls the step response around the final value rather than the initial value. Parabolic filters have slightly less delay time than Bessel filters. Due to their good delay and step response, parabolic filters are useful in pulse filtering applications.

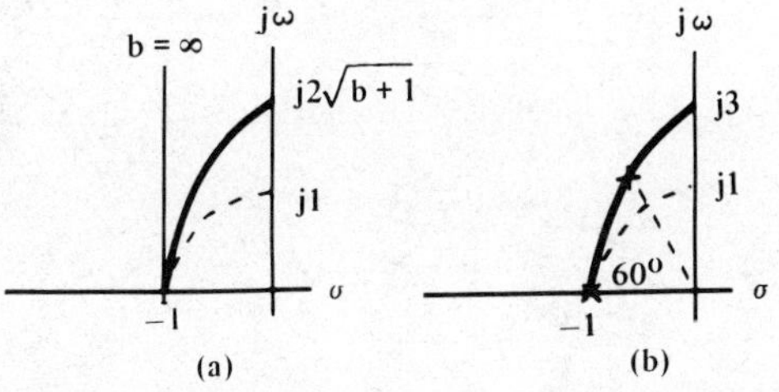

Fig. 4.14.1 (a) General parabola construction and (b) pole locations for third-order parabolic filter (b = 1.25). (The conjugate poles are not shown.)

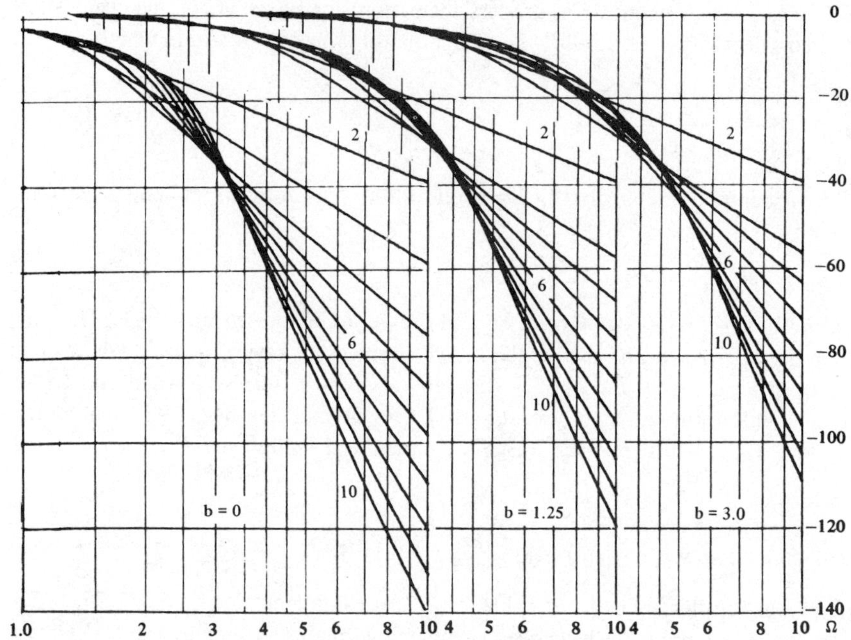

Fig. 4.14.2 Magnitude characteristics of parabolic filters. (From A. D. Taylor, loc. cit.)

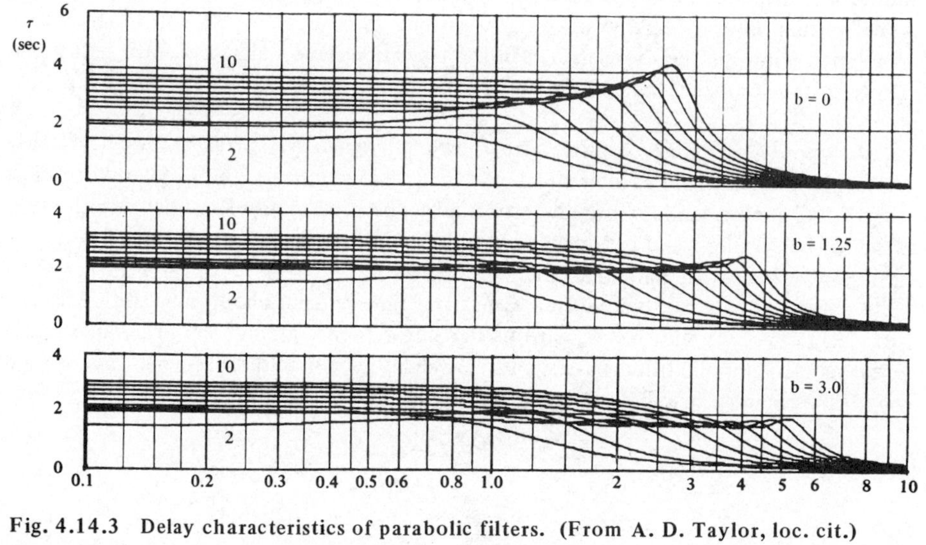

Fig. 4.14.3 Delay characteristics of parabolic filters. (From A. D. Taylor, loc. cit.)

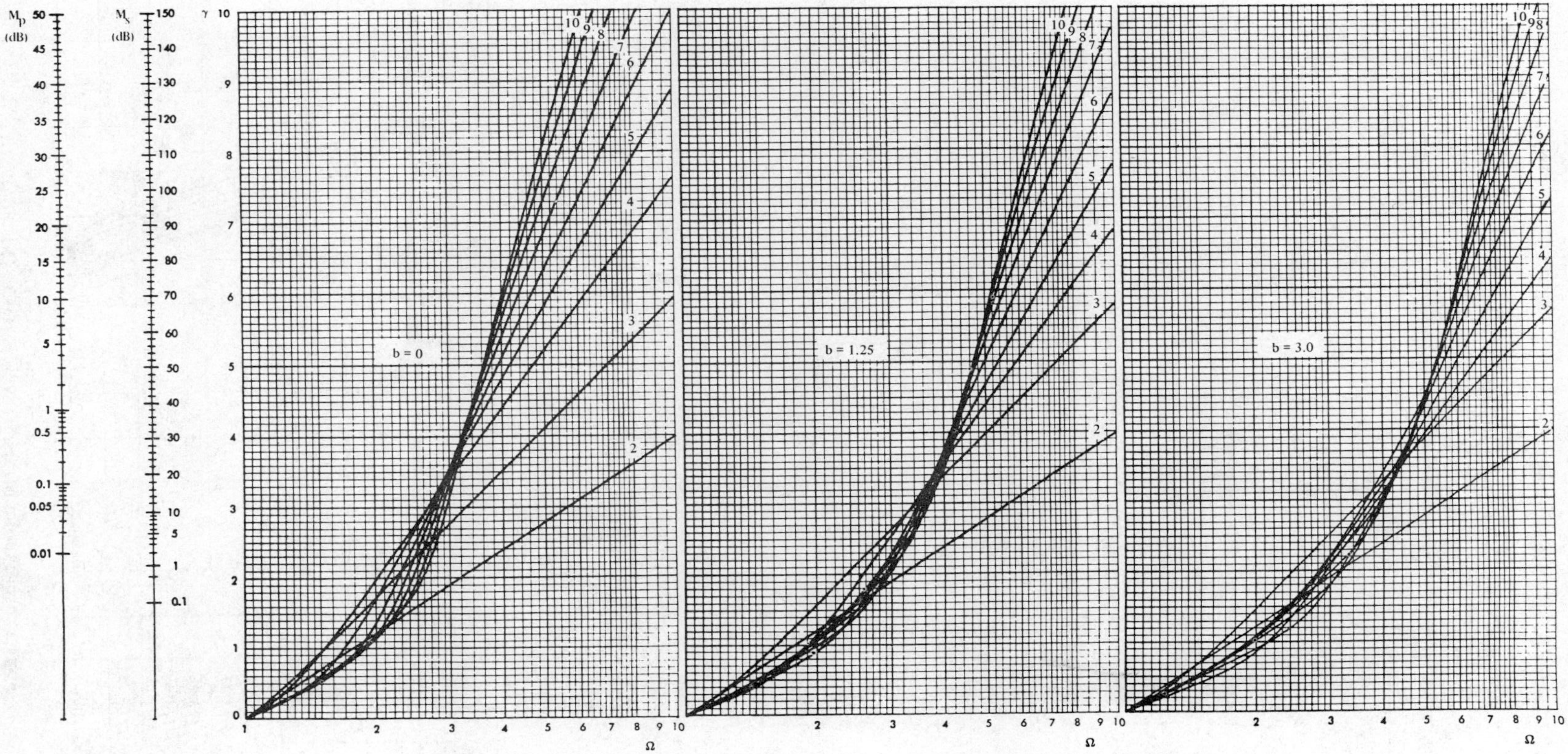

Fig. 4.14.4 Nomographs for parabolic filters. (From A. D. Taylor, loc. cit.)

Table 4.14.1 Parabolic filter poles where 3 dB bandwidth is unity. (From A. D. Taylor, loc. cit.)

n	b = 0		b = 1.25		b = 3.0	
	ω_n	ζ	ω_n	ζ	ω_n	ζ
2	1.0000	0.7071	1.0000	0.7071	1.0000	0.7071
3	1.1266	0.5000	1.2517	0.5000	1.3392	0.5000
	0.8449	real	0.7909	real	0.7771	real
4	1.3077	0.3827	1.0655	0.9239	2.1642	0.3827
	0.9399	0.9239	1.8104	0.3827	1.1387	0.9239
5	1.1627	0.8090	2.3436	0.3090	2.8270	0.3090
	1.6068	0.3090	1.3919	0.8090	1.4834	0.8090
	1.0517	real	1.1886	real	1.2384	real
6	1.8830	0.2588	1.3495	0.9660	1.4029	0.9659
	1.3885	0.7071	1.6877	0.7071	1.8177	0.7071
	1.2057	0.9659	2.7577	0.2588	3.3744	0.2588
7	2.1117	0.2225	3.1352	0.2225	3.8945	0.2225
	1.5902	0.6235	1.9855	0.6235	2.1726	0.6235
	1.3580	0.9010	1.5436	0.9010	1.6160	0.9010
	1.2908	real	1.4257	real	1.4767	real
8	2.3169	0.1951	1.5505	0.9808	1.6095	0.9808
	1.7800	1.5556	1.7538	0.8315	1.8528	0.8315
	1.5119	0.8315	2.2789	0.5556	2.5330	0.5556
	1.3979	0.9808	3.4813	0.1951	4.3782	0.1951
9	2.5035	0.1736	3.8159	0.1736	4.8427	0.1936
	1.9588	0.5000	2.5749	0.5000	2.9011	0.5000
	1.6637	0.7660	1.9796	0.7660	2.1101	0.7660
	1.5148	0.9397	1.7067	0.9397	1.7782	0.9397
	1.4691	real	1.6270	real	1.6847	real
10	2.6862	0.1564	1.7329	0.9877	1.7975	0.9877
	2.1365	0.4540	1.8737	0.8910	1.9642	0.8910
	1.8197	0.7071	2.2047	0.7071	2.3745	0.7071
	1.6428	0.8910	2.8566	0.4540	3.2624	0.4540
	1.5629	0.9877	4.1196	0.1564	5.2727	0.1564

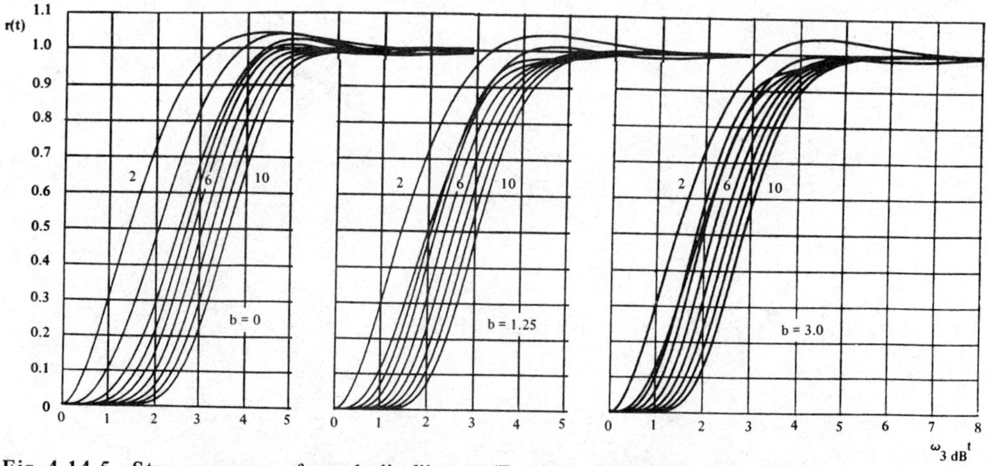

Fig. 4.14.5 Step responses of parabolic filters. (From A. D. Taylor, loc. cit.)

4.15 CATENARY FILTERS

Following the work of Mullick, other contours with arbitrary pole distributions were analyzed. One such filter is the catenary filter introduced by Ghausi and Adamowicz.[42] The poles of a catenary filter lie on a hyperbola

$$\sigma_k = \frac{1}{b-1}(\cosh \omega_k - b) \tag{4.15.1}$$

which passes through the point (−1, j0). The pole location is given by the intersection of the hyperbola and a radial line having Butterworth angle θ_k given by Eq. 4.3.5. The pole locations are shown in Fig. 4.15.1 for b = 0, 2, 4, 5, and 10 where they are compared with the Butterworth (b = 0) and parabolic filter poles. Although the poles have identical damping factors ζ, they have larger resonant frequencies ω_n than their analogous parabolic poles. The pole locations are listed in Table 4.15.1 and have been frequency normalized to yield unity 3 dB bandwidth. b in the range from two to ten gives a useful set of responses.

The magnitude responses of catenary filters are shown in Fig. 4.15.2. In general, we see their decreasing selectivity for increasing b. Catenary filters tend to be Butterworth for $n \leqslant 3$ and become synchronously-tuned for larger n in the transition band. Catenary filters having b = 5.0 have magnitude responses close to those of parabolic filters having b = 1.25 which are convenient reference values. Their nomographs are shown in Fig. 4.15.4.

The delay responses of catenary filters are shown in Fig. 4.15.3. They have fairly flat response in the passband and exhibit peaking near the band-edge in the transition band. This peaking decreases for increasing b and moves into the stopband. The dc delay decreases from that of Butterworth filters (b = 0) to slightly less than that for Bessel filters for b > 5. The delay responses for catenary filters having b = 5.0 is similar to those for parabolic filters having b = 1.25. However, the catenary filters exhibit slightly more delay peaking in the stopband and slightly less bandwidth.

The step responses of catenary filters are shown in Fig. 4.15.5. We see that increasing b decreases the overshoot and delay time of the filter. For small $b \cong 0$, the step response is Butterworth. It is interesting to note that the overshoot remains about constant, for a given b, independent of order. Again, b controls the step response around the final value rather than the initial value. There is little difference between the step response of a b = 5.0 catenary filter and a b = 1.25 parabolic filter.

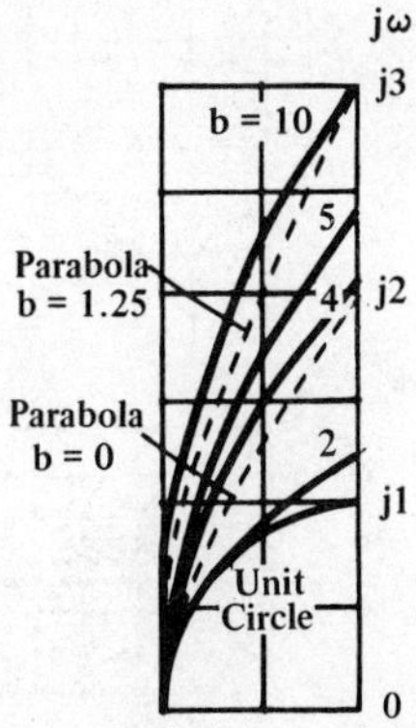

Fig. 4.15.1 Pole locations for catenary filter.[42] (The conjugate poles are not shown.)

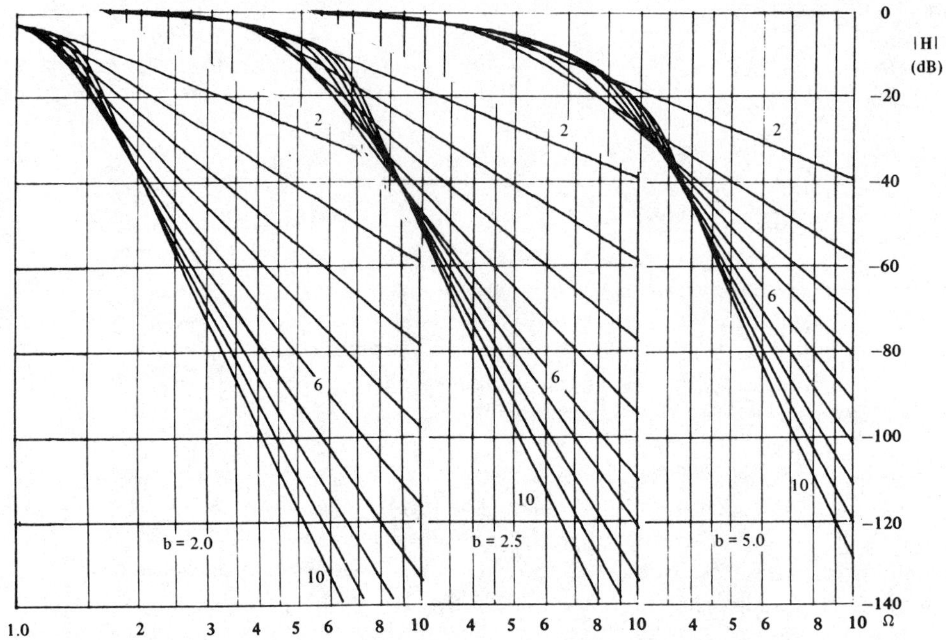

Fig. 4.15.2 Magnitude characteristics of catenary filters. (From A. D. Taylor, loc. cit.)

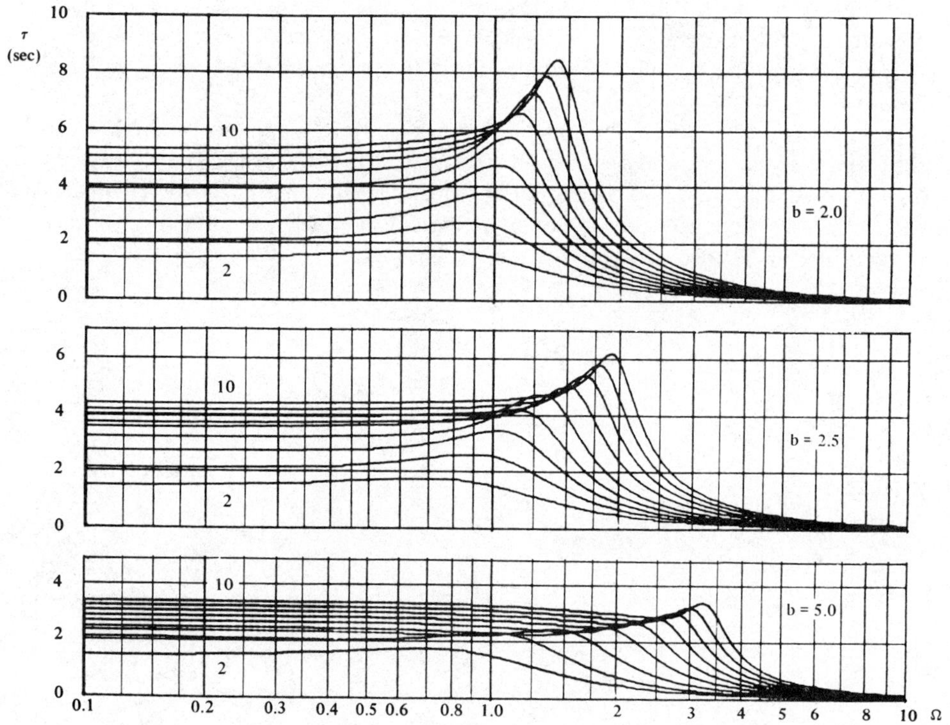

Fig. 4.15.3 Delay characteristics of catenary filters. (From A. D. Taylor, loc. cit.)

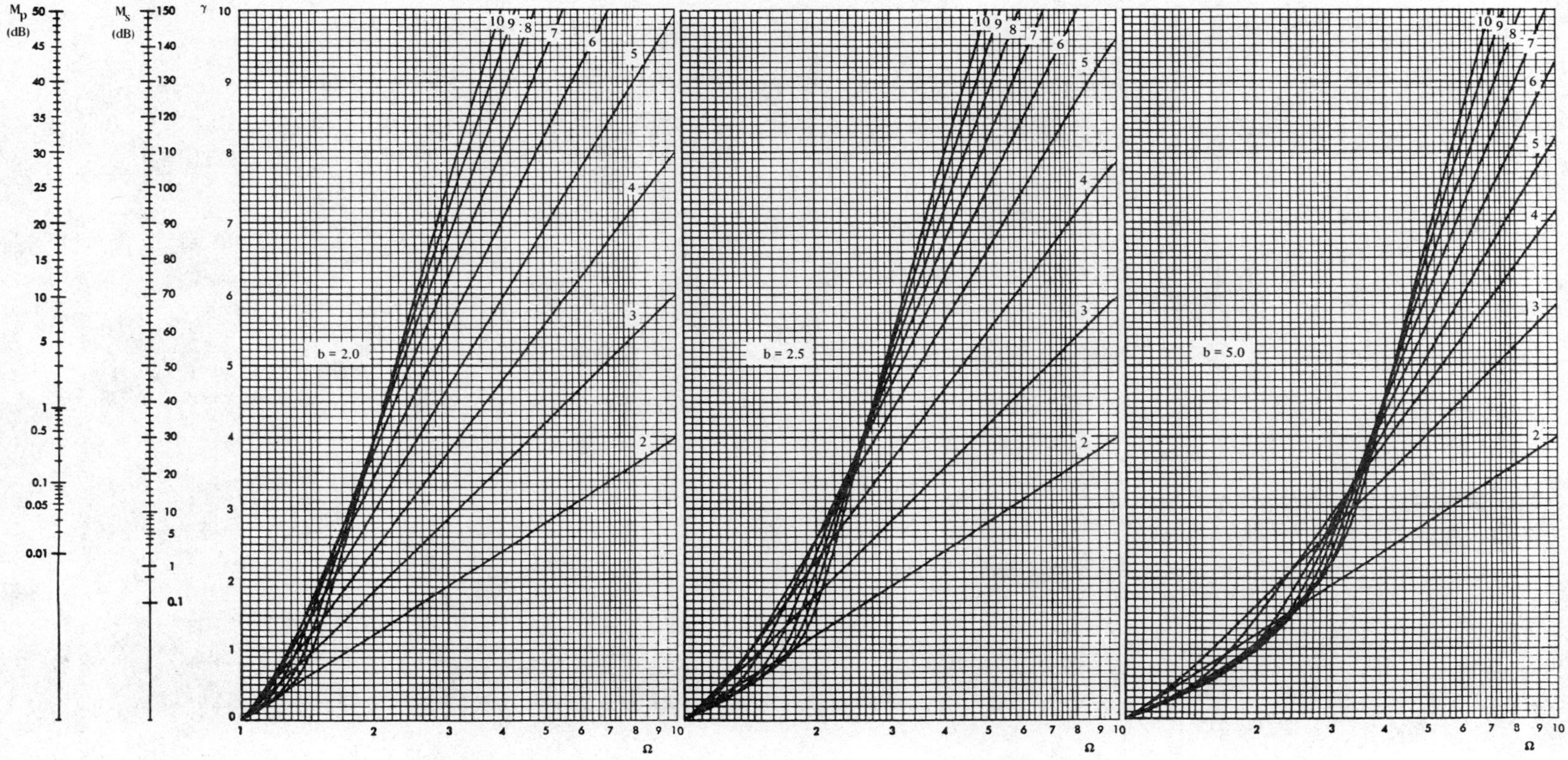

Fig. 4.15.4 Nomographs for catenary filters. (From A. D. Taylor, loc. cit.)

Table 4.15.1 Catenary filter poles where 3 dB bandwidth is unity. (From A. D. Taylor, loc. cit.)

n	b = 2.0		b = 2.5		b = 5.0	
	ω_n	ζ	ω_n	ζ	ω_n	ζ
2	1.0000	0.7071	1.0000	0.7071	1.0000	0.7071
3	1.0258	0.5000	1.0739	0.5000	1.2111	0.5000
	0.9561	real	0.8910	real	0.8027	real
4	1.0605	0.3827	1.1505	0.3827	1.5907	0.3827
	0.9563	0.9239	0.9295	0.9239	1.0099	0.9239
5	1.0967	0.3090	1.2521	0.3090	2.0093	0.3090
	0.9728	0.8090	1.0167	0.8090	1.3128	0.8090
	0.9620	real	0.9518	real	1.1305	real
6	1.1381	0.2588	1.3840	0.2588	2.3222	0.2588
	1.0044	0.7071	1.0951	0.6784	1.5826	0.7071
	0.9796	0.9659	1.0377	0.9659	1.2852	0.9659
7	1.1948	0.2225	1.5675	0.2225	2.5945	0.2225
	1.0552	0.6235	1.3061	0.6235	1.8417	0.6235
	1.0160	0.9010	1.1791	0.9010	1.4649	0.9010
	1.0129	real	1.1401	real	1.3577	real
8	1.2738	0.1951	1.7104	0.1951	2.8486	0.1951
	1.1289	0.5556	1.4435	0.5556	2.0956	0.5556
	1.0766	0.8315	1.2991	0.8315	1.6617	0.8315
	1.0674	0.9808	1.2338	0.9808	1.4785	0.9808
9	1.3610	0.1736	1.8385	0.1736	3.0845	0.1736
	1.2117	0.5000	1.5698	0.5000	2.3391	0.5000
	1.1482	0.7660	1.4132	0.7660	1.8649	0.7660
	1.1308	0.9397	1.3291	0.9397	1.6231	0.9397
	1.1294	real	1.3024	real	1.5503	real
10	1.4422	0.1564	1.9582	0.1564	3.3059	0.1564
	1.2905	0.4540	1.6895	0.4540	2.5721	0.4540
	1.2180	0.7071	1.5239	0.7071	2.0699	0.7071
	1.1920	0.8910	1.4258	0.8910	1.7815	0.8910
	1.1876	0.9877	1.3797	0.9877	1.6535	0.9877

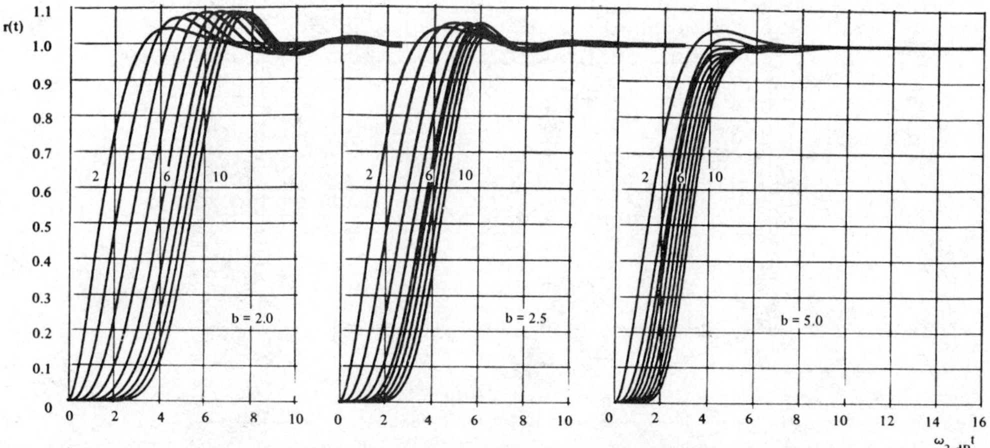

Fig. 4.15.5 Step responses of catenary filters. (From A. D. Taylor, loc. cit.)

4.16 ELLIPTIC CONTOUR FILTERS

The elliptic contour filter was investigated by Kuh[43] and later by Scanlan.[44] The poles of the elliptic contour filter lie on an ellipse

$$-\sigma_k = \left\{(k - 1/k)\left[1 - \left(\frac{\omega_k}{k + 1/k}\right)^2\right]\right\}^{1/2} \tag{4.16.1}$$

whose eccentricity ratio a equals

$$a = \frac{k - 1/k}{k + 1/k} = \frac{k^2 - 1}{k^2 + 1} \tag{4.16.2}$$

The ratio a approaches unity when k approaches infinity and the ellipse becomes a circle. Choosing ratio a establishes the elliptic contour. Scanlan chose the pole locations to have equal-frequency spacing with respect to the $j\omega$-axis. Thus, when a = 1, the elliptic contour filter is almost Bessel as shown in Fig. 4.10.1 and the poles are separated by $2(k + 1/k)/n$. Of course, equal-angle spacing could also be used as in the parablic and catenary filter cases, but this has not yet been investigated. Elliptic contour filters are all-pole filters and must not be confused with the elliptic filters discussed earlier which have zeros of transmission.

The poles for the elliptic contour filter are listed in Table 4.16.1 for a = 0.4, 0.6, and 0.8. They have been frequency normalized to yield unity 3 dB bandwidth. b in the range from 0.4 to 0.8 gives a useful set of responses.

The magnitude responses of elliptic contour filters are shown in Fig. 4.16.2. They exhibit slightly less selectivity for increasing b in their transition band, and less rejection in their stopband. They tend to have a transition band response which is independent of order for $n > 3$ which is different than the parabolic and catenary filters. Elliptic contour filters have magnitude responses which tend to be similar to b = 0 parabolic and b = 2.5 catenary filters. Their nomographs are shown in Fig. 4.16.4.

The delay responses of elliptic contour filters are shown in Fig. 4.16.3. They have almost flat response in the passband and exhibit slight peaking at the band-edge in the transition band. This peaking decreases for increasing a. The bandwidths of the delay responses are almost independent of a and are slightly wider than those of Bessel filters. The dc delay decreases slightly for increasing a. Elliptic contour filters have delay responses similar to those for b = 5.0 catenary filters, but which are unlike those for parabolic filters.

The unit step responses for elliptic contour filters are shown in Fig. 4.16.5. Excluding n = 2. the step responses are almost independent of a. The overshoot remains constant at about 3%. The rise time is constant and the delay time decreases slightly for increasing a. The step responses are somewhat similar to b = 0 parabolic and b = 5.0 catenary filters.

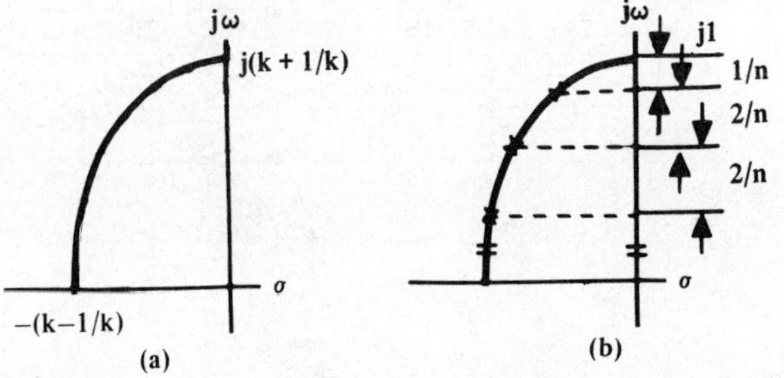

Fig. 4.16.1 (a) General ellipse construction and (b) pole locations for elliptic contour filter. (The conjugate poles are not shown.)

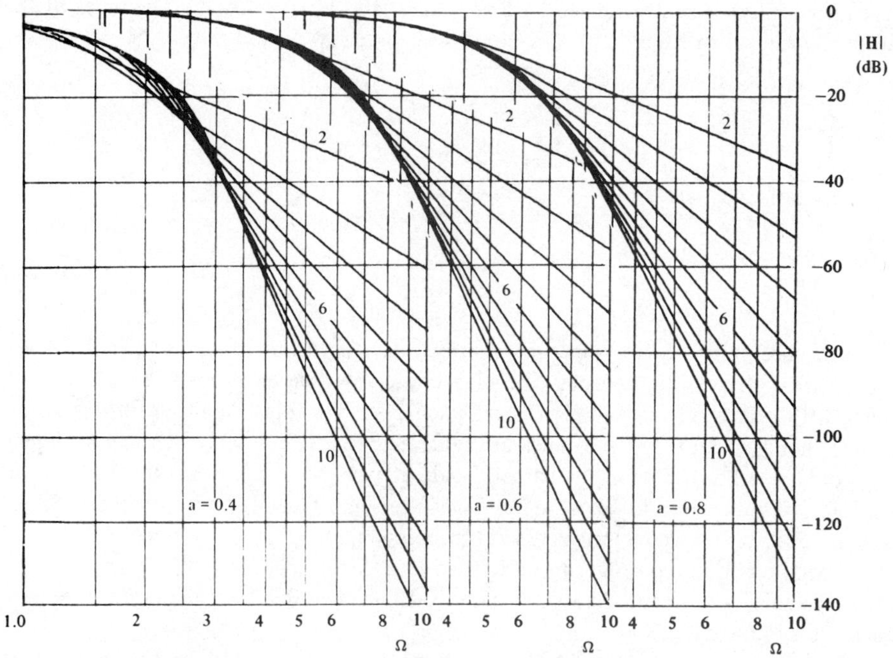

Fig. 4.16.2 Magnitude characteristics of elliptic contour filters. (From A. D. Taylor, loc. cit.)

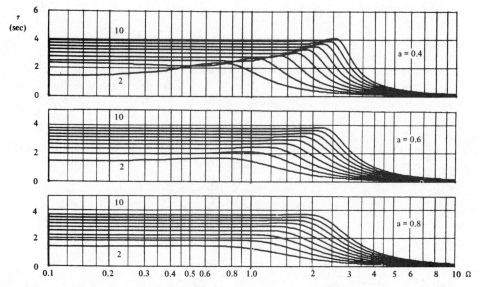

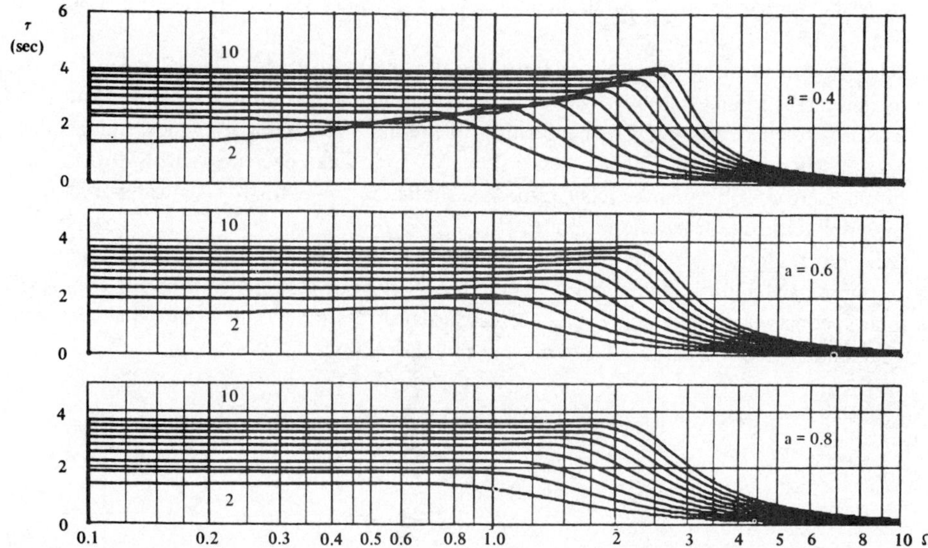

Fig. 4.16.3 Delay characteristics of elliptic contour filters. (From A. D. Taylor, loc. cit.)

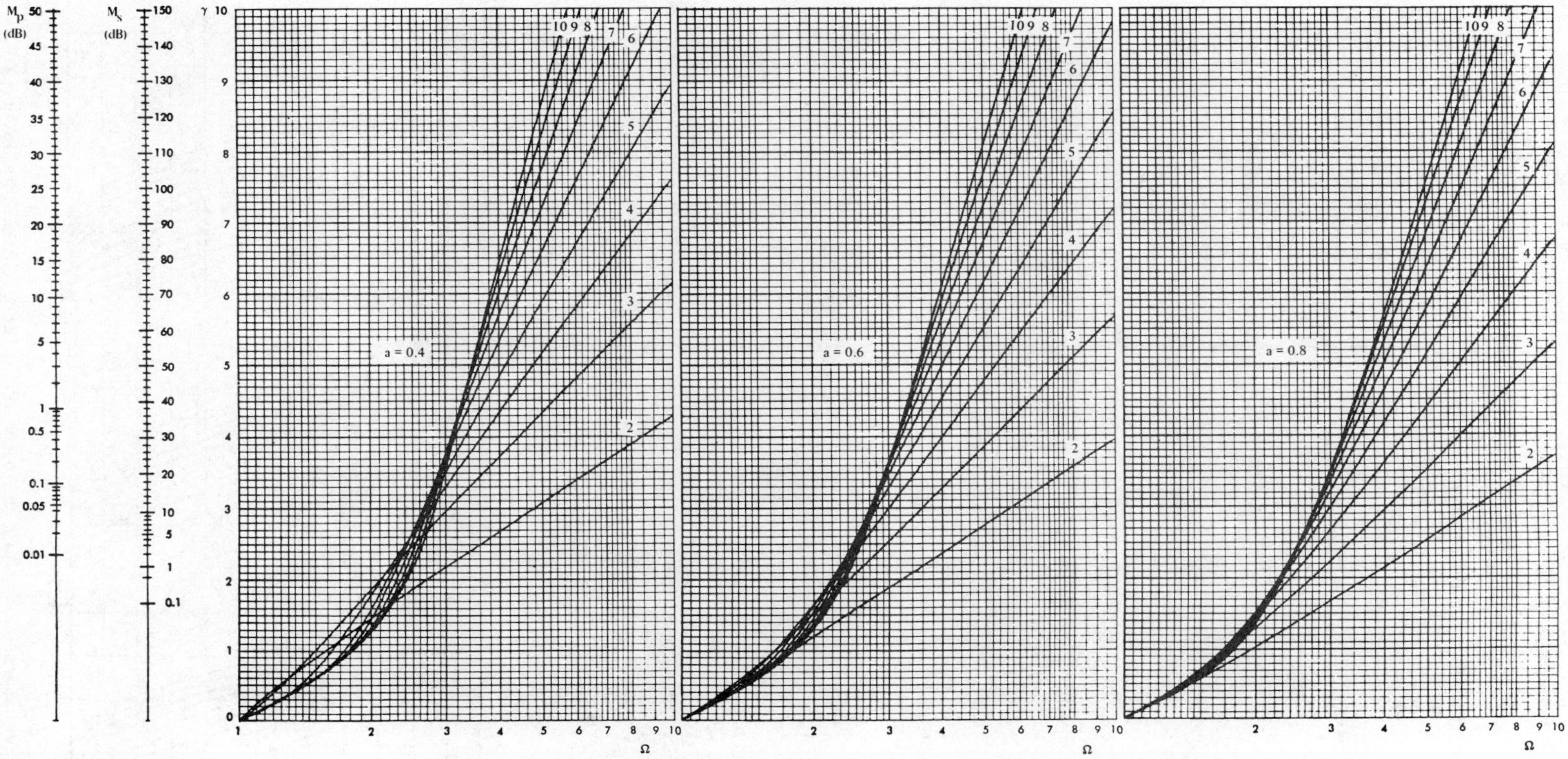

Fig. 4.16.4 Nomographs for elliptic contour filters. (From A. D. Taylor, loc. cit.)

Table 4.16.1 Elliptic contour filter poles where the 3 dB bandwidth is unity. (From A. D. Taylor, loc. cit.)

n	a = 0.4		a = 0.6		a = 0.8	
	ω_n	ζ	ω_n	ζ	ω_n	ζ
2	0.8475	0.5695	1.0204	0.7206	1.1682	0.8109
3	1.1530	0.4082	1.2451	0.5571	1.3462	0.6667
	0.6315	real	0.9306	real	1.2044	real
4	1.4643	0.3327	1.4570	0.4677	1.5063	0.5765
	0.8488	0.8402	1.0860	0.9186	1.3357	0.9517
5	1.7473	0.2873	1.6639	0.4104	1.6609	0.5145
	1.1351	0.6757	1.2897	0.8087	1.4869	0.8779
	0.8368	real	1.1380	real	1.4242	real
6	1.9619	0.2565	1.8538	0.3698	1.8122	0.4687
	1.3842	0.5695	1.4905	0.7206	1.6413	0.8109
	0.9743	0.9211	1.2704	0.9625	1.5487	0.9784
7	2.1691	0.2337	2.0299	0.3392	1.9528	0.4333
	1.6215	0.4981	1.6804	0.6528	1.7872	0.7543
	1.1764	0.8018	1.4304	0.8955	1.6800	0.9370
	0.9842	real	1.3367	real	1.6427	real
8	2.3552	0.2161	2.1892	0.3151	2.0908	0.4048
	1.8361	0.4469	1.8546	0.5997	1.9305	0.7068
	1.3860	0.7031	1.5930	0.8292	1.8158	0.8924
	1.0935	0.9538	1.4444	0.9787	1.7556	0.9878
9	2.5255	0.2019	2.3394	0.2954	2.2180	0.3812
	2.0322	0.4082	2.0185	0.5571	2.0633	0.6667
	1.5886	0.6276	1.7586	0.7707	1.9453	0.8498
	1.2490	0.8689	1.5735	0.9348	1.8709	0.9617
	1.1131	real	1.5076	real	1.8455	real
10	2.6915	0.1902	2.4800	0.2791	2.3385	0.3613
	2.2198	0.3778	2.1717	0.5221	2.1891	0.6323
	1.7860	0.5695	1.9081	0.7206	2.0701	0.8109
	1.4251	0.7861	1.7100	0.8857	1.9867	0.9307
	1.2048	0.9699	1.6017	0.9863	1.9437	0.9922

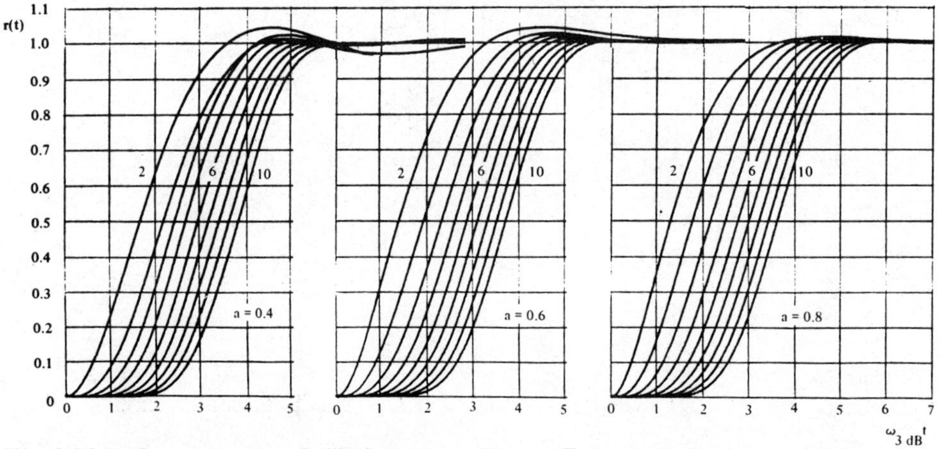

Fig. 4.16.5 Step responses of elliptic contour filters. (From A. D. Taylor, loc. cit.)

4.17 TRANSITIONAL FILTERS

The parabolic, catenary, and elliptic contour filters have different magnitude/delay characteristics than all of the other filter types discussed. Their characteristics tended to be those of a constant delay (and low selectivity) type filter (e.g., Bessel) in the passband, and those of a constant magnitude (and high delay distortion) type filter (e.g., Butterworth) in the stopband. Filters that have such behavior are said to be *transitional filters*. Historically, a transitional filter has been considered as any filter whose characteristic is produced by combining the characteristics of two other filters. Of these two filters, one was usually a constant delay type and the other a constant magnitude type. For example, several transitional filters include the (transitional-) Butterworth-Thomson (TBT),[45] Legendre-Thomson (TLT),[46] Gaussian to 6 or 12 dB,[47] Chebyshev-equiripple delay (TCERD),[48] Papoulis-equiripple delay (TPERD),[48] and Butterworth-Chebyshev (TBC) filters.[49]

Transitional filters provide a means of making compromises in the magnitude, delay, and step response characteristics of a filter. Thus, they allow the designer to combine the characteristics of the two filters and, therefore, anticipate the characteristics of the transitional filter. Also, it is easy to interpolate the poles of the two filters to produce the poles of the transitional filter. We choose to adopt the general viewpoint that any filters having transitional type characteristics (which are generated by any methods such as choosing certain contours) are transitional filters. This is useful when choosing filter types to meet specific applications as we shall soon discuss.

Although we shall not devote more time to investigating the transitional filter listed above, we shall mention several interpolation schemes. These are useful for enlarging our viewpoint of transitional filters. The TBT filter poles were determined from

$$|s_m| = |s_T|^m |s_B|^{1-m}, \qquad \arg s_m = \arg s_B - m(\arg s_B - \arg s_T) \tag{4.17.1}$$

where every pole is expressed in polar form. s_T and s_B denote the *i*th pole of the Thomson and Butterworth filters, respectively. Parameter m varies as $0 < m < 1$ and controls the poles of the TBT filter. When $m = 0$, the poles are Butterworth and when $m = 1$, they are Thomson. Therefore, the parameter m provides linear interpolation in the pole angles and an *m*th power law interpolation in the pole magnitudes. It should be noted that the poles so obtained in general need to be frequency-normalized to maintain the 3 dB filter bandwidth to be unity. The TLT filter poles were found in the same way using Eq. 4.17.1.

The TCERD (and TPERD) filter poles were determined from

$$|s_m| = |s_C| - m(|s_C| - |s_{ERD}|), \qquad \arg s_m = \arg s_C - m(\arg s_C - \arg s_{ERD}) \tag{4.17.2}$$

which gives a linear interpolation in pole magnitude unlike that in Eq. 4.17.1.

The TBC filter interpolated the filter magnitude response as

$$|H_{n,k}(\omega)|^2 = \frac{1}{1 + \omega^{2k} T^2_{n-k}(\omega)}, \qquad 0 \leqslant k \leqslant n \tag{4.17.3}$$

rather than the filter poles as before. For $k = 0$, the response is Chebyshev while for $k = n$, the response is Butterworth. The poles of $H_{n,k}$ are found using analytic continuation, and solving for the left-half-plane zeros of

$$1 + (-js)^{2k} T^2_{n-k}(-js) = 0 \tag{4.17.4}$$

This interpolation scheme produces a magnitude response which is similar to that for an ultraspherical filter ($\alpha > -0.5$). The filter poles no longer follow a linear or power law curve as before.

Every interpolation scheme generates a unique transitional filter. Their characteristics differ and depend ultimately upon the contour and pole placement chosen.

4.18 NOISE RESPONSE OF FILTERS

An important consideration in filter design in addition to its frequency and time domain responses to impressed signals is its noise response. In general, we shall be concerned with "white noise" applied to the filter input. Noise is said to be "white" if its power spectrum $S(\omega)$ is constant for all frequencies ω, i.e., $S(\omega) = N_o/2$ for all ω. It is easy to show that the power spectrum $S_o(\omega)$ at the output of the filter having transfer function $H(j\omega)$ equals

$$S_o(\omega) = S_i(\omega)|H(j\omega)|^2 \tag{4.18.1}$$

where $S_i(\omega)$ is the power spectrum at its input.[50] Thus, when the input spectrum is white noise, the output spectrum of the filter varies as the squared-magnitude of the filter.

To quantitatively evaluate and compare the noise characteristics of filters, we evaluate the energy E contained in the filter output as

$$E = \frac{1}{2\pi}\int_{-\infty}^{\infty} S_o(\omega)\,d\omega = \int_{-\infty}^{\infty} S_o(f)\,df = \int_0^{\infty} s_o^2(t)\,dt \tag{4.18.2}$$

where $s_o(t)$ is the output signal of the filter. The equivalence between integration in the time and frequency domains is called *Parseval's theorem*. Assuming a flat input noise spectrum where $S(\omega) = 1$, then the output energy of the filter equals

$$E = \frac{1}{2\pi}\int_{-\infty}^{\infty} |H(j\omega)|^2\,d\omega = \frac{1}{\pi}\int_0^{\infty} |H(j\omega)|^2\,d\omega = \int_{-\infty}^{\infty} h^2(t)\,dt \tag{4.18.3}$$

where $h(t)$ is the inpulse response of the filter. The ideal low-pass filter with unity 3 dB bandwidth had a magnitude function given by Eq. 4.1.1 where $|H| = 1$ for $|\omega| < 1$ and zero elsewhere. Therefore from Eq. 4.18.3, its output energy E would equal $1/\pi = 0.318$ which forms a convenient reference value. If the filter is causal so $h(t) = 0$ for negative t, then the last integral of Eq. 4.18.3 is zero over negative time. This is the situation for the filters in this chapter. It is important to note that when comparing filters on an energy basis, they must all have the same 3 dB bandwidth which we shall take to be unity. We anticipate that filters having increasing selectivity will have decreasing energy E values.

Recall that the Butterworth filter has a gain given by Eq. 4.3.2. Then its output energy is equal to

$$E_n = \frac{1}{\pi}\int_0^{\infty} \frac{1}{1+\omega^{2n}}\,d\omega = \frac{1}{2n\sin(\pi/2n)} \tag{4.18.4}$$

Table 4.18.1 Energy of various classical filters and their limiting values. (From H. Blinchikoff, "High-pass filter step-response energy: A new performance measure," IEEE Trans. Circuit Theory, vol. CT-20, pp. 593–596, Sept., 1973.)

	Butterworth	Chebyshev	Synchronous	Gaussian
$\lvert H_l(j\omega)\rvert^2$	$\dfrac{1}{1+\omega^{2n}}$	$\dfrac{1}{1+\epsilon^2 C_n^2(\omega\omega_c)}$	$\dfrac{\omega_c^{2n}}{(\omega^2+\omega_c^2)^n}$	$\exp\left[-2\left(\dfrac{\omega}{\omega_c}\right)^2\right]$
E	$\dfrac{1}{2n\sin(\pi/2n)}$	$\dfrac{\cosh\left[\dfrac{1}{n}\ln\left(\dfrac{1+\sqrt{1+\epsilon^2}}{\epsilon}\right)\right]}{\omega_c\sqrt{1+\epsilon^2}\,2n\sin(\pi/2n)}$	$\dfrac{\Gamma(n-1/2)}{2\omega_c\sqrt{\pi}\,(n-1)!}$	$\dfrac{1}{2\sqrt{\pi\ln 2}}$
$E_L = \lim\limits_{n\to\infty} E$	$\dfrac{1}{\pi}$	$\dfrac{1}{\pi\sqrt{1+\epsilon^2}}$	$\dfrac{1}{2\sqrt{\pi\ln 2}}$	$\dfrac{1}{2\sqrt{\pi\ln 2}}$
Notes		$\omega_c = \cosh\left[\dfrac{1}{n}\cosh^{-1}\dfrac{1}{\epsilon}\right]$	$\omega_c = (2^{1/n}-1)^{-1/2}$ Γ(x) is the gamma function	$\omega_c = \sqrt{\dfrac{2}{\ln 2}}$

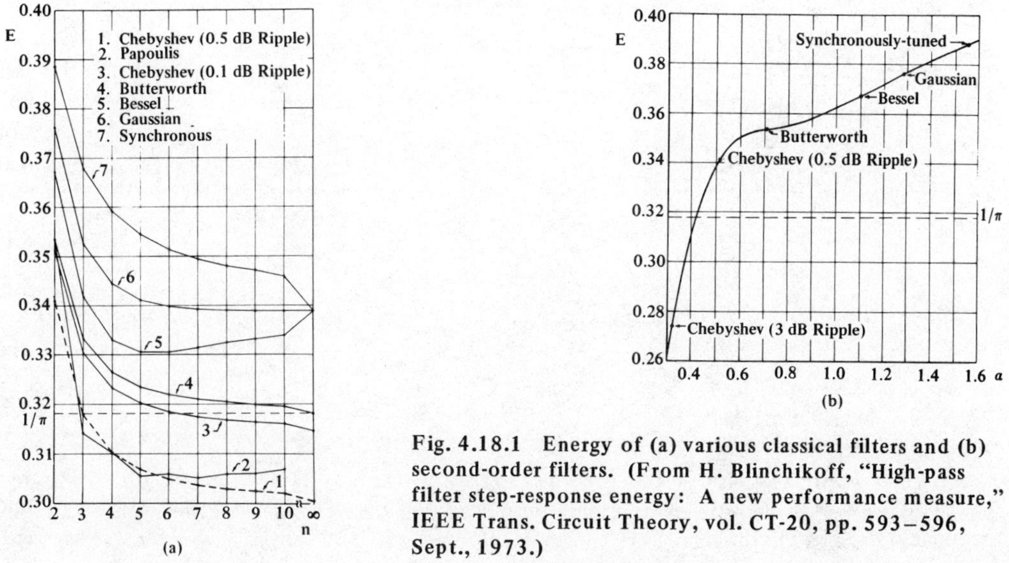

Fig. 4.18.1 Energy of (a) various classical filters and (b) second-order filters. (From H. Blinchikoff, "High-pass filter step-response energy: A new performance measure," IEEE Trans. Circuit Theory, vol. CT-20, pp. 593–596, Sept., 1973.)

which has the limiting value of $1/\pi$ as $n \to \infty$. Thus, the limiting value of E_n is equal to E of the ideal filter. The expressions for other filter energies are listed in Table 4.18.1 and are plotted in Fig. 4.18.1a. Their values can be more easily determined using the resistance-integral theorem from passive network theory.[51]

EXAMPLE 4.18.1 Determine the energy expression of second-order all-pole filters having transfer function[52]

$$H(s) = \frac{K}{(s+a)^2 + \beta^2} \tag{4.18.5}$$

Plot the energy results and compare values for different classical filters.

Solution The gain expression equals

$$|H(j\omega)|^2 = \frac{K^2}{(a^2+\beta^2-\omega^2)^2 + 4a^2\omega^2} = \frac{K^2}{\omega^4 + 2\omega^2(a^2-\beta^2) + (a^2+\beta^2)^2} \tag{4.18.6}$$

Substituting $|H|^2$ into Eq. 4.18.3 and evaluating yields

$$E = \frac{1}{\pi}\int_0^\infty |H|^2\, d\omega = \frac{K^2}{4a(a^2+\beta^2)} \tag{4.18.7}$$

For monotonically nonincreasing responses, unity dc gain requires $K = a^2 + \beta^2$. Unity 3 dB bandwidth requires

$$a^2 + \beta^2 = (2 + 4a^2)^{1/2} - 1 \tag{4.18.8}$$

from Eq. 4.18.6. Substituting these two conditions into Eq. 4.18.7, the energy equals

$$E = [(2 + 4a^2)^{1/2} - 1]/4a \tag{4.18.9}$$

E is plotted for various a's in Fig. 4.18.1b. E attains the minimum value of $1/2\sqrt{2}$ when $a = \beta = 1/\sqrt{2}$ which corresponds to a Butterworth filter. As anticipated from our previous results, the synchronously-tuned filter has the largest E value.

When the gain ripples in the passband, its maximum value occurs at frequency $\omega_p = (\beta^2 - a^2)^{1/2}$. For the maximum gain to equal unity, then $K = 2a\beta$. Unity 3 dB bandwidth then requires $a + \beta = (1 + 2a^2)^{1/2}$. Substituting these results into the energy equation, Eq. 4.18.7, gives

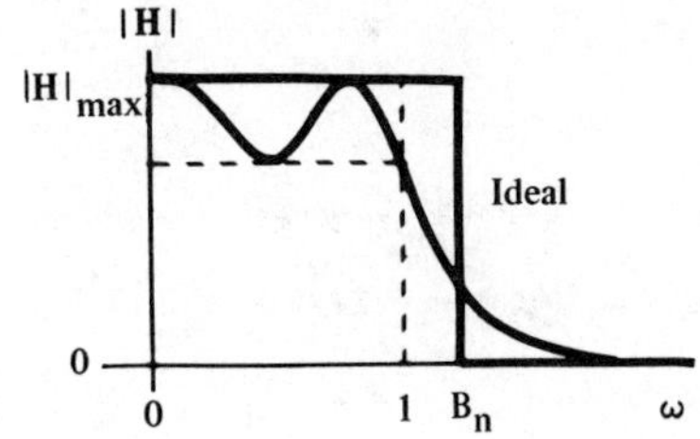

Fig. 4.18.2 Effective noise bandwidth of low-pass filter.

$$E = \frac{a\beta^2}{a^2 + \beta^2} = \frac{a[(1 + 2a^2)^{1/2} - a]^2}{a^2 + [(1 + 2a^2)^{1/2} - a]^2} \tag{4.18.10}$$

which is also plotted in Fig. 4.18.1b. $E \cong a$ as $a \to 0$. We see that Chebyshev filters have decreasing energy with increasing ripple.

Another useful measure of the noise performance of a filter is its *noise margin*. The noise margin of a filter is the ratio of its energy output to that of the equivalent ideal low-pass filter. Thus, from Eq. 4.18.3,

$$NM = \tfrac{1}{2}\int_{-\infty}^{\infty} |H(j\omega)|^2\, d\omega = \int_0^{\infty} |H(j\omega)|^2\, d\omega \tag{4.18.11}$$

assuming a flat input noise spectrum (for another, see Ref. 53). We see from Eq. 4.18.3 that the noise margin is related to energy as $NM = \pi E$. The ideal low-pass filter has an NM of unity or 0 dB.

The *noise bandwidth* B_n of a filter is also of considerable interest. It equals the effective bandwidth of the ideal low-pass filter which passes white noise with the same energy value as the actual filter or

$$B_n = |H(j\omega)|_{max}^{-2} \int_0^{\infty} |H(j\omega)|^2\, d\omega \tag{4.18.12}$$

This is shown in Fig. 4.18.2. The ideal low-pass filter has unity noise bandwidth. Actual filters have a B_n greater than unity. When the maximum in-band gain $|H|_{max}$ equals unity, then the effective noise bandwidth $B_n = \pi E$ from Eq. 4.18.3. Thus, when the noise bandwidth and 3 dB bandwidth of a filter coincide (i.e., $B_n = 1$), the energy equals $1/\pi$ which is shown in Fig. 4.18.1.

Although the step response performance of low-pass filters is usually of interest, there are radar and other similar areas in which *pulsed-cosine response* is of interest. In this situation, the low-pass filter input equals

$$s_i(t) = \cos \omega_o t\, [U_{-1}(t + T/2) - U_{-1}(t - T/2)] \tag{4.18.13}$$

where ω_o is the frequency of the cosine or carrier signal and T is the duration of the cosine pulse. Although low-pass filters may provide a certain energy rejection at a frequency ω_s, it may not provide the same energy rejection for pulsed operation. Schafer and Wang have investigated the behavior of Butterworth low-pass filters under pulsed-cosine operation.[54] We determined the input spectrum $S_i(\omega)$ to the low-pass filter in Example 1.9.6 and found it had the familiar sin x/x characteristics (see Eq. 1.9.30). The output energy of the filter equals

$$E_o = \frac{1}{2\pi}\int_{-\infty}^{\infty} |S_i(\omega)|^2 |H_n(j\omega)|^2\, d\omega = \frac{1}{2\pi}\int_{-\infty}^{\infty} E_i(\omega)|H_n(j\omega)|^2\, d\omega \tag{4.18.14}$$

This is a complicated expression for even Butterworth filters which have a simple gain expression (cf., Ref. 55). E_o is plotted in Fig. 4.18.3 for a fourth-order Butterworth filter where E_o has been normalized to the input energy E_i given by Eq. 1.9.31. The curves are labelled in terms of the

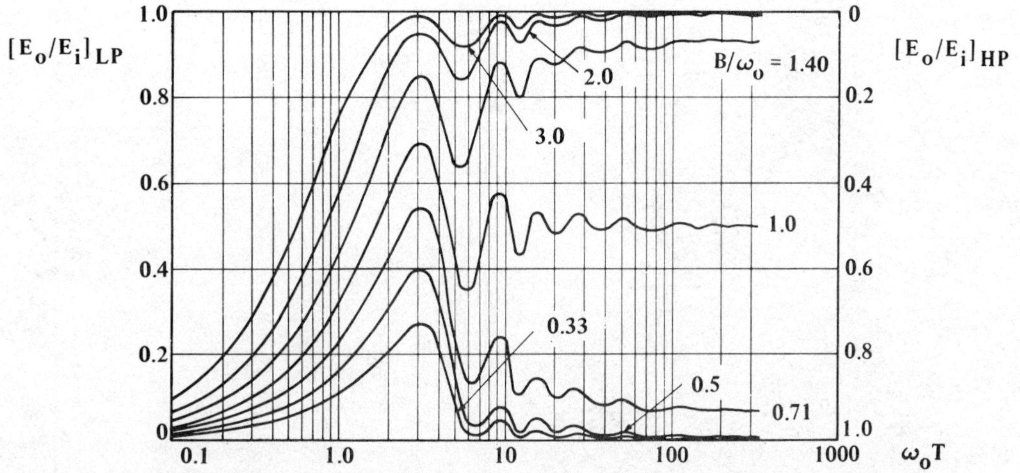

Fig. 4.18.3 Normalized output energies of fourth-order Butterworth filters for pulsed-cosine operation. (From R. H. Schafer and J. J. H. Wang, "Energy transfer characteristics of Butterworth resonant circuits under pulsed-carrier operation," IEEE Trans. Circuit Theory, vol. CT-19, pp. 221–223, March, 1972.)

ratio B/ω_o which equals the 3 dB filter bandwidth divided by the carrier frequency. The B/ω_o values are 0.33, 0.50, 0.71, 1, 1.4, 2, and 3. These curves show that for a fixed B/ω_o ratio, there is a range of normalized time $\omega_o T$ (in radians) required to pass a reasonable amount of energy through the filter. For example, for a filter bandwidth B of 1 KHz and a signal of 2 KHz, then $1.3 \leqslant \omega_o T \leqslant 4.5$ to transfer between 20 and 40% of the input energy. However, if we increase the filter bandwidth to 4 KHz, then $\omega_o T \geqslant 1.5$ insures that at least 80% of the input energy will be transferred. This requires the pulse duration $T \geqslant 1.5/2\pi(2\text{ KHz}) = 0.12$ msec.

It is interesting to note that when the cosine pulse length is only one-half cycle, a significant amount of energy is transmitted through the filter independent of B/ω_o. This is true even for other filter types such as Chebyshev and elliptic filters which have similar energy curves.[56] These results are very useful in design and give us another aspect from which to view filter design.

4.19 CLASSICAL FILTERS IN RETROSPECT

We have seen in this chapter that there are a variety of classical filter responses which can be utilized in design. These filters furnish a continuum of choices from the highly selective types to constant delay/linear phase types. For any application, there will be several response forms which would be adequate and will be of comparable order. The final selection is often based upon experience and intuition and always involves certain compromises and tradeoffs. Usually these tradeoffs are between high filter selectivity, low delay distortion, and well-behaved step response. To facilitate selection, the filter characteristics of primary importance are tabulated in Table 4.19.1. The filters have been arranged in order of decreasing selectivity (or increasing width of the transition band). Thus, elliptic filters rank first and synchronously-tuned filters rank last.

We can loosely put these filters into three groups as: (1) high selectivity filters, (2) transitional or compromise type filters, and (3) constant delay (or linear phase) filters. Typical applications for these filter groups are listed in Table 4.19.2. Under special requirements, an application may move over one column. In general, for applications which require high selectivity and are phase insensitive, the first few filters of Table 4.19.1 can be utilized. For applications which are phase sensitive and do not require high selectivity, the last few filters in Table 4.19.1 can be utilized. Phase sensitive applications requiring high selectivity require compromises.

Table 4.19.1 Comparison of classical filters.

Filter Type	In-band Gain	Stopband Gain	Band-edge Selectivity & NBW	Transition Bandwidth	In-band Delay	Pole Q	Step Response Overshoot	Step Response Rise Time	Step Response Delay Time
Elliptic	Equiripple	Equiripple	Highest	Lowest	Ripples & increases	Highest	Highest	2.2	Highest
Modified Inverse Chebyshev	MFM	Equiripple	Higher	Lower	Ripples & increases	Higher	Higher	2.2	Higher
Ultraspherical	Non-equiripple	Mono. dec.	Higher	Lower	Ripples & increases	Higher	Higher	2.2	Higher
Chebyshev	Equiripple	Mono. dec.	High	Low	Ripples & increases	High	Medium	2.2	High
Inverse Chebyshev	MFM	Equiripple	High	Low	Ripples & increases	High	Medium	2.2	High
Papoulis/ Halpern	Mono. dec.	Mono. dec.	High	Low	Ripples & increases	High	Medium	2.2	Medium
Butterworth	MFM	Mono. dec.	Medium	Medium	No ripple & increases	Medium	Medium	2.2	Medium
Bessel	Mono. dec.	Mono. dec.	Low	High	MFD	Medium	Negligible	2.2	Low
Gaussian	Mono. dec.	Mono. dec.	Low	High	Mono. dec.	Medium	Negligible	2.2	Low
Equiripple Delay	Mono. dec.	Mono. dec.	Low	High	Ripples	Medium	Low	2.2	Low
Parabolic/Catenary/ Elliptic Contour	Mono. dec.	Mono. dec.	Lower	Higher	Ripples & increases	Medium	Low	2.2	Lower
Synchronously-tuned	Mono. dec.	Mono. dec.	Lowest	Highest	Mono. dec.	Lowest	None	2.2	Lowest

Table 4.19.2 Classical filter applications.

High Selectivity Filters	Compromise Filters	Linear Phase Filters
Acoustical Data Couplers	A/D and D/A Converters	Modems
AM/FM Receivers/Transmitters	Automatic Gain Control	Radar
Digital Multimeters	Anti-aliasing Filters	Telemetry
Distortion Analysis	Automatic Phase Control	Video
Harmonic Analysis	Audio Compensation	
Power Supplies	Data Recording/Playback	
Selective Calling Filters	Data Smoothing	
Spectrum Analysis	Electronic Counter Measures	
Stress Analysis	EKG/ECG	
Telephone Noise Analysis	FDM/PCM	
Tone Detection	Medical Electronics	
Vibration Analysis	MUX/DEMUX	
Voice Analysis	Optoelectronics	
	Pulse Noise	
	Sampled Data Processing	
	Seismic Analysis	
	Sonar	
	Transducer Interfaces	
	VCO	

PROBLEMS

4.1 The magnitude responses of a variety of medium- and sharp-cutoff low-pass filters are shown in Fig. P4.1. Determine what type of low-pass filters can be used and their order.

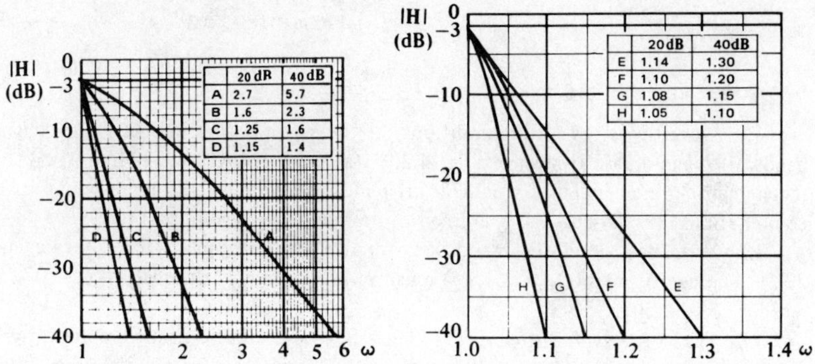

Fig. P4.1 (Courtesy of Allen Avionics[57])

4.2 The magnitude and delay responses of a variety of linear phase low-pass filters are shown in Fig. P4.2. Determine what type of low-pass filters can be used and their order.

4.3 The magnitude responses of a variety of low-pass filters are shown in Fig. P4.3. Determine the types and orders of the: (a) 2.7 KHz speech filter, (b) 400 Hz constant phase filter, (c) delay line.

4.4 Nomographs are tremendously useful in filter design. It can be shown that γ equals

$$\gamma = \log(10^{M_s/10} - 1) - \log(10^{M_p/10} - 1)$$

in Fig. 4.3.4b. (a) If $M_p = 3$ dB, then what does γ equal? (b) Suppose that the filter has the slope requirement shown in Fig. P4.27. If the required stopband rejection M_s equals $10k \log \omega$, determine γ as a function of ω in part (a). (c) Plot $\gamma(\omega)$ found in part (b) on a nomograph. Why is this plot useful?

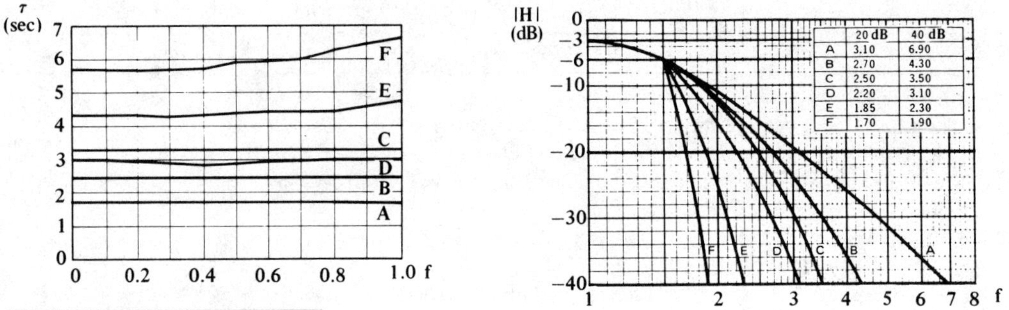

Shape Factor	Max. Phase Distortion (Degrees)	Maximum Overshoot (Percent)	Typical Delay Variation (±Percent)
A	±2°	1.5%	3%
B	±2°	1.5%	3%
C	±2°	1.5%	3%
D	±3°	3%	8%
E	±7°	6%	13%
F	±12°	9%	17%

Fig. P4.2 (Courtesy of Allen Avionics[57])

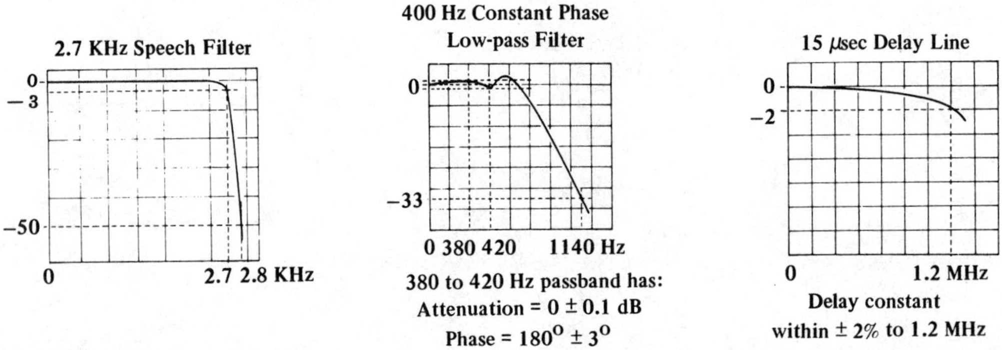

Fig. P4.3 (Courtesy of BG Electronics[58])

4.5 Investigate the MFM conditions for the second-order low-pass filter having a parasitic zero, unity bandwidth, and a gain H given by Eq. 4.2.9. (a) How are a_1, b_1, and b_2 related? How many of these parameters can be independently specified? (b) Plot the Bode magnitude responses of H for several (a_1, b_1, b_2) combinations. (c) Discuss the root locus of the poles and zero in part (b).

4.6 Investigate the MFM conditions for the first-order band-stop filter having the gain given in Prob. 2.33. The coefficients $(\omega_{np}, \zeta, \omega_{nz})$ must be normalized so that $|H(j1)| = 0.707$. Plot the Bode magnitude response of the filter.[59]

4.7 The orders of Butterworth, Chebyshev, and elliptic filters are given by Eqs. 4.3.13, 4.4.15, and 4.8.7, respectively. (a) Derive the equations for Butterworth and Chebyshev filters. (b) For a given ϵ_1, ϵ_2, ω_1, and ω_2, discuss how the order changes between these three filter types. (c) What are the approximate improvement factors?

4.8 (a) Prove that m cascaded stages, each of which is an nth-order Butterworth filter, have a 6–60 dB shaping factor given by Eq. 4.3.11. (b) Are Butterworth or synchronously-tuned filters more efficient in terms of minimizing filter order?

4.9 A fourth-order Butterworth filter having a dc gain of 20 dB and a 3 dB bandwidth of 2 KHz must be designed. Determine the transfer function of the filter and draw its block diagram realization. Plot its magnitude response.

4.10 A delay equalizer was designed earlier for each of the following filters; repeat the problem listed: (a) second-order Butterworth filter in Prob. 2.45, (b) fourth-order Butterworth filter in Prob. 2.48a, (c) fourth-order Chebyshev filter in Prob. 2.48b.

4.11 A fifth-order Butterworth filter has the delay response shown in Fig. 4.3.2. (a) Plot the Bode delay response of the filter. (b) Determine the parameters of the second-order delay equalizer which, when cascaded with the Butterworth filter, will reduce the overall in-band delay variation. (c) Plot the overall delay characteristic. Has the filter been effectively delay equalized?

4.12 A variety of medium- and sharp-cutoff low-pass filters were analyzed in Prob. 4.1. Two of the resulting filter types and their orders are listed below. Design the filters in block diagram form. Assume that the 3 dB bandwidth required is 3.2 KHz. (a) Filter A which is third-order Butterworth. (b) Filter B which is fourth-order Chebyshev (use 0.5 dB ripple). (Hint: Use the nomograph to find the 3 dB frequency.)

4.13 The hydrophone of Prob. 2.7 requires an amplitude equalizer whose response is shown in Fig. P4.13 to extend its bandwidth. Determine the transfer function of the equalizer using (a) Butterworth and (b) Chebyshev filter characteristics. (Hint: Is inverse gain useful?) (c) Plot their magnitude and delay responses. (d) Which filter is best for minimizing delay distortion? Can the delay distortion be reduced?

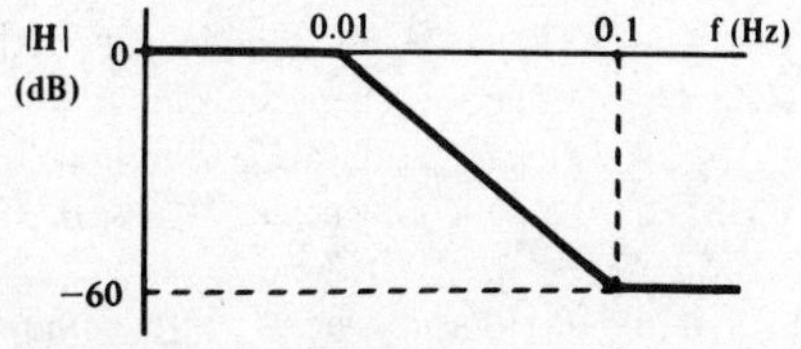

Fig. P4.13

4.14 A band-limiting filter in a sonar processing system was analyzed in Example 2.4.3. Its 1.5 dB frequency = 300 Hz and its 40 dB frequency = 400 Hz. Determine the orders of the Butterworth, Chebyshev, and elliptic filters which meet this specification. Plot the magnitude response of the minimum order elliptic filter and draw its block diagram realization.

4.15 (a) A Touch-Tone band-splitting filter was analyzed in Example 2.6.3. Its 3 dB frequency = 941 Hz and its 20 dB frequency = 1209 Hz. Determine the orders of the Butterworth, Chebyshev, and elliptic filters which meet this specification. (b) Now suppose that the 1.25 dB (not 3 dB) frequency = 941 Hz. Draw the block diagram realization of the minimum order filter which meets this specification.

4.16 Several standard noise weighting filters were considered in Example 2.6.4 and had the magnitude responses shown in Fig. 2.6.7. The filters can be realized by cascading a high-pass filter (for $f \leqslant 1$ KHz) and a low-pass filter (for $f \geqslant 1$ KHz). Determine the order of a Bessel, Butterworth, Chebyshev, and elliptic low-pass filter needed for the: (a) C filter, (b) F1A filter, (c) 144 filter, (d) psophometric filter. (Hint: Begin by specifying the response required.)

4.17 Standard telephone line conditioning was discussed in Prob. 2.27. The magnitude specification and response of a C2 line were shown in Fig. P2.27. (a) Determine the orders of the Butterworth, Chebyshev, and elliptic filters needed to obtain the response beyond 1.7 KHz. (b) Discuss the tradeoffs between the filter order and the required delay characteristics for the C2 filter. Recognizing that a delay equalizer will be required, which filter appears to be the most practical?

4.18 The average speech spectra of humans covers 100–8000 Hz. For good intelligibility, it is unnecessary to transmit this entire spectrum. Since most of the spectral energy is contained between 250–2500 Hz, the standard band used by the telephone company for speech transmission is 200–3200 Hz. Low-pass filters are used to restrict voice to this band before it is transmitted over telephone links.[60] Determine the order of the Bessel, Butterworth, Chebyshev, and elliptic filters which meet the following gain specifications: (1) 3 dB frequency = 3200 Hz, (2) 20 dB frequency = 3700 Hz, and (3) 40 dB frequency = 5000 Hz.

4.19 In Prob. 2.23, we analyzed a parallel array of EEG filters and their responses. Considering only the Delta filter: (a) Determine the minimum order Butterworth, Chebyshev, and elliptic filters which meet the magnitude response shown in Fig. P2.23. If only the (b) appearance or (c) spectral energy of the Delta wave is important, which filter type is best to use? (d) Determine the transfer function of the elliptic filter and draw its block diagram realization.

4.20 The phase detector shown in Fig. P4.20 measures the phase θ between two square waves by filtering the output of an exclusive-or. The input frequency range is 2 Hz–100 KHz; the fundamental frequency of the exclusive-or output is, therefore, 4 Hz–200 KHz. We require 60 dB rejection at 4 Hz and select a 1.25 dB bandwidth of 1 Hz. (a) Determine the orders of the Butterworth, Chebyshev, and elliptic filters which meet this specification. (b) If a third-order elliptic filter is desired and M_p, M_s, and ω_s must remain fixed, what bandwidth ω_p should be specified?

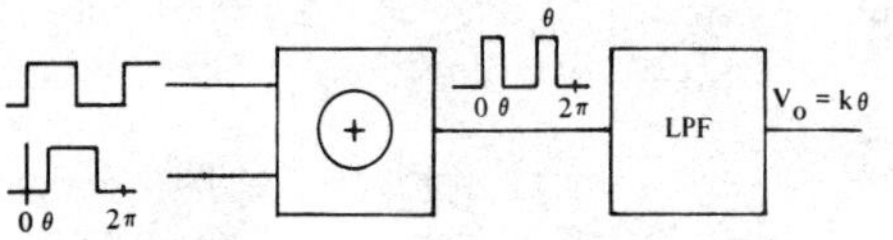

Fig. P4.20

4.21 (a) Determine the orders of the Butterworth, Chebyshev, and elliptic filters which meet the following gain specifications: (1) maximum low-frequency gain = 0 dB, (2) 0.5 dB frequency = 2 KHz, (3) 40 dB frequency = 3 KHz, and (4) 60 dB frequency = 4 KHz. (b) Plot the magnitude response of the elliptic filter. How much rejection can actually be obtained?

4.22 Repeat Prob. 4.21 using the following gain specifications: (1) maximum low-frequency gain = 0 dB, (2) 0.5 dB frequency = 1 KHz, (3) 40 dB frequency = 2 KHz, and (4) 60 dB frequency = 3 KHz.

4.23 (a) Repeat Prob. 4.21a using the following gain specifications: (1) maximum low-frequency gain = 0 dB, (2) 1.25 dB frequency = 1 KHz, (3) 50 dB frequency = 2 KHz, and (4) 80 dB frequency = 3 KHz. (b) Design the Chebyshev and elliptic filters in block diagram form.

4.24 Repeat Prob. 4.21 using the following gain specifications: (1) maximum low-frequency gain = 0 dB, (2) 0.5 dB frequency = 100 KHz, (3) 40 dB frequency = 150 KHz, and (4) 80 dB frequency = 200 KHz.

4.25 (a) Expressing the filter gain using Eq. 4.3.12 where S(1) = 1, show that the advantage of using a Chebyshev filter in place of a Butterworth filter is an additional stopband rejection of 6(n – 1) dB. (b) Now assume that the 3 dB bandwidth is unity (not ripple bandwidth as in part (a)). Determine the additional rejection obtained. Show that it lies between 0 and 6(n – 1) dB, and that it approaches 0 dB as $\epsilon \to 0$. (Hint: It involves $-20 \log \epsilon$ dB.) (c) Calculate the ripple bandwidth for second-order Chebyshev filters having unity 3 dB bandwidth and 0.1 and 1 dB of ripple. Compare the results with Fig. 4.4.3.

4.26 Determine the order of the Chebyshev filter required to meet the specification of Example 4.3.3.

4.27 Determine the order of the Butterworth, Chebyshev, and elliptic filters which meet the magnitude response shown in Fig. P4.27. (Hint: Also check the band-edge selectivity or use Prob. 4.4.)

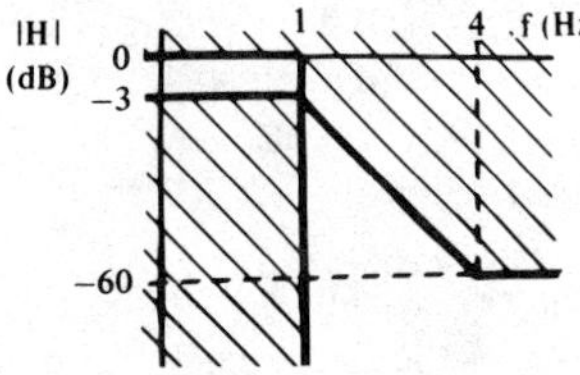

Fig. P4.27

4.28 The ultraspherical filter has parameters n, ϵ, and α with which to design. (a) Show that Eq. 4.5.7 gives the proper selectivity values for Butterworth and Chebyshev (B/C) filters. (b) Determine the α required if the selectivity of an ultraspherical filter is to be halfway between those of B/C filters. Interpret the result using both the magnitude responses of Fig. 4.5.2 and the root locus of Fig. 4.5.3. (c) Show that Eq. 4.5.5 gives the proper asymptotic gain values for B/C filters. (d) Determine the α required if the asymptotic gain of an ultraspherical filter is to be halfway (in dB) between those of B/C filters. Interpret the result as in part (b).

4.29 (a) Determine the order of the Papoulis filter which meets the following gain specifications: (1) dc gain = 0 dB, (2) 3 dB frequency = 5 KHz, and (3) 60 dB frequency = 15 KHz. (b) Determine the transfer function of the filter and draw its block diagram realization.

4.30 Repeat Prob. 4.29 using the following gain specifications: (1) dc gain = 0 dB, (2) 3 dB frequency = 10 KHz, (3) 20 dB frequency = 15 KHz, and (4) 40 dB frequency = 20 KHz.

4.31 Repeat Prob. 4.29 using the following gain specifications: (1) dc gain = 20 dB, (2) 3 dB frequency = 1 KHz, (3) 20 dB frequency = 1.5 KHz, (4) 60 dB frequency = 3 KHz, and (5) minimum high-frequency rolloff = –60 dB/dec.

4.32 Determine the orders of the Chebyshev and Papoulis filters which meet the frequency and time domain specifications shown in Fig. 4.3.7 with the following changes: |H| has its axes relabelled as (0, –1, –20, –40) dB and (1, 3, 5) KHz; r(t) has its axes relabelled as (0, 0.5, 0.95, 1.0, 1.05, 1.2) and (0, 1, 1.5) msec.

4.33 Fourth-order (a) Papoulis, (b) Chebyshev, and (c) elliptic filters having 3 dB bandwidths of 1 KHz and maximum low-frequency gains of unity must be designed. Determine the transfer function for each filter and draw its block diagram realization.

4.34 Generalized inverse Chebyshev filters have an arbitrary number of transmission zeros. (a) How do their orders compare with those of Butterworth and Chebyshev filters? (b) Why are inverse Chebyshev filters not often used? (c) A closely related filter was considered in Fig. 3.8.15. Compare its response with that of a generalized inverse Chebyshev filter. What are their similarities and differences?

4.35 Determine the transfer function of a fourth-order elliptic filter having a maximum low-frequency gain of 10, an in-band ripple of 1.25 dB, a corner frequency of 10 KHz, and a minimum stopband rejection of 40 dB. Draw its block diagram realization.

4.36 (a) The ideal delay filter has a transfer function of e^{-s}. Plot its unit step response. (b) Plot the unit step response of a fourth-order Bessel filter (assume a delay of 1 sec). Compare it with the response of part (a). (c) Draw the block diagram of a fourth-order Bessel filter which will yield a delay of 1 msec. (Hint: Use Eq. 4.10.14 and Table 4.10.1.)

4.37 (a) An ideal delay filter has a transfer function of e^{-s}. Plot its magnitude and delay responses. Classify the filter (e.g., low-pass). (b) The Bessel filter has an MFD characteristic. Therefore, a good gain approximation for constant delay is $H_n(s) = P_n(-s)/P_n(s)$ where P_n is the nth-order Bessel filter polynomial listed in Table 4.10.1. Plot the magnitude and delay responses of this filter. (c) Suppose that a third-order filter of part (b) is used to obtain 1 msec of delay. Design the filter in block diagram form.[61]

4.38 Delay or echo generators are used to simulate data transmission lines having a variety of delay, echo, and return loss characteristics. Such generators are used for testing modems, facsimile systems, and communication systems. Typical specifications are:[62] (1) passband: 200 Hz–3200 Hz, (2) gain = 0 ± 0.5 dB, (3) delay: 2–101 msec adjustable in 1 msec steps, and (4) delay distortion $\leqslant$ 50 μsec throughout the passband. (a) Assume that an all-pass filter having an MFD characteristic is used to obtain the delay (see Prob. 4.37). Determine the filter order required. (b) Is this a desirable design approach?

4.39 A correlation detector is often used in communication systems. It consists of a delay element, multiplier, and integrator as shown in Fig. P4.39. Algebraically, it performs the operation

$$R(\tau) = \int_{-\infty}^{\infty} f(t)f(t+\tau)\,dt$$

Suppose that a Bessel filter is used for the delay element. (a) Plot the step response of an ideal delay filter. (b) Discuss the step response and magnitude characteristic of a Bessel filter. (c) Suppose that a third-order Bessel filter is used to obtain 1 msec of delay. Design the filter in block diagram form. (d) Describe what filter parameters to vary to obtain delays from 0 to 1 msec.

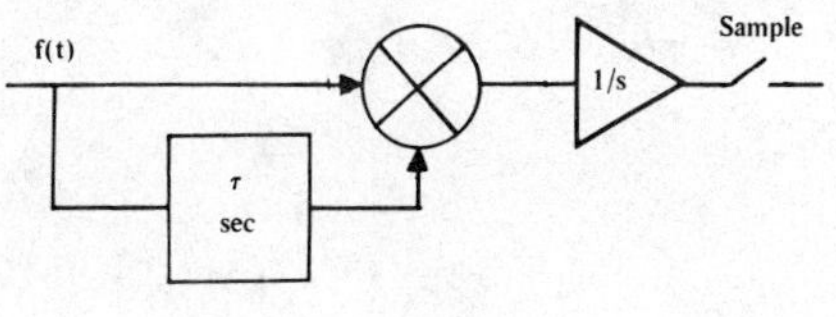

Fig. P4.39

4.40 A second-order noise suppression filter was designed in Examples 3.8.1 and 3.8.2 for a 1000 Bps data stream. It had: (1) overshoot $\gamma \leqslant 20\%$ (2) peak time $T_p \leqslant 0.1$ msec, and (3) settling time $T_s \leqslant 0.5$ msec for $\delta \leqslant 5\%$. (a) Determine the transfer functions of third-order Butterworth, elliptic, and Bessel filters which meet these specifications. Design for minimum bandwidth. (b) Plot their frequency responses. Which filter is best to use?

4.41 A second-order noise suppression filter was designed in Examples 3.8.1 and 3.8.2. We can improve the design by maintaining settling time $T_s \leqslant 0.5$ msec, deleting the peaking time T_p requirement, and increasing overshoot $\gamma \leqslant 50\%$. The resulting filter has a 3 dB bandwidth of 2.2 KHz. (a) Design a second-order Bessel filter to satisfy the same time domain specifications. Draw its block diagram realization. (b) Plot its step response and compare with the earlier solution.

4.42 (a) Determine the orders of the Butterworth, Bessel, and synchronously-tuned filters which meet the frequency domain specification given in Prob. 4.32. (b) When used as a smoothing filter for a digital data stream, which filter is best for minimizing delay distortion? (c) Suppose that the time domain specification given in Prob. 4.32 must also be satisfied. Can the filters still be realized?

4.43 Determine if Butterworth, synchronously-tuned, and Bessel filters can be designed to meet the frequency and time domain specifications shown in Fig. 4.3.7 with the following changes: |H| has its frequency axis relabelled as (1, 2, 4) KHz; r(t) has its time axis relabelled as (5, 7.5, 10) msec. Design the minimum order filter in block diagram form. Plot its step response.

4.44 Determine if Butterworth, synchronously-tuned, and Bessel filters can be designed to meet the frequency and time domain specifications shown in Fig. 4.3.7 with the following changes: r(t) has its time axis relabelled as (2, 4, 6) msec. Design the minimum order filter in block diagram form. Plot its step response.

4.45 Determine the limiting magnitude response of the synchronously-tuned filter as the order $n \to \infty$. Maintain the 3 dB bandwidth to be unity.

4.46 Design a fourth-order parabolic filter in block diagram form having a 3 dB bandwidth of 1000 Hz and the fastest step response. Which b should be used?

4.47 Repeat Prob. 4.46 for a fourth-order catenary filter.

4.48 Repeat Prob. 4.46 for a fourth-order elliptic contour filter.

4.49 Compare the parabolic, catenary, and elliptic contour filters with the Butterworth and Bessel filters on the basis of their nomographs. Why can they be viewed as transitional filters?

4.50 A random noise generator can be constructed using a clocked random ("coin-toss") binary wave n(t). This wave is low-pass filtered to obtain the noise signal s(t) shown in Fig. P4.50. The power spectrum from the noise generator is $N(f) = 25T$ for $f \ll 1/T$ where T is the clock period; when T equals 1 msec, then N(f) equals 0.025 V^2/Hz.[63] (a) Determine the power spectrum outputted by an ideal low-pass filter and (b) the rms output value. (c) Discuss the effects of using different types of low-pass filters.

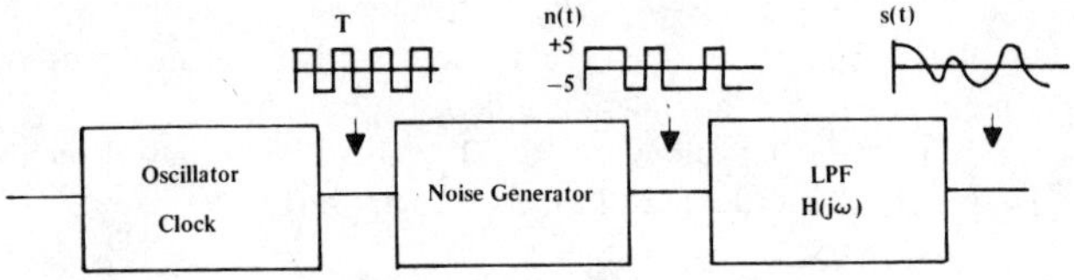

Fig. P4.50

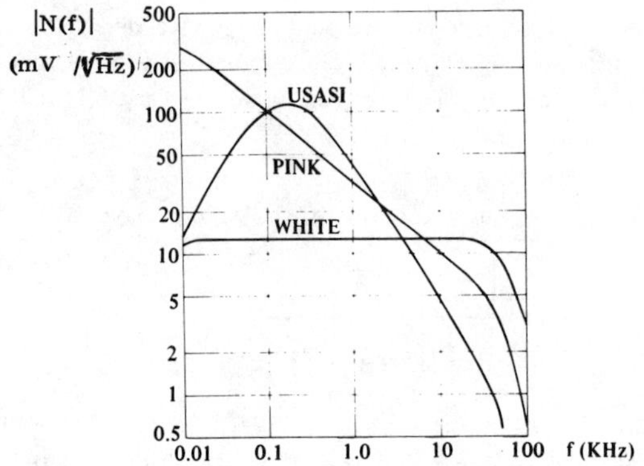

Fig. P4.51 (Courtesy of General Radio[64])

4.51 Random noise generators are used for testing equipment and communication links. The noise output of a typical noise generator is shown in Fig. P4.51 in its three modes of operation: (1) white noise mode: constant energy per Hz bandwidth, (2) pink noise mode: constant energy per octave bandwidth, and (3) USASI noise mode: as specified in USA Standard S1.4-1961. (a) Explain the difference between these three modes. (b) Assuming that white noise is generated, determine the transfer functions required to obtain pink noise and USASI noise. (Hint: The block diagram is shown in Fig. P4.50.)

4.52 (a) Show that Gaussian (ideal) and synchronously-tuned filters have the energy E values listed in Table 4.18.1. (b) What are the limiting values for E as $n \to \infty$? (c) What is the integral that must be evaluated to determine E for an ultraspherical filter? (Do not solve.)

4.53 We are interested in the pulsed-cosine characteristics of a band-splitting low-pass/high-pass filter centered at 1 KHz. The filters are used in an FSK demodulator to separate tone frequencies of 600 and 1400 Hz. Assume that the filters have output energy curves similar to those shown in Fig. 4.18.3. (a) Plot the normalized output energies of the low-pass filter. (b) To insure that at least 50% of the input energy is transmitted or rejected, what should be the duration of the tone? Interpret your result.

4.54 Repeat Prob. 4.53 assuming that the low-pass/high-pass filters have 3 dB corner frequencies of 600 and 1400 Hz, respectively, rather than 1 KHz.

4.55 A Touch-Tone band-splitting filter was analyzed in Example 2.6.3. Assume that the low-pass filter has output energy curves similar to those shown in Fig. 4.18.4. What should be the duration of the tone to pass or reject at least 50% of the input energy if B = 941 Hz? Interpret your result.

REFERENCES

1. Butterworth, S., "On the theory of filter amplifiers," Wireless Engineer, vol. 7, pp. 536–541, Oct., 1930.
2. Churchill, R. V., *Complex Variables and Applications*, 2nd ed., Chap. 12, McGraw-Hill, NY, 1960.
   Tuttle, D. F., Jr., *Network Synthesis*, vol. 1, Chaps. 3 and 8, Wiley, NY, 1958.
3. Churchill, R. V., Ref. 2, Chap. 1.
4. Petit, J. M., and M. M. McWhorter, *Electronic Amplifier Circuits*, p. 238, McGraw-Hill, NY, 1961.
5. Kawakami, M., "Nomographs for Butterworth and Chebyshev filters," IEEE Trans. Circuit Theory, vol. CT-10, pp. 288–289, June, 1963.
6. Hallberg, J. N., and C. S. Lindquist, "Nomographs and filters," J. Franklin Inst., to be published late 1976.
7. Weinberg, L., *Network Analysis and Synthesis*, Chap. 11, McGraw-Hill, NY, 1962.
8. Chebyshev, P. L., "Theorie des mecanismes connus sons le non de parallelogrammes," Oeuvres, vol. 1, St. Petersburg, 1899.
9. Abramowitz, M., and I. A. Stegun (eds.), *Handbook of Mathematical Functions*, Natl. B. of Standards, vol. 55, Sec. 22, 1972.
10. Selby, S. M. (ed.), *Standard Mathematical Tables*, 21st ed., p. 341, Chemical Rubber Co., Cleveland, OH, 1973.
11. Christian, E., and E. Eisenmann, *Filter Design Tables and Graphs*, Wiley, NY, 1966.
12. Vlach, J., *Computerized Approximation and Synthesis of Linear Networks,* Chap. 8, Wiley, NY, 1969.
13. Hansell, G. E., *Filter Design and Evaluation*, Van Nostrand Reinhold, NY, 1969.
14. Mager, H., "The Chebyshev normalized low-pass 3-dB frequency–a 'bone from the technical graveyard?'," IEEE Trans. Circuit Theory, vol. CT-10, pp. 287–288, June, 1963.
15. Johnson, D. E., and J. R. Johnson, "Low-pass filters using ultraspherical polynomials," IEEE Trans. Circuit Theory, vol. CT-13, pp. 364–369, Dec., 1966.
16. Lim, J. T., and J. O. Scanlan, "Group delay characteristics of Chebyshev filters," IEEE Trans. Circuit Theory, vol. CT-11, pp. 427–430, Sept., 1964.
17. Goethals, J. M., and J. Neirynck, "Pseudo-echos interpretation of Chebyshev low-pass filter transient behavior," IEEE Trans. Circuit Theory, vol. CT-11, pp. 504–507, Dec., 1964.
18. Ku, Y. H., and M. Drubin, "Network synthesis using Legendre and Hermite polynomials," J. Franklin Inst., vol. 273, pp. 138–157, Feb., 1962.
19. Petrela, D. M., and A. Budak, "Pole locations for ultraspherical filters," IEEE Trans. Circuit Theory, vol. CT-17, pp. 668–670, Nov., 1970.
20. Papoulis, A., "Optimum filters with monotonic response," Proc. IRE, vol. 46, pp. 606–609, March, 1958.
    ———, "On monotonic response of filters," Proc. IRE, vol. 47, pp. 332–333, Feb., 1959.
21. Halpern, P. H., "Optimum monotonic low-pass filters," IEEE Trans. Circuit Theory, vol. CT-16, pp. 240–242, May, 1969.
22. Rakovich, B. D., and S. M. Lazovich, "Monotonic low-pass filters with improved stopband performance," IEEE Trans. Circuit Theory, vol. CT-19, pp. 218–221, March, 1972.
23. Aronhime, P., and A. Budak, "Maximally flat magnitude beyond the origin," IEEE Trans. Circuit Theory, vol. CT-18, pp. 409–411, May, 1971.
24. Taylor, A. D., and C. S. Lindquist, "MFMBO filter response," IEEE Trans. Circuits and Systems, vol. CAS-23, pp. 477–478, July, 1976.
25. Henderson, K. W., and W. H. Kautz, "Transient responses of conventional filters," IRE Trans. Circuit

Theory, vol. CT-5, pp. 333–347, Dec., 1958.

26. Chang, C. Y., "Maximally flat amplitude low-pass filter with arbitrary number of pairs of real frequency transmission zeros," IEEE Trans. Circuit Theory, vol. CT-15, pp. 465–467, Dec., 1968.
    ———, "Attenuation characteristics and realization of odd-order generalized inverse Chebyshev filters," IEEE Trans. Circuit Theory, vol. CT-15, pp. 467–471, Dec., 1968.
27. Calahan, D. A., *Modern Network Synthesis*, vol. 1, Chaps. 2 and 3, Hayden, NY, 1964.
28. Ref. 9, Sec. 17.
29. Zverev, A. I., *Handbook of Filter Synthesis*, Chap. 5, Wiley, NY, 1967.
30. Thomson, W. E., "Delay networks having maximally flat frequency characteristics," Proc. IEEE, vol. 96, pt. 3, pp. 487–490, Nov., 1949.
    ———, "Maximally-flat delay networks," IRE Trans. Circuit Theory, vol. CT-6, p. 235, June, 1959.
31. Orchard, H. J., "Roots of the maximally flat-delay polynomials," IEEE Trans. Circuit Theory, vol. CT-12, pp. 452–454, Sept., 1965.
32. Storch, L., "Synthesis of constant-delay ladder networks using Bessel polynomials," Proc. IRE, vol. 42, pp. 1666–1675, Nov., 1954.
33. Scanlan, J. O., "A class of transfer functions having approximately maximally flat group delay characteristics," IEEE Trans. Circuit Theory, vol. CT-10, p. 122, March, 1963.
34. Ulbrich, E., and H. Piloty, "Uber den Entwurf von Allpassen, Tiefpassen und Bandpassen mit einer im Tschebyscheffenschen Sinne approximierten konstanten Gruppenlaufzeit," Arch. Elekt. Ubertragung, vol. 14, pp. 451–467, Oct., 1960.
35. Abele, T. A., "Ubertragungsfaktoren mit Tschebyscheffscher Approximation konstanter Gruppenlaufzeit," Arch. Elekt. Ubertragung, vol. 16, pp. 9–18, Jan., 1962.
36. Macnee, A. B., "Chebyshev approximation of a constant group delay," IEEE Trans. Circuit Theory, vol. CT-10, pp. 284–285, June, 1963.
37. Su, K. L., *Time-Domain Synthesis of Linear Networks*, Chap. 7, Prentice-Hall, NJ, 1971.
38. Rakovich, B. D., and B. M. Djurich, "Chebyshev approximation of a constant group delay with constraints at the origin," IEEE Trans. Circuit Theory, vol. CT-19, pp. 466–475, Sept., 1972.
39. Neirynck, J. J., "Transient behavior of systems with equal-ripple delay," IEEE Trans. Circuit Theory, vol. CT-11, pp. 302–303, June, 1964.
40. Dishal, M., "Gaussian-response filter design," Electrical Communication, vol. 36, pp. 3–26, Jan., 1959.
41. Mullick, S. K., "Pulse networks with parabolic distribution of poles," IRE Trans. Circuit Theory, vol. CT-8, pp. 302–305, Sept., 1961.
42. Ghausi, M. S., and M. Adamowicz, "A new class of filters for pulse applications," J. Franklin Inst., vol. 282, pp. 20–30, July, 1966.
43. Kuh, E. S., "Synthesis of lumped parameter precision delay line," Proc. IRE, vol. 45, pp. 1632–1642, Dec., 1957.
44. Scanlan, J. O., "Transfer functions with elliptic distribution of poles at equal frequency spacings," IEEE Trans. Circuit Theory, vol. CT-12, pp. 260–266, June, 1965.
45. Peless, Y., and T. Murakami, "Analysis and synthesis of transitional Butterworth-Thompson filters and bandpass amplifiers," RCA Review, pp. 60–94, March, 1957.
    Hindin, H. J., "Impulse response and transfer phase of transitional Butterworth-Thompson filters," IEEE Trans. Circuit Theory, vol. CT-15, pp. 471–474, Dec., 1968.
46. Aiello, G. L., and P. M. Angelo, "Transitional Legendre-Thomson filters," IEEE Trans. Circuits and Systems, vol. CAS-21, pp. 159–162, Jan., 1974.
47. Ref. 29, Chaps. 3 and 7.
48. Taylor, A. D., "A study of transitional filters," M.S.E.E. Directed Research, California State Univ., Long Beach, Aug., 1975.
49. Budak, A. and P. Aronhime, "Transitional Butterworth-Chebyshev filters," IEEE Trans. Circuit Theory, vol. CT-18, pp. 413–415, May, 1971.
50. Papoulis, A., *Probability, Random Variables, and Stochastic Processes*, p. 347, McGraw-Hill, NY, 1965.
51. Bode, H. W., *Network Analysis and Feedback Amplifier Design*, Chap. 17, D. Van Nostrand, NY, 1945.
52. Bobis, J. P., " 'Energy' of low pass filters," Proc. IEEE, vol. 51, p. 481, March, 1963.
53. Vandivere, E. F., "Noise output of a multipole filter relative to that of the ideal square-response filter," Proc. IEEE, vol. 51, p. 1771, Dec., 1963.
54. Schafer, R. H., and J. J. H. Wang, "Energy transfer characteristics of Butterworth resonant circuits under

pulsed-carrier operation," IEEE Trans. Circuit Theory, vol. CT-19, pp. 221–223, March, 1972.

55. Hancock, J. C., H. Schwarzlander, and R. E. Totty, "Optimization of pulse transmission," Proc. IRE, vol. 50, p. 2136, Oct., 1962.
56. Stones, I., unpublished results.
57. Precision L-C Filters, Catalog 14F, 16 p., Allen Avionics, Inc., Mineola, NY, 1975.
58. Catalog, p. 4, BG Electronics, Inc., Mt Vernon, NY.
59. Budak, A., and P. Aronhime, "Maximally flat low-pass filters with steeper slopes at cutoff," IEEE Trans. Audio and Electro., vol. AU-18, pp. 63–66, March, 1970.
60. Talley, D., *Basic Carrier Telephony*, rev. 2nd ed., pp. 10–12, Hayden, NY, 1966.
61. Marshak, A. H., D. E. Johnson, and J. R. Johnson, "A Bessel rational filter," IEEE Trans. Circuits and Systems, vol. CAS-21, pp. 797–799, Nov., 1974.
62. Delay (Echo) Generator FA-1755, Data Sheet 2855M573, p. 1, SEG Electronics, Richmond Hill, NY, 5/73.
63. Catalog PDS-203B, p. 11, Burr-Brown Research Corp., Tucson, AZ, April, 1969.
64. Random Noise Generators Type 1381 and 1382, Data Sheet, p. 2, General Radio, West Concord, MA, 4/68.

5 OPTIMUM FILTER RESPONSE

Cannot tell where path lead until reach end of road
Oriental Proverb

In the previous chapter, we considered classical filters which were filters described by classical mathematical polynomials or curves. For example Butterworth, Chebyshev, Papoulis, and Bessel filters had magnitude characteristics related to these classical polynomials.

However, the current thrust of filter theory is to develop *optimum filters*. These are filters which satisfy some optimization criterion rather than filters which have transfer functions related to classical functions. The optimization criterion involves the minimization of some performance index subject to certain constraints. Usually the solution cannot be expressed in closed form so computerized iterative solution methods must be used. Tables of optimum filter coefficients are then formed similar to those of the previous chapter for convenient reference by the engineer.

Caution must be exercised when choosing an optimum filter because of certain undesirable peculiarities which these filters sometimes exhibit. These peculiarities often become evident *only* after close scrutiny. Nevertheless, optimum filters can often provide advantages over classical filters. They can also be tailored to meet specialized design requirements as we shall see.

We first review the commonly used performance indices and optimization criteria. A variety of optimum filters derived on these bases will also be examined. We shall also consider several filters which are approximations to ideal filters, but which are not derived using optimization.

5.1 FILTER OPTIMIZATION IN THE TIME DOMAIN

The optimum filter is the filter which optimizes some criterion under certain constraints. Usually the criterion used requires the minimization of a performance or error index E_n. The *performance index* provides a quantitative measure of the performance of the optimum filter. It is chosen to emphasize the most desirable filter characteristics and de-emphasize the undersirable filter characteristics. Performance indices involving integrals are the most universally utilized and have been given standard names.

In time domain optimization, the common performance index integrals are

$$\begin{aligned} IAE &= \int_0^T |e(t)|\,dt & ITSE &= \int_0^T te^2(t)\,dt \\ ISE &= \int_0^T e^2(t)\,dt = \int_0^T |e(t)|^2\,dt & ISTSE &= \int_0^T t^2e^2(t)\,dt \\ ITAE &= \int_0^T t|e(t)|\,dt & IEXSE &= \int_0^T \exp(2kt)\,e^2(t)\,dt \end{aligned} \qquad (5.1.1)$$

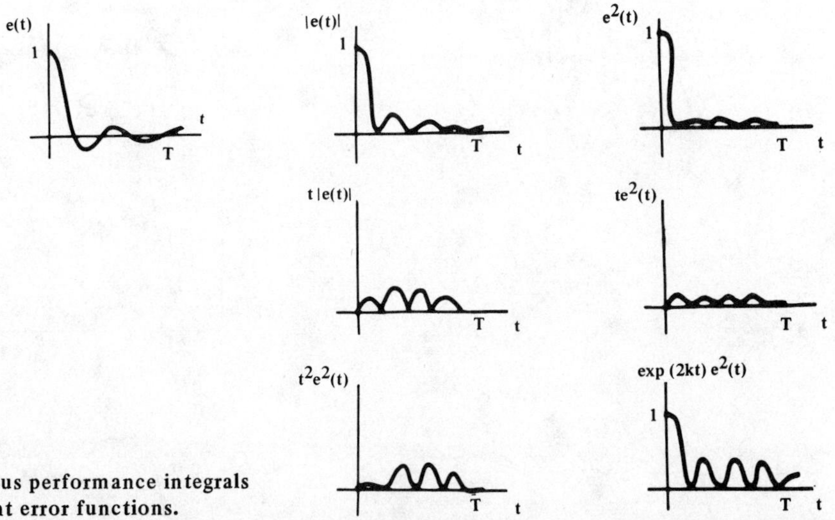

Fig. 5.1.1 Various performance integrals involving different error functions.

where e(t) is the error between desired and the actual filter time domain responses and T is some arbitrary time between zero and infinity. These performance indices are integrals of absolute error (IAE), squared-error (ISE), time-weighted absolute error (ITAE), time-weighted squared-error (ITSE), time-squared weighted squared-error (ISTSE), and exponentially-weighted squared-error (IEXSE). Note that any time limits can be used.

The performance index is a function of the error e(t). The error is equal to the difference between the desired filter response g(t) and the actual filter response $g_n(t)$, or

$$e(t) = g(t) - g_n(t) \tag{5.1.2}$$

For example, if a unit step response is desired, then $e(t) = U_{-1}(t) - r_n(t)$ where $r_n(t)$ is the step response of the *n*th-order filter. The relative merits and deficiencies of these criteria can be somewhat deduced from the typical error e(t) plotted in Fig. 5.1.1. Here we have assumed that the desired filter response is a step and the actual filter response is oscillatory. The following observations can be made about the various performance indices:

1. *IAE*: Error is equally weighted over the interval from 0 to T. Response errors tend to be distributed over the interval.
2. *ISE*: Although error-squared is equally-weighted over the entire interval, large errors are emphasized (or overrated depending on the requirements) and small errors tend to be neglected (or underrated by the same token). The behavior of the rising edge of the transient essentially determines the optimum filter; and overshoots and ringing tend to be overlooked. Large overshoots and long settling time can be obtained using this criterion.
3. *ITAE*: Error is weighted by time over the entire interval. Thus, possibly large initial errors are neglected and the later oscillatory behavior of the response is emphasized. The large initial errors are overlooked so that the optimum filter is relatively independent of the initial response. Large overshoot but short settling time can be obtained using this criterion.
4. *ITSE*: Error-squared is weighted by t over the time interval. This tends to further de-emphasize the initial response errors and emphasize the latter oscillatory behavior. Large overshoot, short settling time, and low-level ringing can be obtained using this criterion.
5. *ISTSE*: Error-squared is weighted by t^2 over the time interval. This further de-emphasizes the initial response errors and greatly emphasizes the later oscillatory behavior. Large overshoot, low level ringing, and short settling time can also be obtained using this criterion.
6. *IEXSE*: Error-squared is exponentially-weighted over the time interval. This is made up, in

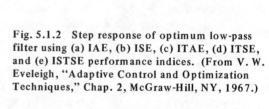

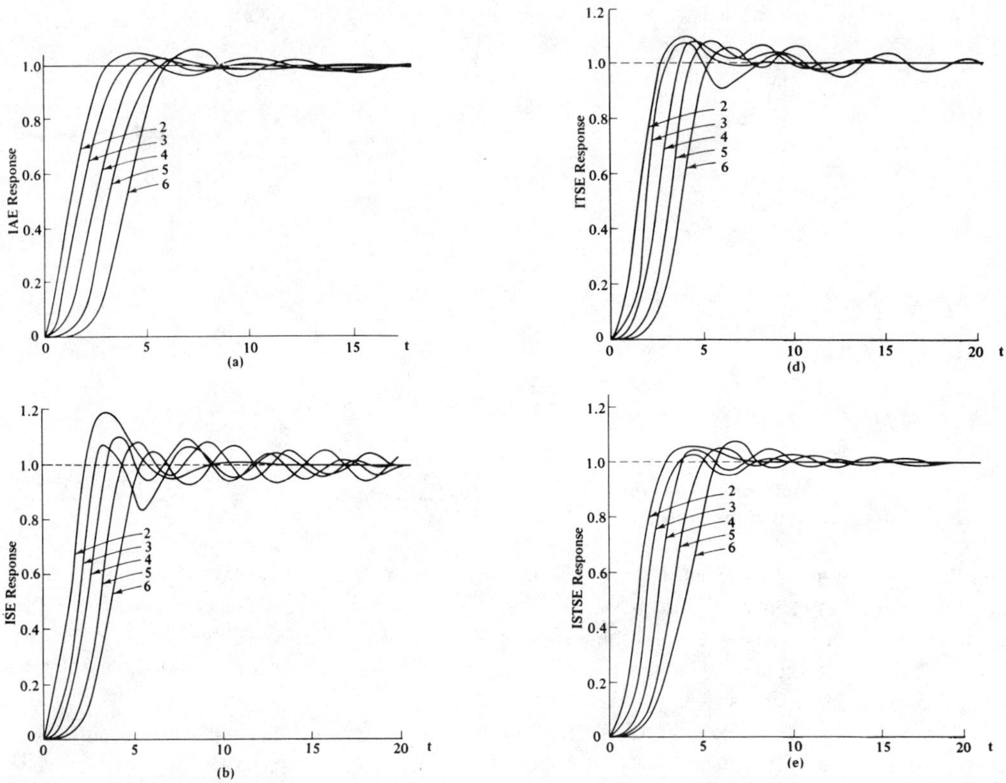

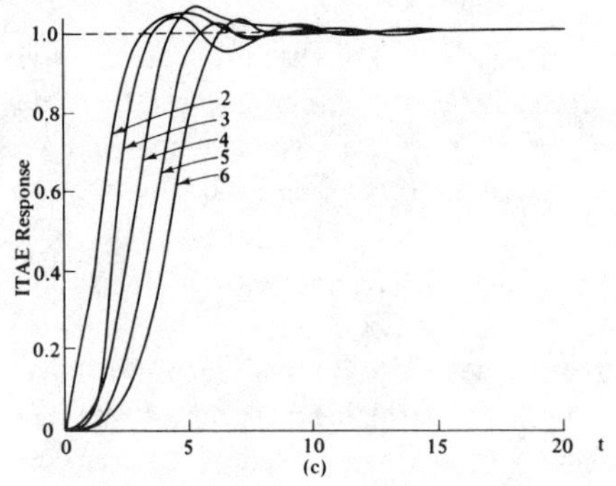

Fig. 5.1.2 Step response of optimum low-pass filter using (a) IAE, (b) ISE, (c) ITAE, (d) ITSE, and (e) ISTSE performance indices. (From V. W. Eveleigh, "Adaptive Control and Optimization Techniques," Chap. 2, McGraw-Hill, NY, 1967.)

part, of ISE and ISTSE. Thus, large errors are emphasized and small errors neglected over the entire interval. Large overshoot and short settling time are again obtained.

Other performance indices are available, but have not found general usage.[1,2]

In the general time-domain optimization, the input is f(t). Since the filter transfer function H_{nm} equals

$$H_{nm}(s) = \sum_{j=0}^{m} a_j s^j \Big/ \sum_{i=0}^{n} b_i s^i \tag{5.1.3}$$

the filter response g(t) to the input f(t) can be calculated to equal

$$g_{nm}(t) = h_{nm}(t) * f(t) = \mathcal{L}^{-1}[H_{nm}(s)\,\mathcal{L}[f(t)]] \tag{5.1.4}$$

In turn, the resulting error is given by Eq. 5.1.2. e(t) can then be substituted into the desired per-

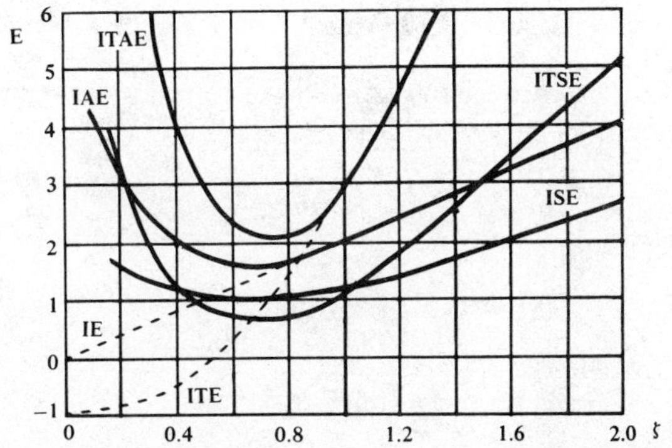

Fig. 5.1.3 Various performance indices for step response of second-order low-pass filter. (Adapted from J. J. D'Azzo and C. H. Houpis, "Control System Analysis and Synthesis," Chap. 17 McGraw-Hill, NY, 1960.)

formance index of Eq. 5.1.1. The optimum filter results by *minimizing* the performance index by properly choosing the a_i and b_i coefficients, under the constraint that $H_{nm}(s)$ is realizable, i.e., $h_{nm}(t) = \mathcal{L}^{-1}[H_{nm}(s)] = 0$ for $t < 0$. In general, closed-form solutions *do not exist* so computerized iterative techniques are used to determine solutions.[3] The coefficients so obtained are then tabulated for ready reference.

Consider the all-pole low-pass filter having a transfer function

$$H_n(s) = \frac{a_0}{s^n + a_{n-1}s^{n-1} + \ldots + a_1 s + a_0} \tag{5.1.5}$$

where its dc gain equals unity. Suppose that $a_0 = 1$ and the desired output equals a unit step where the error e(t) is given by Eq. 5.1.2. The optimum filters which result using the IAE, ISE, ITAE, ITSE, and ISTSE performance indices have the responses shown in Fig. 5.1.2. Comparing these responses with one another tend to verify our comments concerning the peculiarities of the different performance indices.

To further interpret these performance indices, consider a second-order low-pass filter having gain function $H_2(s) = 1/(s^2 + 2\zeta s + 1)$. Various performance indices are shown in Fig. 5.1.3 for a unit step input which is also the desired output. The optimum filter is that whose ζ minimizes the performance index. The optimum filters which result have different damping factors where for IAE/ITAE: $\zeta \cong 0.7$; and ISE/ITSE: $\zeta \cong 0.6$ (also shown are IE: $\zeta = 0$ and ITE: $\zeta \cong 0.5$).

The minimum values of the various performance indices are not comparable. Although the minimum ITSE index is less than the other indices. This does *not* imply that ITSE derived filters are better. Filter comparisons must be made using the same performance index with different inpulse responses $h_n(t)$ or H(s). However, the "selectivity" quality of the performance indices *can* be compared. The selectivity is a measure of the degree of concavity of the performance index (e.g., the value of $d^2I/d\zeta^2$ at $\zeta = \zeta_{opt}$ in Fig. 5.1.3). From Fig. 5.1.3, the ITAE is most selective and the ISE is the least selective.

We should note in passing that one of the most general performance indices, of which the IAE, ISE, ITAE, ITSE, ISTSE, and IEXSE indices are subclasses, is the least *p*th approximation having

$$E_n = \int_a^b W(t)e^p(t)\,dt \tag{5.1.6}$$

W(t) is some arbitrary weighting function, e(t) is the error, p is the power to which the error is raised, and (a,b) represents the time interval between which the error is monitored.[4] When absolute error is utilized, we use $|e(t)|^p = (e^{2p}(t))^{1/2}$ in place of $e^p(t)$ in Eq. 5.1.6.

5.2 FILTER OPTIMIZATION IN THE FREQUENCY DOMAIN

Optimization in the frequency domain is analogous to that in the time domain. The same performance indices are generally used:

$$\begin{aligned} \text{IAE} &= \int_0^{\Omega} f(E(\omega))\, d\omega & \text{IFSE} &= \int_0^{\Omega} \omega f(E^2(\omega))\, d\omega \\ \text{ISE} &= \int_0^{\Omega} f(E^2(\omega))\, d\omega & \text{ISFSE} &= \int_0^{\Omega} \omega^2 f(E^2(\omega))\, d\omega \\ \text{IFAE} &= \int_0^{\Omega} \omega f(E(\omega))\, d\omega & \text{IEXSE} &= \int_0^{\Omega} e^{2k\omega} f(E^2(\omega))\, d\omega \end{aligned} \tag{5.2.1}$$

where $f(E(\omega))$ is some function of the error between the desired and the actual filter frequency responses and Ω is some arbitrary frequency between zero and infinity (note that any frequency limits can be used). The same error interpretations discussed previously apply here. However, it must be remembered that $E(\omega)$ is generally a complex number having a magnitude and phase, where $E(\omega) = |E(\omega)| \exp(j \arg E(\omega))$ so the various indices must be carefully applied. This will be illustrated later in the chapter.

It should also be noted in passing that one of the most general performance indices, of which the IAE, ISE, IFAE, IFSE, ISFSE, and IEXSE indices are subclasses, is the least *p*th approximation having

$$E_n = \int_a^b W_1(\omega)|E(\omega)|^p\, d\omega + \int_a^b W_2(\omega) \arg E(\omega)\, d\omega + \int_a^b W_3(\omega)[d \arg E(\omega)/d\omega]\, d\omega \tag{5.2.2}$$

Here W_1, W_2, and W_3 are arbitrary weighting functions chosen to emphasize or de-emphasize portions of the magnitude, phase, and delay responses of the filter, respectively.

Filters can be simultaneously optimized in both the frequency and time domains. This requires simply combining a frequency domain performance index and a time domain performance index. For example, simple summing can be used. However, because of the increased computation required, optimization in both domains is less often used.

5.3 LOW-PASS FILTER–ITAE STEP RESPONSE APPROXIMATION

Graham and Lathrop[5] derived an optimum low-pass filter having an all-pole transfer function given by Eq. 5.1.5 by minimizing the time-weighted absolute error performance index (ITAE)

$$E_n = \int_0^{\infty} t|1 - r_n(t)|\, dt \tag{5.3.1}$$

in the case where a unit step output $U_{-1}(t)$ is desired. The optimum denominator polynomials are listed in Table 5.3.1 where the 3 dB filter bandwidths have *not* been normalized to unity. The coefficients are very close to the Butterworth filter coefficients so we expect frequency domain responses similar to those shown in Sec. 4.3. The step responses of the optimum filter are shown in Fig. 5.1.2c. Comparing these responses with those of the Butterworth filter, we see that overshoot has been reduced in the higher-order filters. Although settling time appears to be reduced and the delay remains about the same, we cannot jump to these conclusions since the 3 dB filter bandwidths have not been normalized to unity. Nevertheless, we see that the ITAE criteria has been successful in improving the transient response.

Table 5.3.1 Optimum filter polynomials.[5]

$D_1 = s + 1$
$D_2 = s^2 + 1.4s + 1$
$D_3 = s^3 + 1.75s^2 + 2.15s + 1$
$D_4 = s^4 + 2.1s^3 + 3.4s^2 + 2.7s + 1$
$D_5 = s^5 + 2.8s^4 + 5.0s^3 + 5.5s^2 + 3.4s + 1$
$D_6 = s^6 + 3.25s^5 + 6.60s^4 + 8.60s^3 + 7.45s^2 + 3.95s + 1$

5.4 IDEAL LOW-PASS FILTER–ISE STEP RESPONSE APPROXIMATION

The ideal low-pass filter with one second delay has a transfer function and step response of

$$H(j\omega) = e^{-j\omega\tau_0}, \quad |\omega| \leq 1 \quad \text{and} \quad 0, \quad |\omega| > 1$$
$$r(t) = \frac{1}{\pi}\int_{-\infty}^{t} \frac{\sin(x - \tau_0)}{(x - \tau_0)}\, dx = \tfrac{1}{2}\left[1 + \frac{2}{\pi}\mathrm{Si}\,(t - \tau_0)\right] \tag{5.4.1}$$

where $\tau_0 = 1$ and $S_i(x)$ is the tabulated sine integral.[6] McBride, Schaefgen, and Steiglitz[7] derived an optimum low-pass filter having a transfer function given by Eq. 5.1.3 where $m = n - 1$ by finding the poles p_i and zeros z_j which minimized the squared-error performance index (ISE)

$$E_n = \int_0^{T=6} [r(t) - r_n(t)]^2\, dt \tag{5.4.2}$$

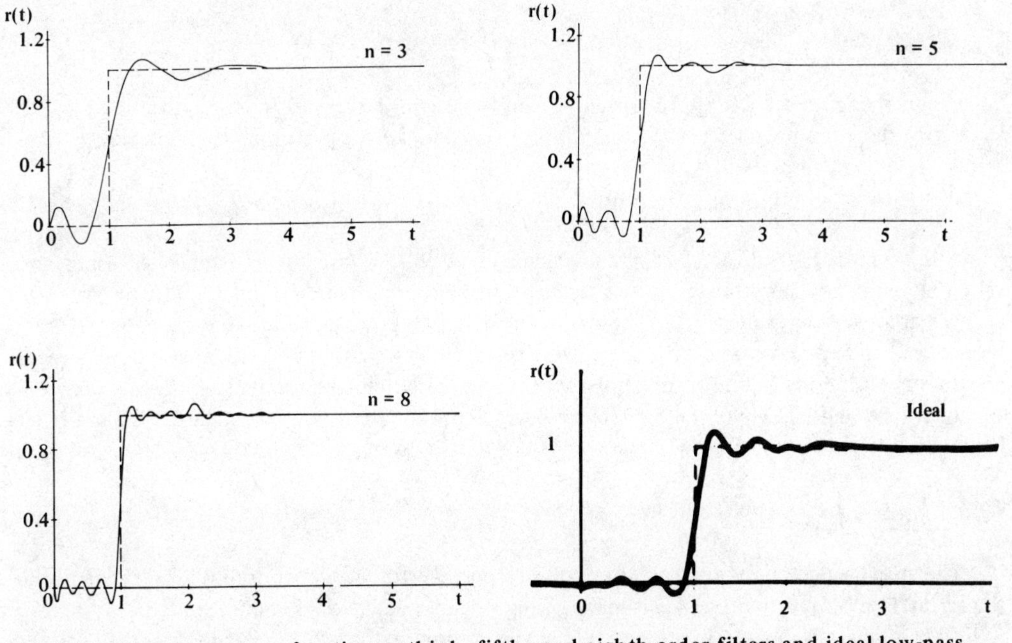

Fig. 5.4.1 Step responses of optimum third-, fifth-, and eighth-order filters and ideal low-pass filter. (From L. E. McBride, Jr., H. W. Schaefgen, and K. Steiglitz, "Time-domain approximation by iterative methods," IEEE Trans. Circuit Theory, vol. CT-13, pp. 381–387, Dec., 1966.)

Table 5.4.1 Optimum poles and zeros.[7]

n	E_n	Poles α	Poles β	Zeros α	Zeros β
3	0.05459	1.40 2.10	4.00 0	−3.10	2.59
5	0.02886	2.37 1.46 2.89	4.50 9.36 0	−3.95 −3.13	2.61 8.31
8	0.01678	3.08 2.40 1.75 1.12	2.31 7.43 12.9 18.4	−4.02 −3.36 −2.72 −4.45	5.41 11.4 17.5 0

evaluated over a six second interval. The optimum poles and zeros are listed in Table 5.4.1. Note the optimum zeros lie in the right-half-plane so that the filter is nonminimum phase. The performance index E_n decreases with increasing n. The step responses for optimum third-, fifth-, and eighth-order filters are shown in Fig. 5.4.1. The ideal step response is also shown. The delay time is seen to be one second and the rise time is less than one-half second and decreases with filter order. The pre- and post-ringing about t = 1 may be objectionable in some systems. It is similar to that found by Budak in his linear phase filter approximation to be discussed in Sec. 5.12.

5.5 IDEAL LOW-PASS FILTER— ISE IMPULSE RESPONSE/GAIN APPROXIMATION

The ideal low-pass filter with τ_o second delay has a transfer function given by Eq. 5.4.1 and an impulse response of

$$h(t) = \frac{1}{\pi}\frac{\sin(t-\tau_o)}{(t-\tau_o)} \tag{5.5.1}$$

Pottle and Wong[8] derived an optimum low-pass filter having a transfer function given by Eq. 5.1.3 by finding the poles p_i and zeros z_j to minimize the squared-error performance index (ISE)

$$E_n = \int_{-\infty}^{\infty} [h(t) - h_n(t)]^2\, dt = \frac{1}{2\pi}\int_{-\infty}^{\infty} |H(j\omega) - H_n(j\omega)|^2\, d\omega \tag{5.5.2}$$

where $h_n(t)$ must be realizable. The equivalence between the integrals is established using Parseval's theorem.[9] This optimization was carried out in the frequency domain. The results of the analysis are listed in Table 5.5.1. The performance index I_{min} listed in the table equals $100\pi E_n$. We see that the approximation improves with filter order since the performance index decreases. The number of zeros is one (n odd) or two (n even) less than the number of poles. Since only the main lobe and right-hand tail of h(t) are being approximated, the error includes the entire left-hand tail of H(t) (see Fig. 1.5.2a). The unavoidable error, as order $n \to \infty$, equals

$$100\pi \int_{-\infty}^{-\pi} \left(\frac{1}{\pi}\frac{\sin x}{x}\right)^2 dx = 4.858\% \tag{5.5.3}$$

The magnitude, phase error, and impulse response error of the optimum and ideal filter are shown in Fig. 5.5.1. Large magnitude peaking occurs near the band-edge and the asymptotic rolloff is either −20 or −40 dB/dec. Since the optimum filter has a phase of either −90° or −180° as $\omega \to \infty$ and the ideal phase equals $-\omega\tau_o$, the phase error decreases linearly as $\omega \to \infty$. Note that the optimum filter has fairly linear phase through the passband.

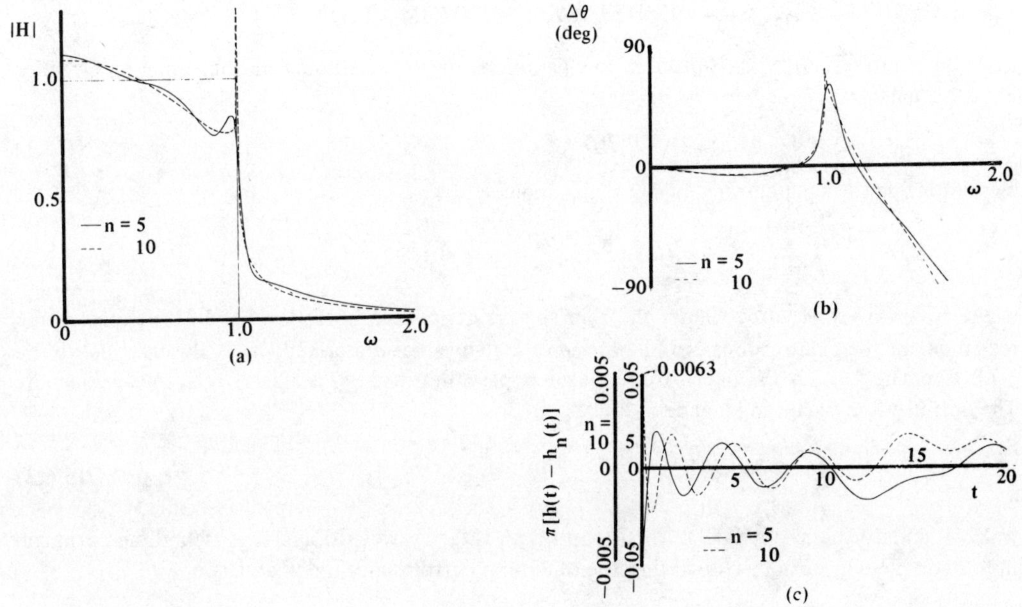

Fig. 5.5.1 (a) Magnitudes, (b) phase errors, and (c) impulse response errors of optimum fifth- and tenth-order filters ($\tau_o = \pi$). (From C. Pottle and J. C. K. Wong, "Optimum least-squares approximations to the ideal low-pass filter," IEEE Trans. Circuit Theory, vol. CT-17, pp. 282–284, May, 1970.)

Table 5.5.1 Optimum poles and zeros.[8]

n	τ_o	I_{min} (%)	Poles		Zeros	
			α	β	α	β
5	2.9882	5.142	0.3259 0.0416 0.4811	0.7325 0.9948	0.0631 1.0307	1.0572 2.8654
6	3.0456	4.977	0.4665 0.2011 0.0162	0.3727 0.9114 0.9992	0.0260 0.3976	1.0165 1.3558
7	3.0791	4.911	0.3864 0.0997 0.00673 0.5212	0.6690 0.9786 0.9908 0	0.0110 0.1552 3.1565	1.0051 1.1062 3.2080
8	3.1001	4.883	0.5055 0.2661 0.0459 0.00300	0.3422 0.8646 0.9953 1.0000	0.00478 0.0678 0.6465	1.0017 1.0364 1.3720
9	3.1132	4.871	0.4299 0.1521 0.0213 0.00136 0.5523	0.6260 0.9577 0.9990 1.0000 0	0.00215 0.0312 0.2510 3.8447 12.1139	1.0006 1.0133 1.1350 0 0
10	3.1219	4.865	0.5355 0.3146 0.0787 0.0103 0.000654	0.3209 0.8267 0.9886 1.0000 1.0000	0.00100 0.0149 0.1150 0.8425	1.0002 1.0050 1.0535 1.3153

5.6 LOW-PASS FILTER–ISE DELAY APPROXIMATION

Ariga and Sato[10] derived an optimum low-pass filter having an all-pole transfer function given by Eq. 5.1.5 having only the constraints that

$$|H_n(0)| = 1, \qquad |H_n(j\omega_c)| = 0.707 \tag{5.6.1}$$

by minimizing the squared-error performance index (ISE)

$$E_n = \frac{1}{\omega_d}\int_0^{\omega_d} [\tau_0 - \tau_n(j\omega)]^2 \, d\omega \tag{5.6.2}$$

where $\tau_n = -d \arg H_n/d\omega$. Under the gain constraints of Eq. 5.6.1, Ariga and Sato expected the remainder of the gain response to lie between the two values prescribed; ω_c is always equal to the 3 dB frequency. τ_0 is the delay of the ideal low-pass filter and ω_d is a delay reference-frequency. The optimization yields an ideal delay τ_0 of

$$\tau_0 = \frac{1}{\omega_d}\int_0^{\omega_d} \tau_n(j\omega) \, d\omega \tag{5.6.3}$$

which is simply the average delay of the optimum filter between 0 and ω_d. When the optimization is completed, it can be shown that the minimum performance index equals

$$\min E_n = \tau_0 - \tau_n(j\omega_d) \tag{5.6.4}$$

Assuming $\omega_d = \omega_c$, the optimum pole positions are listed in Table 5.6.1 where $s_i = \sigma_i \pm j\omega_i$. The magnitude and delay characteristics of the optimum fifth-order filter are shown in Fig. 5.6.1. The magnitude appears to be monotonically decreasing but the delay characteristics exhibit peaking in the transition band. The step response of the optimum fifth-order filter is shown in Fig. 5.6.2a. The optimum filter has small overshoot.

Another optimization arises when ω_d is optimized to yield a relative minimum in E_n rather than remaining fixed as before. The optimum poles and ω_d in this case are listed in Table 5.6.2. In general, the performance index is not as good as that in the preceding case for a given n and

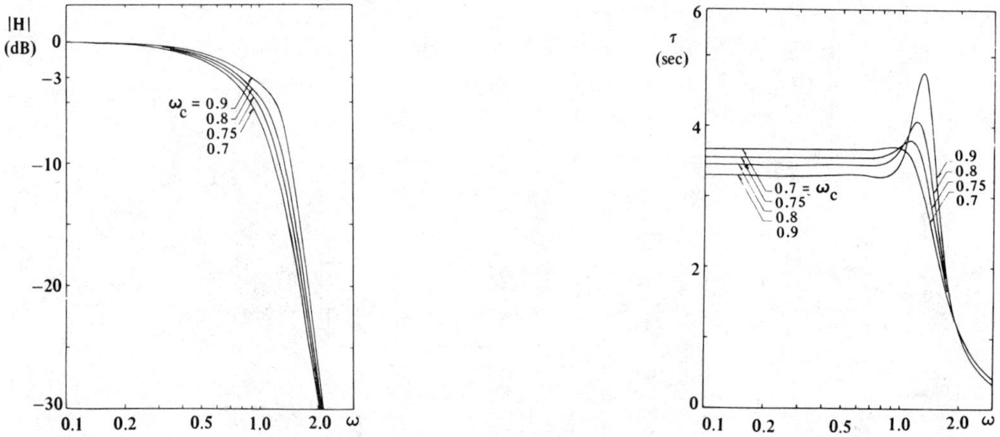

Fig. 5.6.1 Magnitude and delay characteristics of optimum fifth-order filter for $\omega_d = \omega_c$. (From M. Ariga and M. Sato, "An extremum approach to constant-delay approximations to the ideal low-pass filter," IEEE Trans. Circuit Theory, vol. CT-17, pp. 121–125, Feb., 1970.)

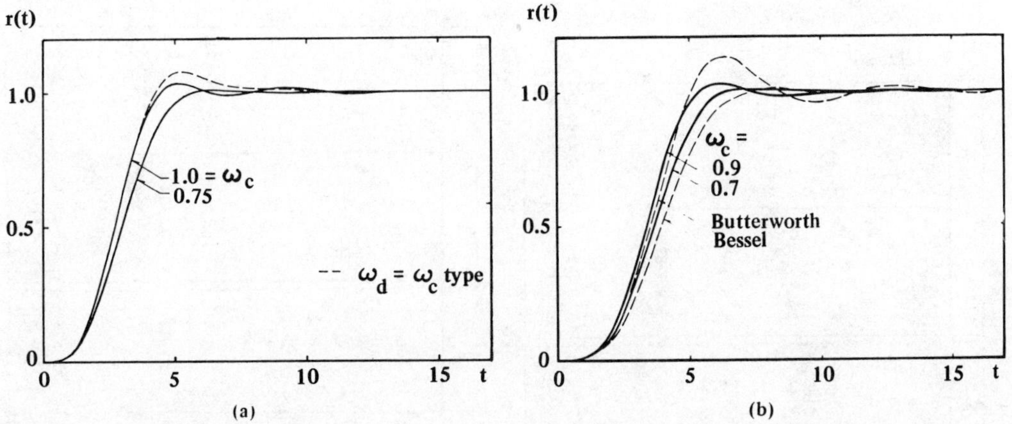

Fig. 5.6.2 Step responses of optimum fifth-order filter having (a) $\omega_d = \omega_c$ and (b) variable ω_d. (From M. Ariga and M. Sato, "An extremum approach to constant-delay approximations to the ideal low-pass filter," IEEE Trans. Circuit Theory, vol. CT-17, pp. 121–125, Feb., 1970.)

ω_c. The magnitude and delay characteristics of the optimum fifth-order filter are shown in Fig. 5.6.3. The magnitude characteristics are not significantly different from those in the preceding case. They lie between Butterworth and Bessel (Thomson) filters in rolloff rate. Their delay characteristics are improved from those of the preceding filter since the transition band delay peaking is eliminated. However, more passband delay variation is present. The step response is shown in Fig. 5.6.2b; it is seen to have slightly more overshoot than that of the preceding filter.

The delay behavior of these optimum filters is determined by the relative value of ω_c and ω_d. More in-band ripple is obtained as their difference increases. Ariga and Sato note that the optimum filters using variable ω_d have similar characteristics to the equiripple delay filters of Chap. 4.

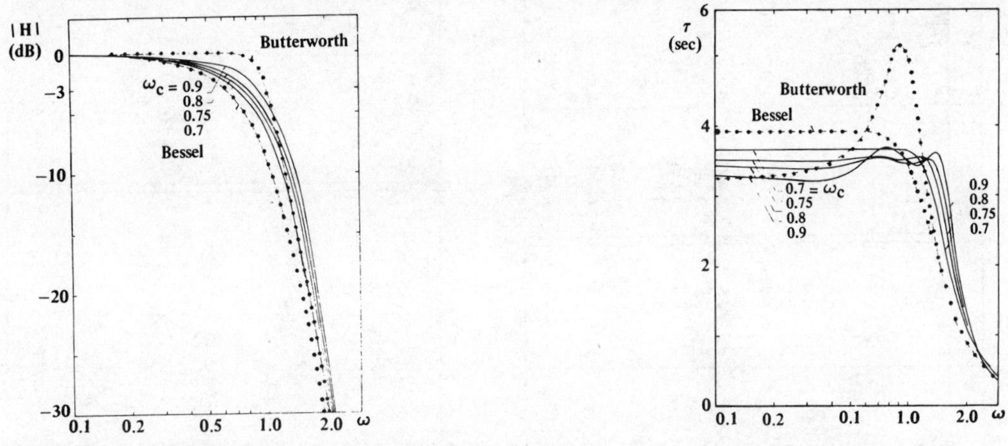

Fig. 5.6.3 Magnitude and delay characteristics of optimum fifth-order filter for variable ω_d. (From M. Ariga and M. Sato, "An extremum approach to constant-delay approximations to the ideal low-pass filter," IEEE Trans. Circuit Theory, vol. CT-17, pp. 121–125, Feb., 1970.)

Table 5.6.1 Optimum poles for $\omega_d = \omega_c$.[10]

n	ω_c	τ_o	E_n	α_1	β_1	α_2	β_2	α_3	β_3
3	1.0	2.1317	0.1159	0.5355	1.0868	0.6813	0		
	0.9	2.2117	0.5136×10^{-1}	0.6334	0.9943	0.7392	0		
	0.8	2.3250	0.8429×10^{-2}	0.6805	0.8597	0.8318	0		
4	1.0	2.6724	0.6090×10^{-1}	0.6099	0.4303	0.3727	1.2869		
	0.9	2.7660	0.2878×10^{-1}	0.6581	0.4037	0.4401	1.2182		
	0.8	2.9041	0.9457×10^{-2}	0.7193	0.3717	0.5324	1.1145		
	0.75	2.9968	0.3170×10^{-2}	0.7685	0.3477	0.5849	1.0312		
5	0.9	3.2976	0.9097×10^{-2}	0.6164	0.6552	0.2859	1.3168	0.6806	0
	0.8	3.4462	0.3237×10^{-2}	0.6556	0.6137	0.3744	1.2579	0.7199	0
	0.75	3.5461	0.1641×10^{-2}	0.6812	0.5907	0.4358	1.2103	0.7433	0
	0.7	3.6701	0.5935×10^{-3}	0.7206	0.5615	0.5073	1.1323	0.7783	0
6	0.8	3.9947	0.7108×10^{-3}	0.7164	0.2602	0.6084	0.7747	0.2426	0.3096
	0.75	4.0915	0.3641×10^{-3}	0.7318	0.2513	0.2653	0.7508	0.2943	1.2896
	0.7	4.2140	0.1641×10^{-3}	0.7494	0.2419	0.6472	0.7252	0.3642	1.2548
	0.65	4.3717	0.5241×10^{-4}	0.7774	0.2308	0.6840	0.6935	0.4532	1.1821

Table 5.6.2 Optimum poles for variable ω_d.[10]

n	ω_c	τ_o	ω_d	E_n	α_1	β_1	α_2	β_2	α_3	β_3
3	1.0	2.1878	1.2630	0.1302	0.5389	1.0602	0.7070	0		
	0.9	2.2245	1.0880	0.5404×10^{-1}	0.6039	0.9898	0.7439	0		
	0.8	2.3258	0.7460	0.6972×10^{-2}	0.6806	0.8605	0.8308	0		
4	1.0	2.8615	1.4238	0.1837	0.5475	0.5051	0.4438	1.2671		
	0.9	2.8560	1.3281	0.9606×10^{-1}	0.5919	0.4659	0.4869	1.2350		
	0.8	2.9052	1.1130	0.2120×10^{-1}	0.6810	0.3995	0.5429	1.1443		
	0.75	2.9956	0.8686	0.3540×10^{-2}	0.7634	0.3514	0.5863	1.0355		
5	0.9	3.4472	1.5266	0.1536	0.4652	0.7696	0.4038	1.4389	0.5536	0
	0.8	3.4699	1.3938	0.5534×10^{-1}	0.5401	0.7166	0.4406	1.3772	0.5940	0
	0.75	3.5264	1.2467	0.1822×10^{-1}	0.6032	0.6716	0.4712	1.3012	0.6407	0
	0.7	3.6611	0.9551	0.1752×10^{-2}	0.7006	0.5885	0.5188	1.1554	0.7447	0
6	0.9	4.0644	1.6456	0.1751	0.4541	0.3697	0.4056	0.9792	0.3450	1.5738
	0.8	4.0742	1.5538	0.8558×10^{-1}	0.5008	0.3432	0.4620	0.9421	0.3723	1.5249
	0.7	4.1762	1.3002	0.1024×10^{-1}	0.6044	0.2022	0.5625	0.8575	0.4257	1.3887
	0.65	4.3600	0.9365	0.4343×10^{-3}	0.7323	0.2486	0.6652	0.7377	0.4761	1.2117

5.7 IDEAL LOW-PASS FILTER–ISE GAIN/PHASE APPROXIMATION

Haas[11] derived an optimum filter by combining time and frequency domain ISE performance indices. He used an all-pole filter having a transfer function given by Eq. 5.1.5 where $|H_n(j\omega)| = M(\omega)$ and $\arg H_n(j\omega) = \phi(\omega)$. Assuming ac steady-state conditions, if a signal $\sin \omega t$ is inputted to an ideal low-pass filter having unity bandwidth whose gain is given by Eq. 1.5.8a, then its response is $M(\omega) \sin [\omega(t - \tau_0) + \phi(\omega)]$ if $|\omega| \leqslant 1$ and zero if $|\omega| > 1$. The ISE time domain distortion D_n over a single cycle of the signal then equals

$$
\begin{aligned}
D_n(\omega) &= \int_0^{2\pi/\omega} \left\{ \sin \omega t - M(\omega) \sin [\omega(t - \tau_0) + \phi(\omega)] \right\}^2 dt, \qquad |\omega| \leqslant 1 \\
&= \int_0^{2\pi/\omega} [M(\omega) \sin \omega t]^2 \, dt, \qquad |\omega| > 1
\end{aligned}
\tag{5.7.1}
$$

Performing the integration, D_n can be re-expressed as

$$
\begin{aligned}
D_n(\omega) &= (\pi/\omega) \left\{ [(1 - M(\omega)]^2 + 2M(\omega)(1 - \cos [\phi(\omega) - \omega\tau_0]) \right\}, \qquad |\omega| \leqslant 1 \\
&= \pi M^2(\omega)/\omega, \qquad |\omega| > 1
\end{aligned}
\tag{5.7.2}
$$

The ISE frequency domain distortion E_n is then defined to equal

$$
E_n(\omega) = \frac{1}{\pi} \int_0^{\infty} D_n(\omega) \, d\omega = \frac{\log_{10} e}{\pi} \int_{-\infty}^{\infty} \omega D_n(\omega) \, d(\log_{10} \omega) \tag{5.7.3}
$$

where D_n is given by Eq. 5.7.2. Therefore, we see the $1/\omega$ in the first integral forms a weighting factor discussed in Eq. 5.2.2. The second integral shows that $1/\omega$ weighting is equivalent to a logarithmic weighting of frequency. E_n is an example of the more general performance index involving magnitude and phase.

The optimum poles are listed in Table 5.7.1. The performance index E_n decreases with increasing n. The magnitude and delay characteristics of the optimum filter are shown in Fig. 5.7.1. The 3 dB filter bandwidths are all about 0.87 and the magnitude responses are monotonic. The delay responses exhibit peaking near the band-edge.

The step responses of the optimum filter are shown in Fig. 5.7.2. They all exhibit an overshoot of about 10% (except for n = 2) and have a fairly short settling time. Comparing these step responses with those in Fig. 5.1.2, they are closest to those of the ITAE optimum filter.

Other optimization criteria are possible by modifying E_n given by Eq. 5.7.3. For example, we can: (1) remove the magnitude M weighting of phase in D_n given by Eq. 5.7.2; (2) neglect the stopband distortion by assuming $D_n = 0$ for $|\omega| > 1$; or (3) neglect the phase distortion term in D_n by omitting the $(1 - \cos \theta)$ term. The first approach results in filters having slightly lower delay distortion, but are otherwise very similar to the original optimum filter of Table 5.7.1; the second approach yields filters which are also very similar to the original optimum filter; the third approach yields filters having almost equiripple (about 2 dB) magnitude response (except for n = 2), a delay response which ripples and peaks near the band-edge, and a step response having a longer settling time than that shown in Fig. 5.7.2.[11]

Another ISE gain/phase approximation has been applied to the ideal Gaussian (Sec. 4.12) and raised-cosine filters.[12] Both filters are useful in pulse applications. The distortion D_n was defined to equal

$$
D_n(\omega) = [|H(j\omega)| - |H_n(j\omega)|]^2 + |H_n(j\omega)| [\arg H(j\omega) - \arg H_n(j\omega)]^2 \tag{5.7.4}
$$

where the performance index is then given by Eq. 5.7.3. H and H_n are the transfer functions of the ideal filter and the optimum filter, respectively. Note that both the magnitude error and the

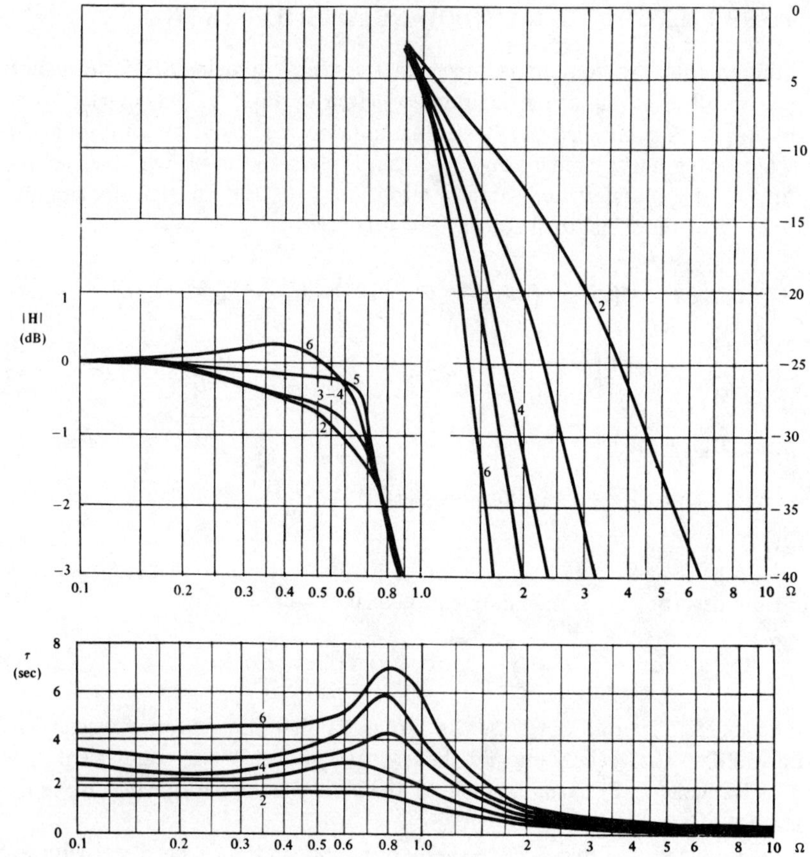

Fig. 5.7.1 Magnitude and delay characteristics of optimum filters.[11]

phase error are considered as in Eq. 5.7.2. The phase error is weighted by the gain magnitude $|H_n|$ so that large phase errors are tolerated only when the filter gain magnitude is small.

Therefore, these optimum filters illustrate the way in which time and frequency domain performance indices can be combined, manipulated, and modified. The choices in optimization criteria are virtually limitless.

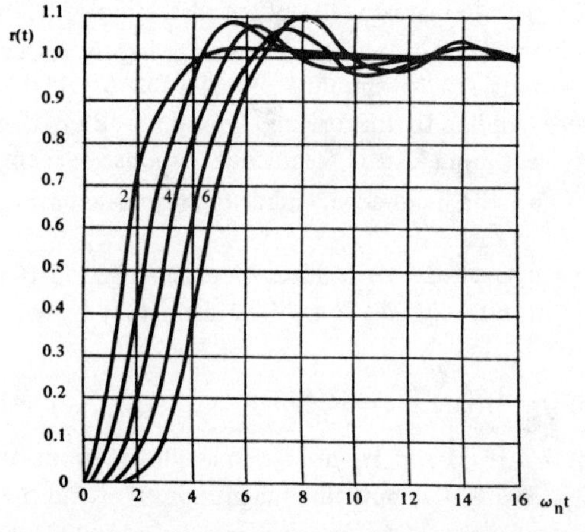

Fig. 5.7.2 Step response of optimum filter.[11]

Table 5.7.1 Optimum poles.[11]

n	E_n	Poles ω_n	ζ	Poles ω_n	ζ	Poles ω_n	ζ
2	0.5592	1.0000	0.7976				
3	0.3407	0.8269	0.5785	1.4625	real		
4	0.2648	1.1594	1.1984	0.8625	0.3712		
5	0.2648	1.3624	1.0720	0.8700	0.2986	0.7118	real
6	0.2611	1.4850	1.4032	0.7106	0.6764	0.9476	0.2260

5.8 LOW-PASS FILTER–MINIMUM RISE TIME APPROXIMATION

In pulse applications, it is desirable to have a step response with small rise time or an impulse response with small width.[13] where both responses have short settling times. Jess and Schussler[14] have investigated optimum low-pass filters for pulse transmission. Their filters have the shortest rise time for a given overshoot and stopband rejection. They constrain both the time domain and frequency domain responses simultaneously as shown in Fig. 5.8.1. In the frequency domain, the stopband rejection satisfies

$$|H(j\omega)| \leqslant q_f H(0), \qquad |\omega| \geqslant \omega_s \tag{5.8.1}$$

where ω_s marks the edge of the stopband. The minimum stopband rejection equals 20 $\log_{10} q_f$ and is, therefore, controlled by q_f. In the time domain, the step response r(t) satisfies

$$|r(t)| \leqslant q_t H(0), \ t \leqslant t_1 \qquad \text{and} \qquad |r(t) - H(0)| \leqslant q_t H(0), \ t \geqslant t_2 \tag{5.8.2}$$

Thus, q_t fixes the maximum overshoot and ringing. For example if $q_t = 0.1$, then the 10–90% rise time $t_R = t_2 - t_1$ and the overshoot cannot exceed 10%. The impulse response h(t) satisfies a similar equation as

$$|h(t)| \leqslant q_t |h_{max}|, \qquad t \leqslant t_1 \qquad \text{and} \qquad t \geqslant t_2 \tag{5.8.3}$$

where the pulse width $t_W = t_2 - t_1$. For minimization purposes, we define the time bandwidth products

$$M_1 = t_R f_s, \qquad M_2 = t_W f_s \tag{5.8.4}$$

Jess and Schussler then minimize M_1 for a step input, or alternatively. M_2 for an impulse input, for a given stopband rejection (i.e., q_f) by appropriately choosing the parameters of the transfer function

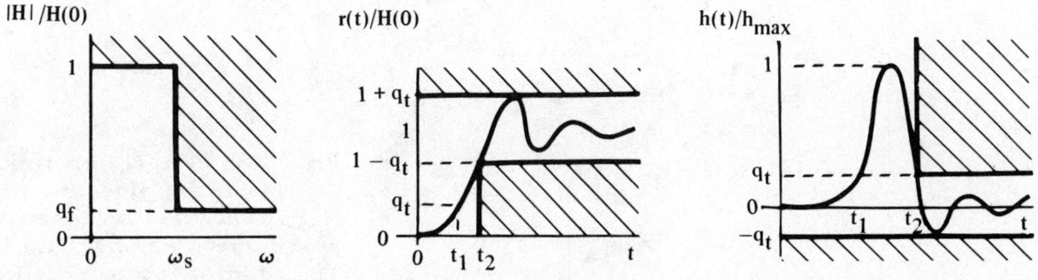

Fig. 5.8.1 Frequency and time domain constraints.

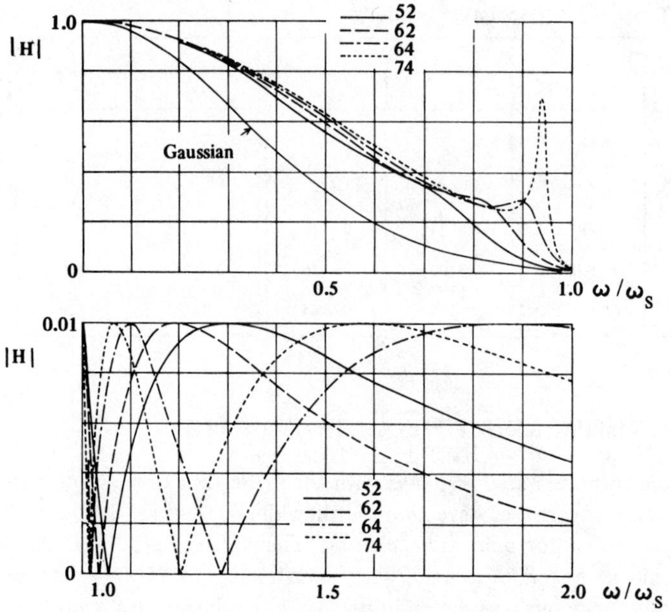

Fig. 5.8.2 Passband and stopband magnitude characteristics of optimum filter. (From J. Jess and H. W. Schussler, "On the design of pulse-forming networks," IEEE Trans. Circuit Theory, vol. CT-12, pp. 393–400, Sept., 1965.)

$$H_{nm}(s) = \prod_{j=1}^{m/2} (s^2 + z_j^2) \Big/ \prod_{i=1}^{n} (s + s_i) \tag{5.8.5}$$

where the number of poles and zeros are selected. Note that the optimum transfer function has m/2 zeros of transmission. The normalized optimum pole-zero positions are tabulated in Tables 5.8.1 (for step inputs) and 5.8.2 (for impulse inputs) for the case where $q_t = 0.01$ (i.e., 1 – 99% rise time and not more than 1% overshoot), $q_f = 0.01 = -40$ dB, and different (n, m) combinations (i.e., number of poles and zeros). The pole-zero positions are normalized by the stopband frequency ω_s. Now we shall interpret these results for *step inputs*. The impulse results have similar interpretations.

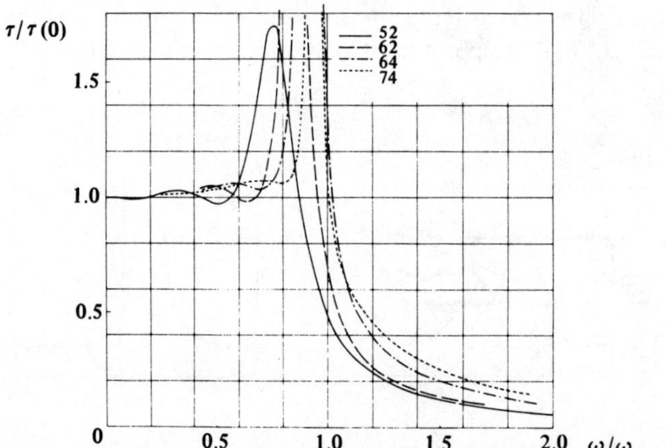

Fig. 5.8.3 Delay characteristics of optimum filters. (From J. Jess and H. W. Schussler, "On the design of pulse-forming networks," IEEE Trans. Circuit Theory, vol. CT-12, pp. 393–400, Sept., 1965.)

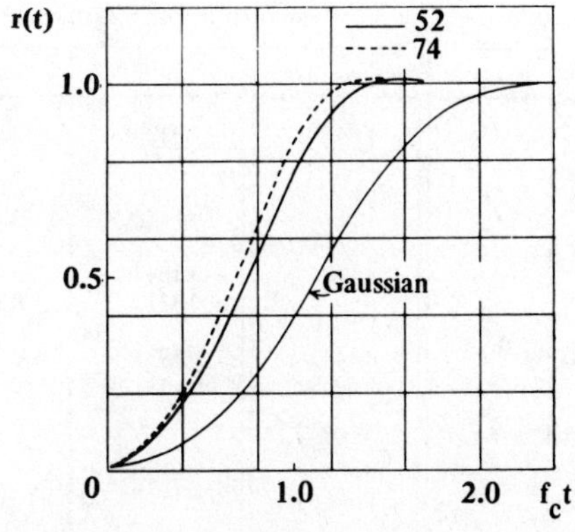

Fig. 5.8.4 Step response of optimum filters. (From J. Jess and H. W. Schussler, "On the design of pulse-forming networks," IEEE Trans. Circuit Theory, vol. CT-12, pp. 393–400, Sept., 1965.)

The magnitude characteristics of these optimum filters are shown in Fig. 5.8.2. We see there is peaking for the larger-order filters near the band-edge of the stopband ω_s. This is due to a high-Q pole pair near the $j\omega$-axis. The stopband response of the filter is shown in Fig. 5.8.2. The responses go to zero at the zeros of transmission. We see that they are equiripple in the stopband which is an interesting result. Thus, this optimum filter is very similar to the inverse Chebyshev filter which has equiripple stopband response. Recall, however, that inverse Chebyshev filters had monotonic response in their transition bands unlike the Jess/Schussler filter.

The delay characteristics of the filters are shown in Fig. 5.8.3. We see that there is significant peaking near the edge of the stopband which increases with filter order. This peaking is due to the high-Q pole pair near the $j\omega$-axis. These responses differ greatly from those of the classical linear phase filters in which the passband delay was fairly constant.

The step responses of the filters are shown in Fig. 5.8.4. They are extremely well-behaved although they exhibit sustained ringing bounded by $\pm q_t$. Jess and Schussler recognized that their criteria allowed such lightly damped ringing. The ringing frequency corresponds to that where the magnitude response exhibits peaking. These results show that delay distortion is *not* always objectionable. Stated differently, good transient response does *not* require fairly constant delay response. This unique and historically unaccepted result will undoubtedly lead to many future investigations.

Table 5.8.1 Optimum poles and zeros for step input.[14]

nm	30	32	42	54	62	64	74
M_1	2.941	2.018	1.521	1.347	1.331	1.287	1.259
z_1		1.1521	1.0872	1.0336	1.0356	1.0187	1.0134
z_2				1.5088		1.2881	1.2059
α_1	0.1617	0.2575	0.3096	0.4335	0.3641	0.4844	0.5620
β_1	0	0	0.1876	0	0.1720	0.2099	0
α_2	0.1316	0.2041	0.1842	0.3588	0.2762	0.3529	0.5112
β_2	0.2092	0.3335	0.5890	0.4380	0.5236	0.6276	0.3922
α_3				0.1013	0.0674	0.0332	0.3398
β_3				0.8484	0.8544	0.9175	0.7684
α_4							0.00790
β_4							0.9391

Table 5.8.2 Optimum poles and zeros for impulse input.[14]

nm	30	40	42	52	62	64	74
M_2	4.047	2.932	2.069	1.912	1.891	1.810	1.799
z_1			1.0903	1.0583	1.0391	1.0206	1.0094
z_2						1.2601	1.1665
α_1	0.1552	0.1643	0.3018	0.3310	0.3283	0.4245	0.4914
β_1	0	0.3813	0.1913		0.1762	0.2028	0
α_2	0.1453	0.1935	0.2400	0.3017	0.2771	0.3474	0.4599
β_2	0.2069	0.1241	0.5864	0.3818	0.5304	0.6098	0.3756
α_3				0.1966	0.1354	0.0782	0.3461
β_3				0.7791	0.8940	0.9840	0.7509
α_4							0.0215
β_4							0.9797

5.9 LINEAR PHASE LOW-PASS FILTER–MINIMAX DELAY APPROXIMATION

In the last chapter, we discussed the equiripple delay filter. The equiripple delay filter approximated an MFD response in the way that the Chebyshev filter approximated an MFM response. The equiripple delay filter approximated constant delay over a wider frequency range than the Bessel filter. Now we want to consider a slightly modified filter form introduced by Bunker[15] called the *symmetrical-ripple delay filter*. The symmetrical-ripple delay filter has a delay characteristic constrained to be equiripple about the nominal delay τ_o as shown in Fig. 5.9.1. The low-frequency delay is bounded between $\tau_o/(1+\epsilon)$ and $\tau_o/(1-\epsilon)$. However, its dc delay value equals τ_o, and *not* $\tau_o/(1 \pm \epsilon)$ as in the equiripple delay filter. The approximate passband delay of the symmetrical-ripple delay filter is given by Eq. 4.11.1. The filter order n equals the number of delay maxima and minima in the filter passband $|\omega| \leqslant 1$ (excluding the minimum at $\omega = 1$).

Bunker determined the optimum pole locations for the symmetrical-ripple delay filter using an iterative procedure and an all-pole transfer function given by Eq. 5.1.5. These are listed in Table 5.9.1. The pole locations have been normalized to produce a dc delay of one second.

A useful observation at this point is to note that Rabovich and Djurich[16] have considered generalized symmetrical-ripple delay filters having arbitrary normalized dc delays of $\tau(0)$ where the initial delay error $\epsilon(0)$ equals

$$\epsilon(0) = \tau(0)/\tau_0 - 1 \tag{5.9.1}$$

For the symmetrical-ripple delay filter, $\epsilon(0) = 0$ since $\tau(0) = \tau_o$. However, Rabovich and Djurich allow $\epsilon(0)$ to be nonzero. For the equiripple (or Abele) delay filter of Chap. 4, $\epsilon(0) = \epsilon$ where ϵ is the ripple factor. The delay characteristics for several third- and fifth-order filters of this more general type are shown in Fig. 5.9.2. The passband responses of several generalized symmetrical-

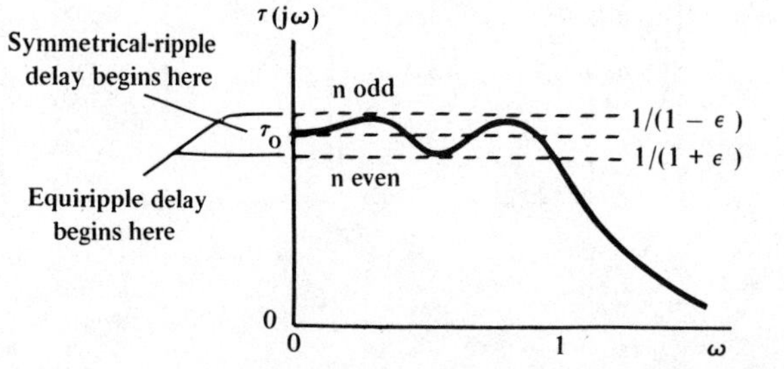

Fig. 5.9.1 Delay characteristics of symmetrical-ripple delay filter.

ripple delay filters of the same order are shown in Fig. 5.9.3. We see that symmetrical-ripple delay filters have more passband ripple than their equiripple delay counterparts. This is accentuated by decreasing $\epsilon(0)$ from $+\epsilon$ to $-\epsilon$. The stopband attenuation is similarly increased beyond that provided by the equiripple delay filter. This improvement is somewhat analogous to that obtained using the Papoulis and Halpern filters of Chap. 4.

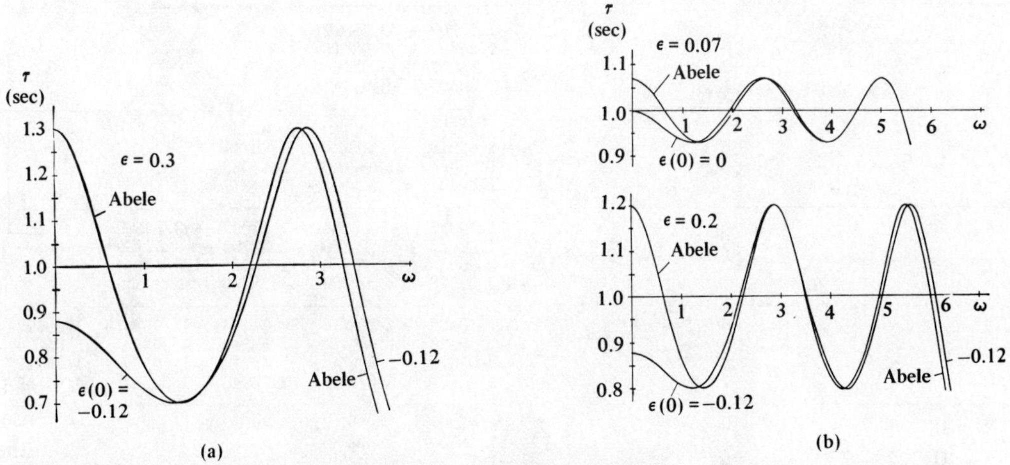

Fig. 5.9.2 Delay characteristics of (a) third- and (b) fifth-order generalized symmetrical-ripple delay filters. (From B. D. Rakovich and B. M. Djurich, "Chebyshev approximation of a constant group delay with constraints at the origin," IEEE Trans. Circuit Theory, vol. CT-19, pp. 466–475, Sept., 1972.)

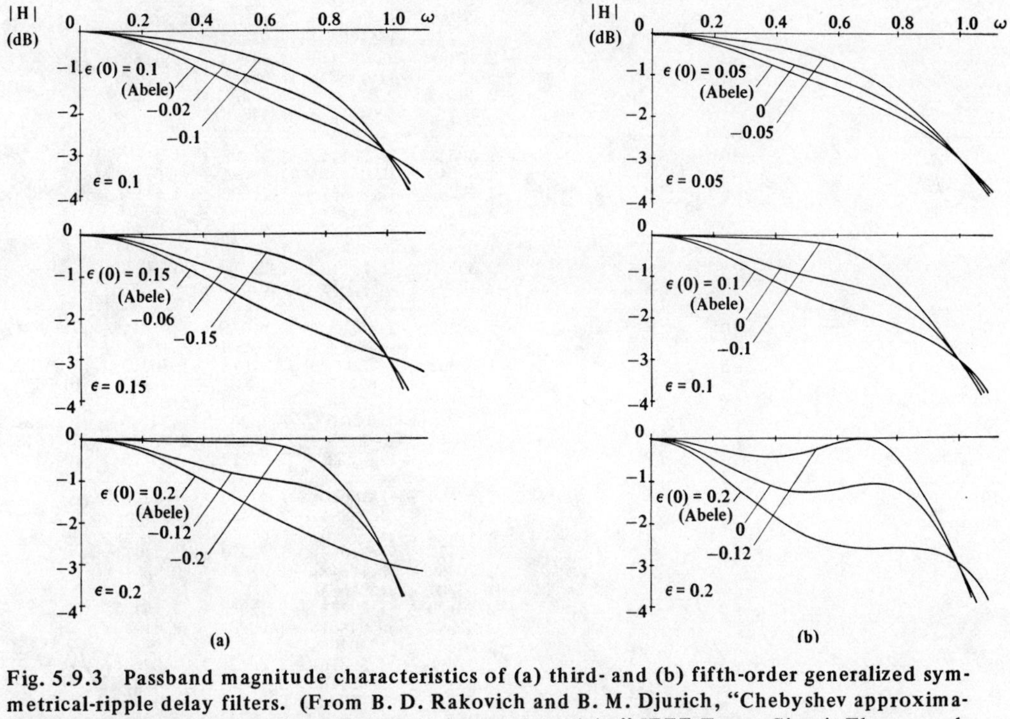

Fig. 5.9.3 Passband magnitude characteristics of (a) third- and (b) fifth-order generalized symmetrical-ripple delay filters. (From B. D. Rakovich and B. M. Djurich, "Chebyshev approximation of a constant group delay with constraints at the origin," IEEE Trans. Circuit Theory, vol. CT-19, pp. 466–475, Sept., 1972.)

Table 5.9.1 Symmetrical-ripple delay filter poles.
(From W. M. Bunker, "Symmetrical equal-ripple delay and symmetrical equal-ripple phase filters," IEEE Trans. Circuit Theory, vol. CT-17, pp. 455–458, Aug., 1970.)

n	ϵ (%)	Poles $-a \pm j\beta$
2	±10	−1.15303 ± j0.988221
	±5	−1.25797 ± j0.966152
	±2	−1.35017 ± j0.936687
	±1	−1.39555 ± j0.918446
3	±10	−1.48229; −1.16302 ± j2.40756
	±5	−1.62273; −1.30365 ± j2.25714
	±2	−1.78364; −1.44606 ± j2.11935
	±1	−1.88491; −1.52787 ± j2.04317
4	±10	−1.40027 ± j1.16084; −1.17032 ± j3.72566
	±5	−1.62172 ± j1.15479; −1.32192 ± j3.57839
	±2	−1.86935 ± j1.12584; −1.48394 ± j3.40724
	±1	−2.02573 ± j1.09796; −1.58295 ± j3.29530
5	±10	−1.60422; −1.36860 ± j2.71144; −1.17648 ± j5.29672
	±5	−1.80326; −1.60975 ± j2.58241; −1.33375 ± j5.05004
	±2	−2.05510; −1.88959 ± j2.45212; −1.50554 ± j4.79829
	±1	−2.23177; −2.07275 ± j2.36946; −1.61341 ± j4.64145
6	±10	−1.47207 ± j1.23022; −1.36670 ± j4.06697; −1.18050 ± j6.66280
	±5	−1.73788 ± j1.24249; −1.61292 ± j3.95851; −1.34127 ± j6.44565
	±2	−2.05666 ± j1.23206; −1.90440 ± j4.81381; −1.51909 ± j6.19084
	±1	−2.27363 ± j1.21355; −2.09937 ± j3.70654; −1.63243 ± j6.01690
7	±10	−1.65688; −1.42634 ± j2.84059; −1.36838 ± j5.67627; −1.18393 ± j8.28178
	±5	−1.88269; −1.70502 ± j2.73502; −1.61819 ± j5.47276; −1.34705 ± j7.97420
	±2	−2.17898; −2.04601 ± j2.63113; −1.91652 ± j5.25501; −1.52882 ± j7.65231
	±1	−2.39554; −2.28192 ± j2.56371; −2.11822 ± j5.10902; −1.64573 ± j7.44398
8	±10	−1.50553 ± j1.26534; −1.42027 ± j4.21758; −1.37049 ± j7.05575; −1.18624 ± j9.66823
	±5	−1.79289 ± j1.28855; −1.70090 ± j4.14187; −1.62273 ± j6.88928; −1.35111 ± j9.40075
	±2	−2.14794 ± j1.29118; −2.04854 ± j4.03426; −1.92572 ± j6.67750; −1.53579 ± j9.08890
	±1	−2.39759 ± j1.28115; −2.29210 ± j3.94920; −2.13194 ± j6.52058; −1.65532 ± j8.87264
9	±10	−1.68592; −1.45333 ± j2.91021; −1.41944 ± j5.85004; −1.37264 ± j8.69286; −1.18834 ± j11.3118
	±5	−1.92662; −1.75033 ± j2.81918; −1.70219 ± j5.68196; −1.62675 ± j8.43802; −1.35449 ± j10.9578
	±2	−2.24816; −2.12260 ± j2.73403; −2.05429 ± j5.50595; −1.93310 ± j8.16302; −1.54130 ± j10.5854
	±1	−2.48801; −2.38698 ± j2.67961; −2.30248 ± j5.38613; −2.14253 ± j7.97512; −1.66273 ± j10.3402
10	±10	−1.52484 ± j1.28630; −1.44506 ± j4.30140; −1.42032 ± j7.23884; −1.37428 ± j10.0861; −1.18982 ± j12.7096
	±5	−1.82477 ± j1.31640; −1.74230 ± j4.24613; −1.70462 ± j7.11242; −1.62984 ± j9.87547; −1.35701 ± j12.4015
	±2	−2.20129 ± j1.32771; −2.11839 ± j4.16425; −2.05995 ± j6.94801; −1.93881 ± j9.61550; −1.54552 ± j12.0463
	±1	−2.47066 ± j1.32375; −2.38794 ± j4.09691; −2.31144 ± j6.82118; −2.15070 ± j9.42318; −1.66847 ± j11.7982

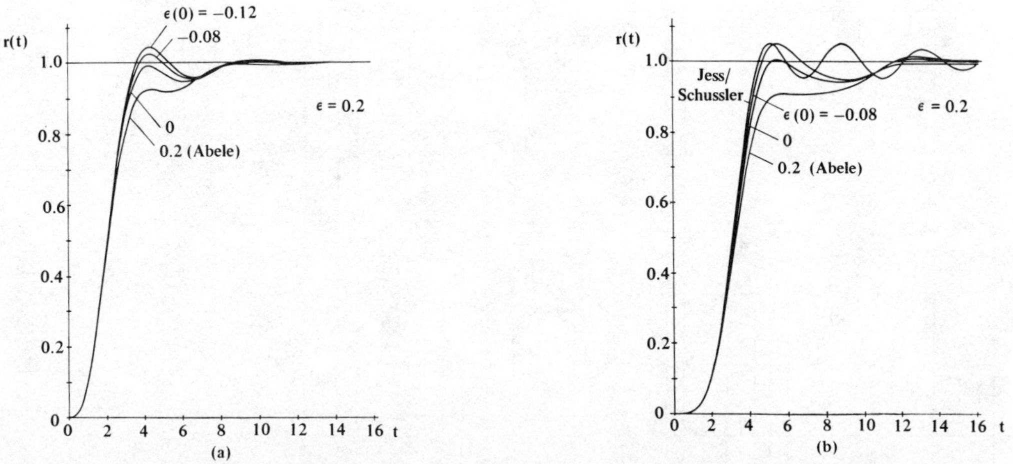

Fig. 5.9.4 Step responses of (a) third- and (b) fifth-order generalized symmetrical-ripple delay filters. (From B. D. Rakovich and B. M. Djurich, "Chebyshev approximation of a constant group delay with constraints at the origin," IEEE Trans. Circuit Theory, vol. CT-19, pp. 466–475, Sept., 1972.)

The step responses of several third- and fifth-order generalized symmetrical-ripple delay filters are shown in Fig. 5.9.4. By decreasing $\epsilon(0)$, we reduce and finally eliminate the plateau effect present in the equiripple delay filter. In these responses, the product of the pole magnitudes is unity. The step response of a fifth-order Jess/Schussler filter is also shown. We see that the generalized symmetrical-ripple delay filters can have much smaller settling times but only slightly greater rise time than the Jess/Schussler filter.

5.10 LINEAR PHASE LOW-PASS FILTER–MINIMAX PHASE APPROXIMATION

An alternative approach for designing linear phase filters is to approximate linear phase itself, rather than constant delay, in the equiripple (i.e., minimax or Chebyshev) sense. These filters have been studied by Humpherys,[17] Bunker,[18] and others. They are usually called *equiripple phase filters* although Bunker refers to them as *symmetrical phase filters*. We choose the former terminology. Equiripple phase filters have phase characteristics which are constrained to be equiripple about the linear phase value $\omega n\pi/2$ as shown in Fig. 5.10.1 where the phase ripple equals ϵ. Ideally, the phase can be expressed as

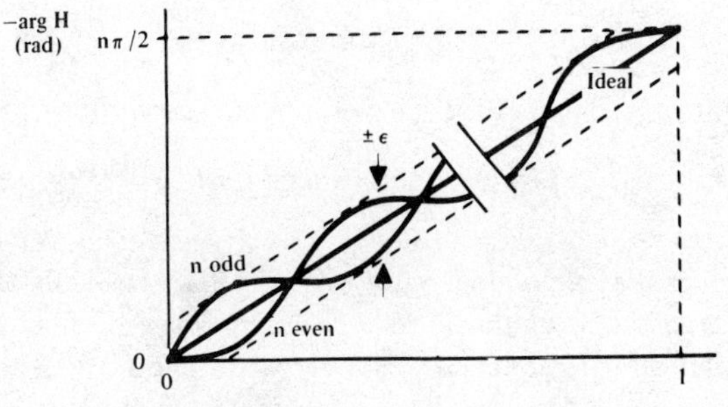

Fig. 5.10.1 Phase characteristic of equiripple phase filter.

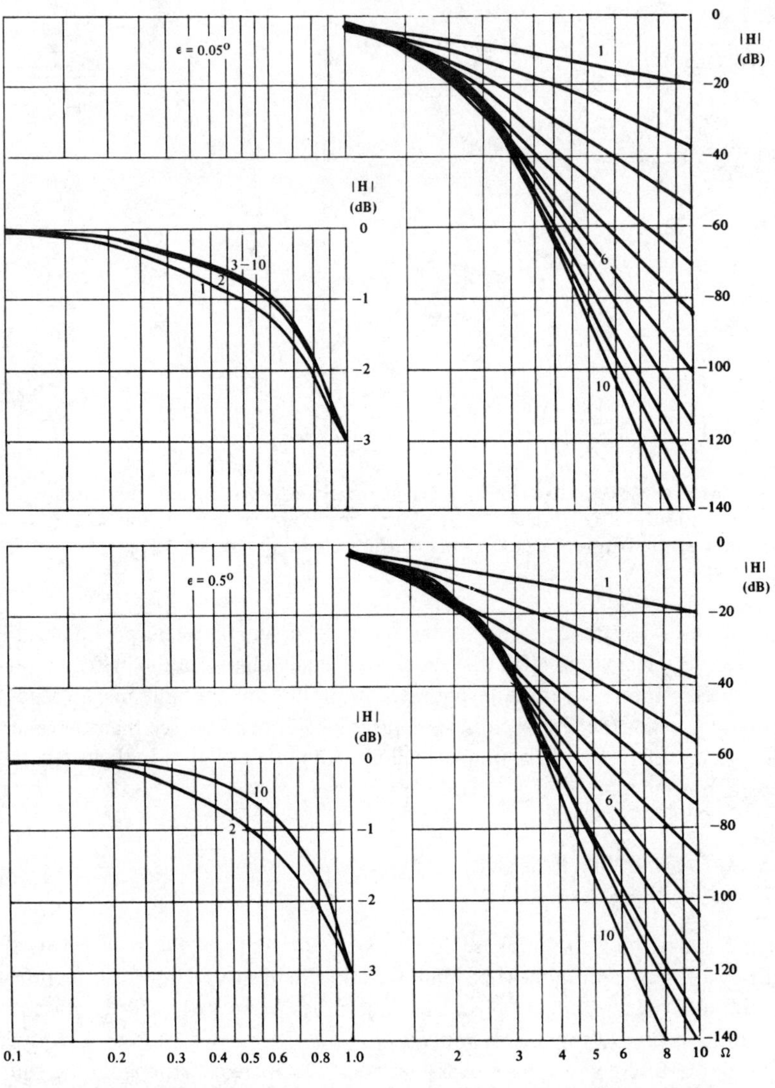

Fig. 5.10.2 Magnitude characteristics of equiripple phase filters having ripples of 0.05° and 0.5°.

$$\theta(j\omega) = \arg H(j\omega) = -(n\pi/2)\omega + (-1)^n \epsilon \sin n\pi\omega, \qquad |\omega| \leqslant 1$$
$$= -(n\pi/2) \operatorname{sgn} \omega, \qquad |\omega| > 1 \tag{5.10.1}$$

Thus, the delay of the ideal equiripple phase filter equals

$$\tau(j\omega) = -d\theta/d\omega = (n\pi/2)[1 + (-1)^{n+1} 2\epsilon \cos n\pi\omega], \ |\omega| \leqslant 1 \qquad \text{and} \qquad 0, \ |\omega| > 1 \tag{5.10.2}$$

which has a nominal value of $\tau_o = n\pi/2$ seconds and a ripple of $n\pi\epsilon$ seconds. Thus, the delay associated with the ideal equiripple phase filter is also equiripple with a cosine variation. It is interesting to compare this delay with that of the equiripple delay filter of Chap. 4 where

$$\tau(j\omega) = \tau_o/[1 + \epsilon T_{2n}(\omega)] \cong \tau_o[1 - \epsilon T_{2n}(\omega)], \qquad \epsilon \ll 1 \tag{5.10.3}$$

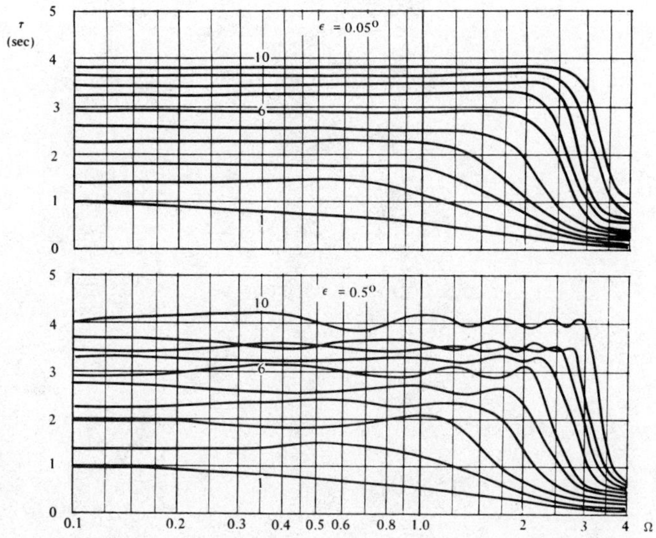

Fig. 5.10.3 Delay characteristics of equiripple filters having ripples of 0.05° and 0.5°.

from Eq. 4.11.1. For small ripple, the equiripple delay filter has a Chebyshev delay variation while from Eq. 5.10.2, the ideal equiripple phase filter has a trignometric (i.e., cosine) delay variation. This is the mathematical difference between these two filter types.

Bunker determined the optimum pole positions for the equiripple phase filters using an iterative minimax procedure and an all-pole transfer function given by Eq. 5.1.5. They are listed in Table 5.10.1. The pole positions have been normalized to produce a dc (not nominal) delay of one second. Humpherys gives an interpolation formula to find the pole locations for other phase ripples than those listed in Table 5.10.1.[19]

The magnitude and delay characteristics for 0.05° and 0.5° equiripple phase filters are drawn in Figs. 5.10.2 and 5.10.3. Note that in these figures, the transfer function has been frequency normalized so the 3 dB bandwidth equals unity. We see from Fig. 4.10.2 that the equiripple phase filter has a greater stopband rejection than the Bessel filter. It also has about 50% wider frequency range for almost constant delay over the Bessel filter. Small delay distortion occurs because of the

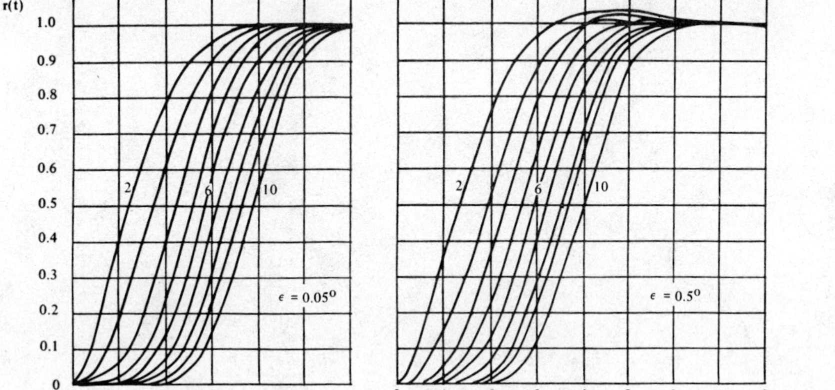

Fig. 5.10.4 Step response of equiripple phase filters having ripples of 0.05° and 0.5° and unity 3 dB bandwidths.

Table 5.10.1 Equiripple phase filter poles.
(From W. M. Bunker, "Symmetrical equal-ripple delay and symmetrical equal-ripple phase filters," IEEE Trans. Circuit Theory, vol. CT-17, pp. 455–458, Aug., 1970.)

n	ϵ (deg)	Poles $-\alpha \pm j\beta$
2	−2.5°	−1.21489 ± j0.976637
	−1°	−1.30793 ± j0.951410
	−0.5°	−1.35688 ± j0.934150
3	+5° −0°	−1.48154; −1.12549 ± j2.37883
	±2.5°	−1.56601; −1.17296 ± j2.26158
	±1°	−1.71576; −1.34213 ± j2.15248
	±0.5°	−1.81355; −1.43936 ± j2.08457
4	−5° +0°	−1.40844 ± j1.15227; −1.12775 ± j3.71899
	±2.5°	−1.54241 ± j1.12618; −1.15150 ± j3.68877
	±1°	−1.77492 ± j1.11181; −1.34391 ± j3.50518
	±0.5°	−1.92589 ± j1.09381; −1.46149 ± j3.38701
5	+5° −0°	−1.63705; −1.37215 ± j2.63852; −1.13497 ± j5.24347
	±2.5°	−1.73823; −1.42944 ± j2.51192; −1.14735 ± j5.14947
	±1°	−1.97051; −1.72406 ± j2.42822; −1.34810 ± j4.91710
	±0.5°	−2.13630; −1.91659 ± j2.36691; −1.47428 ± j4.76213
6	−5° +0°	−1.51234 ± j1.22361; −1.36080 ± j4.02760; −1.13820 ± j6.63975
	±2.5°	−1.65637 ± j1.19475; −1.38797 ± j3.99557; −1.14675 ± j6.63360
	±1°	−1.95288 ± j1.19732; −1.69793 ± j3.85077; −1.35248 ± j6.36238
	±0.5°	−2.15828 ± j1.18907; −1.90578 ± j3.74769; −1.48354 ± j6.17831
7	+5° −0°	−1.17092; −1.45699 ± j2.75980; −1.36236 ± j5.58459; −1.14260 ± j8.20689
	±2.5°	−1.81668; −1.51776 ± j2.62853; −1.37663 ± j5.48897; −1.14800 ± j8.12749
	±1°	−2.09102; −1.86769 ± j2.57230; −1.69150 ± j5.30523; −1.35675 ± j7.82691
	±0.5°	−2.29395; −2.10804 ± j2.52773; −1.90551 ± j5.17230; −1.49088 ± j7.61986
8	−5° +0°	−1.56391 ± j1.26181; −1.43866 ± j4.17671; −1.36296 ± j7.00025; −1.14482 ± j9.62716
	±2.5°	−1.71276 ± j1.23166; −1.46692 ± j4.14340; −1.37264 ± j6.99434; −1.14916 ± j9.63381
	±1°	−2.04309 ± j1.24568; −1.82731 ± j4.03411; −1.69097 ± j6.77866; −1.36028 ± j9.30709
	±0.5°	−2.27869 ± j1.24524; −2.07909 ± j3.95339; −1.90878 ± j6.62177; −1.49665 ± j9.08024
9	+5° −0°	−1.75016; −1.49932 ± j2.82778; −1.43653 ± j5.75401; −1.36597 ± j8.58278; −1.14762 ± j11.2163
	±2.5°	−1.86083; −1.56188 ± j2.69377; −1.45144 ± j5.65703; −1.37216 ± j8.50310; −1.15062 ± j11.1451
	±1°	−2.15973; −1.94115 ± j2.65607; −1.81423 ± j5.51487; −1.69278 ± j8.26308; −1.36340 ± j10.7973
	±0.5°	−2.38489; −2.20801 ± j2.62439; −2.07004 ± j5.40872; −1.91315 ± j8.08703; −1.50139 ± j10.5539
10	−5° +0°	−1.59449 ± j1.28521; −1.47708 ± j4.26285; −1.43519 ± j7.18271; −1.36737 ± j10.0133; −1.14914 ± j12.6502
	±2.5°	−1.74617 ± j1.25432; −1.50592 ± j4.22871; −1.44518 ± j7.17661; −1.37230 ± j10.0204; −1.15175 ± j12.6645
	±1°	−2.09696 ± j1.27599; −1.89280 ± j4.14340; −1.81005 ± j7.00694; −1.69492 ± j9.75806; −1.36595 ± j12.2970
	±0.5°	−2.35120 ± j1.28109; −2.16871 ± j4.07948; −2.06848 ± j6.88019; −1.91731 ± j9.56514; −1.50525 ± j12.0386

oscillating delay.[20] Increasing the delay ripple parameter ϵ and/or filter order n increases the ripple magnitude since the delay ripple magnitude is equal to $n\pi\epsilon/\omega_{3dB}$.

The equiripple phase filter has the step response shown in Fig. 5.10.4. Its form is very similar to that as Bessel and Gaussian filters with the exception that delay time is increased. The response has increasing overshoot for increasing ϵ. Humpherys gives the empirical relationship between overshoot γ (in %) and ripple ϵ (in degrees) as $\gamma = 1.75\epsilon$.[17] Echo affects become noticeable for $\epsilon \gg 1$. As in the equiripple delay filter of Sec. 4.11, the echos arise from the oscillatory delay of the filter.

5.11 LINEAR PHASE LOW-PASS FILTER–VALAND'S APPROXIMATION

Valand[21] has investigated all-pole approximations to linear phase filters. Ideal linear phase filters have transfer functions

$$H(s) = e^{-s} = \frac{1}{\sinh s + \cosh s} \cong \frac{M_n(0)}{M_n(s) + N_n(s)} = \frac{P_n(0)}{P_n(s)} \tag{5.11.1}$$

Recall that the Bessel filter resulted by finding sinh s and cosh s approximations using the truncated continued fraction expansion of coth s, where coth s = cosh s/sinh s $\cong M_n(s)/N_n(s)$. Then the *n*th-order approximation of e^{-s} equalled $1/P_n(s)$ where $P_n(s)$ was obtained from the *n*th-order Bessel polynomial in Eq. 4.10.2.

Valand instead approximates e^s using the product expansion for cosh and sinh s where[22]

$$\cosh s = \prod_{n=1}^{\infty} [1 + 4s^2/(2n-1)^2\pi^2] = (1 + 4s^2/\pi^2)(1 + 4s^2/9\pi^2)\ldots$$
$$\sinh s = s\prod_{n=1}^{\infty} [1 + 4s^2/n^2\pi^2] = s(1 + s^2/\pi^2)(1 + s^2/4\pi^2)\ldots \tag{5.11.2}$$

Then the *n*th-order approximation for e^s is given by Eq. 5.11.1 where M_n and N_n are the product expansions of cosh s (even part of P_n) and sinh s (odd part of P_n), respectively, truncated at the *n*th term. M_n and N_n have their zeros interlaced on the $j\omega$-axis. Parameter k is chosen to improve the approximation.

The linear phase approximation filter has a transfer function

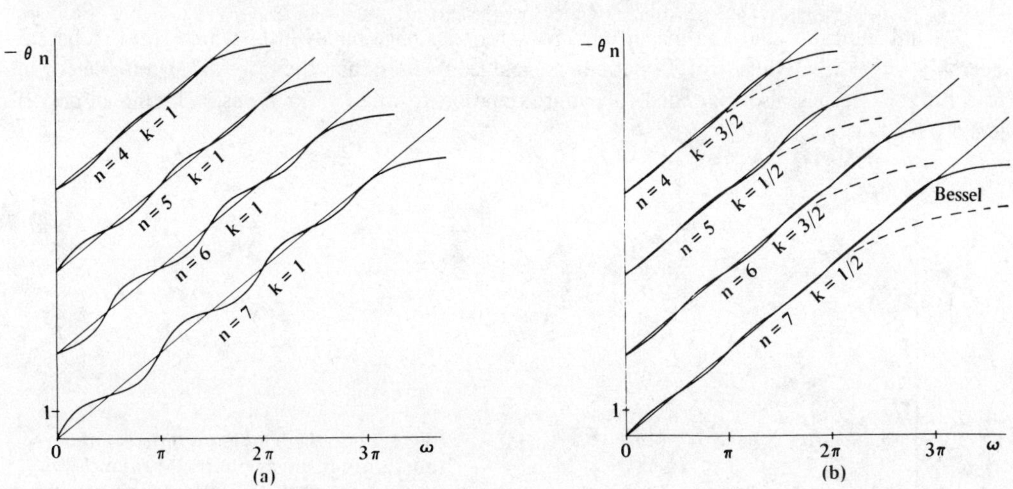

Fig. 5.11.1 Phase characteristics of Valand's linear phase approximation filters. (From J. Valand, "On the linear phase approximation," Proc. IEEE, vol. 55, pp. 1627–1628, Sept., 1967.)

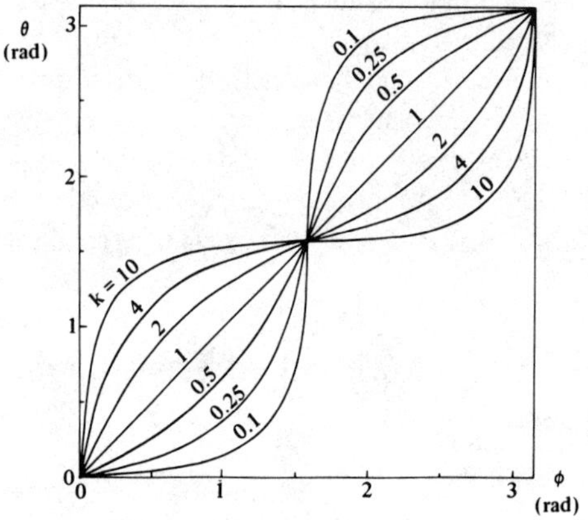

Fig. 5.11.2 Effect of k on phase characteristics. (From J. Valand, "On the linear phase approximation," Proc. IEEE, vol. 55, pp. 1627–1628, Sept., 1967.)

$$H_n(s) = \frac{1}{P_n(s)} = \frac{P_n(0)}{ks(s^2 + \pi^2)(s^2 + 4\pi^2) \ldots + (s^2 + \pi^2/4)(s^2 + 9\pi^2/4) \ldots} \tag{5.11.3}$$

Its phase response equals

$$\theta_n(j\omega) = \arg H_n(j\omega) = -\arg P_n(j\omega) = -\tan^{-1}[kN_n(\omega^2)/M_n(\omega^2)] \tag{5.11.4}$$

The phase characteristics are shown in Fig. 5.11.1a for various order filters where k = 1. In Valand's approach, the phase error equals zero at (n – 1) points equally spaced from $\omega = 0$. A nonunity k can be used to produce eqùiripple phase variation as shown in Fig. 5.11.1b. Denoting the phase $\phi_n = \tan^{-1}(N_n/M_n)$, then the phase response of this filter can be expressed as

$$\theta_n(j\omega) = -\tan^{-1}[k \tan \phi_n(j\omega)] \tag{5.11.5}$$

ϕ_n is plotted in Fig. 5.11.2. The delay of the filter equals

$$\tau_n(j\omega) = -d\phi_n(j\omega)/d\omega = \frac{k}{M_n{}^2 + k^2N_n{}^2}\left(N_n \frac{dM_n}{d\omega} - M_n \frac{dN_n}{d\omega}\right) \tag{5.11.6}$$

Valand indicates that the magnitude characteristics have bandwidths which seem to be considerably wider than those for Bessel filters, and concludes that they are more suitable for all-pass filters. He has also extended this approximation to other filter types including all-pass filters.[23]

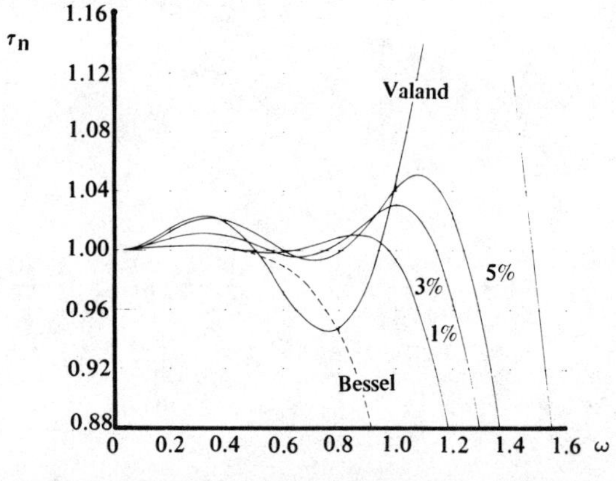

Fig. 5.11.3 Delay characteristics of several fourth-order linear phase approximation filters. (From B. D. Rakovich and B. M. Djurich, "A method for approximation of a linear phase characteristic," Proc. IEEE, vol. 59, pp. 1632–1633, Nov., 1971.)

Rakovich and Djurich[24] have proposed another approximation method which may give improved responses. They also force the phase error to equal zero at (n – 1) points, but the points are not necessarily equally spaced. The delay improvement is shown in Fig. 5.11.3. The delay characteristics of Valand's fourth-order linear phase filter is shown in Fig. 5.11.3 for k = 1.4 and unity bandwidth. Selecting k = 1.4 reduces the phase variation to ± 5%. There is large delay peaking near the band-edge. The normalized delay characteristic of the Rakovich and Djurich unity bandwidth filters is shown for phase ripples of (±) 1%, 3%, and 5%. The improvement in delay is obvious. It is interesting to note also that the Rakovich and Djurich approach yields filters which can be almost identical to the equiripple delay and phase filters.

5.12 LINEAR PHASE LOW-PASS FILTER–BUDAK'S APPROXIMATION

Budak[25] has investigated approximations for linear phase filters and found a useful form having finite zeros. The ideal linear phase filter having one second delay has a transfer function which can be expressed as

$$H(s) = e^{-s} = e^{-ks}/e^{-(k-1)s}, \quad 0 < k \leqslant 1 \tag{5.12.1}$$

Budak approximates numerator and denominator using the Bessel filter polynomials of Eq. 4.10.2 as

$$H(s) \cong H_{nm}(s) = \frac{P_n(0)}{P_m(0)} \frac{P_m[(k-1)s]}{P_n(ks)} \tag{5.12.2}$$

for (k – 1) and k seconds of delay, respectively. $H_{nm}(s)$, therefore, has m zeros and n poles. Note that when k = 1, $H_{no}(s)$ becomes the transfer function for the Bessel filter which forms a convenient reference.

Budak considers the case where m = n – 1. For a fourth-order filter, since the $P_n(s)$ polynomials equal

$$\begin{aligned} P_4(ks) &= (ks)^4 + 10(ks)^3 + 45(ks)^2 + 105(ks) + 105 \\ P_3[(k-1)s] &= [(k-1)s]^3 + 6[(k-1)s]^2 + 15[(k-1)s] + 15 \end{aligned} \tag{5.12.3}$$

then the gain equals

$$H_4(s) = \frac{15}{105} \frac{P_3[(k-1)s]}{P_4(ks)} = 7\,\frac{[(k-1)s]^3 + 6[(k-1)s]^2 + 15[(k-1)s] + 15}{(ks)^4 + 10(ks)^3 + 45(ks)^2 + 105(ks) + 105} \tag{5.12.4}$$

The magnitude and phase error characteristics of H_4 are shown in Figs. 5.12.1a and 5.12.1b. The filter bandwidth increases and filter selectivity decreases for decreasing k. For k = ½, the filter becomes all-pass. The decrease in selectivity is undesirable. However, the phase error is reduced for decreasing k, so a compromise is required.

The step response of the filter is shown in Fig. 5.12.1c. Decreasing k improves the response in that the rise time is decreased (since ω_{3dB} increases). Slight overshoot occurs and pre-ringing increases as k decreases. Poles and zeros migrate along radial lines as k decreases; zeros move inward and poles move outward.

These results appear to be very similar to those determined by McBride, Schaefgen, and Steiglitz in deriving the optimum low-pass filter using the ISE step response approximation in Sec. 5.4.

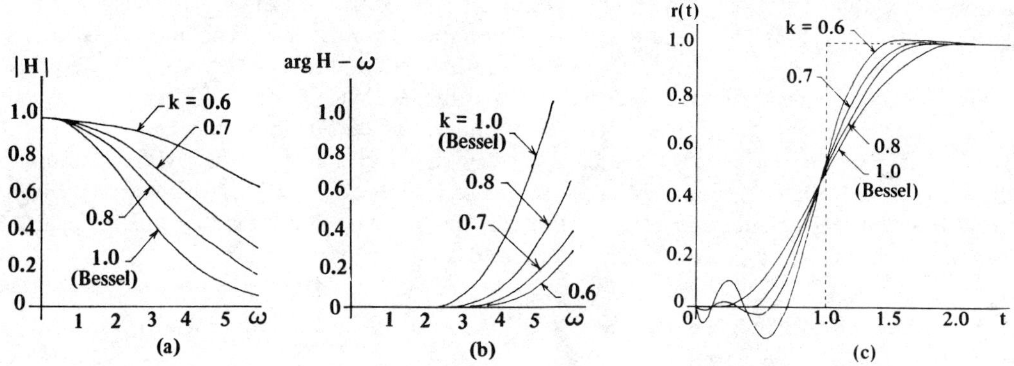

Fig. 5.12.1 (a) Magnitude, (b) phase error, and (c) step response of fourth-order linear phase approximation filter. (From A. Budak, "A maximally flat phase and controllable magnitude approximation," IEEE Trans. Circuit Theory, vol. CT-12, p. 279, June, 1965.)

5.13 LINEAR PHASE FILTER—PADÉ'S APPROXIMATION

Ideal linear phase, or equivalently, constant delay filters having one second delay have a transfer function which equals

$$H(s) = e^{-s} = \sum_{k=0}^{\infty} (-1)^k s^k/k! \tag{5.13.1}$$

Padé introduced a technique in 1892 for approximating any analytic H(s) using a rational function H_{nm} where[26]

$$H_{nm}(s) = P_m(s)/Q_n(s) = \sum_{k=0}^{m} a_k s^k \Big/ \sum_{k=0}^{n} b_k s^k \tag{5.13.2}$$

The a_k and b_k coefficients in the P_m and Q_n polynomials are chosen to make the Maclaurin series expansion of P_m/Q_n coincide with that of e^{-s} up to the $(n + m)$th term. For example, the biquadratic Padé approximation of e^{-s} is found from

$$H_{22}(s) = \frac{1 + a_1 s + a_2 s^2}{1 + b_1 s + b_2 s^2} = \sum_{k=0}^{4} (-1)^k s^k/k! = 1 - s + s^2/2 - s^3/6 + s^4/24 \tag{5.13.3}$$

Cross-multiplying and equating coefficients gives

$$a_1 = 1 + b_1, \qquad a_2 = 1/2 + b_1 + b_2, \qquad 0 = 1/6 + b_1/2 + b_2, \qquad 0 = 1/24 + b_1/6 + b_2/2 \tag{5.13.4}$$

Solving the last two equations yields $b_1 = 1/2$ and $b_2 = 1/12$. Substituting b_1 and b_2 into the first two equations and solving for a_1 and a_2 gives $a_1 = -1/2$ and $a_2 = 1/12$. Ream shows that, in general, the a_k and b_k satisfy

$$\frac{a_k}{a_0} = \frac{(-1)^k (N-k)!\, m!}{k!\,(m-k)!\, N!}, \qquad k = 0, \ldots, m$$
$$\frac{b_k}{b_0} = \frac{(N-k)!\, n!}{k!\,(n-k)!\, N!}, \qquad k = 0, \ldots, n \tag{5.13.5}$$

where $N = n + m$ and $a_o = b_o = 1$. We see that $a_k = (-1)b_k$ for $k = 0, \ldots, \min(m, n)$. The opti-

Table 5.13.1 Transfer functions for Padé's linear phase approximation filters. (Adapted from K. L. Su, "Time-Domain Synthesis of Linear Networks," copyright 1971, p. 25. Reprinted by permission of Prentice-Hall, Inc., Englewood Cliffs, New Jersey.)

m / n	0	1	2	3	4
0	$\frac{1}{1}$	$\frac{1-s}{1}$	$\frac{1-s+\frac{1}{2}s^2}{1}$	$\frac{1-s+\frac{1}{2}s^2-\frac{1}{6}s^3}{1}$	$\frac{1-s+\frac{1}{2}s^2-\frac{1}{6}s^3+\frac{1}{24}s^4}{1}$
1	$\frac{1}{1+s}$	$\frac{1-\frac{1}{2}s}{1+\frac{1}{2}s}$	$\frac{1-\frac{2}{3}s+\frac{1}{6}s^2}{1+\frac{1}{3}s}$	$\frac{1-\frac{3}{4}s+\frac{1}{4}s^2-\frac{1}{24}s^3}{1+\frac{1}{4}s}$	$\frac{1-\frac{4}{5}s+\frac{3}{10}s^2-\frac{1}{15}s^3+\frac{1}{120}s^4}{1+\frac{1}{5}s}$
2	$\frac{1}{1+s+\frac{1}{2}s^2}$	$\frac{1-\frac{1}{3}s}{1+\frac{2}{3}s+\frac{1}{6}s^2}$	$\frac{1-\frac{1}{2}s+\frac{1}{12}s^2}{1+\frac{1}{2}s+\frac{1}{12}s^2}$	$\frac{1-\frac{3}{5}s+\frac{3}{20}s^2-\frac{1}{60}s^3}{1+\frac{2}{5}s+\frac{1}{20}s^2}$	$\frac{1-\frac{2}{3}s+\frac{1}{5}s^2-\frac{1}{30}s^3+\frac{1}{360}s^4}{1+\frac{1}{3}s+\frac{1}{30}s^2}$
3	$\frac{1}{1+s+\frac{1}{2}s^2+\frac{1}{6}s^3}$	$\frac{1-\frac{1}{4}s}{1+\frac{3}{4}s+\frac{1}{4}s^2+\frac{1}{24}s^3}$	$\frac{1-\frac{2}{5}s+\frac{1}{20}s^2}{1+\frac{3}{5}s+\frac{3}{20}s^2+\frac{1}{60}s^3}$	$\frac{1-\frac{1}{2}s+\frac{1}{10}s^2-\frac{1}{120}s^3}{1+\frac{1}{2}s+\frac{1}{10}s^2+\frac{1}{120}s^3}$	$\frac{1-\frac{4}{7}s+\frac{1}{7}s^2-\frac{2}{105}s^3+\frac{1}{840}s^4}{1+\frac{3}{7}s+\frac{1}{14}s^2+\frac{1}{120}s^3}$
4	$\frac{1}{1+s+\frac{1}{2}s^2+\frac{1}{6}s^3+\frac{1}{24}s^4}$	$\frac{1-\frac{1}{5}s}{1+\frac{4}{5}s+\frac{3}{10}s^2+\frac{1}{15}s^3+\frac{1}{120}s^4}$	$\frac{1-\frac{1}{3}s+\frac{1}{30}s^2}{1+\frac{2}{3}s+\frac{1}{5}s^2+\frac{1}{30}s^3+\frac{1}{360}s^4}$	$\frac{1-\frac{3}{7}s+\frac{1}{14}s^2-\frac{1}{210}s^3}{1+\frac{4}{7}s+\frac{1}{7}s^2+\frac{2}{105}s^3+\frac{1}{840}s^4}$	$\frac{1-\frac{1}{2}s+\frac{3}{28}s^2-\frac{1}{84}s^3+\frac{1}{1680}s^4}{1+\frac{1}{2}s+\frac{3}{28}s^2+\frac{1}{84}s^3+\frac{1}{1680}s^4}$

Table 5.14.1 Comparison of optimum filters.

Filter Type	In-band Gain	Stopband Gain	Band-edge Selectivity & NBW	Transition Bandwidth	In-band Delay	Pole Q	Step Response Overshoot	Step Response Rise Time	Step Response Delay
ITAE Step Response	No ripple	Mono. dec.	Medium	Medium	No ripple & increases	Medium	Low	2.2	Medium
ISE Step Response	Ripples	Mono. dec.	Medium	High	Almost constant	High	Medium	2.2	Low
ISE Gain/Impulse Response	Dec. with peaking	Mono. dec.	High	High	Ripples with peaking	High	Medium	2.2	Low
ISE Delay Response	Mono. dec.	Mono. dec.	Low	High	Constant with peaking	Low	Low	2.2	Low
ISE Gain/Phase Response	Dec. with peaking	Mono. dec.	Medium	Medium	Ripples with peaking	Low	Low	2.2	Low
Minimum Rise Time Response	Mono. dec.	Equiripple	Medium	Low	Ripples & increases	High	Low	Lowest	Low
Minimax Delay Response	Ripples	Mono. dec.	Low	High	Equiripple (except $\tau(0)$)	Medium	Low	2.2	Low
Minimax Phase Response	Mono. dec.	Mono. dec.	Low	High	Almost equiripple	Medium	Low	2.2	Low
Valand's MFD Response	Mono. dec.	Mono. dec.	Low	High	Ripples with peaking	Medium	Medium	2.2	Medium
Budak's MFD Response	Mono. dec.	Mono. dec.	Low	High	Mono. dec.	Medium	Negligible	2.2	Low
Padé's MFD Response (for LPF)	Mono. dec.	Mono. dec. or constant	Low	High	Mono. dec.	Medium	Low	2.2	Low

mum transfer functions $H_{nm}(s)$, in the Padé sense, are listed in Table 5.13.1. It is interesting to note that when n = m, then the numerators and denominators of the gain function satisfy $P_n(s) = Q_n(-s)$ so that the filter is all-pass. When $m < n$, the filter is low-pass, and when $m > n$, the filter is high-pass. Thus, the Padé approximation is very flexible in that the orders of numerator and denominator can be selected.

Another interesting observation is that when n = m, comparing the Padé polynomial Q_n coefficients given by Eq. 5.13.5 with the Bessel filter polynomial P_n coefficients given by Eq. 4.10.2, we see that $Q_n(s) \sim P_n(s/2)$. Therefore, the polynomials are scaled versions of one another so the Padé all-pass filter uses the MFD polynomials. This filter is a special case of Budak's filter having the transfer function given by Eq. 5.12.1 where n = m and k = ½.[27]

5.14 OPTIMUM FILTERS IN RETROSPECT

A number of optimum filters have been considered in this chapter. We have seen that optimization criteria allow us to optimize certain aspects of a filter's response. However, we have also seen that optimization of one response usually produces pecularities in some other responses of a filter. Therefore, it is very important that the engineer fully investigates an optimum filter to insure that it has satisfactory characteristics. When this is done, optimum filters can provide advantages over classical filters.

Optimization criteria must also be used in the design of amplitude and delay equalizers as discussed in Chap. 2. Thus, optimum filters form an indispensible part of an engineer's background. To facilitate selection of an optimum filter or an optimization criterion, the filter characteristics of primary importance are tabulated in Table 5.14.1. It is useful to compare this table with Table 4.19.1 which summarizes the characteristics of classical filters.

PROBLEMS

5.1 (a) Determine the gains of the Graham/Lathop optimum ITAE filters at unity frequency. Based on this result, how will the step responses change under unity 3 dB bandwidth conditions? (b) Compare the optimum polynomial coefficients and step responses with those of the Butterworth filter.

5.2 (a) The McBride/Schaefgen/Steiglitz optimum ISE filter approximates the ideal step response shown in Fig. 5.4.1. What is the maximum overshoot of the ideal filter? (b) How does increasing filter order appear to improve the response? (c) The ideal filter has unity 3 dB bandwidth. Plot the magnitude response of the optimum filters. Is unity bandwidth obtained (note that unity time delay was obtained)?

5.3 (a) Write the transfer function H(s) for the McBride/Schaefgen/Steiglitz optimum third-order filter. Is it a minimum-phase filter? (b) Show how an all-pass function can be used in conjunction with a minimum-phase function to obtain H(s). Rewrite H(s) in this form. (c) Draw a block diagram realization of the filter.

5.4 (a) Draw the pole-zero pattern for the McBride/Schaefgen/Steiglitz optimum third-order filter. (b) Plot its magnitude and phase responses. What is the approximate 3 dB bandwidth B? (c) Plot the step response for the filter having B = 1 KHz.

5.5 (a) How does increasing filter order improve the response of the Pottle/Wong optimum ISE gain filter? (b) Draw the block diagram realization of the optimum fifth-order filter.

5.6 (a) Referring to the Pottle/Wong optimum fifth- and tenth-order filters, estimate the amount of magnitude peaking near their band-edges using Table 5.5.1. Compare with that in Fig. 5.5.1. Why is this peaking undesirable? (b) Plot the approximate delay response of the fifth-order filter. How much delay peaking is there near the band-edge?

5.7 Design a fourth-order Ariga/Sato optimum ISE filter in block diagram form. Use the type that has the narrowest transition band with the least delay peaking. The 3 dB bandwidth must equal 1 KHz.

5.8 The step response of the Ariga/Sato optimum fifth-order filter is shown in Fig. 5.6.2. The step responses of fifth-order Butterworth and Bessel filters are also shown. However, the bandwidths of all three filters are different. Normalize their 3 dB bandwidths to unity; then replot and compare their step responses.

5.9 (a) Write the transfer function of the Ariga/Sato optimum third-order filter assuming $\omega_c = \omega_d = 0.8$. Draw its block diagram realization. (b) Plot the delay response of the filter.

5.10 (a) Design a Haas optimum filter in block diagram form. It must provide 20 dB of rejection at 1.85B where the 3 dB bandwidth B equals 1 KHz. (b) Plot the delay response of the filter.

5.11 Compare the ISE approximation used by Pottle and Wong with that used by Haas. Discuss their similarities and differences.

5.12 Compare the shapes of the magnitude responses of Gaussian (ideal) and raised-cosine filters. The raised-cosine (or Hanning) filter has a magnitude response which equals $\cos^2(0.572\omega)$ for $|\omega| < 2.75$ and zero elsewhere (see Table 1.9.3).

5.13 (a) Design a fourth-order Jess/Schussler optimum filter (step input) having a pair of complex filter zeros in block diagram form. Assume that the passband frequency response is similar to those having parameters 52 and 62 in Fig. 5.8.2. The 3 dB bandwidth must equal 1 KHz. (b) Plot the magnitude and step responses of the filter. (c) What is the unusual result between the delay and step responses for these optimum filters?

5.14 Repeat Prob. 5.13 for a fifth-order optimum filter (impulse input) having a pair of complex filter zeros.

5.15 (a) Explain the difference between the equiripple (or Chebyshev) delay filter of Sec. 4.11 and the symmetrical-ripple delay filter. (b) Design a fourth-order symmetrical delay filter in block diagram form. It must have an in-band delay variation not exceeding ± 5% and a dc delay of 1 msec. (c) Plot the delay response of the filter.

5.16 (a) Determine the orders of the Bessel and equiripple phase (±0.5° ripple) filters which meet the following gain specifications: (a) 3 dB frequency = 1 KHz, 10 dB frequency = 2 KHz, 20 dB frequency = 3 KHz, and 30 dB frequency = 4 KHz. (b) Write the transfer function, (c) draw a block diagram, and (d) plot the magnitude response of the equiripple phase filter.

5.17 Design a fourth-order symmetrical phase filter in block diagram form. Its phase ripple must not exceed ±2.5° and it must have a 3 dB bandwidth of 1 KHz.

5.18 (a) Explain the difference in approaches used when determining the filter polynomials for Valand's linear phase filter and the Bessel filter. (b) Compare the phase responses of the two filters.

5.19 (a) Compare Budak's optimum linear phase filter and McBride/Schaefgen/Steiglitz's optimum ISE filter. Discuss their similarities and differences. (b) Which filter is preferable for data pulse smoothing?

5.20 The step response of Budak's optimum fourth-order filter is shown in Fig. 5.12.1 for various k values. However, the bandwidths vary with k. Normalize the 3 dB bandwidths to unity; then replot and compare the step responses.

5.21 (a) Design a 1 msec Padé delay filter in block diagram form. Use first- and second-order low-pass and all-pass filter approximations. (b) Compare their magnitude responses and bandwidths.

5.22 An ideal delay filter has a transfer function of e^{-s} as discussed in Prob. 4.37. Repeat that problem and show that $H_n(s) = P_n(-s)/P_n(s)$ is the gain the a Padé filter having equal indices.

REFERENCES

1. Su, K. L., "The nominal delay and rise times of lumped delay networks," IEEE Trans. Circuit Theory, vol. CT-16, pp. 574–577, Nov., 1969.
2. Marinkovic, V., "Integral criterion as a measure of distortion of a communication system," IEEE Trans. Circuit Theory, vol. CT-13, pp. 200–204, June, 1966.
   ———, "Integral criteria and response to unit impulse," IEEE Trans. Circuit Theory, vol. CT-13, pp. 204–205, June, 1966.
3. D'Azzo, J. J., and C. H. Houpis, *Control System Analysis and Synthesis,* Chap. 17, McGraw-Hill, NY, 1960.
   Dorf, R. C., *Modern Control Systems*, Chap. 4, Addison-Wesley, MA, 1967.
4. Bandler, J. W., and C. Charalambous, "Theory of generalized least *p*th approximation," IEEE Trans. Circuit Theory, vol. CT-19, pp. 287–289, May, 1972.
5. Graham, D., and R. C. Lathrop, "The synthesis of optimum response: criteria and standard forms," Trans. AIEE, vol. 72, pt. II, pp. 273–288, Nov., 1953.
6. Papoulis, A., *The Fourier Integral and Its Applications*, Chap. 6, McGraw-Hill, NY, 1962.

7. McBride, L. E., Jr., H. W. Schaefgen, and K. Steiglitz, "Time-domain approximation by iterative methods," IEEE Trans. Circuit Theory, vol. CT-13, pp. 381–387, Dec., 1966.
8. Pottle, C., and J. C. K. Wong, "Optimum least-squares approximations to the ideal low-pass filter," IEEE Trans. Circuit Theory, vol. CT-17, pp. 282–284, May, 1970.
9. Craig, J. W., and L. M. Goodman, "Approximation by realizable transfer functions," Proc. IEEE, vol. 54, pp. 63–64, Jan., 1966.
10. Ariga, M. and M. Sato, "An extremum approach to constant-delay transfer functions providing large amplitude bandwidth," IEEE Trans. Circuit Theory, vol. CT-17, pp. 121–125, Feb., 1970.
11. Haas, W. H., "A class of optimum low-pass filters," M.S.E. Directed Research, California State Univ., Long Beach, Dec., 1975.
12. Carroll, R. W., "On the design of raised cosine and Gaussian filters," Monograph WP-3370, Collins Radio Group of Rockwell International, Cedar Rapids, IA, Feb., 1969.
13. Papoulis, A., and M. S. Bertran, "Digital filtering and prolate functions," IEEE Trans. Circuit Theory, vol. CT-19, pp. 674–681, Nov., 1972.
14. Jess, J., and H. W. Schussler, "On the design of pulse-forming networks," IEEE Trans. Circuit Theory, vol. CT-12, pp. 393–400, Sept., 1965.
15. Bunker, W. M., "Symmetrical equal-ripple delay and symmetrical equal-ripple phase filters," IEEE Trans. Circuit Theory, vol. CT-17, pp. 455–458, Aug., 1970.
16. Rakovich, B. D., and B. M. Djurich, "Chebyshev approximation of a constant group delay with constraints at the origin," IEEE Trans. Circuit Theory, vol. CT-19, pp. 466–475, Sept., 1972.
17. Humpherys, D. S., "A relationship between impulse response overshoot and phase ripple," IEEE Trans. Circuit Theory, vol. CT-10, pp. 450–452, Sept., 1963.
18. Ref. 15
Bunker, W. M., "Symmetrical equal-ripple delay and symmetrical equal-ripple phase filters," Tech. Publ. 69ASD22, General Electric, Daytona Beach, FL, Dec. 1, 1969.
19. Humpherys, D. S., "Chebyshev linear-phase filter poles by interpolation," Proc. IEEE, vol. 60, p. 725, June, 1972.
20. Hansell, G. E., *Filter Design and Evaluation*, App. 3, Van Nostrand Reinhold, NY, 1969.
21. Valand, J., "On the linear phase approximation," Proc. IEEE, vol. 55, pp. 1627–1628, Sept., 1967.
——, "A variation of the linear phase approximation technique," Proc. IEEE, vol. 56, pp. 1141–1143, June, 1968.
22. Ghausi, M. S., and J. J. Kelly, *Introduction to Distributed-Parameter Networks*, App. C, Holt, Rinehart and Winston, NY, 1968.
23. Valand, J., "On the linear-slope delay approximation," Proc. IEEE, vol. 55, pp. 2059–2060, Nov., 1967.
——, "Addendum to 'On the linear-slope delay approximation'," Proc. IEEE, vol. 56, pp. 748–750, April, 1968.
——, "A further note on the linear-slope delay approximation," Proc. IEEE, vol. 56, pp. 1356–1357, Aug., 1968.
——, "Ripple pass function," IEEE Trans. Circuits and Systems, vol. CAS-21, pp. 763–773, Nov., 1974.
24. Rakovich, B. D., and B. M. Djurich, "A method for approximation of a linear phase characteristic," Proc. IEEE, vol. 59, pp. 1632–1633, Nov., 1971.
——, "Synthesis of dispersive networks for pulse compression using iterative techniques," IEEE Trans. Circuit Theory, vol. CT-20, pp. 147–150, March, 1973.
25. Budak, A., "A maximally flat phase and controllable magnitude approximation," IEEE Trans. Circuit Theory, vol. CT-12, p. 279, June, 1965.
26. Ream, N., "The Padé table for e^s," IEEE Trans. Circuit Theory, vol. CT-13, p. 233, June, 1966.
27. Marshak, A. H., D. E. Johnson, and J. R. Johnson, "A Bessel rational filter," IEEE Trans. Circuits and Systems, vol. CAS-21, pp. 797–799, Nov., 1974.

6 FREQUENCY TRANSFORMATIONS

Good tools shorten labor
Oriental Proverb

In the last two chapters, we investigated the behavior of a variety of classical and optimum low-pass filters. In the frequency domain and time domain analyses of Chaps. 2 and 3, we briefly discussed the concept of frequency transformations. Frequency transformations allowed high-pass, band-pass, band-stop, and all-pass filters to be derived from low-pass filters. We now want to explore this important topic in detail for it will allow us to utilize and exploit all the low-pass filter information we have derived in previous chapters for designing other filter types.

We begin by considering frequency scaling and frequency translation which are the simplest forms of frequency transformations. Then we shall consider the frequency transformations which are used to obtain high-pass, band-pass, band-stop, and all-pass filters. The frequency and time domain interrelations will be carefully investigated. In general, we will find that although these relationships are easily expressed mathematically, they require computer evaluation. Other important, but less known, transformations will be introduced for use in certain applications.

6.1 FREQUENCY SCALING

One of the simplest frequency transformations is that of *scaling*. We saw in Sec. 1.8 that frequency scaling consisted of replacing p by s/ω_o. The s-plane is therefore equal to the p-plane when it is expanded by a factor of ω_o. Frequency scaling is equivalent to frequency denormalization; it was used extensively in the earlier chapters to obtain maximum simplicity in equations and graphs. If the normalized transfer function equals H(p), then the denormalized transfer function H(s) equals

$$H(s) = H(p)\,|_{p = s/\omega_o} \tag{6.1.1}$$

For example, the first- and second-order low-pass filters had frequency normalized gains of

$$H_1(p) = \frac{1}{p+1}, \qquad H_2(p) = \frac{1}{p^2 + 2\zeta p + 1} \tag{6.1.2}$$

Scaling frequency by ω_o yields frequency denormalized gains of

$$H_1(s) = \frac{1}{s/\omega_o + 1} = \frac{\omega_o}{s + \omega_o}, \qquad H_2(s) = \frac{1}{(s/\omega_o)^2 + 2\zeta(s/\omega_o) + 1} = \frac{\omega_o^2}{s^2 + 2\zeta\omega_o s + \omega_o^2} \tag{6.1.3}$$

We saw in Fig. 2.3.4 that the effect of frequency scaling was to shift the magnitude and phase responses of the filter from unity to ω_o. The amplitudes and shaping of the magnitude and phase responses remain unchanged. We saw that frequency scaling also shifted the delay response of the filter from unity to ω_o. However, the delay was also reduced by a factor of $1/\omega_o$.

Now that we have reviewed the effects of frequency scaling on the ac steady-state response of a filter, let us review its effects on the time domain response. From Table 1.8.2, we see that if the impulse response of the filter equals

$$h(t) = \mathcal{L}^{-1}[H(p)] \tag{6.1.4}$$

then under frequency scaling, the response becomes

$$f(t) = \mathcal{L}^{-1}[F(s)] = \mathcal{L}^{-1}[H(s/\omega_o)] = |\omega_o|\, h(\omega_o t) \tag{6.1.5}$$

Thus, the impulse response has the same shape but its amplitude is increased by a factor of $|\omega_o|$ and time is contracted by a factor of $1/\omega_o$. The step response equals

$$g(t) = \mathcal{L}^{-1}[F(s)/s] = \mathcal{L}^{-1}[H(s/\omega_o)/s] = r(\omega_o t) \tag{6.1.6}$$

Therefore, the step response has the same amplitude and time is contracted by the factor $1/\omega_o$.

6.2 FREQUENCY TRANSLATION

Another basic frequency transformation is that of *translation*. We saw in Sec. 1.8 that frequency translation consisted of replacing p by $s + a$. The s-plane is therefore equal to the p-plane when it is translated by $-a$. If the normalized transfer function equals H(p), then the denormalized transfer function H(s) equals

$$H(s) = H(p)\,|_{p = s + a} \tag{6.2.1}$$

For example, if

$$H_1(p) = \frac{1}{p}, \qquad H_2(p) = \frac{1}{p^2 + \beta^2} \tag{6.2.2}$$

then

$$H_1(s) = \frac{1}{s + a}, \qquad H_2(p) = \frac{1}{(s + a)^2 + \beta^2} \tag{6.2.3}$$

The magnitude, phase, and delay responses are modified considerably. However, the impulse (or step) response is easily written. Since

$$h(t) = \mathcal{L}^{-1}[H(p)] \tag{6.2.4}$$

then

$$f(t) = \mathcal{L}^{-1}[F(s)] = \mathcal{L}^{-1}[H(s + a)] = e^{-at}h(t) \tag{6.2.5}$$

using Table 1.8.2. Thus, translating frequency is equivalent to multiplying the impulse (or step) response by exp $(-at)$.

Now that we have reviewed frequency scaling and translation, let us utilize these results for deriving high-pass, band-pass, band-stop, and all-pass filters from low-pass filters.

6.3 LOW-PASS TO HIGH-PASS TRANSFORMATIONS

The *low-pass to high-pass transformation* converts low-pass filter transfer functions to high-pass filter transfer functions. If the low-pass filter has gain H(p), then the corresponding high-pass filter has gain H(s) where p is replaced by ω_o/s. Thus

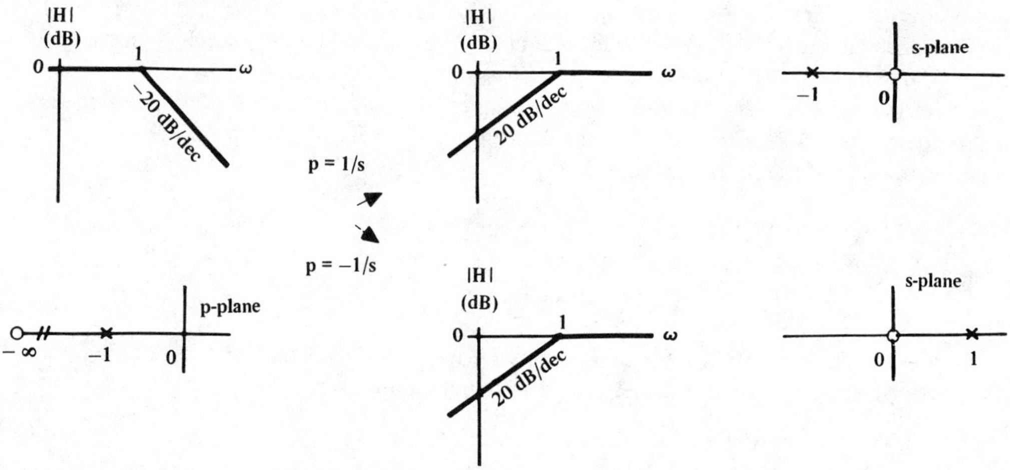

Fig. 6.3.1 Effect of two low-pass to high-pass transformations upon magnitude characteristic and pole-zero pattern for a first-order filter.

$$H_{HP}(s) = H_{LP}(p)\,|_{p = \omega_o/s} \tag{6.3.1}$$

Let us now derive this result. We denote the complex frequency variables p and s as

$$p = u + jv, \qquad s = \sigma + j\omega \tag{6.3.2}$$

In ac steady-state, $p = jv$ and $s = j\omega$. To form a high-pass filter from a low-pass filter, we require the magnitude characteristic to be inverted and to exhibit geometric symmetry as shown in Fig. 6.3.1. The low-pass filter behavior at low frequencies becomes the exact high-pass filter behavior at high frequencies and visa versa. Alternatively stated, we require the frequency axis to be inverted such that: (1) $p = j0$ maps into $s = +j\infty$ (or $-j\infty$), (2) $p = j1$ maps into $s = +j\omega_o$ (or $-j\omega_o$), and (3) $p = j\infty$ maps into $s = j0$. The transformation which produces this inversion is

$$|\omega| = 1/|v| \qquad \text{or} \qquad \omega = \pm 1/v \tag{6.3.3}$$

Thus, substituting $\omega = s/j$ and $v = p/j$ (i.e., using analytic continuation), the general low-pass to high-pass transformation must equal

$$s/j = \pm j/p \qquad \text{or} \qquad s = \mp 1/p \tag{6.3.4}$$

6.3.1 EFFECT ON THE S-PLANE

Which of the two transformations should be used? In general, we require minimum-phase filters (which have no right-half-plane zeros or poles) to generate minimum-phase filters under the transformation. Inspecting the two transformations of Eq. 6.3.4, and writing

$$s = |s| \exp[j \arg s], \qquad p = |p| \exp[j \arg p] \tag{6.3.5}$$

then the magnitudes satisfy $|s| = 1/|p|$ in both cases. Thus, the critical frequencies are located at reciprocal distances from the origin. Their angles equal

$$\arg s = -\arg p \ \ (\text{for } s = 1/p), \qquad \arg s = -\arg p + \pi \ \ (\text{for } s = -1/p) \tag{6.3.6}$$

In the second case, the angles are negatives of each other. However, in the first case, an additional 180° rotation must be added. Thus, if the low-pass filter was minimum-phase, the associated

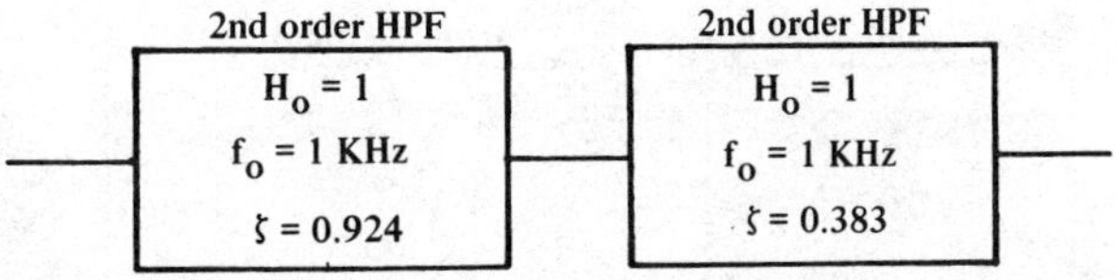

Fig. 6.3.2 Block diagram of fourth-order Butterworth high-pass filter of Example 6.3.1.

high-pass filter would also be minimum-phase if we used the transformation $s = 1/p$. However, if we use the other transformation having a negative sign, then the high-pass filter would be non-minimum-phase. Thus, $s = 1/p$ is the proper transformation.

To allow the frequency-normalized low-pass filter results to be denormalized, we use $s = \omega_o/p$ so that the magnitude characteristic is inverted about $\omega = \omega_o$ rather than $\omega = 1$. For a low-pass filter having any pole-zero distribution in the s-plane, the pole-zero distribution of the high-pass filter is obtained by simply *inverting* the s-plane around ω_o. Thus, low-pass poles or zeros at $p = 0$, $\omega_n e^{j\theta}$, and ∞ become high-pass poles or zeros at $s = \infty$, $\omega_o e^{-j\theta}/\omega_n$, and 0. Note that the damping factors and Q's of all the poles and zeros remain unchanged. Also note that if the low-pass filter has n zeros at infinity, then the transformation produces n zeros at the origin (reciprocal of infinity) for the high-pass filter. Summarizing, high-pass filter poles and zeros are easily obtained from low-pass filter poles and zeros by simple inversion.

EXAMPLE 6.3.1 Determine the transfer function for a fourth-order Butterworth high-pass filter having unity high-frequency gain and a 3 dB frequency of 1000 Hz. Draw its block diagram realization.

Solution We first determine the transfer function of the equivalent low-pass filter and then use the low-pass to high-pass transformation. From Table 4.3.1, the transfer function of the low-pass Butterworth filter equals

$$H(p) = \frac{1}{p^2 + 2(0.924)p + 1} \frac{1}{p^2 + 2(0.383)p + 1} \tag{6.3.7}$$

Using the low-pass to high-pass transformation $p = \omega_o/s = 1/s_n$, then

$$H(s) = \frac{s_n^2}{s_n^2 + 2(0.924)s_n + 1} \frac{s_n^2}{s_n^2 + 2(0.383)s_n + 1} \tag{6.3.8}$$

where $s_n = s/2\pi(1000 \text{ Hz})$. The block diagram of the high-pass filter is shown in Fig. 6.3.2. It is usually easier to convert low-pass filter blocks directly into high-pass filter blocks as shown in the next example.

EXAMPLE 6.3.2 Determine the transfer function for a fourth-order Chebyshev high-pass filter having unity high-frequency gain, a maximum in-band ripple of 3 dB, and a 3 dB cutoff frequency of 1000 Hz. First, use the low-pass to high-pass transformation. Then simply transform the block diagram of the low-pass filter directly.

Solution From Table 4.4.1, the fourth-order Chebyshev low-pass filter has a transfer function

$$H(p) = 0.707 \frac{1}{p_{n1}^2 + 2(0.464)p_{n1} + 1} \frac{1}{p_{n2}^2 + 2(0.0896)p_{n2} + 1} \tag{6.3.9}$$

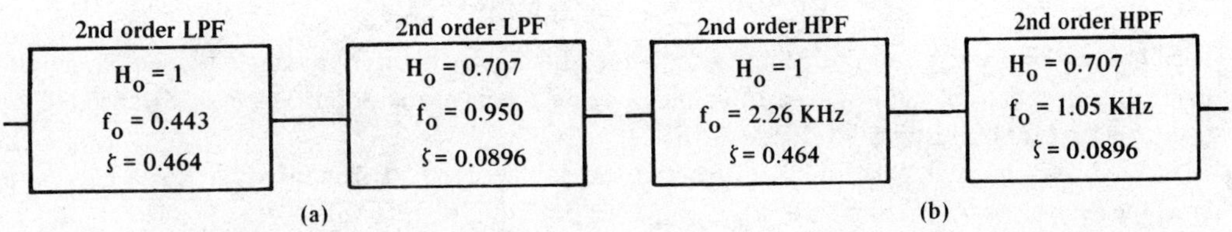

Fig. 6.3.3 Conversion of block diagram realization of (a) fourth-order Chebyshev low-pass filter to that for the (b) equivalent high-pass filter.

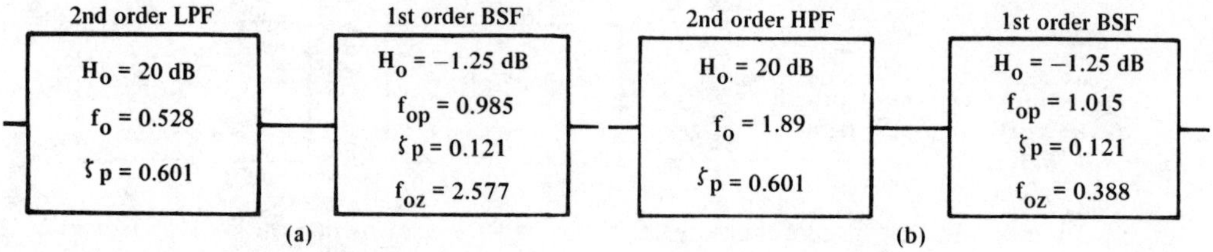

Fig. 6.3.4 Conversion of block diagram realization of (a) fourth-order elliptic low-pass filter to that for the (b) equivalent high-pass filter.

where $p_{n1} = p/0.443$ and $p_{n2} = p/0.950$. Letting $p = 1/s_n$, the high-pass filter has a transfer function tion

$$H(s) = 0.707 \frac{(s_n/2.26)^2}{(s_n/2.26)^2 + 2(0.464)(s/2.26) + 1} \frac{(s_n/1.05)^2}{(s_n/1.05)^2 + 2(0.0896)(s_n/1.05) + 1} \tag{6.3.10}$$

where $s_n = s/2\pi(1000 \text{ Hz})$. Notice that we have used the frequency-normalized form so that the corner frequency and damping factor of each stage can be easily identified.

Now we obtain equivalent information directly from the block diagram realization of the low-pass filter which is shown in Fig. 6.3.3a. With this conversion method, the normalized frequencies are first inverted and then denormalized; damping factors and Q's are left unchanged. Thus, we may easily convert the low-pass filter into a high-pass filter realization as shown in Fig. 6.3.3b.

EXAMPLE 6.3.3 Convert the fourth-order elliptic low-pass filter of Example 4.8.2 to an elliptic high-pass filter having analogous parameters and a band-edge of 1 KHz.

Solution The low-pass filter has the block diagram shown in Fig. 6.3.4a assuming it has unity bandwidth. Inverting normalized frequency gives the equivalent high-pass filter frequencies. Relabelling blocks completes the design (note that LPF becomes HPF, but BSF remains BSF under the transformation). To emphasize the frequency inversion, we have labelled the blocks in terms of normalized frequency where $f_n = f/1000$ Hz.

6.3.2 MAGNITUDE, PHASE, AND DELAY RESPONSES

Magnitude, phase, and delay responses are easily determined from Eq. 6.3.1. The magnitude responses of high-pass filters are related to those of low-pass filters as

$$|H_{HP}(j\omega/\omega_o)| = |H_{LP}(-j/\omega)| = |H_{LP}(j/\omega)| \tag{6.3.11}$$

(recalling $|H|$ is always an even function). The frequency inversion of the magnitude characteristic is shown in Fig. 6.3.5a. An alternative plot which is more general is shown in Fig. 6.3.6. Here gain magnitudes are drawn over the entire p- and s-planes. We see that $p = 0$ where $H_{LP}(0) = 1$ maps into $|s| = \infty$ where $H_{HP}(\infty) = 1$. This forms the "drumhead" around the perimeter of $H_{HP}(s)$. We also see that $|p| = \infty$ where $H_{LP}(\infty) = 0$ maps into the origin $s = 0$ where $H_{HP}(0) = 0$. This vividly shows the process of complex frequency inversion in the low-pass to high-pass transformation.

The phase responses of high-pass filters can also be easily expressed as

$$\arg H_{HP}(j\omega/\omega_o) = \arg H_{LP}(-j/\omega) = -\arg H_{LP}(j/\omega) \tag{6.3.12}$$

(recalling arg H is always an odd function). Thus, the high-pass filter phase is obtained by simply taking the *negative* of the low-pass filter phase after it is inverted about $v = 1$ and translated to $v = \omega_o$. This is also illustrated in Fig. 6.3.5b.

The delays of high-pass filters can also be easily written. Differentiating Eq. 6.3.12 and remembering that $v = -1/\omega$ and τ is always an even function, then for $\omega_o = 1$,

$$\tau_{HP}(j\omega) = -\frac{d \arg H_{HP}(j\omega)}{d\omega} = -\frac{1}{\omega^2} \frac{d \arg H_{LP}(-j/\omega)}{d(-1/\omega)} = \frac{1}{\omega^2} \tau_{LP}(j/\omega) \tag{6.3.13}$$

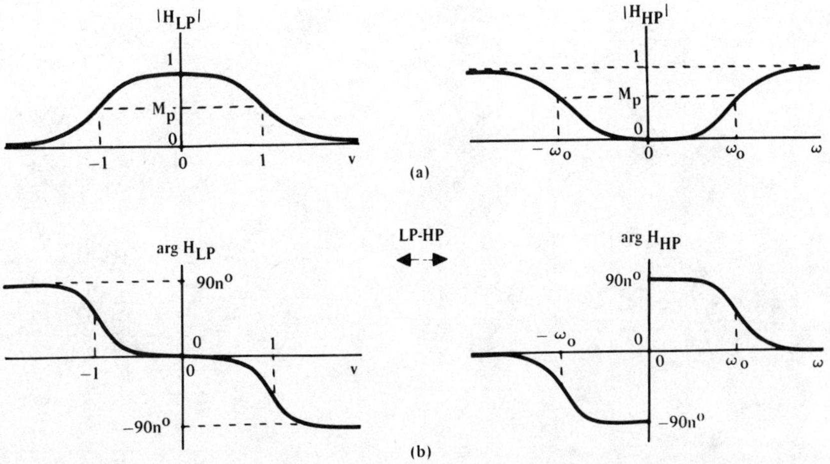

Fig. 6.3.5 Effect of low-pass to high-pass transformation upon (a) magnitude and (b) phase characteristics.

Thus, to obtain the delay of the high-pass filter, we simply invert the low-pass filter delay characteristic about $\omega = 1$ and multiply by ω^{-2}. In general, high-pass and low-pass filters have quite different delay characteristics. On a frequency-denormalized basis, it is easy to show that $\omega_o \tau_{HP}(j\omega/\omega_o)$ is given by Eq. 6.3.13. The low-frequency and high-frequency delay values equal

$$\begin{aligned} \tau_{HP}(j\omega) &= \tau_{LP}(j\infty)/\omega^2 = (b_{n-1}/b_n - a_{m-1}/a_m), \qquad \omega \ll \omega_o \\ &= \tau_{LP}(j0)/\omega^2 = (b_1/b_0 - a_1/a_0)/\omega^2, \qquad \omega \gg \omega_o \end{aligned} \tag{6.3.14}$$

where the gain of the low-pass filter is given in the summation form of Eq. 2.0.1. This is easily proved using Eqs. 2.10.34, 2.10.36, and 6.3.13. Eq. 6.3.14 shows the high-frequency slope of τ_{LP} (defined as $d\tau_{LP}/d(1/\omega^2)$) equals the dc delay of the high-pass filter and vice versa. From a pole-zero standpoint, letting $s = \omega/j$ in Eq. 6.3.13 gives

$$\tau_{HP}(s) = -\tau_{LP}(-1/s)/s^2 = -\tau_{LP}(1/s)/s^2 \tag{6.3.15}$$

Thus, the delay pole-zero diagram of the high-pass filter is equal to an inverted version of the delay pole-zero pattern for the low-pass filter with the addition of two poles at $s = 0$.

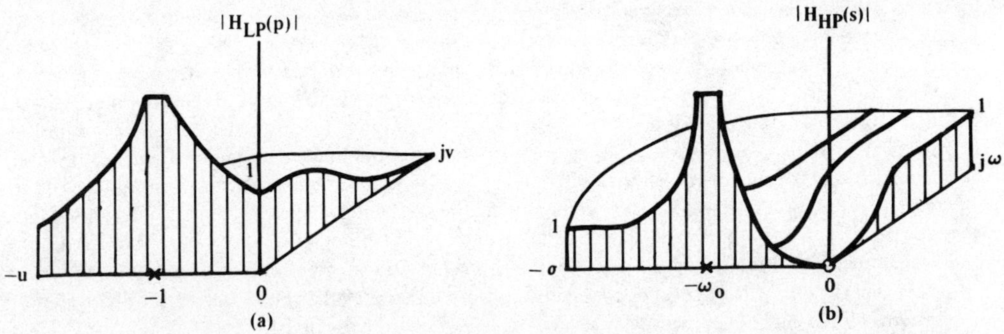

Fig. 6.3.6 Magnitudes of first-order (a) low-pass filter gain $H_{LP}(p)$ and (b) high-pass filter gain $H_{HP}(s)$ in the p- and s-planes, respectively.

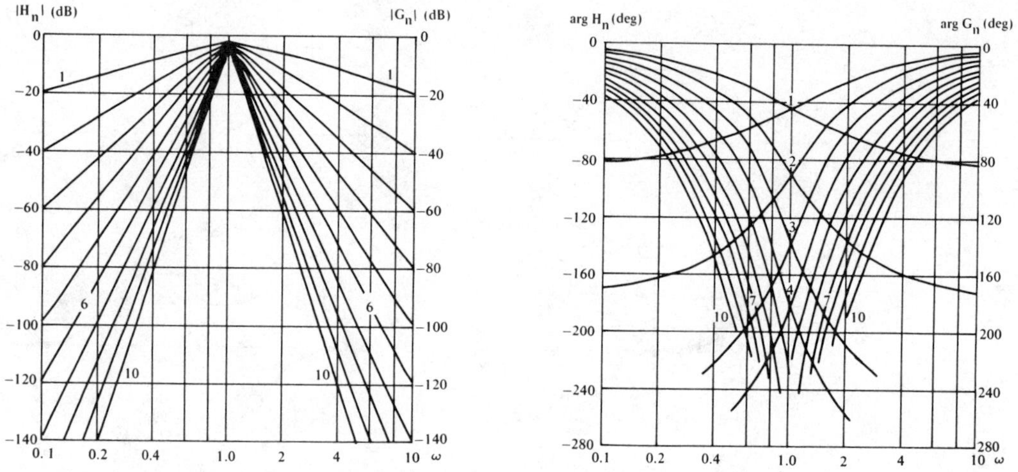

Fig. 6.3.7 Magnitude and phase characteristics of Butterworth low-pass and high-pass filters.[1]

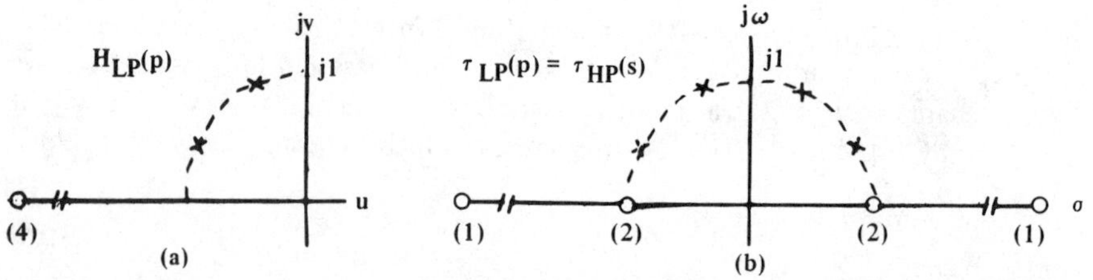

Fig. 6.3.8 Pole-zero pattern for (a) gain and (b) delay of fourth-order Butterworth low-pass and high-pass filters of Example 6.3.5. (The conjugate poles are not shown.)

EXAMPLE 6.3.4 Determine the magnitude and phase responses of Butterworth high-pass filters from the magnitude and phase responses of unity-bandwidth Butterworth low-pass filters shown in Fig. 6.3.7.
Solution The magnitude characteristic H_n of the high-pass filter is obtained by rotating the magnitude characteristic G_n of the low-pass filter about v = 1. To obtain the phase characteristic arg H_n, we rotate the phase characteristic arg G_n of the low-pass filter about v = 1 and change its sign.

EXAMPLE 6.3.5 Relate the delay responses of Butterworth high-pass filters to the delay responses of unity-bandwidth Butterworth low-pass filters shown in Fig. 4.3.2.
Solution This problem is easily solved from the pole-zero standpoint. The delay pole-zero configuration for a fourth-order low-pass Butterworth filter is shown in Fig. 6.3.8b. This is obtained using Fig. 2.10.1 and the gain poles-zeros of the Butterworth filter. Inverting the delay pattern and adding two poles at s = 0 using Eq. 6.3.15, we obtain the delay pole-zero configuration of the fourth-order high-pass Butterworth filter. Because all poles and zeros lie on a unit circle for any order Butterworth filter, the configuration remains unchanged. Therefore, we can make the immediate observation that the delay characteristic of Butterworth high-pass filters must be *identical* to that of Butterworth low-pass filters, except perhaps for a scaling constant. To determine the constant, we note that the dc delay of the high-pass filter $\tau_{HP}(j0) = b_{n-1}/b_n$ and the dc delay of the low-pass filter $\tau_{LP}(j0) = b_1/b_0$ from Eq. 6.3.14. Since Butterworth filters have $b_0 = b_n = 1$ and $b_1 = b_{n-1} = 2.63131$ (see Table 4.3.1), $\tau_{HP}(0) = \tau_{LP}(0) = 2.6131$ and the delay characteristics *are* identical. Note that since other filter types do not have all poles and zeros on the unit circle, their delay characteristics will *not* be preserved.

High-pass filters are specified in the frequency domain, the time domain, or in both domains simultaneously. Frequency domain specifications are especially convenient since we can utilize the classical and optimum filters developed in Chaps. 4 and 5. The nomographs of Chap. 4 are

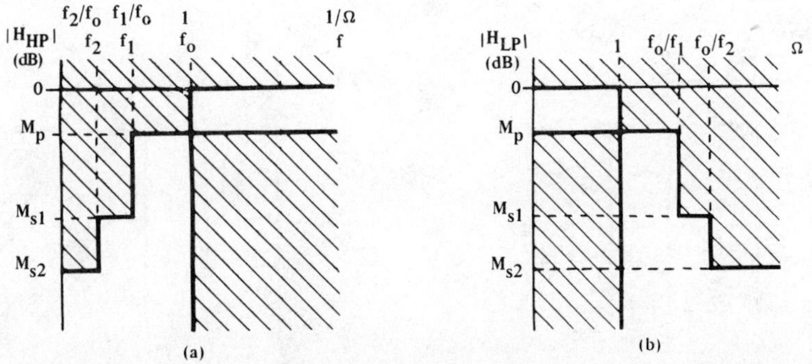

Fig. 6.3.9 Conversion of magnitude specification for (a) high-pass filters into equivalent specification for (b) low-pass filters.

again invaluable in determining the required filter order.

In general, the frequency domain specifications of high-pass filters have the form shown in Fig. 6.3.9a. The maximum passband ripple is M_p for frequencies greater than f_o. In the stopband of the high-pass filter, the minimum rejection is M_{s1} for $f_1 \leqslant f \leqslant f_o$, and so forth. To utilize the design data of earlier chapters, we convert this into equivalent information for a low-pass filter. The conversion consists of simply normalizing frequencies in the high-pass filter relative to f_o. We then form the reciprocal normalized frequency which describes frequency in the low-pass filter. In this form, we can now utilize the low-pass filter magnitude responses and their associated nomographs. After the desired filter type has been selected and its order determined, the normalized poles and zeros of the low-pass filter are converted to those for the high-pass filter using the low-pass to high-pass transformation just discussed.

EXAMPLE 6.3.6 Determine the minimum filter order required to satisfy the high-pass characteristics shown in Fig. 6.3.10a. Consider Butterworth, Chebyshev, and elliptic filters.

Solution The stopband frequencies are normalized by the corner frequency as shown in Fig. 6.3.10a. Inverting normalized frequency results in the low-pass filter specification of Fig. 6.3.10b. From the nomographs of Chap. 4, we find

Butterworth: $n_1 \geqslant 17$ and $n_2 \geqslant 10$ (use $n \geqslant 17$)
Chebyshev: $n_1 \geqslant 8$ and $n_2 \geqslant 7$ (use $n \geqslant 8$)
Elliptic: $n_1 \geqslant 5$ and $n_2 \geqslant 5$ (use $n \geqslant 5$)

As we anticipate, the elliptic type yields the minimum order filter.

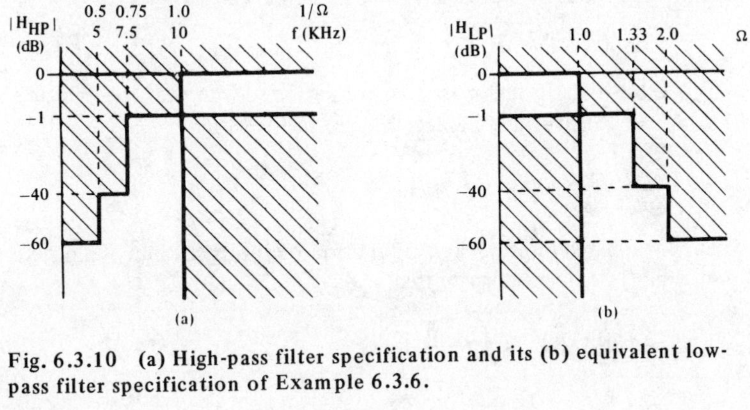

Fig. 6.3.10 (a) High-pass filter specification and its (b) equivalent low-pass filter specification of Example 6.3.6.

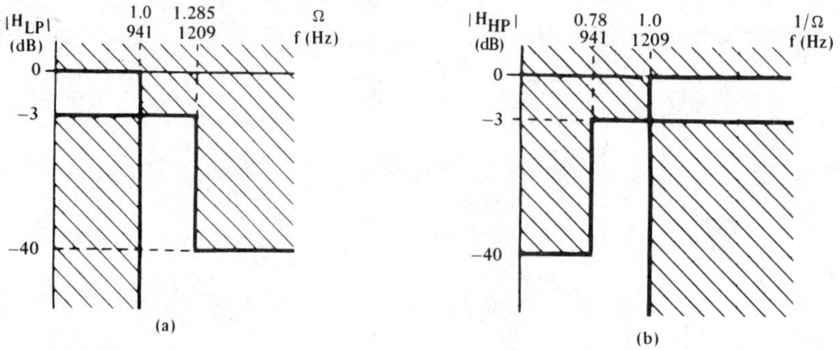

Fig. 6.3.11 (a) Low-pass and (b) high-pass band-splitting filter specifications in Example 6.3.7.

EXAMPLE 6.3.7 Touch-Tone telephone systems require two band-splitting filters to separate low- and high-frequency groups as discussed in Example 2.6.3. Determine the required order of Butterworth, Chebyshev, and elliptic low-pass and high-pass filters to obtain at least 40 dB of stopband rejection. Which filter would you recommend using and why?

Solution The desired magnitude characteristics are shown in Fig. 6.3.11 where we have chosen to allow 3 dB of in-band ripple. The maximum frequency from the low group (941 Hz) and the minimum frequency from the high group (1209 Hz) form the band-edges of the passband and stopband. Normalizing these frequencies, we see that the low-pass and high-pass filters will be of identical order. Entering this data on the nomographs of Chap. 4, we find

Butterworth: $n \geq 19$, Chebyshev: $n \geq 8$, Elliptic: $n \geq 5$

The elliptic filter is of lowest degree because of its narrow transition band. Due to its low order, it is useful in this application. We must assure that the amplitude limiter (see Fig. 2.7.3) can accept the large step response overshoot and the settling time for the filters.

6.3.3 IMPULSE AND STEP RESPONSES

The step and impulse responses of high-pass filters are easily expressed in terms of their analogous low-pass filter responses. If the low-pass filters have step response $r_{LP}(t)$ and impulse response $h_{LP}(t)$ which have Laplace transforms of

$$H_{LP}(p) = \mathcal{L}[h_{LP}(t)], \qquad R_{LP}(p) = \mathcal{L}[r_{LP}(t)] = H_{LP}(p)/p = \mathcal{L}\left[\int_{-\infty}^{t} h_{LP}(\tau)\, d\tau\right] \quad (6.3.16)$$

then the analogous high-pass filter responses must equal

$$h_{HP}(t) = \mathcal{L}^{-1}[H_{LP}(p)\,|_{p=1/s}] = \mathcal{L}^{-1}[H_{LP}(1/s)], \qquad r_{HP}(t) = \mathcal{L}^{-1}[H_{LP}(1/s)/s] \quad (6.3.17)$$

using the low-pass to high-pass transformation. Note that r_{HP} is *not* equal to $\mathcal{L}^{-1}[R_{LP}]$. It can be shown that if f(t) has a Laplace transform F(s), then[2]

$$\mathcal{L}^{-1}[F(1/s)/s] = \int_0^{\infty} J_0(2\sqrt{t\tau})f(\tau)\, d\tau\, U_{-1}(t) \quad (6.3.18)$$

where J_0 is the zero-order Bessel function of the first kind. Using the time integration theorem from Table 1.8.2, we can write that

$$\mathcal{L}^{-1}[F(1/s)] = \int_0^{\infty} \frac{d}{dt}[J_0(2\sqrt{t\tau})]\, f(\tau)\, d\tau\, U_{-1}(t) + \int_0^{\infty} J_0(0) f(\tau)\, d\tau\, U_0(t)$$

$$= -t^{-1}\int_0^{\infty} \sqrt{t\tau}\, J_1(2\sqrt{t\tau}) f(\tau)\, d\tau\, U_{-1}(t) + \int_0^{\infty} f(\tau)\, d\tau\, U_0(t) \quad (6.3.19)$$

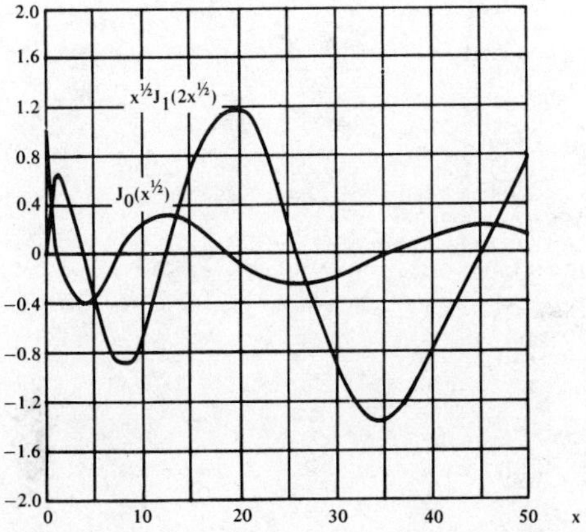

Fig. 6.3.12 Bessel functions $J_0(2x^{1/2})$ and $x^{1/2}J_1(2x^{1/2})$.[3]

J_1 is the first-order Bessel function of the first kind. The impulse response of the high-pass filter must therefore equal

$$h_{HP}(t) = \mathcal{L}^{-1}[H_{LP}(1/s)] = -t^{-1}\int_0^{\infty} \sqrt{t\tau}\, J_1(2\sqrt{t\tau})h_{LP}(\tau)\, d\tau\, U_{-1}(t) + r_{LP}(\infty)\, U_0(t) \tag{6.3.20}$$

The step response of the high-pass filter equals

$$r_{HP}(t) = \int_{-\infty}^{t} h_{HP}(\tau)\, d\tau = \int_0^{\infty} J_0(2\sqrt{t\tau})h_{LP}(\tau)\, d\tau\, U_{-1}(t) \tag{6.3.21}$$

These are very useful results. They show that the step (or impulse) response of a high-pass filter is the integral of the product of the low-pass filter impulse response times J_0 (or J_0' plus a U_0 term).

Although h_{LP} may be a monotonic response, J_0 or J_0' can cause h_{HP} or r_{HP} to be oscillatory since J_0 and J_0' are themselves oscillatory as shown in Fig. 6.3.12. The second term in Eq. 6.3.20 represents an impulse in h_{HP} at $t = 0$ of area $r_{LP}(\infty)$. This impulse allows r_{HP} to make an instantaneous transition from a value 0 to $r_{LP}(\infty)$ at time $t = 0$. Although these results are easily written mathematically and are useful conceptually, they require a computer for evaluation in most practical filters. Inverse Laplace transform solutions are more practical and direct although they also require computer evaluation.

The responses of several classical filters are shown in the following figures: the step response of Butterworth high-pass filters is shown in Fig. 6.3.13;[4] the impulse and step responses of Chebyshev high-pass filters having ripples of 0.5 and 2 dB and unity ripple bandwidths are shown in Fig. 6.3.14.

Another useful result concerns the initial and final values of the high-pass filter unit step response. These are easily related to the responses of the analogous low-pass filter as

$$\begin{aligned} r_{HP}(0) &= \lim_{s\to\infty} sR_{HP}(s) = H_{HP}(\infty) = \lim_{p\to 0} pR_{LP}(p) = H_{LP}(0) = r_{LP}(\infty) \\ r_{HP}(\infty) &= \lim_{s\to 0} sR_{HP}(s) = H_{HP}(0) = \lim_{p\to\infty} pR_{LP}(p) = H_{LP}(\infty) = r_{LP}(0) \end{aligned} \tag{6.3.22}$$

Thus, the initial value of the step response of a high-pass filter is *equal* to the final value of the step response of its analogous low-pass filter, and vice versa. This becomes obvious as soon as we recall that low-frequency and high-frequency behaviors are interchanged in the low-pass to high-pass transformation.

The *sag* or *droop* of the high-pass filter step response can also be easily determined. Sag δ is defined as the negative slope of the step response at $t = 0$, or

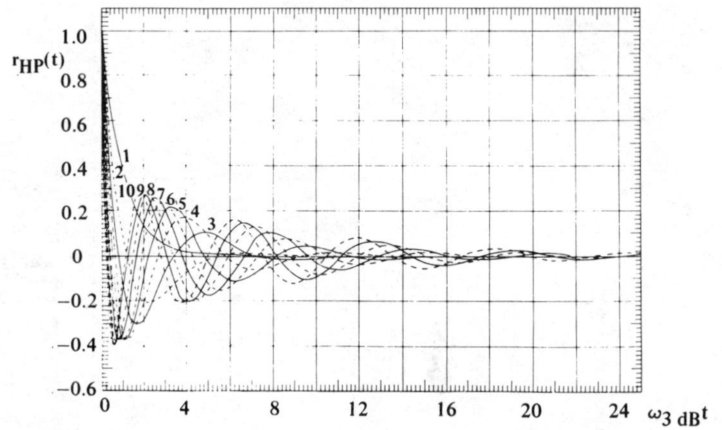

Fig. 6.3.13 Step response of Butterworth high-pass filters having unity 3 dB bandwidth. (From G. A. Beck, "Comments on 'Transient responses of conventional filters'," IRE Trans. Circuit Theory, vol. CT-8, pp. 166–167, June, 1961.)

$$\delta \cong -r_{HP}'(0) = -\lim_{s\to\infty} [sR_{HP}(s) - r_{HP}(0)] = -\lim_{s\to\infty} [H_{HP}(s) - H_{HP}(\infty)] \qquad (6.3.23)$$

In terms of the analogous low-pass filter from which H_{HP} is derived, the sag equals

$$\delta \cong -\lim_{s\to 0} [H_{LP}(s) - r_{LP}(\infty)] = -\lim_{s\to 0} [H_{LP}(s) - H_{LP}(0)] = b_1/b_0 - a_1/a_0 \ \text{sec}^{-1} \qquad (6.3.24)$$

where H_{LP} is given by Eq. 2.0.1. Thus, the sag in the high-pass filter step response is equal to the dc delay of the analogous low-pass filter.

Meyer has found a useful result concerning step response overshoot.[5] All high-pass filters having *more* than one zero at the origin (i.e., more than +6 dB/oct or +20 dB/dec low-frequency rolloff in its magnitude characteristic) *must always* have step response overshoot. Thus, no high-pass filter having greater than +20 dB/dec low-frequency rolloff can be constructed that will not exhibit step response overshoot. However, high-pass filters having a single zero at the origin may or may not exhibit overshoot.

In Sec. 4.18, we discussed the pulsed-cosine response of low-pass filters. In like manner, it is of interest to investigate the pulsed-cosine response of high-pass filters. The pulsed-cosine input s_i to the high-pass filter is given by Eq. 4.18.13, its spectrum S_i by Eq. 1.9.30, and its energy E_i by Eq. 1.9.31. The output energy E_o of the filter is given by Eq. 4.18.14 where $|H_n|^2$ is the squared-magnitude response of the high-pass filter. After some manipulation, it can be shown that the E_o/E_i ratio for Butterworth high-pass filters is simply one minus that for Butterworth low-pass filters. Thus, with a simple relabelling of the ordinate in Fig. 4.18.3, the same figure can be used for analyzing the pulsed-cosine response of fourth-order Butterworth high-pass filters.

For example, $E_o/E_i \to 1$ as $\omega_o T \to 0$ since reducing the pulse duration flattens the sin x/x spectrum which allows more energy to be transmitted through the high-pass filter. For a given $\omega_o T$, reducing B/ω_o increases E_o/E_i since more bandwidth is available for transmission. For $B/\omega_o = 3.0$, in continuous wave or CW operation (meaning $T \to \infty$), less than 0.3% of the energy is transmitted. However, under pulsed operation when $\omega_o T = 5.3$, then almost 9% of the energy is transmitted. Thus, this different type of response allows us to gain another perspective of high-pass filter response.

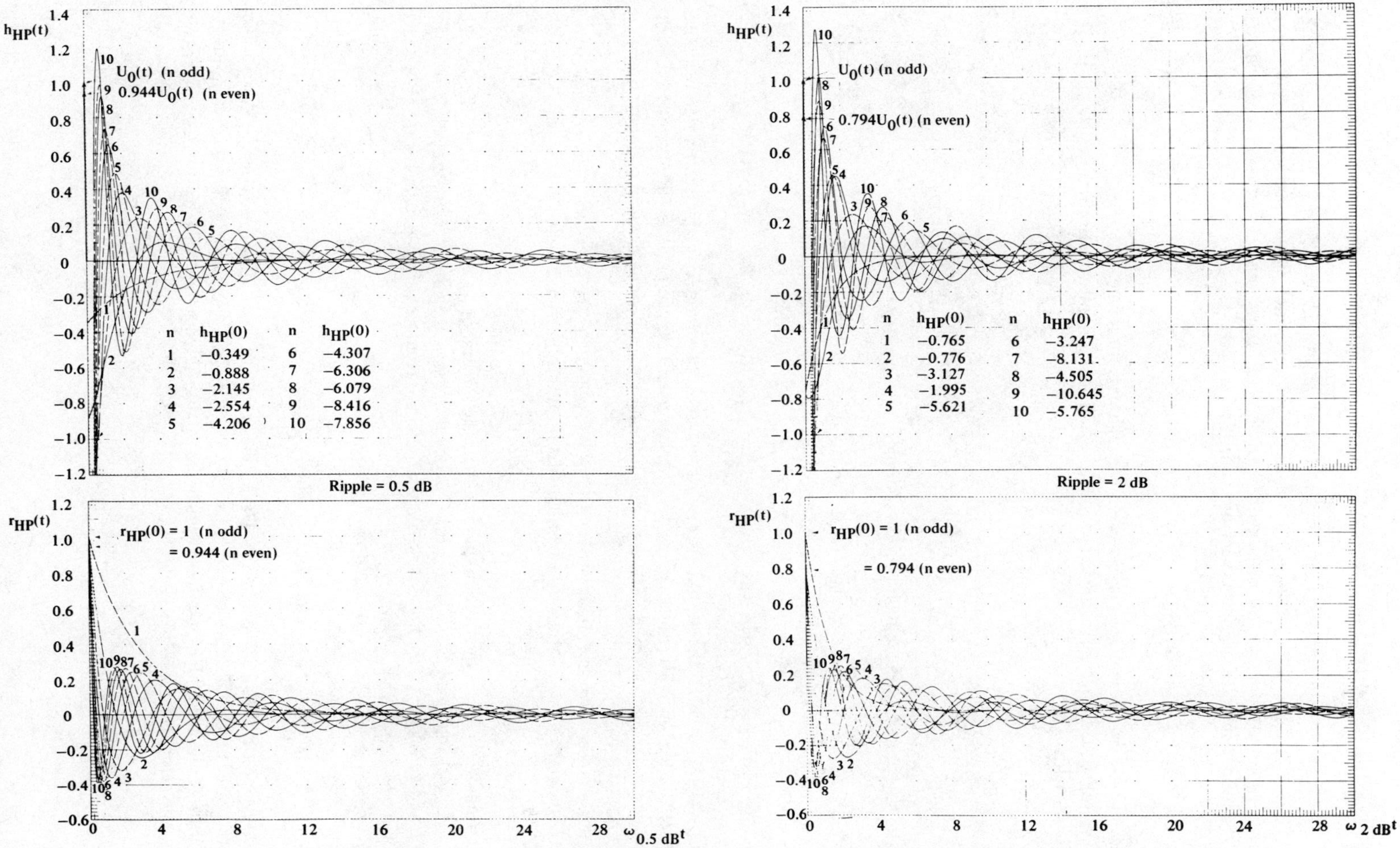

Fig. 6.3.14 Impulse and step responses of Chebyshev high-pass filters having ripples of 0.5 and 2 dB and unity ripple bandwidths. (From K. W. Henderson and W. H. Kautz, "Transient responses of conventional filters," IRE Trans. Circuit Theory, vol. CT-5, pp. 333–347, Dec., 1958.)

6.3.4 NOISE RESPONSE

In Sec. 4.18, we investigated the noise bandwidths of various classical filters. We found that the more highly selective a filter, the smaller was its output noise energy and noise bandwidth. From Eq. 4.18.3, the output energy of a low-pass filter contained in its impulse response, or alternatively, its response to a flat input noise spectrum equalled

$$E = \pi^{-1}\int_0^\infty |H_{LP}(jv)|^2\, dv = \int_{-\infty}^{\infty} h_{LP}{}^2(t)\, dt \tag{6.3.25}$$

Now let us see how the energy E is related to the high-pass filter characteristics.[6]

Performing a change of variable $v = -1/\omega$ in Eq. 6.3.25 and substitution of $|H_{LP}(-j/\omega)| = |H_{HP}(j\omega)|$ yields

$$E = \pi^{-1}\int_{-\infty}^{0} |H_{LP}(-j/\omega)|^2\, d(-1/\omega)$$

$$= \pi^{-1}\int_{-\infty}^{0} \omega^{-2}|H_{HP}(j\omega)|^2\, d\omega = \pi^{-1}\int_0^\infty \omega^{-2}|H_{HP}(j\omega)|^2\, d\omega \tag{6.3.26}$$

Since the step response of the high-pass filter equals

$$r_{HP}(t) = \mathcal{L}^{-1}[R_{HP}(s)] = \mathcal{L}^{-1}[H_{HP}(s)/s] = F^{-1}[H_{HP}(j\omega)/j\omega] \tag{6.3.27}$$

then combining Eqs. 6.3.26 and 6.3.27, we can re-express Eq. 6.3.25 as

$$E = \pi^{-1}\int_0^\infty \omega^{-2}|H_{HP}(j\omega)|^2\, d\omega = \int_{-\infty}^{\infty} r_{HP}{}^2(t)\, dt = \int_{-\infty}^{\infty} h_{LP}{}^2(t)\, dt \tag{6.3.28}$$

Thus in a high-pass filter, the output energy E is equal to the energy contained in its step response. Therefore, the results concerning energy for the low-pass filter can be generalized to the high-pass filter when properly interpreted. The step response energies of various classical high-pass filters are plotted in Fig. 4.18.1.

From a noise viewpoint, integrated white noise is input to the high-pass filter (rather than a step) where $S_i(\omega) = 1/\omega^2$ for all ω. The high-pass filter output then equals

$$S_o(\omega) = S_i(\omega)|H_{HP}(j\omega)|^2 = \omega^{-2}|H_{HP}(j\omega)|^2 \tag{6.3.29}$$

so that using Eq. 4.18.2, the output energy equals the integral of S_o which agrees with Eq. 6.3.28. Since the ideal high-pass filter with unity bandwidth has a magnitude response $|H_{HP}| = 1$ for $|\omega| \geqslant 1$ and zero elsewhere, Eq. 6.3.28 shows that its output energy E equals $1/\pi = 0.318$ which forms a convenient reference value.

The *noise margin* of a high-pass filter is defined as

$$NM = \int_0^\infty \omega^{-2}|H_{HP}(j\omega)|^2\, d\omega \tag{6.3.30}$$

by analogy with Eq. 4.18.11 assuming a $1/f^2$ input noise spectrum. For convenience, this is called the $1/f^2$ noise margin. The *noise bandwidth* B_s of a high-pass filter equals the effective stopband bandwidth of the ideal high-pass filter which passes integrated white noise with the same energy value as the actual filter, or

$$B_s = |H_{HP}(j\omega)|^2_{max} \Big/ \int_0^\infty \omega^{-2}|H_{HP}(j\omega)|^2\, d\omega \tag{6.3.31}$$

6.3.5 COMPLEMENTARY TRANSFORMATION

In general, the low-pass to high-pass transformation preserves the magnitude characteristic of a filter but modifies its step response. There is a different transformation which preserves the step response characteristic but modifies the magnitude characteristic.[7] This is desirable in some applications. This transformation is called the *complementary* or *low-transient* low-pass to high-pass transformation.

The step response of a Butterworth low-pass filter is shown in Fig. 6.3.15. If we are to maintain the step response characteristics in terms of overshoot (undershoot), rise time (fall time), delay time (storage time), settling time, etc., then the high-pass filter step response must equal

$$r_{HP}(t) = U_{-1}(t) - r_{LP}(t) \tag{6.3.32}$$

Equivalently, the impulse responses must satisfy

$$h_{HP}(t) = U_0(t) - h_{LP}(t) \tag{6.3.33}$$

Thus, the time domain responses are complements of one another. Now let us determine the relation between the filter transfer functions.

Taking the Laplace transform of the impulse responses in Eq. 6.3.33 yields

$$H_{HP}(s) = 1 - H_{LP}(s) \tag{6.3.34}$$

where the region of convergence of H_{HP} coincides with that of H_{LP}. Thus, if the low-pass filter has a transfer function

$$H_{LP}(s) = \sum_{i=0}^{m} a_i s^i \Big/ \sum_{i=0}^{n} b_i s^i, \qquad m \leqslant n \tag{6.3.35}$$

then using Eq. 6.3.34, the high-pass filter has transfer function

$$H_{HP}(s) = \sum_{i=0}^{n} (b_i - a_i)s^i \Big/ \sum_{i=0}^{n} b_i s^i \tag{6.3.36}$$

We see that the poles are unchanged but that the original zeros are modified and $(n - m)$ additional zeros are introduced. Thus, a stable low-pass filter remains stable under the transformation, but a minimum phase filter may become nonminimum phase. If we consider a low-pass filter having no finite zeros, then $a_i = 0$ except for $a_0 \neq 0$ and Eq. 6.3.36 becomes

$$H_{HP}(s) = \sum_{i=0}^{n} b_i s^i - b_0 \Big/ \sum_{i=0}^{n} b_i s^i = s \sum_{i=1}^{n} b_i s^{i-1} \Big/ \sum_{i=0}^{n} b_i s^i \tag{6.3.37}$$

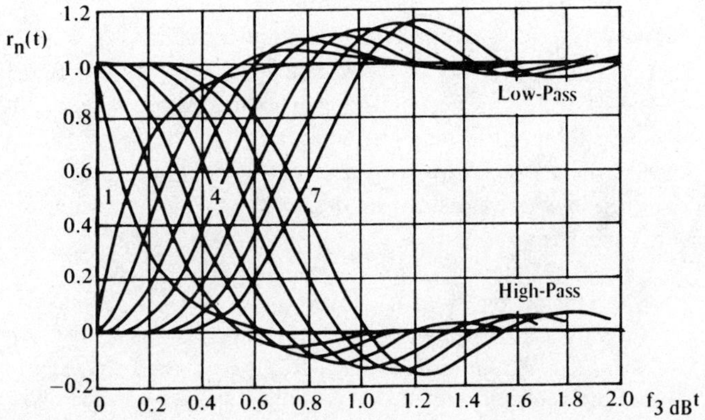

Fig. 6.3.15 Step responses of Butterworth low-pass filters and their complementary high-pass filters.

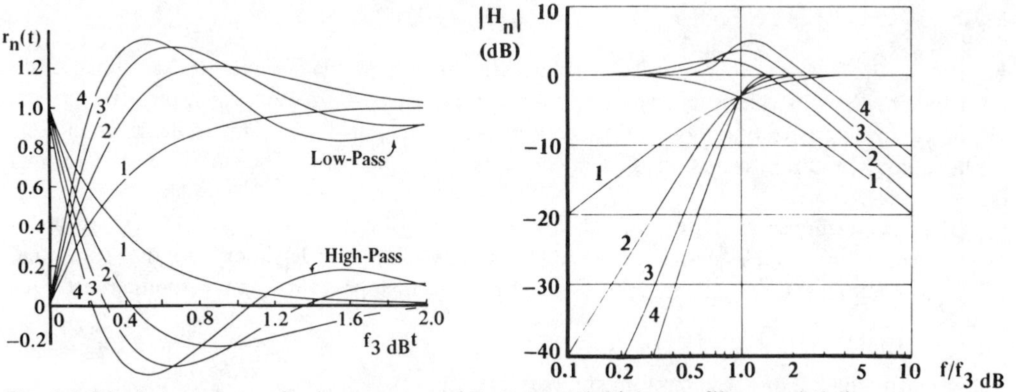

Fig. 6.3.16 Step and magnitude responses of Butterworth high-pass filters and their complementary low-pass filters. (From J. R. Ashley, "Butterworth filters as loudspeaker frequency-dividing networks," Proc. IEEE, vol. 58, pp. 959–960, June, 1970.)

Thus, all-pole filters have n finite zeros where one of these zeros is located at the origin.

Let us consider the ac steady-state behavior of filters related by this transformation. Using Eq. 6.3.34, it is easily shown that

$$|H_{HP}| = [(1 - \text{Re}\,H_{LP})^2 + \text{Im}\,H_{LP}{}^2]^{1/2}, \qquad \arg H_{HP} = \tan^{-1}[\text{Im}\,H_{LP}/(1 - \text{Re}\,H_{LP})]$$

$$\tau_{HP} = (\text{Re}\,H_{LP})^2[\tau_{LP} - d\,\text{Im}\,H_{LP}/d\omega]/[(1 - \text{Re}\,H_{LP})^2 + (\text{Im}\,H_{LP})^2] \qquad (6.3.38)$$

Thus, the magnitude, phase, and delay characteristics are related in a complicated manner and must be calculated using Eq. 6.3.38. The high-pass filter characteristics cannot be drawn directly from the low-pass filter characteristics.

For example, consider a Butterworth high-pass filter whose step and frequency responses are shown in Fig. 6.3.16. Using the complementary transformation of Eqs. 6.3.32 and 6.3.34, the analogous low-pass filters having the characteristics shown in Fig. 6.3.16 result. We see that the time domain characteristics are preserved. However, the frequency domain characteristics are changed. It is interesting to observe that gain peaking is introduced. We also see that the asymptotic rolloff of the low-pass filter is –20 dB/dec for any order. Thus, the primary benefit of using a higher-order filter is to obtain the desired step response characteristic.

For another example, consider a Bessel low-pass filter having transfer function $H_{LP}(s_n) = P_n(0)/P_n(s_n)$ as discussed in Sec. 4.10. Then the analogous high-pass filter has transfer function

$$H_{HP}(s_n) = 1 - H_{LP}(s_n) = [P_n(s_n) - P_n(0)]/P_n(s_n) \qquad (6.3.39)$$

The step responses of the two filters are shown in Fig. 6.3.17. Normalizing the bandwidth of the high-pass filter to unity, the frequency responses of the two filters are also shown in Fig. 6.3.18. We see that the frequency domain characteristics are modified. Peaking is introduced in the high-pass filter magnitude characteristic, and the asymptotic rolloff is maintained at +20 dB/dec for all orders. Again we see that out-of-band rejection is not increased by increasing filter order. Thus, the only advantage of increasing the high-pass filter order here is to increase the storage time of the step response.

EXAMPLE 6.3.8 Determine the frequency responses of a Butterworth low-pass filter and its complementary high-pass filter. Their step responses are shown in Fig. 6.3.15.

Solution A Butterworth high-pass filter has the frequency response shown in Fig. 6.3.16. To obtain a Butterworth low-pass filter, we simply apply the standard low-pass to high-pass transformation to this

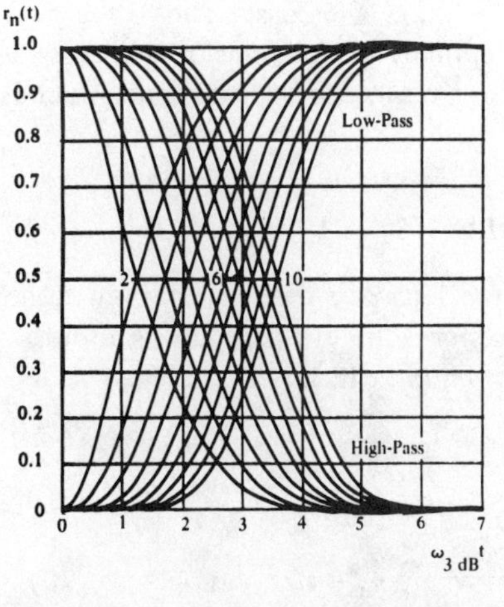

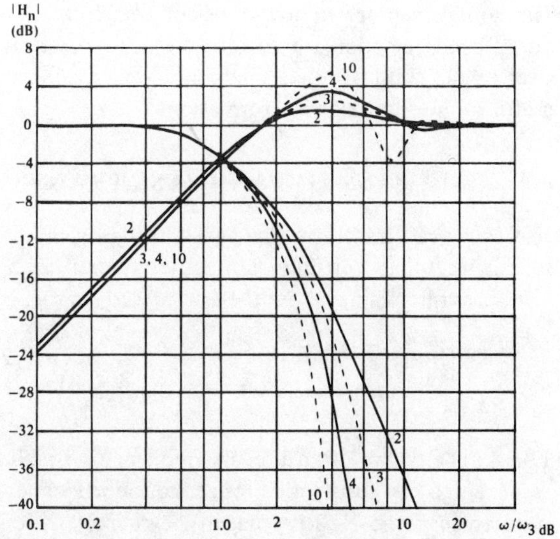

Fig. 6.3.17 Step and magnitude[7] responses of low-transient Bessel filters.

frequency response. Inverting frequency, we obtain the desired responses as shown in Fig. 6.3.18.

EXAMPLE 6.3.9 Design two second-order band-splitting filters having an overall gain of unity and analogous step response characteristics. Design the low-pass filter to have maximally flat magnitude (MFM) response and unity bandwidth.

Solution The band-splitting filter consists of a parallel combination of an MFM low-pass filter and a complementary high-pass filter (e.g., see Fig. 2.7.3a). Assume the low-pass filter has transfer function

$$H_{LP}(s) = \frac{1 + a_1 s}{1 + b_1 s + b_2 s^2} \tag{6.3.40}$$

For H_{LP} to have an MFM response, we found in Example 4.2.2 that $b_1{}^2 - 2b_2 = a_1{}^2$ and $a_1{}^2 = b_2{}^2 - 1$. Therefore, the high-pass filter must have a transfer function

$$H_{HP}(s) = 1 - H_{LP}(s) = \frac{s[b_2 s + (b_1 - a_1)]}{1 + b_1 s + b_2 s^2} = \frac{b_2 s[s + 2/(a_1 + b_1)]}{1 + b_1 s + b_2 s^2} \tag{6.3.41}$$

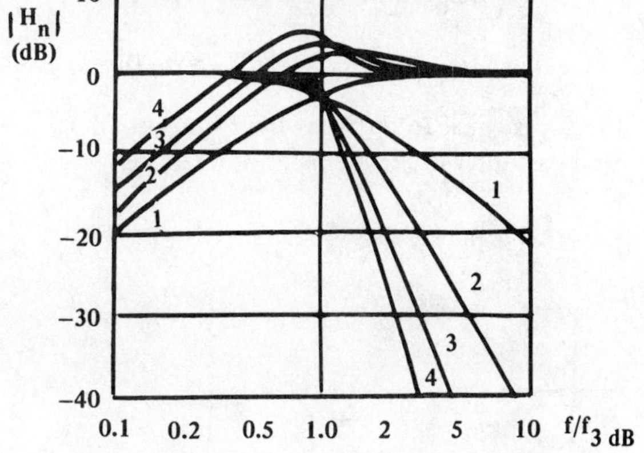

Fig. 6.3.18 Magnitude responses of Butterworth low-pass filters and their complementary high-pass filters in Example 6.3.8.

The complementary or low-transient transformation has not found wide usage due to the poor out-of-band rejection obtained. Nevertheless, it is a conceptually useful transform because it gives us the ability to maintain time domain behavior. It also gives us another viewpoint which is useful for interpreting transformations.

6.4 LOW-PASS TO BAND-PASS TRANSFORMATIONS

Just as we can transform low-pass filter transfer functions into high-pass filter transfer functions, so can we transform them into other filter types. To transform the low-pass filter gain into a band-pass filter gain, we use the *low-pass to band-pass transformation* which is

$$H_{BP}(s) = H_{LP}(p)\Big|_{p = \frac{\omega_o}{B}\left(\frac{s}{\omega_o} + \frac{\omega_o}{s}\right) = \frac{s^2 + \omega_o^2}{Bs}} \tag{6.4.1}$$

For simplicity, we often use the frequency normalized form where $s_n = s/\omega_o$ and $p = (\omega_o/B) \times (s_n + 1/s_n)$. To justify this result, consider Figs. 6.4.1 and 6.4.8. From a mapping viewpoint, we need to map the $H_{LP}(jv)$ magnitude characteristic into the $H_{BP}(j\omega)$ magnitude characteristic as shown. Thus, we must map the jv-axis of the p-plane into the jω-axis of the s-plane with the following constraints: (1) $p = j0$ maps into $s = +j\omega_o$ (and $-j\omega_o$), (2) $p = j1$ maps into $s = +j\omega_U$ (and $-j\omega_L$), and (3) $p = -j1$ maps into $s = +j\omega_L$ (and $-j\omega_U$). We also wish to maintain the geometric symmetry of $H_{LP}(jv)$. A transformation which produces this mapping is[8]

$$p = k(s/\omega_o + \omega_o/s) \tag{6.4.2}$$

Setting $p = jv$ and $s = j\omega$, then Eq. 6.4.2 becomes

$$v = k(\omega_o^2 - \omega^2)/\omega\omega_o \tag{6.4.3}$$

When $v = 0$, then $\omega = \pm\omega_o$. When $v = +1$ and -1, then Eq. 6.4.3 requires that

$$1 = k(\omega_o^2 - \omega_L^2)/\omega_o\omega_L, \qquad -1 = k(\omega_o^2 - \omega_U^2)/\omega_o\omega_U \tag{6.4.4}$$

Solving both equations for k and equating shows that ω_o equals

$$\omega_o = \sqrt{\omega_U\omega_L} \tag{6.4.5}$$

which is the (geometric) center frequency of the band-pass filter. Substituting ω_o into Eq. 6.4.4 gives k as

$$k = (\omega_o/\omega_L - \omega_U/\omega_o)^{-1} = [(\omega_L/\omega_U)^{1/2} - (\omega_U/\omega_L)^{1/2}]^{-1}$$

$$= (\omega_U\omega_L)^{1/2}/(\omega_L - \omega_U) = \omega_o/B = Q \tag{6.4.6}$$

Thus, k is equal to the Q of the band-pass filter. 1/k must equal the fractional bandwidth of the band-pass filter where the bandwidth equals

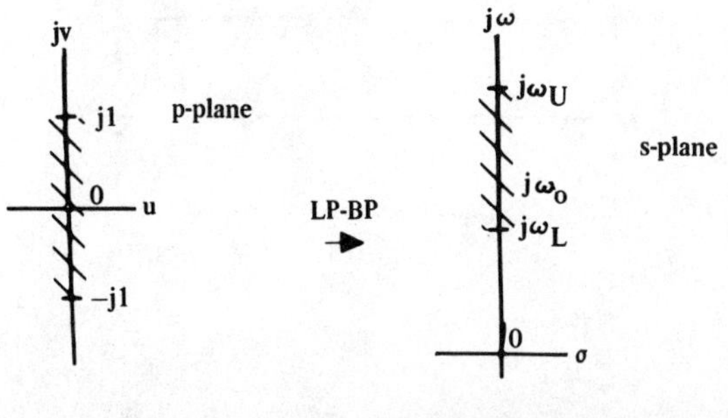

Fig. 6.4.1 Mapping of p-plane into s-plane using the low-pass to band-pass transformation. (The lower-half s-plane is not shown.)

$$B = \omega_U - \omega_L \tag{6.4.7}$$

It is important to note from Fig. 6.4.1 that Q is defined in terms of the M_p (dB) bandwidth. M_p can be any value such as 0.01, 0.5, or 3 dB.

6.4.1 EFFECT ON THE S-PLANE

Now let us investigate the effect this transformation has upon the poles and zeros of the low-pass filter. Rewriting Eq. 6.4.1, we see that s must satisfy

$$s^2 - pBs + \omega_o^2 = 0 \tag{6.4.8}$$

Solving for s using the biquadratic equation gives

$$s = (pB/2) \pm [(pB/2)^2 - \omega_o^2]^{1/2} \tag{6.4.9}$$

so normalized s, denoted as s_n, equals

$$s_n = s/\omega_o = (p/2Q) \pm [(p/2Q)^2 - 1]^{1/2} \tag{6.4.10}$$

Every pole and zero p of the low-pass filter transforms into a *pair* of poles and zeros in the band-pass filter. The location of these critical frequencies depends upon p and the Q of the transformation. When $|p/2| \ll Q$, then s equals

$$s = (pB/2) \pm j\omega_o[1 - (pB/2\omega_o)^2]^{1/2} \cong (pB/2) \pm j\omega_o[1 - (pB/2\omega_o)^2/2] \cong pB/2 \pm j\omega_o \tag{6.4.11}$$

so s_n equals

$$s_n = s/\omega_o \cong p/2Q \pm j1 \tag{6.4.12}$$

When $|p/2| \gg Q$, then s equals

$$s = (pB/2)\left\{1 \pm [1 - (2\omega_o/pB)^2]^{1/2}\right\} \cong (pB/2)\left\{1 \pm [1 - \tfrac{1}{2}(2\omega_o/pB)^2]\right\} \cong pB, \quad Q\omega_o/p \tag{6.4.13}$$

so s_n equals

$$s_n = s/\omega_o \cong p/Q, \qquad Q/p \tag{6.4.14}$$

Therefore, we see that when $|p/2| \ll Q$, the band-pass filter poles and zeros are obtained from the low-pass filter poles and zeros by scaling p by half the bandwidth and then translating vertically to $\pm j\omega_o$. However, when $|p/2| \gg Q$, then one band-pass pole-zero is obtained by scaling p by B. The second pole-zero is obtained by inverting the first pole-zero and scaling by ω_o^2. For intermediate values of p, the pole-zero locations must be calculated using Eqs. 6.4.9 or 6.4.10. These results show that real low-pass poles-zeros remain real under low-Q transformations but become complex under high-Q transformations. Alternatively, the values may be obtained directly from Fig. 6.4.2. Here we scale p as

$$p/Q = x + jy \tag{6.4.15}$$

and simply read off the s_n values as

$$s_n = s/\omega_o = \sigma + j\omega \tag{6.4.16}$$

These results are illustrated in Fig. 6.4.3. It shows the mapping of the pole-zero pattern for a second-order low-pass Butterworth filter of unity center frequency where $p = -0.707 \pm j0.707$. In the high-Q case, the band-pass filter poles equal

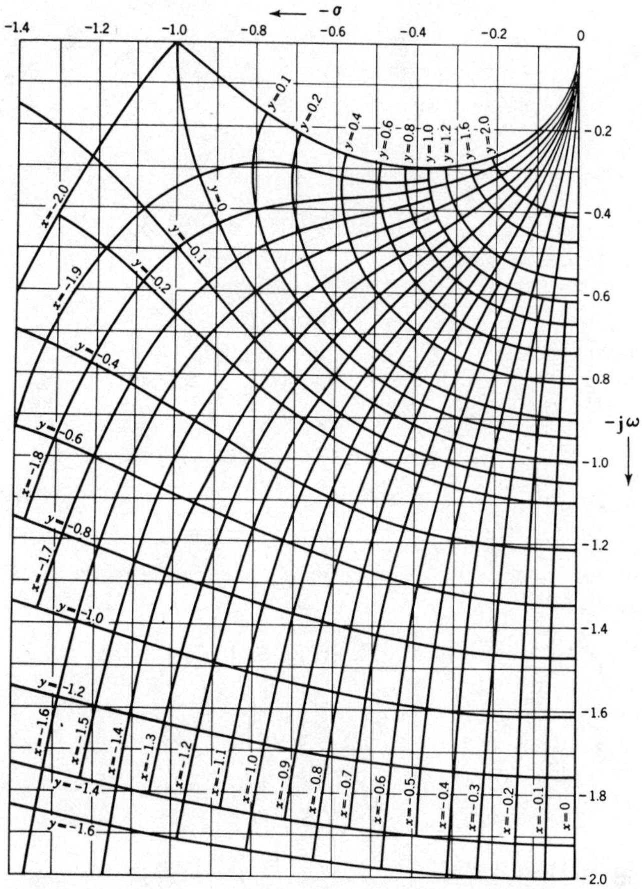

Fig. 6.4.2 Relation between critical frequencies of low-pass and band-pass filters. (From M. S. Ghausi, "Principles and Design of Linear Active Circuits," p. 437, Fig. 15-6, McGraw-Hill, NY, 1965.)

$$s_{n1,2,3,4} = (-0.707 \pm j0.707)/2Q \pm j1 \tag{6.4.17}$$

from Eq. 6.4.12. For the low-Q case, the band-pass filter poles equal

$$s_{n1,2} = Q^{-1} \exp\,[j(180^\circ \pm 45^\circ)], \qquad s_{n3,4} = Q \exp\,[j(180^\circ \pm 45^\circ)] \tag{6.4.18}$$

from Eq. 6.4.14. For the intermediate-Q case, we use Fig. 6.4.2. For example, when Q = 1, then $p/Q = -0.707 \pm j0.707$ and the band-pass filter poles equal

$$\begin{aligned} s_{n1,2} &= -0.23 \pm j0.65 = 0.688 \exp\,[j(180^\circ \pm 70.5^\circ)] \\ s_{n3,4} &= -0.47 \pm j1.36 = 1.69 \exp\,[j(180^\circ \pm 70.5^\circ)] \end{aligned} \tag{6.4.19}$$

It is important to observe that the two sets of band-pass filter poles obtained from one pair of low-pass filter poles always have the same Q and damping factor as we shall soon discuss.

Now let us consider the mapping of low-pass filter zeros at infinity. Since these are equivalently low-Q zeros, each such low-pass filter zero maps into two band-pass filter zeros; one is located at the origin and the other at infinity. Thus, if the low-pass filter is the all-pole type of order n, then its associated band-pass filter will have n zeros at both the origin and infinity. If the

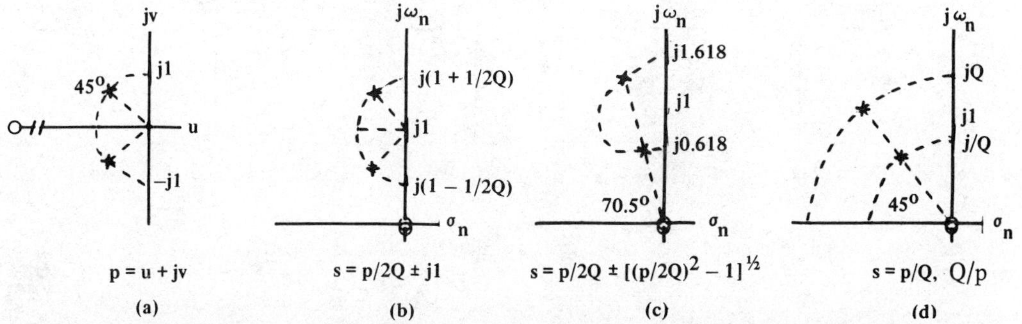

Fig. 6.4.3 (a) Pole movement in low-pass to band-pass transformations for (b) high-Q, (c) intermediate-Q (here Q = 1), and (d) low-Q cases. (The conjugate poles are not shown.)

low-pass filter has n finite poles and m finite zeros, then its associated band-pass filter will have (n – m) zeros at both the origin and infinity.

EXAMPLE 6.4.1 In Example 2.7.3, we designed a second-order band-pass filter using trial-and-error methods. Now design the filter to have a Butterworth characteristic using transformations.

Solution A second-order band-pass filter is obtained from a second-order low-pass filter. The Butterworth filter having unity 3 dB bandwidth has a transfer function

$$H_{LP}(p) = \frac{10}{p^2 + 1.414p + 1} \tag{6.4.20}$$

where $p = -0.707 \pm j0.707 = \exp\,[j(180^\circ \pm 45^\circ)]$. To determine the poles of the band-pass filter, we must know its Q. The center frequency ω_o, 3 dB bandwidth B, and Q of the band-pass filter equal

$$f_o = [600(3000)]^{1/2} = 1340 \text{ Hz}, \qquad B = 3000 - 600 = 2400 \text{ Hz}, \qquad Q = 1340/2400 = 0.558 \tag{6.4.21}$$

Since $|p/2|$ is the same order of magnitude as Q, this is an intermediate–Q situation. Therefore, the scaled low-pass filter pole equals

$$\frac{p}{Q} = \frac{-0.707 \pm j0.707}{0.558} = -1.267 \pm j1.267 = x + jy \tag{6.4.22}$$

From Fig. 6.4.2, we find that the normalized band-pass filter poles equal

$$\begin{aligned} s_n = s/\omega_o = \sigma + j\omega &= -0.26 \pm j0.44 = 0.51 \exp\,[j(180^o \pm 59^o)] \\ &= -1.02 \pm j1.70 = 1.98 \exp\,[j(180^o \pm 59^o)] \end{aligned} \tag{6.4.23}$$

Therefore, the band-pass filter transfer function equals

$$H_{BP}(s_n) = \frac{10s_n{}^2/0.558^2}{[(s_n + 0.26)^2 + 0.44^2]\,[(s_n + 1.02)^2 + 1.70^2]} \tag{6.4.24}$$

where $s_n = s/2\pi(1340 \text{ Hz})$. The block diagram of the band-pass filter is shown in Fig. 6.4.4.

EXAMPLE 6.4.2 Design a fourth-order Butterworth band-pass filter in block diagram form having a center frequency of 1 KHz, a 3 dB bandwidth of 1 KHz, and a midband gain of 10.

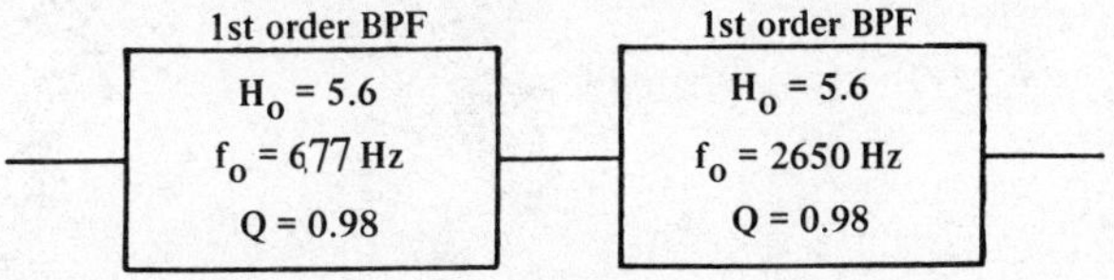

Fig. 6.4.4 Block diagram realization of second-order Butterworth band-pass filter of Example 6.4.1.

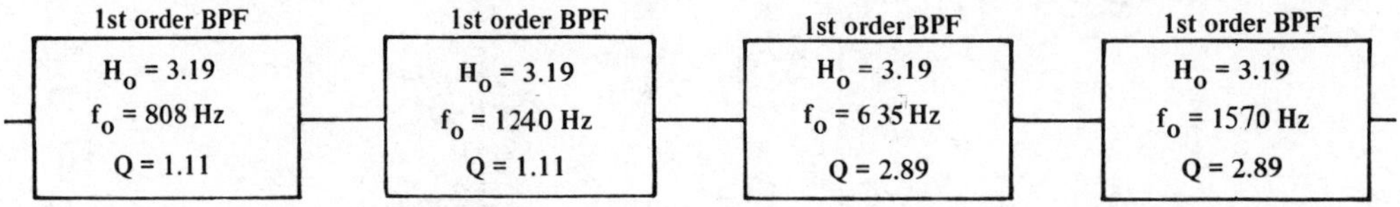

Fig. 6.4.5 Block diagram realization of fourth-order Butterworth band-pass filter of Example 6.4.2.

Solution The fourth-order Butterworth low-pass filter has a transfer function

$$H(p) = \frac{10}{(p^2 + 0.765p + 1)(p^2 + 1.848p + 1)} \tag{6.4.25}$$

Since Q = 1 KHz/1 KHz = 1 and $s_n = s/2\pi(1000\text{ Hz})$, substituting $p = (s_n^2 + 1)/s_n$ into the transfer function yields

$$H(s) = \frac{10s_n^4}{[(s_n^2 + 1)^2 + 0.765s_n(s_n^2 + 1) + s_n^2]\,[(s_n^2 + 1)^2 + 1.848s_n(s_n^2 + 1) + s_n^2]}$$

$$= \frac{10s_n^4}{(s_n^4 + 0.765s_n^3 + 3s_n^2 + 0.765s_n + 1)(s_n^4 + 1.848s_n^3 + 3s_n^2 + 1.848s_n + 1)} \tag{6.4.26}$$

The band-pass poles are easily found from Fig. 6.4.2. For the low-pass filter pole pair $p_1, p_1^* = -0.383 \pm j0.924$, the band-pass filter poles equal

$$\begin{aligned} s_{n1,2} &= -0.11 \pm j0.61 = 0.64 \exp[j(180^\circ \pm 80^\circ)] \\ s_{n3,4} &= -0.28 \pm j1.58 = 1.57 \exp[j(180^\circ \pm 80^\circ)] \end{aligned} \tag{6.4.27}$$

For the low-pass filter pole pair $p_2, p_2^* = -0.924 \pm j0.383$, then the band-pass filter poles are

$$\begin{aligned} s_{n5,6} &= -0.36 \pm j0.71 = 0.81 \exp[j(180^\circ \pm 63^\circ)] \\ s_{n7,8} &= -0.57 \pm j1.11 = 1.24 \exp[j(180^\circ \pm 63^\circ)] \end{aligned} \tag{6.4.28}$$

The block diagram of the band-pass filter is easily drawn in Fig. 6.4.5.

The band-pass filter poles and zeros can be obtained from the low-pass filter poles and zeros in polar form (rather than rectangular form as in Fig. 6.4.2) using a different approach. Jones has shown[9] that under the low-pass to band-pass transformation, a pair of low-pass filter roots having magnitude ω_n and a Q of Q_{LP} map into a pair of band-pass filter roots which always have *identical* Q_{BP}'s. Defining a constant δ, to equal $\delta = Q/\omega_n$, then Q_{BP} is equal to

$$Q_{BP} = (Q_{LP}/2^{1/2})\left\{1 + 4\delta^2 + [(1 + 4\delta^2)^2 - 4\delta^2/Q_{LP}^2]^{1/2}\right\}^{1/2} \tag{6.4.29}$$

We already observed in Figs. 6.4.4 and 6.4.5 that the band-pass filter poles always have the same damping factor. The normalized critical frequencies equal

$$\omega_{o1}/\omega_o, \omega_{o2}/\omega_o = \tfrac{1}{2}\left\{(Q_{BP}/\delta Q_{LP}) \pm [(Q_{BP}/\delta Q_{LP})^2 - 4]^{1/2}\right\} \tag{6.4.30}$$

Under the limiting condition that $\delta \to \infty$ or 0, then

$$\begin{aligned} &Q_{BP} \cong 2\delta Q_{LP}, \quad \omega_{oi}/\omega_o \cong 1 \pm (1 - 1/8Q_{LP}^2)/2\delta \cong 1 \pm 1/2\delta \quad \text{for} \quad \delta \to \infty \\ &Q_{BP} \cong (1 + 2\delta^2)Q_{LP} \cong Q_{LP}, \quad \omega_{oi}/\omega_o \cong \delta(1 - 2\delta^2) \cong \delta \\ &\qquad \cong (1 + 2\delta^3)/\delta \cong 1/\delta \quad \text{for} \quad \delta \to 0 \end{aligned} \tag{6.4.31}$$

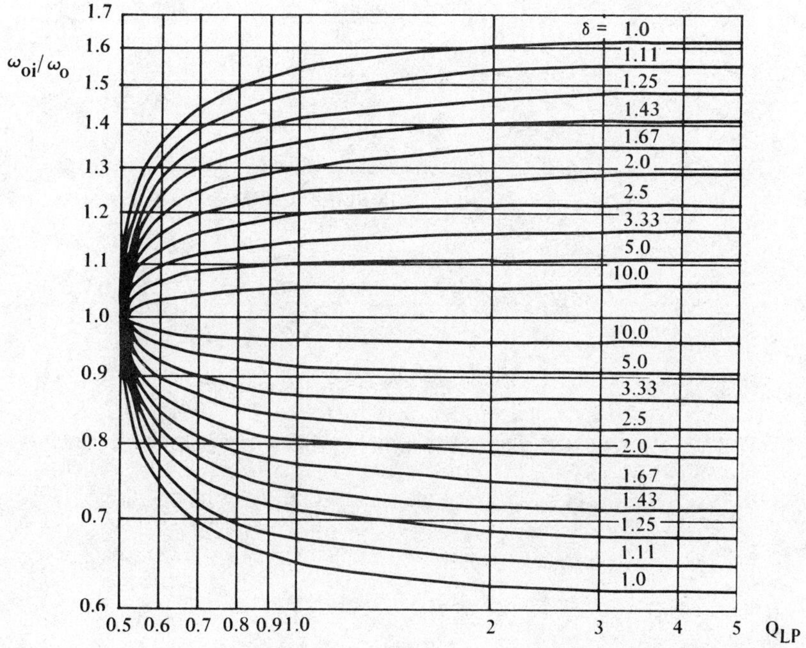

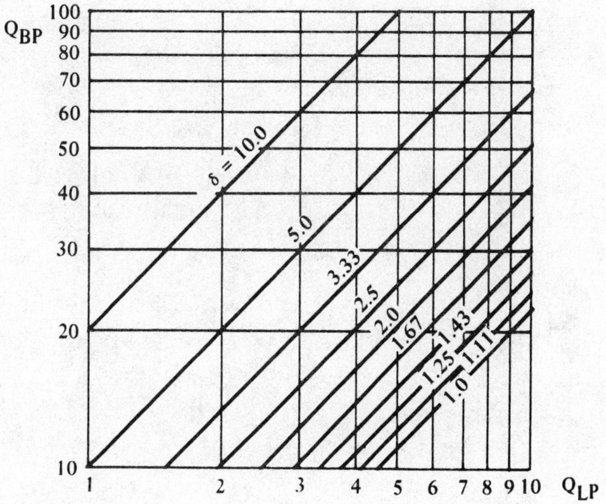

Fig. 6.4.6 Relation between Q and ω_o of critical frequencies of low-pass and band-pass filters.

The normalized critical frequencies and the Q_{BP} of the roots are plotted in Fig. 6.4.6. These figures are useful primarily for the narrowband case.

EXAMPLE 6.4.3 Determine the band-pass filter poles of Example 6.4.1 in polar form.

Solution In Example 6.4.1, we found that Q = 0.558 and that the Butterworth low-pass filter poles had $\omega_n = 1$ and $Q_{LP} = 0.707$. Therefore, since $\delta = Q/\omega_n = 0.558$, the band-pass filter poles have a Q_{BP} given by Eq. 6.4.29 of

$$Q_{BP} = (0.707/2^{1/2})\left\{1 + 4(0.558^2) + [(1 + 4(0.558^2))^2 - 4(0.558^2)/0.707^2]^{1/2}\right\}^{1/2}$$
$$= 0.5[1 + 1.25 + (2.25^2 - 2.49)^{1/2}]^{1/2} = 0.5(2.25 + 1.60)^{1/2} = 0.98 \qquad (6.4.32)$$

The normalized band-pass filter pole frequencies equal

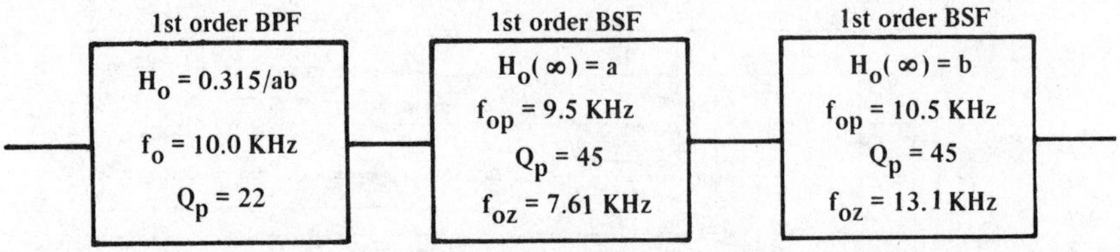

Fig. 6.4.7 Block diagram realization of third-order elliptic band-pass filter of Example 6.4.4.

$$\omega_{o1}/\omega_o, \omega_{o2}/\omega_o = ½\left\{0.98/(0.558)(0.707) \pm [(0.98/(0.558)(0.707))^2 - 4]^{½}\right\}$$
$$= 0.5(2.48 \pm 2.17^{½}) = 0.51, \quad 1.98 \qquad (6.4.33)$$

from Eq. 6.4.30. We determined these same poles in Example 6.4.1 using Fig. 6.4.2.

EXAMPLE 6.4.4 Determine the transfer function and block diagram for a third-order elliptic band-pass filter having a center frequency of 10 KHz, a bandwidth of 1 KHz, and a maximum gain of 10. The in-band ripple equals 1.25 dB and the minimum stopband rejection equals 60 dB. Use the narrowband approximation and then verify the results using Fig. 6.4.6.

Solution The third-order elliptic low-pass filter has a transfer function

$$H(p) = 0.143 \frac{p^2 + 5.54^2}{(p + 0.459)[(p + 0.222)^2 + 0.953^2]} \qquad (6.4.34)$$

from Table 4.8.2 where $|H(j0)| = 10$. Since the band-pass filter has $f_o = 10$ KHz and $B = 1$ KHz, then $Q = 10$ KHz/1 KHz $= 10$. Using the narrowband approximation $s_n = p/2Q \pm j1 = 0.05p \pm j1$, then the individual low-pass filter poles p_i and their corresponding band-pass filter poles s_{ni} must equal

$$p_1 = -0.459 = 0.459 \exp(\pm j180^o) \quad \text{so} \quad s_{n1,2} \cong -0.023 \pm j1$$
$$p_2, p_2^* = -0.222 \pm j0.953 = 0.98 \exp[j(180^o \pm 76.9^o)] \quad \text{so} \qquad (6.4.35)$$
$$s_{n3,4,5,6} \cong -0.011 \pm j1(1 \pm 0.048) = -0.011 \pm j0.952, \quad -0.011 \pm j1.048$$

Likewise for the zeros z_i,

$$z_1, z_1^* = \pm j5.54 = 5.54 \exp(\pm j90^o) \quad \text{so} \quad s_{n7,8} \cong \pm j(1 \pm 0.277) = \pm j0.723, \quad \pm j1.277 \qquad (6.4.36)$$

Now let us use Fig. 6.4.6 to find the exact poles and zeros. Treating the real low-pass pole as complex with $Q_{LP} = 0.5$, since $\delta = 10/0.459 = 21.8$, then from Eqs. 6.4.29 and 6.4.30

$$|s_{n1,2}| = 1.0; \quad Q_{BP} = 22 \qquad (6.4.37)$$

Since the complex poles p_2 and p_2^* have a $Q_{LP} = 1/(2 \cos 76.9°) = 2.21$, and $\delta = 10/0.98 = 10.2$, then from Fig. 6.4.6,

$$|s_{n3,4,5,6}| = 0.95, \ 1.05; \quad Q_{BP} = 45 \qquad (6.4.38)$$

The approximate results of Eq. 6.4.35 are in close agreement with the exact results of Eqs. 6.4.37 and 6.4.38. The complex zeros z_1 and z_1^* have a $Q_{LP} = 1/(2 \cos 90°) = \infty$. Since $\delta = 10/5.54 = 1.8$, then from Fig. 6.4.6,

$$|s_{n7,8}| = 0.76, \ 1.31; \quad Q_{BP} = \infty \qquad (6.4.39)$$

We see from Eq. 6.4.39 that the approximate results of Eq. 6.4.36 are slightly in error. We also see that either approach requires some algebra. The transfer function equals

$$H_{BP}(s) = H_{LP}(p)\,|_{p = 10(s_n + 1/s_n)}$$

$$= \frac{0.0143 s_n(s_n^2 + 0.76^2)(s_n^2 + 1.32^2)}{(s_n^2 + s_n/22 + 1)(s_n^2 + 0.95 s_n/45 + 0.95^2)(s_n^2 + 1.05 s_n/45 + 1.05^2)} \tag{6.4.40}$$

for $s_n = s/2\pi(10\text{ KHz})$ and $|H_{BP}(j1)| = 10$. The block diagram of the filter is shown in Fig. 6.4.7.

We should make an important observation concerning the midband gain H_o of the band-pass filter and the gains of the individual blocks in its block diagram realization. First-order band-pass filters have transfer functions

$$H_1(p) = \frac{H_o}{p+1} \quad \rightarrow \quad H_1(s) = \frac{H_o s_n/Q}{s_n^2 + s_n/Q + 1} \tag{6.4.41}$$

so their midband gains equal H_o. Therefore, the low-pass and band-pass filter blocks have identical gains. However, the transfer function of a second-order band-pass filter equals

$$H_2(p) = \frac{H_o}{p^2 + p/Q_{LP} + 1} \quad \rightarrow \tag{6.4.42}$$

$$H_2(s) = \frac{H_o s_n^2/Q^2}{s_n^4 + s_n^3/QQ_{LP} + (2 + 1/Q^2\quad)s_n^2 + s_n/QQ_{LP} + 1}$$

which can be factored as

$$H_2(s) = \frac{(H_o^{1/2} Q_{BP}/Q)k s_n/Q_{BP}}{s_n^2 + k s_n/Q_{BP} + k^2} \frac{(H_o^{1/2} Q_{BP}/Q)s_n/kQ_{BP}}{s_n^2 + s_n/kQ_{BP} + 1/k^2} \tag{6.4.43}$$

where k is the order of unity. Here the midband gain of each second-order band-pass filter stage equals $\sqrt{H_o}\, Q_{BP}/Q$ which is a factor $Q_{BP}/Q\sqrt{H_o}$ higher than that in the first-order case.

This result is useful for determining the proper gains. For example in the second-order Butterworth filter of Fig. 6.4.4, the gains must equal $[10(0.98/0.558)^2]^{1/2} = 5.6$. In the fourth-order Butterworth filter of Fig. 6.4.5, the gains must equal $[10(1.11^2)(2.89^2)]^{1/4} = 3.19$. This is obtained by factoring each half of Eq. 6.4.26 as shown in Eq. 6.4.43.

A simpler approach for determining the gain constant H_o of a higher order band-pass filter is to use Eq. 6.4.1 directly. Here we see that at high-frequencies when $p \rightarrow \infty$, then $s \rightarrow \infty$ and the low-pass and band-pass filter gains equal

$$H_{BP}(s_n) = H_{LP}(p)\Big|_{p = Qs_n}, \qquad s_n,\ p \rightarrow \infty \tag{6.4.44}$$

Hence, when the low-pass filter has an asymptotic gain given by $H_{LP} \sim H_o/p^n$, then the band-pass filter has an asymptotic gain $H_{BP} \sim H_o/(Qs_n)^n = (H_o/Q^n)/s_n^n$. Thus, the multiplying coefficient of H_{BP} is $H_o' = H_o/Q^n$. For example, in the third-order elliptic filter of Fig. 6.4.7, $H_{LP}(p) \sim 0.143/p$ at high-frequencies using Eq. 6.4.34. Therefore, H_o must equal $0.143/10 = 0.0143$ in Eq. 6.4.40; when the high-frequency gain of the two BSF stages is unity, then the midband gain of the BPF stage must equal $22(0.0143) = 0.315$ using Eq. 6.4.41.

We should also make one comment about the form of our low-pass to band-pass transformation. We have used $p = (\omega_o/B)(s/\omega_o + \omega_o/s)$. This transformation maps a unity-bandwidth low-pass filter into a band-pass filter having bandwidth B. This is especially convenient since most of our classical and optimum filters tabulated in Chaps. 4 and 5 had unity bandwidths. Of course, we may apply this transformation to any bandwidth filter. Other authors have chosen to use the transformation $p = \omega_o(s/\omega_o + \omega_o/s)$, or in terms of normalized frequency when $\omega_o = 1$, $p = s +$

1/s. Here the bandwidth of the band-pass filter *equals* that of the low-pass filter. We used this form in Chap. 2 when we introduced the various transformations, and indeed, we saw that the bandwidth was preserved in the examples discussed there. However, we feel that our first form is more advantageous for present purposes.

6.4.2 MAGNITUDE, PHASE, AND DELAY RESPONSES

The magnitude characteristic of a band-pass filter has geometric symmetry about its center frequency ω_o using the low-pass to band-pass transformation. Thus, its gain at frequency ω is identical to that at frequency ω_o/ω. Therefore, the shape of the characteristic is preserved for transformations of any Q (i.e., low, intermediate, or high). A magnitude characteristic is shown in Fig. 6.4.8a. A more general plot is drawn in Fig. 6.4.9 to show the entire s-plane. Note that $H_{LP}(0)$ maps into $H_{BP}(\pm j\omega_o)$ and $H_{LP}(\infty)$ maps into $H_{BP}(\infty)$.

The phase characteristic also has geometric symmetry about ω_o. It is identical to the phase of the low-pass filter after it is recentered from 0 to ω_o. This is shown in Fig. 6.4.8b.

The delay of the band-pass filter can be determined from the low-pass filter delay. The band-pass filter delays equals

$$\tau_{BP}(j\omega) = -\frac{d \arg H_{BP}(j\omega)}{d\omega} = -\frac{d \arg H_{LP}(jv)}{dv}\frac{dv}{d\omega} = \tau_{LP}(jv)\frac{dv}{d\omega} \tag{6.4.45}$$

where v is given by Eq. 6.4.3 as

$$v = (\omega_o/B)(\omega/\omega_o - \omega_o/\omega) = (\omega - \omega_o^2/\omega)/B \tag{6.4.46}$$

Therefore, since

$$dv/d\omega = [1 + (\omega_o/\omega)^2]/B \tag{6.4.47}$$

then substituting Eq. 6.4.47 into Eq. 6.4.45, the delay of the band-pass filter can be expressed as

$$\tau_{BP}(j\omega) = B^{-1}[1 + (\omega_o/\omega)^2]\tau_{LP}(jv)\,\Big|_{v = Q(\omega/\omega_o - \omega_o/\omega)} \tag{6.4.48}$$

We can write the passband delay of a narrowband filter. If we express the frequency variation from center frequency ω_o as $\Delta\omega = \omega - \omega_o$, then we can express v given by Eq. 6.4.46 as

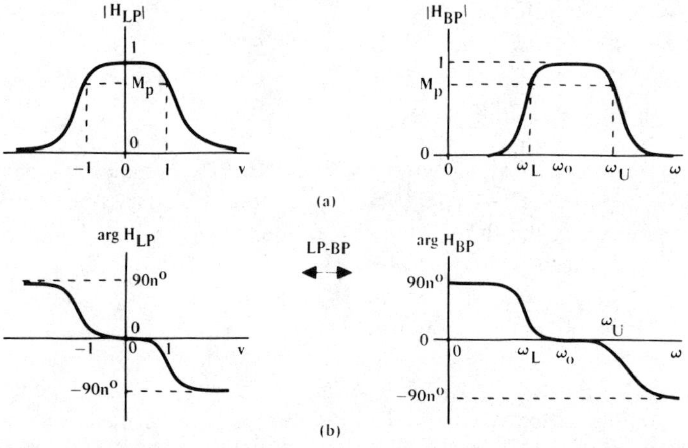

Fig. 6.4.8 Effect of low-pass to band-pass transformation upon (a) magnitude and (b) phase characteristics.

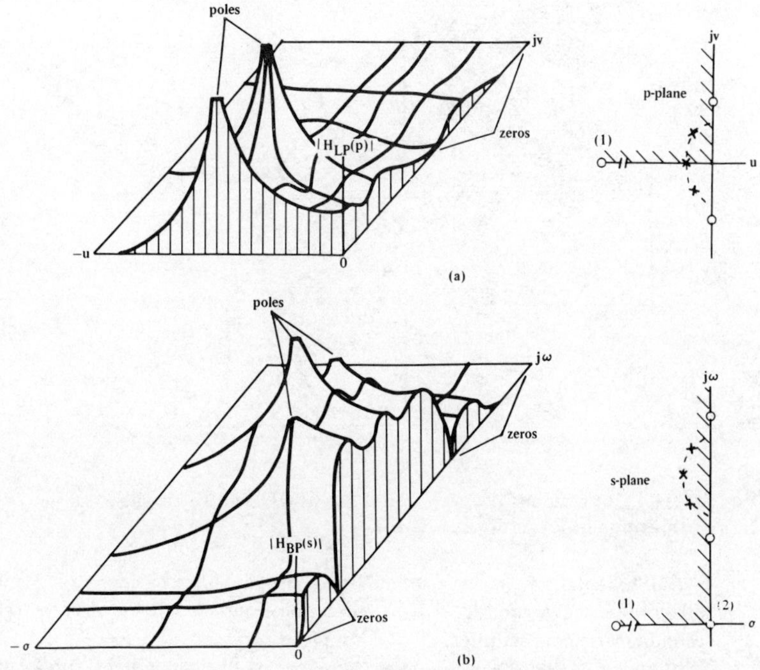

Fig. 6.4.9 Magnitudes of third-order elliptic (a) low-pass filter gain $H_{LP}(p)$ and (b) band-pass filter gain $H_{BP}(s)$ in the p- and s-planes, respectively.

$$v = (\omega^2 - \omega_o^2)/B\omega = \Delta\omega(\omega + \omega_o)/B\omega \tag{6.4.49}$$

When the frequency derivation is small so that $\Delta\omega \cong 0$, then $\omega \cong \omega_o$ and $v \cong 2\Delta\omega/B$. Thus, the passband delay of a band-pass filter given by Eq. 6.4.48 equals

$$\tau_{BP}(j(\omega_o + \Delta\omega)) \cong (B/2)^{-1}\tau_{LP}(j\Delta\omega/(B/2)) \tag{6.4.50}$$

Since τ_{LP} is even, then τ_{BP} is symmetrical about the center of the passband. However the $dv/d\omega$ term in the τ_{BP} expression introduces asymmetry; the delay becomes more asymmetrical with increasing deviation from the center frequency and decreasing Q^{10}. We will illustrate this in a moment. The delay at the center frequency of the band-pass filter equals

$$\tau_{BP}(j\omega_o) = (B/2)^{-1}\tau_{LP}(j0) = (B/2)^{-1}(b_1/b_0 - a_1/a_0) \tag{6.4.51}$$

It is 2/B times the dc delay of the low-pass filter whose gain is given by Eq. 2.0.1. Thus, the midband delay is inversely proportional to half the filter bandwidth. The low-frequency delay of the band-pass filter equals

$$\tau_{BP}(j\omega) = (Q\omega_o)^{-1}\, d\tau_{LP}(\infty)/d\,(1/\omega^2) = (Q\omega_o)^{-1}(b_{n-1}/b_n - a_{m-1}/a_m), \qquad \omega \ll \omega_o \tag{6.4.52}$$

while the high-frequency delay equals

$$\tau_{BP}(j\omega) = (B/\omega^2)\, d\tau_{LP}(\infty)/d\,(1/\omega^2) = (B/\omega^2)\,(b_{n-1}/b_n - a_{m-1}/a_m), \qquad \omega \gg \omega_o \tag{6.4.53}$$

This is easily proved using Eqs. 2.10.34, 2.10.36, and 6.4.45. The low-frequency delay is constant and the high-frequency delay rolls off as $1/\omega^2$.

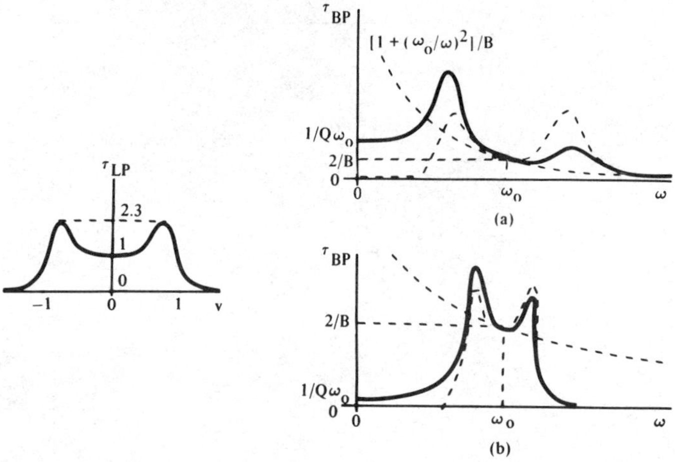

Fig. 6.4.10 Conversion of delay under (a) low-Q and (b) high-Q transformations in Example 6.4.5.

EXAMPLE 6.4.5 Consider a second-order low-pass filter having $\omega_n = 1$ and $\zeta = 0.5$. Its delay characteristics are shown in Fig. 2.10.2. Determine and sketch the delay characteristic of the analogous second-order band-pass filter.

Solution The transfer function of the low-pass filter equals $H_{LP}(p) = 1/(p^2 + p + 1)$. The transfer function of the band-pass filter is given by Eq. 6.4.1 where ω_o and B must be specified. The delay of the band-pass filter is given by Eq. 6.4.45. Since the low-pass filter delay equals

$$\tau_{LP}(jv) = \frac{1 + v^2}{1 - v^2 + v^4} \tag{6.4.54}$$

from Eq. 2.10.5, the dc value equals one second while $\tau_{LP}(jv) \cong 1/v^2$ for $|v| \gg 1$. Thus, the midband delay of the band-pass filter equals 2/B from Eq. 6.4.51. The low-frequency delay equals $1/Q\omega_o$ for $\omega \ll \omega_o$ from Eq. 6.4.52, while the high-frequency delay equals B/ω^2 for $\omega \gg \omega_o$ from Eq. 6.4.53. The delay of a low-Q and high-Q band-pass filter is sketched in Fig. 6.4.10. We see that the low-Q filter has asymmetrical passband delay but that the high-Q filter has almost symmetrical passband delay.

Band-pass filters are specified in the frequency domain, the time domain, or in both domains simultaneously. Just as with low-pass filters, we can utilize the frequency domain results and nomographs of Chaps. 4 and 5. We shall soon see that we can also utilize the time domain results for narrowband band-pass filters. In general, the frequency domain specifications of band-pass filters have the form shown in Fig. 6.4.11. f_L and f_U are the required corner frequencies for less than M_p in-band gain variation and f_1, f_2, f_3, f_4, etc., are the frequencies for stopband rejections of M_{s1}, M_{s2}, etc. In many applications, the gain characteristic will have geometric symmetry about the center frequency f_o where $f_o^2 = f_L f_U = f_1 f_3 = f_2 f_4 = \ldots$. To utilize the design data of the previous chapters, we convert this into equivalent information for a low-pass filter using

$$\Omega_i = Q\left|\frac{f_i}{f_o} - \frac{f_o}{f_i}\right| \tag{6.4.55}$$

We normalize each stopband frequency f_i by f_o, form its reciprocal, take the absolute value of the difference, and multiply by Q. This gives us the normalized stopband frequencies of the equivalent low-pass filter. Since the upper and lower frequencies are assumed to have geometric symmetry, their normalized Ω_i's will be equal to one another (i.e., $\Omega_1 = \Omega_3$, etc.). We then draw

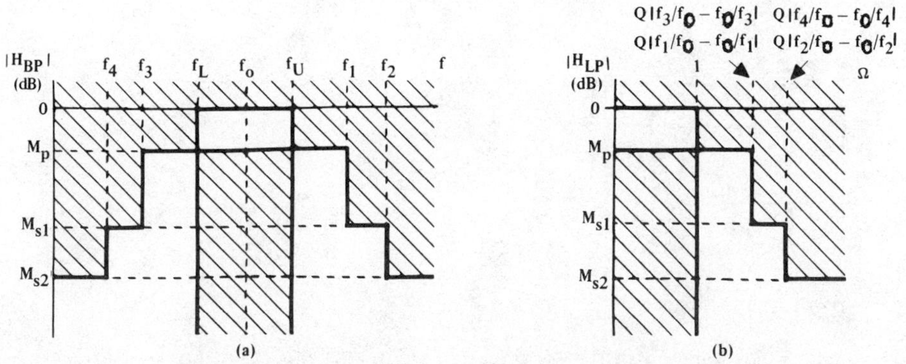

Fig. 6.4.11 Conversion of magnitude specification for (a) band-pass filters into equivalent specification for (b) low-pass filters.

the equivalent low-pass filter specification as shown in Fig. 6.4.11b where f_o corresponds to $\Omega = 0$, the upper and lower band-edge frequencies correspond to $\Omega = 1$, and the various cutoff frequencies are as shown. Using this specification, we now determine the characteristics for the low-pass filter. The filter type is selected, the order determined, and the normalized low-pass filter pole-zero data obtained from the tables. Then using the low-pass to band-pass transformation, the required transfer function of the band-pass filter can be written.

EXAMPLE 6.4.6 Determine the minimum order Butterworth, Chebyshev, and elliptic band-pass filters required to meet the magnitude characteristics shown in Fig. 6.4.12a.

Solution To enable us to determine the order of the band-pass filters, we need to first determine the Q and f_o for the filter. Since the center frequency and bandwidth equal

$$f_o = [500(2000)]^{1/2} = 1000 \text{ Hz}, \qquad B = 2000 - 500 = 1500 \text{ Hz} \tag{6.4.56}$$

using Eqs. 6.4.5 and 6.4.7, then from Eq. 6.4.6, Q equals

$$Q = 1000/1500 = 0.667 \tag{6.4.57}$$

Therefore, using Eq. 6.4.55, the normalized stopband frequencies are

$$\Omega_s = 0.667\ |4000/1000 - 1000/4000| = 0.667\ |250/1000 - 1000/250| = 2.5 \tag{6.4.58}$$

which are equal since they have geometric symmetry about f_o. We now express the band-pass filter requirements in terms of the equivalent low-pass filter requirements. This is shown in Fig. 6.4.12b. From the nomographs of Chap. 4, we find

Butterworth: $n \geqslant 6$, Chebyshev: $n \geqslant 4$, Elliptic: $n \geqslant 3$

Therefore, a third-order elliptic band-pass filter will meet this gain requirement.

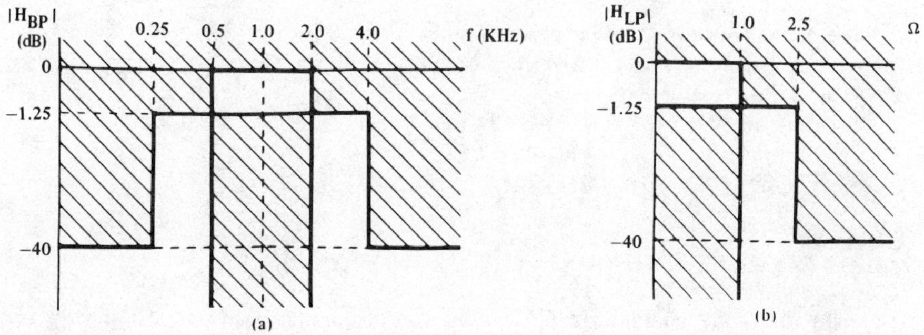

Fig. 6.4.12 (a) Band-pass filter specification and its (b) equivalent low-pass filter specification of Example 6.4.6.

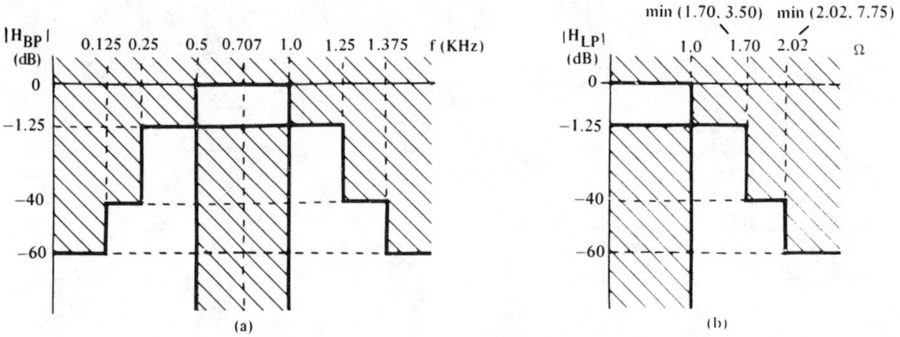

Fig. 6.4.13 (a) Band-pass filter specification and its (b) equivalent low-pass filter specification of Example 6.4.7.

Another useful result which simplifies determining filter order is use of the $M_1 - M_2$ dB shaping factor $S = BW_1/BW_2$ where M_1 and M_2 are arbitrary rejections. It is easily shown that S is independent of Q and is invariant under the low-pass to band-pass transformation. Thus, the shaping factor can be calculated directly from the bandwidth ratio for the band-pass filter. Then using this as the normalized stopband frequency Ω_s for the low-pass filter, the order is determined directly. For instance, in Example 6.4.6, since $BW_{1.25\ dB} = 1500$ Hz and $BW_{40\ dB} = 3750$ Hz, then the 1.25–40 dB shaping factor $S = 3750/1500 = 2.5$. Thus, $\Omega_s = 2.5$ directly in Fig. 6.4.12b without the need of Eqs. 6.4.56–6.4.58. The filter order is then determined as usual. This approach considerably reduces the work required to find the orders of filters having geometric symmetry.

In some filter applications, asymmetrical magnitude specifications may be given. We shall discuss this in connection with filter magnitude responses which have arithmetic symmetry rather than geometric symmetry. In such asymmetrical gain situations, we can still utilize the filter nomographs, assuming of course that filters having geometric symmetry are acceptable. The technique merely requires selection of the most stringent (i.e., minimum) stopband frequency Ω_s at a given attenuation as we show in the following example.

EXAMPLE 6.4.7 Determine the minimum order Butterworth, Chebyshev, and elliptic band-pass filters required to meet the magnitude characteristics shown in Fig. 6.4.13a.

Solution In this case, we have

$$f_o = [500(1000)]^{1/2} = 707 \text{ Hz}, \qquad B = 1000 - 500 = 500 \text{ Hz}, \qquad Q = 707/500 = 1.41 \qquad (6.4.59)$$

The upper and lower stopband frequencies of the equivalent low-pass filter are found to be $\Omega_1 = 1.70$, $\Omega_2 = 2.02$, $\Omega_3 = 3.50$, and $\Omega_4 = 7.75$ using

$$\Omega_i = 1.41\ |f_i/707 - 707/f_i| \qquad (6.4.60)$$

The equivalent low-pass filter gain is drawn in Fig. 6.14.13b. The required stopband frequencies are unequal and so the *smallest* frequency is chosen. This gives the *most* stringent gain requirement. From Chap. 4, then

Butterworth: $n_1 \geq 10$ and $n_2 \geq 11$ (use $n \geq 11$)
Chebyshev: $n_1 \geq 6$ and $n_2 \geq 6$ (use $n \geq 6$)
Elliptic: $n_1 \geq 4$ and $n_2 \geq 5$ (use $n \geq 5$)

6.4.3 IMPULSE AND COSINE STEP RESPONSES

Low-pass filters are characterized by their step responses. Band-pass filters are characterized by their responses to a unit cosine step input $\cos \omega_o t\, U_{-1}(t)$ where ω_o is the center frequency of the filter. Note that this band-pass filter input is analogous to the low-pass filter step input, since using the low-pass to band-pass transformation,

$$\mathcal{L}^{-1}[1/p\,|_{p=(s^2+\omega_o^2)/Bs}] = \mathcal{L}^{-1}[Bs/(s^2+\omega_o^2)] = B\cos\omega_o t\, U_{-1}(t) \tag{6.4.61}$$

from Table 1.8.1. When the impulse response of the analogous low-pass filter is known, then the unit cosine step response of the band-pass filter can be found as we will now show.

The impulse response of the band-pass filter equals

$$h_{BP}(t) = \mathcal{L}^{-1}[H_{BP}(s)] = \mathcal{L}^{-1}[H_{LP}(p)\,|_{p=Q(s/\omega_o+\omega_o/s)}] \tag{6.4.62}$$

It can be shown that if f(t) has a Laplace transform F(s), then[2]

$$\mathcal{L}^{-1}[F(s+1/s)/s] = \int_0^t J_0(2\sqrt{(t-\tau)\tau}\,)f(\tau)\,d\tau \tag{6.4.63}$$

Applying the time differentiation theorem from Table 1.8.2 to Eq. 6.4.63, then

$$\mathcal{L}^{-1}[F(s+1/s)] = \frac{d}{dt}\int_0^t J_0(2\sqrt{(t-\tau)\tau}\,)f(\tau)\,d\tau\, U_{-1}(t) + (0)U_0(t) \tag{6.4.64}$$

Since the derivative of an integral equals

$$\frac{d}{dt}\int_0^t f(t,\tau)\,d\tau\, U_{-1}(t) = [f(t,t) + \int_0^t \frac{df(t,\tau)}{dt}\,d\tau]\, U_{-1}(t) \tag{6.4.65}$$

then we can re-express Eq. 6.4.64 as

$$\mathcal{L}^{-1}[F(s+1/s)] = [f(t) - \int_0^t \sqrt{\tau/(t-\tau)}\, J_1(2\sqrt{(t-\tau)\tau}\,)f(\tau)\,d\tau]\, U_{-1}(t) \tag{6.4.66}$$

Applying this result to a low-pass filter where $\omega_o = 1$, the impulse response of the band-pass filter equals

$$h_{BP}(t) = Q[h_{LP}(t') - \int_0^{t'} \sqrt{\tau/(t'-\tau)}\, J_1(2\sqrt{(t'-\tau)\tau}\,)h_{LP}(\tau)\,d\tau]\, U_{-1}(t) \tag{6.4.67}$$

from Eq. 6.4.62 (note $t' = t/Q$). Therefore, the unit cosine step response equals

$$r_{BP}(t) = h_{BP}(t) * [\cos t\, U_{-1}(t)] \tag{6.4.68}$$

using the convolution theorem of Table 1.8.2. These are very useful results. They show that the impulse response of a band-pass filter is proportional to the integral of the product of the low-pass filter impulse response times J_0' An analogous result was found for the high-pass filter.

Now let us find the responses for the two limiting cases of narrowband and wideband band-pass filters. In the narrowband case, we found that $p = (s \pm j\omega_o)/(B/2)$ from Eq. 6.4.11. The approximate transfer function of the band-pass filter can be expressed as[11]

$$H_{BP}(s) \cong H_{LP}(p)\,|_{p=2(s+j\omega_o)/B} + H_{LP}(p)\,|_{p=2(s-j\omega_o)/B} \tag{6.4.69}$$

Therefore, the impulse response of the band-pass filter must equal

$$\begin{aligned} h_{BP}(t) &= \mathcal{L}^{-1}[H_{BP}(s)] \\ &\cong \mathcal{L}^{-1}[H_{LP}(p)\,|_{p=2(s+j\omega_o)/B}] + \mathcal{L}^{-1}[H_{LP}(p)\,|_{p=2(s-j\omega_o)/B}] \\ &= (B/2)h_{LP}(Bt/2)[e^{-j\omega_o t} + e^{j\omega_o t}]\, U_{-1}(t) = Bh_{LP}(Bt/2)\cos\omega_o t\, U_{-1}(t) \end{aligned} \tag{6.4.70}$$

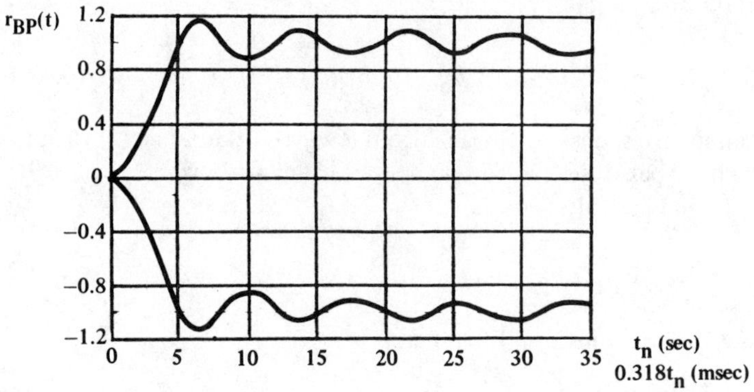

Fig. 6.4.14 Cosine step response envelope of third-order elliptic band-pass filter of Example 6.4.8.

using the time scaling and frequency shifting theorems of Table 1.8.2 and the Laplace transforms of Table 1.8.1. The response is a cosine step whose envelope equals $Bh_{LP}(Bt/2)$ where h_{LP} is the impulse response of the low-pass filter. In like manner, the unit cosine step response equals

$$\begin{aligned} r_{BP}(t) &= \mathcal{L}^{-1}[R_{BP}(s)] \\ &= B^{-1}\mathcal{L}^{-1}[H_{LP}(p)/p\,|_{p=2(s+j\omega_o)/B}] + B^{-1}\mathcal{L}^{-1}[H_{LP}(p)/p\,|_{p=2(s-j\omega_o)/B}] \\ &= r_{LP}(Bt/2)\cos\omega_o t\, U_{-1}(t) \end{aligned} \tag{6.4.71}$$

Therefore, narrowband band-pass filters have impulse and cosine step responses which can be drawn by inspection using the impulse and step responses of their analogous low-pass filters.

In wideband band-pass filters, this is not true. In this case, the poles and zeros are determined using Eq. 6.4.13 where $p = s/B$ and $Q\omega_o/s$. The transfer function of the band-pass filter can be expressed as

$$H_{BP}(s) = H_{LP}(p)\,|_{p=s/B} \times H_{LP}(p)\,|_{p=Q\omega_o/s} \tag{6.4.72}$$

Therefore, the filter impulse response must equal

$$\begin{aligned} h_{BP}(t) &= \mathcal{L}^{-1}[H_{BP}(s)] = \mathcal{L}^{-1}[H_{LP}(p)\,|_{p=s/B}] * \mathcal{L}^{-1}[H_{HP}(p)\,|_{p=s/Q\omega_o}] \\ &= Bh_{LP}(Bt) * Q\omega_o h_{HP}(Q\omega_o t) = \omega_o^{\,2} h_{LP}(Bt) * h_{HP}(Q\omega_o t) \end{aligned} \tag{6.4.73}$$

using the high-pass filter result of Eq. 6.3.17. Thus, we convolve the impulse responses of low-pass and high-pass filters to determine the impulse response of a wideband band-pass filter. The cosine step response is then obtained using h_{BP} and Eq. 6.4.68.

EXAMPLE 6.4.8 A third-order elliptic band-pass filter having a center frequency f_o of 10 KHz, a bandwidth B of 1 KHz, and a Q of 10 was analyzed in Example 6.4.4. Sketch its cosine step response assuming unity passband gain.

Solution Treating this as a high-Q filter, its cosine step response is easily sketched using its analogous low-pass filter step response which is shown in Fig. 4.8.5. Using $M_p = 1.25 \cong 1$ dB and $\theta = 12° \cong 10°$ since $M_s = 60$ dB (see Table 4.8.2), we first sketch the envelope of the band-pass filter response $r_{LP}(t_n)$ as shown in Fig. 6.4.14. We then denormalize the time scale as

$$t = \frac{t_n}{B/2} = \frac{t_n}{2\pi(1\text{ KHz})/2} = 0.318t_n \text{ (msec)} \tag{6.4.74}$$

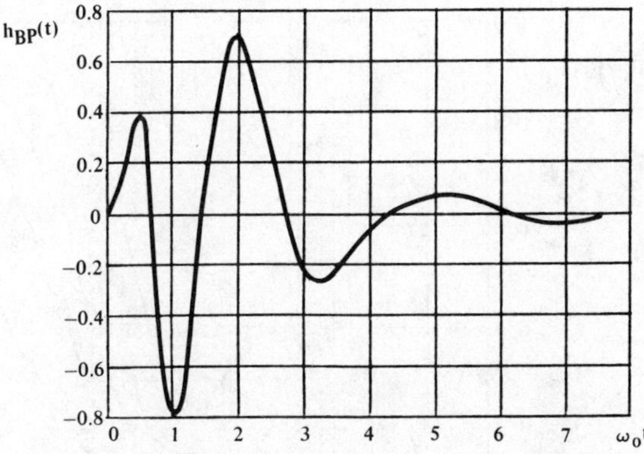

Fig. 6.4.15 Impulse response of eighth-order Butterworth octave band-pass filter of Example 6.4.9.[4]

Next, we "fill in" this envelope with the cosine signal cos $[2\pi(10\text{ KHz})t]$. Because $f_o \gg B$, this signal simply "darkens" the envelope in Fig. 6.4.14.

EXAMPLE 6.4.9 Determine the transfer function form and sketch the impulse response of a wideband Butterworth band-pass filter having Q = ½ so $B/\omega_o = 2$. As discussed in Prob. 2.21, such filters are called *octave-bandwidth* filters because their fractional bandwidths equal two.

Solution The *n*th-order Butterworth band-pass filter having a wide bandwidth has a transfer function given by Eq. 6.4.72. The octave-bandwidth filter having unity center frequency has a transfer function

$$H_{BP}{}^{(n)}(s) = H_{LP}{}^{(n)}(s/2)\, H_{HP}{}^{(n)}(2s) \tag{6.4.75}$$

where the *n*th-order Butterworth polynomials for H_{LP} are listed in Table 4.3.1. H_{HP} is obtained using the low-pass to high-pass transformation. The impulse response of the octave-bandwidth filter equals

$$h_{BP}{}^{(n)}(t) = h_{LP}{}^{(n)}(2t) * h_{HP}{}^{(n)}(t/2) \tag{6.4.76}$$

from Eq. 6.4.73. The result of this convolution for an eighth-order Butterworth octave-bandwidth band-pass filter is shown in Fig. 6.4.15.

Sometimes it is necessary to calculate filter response to inputs other than a cosine step. One such example arises in video processing applications in which a band-pass filter is excited by a Gaussian cosine pulse having a value[12]

$$f(t) = e^{-(2\ln 2)(t/T)^2} \cos \omega_o t\, U_{-1}(t) \tag{6.4.77}$$

The 3 dB pulse duration equals T. In such instances, Laplace or Fourier transforms are used to calculate responses. Although the method is straightforward, the results become complicated.

Another closely related area is that of the pulsed-cosine response of band-pass filters. This is important in radar and other similar applications. In this situation, the filter input becomes

$$s_i(t) = \cos \omega_o t\, [U_{-1}(t + T/2) - U_{-1}(t - T/2)] \tag{6.4.78}$$

where ω_o is the center frequency of the filter and T is the duration of the cosine pulse. Schafer and Wang have investigated the behavior of Butterworth band-pass filters under pulsed-cosine operation. The output energy of the filter is given by Eq. 4.18.14 where $|H_n|^2$ is the squared-magnitude response of the band-pass filter. This is a complicated expression for even a Butterworth filter.[13] E_o is plotted in Fig. 6.4.16 for a fourth-order Butterworth band-pass filter, where E_o has been normalized to the input energy E_i given by Eq. 1.9.31. The fractional 3 dB bandwidths (1/Q) equal 0.001, 0.004, 0.02, 0.1, 0.2, 0.3, and 0.6. The curves show that for a fixed fractional bandwidth B/ω_o, there is a minimum normalized time $\omega_o T$ required to pass a reasonable amount of energy through the filter. For example, for a Q = 10, then $\omega_o T \geq 35$ to transfer at

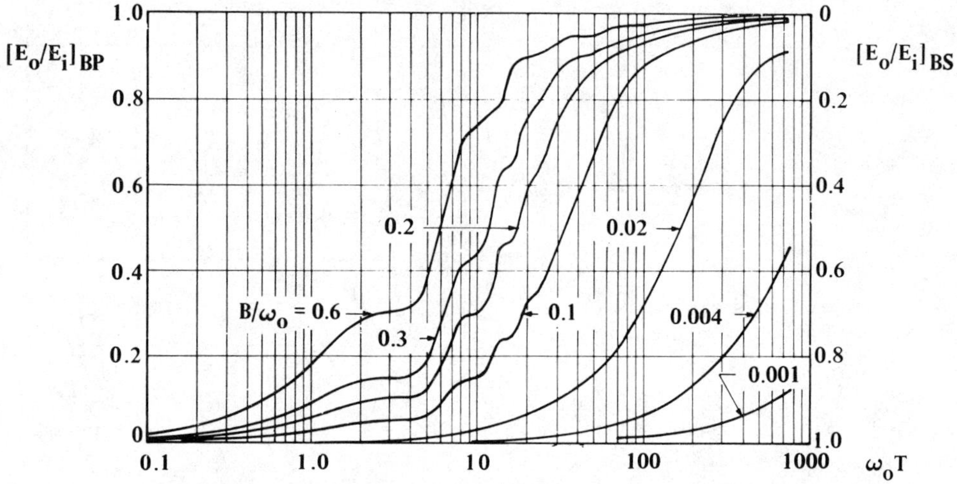

Fig. 6.4.16 Normalized output energies of fourth-order Butterworth band-pass and band-stop filters for pulsed-cosine operation. (From R. H. Schafer and J. J. H. Wang, "Energy transfer characteristics of Butterworth resonant circuits under pulsed-carrier operation," IEEE Trans. Circuit Theory, vol. CT-19, pp. 221–223, March, 1972.)

least 50% of the input energy through the filter. If $f_o = 10$ KHz, then the pulse duration $T \geqslant 35/(2\pi \times 10^4) = 0.56$ msec. For a discussion of pulsed-cosine signal distortion, see Ref. 14.

6.4.4 NOISE RESPONSE

Now let us consider the noise energy E of a band-pass filter. Making the low-pass to band-pass transformation in Eq. 4.18.3 gives

$$\begin{aligned} E &= (2\pi)^{-1}\int_{-\infty}^{\infty}|H_{LP}(jv)|^2\,dv = (2B\pi)^{-1}\int_0^{\infty}|H_{BP}(j\omega)|^2[1+(\omega_o/\omega)^2]\,d\omega \\ &= (2B\pi)^{-1}\int_0^{\infty}|H_{BP}(j\omega)|^2\,d\omega + (Q\omega_o/2\pi)\int_0^{\infty}\omega^{-2}|H_{BP}(j\omega)|^2\,d\omega \end{aligned} \tag{6.4.79}$$

E equals the weighted sum of the energies in the white noise response and the $(1/f^2)$ noise response of the band-pass filter. Trofimenkoff shows that these noise energies are equal so that E equals[15]

$$E = (B\pi)^{-1}\int_0^{\infty}|H_{BP}(j\omega)|^2\,d\omega = (Q\omega_o/\pi)\int_0^{\infty}\omega^{-2}|H_{BP}(j\omega)|^2\,d\omega \tag{6.4.80}$$

Thus, the same performance indices determined for the low-pass filter apply to the band-pass filter when scaled by the bandwidth B (e.g., see Fig. 4.18.1). In terms of the impulse of the band-pass filter, E equals

$$E = (B/2)^{-1}\int_{-\infty}^{\infty}h_{BP}^2(t)\,dt \tag{6.4.81}$$

using Parseval's theorem of Eq. 4.18.2.

6.4.5 ARITHMETICALLY-SYMMETRICAL TRANSFORMATION

In some applications, it is desirable for filters to have magnitude and delay characteristics that exhibit arithmetic symmetry about ω_o rather than geometric symmetry.[16] These include radar, television, telephone, and other communication systems which have signal frequencies distributed arithmetically about their carrier frequencies. In order for band-pass filters to have arithmetic symmetry, they must have a periodic magnitude response. Therefore, they have an infinite number of passbands and stopbands. The additional passbands introduce spurious responses which are undesirable. Thus, we must use a transformation which produces approximate arithmetic symmetry in the magnitude and delay characteristics, or use the optimization techniques of Chap. 5. A transformation which produces almost symmetrical delay and fairly symmetrical magnitude characteristics in the passband (for large Q) is the narrowband or *arithmetically-symmetrical* transformation where[17]

$$s = (B/2)p \pm j\omega_o \tag{6.4.82}$$

Letting $s = j\omega$ and $p = jv$ for ac steady-state, then

$$v = (\omega \pm \omega_o)/(B/2) \tag{6.4.83}$$

where

$$\omega_o = (\omega_U + \omega_L)/2, \qquad B = \omega_U - \omega_L, \qquad Q = \omega_o/B \tag{6.4.84}$$

Here we see that the bandwidth remains constant but that the center frequency is the *arithmetic mean* of the corner frequencies rather than the geometric mean (of Eqs. 6.4.5–6.4.7).

The band-pass filter transfer function is defined to equal

$$H_{BP}(s) = (s/\omega_o)^n H_{LP}(p)\big|_{p = 2(s - j\omega_o)/B} H_{LP}(p)\big|_{p = 2(s + j\omega_o)/B} \tag{6.4.85}$$

This transformation scales the entire pole/zero pattern of the low-pass filter by B/2 and translates it to frequencies $\pm j\omega_o$. It also inserts n zeros at the origin. This produces the narrowband pole-zero distribution shown in Fig. 6.4.3b. Expressing the frequency deviation from center frequency ω_o as $\Delta\omega = \omega - \omega_o$, then the gain equals

$$H_{BP}(j(\omega_o + \Delta\omega)) = (1 + \Delta\omega/\omega_o)^n H_{LP}(j\Delta\omega/(B/2))\, H_{LP}(j\,[4Q + \Delta\omega/(B/2)]) \tag{6.4.86}$$

When $\Delta\omega \ll \omega_o$, the first and third terms are constant with values 1 and H_{LP} (j4Q), respectively, so that $H_{BP}(j(\omega_o + \Delta\omega)) \sim H_{LP}(j2\Delta\omega/B)$. Therefore, H_{BP} exhibits arithmetic symmetry in the immediate vicinity of ω_o. The gains at the band-edges where $\Delta\omega = \pm B/2$ equal

$$H_{BP}(j(\omega_o \pm B/2)) = (1 \pm 1/2Q)^n H_{LP}(\pm j1)\, H_{LP}(j(4Q \pm 1)) \tag{6.4.87}$$

The difference between these gains, or the gain unbalance, becomes negligible for large Q. Calculating the gains at dc, ω_o, and $2\omega_o$ shows that

$$H_{BP}(0) = 0, \quad H_{BP}(j\omega_o) = j^n H_{LP}(0) H_{LP}(j4Q), \quad H_{BP}(j2\omega_o) = (j2)^n H_{LP}(j2Q) H_{LP}(j6Q) \tag{6.4.88}$$

Although the dc gain is zero, the gain at frequency $2\omega_o$ is not quite zero, although it approaches zero for increasing Q and filter order. We also note from Eq. 6.4.85 that the asymptotic gain slopes equal ±20n dB/dec.

The phase of the band-pass filter equals

$$\arg H_{BP}(j(\omega_o + \Delta\omega)) = \arg H_{LP}(j\Delta\omega/(B/2)) + \arg H_{LP}(j\,[4Q + \Delta\omega/(B/2)]) + 90n^o \tag{6.4.89}$$

The second term is constant with a value arg H_{LP}(j4Q) for small $\Delta\omega \ll 2\omega_o$. Thus, the phase in the vicinity of the passband is equal to the low-pass filter phase (around dc) augumented by (arg H_{LP}(j4Q) + n90°). Therefore, if arg H_{LP} is linear in the passband, then arg H_{BP} will also be linear. For this reason, this transformation might also be called the *linear phase* low-pass to band-pass transformation.

The delay of the band-pass filter equals (excluding the impulse of area $n\pi$ at $\omega = 0$)

$$\tau_{BP}(j\omega) = \tau_1(j\omega) + \tau_2(j\omega) \tag{6.4.90}$$

where τ_1 and τ_2 are the delays of the individual low-pass filter gain terms in Eq. 6.4.85. These delay terms equal

$$\tau_{1,2}(j\omega) = -\frac{d \arg H_{BP}(j\omega)}{d\omega} = -\frac{d \arg H_{LP}(jv)}{dv}\frac{dv}{d\omega} = \tau_{LP}(jv)\frac{dv}{d\omega} \tag{6.4.91}$$

where τ_{LP} is the delay of one of the low-pass filters and v is given by Eq. 6.4.83. Therefore, since

$$dv/d\omega = 2/B \tag{6.4.92}$$

then combining Eqs. 6.4.90 and 6.4.91 gives

$$\tau_{BP}(j\omega) = (B/2)^{-1}[\tau_{LP}(jv)\,|_{v=(\omega-\omega_o)/(B/2)} + \tau_{LP}(jv)\,|_{v=(\omega+\omega_o)/(B/2)}] \tag{6.4.93}$$

Here we note that $dv/d\omega$ is constant rather than being frequency dependent as in the regular low-pass to band-pass transformation (see Eq. 6.4.47). In terms of the frequency deviation from center frequency ω_o, then Eq. 6.4.93 can be rewritten as[18]

$$\tau_{BP}(j(\omega_o + \Delta\omega)) = (B/2)^{-1}[\tau_{LP}(j\Delta\omega/(B/2)) + \tau_{LP}(j[4Q + \Delta\omega/(B/2)])) \tag{6.4.94}$$

This equation shows us why the linear phase transformation well-preserves the delay characteristics. The first term is the transformed delay characteristic of the low-pass filter. The second term represents a delay error term. It is small since 4Q significantly increases the value of the argument for $\Delta\omega = 0$ and since $\tau_{LP} \to 0$ as $\omega \to \infty$. It is interesting to note that the first term is the delay of a filter using the "half-transformation"[19] where $s = pB/2 + j\omega_o$. This transformation scales and translates the entire pole-zero cluster of the low-pass filter to frequency ω_o. Thus, a low-pass filter having constant delay in its passband becomes a band-pass filter also having constant passband delay. Of course, it is nonrealizable since the poles and zeros do not have complex conjugate values. These conjugate poles and zeros must be added for realizability, and this introduces delay distortion.

EXAMPLE 6.4.10 Determine the transfer function for a fourth-order Butterworth band-pass filter which is arithmetically symmetrical about center frequency $\omega_o = 1$. Design for a bandwidth of ½ where Q = 2.

Solution The fourth-order Butterworth low-pass filter has a transfer function

$$H_{LP}(p) = \frac{1}{(p+0.924)^2 + 0.382^2}\,\frac{1}{(p+0.382)^2+0.924^2} \tag{6.4.95}$$

The proper transformation to obtain approximate arithmetic symmetry is $p = 4(s \pm j)$ from Eq. 6.4.82. The pole-zero pattern of the resulting band-pass filter is shown in Fig. 6.4.17. The pattern is scaled by B/2 = ¼ and then translated to $\pm j\omega_o = \pm j1$. The gain of the band-pass filter, given by Eq. 6.4.85, is

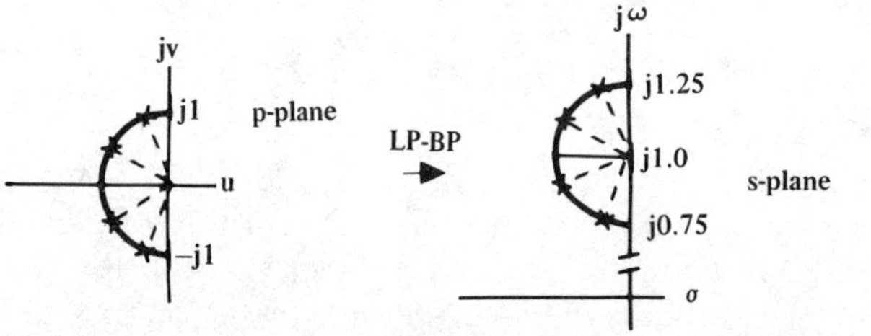

Fig. 6.4.17 Pole transformation of low-pass filter into a quasi-band-pass filter having arithmetically-symmetrical magnitude and delay responses. (The conjugate poles are not shown.)

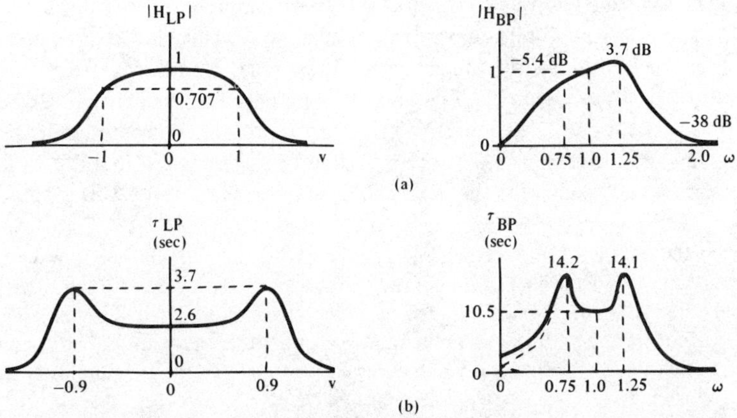

Fig. 6.4.18 Transformation of (a) magnitude and (b) delay characteristics of Example 6.4.10.

$$H_{BP}(s) = \frac{s^4}{|H_{LP}(j8)|} \frac{\omega_{o1}^2}{(s+0.231)^2 + 1.096^2} \frac{\omega_{o2}^2}{(s+0.231)^2 + 0.904^2}$$
$$\times \frac{\omega_{o3}^2}{(s+0.096)^2 + 1.231^2} \frac{\omega_{o4}^2}{(s+0.096)^2 + 0.769^2} \tag{6.4.96}$$

where $|H_{LP}(j8)| = 72$ dB from Fig. 4.3.2. The magnitude characteristic is shown in Fig. 6.4.18a. Due to the relatively low Q, it does not exhibit good arithmetic symmetry in the passband. The band-edge gains of −5.4 and +3.7 dB are calculated using Eq. 6.4.87. The gain also exhibits asymmetry in the stopband; at frequencies $\omega = 0$ and 2, the gains equal $-\infty$ and −38 dB, respectively, which are easily calculated using Eq. 6.4.88. The symmetry would rapidly improve with increasing Q.

The delay is shown in Fig. 6.4.18b and is calculated using Eq. 6.4.94. Noting that $\tau_{LP}(0) = 2.613$ and $\tau_{LP}(j\omega) = 2.613/\omega^2$ for $\omega \gg 1$ from Eq. 4.3.17 and Table 4.3.1, then the delay of the band-pass filter at its center frequency equals

$$\tau_{BP}(j1) = 4[\tau_{LP}(0) + \tau_{LP}(j8)] = 4(2.61 + 0.04) = 10.6 \text{ sec} \tag{6.4.97}$$

At the lower 3 dB frequency where $\Delta\omega = -B/2$, the delay equals

$$\tau_{BP}(j0.75) = 4[\tau_{LP}(-j1) + \tau_{LP}(j7)] = 4(3.50 + 0.05) = 14.2 \text{ sec} \tag{6.4.98}$$

since $\tau_{LP}(-j1) = \tau_{LP}(j1) = 3.50$ (see Fig. 4.3.2) and $\tau_{LP}(j7) = 0.053$. At the upper 3 dB frequency where $\Delta\omega = +B/2$, the delay equals

$$\tau_{BP}(j1.25) = 4[\tau_{LP}(j1) + \tau_{LP}(j9)] = 4(3.50 + 0.03) = 14.1 \text{ sec} \tag{6.4.99}$$

since $\tau_{LP}(j9) = 0.032$. Thus, we see that the delay maintains its approximate arithmetic shaping under this transformation.

The frequency domain specifications of band-pass filters having ideal arithmetic symmetry are shown in Fig. 6.4.11a where $f_U - f_o = f_o - f_L$, $f_1 - f_o = f_3 - f_o$, etc. We convert this data into equivalent information for a low-pass filter by using

$$\Omega_i = \frac{|f_i - f_o|}{B/2} \tag{6.4.100}$$

from Eq. 6.4.83. Here we simply determine the deviation of the stopband frequencies from the center frequency and normalize by half the bandwidth. This gives us the normalized stopband frequencies of the equivalent low-pass filter. We can now utilize the various magnitude characteristics for the low-pass filters of the earlier chapters, select the desired type, determine the required orders, and obtain the normalized filter poles and zeros from the tables. Then using the arithmetically-symmetrical low-pass to band-pass transformation, we can write the transfer function of the required band-pass filter. It is important to always compare the gain unbalance at the band-edges using Eq. 6.4.87, and at dc and $2\omega_o$ using Eq. 6.4.88, to insure that the actual filter response will be close to the ideal response on which Eq. 6.4.100 is based.

EXAMPLE 6.4.11 A band-pass filter having an arithmetically-symmetrical magnitude characteristic was considered in Example 6.4.7. However, it was realized using the standard low-pass to band-pass transformation which resulted in a filter having geometrically-symmetrical magnitude characteristics. Now realize the filter using the transformation to preserve arithmetic symmetry.

Solution We first determine the equivalent low-pass filter requirement. In this case, we have

$$f_o = (1000 + 500)/2 = 750 \text{ Hz}, \qquad B = 1000 - 500 = 500 \text{ Hz}, \qquad Q = 750/500 = 1.5 \quad (6.4.101)$$

from Eq. 6.4.84. Now we can determine the normalized stopband frequencies of the equivalent low-pass filter as

$$\Omega_{s1} = \frac{750 - 250}{500/2} = \frac{1250 - 750}{250} = 2, \qquad \Omega_{s2} = \frac{750 - 125}{500/2} = \frac{1375 - 750}{250} = 2.5 \quad (6.4.102)$$

which correspond to stopband rejections of 40 and 60 dB, respectively. Thus, the equivalent low-pass filter has the magnitude requirement shown in Fig. 6.4.13b where the Ω-axis is relabelled as (1, 2, 2.5). From the nomographs of Chap. 4, we find that

Butterworth: $n_1 \geqslant 7$ and $n_2 \geqslant 9$ (use $n \geqslant 9$)
Chebyshev: $n_1 \geqslant 5$ and $n_2 \geqslant 6$ (use $n \geqslant 6$)
Elliptic: $n_1 \geqslant 4$ and $n_2 \geqslant 4$ (use $n \geqslant 4$)

Due to the low Q of 1.5, we do not anticipate good arithmetic symmetry in this situation. One way to improve magnitude symmetry is to select the number of zeros m (letting n = m) in Eq. 6.4.85 to minimize the gain unbalance. Taking m = 3 reduces this gain unbalance to about 1 dB (see Prob. 6.40).

It is useful to again note that the M_1–M_2 dB shaping factor $S = BW_2/BW_1$ is invariant under this transformation and is independent of Q. We can again calculate bandwidth ratios to determine stopband frequencies and reduce our work. For instance in Example 6.4.11, $BW_{1.25dB}$ = 500 Hz, BW_{40dB} = 1000 Hz, and BW_{60dB} = 1250 Hz using Fig. 6.4.13a. Thus, the 1.25–40 dB S = 1000/500 = 2 and the 1.25–60 dB S = 2.5 which agree with the results of Eq. 6.4.102. The filter order is then determined as usual.

The impulse and cosine step responses of band-pass filters having transfer functions given by Eq. 6.4.85 are given by Eqs. 6.4.70 and 6.4.71. Thus, we simply use the narrowband filter results discussed previously. It is important to re-emphasize that the transformation of Eq. 6.4.82 will yield magnitude characteristics having arithmetric symmetry only for large Q, but that delay will remain arithmetically-symmetrical even for small Q's.

Before proceeding further, it should be pointed out that little quantitive design data has been tabulated for classical and optimum band-pass filters. In theory, it can be derived directly, so little effort has been expended in this area. However, there are some limited results and actual design data which the engineer may find useful in designing Butterworth,[20] Bessel,[21] Gaussian and raised-cosine (ISE gain/phase),[22] and linear phase (ISE delay)[23] band-pass filters.

6.4.6 FREQUENCY DISCRIMINATOR TRANSFORMATIONS

Another useful transformation is used to design *frequency discriminators* for FM applications. These are band-pass filters whose gain is proportional to input frequency (i.e., they are band-limited differentiators). A low-pass frequency discriminator has a linear magnitude response from

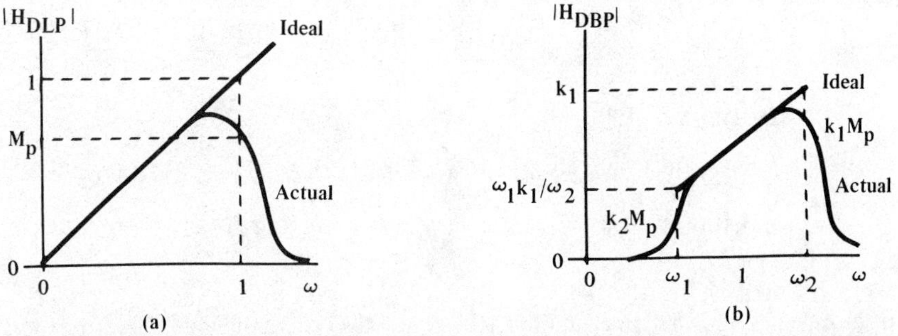

Fig. 6.4.19 (a) Low-pass and (b) band-pass (low-Q) frequency discriminators.

$\omega = 0$ to 1 and then falls off for $\omega > 1$. A band-pass frequency discriminator has a linear magnitude response over a passband $\omega_1 \leqslant \omega \leqslant \omega_2$ where $\omega_2 - \omega_1 = B$. Both types are shown in Fig. 6.4.19. The low-pass discriminator has a transfer function

$$H_{DLP}(s) = sH_{LP}(s) \tag{6.4.103}$$

where H_{LP} is a low-pass filter gain chosen to obtain the desired stopband characteristics (see Prob. 6.46). For a maximally flat passband characteristic, for example, then H_{LP} is selected to be Butterworth where $H_{DLP}(s) = s/B_n(s)$ and B_n is the *n*th-order Butterworth polynomial.[24]

If a (low-Q) band-pass discriminator is desired, then it has a transfer function[25]

$$H_{DBP}(s) = sH_{LP}(p)\,\big|_{p = (s/\omega_o + \omega_o/s)/B} = sH_{BP}(s) \tag{6.4.104}$$

This transformation yields gain linearity with respect to log ω. If we require linearity with respect to ω instead, then we use the narrowband transformation given by Eq. 6.4.82 in Eq. 6.4.104. These transformations are suitable for wide-bandwidth or low-Q discriminators. However, for narrow bandwidths, they are not too useful because of the small change in gain K. In these cases, a high-Q band-pass discriminator is required, and we use the transformation[26]

$$H_{DBP}(s) = pH_{LP}(p)\,\big|_{p = (s/\omega_o + \omega_o/s)/B} = \frac{1}{B\omega_o}\,\frac{s^2 + \omega_o^{\,2}}{s}\,H_{BP}(s) \tag{6.4.105}$$

Its response is shown in Fig. 6.4.20a. By modifying the parameters used in *only* the H_{LP} portion of Eq. 6.4.105 so that $\omega_o' = \sqrt{\omega_o\omega_2}$ and $B' = \omega_2 - \omega_o$, a band-pass filter results which eliminates the lower side of the gain characteristic as shown in Fig. 6.4.20b.[27] Again, the gain exhibits linearity with respect to $(\omega - 1/\omega)$. The narrowband transformation may be used to obtain

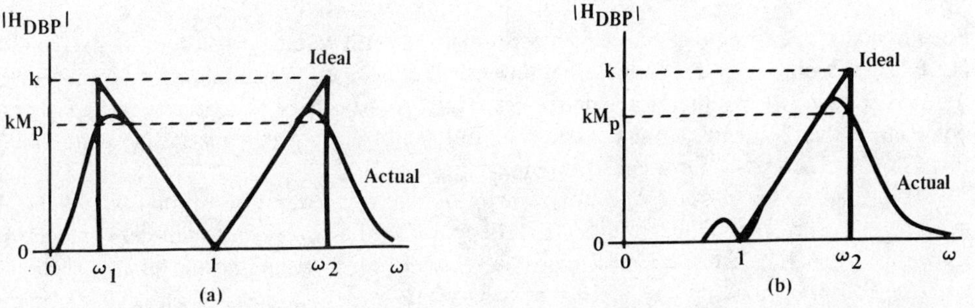

Fig. 6.4.20 Band-pass (high-Q) frequency discriminator using (a) H_{BP} or (b) modified H_{BP}.

linearity with respect to $(\omega - 1)$.

The phase and delay responses of the dsicriminators are easy to determine from the transformations. We can immediately see that

$$\arg H_{DLP}(j\omega) = \arg H_{LP}(j\omega) + (\pi/2)[2U_{-1}(\omega) - 1]$$
$$\arg H_{DBP}(j\omega) = \arg H_{BP}(j\omega) + (\pi/2)[2U_{-1}(\omega) - 1] \qquad \text{(low-Q)} \qquad (6.4.106)$$
$$\arg H_{DBP}(j\omega) = \arg H_{BP}(j\omega) + (\pi/2)[2U_{-1}(\omega + \omega_o) - 1] + (\pi/2)[2U_{-1}(\omega - \omega_o) - 1] \qquad \text{(high–Q)}$$

from Eqs. 6.4.103, 6.4.104, and 6.4.105, respectively. The delays, therefore, equal

$$\tau_{DLP}(j\omega) = \tau_{LP}(j\omega) + \pi U_0(\omega)$$
$$\tau_{DBP}(j\omega) = \tau_{BP}(j\omega) + \pi U_0(\omega) \qquad \text{(low-Q)} \qquad (6.4.107)$$
$$\tau_{DBP}(j\omega) = \tau_{BP}(m) + \pi U_0(\omega + \omega_o) + \pi U_0(\omega - \omega_o) \qquad \text{(high-Q)}$$

In the time domain, the unit step response of low-pass discriminators equal

$$r_{DLP}(t) = h_{LP}(t) \qquad (6.4.108)$$

while the unit step response of the low-Q band-pass discriminator and the unit cosine step response of the high-Q band-pass discriminator equal

$$r_{DBP}(t) = h_{BP}(t) \qquad (6.4.109)$$

Thus, these various discriminator responses can be drawn directly from those of their analogous low-pass and band-pass filters.

Another useful result in band-pass discriminator design is to note that the band-stop transfer function given by Eq. 2.8.3 can be used in place of p in Eq. 6.4.105. This is convenient when we wish to use an existing band-pass filter as part of the band-pass discriminator, because band-stop filters are easier to implement than filters having inverse band-pass responses (i.e., $(s^2 + \omega_o^2)/s$ in Eq. 6.4.105). Parameter γ in Eq. 2.8.3 is determined from the discriminator bandwidth.[27]

6.5 LOW-PASS TO BAND-STOP TRANSFORMATIONS

Low-pass filter transfer functions are transformed into band-stop filter transfer functions using the *low-pass to band-stop transformation* which is

$$H_{BS}(s) = H_{LP}(p)\Big|_{1/p = \frac{\omega_o}{B}\left(\frac{s}{\omega_o} + \frac{\omega_o}{s}\right)} = H_{HP}(p)\Big|_{p = \frac{\omega_o}{B}\left(\frac{s}{\omega_o} + \frac{\omega_o}{s}\right)} \qquad (6.5.1)$$

For simplicity, we often use the frequency normalized form where $s_n = s/\omega_o$ so that $1/p = (\omega_o/B)(s_n + 1/s_n)$. Comparing this transformation with the low-pass to band-pass transformation of the previous section, we see they are reciprocals. Thus, we can make the interesting and very useful observation that band-stop filters can also be obtained by using the low-pass to band-pass transformation on *high-pass* filter transfer functions.

To justify the low-pass to band-stop transformation, this latter observation is very helpful. We need to map the $H_{LP}(jv)$ magnitude charactierstic into the $H_{BS}(j\omega)$ magnitude characteristic as shown in Fig. 6.5.1. Thus, we must map the jv-axis of the p-plane into the $j\omega$-axis of the s-plane with the following constraints: (1) $p = \pm j\infty$ maps into $s = +j\omega_o$ (and $-j\omega_o$), (2) $p = j1$ maps into $s = +j\omega_L$ (and $-j\omega_U$), and (3) $p = -j1$ maps into $s = +j\omega_U$ (and $-j\omega_L$). We also wish to maintain

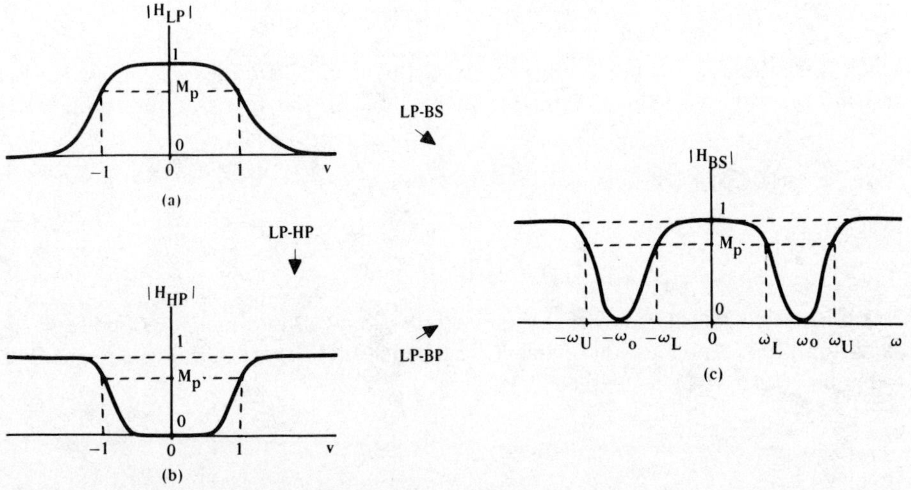

Fig. 6.5.1 Transformation of (a) low-pass and (b) high-pass filter gain characteristics into (c) bandstop filter gain characteristic.

the geometric symmetry of $H_{LP}(jv)$. A transformation which produces this mapping is

$$1/p = k(\omega_o/s + s/\omega_o) \tag{6.5.2}$$

Setting $p = jv$ and $s = j\omega$, then Eq. 6.5.2 becomes

$$1/v = k(\omega_o^2 - \omega^2)/\omega\omega_o \tag{6.5.3}$$

When $v = \infty$, $1/v = 0$, and then $\omega = \pm\omega_o$. When $v = +1$ and -1, then Eq. 6.5.3 requires that

$$1 = k(\omega_o^2 - \omega_L^2)/\omega_o\omega_L, \qquad -1 = k(\omega_o^2 - \omega_U^2)/\omega_o\omega_U \tag{6.5.4}$$

Eq. 6.5.4 is identical to Eq. 6.4.4 of the band-pass filter. Therefore, the (geometric) center frequency ω_o, bandwidth B, and Q of the band-stop filter equal

$$\omega_o = \sqrt{\omega_U\omega_L}, \qquad B = \omega_U - \omega_L, \qquad Q = \omega_o/B = k \tag{6.5.5}$$

from Eqs. 6.4.5–6.4.7. It is important to remember that the bandwidth of the notch filter is the width of its *stopband*.

6.5.1 EFFECT ON THE S-PLANE

The poles and zeros of the band-stop filter can be easily related to those of the low-pass filter. Rewriting Eq. 6.5.1, we find that s satisfies

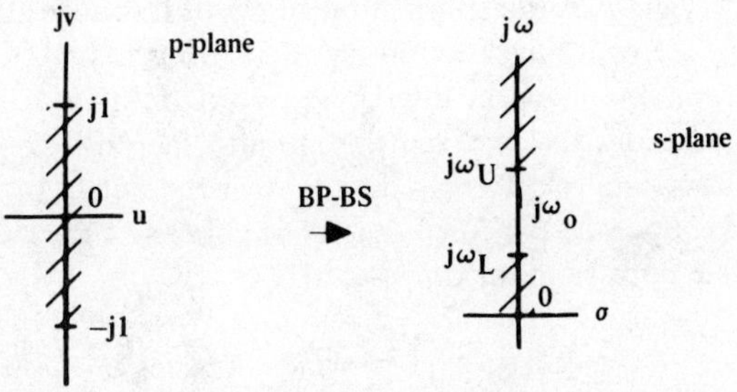

Fig. 6.5.2 Mapping of p-plane into s-plane using the low-pass to band-stop transformation. (The lower-half s-plane is not shown.)

$$s^2 - (B/p)s + \omega_o^2 = 0 \tag{6.5.6}$$

which is identical to Eq. 6.4.8 but p is replaced by 1/p. Therefore, we can use the earlier band-pass filter results by making the (p, 1/p) interchange. Solving Eq. 6.5.6 for s using the biquadratic equation gives

$$s = (B/2p) \pm [(B/2p)^2 - \omega_o^2]^{1/2} \tag{6.5.7}$$

so s_n equals

$$s_n = s/\omega_o = (1/2Qp) \pm [(1/2Qp)^2 - 1]^{1/2} \tag{6.5.8}$$

As before, every pole and zero of the low-pass filter transforms into a pair of poles and zeros in the band-stop filter. The location of the critical frequencies depends upon the p and Q of the transformation. When $|1/2p| \ll Q$, then

$$s \cong B/2p \pm j\omega_o \tag{6.5.9}$$

so s_n equals

$$s_n = s/\omega_o \cong 1/2Qp \pm j1 \tag{6.5.10}$$

from Eqs. 6.4.11 and 6.4.12. When $|1/2p| \gg Q$, then s equals

$$s = B/p, \qquad pQ\omega_o \tag{6.5.11}$$

so s_n equals

$$s_n = s/\omega_o \cong 1/pQ, \qquad pQ \tag{6.5.12}$$

from Eqs. 6.4.13 and 6.4.14. Therefore, when $|1/2p| \ll Q$, the band-stop filter poles and zeros are obtained from the low-pass filter poles and zeros by inverting, scaling 1/p by half the bandwidth, and then translating vertically to $\pm j\omega_o$. However, when $|1/2p| \gg Q$, then one band-stop filter pole-zero is obtained by inverting p and scaling by B. The second pole-zero is obtained by inverting the first pole-zero and scaling by ω_o^2. For intermediate values of p, the pole-zero locations must be calculated using Eq. 6.5.7. Again we see that real low-pass filter poles-zeros remain real under a low-Q transformation, but become complex under a high-Q transformation.

Alternatively, the value may be obtained directly from Fig. 6.4.2 where we let

$$1/pQ = x + jy \tag{6.5.13}$$

and simply read off

$$s_n = s/\omega_o = \sigma + j\omega \tag{6.5.14}$$

We may also use the polar form equations, Eqs. 6.4.29 and 6.4.30, and Fig. 6.4.6 in determining band-stop filter roots. *However*, we must replace ω_n by $1/\omega_n$, so that $\delta = Q\omega_n$. Conceptually, the idea of first transforming a low-pass filter to a high-pass filter and then applying the low-pass to band-pass transformation, allows us to utilize all of the previous band-pass filter results.

This is illustrated in Fig. 6.5.3 for a second-order Butterworth band-stop filter. We first transform the low-pass filter pole-zero pattern into that for a high-pass filter. By simple frequency inversion, the two zeros at infinity map into zeros at the origin. Then we apply a low-pass to band-pass transformation to obtain the pole-zero pattern for the band-stop filter shown. Depending upon Q, the three general patterns of Fig. 6.4.3 also apply to the band-stop filter, if we move the zeros from the origin to $\pm j1$.

EXAMPLE 6.5.1 Determine the transfer function for a second-order Chebyshev band-stop filter having 3 dB in-band ripple. Sketch the gain characteristic of the filter.

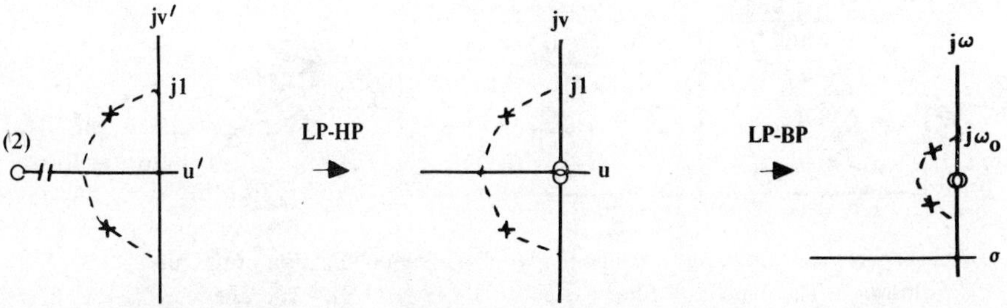

Fig. 6.5.3 Transformation of low-pass filter pole-zero pattern into that for band-stop filter. (The lower-half s-plane is not shown.)

Solution The associated low-pass filter has a transfer function

$$H_{LP}(p) = \frac{0.707(0.841)^2}{(p+0.322)^2 + 0.777^2} = \frac{0.707(0.841)^2}{p^2 + 0.644p + 0.841^2} \tag{6.5.15}$$

Substituting the low-pass to band-stop transformation given by Eq. 6.5.1 into Eq. 6.5.15, then the band-stop filter transfer function equals

$$H_{BS}(s) = 0.707(0.841)^2\left[\frac{1}{Q^2}\left(\frac{s_n}{s_n^2+1}\right)^2 + \frac{0.644}{Q}\left(\frac{s_n}{s_n^2+1}\right) + 0.841^2\right]^{-1} \tag{6.5.16}$$

which can be re-expressed as

$$H_{BS}(s) = 0.707\frac{(s_n^2+1)^2}{s_n^4 + (0.911/Q)s_n^3 + (1 + 1/0.841Q^2)s_n^2 + (0.911/Q)s_n + 1} \tag{6.5.17}$$

EXAMPLE 6.5.2 Determine the poles and zeros of the band-stop filter of Example 6.5.1.

Solution From Eq. 6.5.15, the low-pass filter has poles located at

$$p_{1,2} = -0.322 \pm j0.777 = 0.841 \exp\left[j(180^\circ \pm 67.5^\circ)\right] \tag{6.5.18}$$

and two zeros at infinity. To find the poles of the band-stop filter, we begin by inverting the low-pass filter poles as

$$1/p_{1,2} = 0.841^{-1} \exp\left[-j(180^\circ \pm 67.5^\circ)\right] = 1.19 \exp\left[j(180^\circ \pm 67.5^\circ)\right] = -0.455 \pm j1.10 \tag{6.5.19}$$

In the high-Q case, the transformed poles equal

$$s_{n1,2,3,4} = -0.455/2Q \pm j(1 \pm 1.10/2Q) \tag{6.5.20}$$

from Eq. 6.5.10. For the low-Q case, the transformed poles equal

$$s_{n1,2} = 1.19Q^{-1} \exp\left[j(180^\circ \pm 67.5^\circ)\right], \qquad s_{n3,4} = 0.841Q \exp\left[j(180^\circ \pm 67.5^\circ)\right] \tag{6.5.21}$$

from Eq. 6.5.12. For the intermediate-Q case, we use Figs. 6.4.2 or 6.4.6. For example, when Q = 1, then $1/pQ = -0.455 \pm j1.10 = x + jy$ and using Fig. 6.4.2,

$$\begin{aligned} s_{n1,2} &= -0.12 \pm j0.58 = 0.59 \exp\left[j(180^\circ \pm 78.5^\circ)\right] \\ s_{n3,4} &= -0.34 \pm j\,1.68 = 1.71 \exp\left[j(180^\circ \pm 78.5^\circ)\right] \end{aligned} \tag{6.5.22}$$

We again note that the two pairs of band-stop filter poles are obtained from one pair of low-pass filter poles. They will always have the same Q and damping factor. The zeros are easily determined since each of the two zeros of the low-pass filter at infinity map into two zeros of transmission at $s = \pm j\omega_o$.

EXAMPLE 6.5.3 A second-order Butterworth band-stop filter having a center frequency f_o of 1 KHz, a bandwidth B of 100 Hz, and a maximum gain of 10 is required. Determine its transfer function and

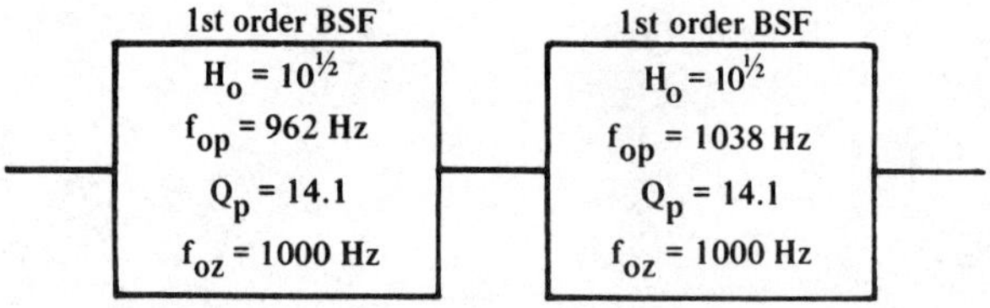

Fig. 6.5.4 Block diagram realization of second-order Butterworth band-stop filter of Example 6.5.3.

sketch its pole-zero pattern. Draw the block diagram realization of the filter.

Solution The band-stop filter has a Q = 1 KHz/100 Hz = 10. The second-order Butterworth low-pass filter has poles located at

$$p = -0.707 \pm j0.707 = \exp\,[j(180^o \pm 45^o)] \tag{6.5.23}$$

Using Fig. 6.4.6 where $\delta = Q\omega_n = 10$ and $Q_{LP} = 0.707$, then the normalized poles of the band-stop filter equal

$$|s_n| = 0.965, \quad 1.036; \quad Q_{BS} = 14.1 \tag{6.5.24}$$

Since the low-pass filter has two zeros at $p = \infty$, the band-stop filter has two zeros at $s_n = \pm j1$. This is verified from Fig. 6.4.6 using $\delta = \infty$ and $Q_{LP} = 1.0$ where

$$|s_n| = 1.0; \quad Q_{BS} = \infty \tag{6.5.25}$$

Thus, the transfer function of the band-stop filter equals

$$H(s) = \frac{10(s_n^2 + 1)^2}{(s_n^2 + 0.962s_n/14.1 + 0.962^2)(s_n^2 + 1.038s_n/14.1 + 1.038^2)} \tag{6.5.26}$$

where $s_n = s/2\pi(1\text{ KHz})$. Of course, we may apply the low-pass to band-stop transformation directly to the low-pass transfer equation as

$$H(s) = H(p)\,\big|_{1/p = Q(s_n + 1/s_n)} = \frac{10}{p^2 + 1.414p + 1}\,\Bigg|_{p = \frac{s_n/Q}{s_n^2 + 1}}$$

$$= \frac{10(s_n^2 + 1)^2}{(s_n^2 + 1)^2 + 1.414\frac{s_n}{Q}\,(s_n^2 + 1) + (\frac{s_n}{Q})^2} \tag{6.5.27}$$

Factoring Eq. 6.5.27 into the product of second-order terms yields Eq. 6.5.26. The block diagram realization of the filter is shown in Fig. 6.5.4.

We should make an important observation concerning the midband gain H_o of the band-stop filter and the gains of the individual blocks in its block diagram realization. From Eq. 6.5.1, we see that at low-frequencies when $p \to 0$, then $s_n \to 0$ or ∞ and the low-pass and band-stop filter gains equal

$$H_{BS}(s_n) = H_{LP}(p)\,\big|_{1/p = Q(s_n + 1/s_n)}, \quad p \to 0 \quad \text{and} \quad s_n \to 0 \text{ or } \infty \tag{6.5.28}$$

Hence, when the low-pass filter has a dc gain given by H_o, then the band-stop filter has an identical dc and high-frequency gain H_o. This is much more convenient than the band-pass filter case where calculations are needed. For example, $H_{LP}(0)$ and $H_{BS}(\infty)$ are identical in Example 6.5.1 (Eqs. 6.5.15 and 6.5.17), and Example 6.5.3 (Eq. 6.5.27) as required.

We shall make the same comment about the form of our low-pass to band-stop transformation as we made for the band-pass case. We have used $1/p = (\omega_o/B)(s/\omega_o + \omega_o/s)$. This transformation maps a unity-bandwidth low-pass filter into a band-stop filter having (stopband) bandwidth B. This is especially convenient since most of our tabulated low-pass filters have unity bandwidths. Other authors have chosen to use the transformation $1/p = \omega_o\,(s/\omega_o + \omega_o/s)$, or in terms of normalized frequency when $\omega_o = 1$, $p = s + 1/s$. Here the bandwidth of the band-stop filter *equals* that of the low-pass filter. We used this form in Chap. 2 when we introduced the various transformations, and indeed, we saw that bandwidth was preserved in the examples discussed there. However, we feel that our first form is more advantageous for present purposes.

6.5.2 MAGNITUDE, PHASE, AND DELAY RESPONSES

The magnitude characteristic of a band-stop filter has geometric symmetry about its center frequency ω_o using the low-pass to band-stop transformation. Thus, its gain at frequency ω is identical to that at frequency ω_o/ω. The shape of the characteristic is preserved for transformations of any Q. A magnitude characteristic is shown in Fig. 6.5.5a. A more general s-plane plot is shown in Fig. 6.5.6. Note that $H_{LP}(0)$ maps into $H_{BS}(0)$ and $H_{BS}(\infty)$ to form the drumhead. $H_{LP}(\infty)$ maps into $H_{BS}(\pm j\omega_o)$.

The phase characteristic also has geometric symmetry about ω_o. It is identical to the phase of the analogous high-pass filter after it is recentered from 0 to ω_o. This is shown in Fig. 6.5.5b, where it is important to note the phase change of $180(n - m)^o$ at ω_o.

The delay of the band-stop filter can be determined from the low-pass filter delay. The band-stop filter delay equals

$$\tau_{BS}(j\omega) = -\frac{d \arg H_{BS}(j\omega)}{d\omega} = -\frac{d \arg H_{LP}(jv)}{dv}\frac{dv}{d\omega} = \tau_{LP}(jv)\frac{dv}{d\omega} \tag{6.5.29}$$

where v is given by Eq. 6.5.3 as

$$-1/v = (\omega_o/B)(\omega/\omega_o - \omega_o/\omega) = (\omega - \omega_o^2/\omega)/B \tag{6.5.30}$$

Therefore, since

$$dv/d\omega = [1 + (\omega_o/\omega)^2]v^2/B = (B/\omega)^2[1 + (\omega_o/\omega)^2]/B[1 - (\omega_o/\omega)^2]^2 \tag{6.5.31}$$

then the band-stop filter delay given by Eq. 6.5.29 can be expressed as

$$\tau_{BS}(j\omega) = (B/\omega)^2[1 + (\omega_o/\omega)^2]/B[1 - (\omega_o/\omega)^2]^2 \; \tau_{LP}(jv)\,\big|_{1/v = Q(\omega_o/\omega - \omega/\omega_o)} \tag{6.5.32}$$

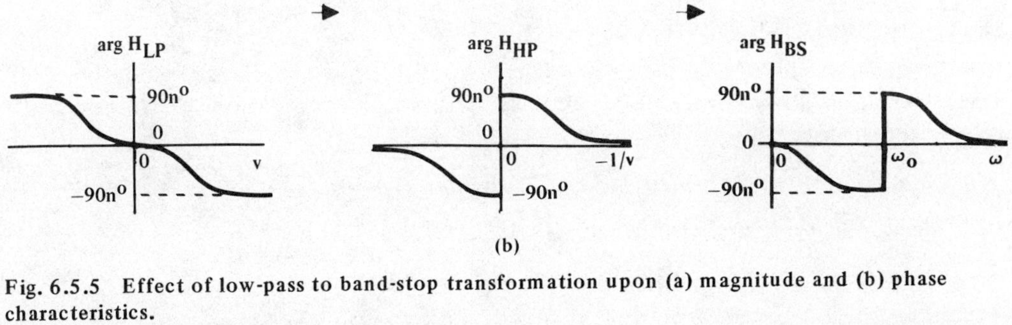

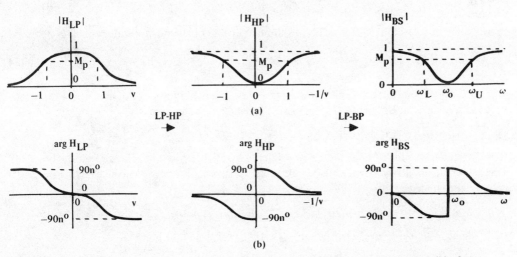

Fig. 6.5.5 Effect of low-pass to band-stop transformation upon (a) magnitude and (b) phase characteristics.

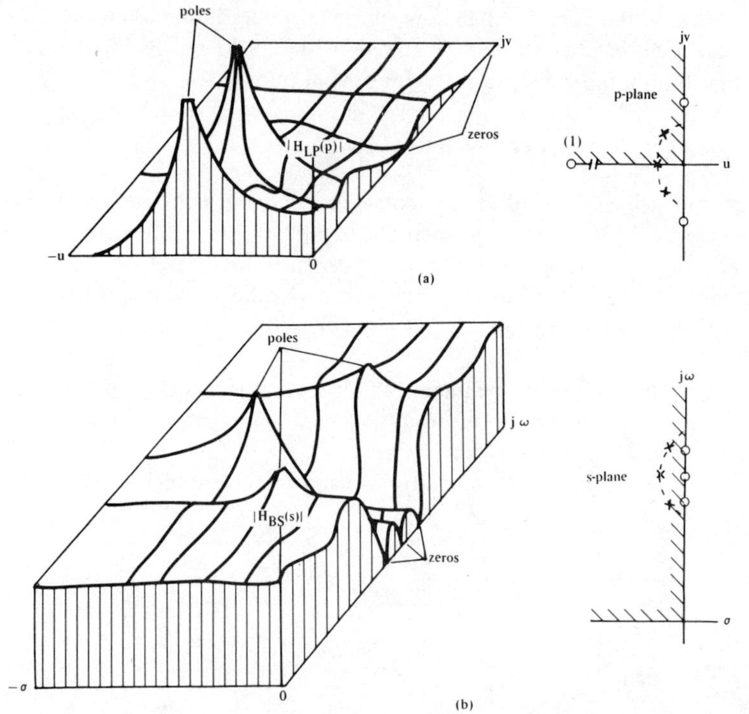

Fig. 6.5.6 Magnitudes of third-order elliptic (a) low-pass filter gain $H_{LP}(p)$ and (b) band-stop filter gain $H_{BS}(s)$ in the p- and s-planes, respectively.

The delay expression is more complicated than that for band-pass filters (cf. Eq. 6.4.48).

We see that the dv/dω term in Eq. 6.5.29 introduces delay asymmetry as in the band-pass filter case. The delay becomes more asymmetrical with increasing deviation from center frequency. We can find the approximate stopband delay of a filter. If we express the frequency variation from center frequency ω_o as $\Delta\omega = \omega - \omega_o$, then we can express Eq. 6.5.30 as

$$-1/v = (\omega^2 - \omega_o^2)/B\omega = \Delta\omega(\omega + \omega_o)/B\omega \tag{6.5.33}$$

Substituting this result into Eq. 6.5.32, the stopband delay of a band-stop filter equals

$$\tau_{BS}(j(\omega_o + \Delta\omega)) \cong \frac{B/2}{(\Delta\omega)^2}\tau_{LP}(j\frac{B/2}{\Delta\omega}) \tag{6.5.34}$$

Due to the instantaneous phase change at $\omega = \omega_o$, the delay has impulses of area $\pi(n - m)$ located at $\pm\omega_o$. The delay at the center frequency of the band-stop filter equals

$$\tau_{BS}(j\omega_o) = (B/2)^{-1}\, d\tau_{LP}(j\infty)/d\,(1/\omega^2) = (B/2)^{-1}(b_{n-1}/b_n - a_{m-1}/a_m) \tag{6.5.35}$$

It is 2/B times the high-frequency slope of the low-pass filter whose gain is given by Eq. 2.0.1. Thus, the midband delay is inversely proportional to half the filter bandwidth. The low-frequency delay of the band-stop filter equals

$$\tau_{BS}(j\omega) = (Q\omega_o)^{-1}\tau_{LP}(0) = (Q\omega_o)^{-1}\,(b_1/b_0 - a_1/a_0), \qquad \omega \ll \omega_o \tag{6.5.36}$$

while the high-frequency delay equals

$$\tau_{BS}(j\omega) = (B/\omega^2)\,\tau_{LP}(0) = (B/\omega^2)\,(b_1/b_0 - a_1/a_0), \qquad \omega \gg \omega_o \tag{6.5.37}$$

This is easily proved using Eqs. 2.10.34, 2.10.36, and 6.5.32. The low-frequency delay is constant

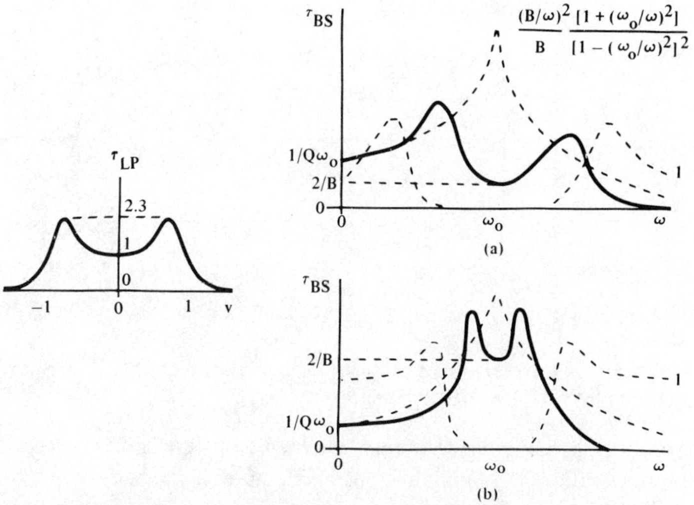

Fig. 6.5.7 Conversion of delay under (a) low-Q and (b) high-Q transformations of Example 6.5.4.

and the high-frequency delay rolls off as $1/\omega^2$.

EXAMPLE 6.5.4 A second-order low-pass filter having $\omega_n = 1$ and $\zeta = 0.5$ was considered in Example 6.4.5. Determine and sketch the delay characteristic of the analogous second-order band-stop filter.
Solution The low-pass filter gain equals $H_{LP}(p) = 1/(p^2 + p + 1)$. The band-stop filter gain is found from Eq. 6.5.1 where ω_o and B must be specified. The low-pass filter has a delay given by Eq. 6.4.54. Since it has a dc delay of one second, the band-stop filter has a low-frequency delay of $1/Q\omega_o$ for $\omega \ll \omega_o$ from Eq. 6.5.36, and a high-frequency delay of B/ω^2 for $\omega \gg \omega_o$ from Eq. 6.5.37. From Eq. 6.5.35, the midband delay equals $\tau_{BS}(j\omega_o) = 2/B$ with delay impulses of area 2π at $\omega = \pm\omega_o$. These delay characteristics are shown in Fig. 6.5.7. The general shape of τ_{BS} is obtained by taking the product of the τ_{LP} and $dv/d\omega$ curves.

Band-stop filters are specified in an analogous fashion to band-pass filters. The specifications may be in the frequency domain, the time domain, or in both domains simultaneously. We can utilize the frequency domain results and nomographs of Chaps. 4 and 5. We can also utilize the time domain results for narrowband notch filters. In general, the frequency domain specifications of band-stop filters have the form shown in Fig. 6.5.8. f_L and f_U are the required corner frequencies for less than M_p in-band gain variation and frequencies f_1, f_2, f_3, f_4, etc., are the frequencies for various stopband rejections of M_{s1}, M_{s2}, etc. In many applications, the gain characteristic will have geometric symmetry about the center frequency f_o where $f_o^2 = f_L f_U = f_1 f_3 = f_2 f_4 = \ldots$. We convert this data to that for the equivalent low-pass filter using Eq. 6.5.3 where

$$\Omega_i = 1 \Big/ Q\left|\frac{f_i}{f_o} - \frac{f_o}{f_i}\right| \tag{6.5.38}$$

We normalize each stopband frequency f_i by f_o, form its reciprocal, take the absolute value of the difference, multiply by Q, and take the reciprocal. Alternatively, in filters having geometric symmetry, we can simply determine the M_1–M_2 dB shaping factor $S = BW_1/BW_2$ (note the *inverted* bandwidth ratio). We then draw the equivalent low-pass filter specification as shown in Fig. 6.5.8b where f_o corresponds to $\Omega = 0$, the upper and lower band-edge frequencies correspond to $\Omega = 1$, and the various cutoff frequencies are as shown. Using the specification, we now determine the characteristics for the low-pass filter. The filter type is selected, the order determined, and the

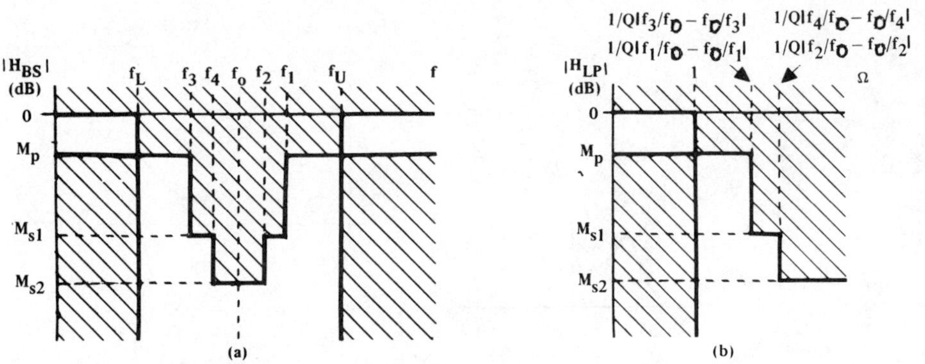

Fig. 6.5.8 Conversion of magnitude specifications for (a) band-stop filters into equivalent specifications for (b) low-pass filters.

normalized filter pole-zero data obtained from the tables. Then using the low-pass to band-stop transformation, the required transfer function of the band-stop filter can be written.

EXAMPLE 6.5.5 Determine the minimum order Butterworth, Chebyshev, and elliptic band-stop filters required to meet the magnitude characteristics shown in Fig. 6.5.9a.

Solution We first find the Q and f_o for the filter. Since

$$f_o = [250(4000)]^{1/2} = 1000 \text{ Hz}, \qquad B = 4000 - 250 = 3750 \text{ Hz} \tag{6.5.39}$$

using Eq. 6.5.5, then Q equals

$$Q = 1000/3750 = 0.267 \tag{6.5.40}$$

Therefore, the normalized stopband frequencies equal

$$\Omega_s = [0.267\ |2000/1000 - 1000/2000|]^{-1} = [0.267\ |500/1000 - 1000/500|]^{-1} = 1/0.4 = 2.5 \tag{6.5.41}$$

using Eq. 6.5.38. Alternatively, since we have geometric symmetry and $B_{1.25dB}$ = 3750 Hz and B_{40dB} = 1500 Hz, then Ω_s = 3750/1500 = 2.5. The equivalent low-pass filter gain is drawn in Fig. 6.5.9b. From the nomographs of Chap. 4, we find

Butterworth: $n \geqslant 6$, Chebyshev: $n \geqslant 4$, Elliptic: $n \geqslant 3$

Thus, a third-order elliptic band-stop filter will meet this gain requirement.

In some filter applications, asymmetrical magnitude specifications may be given. This occurs in filters requiring arithmetic symmetry. In these situations, we can still utilize the nomographs, assuming of course that filters having geometric symmetry are acceptable. We select the most

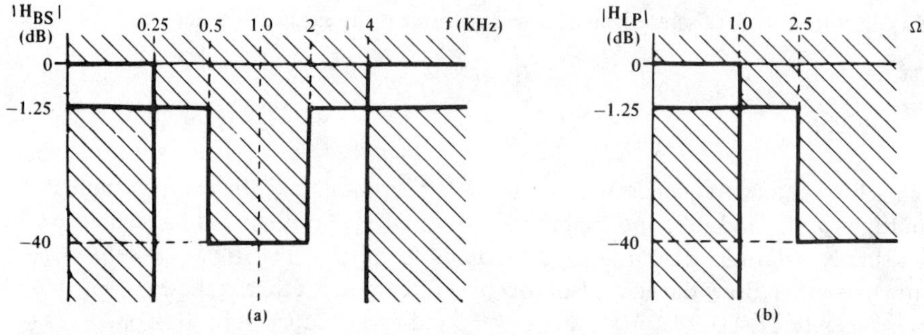

Fig. 6.5.9 (a) Band-stop filter specification and its (b) equivalent low-pass filter specification of Example 6.5.5.

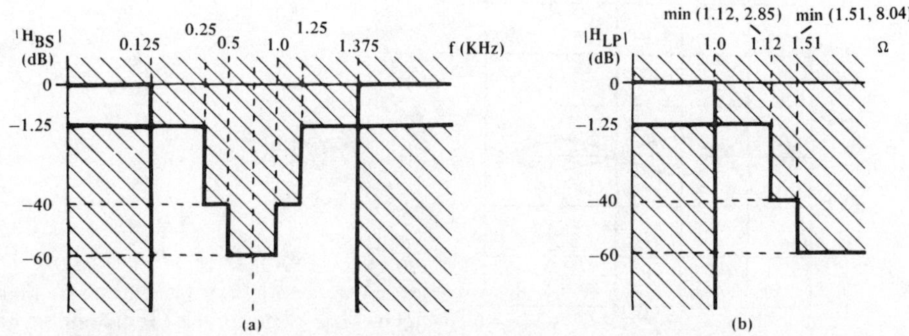

Fig. 6.5.10 (a) Band-stop filter specification and its (b) equivalent low-pass filter specification of Example 6.5.6.

stringent stopband frequency at a given attenuation as we show in the following example.

EXAMPLE 6.5.6 Determine the minimum order Butterworth, Chebyshev, and elliptic band-stop filters required to meet the magnitude requirements shown in Fig. 6.5.10a.

Solution In this case, we have

$$f_o = [125(1375)]^{1/2} = 415 \text{ Hz}, \qquad B = 1375 - 125 = 1250 \text{ Hz}, \qquad Q = 415/1250 = 0.332 \tag{6.5.42}$$

which is a low-Q requirement. The upper and lower stopband frequencies of the equivalent low-pass filter are found to be $\Omega_1 = 1.12$, $\Omega_2 = 1.51$, $\Omega_3 = 2.85$, and $\Omega_4 = 8.04$ using

$$\Omega_i = [0.332\ |f_i/415 - 415/f_i|]^{-1} \tag{6.5.43}$$

The equivalent low-pass filter is drawn in Fig. 6.5.10b. The required stopband frequencies are unequal and so the smallest frequency is chosen at any given attenuation level. This gives the *most* stringent gain requirement. From the nomographs of Chap. 4,

Butterworth: Impractical, Chebyshev: $n \geq 12, 9$ (use $n \geq 12$), Elliptic: $n \geq 6, 6$ (use $n \geq 6$)

Therefore, a sixth-order elliptic band-stop filter can be used.

6.5.3 IMPULSE AND COSINE STEP RESPONSES

Band-stop filters are characterized in the time domain by their responses to a unit cosine step input $\cos \omega_o t\, U_{-1}(t)$ where ω_o is the center frequency of the filter. When the impulse response of the analogous high-pass filter is known, then the impulse response of the band-stop filter can be easily written. The band-stop filter has an impulse response

$$h_{BS}(t) = \mathcal{L}^{-1}[H_{BS}(s)] = \mathcal{L}^{-1}[H_{HP}(p)\ |_{p = Q(s/\omega_o + \omega_o/s)}] \tag{6.5.44}$$

Therefore, by analogy with Eqs. 6.4.62 and 6.4.67,

$$h_{BS}(t) = Q[h_{HP}(t') - \int_0^{t'} \sqrt{\tau/(t'-\tau)}\, J_1(2\sqrt{(t'-\tau)\tau}\,)h_{HP}(\tau)\, d\tau]\ U_{-1}(t) \tag{6.5.45}$$

when $\omega_o = 1$ and $t' = t/Q$. Therefore, the unit cosine step response equals

$$r_{BS}(t) = h_{BS}(t) * [\cos \omega_o t\ U_{-1}(t)] \tag{6.5.46}$$

The step response can be written for the two limiting cases of narrowband and wideband band-stop filters. In the narrowband case, we found $1/p = (s \pm j\omega_o)/(B/2)$ from Eq. 6.5.9. The approximate transfer function of the band-stop filter can be expressed as

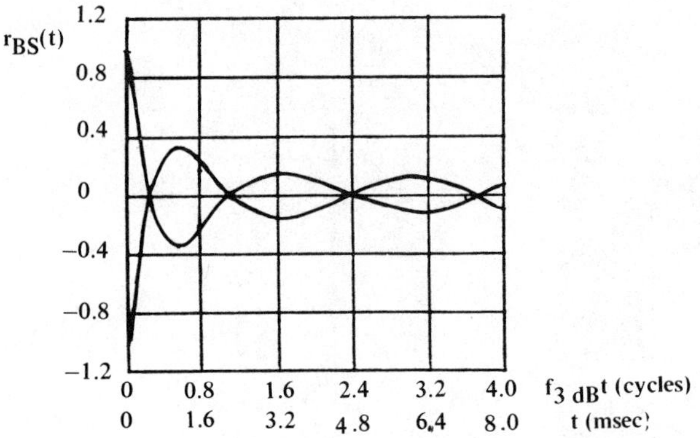

Fig. 6.5.11 Cosine step response envelope of fourth-order Butterworth band-stop filter of Example 6.5.7.

$$H_{BS}(s) \cong H_{HP}(p)\big|_{p=2(s+j\omega_o)/B} + H_{HP}(p)\big|_{p=2(s-j\omega_o)/B} \tag{6.5.47}$$

Therefore, following the same procedure as that in Eq. 6.4.70, the impulse response of the band-stop filter must equal

$$h_{BS}(t) = Bh_{HP}(Bt/2)\cos\omega_o t\, U_{-1}(t) \tag{6.5.48}$$

The unit cosine step response equals

$$r_{BS}(t) = r_{HP}(Bt/2)\cos\omega_o t\, U_{-1}(t) \tag{6.5.49}$$

by analogy with Eq. 6.4.71. Therefore, narrowband band-stop filters have impulse and cosine step responses which can be drawn by inspection using the impulse and step responses of their analogous high-pass filters.

In wideband band-stop filters, this is not true. In this case, the poles and zeros are given by $1/p = s/B$ and $Q\omega_o/s$. The transfer function of the band-stop filter can be expressed as

$$H_{BS}(s) = H_{HP}(p)\big|_{p=s/B} \times H_{HP}(p)\big|_{p=Q\omega_o/s} \tag{6.5.50}$$

Therefore, the filter impulse response must equal

$$h_{BS}(t) = \mathcal{L}^{-1}[H_{BS}(s)] = \omega_o^2 h_{HP}(Bt) * h_{LP}(Q\omega_o t) \tag{6.5.51}$$

by analogy with Eq. 6.4.73. Thus, we convolve the impulse responses of the low-pass and high-pass filters to determine the impulse response of a wideband band-stop filter. The cosine step response is then obtained using h_{BS} and Eq. 6.5.46.

It is important to remember that when *low-transient* or *complementary* band-stop filters are required, they can be obtained by utilizing the *low-transient* high-pass filters discussed earlier, and the low-pass to band-pass transformation. This gives us considerable latitude in choosing band-stop filter responses.

EXAMPLE 6.5.7 A fourth-order Butterworth band-stop filter has a center frequency f_o of 10 KHz, a bandwidth B of 1 KHz, and unity gain. Sketch its cosine step response.

Solution Since Q = 10 KHz/1 KHz = 10, we treat this as a high-Q filter. Its cosine step response is easily sketched using its analogous high-pass filter step response. This step response is shown in Figs. 6.3.13 and 6.3.16. Using Fig. 6.3.16, we first sketch the envelope response $r_{HP}(t_n)$ of the band-stop filter as shown in Fig. 6.5.11. We then denormalize the time scale as

$$t = \frac{t_n}{B/2} = \frac{t_n}{1\text{ KHz}/2} = 2t_n \text{ (msec)} \tag{6.5.52}$$

Next, we "fill in" this envelope with the cosine signal cos [2π(10 KHz)t]. Because $f_o \gg B$, this signal

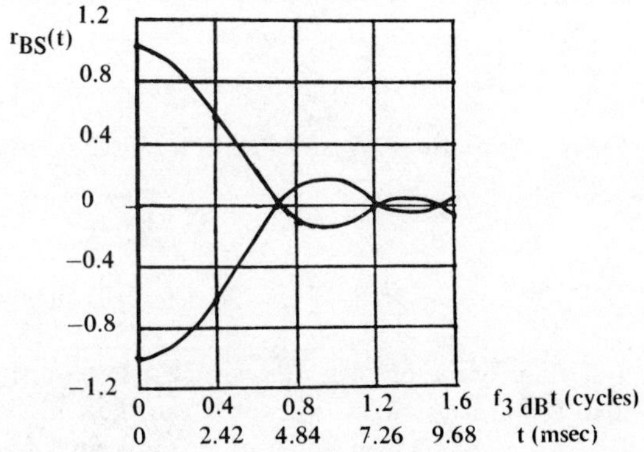

Fig. 6.5.12 Cosine step response envelope of low-transient fourth-order Butterworth band-stop filter of Example 6.5.8.

simply "darkens" the envelope in Fig. 6.5.11.

EXAMPLE 6.5.8 A low-transient fourth-order Butterworth band-stop filter has a center frequency f_o of 10 KHz, a bandwidth B of 1 KHz, and unity gain. Sketch its cosine step response.

Solution Since Q = 10 as in Example 6.5.7, we treat this as a high-Q filter. Its cosine step response is readily drawn using the analogous high-pass filter step response in Fig. 6.3.15. This response gives the envelope response $r_{HP}(t_n)$ of the band-stop filter as shown in Fig. 6.5.12. We then denormalize the time scale as

$$t = \frac{t_n}{0.33B/2} = 6.06t_n \text{ (msec)} \tag{6.5.53}$$

Remember that the low-transient fourth-order Butterworth high-pass filter had a 3 dB bandwidth of $f_{3dB} \cong 0.33$ from Fig. 6.3.18, we we must denormalize $f_{3dB}t$ accordingly. Next we fill in the envelope with the cosine signal cos $[2\pi(10\text{ KHz})t]$. Comparing this result with that of Fig. 6.5.11, we see the reduced overshoot and increased storage time of the response. Of course, the penalty paid is the decreased rate of rejection in the stopband magnitude characteristics.

We considered the pulsed-cosine response of band-pass filters in the last section. Now let us consider the pulsed-cosine response of band-stop filters. The pulsed-cosine input s_i to the band-stop filter is given by Eq. 6.4.78, its spectrum S_i by Eq. 1.9.30, and its energy E_i by Eq. 1.9.31. The output energy E_o of the filter is given by Eq. 6.4.79 where $|H_n|^2$ is the squared-magnitude response of the band-stop filter. It can be shown that the E_o/E_i ratio for Butterworth band-stop filters is simply one minus that for Butterworth band-pass filters. Thus, with a simple relabelling of the ordinate in Fig. 6.4.16, the same figure can be used for analyzing the pulsed-cosine response of fourth-order Butterworth band-stop filters.

We see from this figure that there is a maximum normalized time $\omega_o T$ required to pass a reasonable amount of energy through the filter. For example, for a Q = 10, then $\omega_o T \leqslant 35$ to transfer at least 50% of the input energy through the filter. If f_o = 10 KHz, then the pulse duration $T \leqslant 35/2\pi \times 10^{-4} = 0.56$ msec.

6.5.4 ARITHMETICALLY-SYMMETRICAL TRANSFORMATION

In applications involving signal frequencies which are arithmetically distributed about their carrier frequencies, band-stop filters having arithmetic symmetry in magnitude and/or delay are required. Just as with the analogous band-pass filters, such filters can only be approximated. The narrow-band transformation

$$s = (B/2)/p \pm j\omega_o \tag{6.5.54}$$

produces almost symmetrical passband magnitude and delay characteristics. By analogy with Eq. 6.4.84,

$$\omega_o = (\omega_U + \omega_L)/2, \qquad B = \omega_U - \omega_L, \qquad Q = \omega_o/B \tag{6.5.55}$$

The band-stop filter transfer function is defined to equal

$$\begin{aligned} H_{BS}(s) &= H_{LP}(p)\,\big|_{1/p = 2(s + j\omega_o)/B}\, H_{LP}(p)\,\big|_{1/p = 2(s - j\omega_o)/B} \\ &= H_{HP}(p)\,\big|_{p = 2(s + j\omega_o)/B}\, H_{HP}(p)\,\big|_{p = 2(s - j\omega_o)/B} \end{aligned} \tag{6.5.56}$$

This transformation scales the entire pole-zero pattern of the high-pass filter by B/2 and translates it to frequencies $\pm j\omega_o$. This produces the narrowband pole-zero distribution shown in Fig. 6.5.3. Expressing the frequency deviation from center frequency ω_o as $\Delta\omega = \omega - \omega_o$, then H_{BS} equals

$$H_{BS}(j(\omega_o + \Delta\omega)) = H_{HP}(j\Delta\omega/(B/2))\, H_{HP}(j\,[4Q + \Delta\omega/(B/2)]\,) \tag{6.5.57}$$

When $\Delta\omega \ll \omega_o$, the second term is constant with value $H_{LP}(j4Q)$ so that $H_{BS}(j(\omega_o + \Delta\omega)) \sim H_{HP}(j2\Delta\omega/B)$. Therefore, H_{BS} exhibits arithmetic symmetry in the immediate vicinity of ω_o. The gains at the band-edges where $\Delta\omega = \pm B/2$ equal

$$H_{BS}(j(\omega_o \pm B/2)) = H_{HP}(\pm j1)\, H_{HP}(j(4Q \pm 1)) \tag{6.5.58}$$

The gain unbalance becomes negligible for large Q. Calculating the gains at ω_o, dc, and $2\omega_o$ shows that

$$H_{BS}(j\omega_o) = 0, \qquad H_{BS}(0) = H_{HP}(-j2Q)H_{HP}(j2Q), \qquad H_{BS}(j2\omega_o) = H_{HP}(j2Q)H_{HP}(j6Q) \tag{6.5.59}$$

Although the gain at center frequency ω_o is zero, the gains at frequencies of dc and $2\omega_o$ are slightly unbalanced by the ratio $H_{HP}(-j2Q)/H_{HP}(j6Q)$. This gain unbalance approaches zero for increasing Q.

The phase of the band-stop filter equals

$$\arg H_{BS}(j(\omega_o + \Delta\omega)) = \arg H_{HP}(j\Delta\omega/(B/2)) + \arg H_{HP}(j\,[4Q + \Delta\omega/(B/2)]\,) \tag{6.5.60}$$

The second term is constant with a value $\arg H_{HP}(j4Q)$ for small $\Delta\omega \ll 2\omega_o$. Thus, the phase in the vicinity of the stopband is equal to the phase of the high-pass filter phase (around dc) augmented by $\arg H_{HP}(j4Q)$.

By analogy with Eq. 6.4.94, the delay of the band-stop filter equals

$$\tau_{BS}(j(\omega_o + \Delta\omega)) = (B/2)^{-1}\,[\tau_{HP}(j\Delta\omega/(B/2)) + \tau_{HP}(j\,[4Q + \Delta\omega/(B/2)]\,) \tag{6.5.61}$$

The delay characteristics of the high-pass filter are well-preserved under this transformation. This is due to the second term which represents delay error $\Delta\omega$. It is small for large Q and small $\Delta\omega$.

The frequency domain specifications of band-stop filters having ideal arithmetic symmetry are shown in Fig. 6.5.8a where $f_U - f_o = f_o - f_L$, $f_1 - f_o = f_3 - f_o$, etc. We convert this data into equivalent information for a low-pass filter by using

$$\Omega_i = \left(\frac{|f_i - f_o|}{B/2}\right)^{-1} \tag{6.5.62}$$

from Eq. 6.5.54. Here we simply determine the deviation of the stopband frequencies from the center frequency, normalize by half the bandwidth, and take the reciprocal. Alternatively, we can simply calculate bandwidth ratios and shaping factors. Either approach gives us the normalized stopband frequencies of the equivalent low-pass filter. We can now utilize the various magnitude

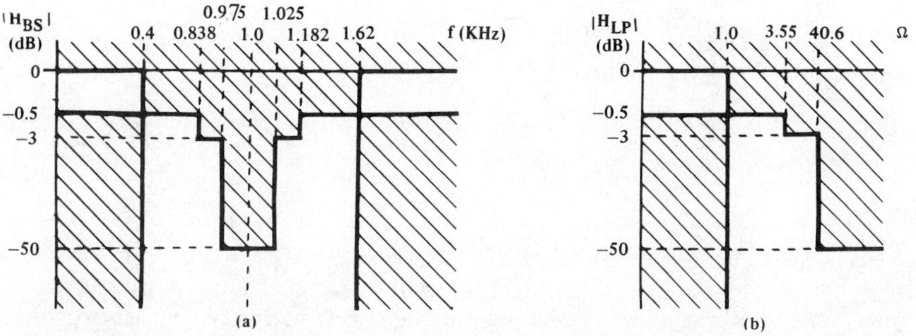

Fig. 6.5.13 (a) Band-stop filter specification and its (b) equivalent low-pass filter specification of Example 6.5.9.

characteristics for the low-pass filters of the earlier chapters, select the desired type, determine the required orders, and obtain the normalized poles and zeros from the tables. Then using the arithmetically-symmetrical low-pass to band-stop transformation, we can write the gain of the required band-stop filter. It is important to always compare the gain unbalance at the band-edges using Eq. 6.5.58, and at dc and $2\omega_o$ using Eq. 6.5.59, to insure that the actual filter response will be close to the ideal response on which Eq. 6.5.62 is based.

EXAMPLE 6.5.9 The telephone system uses holding tones and test tones in measuring impulse noise, gain hits, phase hits, phase jitter, and crosstalk in transmission channels. Generally, the tone frequencies are 1010 and 2805 Hz. Notch filters are often used to eliminate these tones when telephone lines are being monitored for other purposes. Assume that the 1010 Hz notch filter has a passband gain of 0 dB and that the other specifications are: (1) 0.5 dB frequencies $\leqslant 400, \geqslant 1620$ Hz; (2) 3 dB frequencies = 838, 1182 Hz; and (3) 50 dB frequencies = 995, 1025 Hz as shown in Fig. 6.5.13a. What order Butterworth, Chebyshev, and elliptic filter is required? Which filter is most appropriate?

Solution The center frequency, bandwidth, and Q of the band-stop filter equal

$$f_o = (400 + 1620)/2 = 1010 \text{ Hz}, \qquad B = 1620 - 400 = 1220 \text{ Hz}, \qquad Q = 1010/1220 = 0.828 \tag{6.5.63}$$

We normalize the stopband frequencies as

$$\frac{1}{\Omega_{s1}} = \frac{1010 - 838}{1220/2} = \frac{1182 - 1010}{610} = \frac{1}{3.55}, \qquad \frac{1}{\Omega_{s2}} = \frac{1010 - 975}{1220/2} = \frac{1025 - 1010}{610} = \frac{1}{40.7} \tag{6.5.64}$$

Alternatively, since BW_{3dB} = 344 Hz and BW_{50dB} = 30 Hz, the normalized stopband frequencies are Ω_{s1} = 1220/344 = 3.55 and Ω_{s2} = 1220/30 = 40.7. Thus, the equivalent low-pass filter has the magnitude requirements shown in Fig. 6.5.13b. From the nomographs of Chap. 4, we find

Butterworth and Chebyshev: $n_1 \geqslant 1$ and $n_2 \geqslant 2$ (use $n \geqslant 2$)

Elliptic: $n_1 \geqslant 3$ and $n_2 \geqslant 3$ (use $n \geqslant 3$)

For minimum complexity and the best delay and step response characteristics, we shall use a second-order Butterworth notch filter.

We should verify that the resulting filter has approximate arithmetic symmetry. The gain unbalance from $|H_{HP}(\pm j1)| = -0.5$ dB at the edge of the passband equals

$$\begin{aligned} |H_{HP}(j(4Q+1))| &= |H_{HP}(j4.31)| = |H_{LP}(j0.232)| = -0.01 \text{ dB} \\ |H_{HP}(j(4Q-1))| &= |H_{HP}(j2.31)| = |H_{LP}(j0.433)| = -0.15 \text{ dB} \end{aligned} \tag{6.5.65}$$

using Eqs. 6.5.58 and 4.3.8. Even with this low Q, the errors are sufficiently small. The gain unbalance between the gains at frequencies of dc and $2\omega_o$ are

$$\frac{|H_{HP}(j6Q)|}{|H_{HP}(j2Q)|} = \frac{|H_{HP}(j4.97)|}{|H_{HP}(j1.66)|} = \frac{|H_{LP}(j0.201)|}{|H_{LP}(j0.602)|} = -0.007\text{ dB} + 0.54\text{ dB} \cong 0.5\text{ dB} \tag{6.5.66}$$

from Eq. 6.5.59 which is also small. Thus, we assume the band-stop filter will have close to arithmetic symmetry.

The impulse and cosine step responses of band-stop filters having transfer functions given by Eq. 6.5.56 are given by Eqs. 6.5.48 and 6.5.49. Thus, we simply use the narrowband filter results discussed previously. It is important to re-emphasize that the transformation of Eq. 6.5.44 will yield magnitude characteristics having arithmetic symmetry only for large Q, but that delay will remain arithmetically-symmetrical even at small Q's.

6.6 LOW-PASS TO ALL-PASS TRANSFORMATION

Low-pass filters are transformed into all-pass filters using the low-pass to all-pass transformation where

$$H_{AP}(s) = H_{LP}(s)/H_{LP}(-s) = H_{LP}(s)H_{LP}^{-1}(-s) \tag{6.6.1}$$

This transformation produces zeros which are images of the poles, and visa versa. All-pass filters were introduced in Sec. 2.11. Stable, causal all-pass filters (the usual case of interest) have only left-half-plane poles with their right-half-plane zero images. They have no $j\omega$-axis poles or zeros. Thus, only low-pass filters having no finite zeros (except perhaps on the $j\omega$-axis) are used in Eq. 6.6.1. All-pass filters have gains, phase, and delay responses which satisfy

$$|H_{AP}(j\omega)| = 1, \qquad \arg H_{AP}(j\omega) = 2 \arg H_{LP}(j\omega), \qquad \tau_{AP}(j\omega) = 2\tau_{LP}(j\omega) \tag{6.6.2}$$

The phase characteristic of the all-pass filter is twice that of the low-pass filter (excluding any steps due to $j\omega$-axis zeros) and must always be monotonically nonincreasing. All-pass filters can only introduce positive delay (never negative). The delay is twice that of its analogous low-pass filter. The use of Eq. 6.6.2 is illustrated in Examples 2.10.1–2.10.8, 2.11.1, and 2.11.2.

In most cases, the low-pass filter selected is an all-pole filter where $H_{LP}(s) = D_n(0)/D_n(s)$. Then the analogous all-pass filter has a transfer function

$$H_{AP}(s) = D_n(-s)/D_n(s) \tag{6.6.3}$$

Usually, the low-pass filter is selected which has the required delay characteristic. For example, if H_{AP} is a delay element, then a Bessel or equiripple delay low-pass filter may be used. In situations where H_{AP} is a delay equalizer, then we select a low-pass filter having a delay characteristic τ_c which complements that of the delay characteristic to be equalized. In other words, τ_{LP} is chosen so that

$$\tau_c + 2\tau_{LP} = \text{constant} \tag{6.6.4}$$

This was illustrated in Examples 2.10.6, 2.11.4, and 2.11.5. In general, the optimization methods of Chap. 5 are used to determine the parameters of the required delay equalizer.

Although the magnitude, phase, and delay responses of all-pass filters are easy to determine from their transfer functions, their step responses are not. Unfortunately, there are no convenient transformation theorems known which directly relate low-pass and all-pass filter step responses. They must be calculated directly from their transfer functions using Laplace transform methods. This was discussed in Sec. 3.12.

PROBLEMS

6.1 Low-pass, high-pass, band-pass, and band-stop filters often have magnitude response bounds as shown in Fig. P6.1. The typical filter responses are shown by the dotted lines. Describe the parameters required to specify the responses.

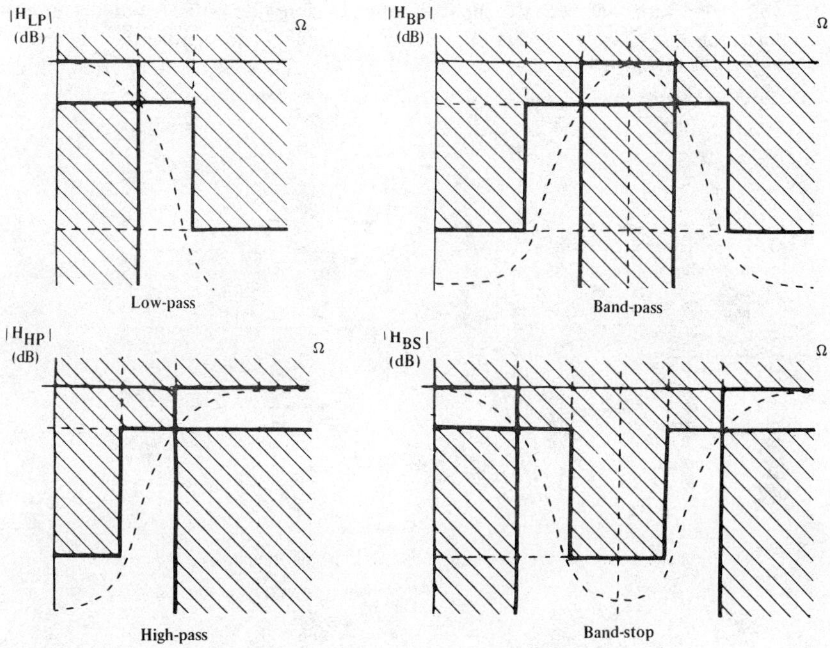

Fig. P6.1

Table P6.2 (Courtesy of General Instrument Corp.[28])

1. Low-Pass _____ High-Pass _____ Band-Pass _____ Band-Stop _____

2a. Magnitude, Phase, and Group Delay
- a. Passband
  1. Frequency range
  2. Nominal passband gain
  3. Maximum ripple
  4. Nominal passband delay
  5. Maximum delay distortion
  6. Maximum phase nonlinearity
- b. Stopband
  1. Frequency range
  2. Minimum stopband gain
  3. Maximum stopband delay
  4. Maximum phase shift

2b. Step Response
  1. Maximum overshoot
  2. Maximum rise time
  3. Maximum ________ % settling time

3. Input Impedance
   Output Impedance
   (If other than resistive, specify.)

4. Temperature Range
   Operating Range
   Storage Range

5. Noise Characteristics (Specify where applicable)
   Noise Figure
   Spot Noise Figure ________ dB at f =
   Maximum Input Voltage
   Maximum Output Voltage
   Required Dynamic Range
   Required Output S/N
   RMS Output Noise
   RMS Equivalent Input Noise

6. Distortion Characteristics
   Allowable RMS Distortion
   Allowable Intermodulation Distortion

7. Power Requirements
   Voltage
   Current
   Power

6.2 The importance of compiling complete filter specifications cannot be over-emphasized. A typical specification sheet describing the electrical characteristics of a filter is shown in Table P6.2. Briefly list the reasons for providing each data entry.

6.3 When delay lines and discriminators are required, the filter specifications of Prob. 6.2 are somewhat modified. The important parameters are listed as follows. Modify the specification sheet of Prob. 6.2 so that it can be used for delay lines and discriminators. (a) Delay lines: (1) delay and delay tolerance, (2) maximum frequency of operation, (3) maximum attenuation, (4) delay taps, and (5) impedance. (b) Discriminators: (1) zero cross-over (center) frequency, (2) linear frequency range, (3) output voltage (sensitivity), and (4) operating circuit data, such as input and output impedance, and operating level and waveform.

6.4 The magnitude responses of a variety of medium- and sharp-cutoff high-pass filters are shown in Fig. P6.4. Can the high-pass filter be obtained from the low-pass filters of Prob. 4.1 using the LP-HP transformation? Determine what type of low-pass filters can be used and their order.

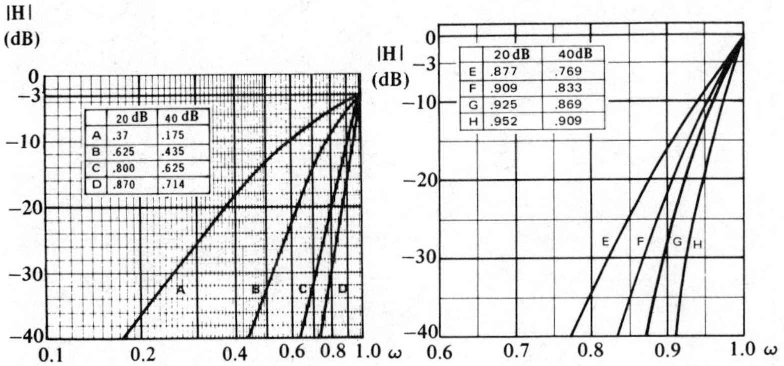

Fig. P6.4 (Courtesy of Allen Avionics[29])

Series	Min. Attn. dB	Cut-off Ratio f/f_c
H60B	30	.45
H62B	40	.35
H64B	50	.25
H66B	60	.19
H67B	30	.72
H69B	40	.65
H71B	50	.56
H73B	60	.50
H74B	30	.79
H76B	40	.73
H78B	50	.67
H80B	60	.58
H81B	30	.83
H83B	40	.79
H85B	50	.73
H87B	60	.67

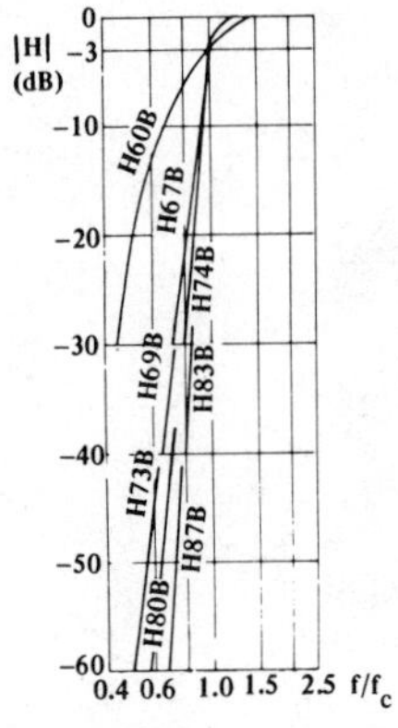

Series	Min. Attn. dB	Cut-off Ratio f/f_c
J50B	30	2.2
J52B	40	2.9
J54B	50	3.9
J56B	60	5.3
J57B	30	1.4
J59B	40	1.6
J61B	50	1.8
J63B	60	2.0
J64B	30	1.2
J66B	40	1.4
J68B	50	1.5
J70B	60	1.7
J71B	30	1.18
J73B	40	1.3
J75B	50	1.4
J77B	60	1.5
*J80B	40	2.0

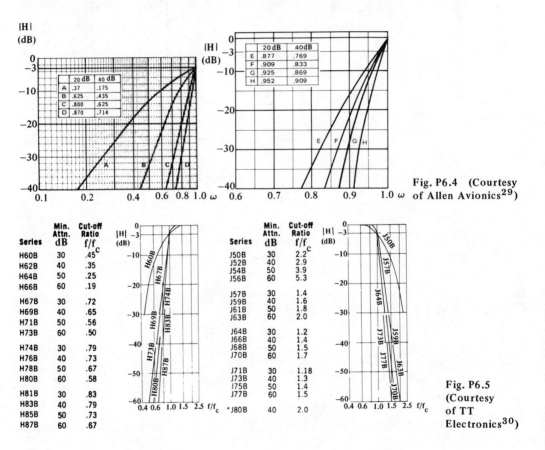

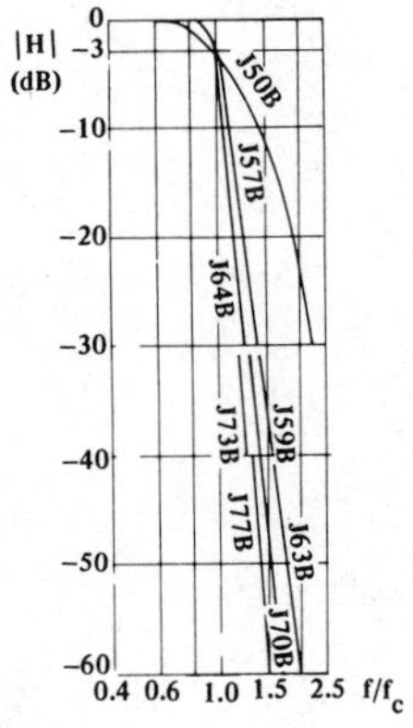

Fig. P6.5 (Courtesy of TT Electronics[30])

6.5 The magnitude responses of a variety of high-pass and low-pass filters are shown in Fig. P6.5. Repeat Prob. 6.4. Assume that the phase is reasonably linear.

6.6 The magnitude responses of a low-pass and a high-pass filter are shown in Fig. P6.6. Several pertinent specifications are also listed. Determine the parameters of the filters. Can the high-pass filter be obtained from the low-pass filter using the LP-HP transformation?

6.7 A low-pass/high-pass band-splitting filter used in speech analysis has the magnitude responses shown in Fig. P6.7. Determine the transfer functions which describe their responses. Design the filters in block diagram form.

6.8 Octave-bandwidth and one-third octave-bandwidth filters were discussed in Prob. 2.21. Their maximum and minimum magnitude response bounds are shown in Fig. P6.8.[32] Determine the order of the Bessel, Butterworth, Chebyshev, and elliptic band-pass filters required to meet these bounds. Use M_p = 5 dB for convenience. (Hint: Cascade a low-pass and a high-pass filter.)

6.9 As discussed in Example 2.6.4, the telephone system uses standard input filters in their noise

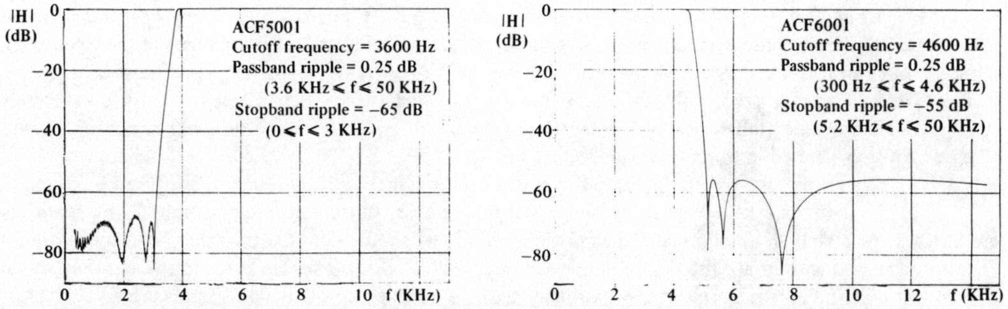

Fig. P6.6 (Courtesy of General Instrument Corp.[31])

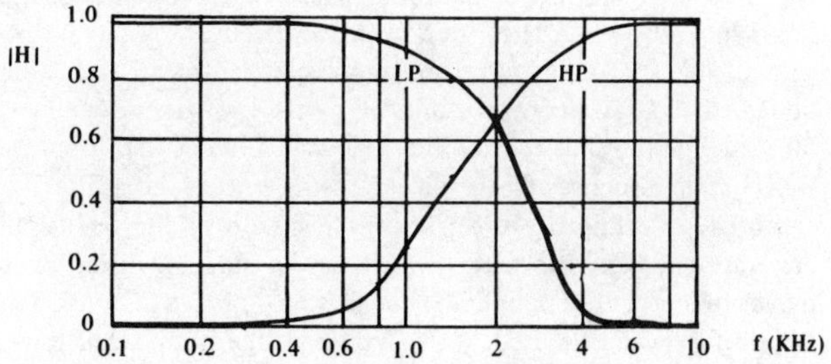

Fig. P6.7

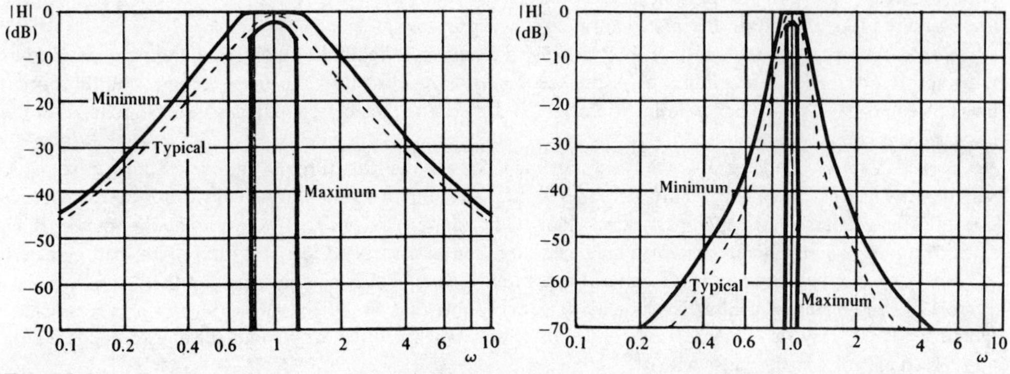

Fig. P6.8

measurement equipment. These input filters have standard magnitude responses as shown in Fig. 2.6.7. The filters can be realized by cascading a high-pass filter (for f ⩽ 1 KHz) and a low-pass filter (for f ⩾ 1 KHz). Determine the orders of Bessel, Butterworth, Chebyshev, and elliptic high-pass and low-pass filters to obtain the: (a) C filter, (b) F1A filter, (c) 144 filter, (d) psophometric filter. (Hint: Begin by specifying the response required.)

6.10 In Prob. 4.16, we found that the C-weighting filter could be realized using a third-order Butterworth high-pass filter cascaded with a fourth-order Chebyshev low-pass filter. The parameters are shown in Fig. P6.10. Design both filters in block diagram form.

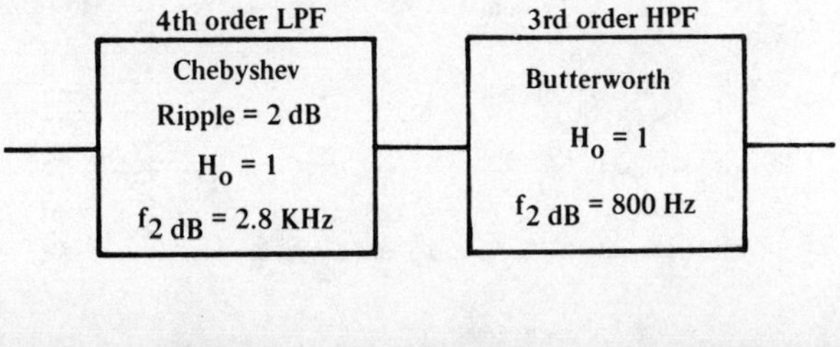

Fig. P6.10

6.11 A band-splitting filter was analyzed in Example 6.3.7. Eighth-order Chebyshev filters can be used to realize the response even when M_p is reduced to 2 dB. (a) Plot the step responses of the Chebyshev low-pass filter and its associated high-pass filter (using the LP-HP transformation). Time must be properly denormalized to be consistent with the 2 dB frequencies listed in Fig. 6.3.11. (b) Compare overshoot (undershoot), rise time (fall time), and delay time (storage time). (c) Based on these responses, should Chebyshev filters be used in this application?

6.12 Technically, we are interested in the pulsed-cosine response of the Touch-Tone filters in Example 6.3.7 since the inputs are keyed tones. Assume that fourth-order Butterworth low-pass and high-pass filters are utilized. (a) What are the normalized bandwidths which we should consider in Touch-Tone applications? (The frequencies involved are listed in Example 2.6.3.) What is the worst-case B/ω_o ratio we should therefore consider? (b) Plot the normalized output energies of the low-pass and high-pass filters using Fig. 4.18.3. (c) To insure that 50% of the input energy is transmitted, what is the minimum and maximum duration of the tone? Interpret your result.

6.13 We are interested in the pulsed-cosine response of the low-pass/high-pass band-splitting filter analyzed in Prob. 6.7. The filters were centered at 2 KHz and we will assume they are fourth-order Butterworth. (a) Plot their output energy responses for a 2 KHz cosine pulse. (b) What is the pulse duration for no less than 40% energy transmission by the low-pass filter? (c) What is the pulse duration for no more than 40% energy transmission by the high-pass filter? (d) Why is it important to distinguish between the ac steady-state response and the pulsed-cosine response of a filter?

6.14 To improve the transient response of the band-splitting filters in Example 6.3.7, let us utilize low-transient high-pass filters which can be obtained from low-pass filters using the complementary LP-HP transformation. For simplicity, let us specify $M_p = 1.25$ dB, $M_s = 20$ dB, and $\Omega_s = 1.285$ so that third-order elliptic filters can be used. (a) Determine the normalized low-pass filter transfer function. (b) Determine the normalized high-pass filter transfer function using the low-transient LP-HP transformation. Identify its poles and zeros and draw the pattern in the s-plane. (c) Using $M_p = 1.25$ dB, plot the step responses of the low-pass and high-pass filters. Be sure to normalize time properly.

6.15 A Papoulis band-splitting low-pass/high-pass filter is required whose step response parameters must be preserved. (a) Determine the normalized transfer functions for the first-, second-, and third-order low-pass filters having 3 dB bandwidths of unity. (b) Determine the corresponding transfer functions for the low-transient high-pass filters.

6.16 A third-order Butterworth band-splitting low-pass/high-pass filter is required whose step response parameters must be preserved. (a) Determine the transfer function of a unity-bandwidth Butterworth low-pass filter and its associated high-pass filter. Plot their pole-zero patterns. (b) Determine the transfer functions of a unity-bandwidth Butterworth high-pass filter and its associated low-pass filter. Plot their pole-zero patterns. (c) Plot and compare the step responses of both pairs of filters in parts (a) and (b).

6.17 Suppose that a filter has a gain H(s). (a) Show that the effect of introducing an excess phase term $e^{-\tau_o s}$ is to delay its response τ_o seconds. (b) Show that the effect of introducing an excess phase term $e^{-\tau_o/s}$ is to convolve its response with

$$c(t) = U_0(t) - \sqrt{\tau_0/2t}\, J_1(\sqrt{2t\tau_0})\, U_{-1}(t)$$

(c) Show that this causes a second oscillatory component in the response which is the convolution of the original response with $J_o'(\sqrt{2t\tau_o})$. Show that this component becomes negligible as $\tau_o \to 0$. (d) Use this result to show the effect of the excess phase term in the high-pass filter of Example 2.9.4.

6.18 The magnitude response of a band-pass filter having various shaping factors is shown in Fig. P6.18. Can the band-pass filter be obtained from a low-pass filter using the LP-BP transformation? Determine what type of low-pass filters can be used and their order.

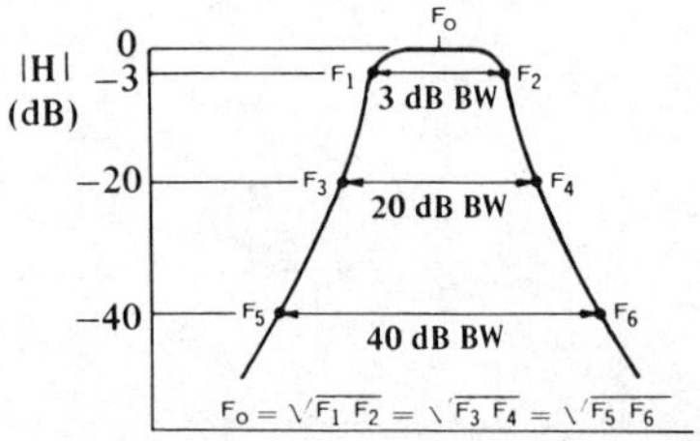

Shape Factor	20db BW / 3db BW	40db BW / 3db BW
Ao	3.65	7.85
A	2.70	5.70
A1	2.00	4.00
B	1.60	2.50
B1	1.50	2.10
C	1.45	1.85
D	1.30	1.55
E	1.20	1.45

Fig. P6.18 (Courtesy of Allen Avionics[29])

6.19 The magnitude responses of a variety of band-pass filters are shown in Fig. P6.19. Repeat Prob. 6.18.

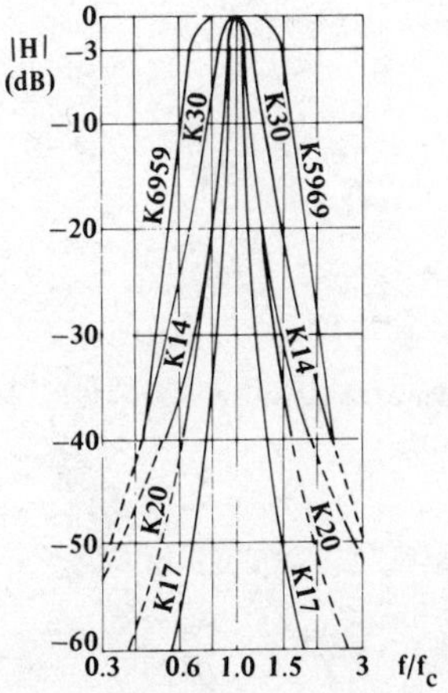

Series	F_c Center Freq. Range Min.	Max.	Bandwidth @ −3db	Attenuation
K10	500Hz	9.9KHz	±1% F_c	30db at .92F_c & 1.1F_c
K11B	500Hz	9.9KHz	±1% F_c	30db at .94F_c & 1.06F_c
K12A	500Hz	9.9KHz	±2% F_c	30db at .92F_c & 1.1F_c
K13	30Hz	99Hz	±5% F_c	60db at .5F_c & 2F_c
K14A	100Hz	100KHz	±5% F_c	40db at .5F_c & 2F_c
K14B	300Hz	999Hz	±5% F_c	35db at .5F_c & 2F_c
K14C	1KHz	99KHz	±5% F_c	43db at .5F_c & 2F_c
K17	100Hz	10KHz	±5% F_c	60db at .5F_c & 2F_c
K17A	300Hz	999Hz	±5% F_c	50db at .5F_c & 2F_c
K20	100Hz	3.9KHz	±7.5% F_c	40db at .57F_c & 1.75F_c
K20A	250Hz	99KHz	±7.5% F_c	35 to 50db at .5F_c & 2F_c
K20B	100KHz	100MHz	±7.5% F_c	40db at .67F_c & 1.5F_c
K30	100Hz	3.9KHz	±15% F_c	40db at .4F_c & 2.5F_c
K30A	150Hz	99KHz	±15% F_c	25db at .45F_c & 2.2F_c
K30B	100KHz	100MHz	±15% F_c	40db at .5F_c & 2F_c

Fig. P6.19 (Courtesy of TT Electronics[30])

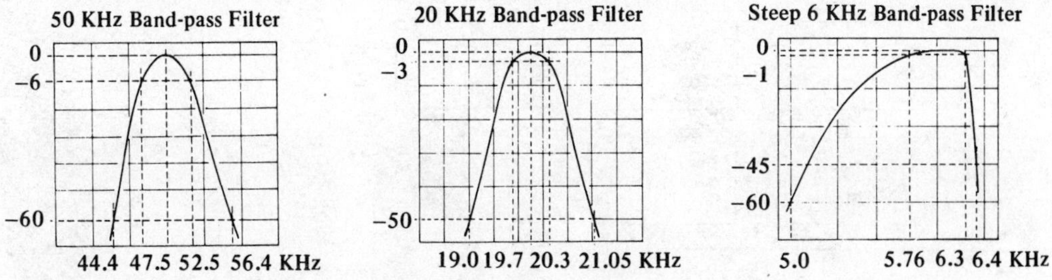

Fig. P6.20 (Courtesy of BG Electronics[33])

6.20 The magnitude responses of a variety of band-pass filters are shown in Fig. P6.20. Determine the types and orders of the: (a) 50 KHz filter, (b) 20 KHz constant delay filter (passband delay variation $< \pm 5\%$), and (c) steep 6 KHz filter.

6.21 The acoustical data coupler shown in Fig. P6.21 is a 300 Baud FSK modem which operates half-duplex. It receives signals at 1070 and 1270 Hz and transmits signals at 2025 and 2225 Hz. To filter extraneous signals, two band-pass filters are used which have the magnitude responses shown. Determine the parameters of the filters.

6.22 Other Transmit/Receive band-pass filters which might be used in the acoustical data coupler of Prob. 6.21 have the magnitude responses shown in Fig. P6.22. Determine the parameters of the filters.

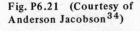

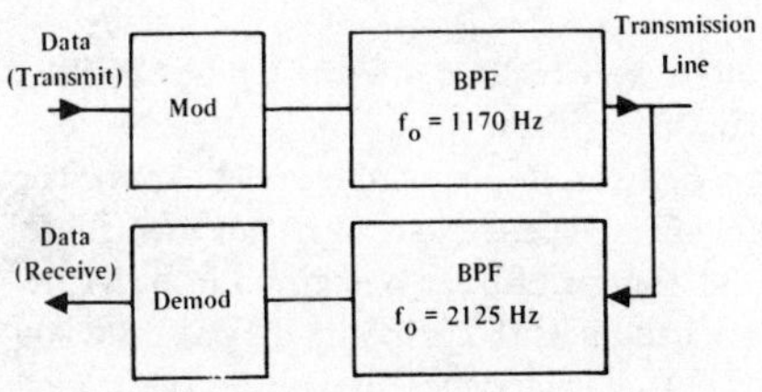

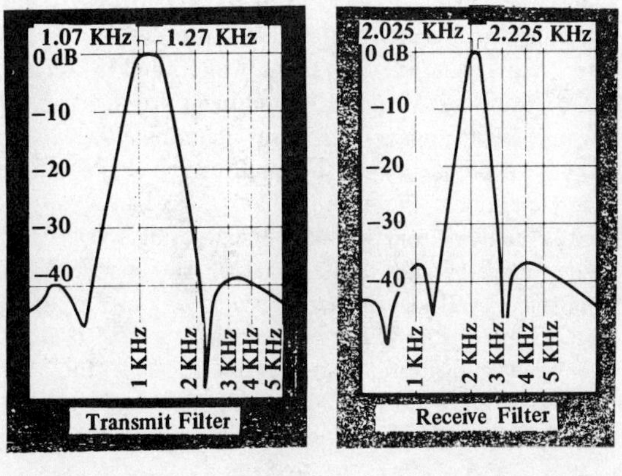

Fig. P6.21 (Courtesy of Anderson Jacobson[34])

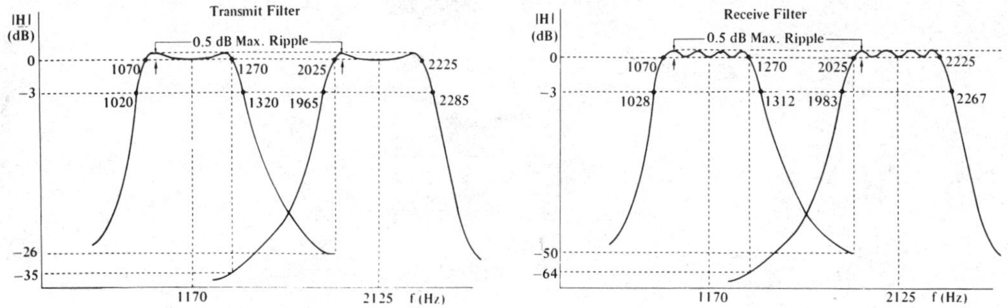

Fig. P6.22 (Courtesy of Cermetek Microelectronics[35])

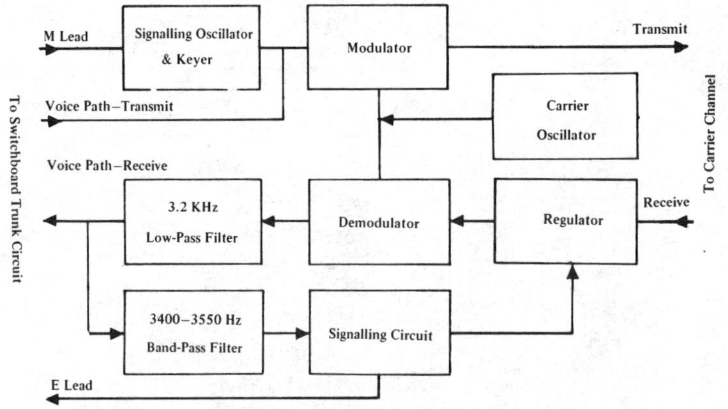

Fig. P6.23

6.23 The Lenkurt Type 45 signalling system is shown in Fig. P6.23. The 3400/3550 Hz band-pass filter is used to recover the signalling tones.[36] Assume that the 3 dB frequencies of the filter are 3325 and 3625 Hz. Suppose the filter must provide 40 dB rejection at 3000 and 3950 Hz. (a) Determine the order of the Butterworth, Chebyshev, and elliptic band-pass filters which meet this specification. (b) To minimize order and maximize rejection, a third-order elliptic band-pass filter shall be used. How much rejection can now be obtained at 3000 and 3950 Hz? (c) What is the filter Q?

6.24 Touch-Tone systems use band-pass filters to decode two frequencies as discussed in Example 2.7.2. Assume that the adjacent filter responses intersect at their 20 dB frequencies and that their Q (based on their 3 dB frequencies) equals 25. Determine the order of the Bessel, Butterworth, Chebyshev, and elliptic band-pass filters required to meet this specification.

6.25 Telegraph systems use FDM to obtain a number of telegraph channels from a single voice channel as discussed in Prob. 2.25. 120 Hz and 170 Hz tone spacing is used. Using the magnitude response data listed in that problem, determine the order of the Bessel, Butterworth, Chebyshev, and elliptic band-pass filters required for the (a) Transmit filters and (b) Receive filters.

6.26 Octave-bandwidth and one-third octave-bandwidth filters were realized in Prob. 6.8 by cascading low-pass and high-pass filters. Now determine their order using band-pass filters.

6.27 Frequency-division multiplexed (FDM) communication systems use standard channel banks. The basic function of the channel bank is to band-limit each of 12 voice channels to 4 KHz and then subsequently combine and translate them (using single-sideband modulation or SSB) as one group into the frequency range between 60–108 KHz. The channel bank filters are band-pass filters having the passband and stopband magnitude characteristics shown in Fig. P6.27. The USA characteristics are used in the United States, while the CCITT characteristics are used overseas. Determine the required order of the Butterworth, Chebyshev, and elliptic band-pass filters to meet these specifications.

6.28 Show that the M_1-M_2 dB shaping factor $S = BW_2/BW_1$ of the low-pass filter is invariant under the LP-BP transformation and is independent of Q. Explain how this fact is useful when determining band-

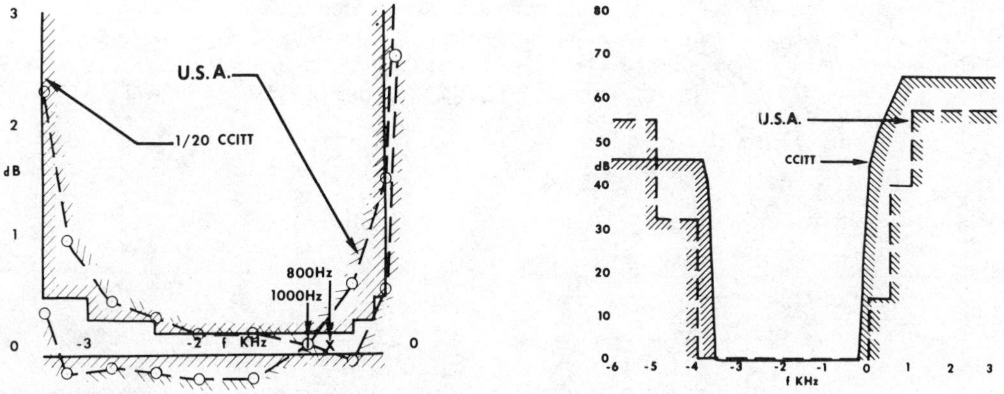

Fig. P6.27 (Courtesy of IEEE[37])

pass filter order.

6.29 The center frequencies and Q_{BP} of a pair of band-pass filter roots are given by Eqs. 6.4.29 and 6.4.30. Show how (ω_{oi}, Q_{BP}) vary for $\delta \to 0$ and $\delta \to \infty$. Relate the results to the curves in Fig. 6.4.6.

6.30 Design the following band-pass filters in block diagram form. (a) Second-order Butterworth filter with a center frequency of 1 KHz, a bandwidth of 100 Hz, and a midband gain of 10 (see Example 10.4.3). (b) Second-order Butterworth filter with a 3 dB frequency range of 300 Hz to 3.4 KHz and unity midband gain (see drop-out filter of Prob. 10.17). (c) Second-order Butterworth filter with a center frequency of 3470 Hz, Q = 11.6, and unity midband gain (see signalling filter of Prob. 6.23). (d) Second-order Chebyshev Transmit filters for acoustical data coupler of Prob. 6.22. (e) Fourth-order Chebyshev Receive filters for acoustical data coupler of Prob. 6.22. (f) Third-order elliptic Transmit filter for acoustical data coupler of Prob. 6.21 (use minimum M_p possible). (g) The third-order elliptic Receive filter for acoustical data coupler of Prob. 6.21 (use 40 dB rejection).

6.31 (a) Show that the transformed cosine step response of a narrowband band-pass filter can be expressed as

$$R_{BP}(s) = \frac{s}{s^2 + \omega_o^2} H_{BP}(s) \cong \frac{s(H_1 + H_2)}{s^2 + \omega_o^2}$$

(b) Show that this can be further reduced to

$$R_{BP}(s) \cong \frac{H_1/2}{s + j\omega_o} + \frac{H_2/2}{s - j\omega_o}$$

(c) Then proceed to verify Eq. 6.4.71.

6.32 Plot the magnitude and delay responses of a fifth-order elliptic band-pass filter having f_o = 1 KHz, B = 40 Hz, a passband ripple of 0.177 dB and a stopband rejection of 60 dB. (b) Plot the response of the filter to a 100 msec cosine pulse.

6.33 Plot the magnitude and delay responses of fifth-order Chebyshev and elliptic band-pass filters having f_o = 3.16 KHz, B = 1.5 KHz, and maximum passband ripple of 0.177 dB. The elliptic filter has a minimum stopband rejection of 60 dB. (b) Plot the cosine step responses of the filters.

6.34 A bank of Touch-Tone decoding filters are needed in Example 2.7.2. To obtain adequate discrimination between channels, Q = 25. Assume that fourth-order Butterworth band-pass filters are used. (a) Plot their cosine step responses. (b) Assuming a pulsed-cosine input, what is the minimum pulse duration to pass 50% of the input energy through the filters?

6.35 A bank of telegraph Receive filters have the center frequencies listed in Prob. 2.25. Assume 3 dB bandwidths of either 64 or 90 Hz. Repeat Prob. 6.34.

6.36 (a) Plot the cosine step responses of the acoustical data coupler filters in Prob. 6.21. (b) Assuming that the filters have output energy curves similar to those shown in Fig. 6.4.16 in pulsed-cosine operation, what should be the duration of the tone to pass 80% of the input energy? Is this compatable with 300 Baud operation?

6.37 Repeat Prob. 6.36 for the acoustical data coupler filters in Prob. 6.22.

6.38 The magnitude response of an arithmetically-symmetrical band-pass filter is shown in Fig. P6.38. Determine what type of low-pass filters can be used and their order. The filters listed in: (a) have Q = 1.4–3.3, delay distortion $\leqslant \pm$ 2.5%, phase distortion $\leqslant \pm 3^\circ$, and an approximate passband delay of $D/2\pi f_o$ second; (b) have Q = 6–50 and the delay and phase distortion listed.

(a)

Percent (%) Bandwidth	20db BW / 3db BW	40db BW / 3db BW	D
30	2.60	4.85	14.62
40	2.58	4.80	10.89
50	2.56	4.70	8.65
60	2.53	4.60	7.14
70	2.51	4.50	6.04

(b)

Shape Factor	20db BW / 3db BW	40db BW / 3db BW	Delay Distortion	Max. Phase Distortion
A	2.60	4.85	5%	$\pm 3^\circ$
B	2.56	4.25	10%	$\pm 6^\circ$
C	2.52	3.75	15%	$\pm 9^\circ$

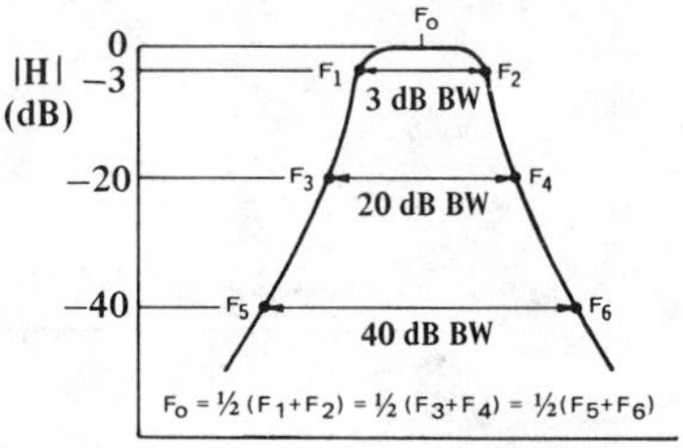

Fig. P6.38 (Courtesy of Allen Avionics[29])

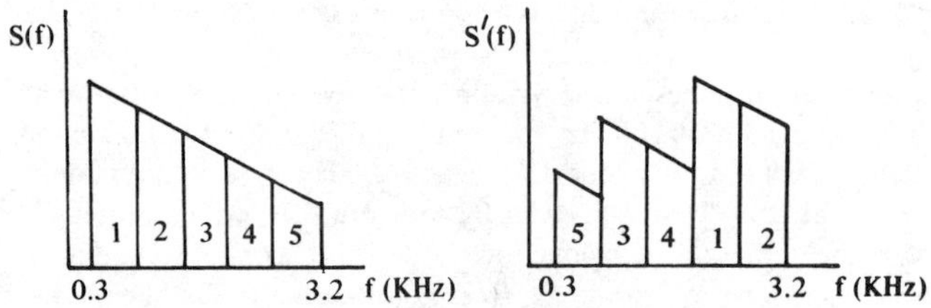

Fig. P6.39

6.39 Some voice communication systems require privacy and protection against eavesdropping. Police, firemen, bank administrators, and bonded trucking firms are typical potential users. "Scramblers" are used to obtain communications security.[38] One of the simplest scramblers are band-splitters which make use of a bank of band-pass filters. The voice band is split into four or five separate frequency bands each having a bandwidth of about 500 Hz. The frequency bands are then transposed for transmission as shown in Fig. P6.39. (a) Assume that five filters, each having a 500 Hz bandwidth, are used to process speech from 300 to 3200 Hz. Determine their center frequency, bandwidth, and Q. (b) Should geometrically- or arithmetically-symmetrical filters be used? Discuss. (c) Determine the order of the Butterworth, Chebyshev, and elliptic band-pass filters. Assume that they have arithmetic symmetry and that they provide 20 dB of rejection at frequencies which are 50 Hz removed from their 3 dB frequencies.

6.40 All-pole low-pass filters have gains $H_{LP}(j\omega) = \omega^{-n}$ for $\omega \gg 1$. If the arithmetically-symmetrical LP-BP transformation is used, prove the following results assuming that $|H_{LP}(j0)| = 1$. (a) The inherent gain unbalance at the upper and lower band-edges equals $|H_{BP}(j\omega_U)|/|H_{BP}(j\omega_L)| \cong [(2Q+1)/(2Q-1)]^n \times [(4Q-1)/(4Q+1)]^n \cong (1+n/Q)(1-n/2Q)$. Thus, the response exhibits passband symmetry only when $Q \gg n$. (b) To reduce the gain unbalance in the passband, let the number of zeros at the origin be m. Then $m \cong (n/2)(1 - n/2Q) \cong n/2$. (c) The rejection at $2\omega_o$ equals $|H_{BP}(j2\omega_o)|/|H_{BP}(j\omega_o)| = (2/3Q)^n$ which increases with increasing n and Q.

6.41 Derive the general transfer function of the first-order band-pass filter having arithmetic symmetry. Assume that the analogous low-pass filter has the transfer function $H_{LP}(p) = (1+p)^{-1}$.

6.42 A second-order Chebyshev band-pass filter having an arithmetically-symmetrical magnitude response is required. Determine its transfer function for a center frequency of 1 and a 3 dB bandwidth of 0.1. Use a ripple of 3 dB. Plot its magnitude and delay responses.

6.43 Dominant pole-zero approximations simplify frequency and time domain analyses. (a) Show that band-pass filters have first- and second-order dominant pole approximations given by Eqs. 6.4.41 and 6.4.42, respectively, where the numerators are multiplied by the excess phase factor $\exp\,[-Q\tau_o(s_n + 1/s_n)]$. (b) Viewing the band-pass filter as the cascade of a low-pass and a high-pass filter, show that the excess phase factor in part (a) is the sum of the excess phase factors for the two filters. (c) Describe how to calculate the argument of the exponent from band-pass filter data. (d) Show that one effect of the excess phase factor is to delay the envelope of the cosine step response regardless of the Q of the band-pass filter.

6.44 Using a first-order dominant pole-zero approximation, plot the envelope responses for the following band-pass filters. (a) Filters having 1, 5, and 15% bandwidths in Prob. 6.19. (b) 50 KHz filter in Prob. 6.20a. (c) 20 KHz filter in Prob. 6.20b.

6.45 Using a second-order dominant pole-zero approximation, plot the envelope responses for the (a) Transmit and (b) Receive filters in Prob. 6.22.

6.46 The magnitude response of a low-pass discriminator is shown in Fig. P6.46. The required low-pass filter response is also shown. (a) Show how $|H_{LP}|$ is established from $|H_{DLP}|$. (b) Suppose that M_p = 0.5 dB, M_s = 40 dB, and Ω_s = 1.1. Determine the order of the Butterworth, Chebyshev, and elliptic filters which meet this specification. (c) Suppose that only third-order filters are used in part (b) where Ω_s is unspecified. What Ω_s's can be achieved? Are they small enough to allow a narrow transition band?

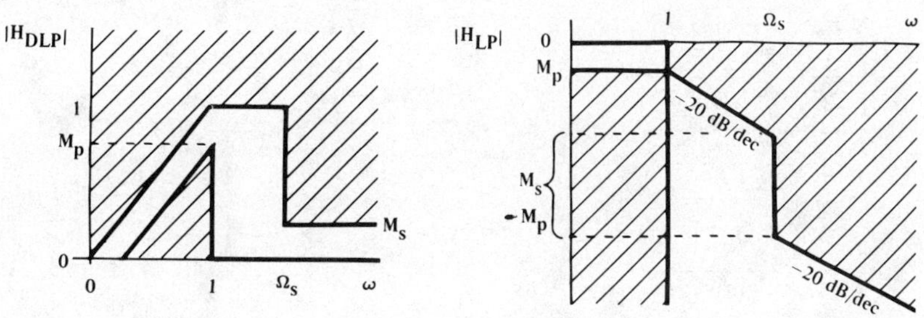

Fig. P6.46

6.47 Band-pass discriminator transformations were discussed in Sec. 6.4.6. (a) Plot the magnitude response which results using the low-Q transformation given by Eq. 6.4.104. (b) Repeat part (a) using the high-Q transformation given by Eq. 6.4.105. (c) Although the response in part (b) is not suitable for FM discrimination, identify possible applications. (d) How can the response of part (c) be modified to yield FM discrimination?

6.48 A data recorder receives an FSK signal over a telephone line from a remote FSK modem operating at 2125 Hz. The data modem transmits a frequency of 2025 Hz for a "0" of data and 2225 Hz for a "1" (see Prob. 6.21). Determine the transfer functions and plot the magnitude responses of the following FSK discriminators used to detect the signals (see Fig. P6.48): (a) Fourth-order Butterworth and Chebyshev low-pass discriminators. (b) First-order Butterworth and Chebyshev band-pass discriminators having geometric symmetry. (c) Repeat part (b) for arithmetic symmetry.

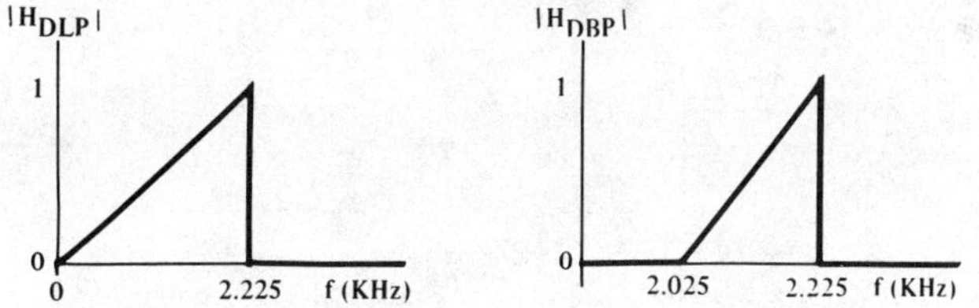

Fig. P6.48

6.49 Design, in block diagram form, a fourth-order Butterworth low-pass discriminator having a 3 dB bandwidth of 500 Hz and a slope of 0.00522 volt/volt/Hz. Plot its magnitude response.

6.50 Design, in block diagram form, a second-order Butterworth band-pass discriminator having a center frequency of 100 Hz, a 20% bandwidth, and a gain slope of 7.615 volt/volt/Hz. Use the high-Q band-pass transformation given by Eq. 6.4.105.

6.51 The magnitude responses of two band-stop filters are shown in Fig. P6.51. Can the band-stop filters be obtained from low-pass filters using the LP-BS transformation? Determine what type of low-pass filters can be used and their order.

6.52 The magnitude responses of two band-stop filters are shown in Fig. P6.52. Determine the types and orders of the: (a) 200 Hz filter (40 dB bandwidth = 6 Hz) and (b) 21.6 KHz filter.

6.53 The telephone company uses tone frequencies within the voice band (200–3200 Hz) to transmit signalling, supervisory, and dialing information between carrier terminals. Single-frequency (SF) signalling

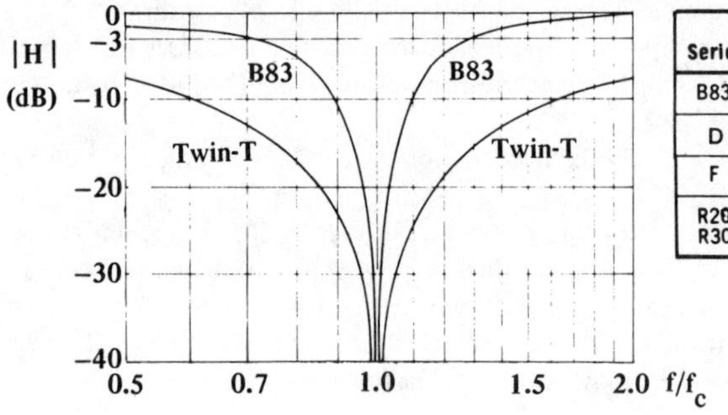

Series	F_C, Center Freq. Range Min.	Max.	Bandwidth −3db	Attenuation
B83	10Hz	1MHz	.77Fc & 1.3Fc	50 db Notch
D	10Hz	100KHz	.25Fc & 4 Fc	40 db Notch
F	10Hz	100KHz	.25Fc & 4 Fc	60 db Notch
R20 R30	100Hz 4KHz	3999Hz 100MHz	{3db Bandwidth to 40db Bandwidth Ratio = 5 or less	

Fig. P6.51 (Courtesy of TT Electronics[30])

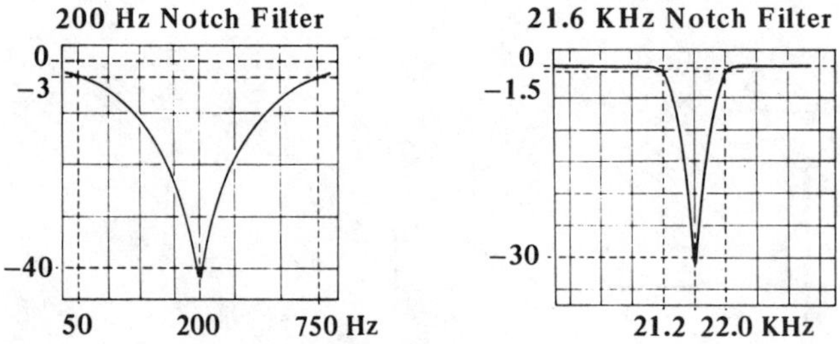

Fig. P6.52 (Courtesy of BG Electronics[33])

systems use a 2600 Hz tone. The SF system is shown in Fig. P6.53.[36] It must be designed to prevent false operation of signalling equipment during speech transmission. A 2600 Hz band-stop filter provides one such safeguard. Assume that is has a 3 dB bandwidth of 60 Hz and that it provides 40 dB of rejection over a 30 Hz bandwidth. Determine the orders of the Butterworth, Chebyshev, and elliptic band-stop filters required to meet this specification. What is the filter Q?

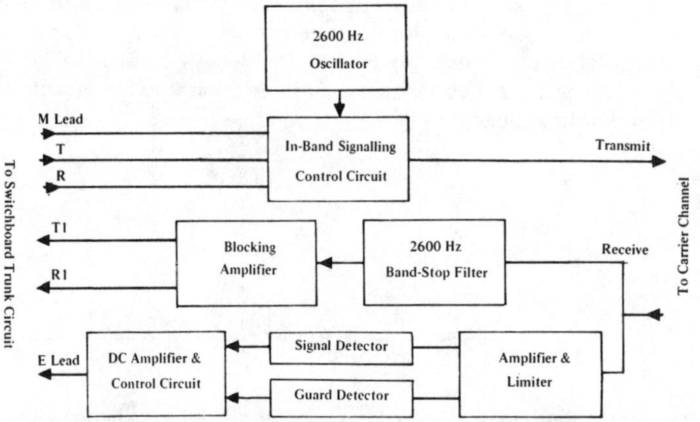

Fig. P6.53

6.54 The 2805 Hz notch filter in Example 6.5.9 has the following gain specifications: −0.5 dB frequencies $\leqslant$ 2100, $\geqslant$ 3500 Hz; −3 dB frequencies = 2650, 2960 Hz; −50 dB frequencies = 2795, 2815 Hz. Determine the filter orders.

6.55 Repeat Prob. 6.28 to show that the M_1-M_2 dB shaping factor $S = BW_1/BW_2$ for band-stop filters is identical to that for their analogous low-pass filters and is independent of Q.

6.56 Design the following band-stop filters having unity passband gain in block diagram form: (a) Second-order Butterworth filter with a center frequency of 1 KHz and a 3 dB bandwidth of 100 Hz (see Example 6.5.3). (b) Second-order Butterworth filter with a center frequency of 2600 Hz and a 3 dB bandwidth of 60 Hz (see Prob. 6.53). (c) Second-order Butterworth filter with a center frequency of 1010 Hz, a 0.5 dB bandwidth of 1220 Hz, and arithmetic symmetry (see Example 6.5.9). (d) Fourth-order Chebyshev filter with a center frequency of 1000 Hz and a 1.25 dB bandwidth of 3750 Hz (see Example 6.5.5). (e) Repeat part (d) for a third-order elliptic filter. Use 40 dB of rejection.

6.57 Plot the cosine step response of the first-order 60 Hz notch filter in Example 2.8.1.

6.58 Plot the cosine step response for the band-stop filters listed in: (a) Prob. 6.56a, (b) Prob. 6.56b, and (c) Prob. 6.56c. Assuming that the filters have output energy curves similar to those shown in Fig. 6.4.16 in pulsed-cosine operation, what should be the duration of the tone to reject 50% of the input energy?

6.59 Dominant pole-zero approximations for band-pass filters were discussed in Prob. 6.43. Analogous results hold for band-stop filters. (a) Show that band-stop filters have first- and second-order dominant pole approximations given by Eqs. 6.4.41 and 6.4.42 where the numerators have the general form $H_o \times (s_n^2 + 1)^m \exp[-\tau_o/Q\ (s_n + 1/s_n)]$. (b) Describe how to calculate the argument of the exponent from band-stop filter data. (c) Repeat part (d) of Prob. 6.43 but use the result of Prob. 6.17.

6.60 Using the first-order dominant pole-zero approximation, plot the envelope responses of the following band-stop filters: (a) B83 filter in Prob. 6.51. (b) 21.6 KHz filter in Prob. 6.52b. (c) 2805 Hz filter in Prob. 6.54.

6.61 A delay equalizer for a second-order Butterworth low-pass filter was considered in Prob. 2.45. Repeat that problem.

6.62 Delay equalizers for fourth-order Butterworth and Chebyshev low-pass filters were considered in Prob. 2.48. Repeat that problem.

6.63 A delay equalizer for a second-order band-pass filter was considered in Prob. 2.46. Repeat that problem.

6.64 Sketch the delay characteristics for a Bessel all-pass filter. (Hint: See Prob. 4.37.)

6.65 (a) Determine the dominant pole-zero approximation for a first-order all-pass filter having ω_n = 1. Obtain a low-frequency and a high-frequency approximation. Compare their magnitude and phase responses. (b) Plot the step responses based on the results of part (a).

6.66 Discuss the pros and cons of using Elmore's results for estimating the delay and rise times of Prob. 6.65. Can the Valley-Wallman result be used?

6.67 As discussed in Probs. 2.31 and 2.32, filters must often be tuned to obtain their required parameters. Repeat those problems.

6.68 As discussed in Prob. 2.33, filters having zeros of transmission are more difficult to tune than those having no finite zeros. Repeat that problem.

REFERENCES

1. Al-Nassar, F., "Tables speed design of low-pass active filters," EDN Magazine, pp. 23–32, March 15, 1971.
2. Doetsch, G., *Guide to the Applications of Laplace Transforms,* p. 229, D. Van Nostrand, NY, 1961.
3. Jahnke, E., and F. Emde, *Tables of Functions*, 4th ed., p. 165, Dover, NY, 1945.
4. van Vollenhoven, E., H. A. Reuver, and J. C. Somer, "Transient response of Butterworth filters," IEEE Trans. Circuit Theory, vol. CT-12, pp. 624–626, Dec., 1965.
5. Meyer, E. R., "A note on the step response of high-pass filters," IEEE Trans. Circuit Theory, vol. CT-15, pp. 481–482, Dec., 1968.
6. Blinchikoff, H. J., "High-pass filter step-response energy: a new performance measure," IEEE Trans. Circuit Theory, vol. CT-20, pp. 593–596, Sept., 1973.
7. Blinchikoff, H. J., "Low-transient high-pass filters," IEEE Trans. Circuit Theory, vol. CT-17, pp. 663–667, Nov., 1970.
8. Churchill, R. V., *Complex Variables and Applications*, 2nd ed., App. 2, McGraw-Hill, NY, 1960.
9. Jones, H. E., "On the roots of an undamped quadratic after a low-pass to bandpass transformation," Proc. IEEE, vol. 57, p. 1451, Aug., 1969.
10. Blinchikoff, H. J., "Derivative of group delay at band center," IEEE Trans. Circuit Theory, vol. CT-17, pp. 636–637, Nov., 1970.
11. Papoulis, A., *The Fourier Integral and Its Application*, Chap. 7, McGraw-Hill, NY, 1962.
12. Bradford, W. R., "Response of a Gaussian band-pass filter to a Gaussian video pulse," Proc. IEEE, vol. 54, pp. 89–90, Jan., 1966.
13. Schafer, R. H., and J. J. H. Wang, "Energy transfer characteristics of Butterworth resonant circuits under pulsed-carrier operation," IEEE Trans. Circuit Theory, vol. CT-19, pp. 221–223, March, 1972.

14. Shelton, R. D., "Optimum filters for narrow-band frequency modulation," Proc. IEEE, vol. 60, pp. 127–128, Jan., 1972.
15. Trofimenkoff, F. N., "Noise margins of bandpass filters," IEEE Trans. Circuit Theory, vol. CT-20, pp. 171–172, March, 1973.
16. Szentirmai, G., "The design of arithmetically symmetrical band-pass filters," IEEE. Trans. Circuit Theory, vol. CT-10, pp. 367–375, Sept., 1963.
17. Ulbrich, E., and H. Piloty, "Uber den Entwurf von Allpassen, Tiefpassen und Bandpassen mit einer im Tschebysheffschen Sinne approximierten konstanten Gruppenlaufzeit," Arch. Elek. Ubertragung, vol. 14, pp. 451–467, Oct., 1960.
    Geffe, P. R., "On the approximation problem for band-pass delay lines," Proc. IEEE, vol. 50, pp. 1986–1987, Sept., 1962.
18. Blinchikoff, H. J., "A note on wide-band group delay," IEEE Trans. Circuit Theory, vol. CT-18, pp. 577–578, Sept. 1971.
19. Geffe, P. R., Ref. 17.
20. Docherty, I. S., and J. L. Casse, "The design of maximally flat wideband amplifiers with double-tuned interstage coupling," Proc. IEEE, vol. 55, pp. 513–522, April, 1967.
21. Halpern, P. H., "Solution of flat time delay at finite frequencies," IEEE Trans. Circuit Theory, vol. CT-18, pp. 241–246, March, 1971.
22. Lindquist, C. S., "A class of optimum raised-cosine and Gaussian bandpass filters," Tech. Rep. WP-2331, Collins Radio Group of Rockwell International, Newport Beach, CA, Sept., 1970.
23. Blinchikoff, H. J., and M. Savetman, "Least-squares approximation to wide-band constant delay," IEEE Trans. Circuit Theory, vol. CT-19, pp. 387–389, July, 1972.
24. Budak, A., and K. E. Waltz, "Linear amplitude Butterworth active filter," Proc. IEEE, vol. 58, pp. 274–275, Feb., 1970.
25. Joseph, R. D., "Maximally linear bandpass frequency discriminator," Proc. IEEE, vol. 59, pp. 1712–1713, Dec., 1971.
26. Budak, A., and K. E. Waltz, "An active Butterworth frequency discriminator," Proc. IEEE, vol. 58, pp. 795–796, May, 1970.
27. Dangl, A., "A study of band-pass discriminators," M.S.E.E. Directed Research, California State Univ., Long Beach, June, 1976.
28. Filter Specification Sheet, 1 p., General Instrument Corp., Hicksville, NY.
29. Precision L-C Filters, Catalog 14F, 16 p., Allen Avionics, Inc., Mineola, NY, 1975.
30. TTE Miniature Filters, 2 p., TT Electronics, Los Angeles, CA.
31. ACF6001, Data Sheet RPC-BPL-146; and ACF5001, Data Sheet RPC-BPL-147, General Instrument Corp., Hicksville, NY.
32. Data Sheet on Model AF3B1-020, 1 p., TDL Electronics, Fayetteville, AR, May, 1973.
    Mauro, R., "Customize your audio filter," Electronic Design, pp. 94–96, May 24, 1974, copyright Hayden Publishing, 1974.
33. Catalog, 4 p., BG Electronics, Inc., Mt. Vernon, NY.
34. Data Coupler ADC300, Data Sheet, 1 p., Anderson Jacobson, Sunnyvale, CA, 12/12/70.
35. Data Sheets CH1252 and CH1257, Cermetek Microelectronics, Mt. View, CA.
36. Tally, D., *Basic Carrier Telephony*, pp. 113–128, Hayden, NY, 1966.
37. Kurth, C. F. "Channel bank filtering in frequency division multiplex communication systems," IEEE Circuits and Systems, vol. 7, pp. 5–13, Dec., 1974.
38. McCalmont, A. M., "Communications security for voice–Techniques, systems and operations," Telecommunications, pp. 35–42, April, 1973.

7 ACTIVE FILTER CLASSIFICATION

Long road sometimes shortest way to end of journey
Oriental Proverb

We now turn our attention to the classifying of active filters. A classification system is essential for the orderly development and analysis of active filters. This becomes particularly evident to the engineer when he must select and design an active filter from hundreds of different forms. In the classification system which we have chosen to use,[1] only the denominator of the gain function is considered for reasons which will become evident. In the following chapters, we will consider in great detail low-pass, high-pass, band-pass, band-stop, and all-pass filters by additionally classifying the numerator of the gain function.

In order to obtain the greatest insight into the relation between active filter topology and their gain characteristics, signal flow graphs will be used. After some practice, the signal flow graphs describing many active filters can be drawn and labelled by inspection.

In active filters, two parameters of primary interest are the amplifier gain values and the filter sensitivities with respect to the active and passive component values. The gain values largely determine the usable frequency range of the filter. The sensitivities determine the maximum selectivity of the filter. We shall calculate the gains and sensitivities for the various filter classes and establish maximum bounds. These bounds are indispensable in the selection of an appropriate active filter, and allow design tradeoffs to be made.

To gain insight into the dependence of the active filter poles upon the filter topology and components, we shall also utilize root locus analysis. The root locus and sensitivity coefficients give the design engineer an added dimension in the understanding of active filters. He may find it useful to review sensitivity and root locus concepts which are fully discussed in Chap. 1.

7.1 SIGNAL FLOW GRAPHS

In Chap. 1, we discussed signal flow graph theory. We found that signal flow graphs were simply a pictorial representation of a set of equations. Signal flow graphs were amenable to manipulation into desired forms, much more so than the manipulation of their associated equations. Also, Mason's gain equation could be used for easily calculating the gain between any two nodes of the graph. This gain could be an open-circuit voltage gain, short-circuit current gain, gain under loaded conditions, transfer immittance, and driving-point immittance. Thus, signal flow graphs are an extremely flexible design tool for the engineer. In general, signal flow graphs are not unique since there are various ways of forming a set of equations which completely describe a system. However, these signal flow graphs can always be reduced to a single canonical form.

The order of a canonical flow graph equals the number of essential nodes (i.e., the nodes

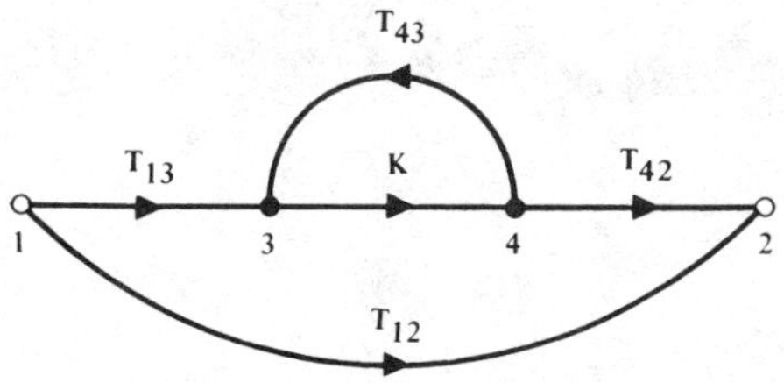

Fig. 7.1.1 First-order canonical flow graph.

which must be removed to eliminate all feedback paths) in the system. In active filter applications, this usually equals the number of controlled or dependent sources contained in the filter being described. A first-order canonical flow graph is shown in Fig. 7.1.1. Here a controlled-source of strength K is embedded in some network. If $K = 0$, there will be signal transmission only through the branch having gain T_{12}. When $K \neq 0$, signal also flows through the upper branch. The filter gain using Mason's gain equation in Sec. 1.14 equals

$$H(s) = T_{12}(s) + \frac{KT_{13}(s)T_{42}(s)}{\Delta(s)} \tag{7.1.1}$$

where the system determinant $\Delta(s)$ equals

$$\Delta(s) = 1 - KT_{43}(s) \tag{7.1.2}$$

Active filters having a single-controlled source can be described by this first-order canonical flow graph.

In the active filters which we shall consider, we will be using operational amplifiers which are modelled by voltage-controlled voltage sources of strength K. The inputs and outputs of the active filter shall also be voltages. Thus, the four nodes of the flow graph will correspond to the node voltages in the active filter. The various transfer functions of the branches are calculated as:

$$\begin{aligned} T_{12} &= V_2/V_1 \Big|_{K=0} & T_{42} &= V_2/V_4 \Big|_{V_1 = 0,\ \text{Replace } K} \\ T_{13} &= V_3/V_1 \Big|_{K=0} & T_{43} &= V_3/V_4 \Big|_{V_1 = 0,\ \text{Replace } K} \end{aligned} \tag{7.1.3}$$

These equations follow by inspection of the flow graph. The measurement conditions indicated by the vertical line must be imposed to insure signal transmission through the appropriate branch. It is important to memorize the convention that the branch having gain T_{ij} originates at node i and terminates on node j.

When calculating gain T_{12}, signal can flow only through this branch so K must be set equal to zero; otherwise signal transmission through the upper branch would augment T_{12}.

When calculating T_{13}, the signal at node 3 must be due only to signal flow through branch T_{13}; otherwise the signal at node 3 will be modified. Thus, to eliminate signal entering node 3 from the T_{43} branch, we set $K = 0$. This is equivalent to forcing the dependent source strength to zero. It is important to note that setting $K = 0$ forces the node 4 signal to be zero. Removing the dependent source K would also insure that no signal was fed back through branch T_{43} but this changes the impedance loading at node 4. Although this represents no problem in measurement, dependent sources cannot in general be removed since this alters the impedance loading conditions within the filter. Removal must be exercised with great caution.

When measuring T_{42} or T_{43}, signal is injected at node 4 from an independent source. To eliminate ambiguity due to feedback through the controlled source of signal $KT_{43}V_4$, we choose to merely *replace* the dependent source of strength K by the independent source of strength K (or

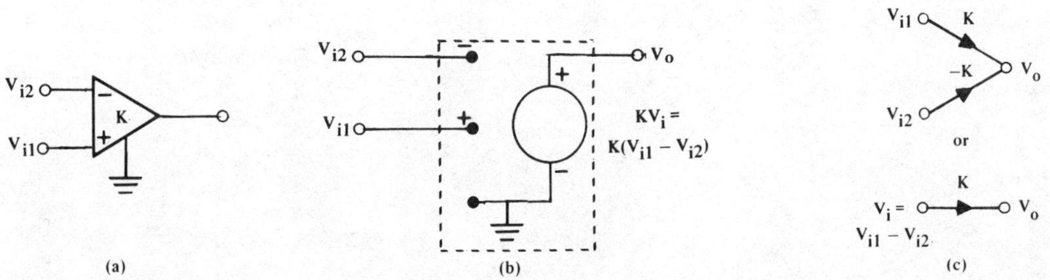

Fig. 7.1.2 Operational amplifier model and flow graph.

unity). This approach is intuitively pleasing to the engineer since the impedance loading is maintained and the feedback is eliminated. Note that the input signal V_1 must equal zero to eliminate signal transmission through the T_{12} branch when calculating T_{42}.

The T_{43} branch is the feedback branch which feeds output signal from the dependent source back into its input. Let us now relate the operational amplifier model to its flow graph. We will then apply these equations to calculate the branch gains for an amplifier operating in its inverting and noninverting modes. These gains are important since they are the gain blocks we shall utilize in our design of active filters.

EXAMPLE 7.1.1 Derive the flow graph for an ideal operational amplifier having infinite input impedances, zero output impedance, and gain K.

Solution The ideal operational amplifier is shown in Fig. 7.1.2a. Its inputs are V_{i1} (noninverting input) and V_{i2} (inverting input). Its output equals

$$V_o = KV_i = K(V_{i1} - V_{i2}) \tag{7.1.4}$$

Its equivalent circuit or model is shown in Fig. 7.1.2b where the input impedances are infinite and the output impedance is zero. The flow graph representation of the amplifier is shown in Fig. 7.1.2c.

EXAMPLE 7.1.2 Derive the gain expression for an ideal operational amplifier connected in the inverting mode as shown in Fig. 7.1.3a.

Solution Using the model of Example 7.1.1, the equivalent circuit is shown in Fig. 7.1.3b. The flow graph is shown in Fig. 7.1.3c. The branch transfer functions equal

$$T_{12} = V_2/V_1\,\big|_{K=0} = 0 \qquad T_{42} = V_2/V_4\,\Big|_{\substack{V_1 = 0 \\ \text{Replace K}}} = 1$$

$$T_{13} = V_3/V_1\,\big|_{K=0} = \frac{R_f}{R_1 + R_f} \qquad T_{43} = V_3/V_4\,\Big|_{\substack{V_1 = 0 \\ \text{Replace K}}} = \frac{R_1}{R_1 + R_f} \tag{7.1.5}$$

Therefore, the overall amplifier gain equals

$$H(s) = -\frac{KT_{13}T_{42}}{1 + KT_{43}} = -\frac{KR_f}{R_1(1 + K) + R_f} \tag{7.1.6}$$

Under limiting gain conditions where $K \to \infty$, then

$$H(s) = -R_f/R_1 \tag{7.1.7}$$

Several comments should be made. Note that then $V_{i1} = 0, V_3 = V_{i2}$, and then $V_4 = -KV_3 = -KV_{i2}$. Therefore, the controlled source has an effective gain of $-K$. Thus, the op amp is said to be operating in its inverting mode. Note also that the noninverting amplifier input is grounded through $R_1||R_f$. This is common practice when the dc offset voltage at the amplifier output due to offset current is important. Offset effects will be thoroughly discussed in Chap. 14.

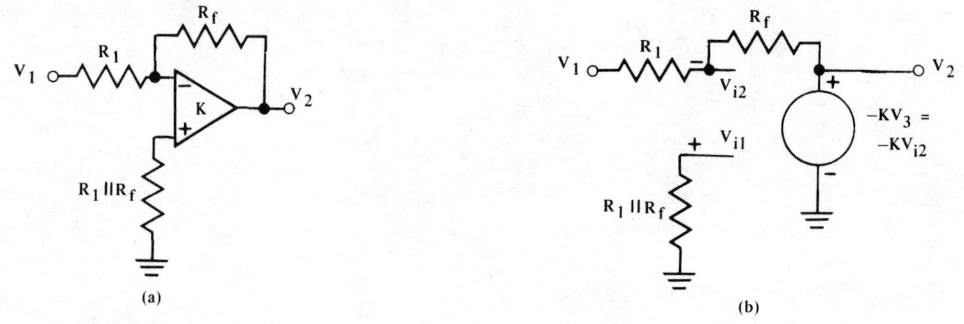

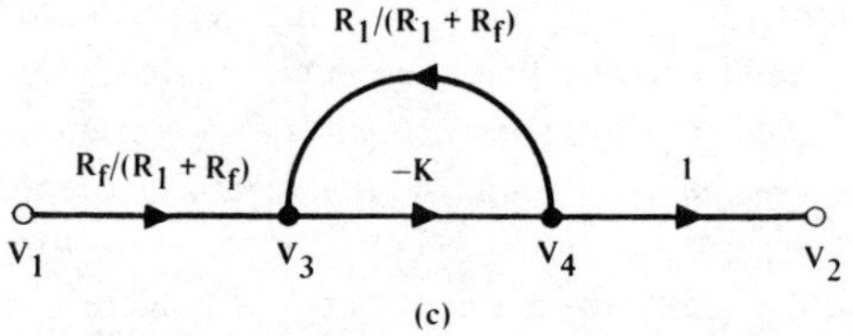

Fig. 7.1.3 Operational amplifier in inverting mode.

EXAMPLE 7.1.3 Derive the gain expression for an ideal operational amplifier connected in the noninverting mode as shown in Fig. 7.1.4a.

Solution Using the model of Example 7.1.1, the equivalent circuit is shown in Fig. 7.1.4b. The flow graph is shown in Fig. 7.1.4c. The branch transfer functions equal

$$T_{12} = V_2/V_1 \big|_{K=0} = 0 \qquad T_{42} = V_2/V_4 \Big|_{\substack{V_1 = 0 \\ \text{Replace K}}} = 1$$

$$T_{13} = V_3/V_1 \big|_{K=0} = \frac{R_3}{R_2 + R_3} \qquad T_{43} = V_3/V_4 \Big|_{\substack{V_1 = 0 \\ \text{Replace K}}} = -\frac{R_1}{R_1 + R_f} \tag{7.1.8}$$

Therefore, the overall amplifier gain equals

$$H(s) = \frac{KT_{13}T_{42}}{1 - KT_{43}} = \frac{R_3}{R_2 + R_3} \frac{K(R_1 + R_f)}{KR_1 + (R_1 + R_f)} \tag{7.1.9}$$

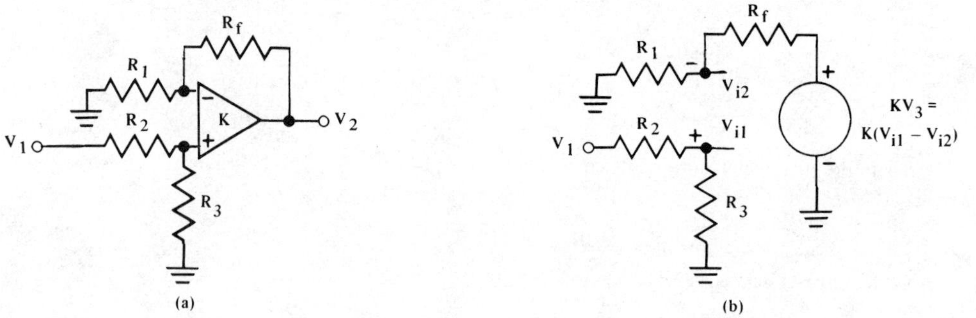

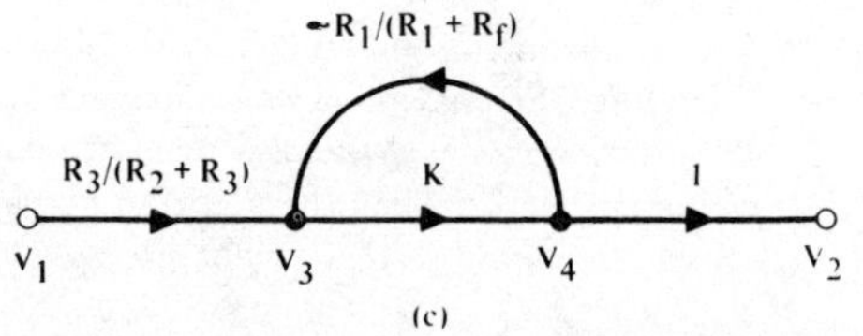

Fig. 7.1.4 Operational amplifier in noninverting mode.

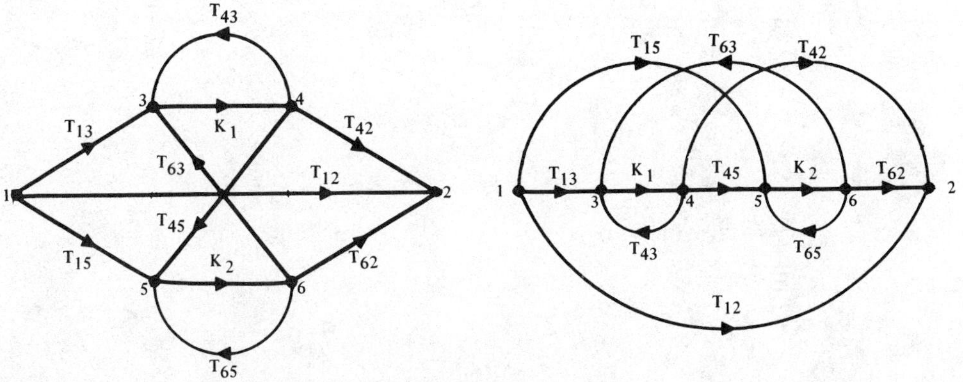

Fig. 7.1.5 Second-order canonical flow graph in two forms.

Under limiting gain conditions where $K \to \infty$, then

$$H(s) = \frac{R_3}{R_2 + R_3} \frac{R_1 + R_f}{R_1} = \frac{1 + R_f/R_1}{1 + R_2/R_3} \tag{7.1.10}$$

Since the noninverting input circuit is a voltage divider, the first term represents its voltage gain. The second term represents the gain due to the amplifier. For $R_1 = \infty$, the amplifier acts as a voltage follower with unity gain. To minimize voltage offsets due to offset current, $R_1 || R_f$ is set equal to $R_2 || R_3$ as will be discussed in Chap. 14.

It should be pointed out before proceeding that the inverting and noninverting amplifiers of Fig. 7.1.3 and 7.1.4 are very important. They are used to realize the amplifiers of gains $\pm K$ in this and the following chapters. We shall discuss their design in Chap. 8 when we begin to actually realize filters with hardware.

We considered the first-order canonical flow graph in Fig. 7.1.1. Two equivalent but rearranged forms of the second-order canonical flow graph are shown in Fig. 7.1.5. An active filter having two controlled-sources with strengths K_1 and K_2 is described by a second-order flow graph. Since many filters have a physical form close to the second graph in Fig. 7.1.5, we will generally use that form. When $K_1 = K_2 = 0$, there is signal transmission only through the T_{12} branch. Otherwise, signals flow through the other branches as well. Branches T_{43} and T_{65} represent *local feedback* around controlled sources K_1 and K_2, respectively. Branches T_{63} and T_{45} represent *cross-coupling* (i.e., global feedback) from the output of controlled source K_2 to the input of controlled source K_1 and vice versa, respectively. The system gain using Mason's gain equation equals

$$H(s) = T_{12} + \frac{K_1 T_{13} T_{42}(1 - K_2 T_{65}) + K_2 T_{15} T_{62}(1 - K_1 T_{43}) + K_1 K_2 (T_{13} T_{45} T_{62} + T_{15} T_{42} T_{63})}{\Delta(s)} \tag{7.1.11}$$

where the system determinant $\Delta(s)$ equals

$$\Delta(s) = 1 - K_1 T_{43} - K_2 T_{65} + K_1 K_2 (T_{43} T_{65} - T_{45} T_{63}) \tag{7.1.12}$$

The branch transfer functions are derived in the same manner as before:

$$T_{13} = V_3/V_1 \,\big|\, K_1 = K_2 = 0 \qquad T_{43} = V_3/V_4 \,\Big|\begin{array}{l} V_1 = K_2 = 0 \\ \text{Replace } K_1 \end{array}$$

$$T_{15} = V_5/V_1 \,\big|\, K_1 = K_2 = 0 \qquad T_{45} = V_5/V_4 \,\Big|\begin{array}{l} V_1 = K_2 = 0 \\ \text{Replace } K_1 \end{array}$$

$$T_{12} = V_2/V_1 \,\big|\, K_1 = K_2 = 0 \qquad T_{42} = V_2/V_4 \,\Big|\begin{array}{l} V_1 = K_2 = 0 \\ \text{Replace } K_1 \end{array}$$

$$T_{65} = V_5/V_6 \,\Big|\begin{array}{l} V_1 = K_1 = 0 \\ \text{Replace } K_2 \end{array}$$

$$T_{63} = V_3/V_6 \,\Big|\begin{array}{l} V_1 = K_1 = 0 \\ \text{Replace } K_2 \end{array} \tag{7.1.13}$$

$$T_{62} = V_2/V_6 \,\Big|\begin{array}{l} V_1 = K_1 = 0 \\ \text{Replace } K_2 \end{array}$$

Again note that T_{ij} represents the gain of the branch originating at node i and terminating at node j. Thus, all gains with identical first subscripts *originate* from the same node. All gains with identical second subscripts *terminate* on the same node.

7.2 RC ACTIVE FILTERS OF SECOND-ORDER

We shall be concerned with classifying active filters made up of one or two active elements using the scheme developed by Mitra and Soderstrand. The single active-element filter is a special case of the two active-element filter. Their approach can be extended to any number of active elements but the algebra becomes tedious to perform. The active elements will be voltage-controlled voltage sources (VCVS) which are realized using operational amplifiers. The theory may also be extended to other types of controlled sources. However, almost all active filters used today are the VCVS type. Therefore, we shall be analyzing active filters described by a second-order canonical flow graph. When $K_2 = 0$ corresponding to a single-amplifier active filter, the second-order canonical flow graph reduces to a first-order graph.

We shall be considering active filters having second-order transfer functions where

$$H(s) = K\frac{s^2 + (\omega_{oz}/Q_z)s + \omega_{oz}^2}{s^2 + (\omega_{op}/Q_p)s + \omega_{op}^2} \tag{7.2.1}$$

*n*th-order active filters shall be realized as the cascade of n/2 (for n even) or (n + 1)/2 second-order stages (for n odd). The main advantage of cascade design is the ease of tuning and temperature compensation. The industrial importance of these features for producing low cost, high quality active filters cannot be overemphasized. Alternative designs realize the *n*th-order active filter using a single *n*th-order stage. One such example is the classical analog computer solution involving n integrators which is currently referred to as a state-variable filter. Although this type of filter will be discussed, it is difficult to tune and compensate in analog form (this filter is excellent in digital form since it can be tuned exactly and has no temperature drift). Thus, cascade design incorporating lower-order stages will be used.

It is important to note that the order of the transfer function of the filter is unrelated to the order of flow graph describing the filter. The order of the transfer function depends only upon the branch gains T_{ij} and not upon the number of controlled sources of the filter.

The transfer function of active filters having second-order canonical flow graphs which we shall consider equals

$$H(s) = (1/\Delta)\,[T_{12}\Delta + K_1T_{13}T_{42}(1 - K_2T_{65}) + K_2T_{15}T_{62}(1 - K_1T_{43}) + K_1K_2(T_{13}T_{45}T_{62} + T_{15}T_{42}T_{63})] \tag{7.2.2}$$

The poles of the filter satisfy

$$\Delta(s) = 1 - K_1T_{43} - K_2T_{65} + K_1K_2(T_{43}T_{65} - T_{45}T_{63}) = 0 \tag{7.2.3}$$

while the zeros satisfy

$$T_{12}\Delta + K_1T_{13}T_{42}(1 - K_2T_{65}) + K_2T_{15}T_{62}(1 - K_1T_{43}) + K_1K_2(T_{13}T_{45}T_{62} + T_{15}T_{42}T_{63}) = 0 \tag{7.2.4}$$

Finding the zeros is considerably more involved than finding the poles of the filter. Thus, it is expedient to classify filters by the properties of only the poles. Expressing the branch gains T_{ij} in the form

$$T_{ij}(s) = N_{ij}(s)/D_{ij}(s) \tag{7.2.5}$$

then the filter poles satisfy

$$\Delta(s) = 1 - K_1\frac{N_{43}}{D_{43}} - K_2\frac{N_{65}}{D_{65}} + K_1K_2\left[\frac{N_{43}}{D_{43}}\frac{N_{65}}{D_{65}} - \frac{N_{45}}{D_{45}}\frac{N_{63}}{D_{63}}\right] \tag{7.2.6}$$

Considerable simplification results by observing that the branch gains T_{ij} describe the voltage transfer characteristics of RC passive networks. These gains must satisfy several properties.

First, all branches *terminating* on the same node in the flow graph have the same denominator.[2] These are branches having gains with identical second subscripts. Thus,

$$D_{13} = D_{43} = D_{63}, \qquad D_{15} = D_{45} = D_{65} \tag{7.2.7}$$

This may be seen from Example 7.1.2 from the voltage divider expressions. In Example 7.1.3, this is true after we rationalize the voltage divider expressions. Rationalizing is usually required when both inputs of the differential amplifier are utilized for signal processing rather than only one. Therefore, the poles of RC active filters having second-order flow graphs satisfy

$$\Delta(s) = D_{43}D_{65} - K_1N_{43}D_{65} - K_2N_{65}D_{43} + K_1K_2(N_{43}N_{65} - N_{45}N_{63}) = 0 \tag{7.2.8}$$

Note that the poles depend only upon the poles and zeros of the various feedback path gains. They are independent of $N_{12}, N_{13}, N_{15}, N_{42}$, and N_{62}.

Second, all branch gains must satisfy the Fialkow-Gerst conditions.[3] This requires that for a branch gain of order n where

$$T_{ij}(s) = \frac{N_{ij}(s)}{D_{ij}(s)} = \frac{\beta_n s^n + \ldots + \beta_1 s + \beta_0}{\gamma_n s^n + \ldots + \gamma_1 s + \gamma_0} \tag{7.2.9}$$

then the coefficients of the gain function are bounded by

$$0 \leqslant \beta_0 \leqslant \gamma_0, \qquad 0 \leqslant \beta_1 \leqslant \gamma_1, \qquad \ldots, \qquad 0 \leqslant \beta_n \leqslant \gamma_n \tag{7.2.10}$$

Class	s^2	s^1	s^0
A	X		
$\overline{A}$			X
B		X	
C	X	X	
$\overline{C}$		X	X
D	X		X
E	X	X	X

Table 7.2.1 Classifying the active portions of $\Delta(s)$.

We will be concerned with only T_{ij} not exceeding second-order. In addition, the poles of T_{ij} must be simple and lie along the interior of the negative real axis of the s-plane (poles cannot be located at either the origin or infinity). The zeros of T_{ij} may have any s-plane location but must occur in conjugate pairs if complex. These bounds are important for they fix limits on various sensitivities of RC active filters. Also, the pole-zero locations are required when constructing the root locus of poles in RC active filters. These limitations are valid regardless of the complexity of the RC passive networks. For example, they may be grounded or ungrounded, and have ladder, bridge, or more general topologies.

The poles of the second-order RC active filters which we are considering satisfy Eq. 7.2.8. Note that the $D_{43}D_{65}$ term is dependent only upon the passive network and does not involve the active parameters K_1 and K_2. We shall refer to this as the *passive portion* of the denominator. The remainder of $\Delta(s)$ involves the active parameters and shall be called the *active portion* of the denominator. Due to the active portion, complex poles can be produced which is the usual case of interest in active filters.

For $\Delta(s)$ to be a second-order polynomial (quadratic), $D_{43}(s)$ and $D_{65}(s)$ must both be first-order polynomials; or $D_{65}(s) = 1$ and $D_{43}(s)$ must be quadratic (or visa versa). This fact is useful for filter classification. Filters which have first-order D_{43} and D_{65} polynomials will be called *first-order decompositions*. Filters which have one zero-order and one second-order D_{43} and D_{65} polynomials will be called *second-order decompositions*. Thus, the character of the passive portion of $\Delta(s)$ determines the decomposition order of the filter.

The active portion of $\Delta(s)$ can also be classified in the analogous manner as follows:

Class A: Active portion varies with s^2 only.
Class $\overline{A}$: Active portion varies with s^0 only. (Class $\overline{A}$ filters can be derived from Class A filters using Mitra's RC:CR transformation.[4])
Class B: Active portion varies with s^1 only.
Class C: Active portion varies with s^2 and s^1.
Class $\overline{C}$: Active portion varies with s^0 and s^1. (Class $\overline{C}$ filters can be from Class C filters using the RC:CR transformation.)
Class D: Active portion varies with s^2 and s^0.
Class E: Active portion varies with s^2, s^1, and s^0.

This classification scheme is exhaustive since it lists all possible combinations of s^2, s^1 and s^0 as shown in Table 7.2.1. We shall now investigate the properties of first-order and second-order decomposition RC active filters of the various classes. These filters will be denoted as Class 1X or Class 2X active filters, respectively, where "1" or "2" refers to the decomposition order and "X" refers to the class of interest.

7.3 FIRST-ORDER DECOMPOSITION FILTERS

In first-order decomposition filters, D_{43} and D_{65} are first-order polynomials. We introduce the convention that

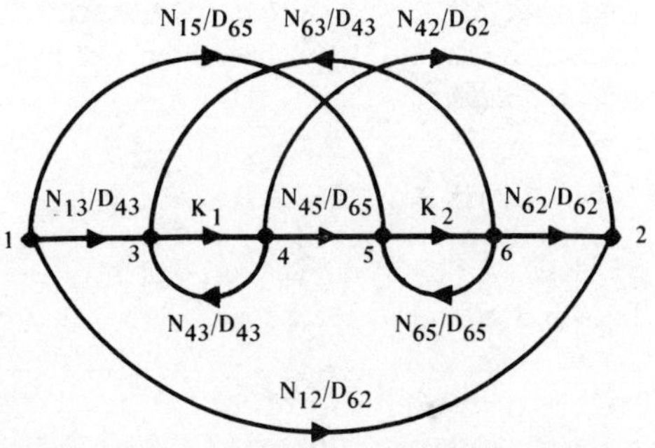

Fig. 7.3.1 General flow graph of first-order decomposition filters.

$$\begin{aligned}
&D_{13} = D_{43} = D_{63} = a_{30} + a_{31}s && D_{15} = D_{45} = D_{65} = a_{50} + a_{51}s \\
&N_{43} = b_{30} + b_{31}s && N_{65} = b_{50} + b_{51}s \\
&N_{63} = c_{30} + c_{31}s && N_{45} = c_{50} + c_{51}s \\
&N_{43}N_{65} - N_{45}N_{63} = d_2s^2 + d_1s + d_0
\end{aligned} \tag{7.3.1}$$

The difference equation is used for notational brevity and equals

$$\begin{aligned}
N_{43}N_{65} - N_{45}N_{63} &= (b_{30} + b_{31}s)(b_{50} + b_{51}s) - (c_{30} + c_{31}s)(c_{50} + c_{51}s) \\
&= (b_{31}b_{51} - c_{31}c_{51})s^2 + (b_{30}b_{51} + b_{31}b_{50} - c_{30}c_{51} - c_{31}c_{50})s \\
&\quad + (b_{30}b_{50} - c_{30}c_{50}) = d_2s^2 + d_1s + d_0
\end{aligned} \tag{7.3.2}$$

Substituting these polynomials into the system determinant and collecting like powers of s yields

$$\begin{aligned}
\Delta(s) &= (a_{30} + a_{31}s)(a_{50} + a_{51}s) - K_1(a_{50} + a_{51}s)(b_{30} + b_{31}s) \\
&\quad - K_2(a_{30} + a_{31}s)(b_{50} + b_{51}s) + K_1K_2(d_2s^2 + d_1s + d_0) \\
&= [a_{31}a_{51} - K_1a_{51}b_{31} - K_2a_{31}b_{51} + K_1K_2d_2]\,s^2 \\
&\quad + [a_{30}a_{51} + a_{31}a_{50} - K_1(a_{50}b_{31} + a_{51}b_{30}) - K_2(a_{30}b_{51} + a_{31}b_{50}) + K_1K_2d_1]\,s \\
&\quad + [a_{30}a_{50} - K_1a_{50}b_{30} - K_2a_{30}b_{50} + K_1K_2d_0]
\end{aligned} \tag{7.3.3}$$

It now remains to determine the a_{ij}, b_{ij}, c_{ij}, and d_i coefficient conditions to produce the various classes of filters listed previously. Note that the Fialkow-Gerst conditions require

$$\begin{aligned}
&0 \leqslant b_{31} \leqslant a_{31}, \quad 0 \leqslant c_{31} \leqslant a_{31}, \quad 0 \leqslant b_{51} \leqslant a_{51}, \quad 0 \leqslant c_{51} \leqslant a_{51} \\
&0 \leqslant b_{30} \leqslant a_{30}, \quad 0 \leqslant c_{30} \leqslant a_{30}, \quad 0 \leqslant b_{50} \leqslant a_{50}, \quad 0 \leqslant c_{50} \leqslant a_{50}
\end{aligned} \tag{7.3.4}$$

Since the d_j coefficients satisfy

$$\begin{aligned}
&d_2 = b_{31}b_{51} - c_{31}c_{51}, \quad d_1 = b_{30}b_{51} + b_{31}b_{50} - c_{30}c_{51} - c_{31}c_{50}, \\
&\qquad\qquad d_0 = b_{30}b_{50} - c_{30}c_{50}
\end{aligned} \tag{7.3.5}$$

these coefficients may be positive, negative, or zero depending upon the b_{ij}'s and c_{ij}'s.

We shall see that two operational amplifiers are required for all Class 1X filters. Class 1D filters will be shown to be nonrealizable. The general flow graph for first-order decomposition filters is shown in Fig. 7.3.1. *To obtain maximum simplicity in the flow graphs to follow, we* *shall omit the T_{12}, T_{15}, and T_{42} branches.* After the engineer grasps the basic concepts of this chapter, he should draw these branches in the flow graphs so he will *not forget their necessity in general analysis.*

7.4 CLASS 1A FILTERS

In Class 1A filters, the active portion of the system determinant varies with s^2 only. Therefore in Eq. 7.3.3, we must set

$$b_{30} = b_{31} = b_{50} = b_{51} = d_0 = d_1 = 0 \tag{7.4.1}$$

to produce this condition. Note that setting $b_{ij} = 0$ takes precedence over setting $a_{ij} = 0$ so the Fialkow-Gerst conditions can be satisfied. The last requirement that $d_0 = d_1 = 0$ requires additionally that

$$c_{30}c_{50} = 0 \tag{7.4.2}$$

and

$$c_{30}c_{51} = 0, \qquad c_{31}c_{50} = 0 \tag{7.4.3}$$

There are several combinations of c_{30}, c_{31}, c_{50}, and c_{51} which allow these equations to be satisfied. These combinations are listed in Table 7.4.1. However, in order for the active portion of Δ to vary with s^2, only setting $c_{30} = c_{50} = 0$ will be of practical importance. Note that since $b_{30} = b_{31} = 0$ and $b_{50} = b_{51} = 0$, then $N_{43} = N_{65} = 0$ so that

$$T_{43} = T_{65} = 0 \tag{7.4.4}$$

Thus, there is no local feedback around the K_1 and K_2 amplifiers. There is only cross-coupling in this type of filter. The cross-coupling transfer functions are listed in Table 7.4.1. Note that the amplifiers are cross-coupled by transfer functions having only first-order terms in the numerators. Thus, the cross-coupling networks are high-pass filters.

The system determinant for Class 1A filters equals

$$\Delta(s) = (a_{31}a_{51} + K_1K_2d_2)s^2 + (a_{31}a_{50} + a_{30}a_{51})s + a_{30}a_{50} \tag{7.4.5}$$

Table 7.4.1 Permissible transfer functions for Class 1A filters.

	$c_{30} = c_{50} = 0$	$c_{30} = c_{31} = 0$	$c_{50} = c_{51} = 0$
T_{45}	$\dfrac{c_{51}s}{a_{50} + a_{51}s}$	$\dfrac{c_{50} + c_{51}s}{a_{50} + a_{51}s}$	0
T_{63}	$\dfrac{c_{31}s}{a_{30} + a_{31}s}$	0	$\dfrac{c_{30} + c_{31}s}{a_{30} + a_{31}s}$

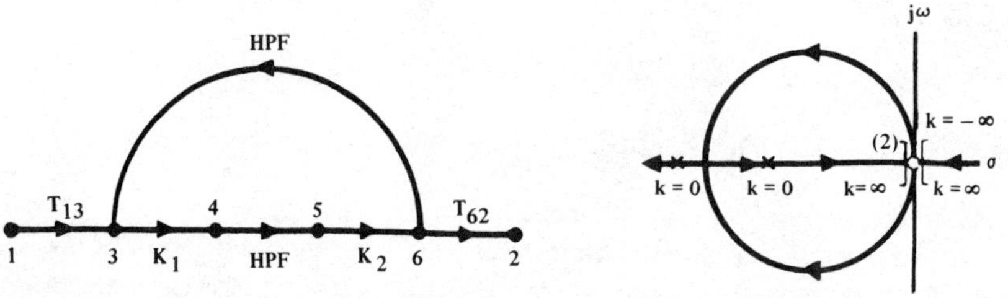

Fig. 7.4.1 Flow graph and root locus for Class 1A filters.

where $d_2 = -c_{31}c_{51}$. Expressing the system determinant as

$$\Delta(s) = (s + a_1)(s + a_2) - ks^2 \tag{7.4.6}$$

then we may draw the root locus of the system poles. We use the alternative standard form where

$$1 - k\frac{s^2}{(s + a_1)(s + a_2)} = 0 \tag{7.4.7}$$

and

$$k = K_1K_2c_{31}c_{51}/a_{31}a_{51} \tag{7.4.8}$$

k equals the high-frequency loop gain, $K_1K_2T_{45}T_{63}$, of the filter. The root locus is drawn in Fig. 7.4.1 which was analyzed in Example 1.16.2. The system poles vary in the following manner as k increases from $-\infty$ to $+\infty$: the system poles originate at the origin and travel around a circle of radius $a_1a_2/(a_1 + a_2)$ centered at $s = -a_1a_2/(a_1 + a_2)$; they break onto the real axis and pass through $s = -a_1, -a_2$ for $k = 0$; one pole migrates toward $s = -\infty$, reappears at $s = +\infty$, travels back along the positive real axis, and terminates at the origin; the other pole travels to the origin along the negative real axis from $-a_1$. The poles lie in the left-half-plane for $k < 0$ and one pole lies in the right-half-plane for large positive k. The poles are located at the origin for $k = \pm\infty$. Class 1A filters are therefore potentially unstable for k both positive and negative. Since complex conjugate poles can be obtained for negative k only, $k < 0$ is the usual mode of filter operation. Using Eq. 7.4.8, complex poles are obtained for $c_{31}c_{51} \neq 0$ and nonzero amplifier gains of opposite signs. Thus, only the T_{63} and T_{45} transfer functions listed in the first column of Table 7.4.1 are used for Class 1A active filters. Also, Class 1A filters require two amplifiers. The useful transfer functions are summarized in Table 7.19.1 and the root loci and flow graphs are drawn in Fig. 7.19.1 for ready reference.

To establish gain and sensitivity bounds,[5] we note that Class 1A filters have a determinant given by Eq. 7.4.6 where k is the high-frequency loop gain of the filter from Eq. 7.4.8. Then the filter poles are characterized by

$$\omega_o = [a_1a_2/(1 - k)]^{1/2}, \qquad Q = [a_1a_2(1 - k)]^{1/2}/(a_1 + a_2) \tag{7.4.9}$$

Therefore, the various sensitivities equal

$$\begin{gathered} \tfrac{1}{2}(1 - 1/4Q^2) \leq -S_k^{\omega_o} = S_k^Q = -k/2(1 - k) \leq \tfrac{1}{2} \\ S_{a_1}^{\omega_o} = S_{a_2}^{\omega_o} = \tfrac{1}{2}, \qquad -1 \leq S_{a_1}^Q = -S_{a_2}^Q = (a_1 - a_2)/(a_1 + a_2) \leq 1 \end{gathered} \tag{7.4.10}$$

where for complex poles, the gain equals

$$-k = [(a_1 + a_2)Q/(a_1a_2)^{1/2}]^2 - 1 \geq 4Q^2 - 1 \tag{7.4.11}$$

from Eq. 7.4.9b. Since when $k = 0$, an RC passive network results which always has $Q \leq \tfrac{1}{2}$ ($Q = \tfrac{1}{2}$ is permissible in first-order decompositions since the first-order RC networks are isolated by amplifiers), then

$$1/Q = (a_1 + a_2)/(a_1a_2)^{1/2} \geq 2 \tag{7.4.12}$$

from Eq. 7.4.9b. Substituting this result and that of Eq. 7.4.11 into Eq. 7.4.10 yields the sensitivity bounds shown.

The active sensitivities, S_k^Q and $S_k^{\omega_o}$, never exceed $\pm\tfrac{1}{2}$. To obtain a filter having minimum active sensitivities, we must minimize gain k in Eq. 7.4.10a. To minimize k, this in turn requires minimizing the separation between a_1 and a_2 so that $a_1 = a_2$ in Eq. 7.4.11. This reduces the active sensitivities to no less than $\pm\tfrac{1}{2}(1 - 1/4Q^2)$ whose value lies between 0 (for $Q = \tfrac{1}{2}$) and $\pm\tfrac{1}{2}$

(for $Q = \infty$) where Q equals the required Q of the filter. Therefore, significant sensitivity improvement is obtained only in low-Q applications.

To obtain a filter having minimum passive Q sensitivities, $S^Q_{a_i}$, we set $a_1 = a_2$ in Eq. 7.4.10c. Although these passive Q sensitivities never exceed ±1, they can thereby be reduced to zero. Note the passive ω_o sensitivity, $S^{\omega_o}_a$, is always ½.

The minimum gain is given by Eq. 7.4.11. To obtain the minimum gain possible, we must set $a_1 = a_2$ so that $-k \geqslant (4Q^2 - 1)$. This result shows that the high-frequency loop gain, $K_1K_2T_{45}T_{63}$, of the filter can be no less than $(4Q^2 - 1)$. Note that since $T_{45}T_{63}$ equals $c_{31}c_{51}/a_{31}a_{51}$ from Eq. 7.4.8, the high-frequency passive loop gain $T_{45}T_{63}$ must equal unity for gains K_1 and K_2 to be minimized. Recall that K_1 and K_2 must have opposite signs to produce complex poles (i.e., $Q > ½$).

Therefore, we reach the important conclusion that equating passive time constants in Class 1A filters simultaneously minimizes not only the gain required, but the active and passive sensitivities of ω_o and Q. This information is summarized in Table 7.19.3. We see that Class 1A filters will always have low sensitivities (the order of ±½). However, high amplifier gains of at least $\pm(4Q^2 - 1)^{1/2} \cong \pm 2Q$ are required.

The importance of the $S^{\omega_o}_K$, $S^{\omega_o}_R$, and $S^{\omega_o}_C$ sensitivities, and the S^Q_K, S^Q_R, and S^Q_C, sensitivities were illustrated in Sec. 1.15 by examples. Since sensitivity analysis will be fully exploited in comparing filter forms in the following chapters, Sec. 1.15 should be reviewed to enhance understanding before proceeding further.

EXAMPLE 7.4.1 Derive the flow graph and transfer function for the active filter shown in Fig. 7.4.2a. Verify that it is a Class 1A filter.

Solution The equivalent circuit of the filter is drawn in Fig. 7.4.2b. The flow graph is shown in Fig. 7.4.2c. The various node voltages of the equivalent circuit are labelled to coincide with those of the flow graph. The branch gains are easily calculated as follows:

$$T_{13} = V_3/V_1 \big|_{K_1 = K_2 = 0} = \frac{1}{1 + sR_1C_1} \qquad T_{43} = V_3/V_4 \Big|_{\substack{V_1 = K_2 = 0 \\ \text{Replace } K_1}} = 0$$

$$T_{15} = V_5/V_1 \big|_{K_1 = K_2 = 0} = 0 \qquad T_{45} = V_5/V_4 \Big|_{\substack{V_1 = K_2 = 0 \\ \text{Replace } K_1}} = \frac{sR_2C_2}{1 + sR_2C_2}$$

$$T_{12} = V_2/V_1 \big|_{K_1 = K_2 = 0} = 0 \qquad T_{42} = V_2/V_4 \Big|_{\substack{V_1 = K_2 = 0 \\ \text{Replace } K_1}} = 0$$

$$T_{65} = V_5/V_6 \Big|_{\substack{V_1 = K_1 = 0 \\ \text{Replace } K_2}} = 0$$

$$T_{63} = V_3/V_6 \Big|_{\substack{V_1 = K_1 = 0 \\ \text{Replace } K_2}} = \frac{sR_1C_1}{1 + sR_1C_1} \tag{7.4.13}$$

$$T_{62} = V_2/V_6 \Big|_{\substack{V_1 = K_1 = 0 \\ \text{Replace } K_2}} = 1$$

Several general comments can be made from direct inspection of the active filter. Neither amplifier has local feedback from its output directly to its input so that $T_{43} = T_{65} = 0$. The amplifiers are cross-coupled by the R_1C_1 and the R_2C_2 networks. The output of K_1 is coupled to the input of K_2 by C_2; the output of K_2 is coupled to the input of K_1 by C_1. The voltage transfer functions of these two networks are calculated for $V_1 = 0$, and it is clear by inspection that both networks are high-pass of first-order. Therefore, from Table 7.19.1, this must be a Class 1A filter. The branch gains calculated in Eq.

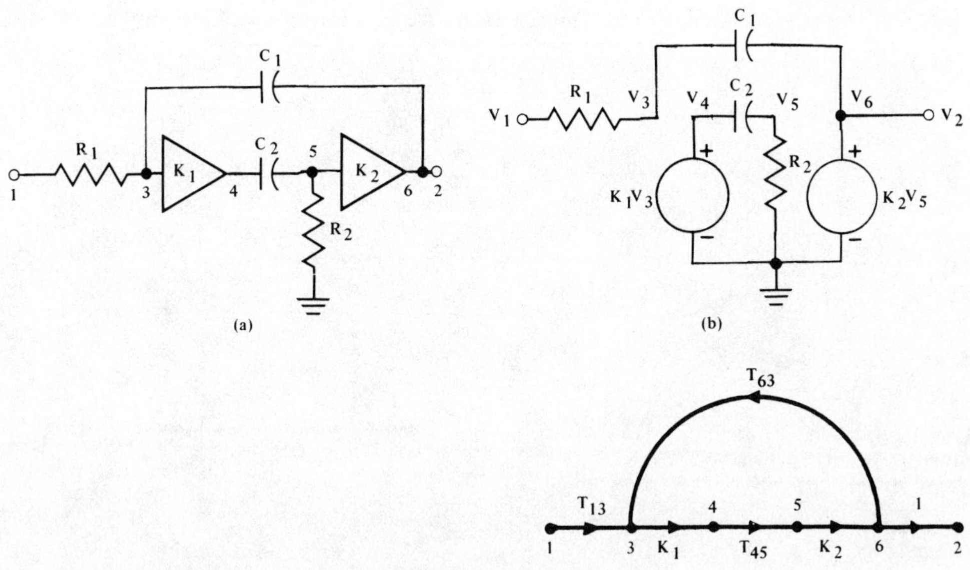

Fig. 7.4.2 Class 1A filter and its flow graph.

7.4.13 substantiate this classification. Also note that the input voltage V_1 is applied only to the input of K_1 by R_1. Thus, $T_{15} = 0$. Likewise, the output voltage V_2 comes directly from the output of K_2. Thus, $T_{62} = 1$ and $T_{42} = 0$. The gain of the active filter equals

$$H(s) = \frac{K_1K_2T_{13}T_{45}}{1 - K_1K_2T_{45}T_{63}} = \frac{K_1K_2sR_2C_2}{(1 + sR_1C_1)(1 + sR_2C_2) - K_1K_2s^2R_1C_1R_2C_2}$$

$$= \frac{K_1K_2sR_2C_2}{s^2(1 - K_1K_2)R_1C_1R_2C_2 + s(R_1C_1 + R_2C_2) + 1} \tag{7.4.14}$$

so the filter is a band-pass type.

7.5 CLASS $1\bar{A}$ FILTERS

In Class $1\bar{A}$ filters, the active portion of the system determinant varies with s^0 only. Class $1\bar{A}$ filters can be obtained directly from Class 1A filters using the RC:CR transformation which will be discussed in Chap. 9. Class $1\bar{A}$ filters have coefficients satisfying

$$b_{30} = b_{31} = b_{50} = b_{51} = d_1 = d_2 = 0 \tag{7.5.1}$$

The last requirements of $d_1 = d_2 = 0$ require additionally that

$$c_{31}c_{50} = 0, \qquad c_{30}c_{51} = 0 \tag{7.5.2}$$

and

$$c_{31}c_{51} = 0 \tag{7.5.3}$$

Note that Class $1\bar{A}$ filters differ from Class 1A filters only in that $d_2 = 0$ rather than $d_0 = 0$. Again there are several combinations of c_{30}, c_{31}, c_{50}, and c_{51} which allow these equations to be satisfied. These are listed in Table 7.5.1. Setting only $c_{31} = c_{51} = 0$ is of practical importance.

Since the coefficient conditions require

$$T_{43} = T_{65} = 0 \tag{7.5.4}$$

Table 7.5.1 Permissible transfer functions for Class $1\overline{A}$ filters.

	$c_{31} = c_{51} = 0$	$c_{30} = c_{31} = 0$	$c_{50} = c_{51} = 0$
T_{45}	$\dfrac{c_{50}}{a_{50} + a_{51}s}$	$\dfrac{c_{50} + c_{51}s}{a_{50} + a_{51}s}$	0
T_{63}	$\dfrac{c_{30}}{a_{30} + a_{31}s}$	0	$\dfrac{c_{30} + c_{31}s}{a_{30} + a_{31}s}$

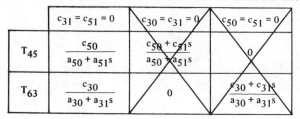

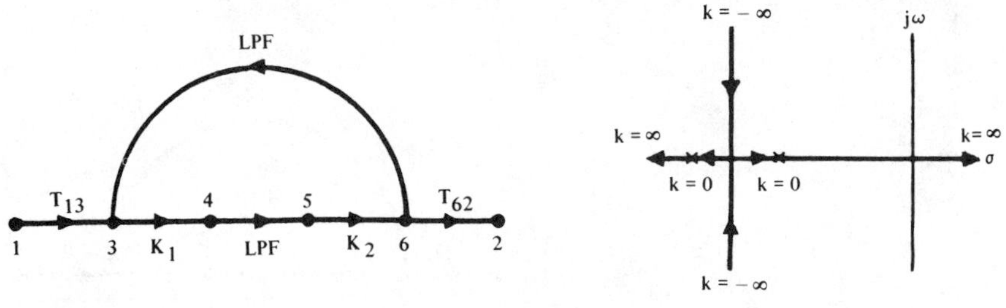

Fig. 7.5.1 Flow graph and root locus for Class $1\overline{A}$ filters.

there is again no local feedback around the K_1 and K_2 amplifiers. There is only cross-coupling in this type of filter, where the cross-coupling forms are listed in Table 7.5.1. Class $1\overline{A}$ filters have cross-couplings with zero-order numerators in contrast to Class 1A filters which have first-order numerators. Thus, Class $1\overline{A}$ filters have low-pass cross-coupling rather than high-pass.

The system determinant for Class $1\overline{A}$ filters equals

$$\Delta(s) = a_{31}a_{51}s^2 + (a_{30}a_{51} + a_{31}a_{50})s + (a_{30}a_{50} + K_1K_2d_0) \tag{7.5.5}$$

where $d_0 = -c_{30}c_{50}$. For nonzero d_0, neither c_{30} nor c_{50} can equal zero so only the cross-coupling form in the first column of Table 7.5.1 is used in this class of filter. We can express the determinant in the root locus form

$$\Delta(s) = (s + a_1)(s + a_2) - ka_1a_2 \tag{7.5.6}$$

where

$$k = K_1K_2c_{30}c_{50}/a_{30}a_{50} \tag{7.5.7}$$

k equals the low-frequency loop gain, $K_1K_2T_{43}T_{65}$, of the filter. The root locus for the Class $1\overline{A}$ filter poles is shown in Fig. 7.5.1 and was also analyzed in Example 1.16.2. The system poles behave in the following manner as k increases from $-\infty$ to $+\infty$: the poles originate at infinity on a vertical asymptote located at $s = -\frac{1}{2}(a_1 + a_2)$; the poles migrate inwards along the vertical asymptote and break onto the negative real axis; they travel to $s = -a_1, -a_2$ for $k = 0$; they continue to travel in opposite directions along the real axis for positive k and terminate at $s = \pm\infty$. The system poles lie in the left-half-plane for $k \leqslant 0$ and one pole lies in the right-half-plane for large positive k. Thus, Class $1\overline{A}$ filters are absolutely stable for negative k, but potentially unstable for positive k. Complex conjugate poles can be obtained for negative k only, so this is the normal mode of filter operation. Using Eq. 7.5.7, complex poles are obtained only when $c_{30}c_{50} \neq 0$ and nonzero amplifier gains of opposite signs. Again, two amplifiers are required. The various transfer functions are listed in Table 7.19.1.

The gain and sensitivity bounds are established in the same manner as those for the Class 1A filters. Since the Class $1\overline{A}$ filter determinant is given by Eq. 7.5.6, the filter poles are characterized by

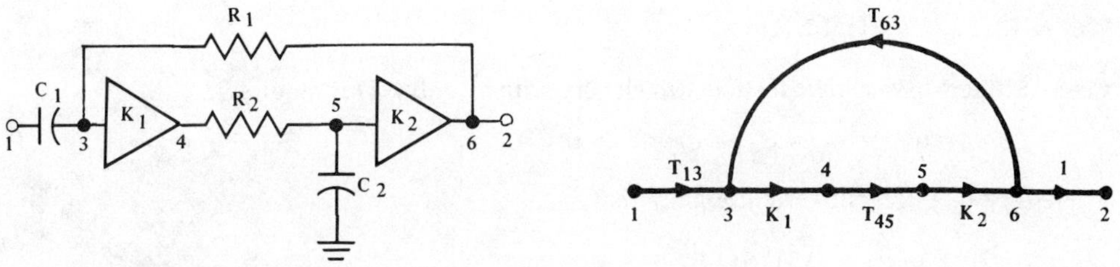

Fig. 7.5.2 Class $1\bar{A}$ filter and its flow graph.

$$\omega_o = [a_1 a_2(1-k)]^{1/2}, \qquad Q = [a_1 a_2(1-k)]^{1/2}/(a_1 + a_2) \tag{7.5.8}$$

Therefore, the various sensitivities equal

$$\tfrac{1}{2}(1 - 1/4Q^2) \leqslant S_k^{\omega_o} = S_k^Q = -k/2(1-k) \leqslant \tfrac{1}{2}$$
$$S_{a_1}^{\omega_o} = S_{a_2}^{\omega_o} = \tfrac{1}{2}, \qquad -1 \leqslant S_{a_1}^Q = -S_{a_2}^Q = (a_1 - a_2)/(a_1 + a_2) \leqslant 1 \tag{7.5.9}$$

where for complex poles, the gain equals

$$-k = [(a_1 + a_2)Q/(a_1 a_2)^{1/2}]^2 - 1 \geqslant 4Q^2 - 1 \tag{7.5.10}$$

from Eq. 7.5.8b. Comparing these results with those of the Class 1A filters given by Eqs. 7.4.9 through 7.4.12, we see they are identical (except for the sign of $S_k^{\omega_o}$ due to the ω_o expression). Therefore, we can immediately observe that equating passive time constants in Class $1\bar{A}$ filters simultaneously minimizes not only the gain required but the active and passive sensitivities of ω_o and Q as in Class 1A filters. By analogy, Class $1\bar{A}$ filters will always have low sensitivities (the order of ½) but will require high amplifier gains (the order of ±2Q). These results are summarized in Table 7.19.3.

EXAMPLE 7.5.1 Derive the flow graph and transfer function for the active filter shown in Fig. 7.5.2. Verify that it is a Class $1\bar{A}$ filter.

Solution The various node voltages of the filter are labelled to correspond with those of the flow graph. The branch gains are easily written by inspection as:

$$T_{13} = \frac{sR_1C_1}{1 + sR_1C_1} \qquad T_{43} = 0 \qquad T_{63} = \frac{1}{1 + sR_1C_1}$$
$$T_{15} = 0 \qquad T_{45} = \frac{1}{1 + sR_2C_2} \qquad T_{65} = 0 \tag{7.5.11}$$
$$T_{12} = 0 \qquad T_{42} = 0 \qquad T_{62} = 1$$

From the flow graph, we see that neither amplifier has local feedback so $T_{43} = T_{65} = 0$. The amplifiers are cross-coupled by the R_1C_1 and R_2C_2 networks which are low-pass filters of first-order. Therefore, from Table 7.19.1, this must be a Class $1\bar{A}$ active filter and can be obtained from the filter in Fig. 7.4.2 using the RC:CR transformation as we shall discuss in Chap. 9. The gain of the active filter equals

$$H(s) = \frac{K_1K_2T_{13}T_{45}}{1 - K_1K_2T_{45}T_{63}} = \frac{K_1K_2sR_1C_1}{(1 + sR_1C_1)(1 + sR_2C_2) - K_1K_2}$$
$$= \frac{K_1K_2sR_1C_1}{s^2R_1C_1R_2C_2 + s(R_1C_1 + R_2C_2) + (1 - K_1K_2)} \tag{7.5.12}$$

so the filter is a band-pass type.

7.6 CLASS 1B FILTERS

Class 1B filters have active portions which vary with s^1 only. This requires

$$b_{30} = b_{31} = b_{50} = b_{51} = d_0 = d_2 = 0 \tag{7.6.1}$$

where $d_0 = d_2 = 0$ requires additionally that

$$c_{30}c_{50} = 0, \qquad c_{31}c_{51} = 0 \tag{7.6.2}$$

Note that Class 1B filters differ from Class 1A and $1\overline{A}$ filters only in that d_1 is nonzero. The various c_{30}, c_{31}, c_{50}, and c_{51} combinations which allow these equations to be satisfied are listed in Table 7.6.1.

The coefficient conditions require that

$$T_{43} = T_{65} = 0 \tag{7.6.3}$$

so there is again no local coupling around the amplifiers. There is only cross-coupling between amplifiers. Examining the entries in Table 7.6.1, the amplifiers are cross-coupled by two transfer functions, one of which has a first-order numerator (high-pass), and the other which has a zero-order numerator (low-pass). Thus, Class 1B filters have both high-pass and low-pass cross-coupling in contrast to Class 1A filters which have only high-pass cross-coupling and Class 1A filters which have only low-pass cross-coupling. Class 1B filters are therefore combination Class 1A and $1\overline{A}$ filters, and have transfer functions listed in Table 7.19.1. Class 1B filters require two amplifiers.

The system determinant for Class 1B filters equals

$$\Delta(s) = a_{31}a_{51}s^2 + (a_{31}a_{50} + a_{30}a_{51} + K_1K_2d_1)s + a_{30}a_{50} \tag{7.6.4}$$

where $d_1 = -c_{30}c_{51} - c_{31}c_{50}$. We can express the system determinant as

$$\Delta(s) = (s + \alpha_1)(s + \alpha_2) - k\alpha_1 s \tag{7.6.5}$$

where

Table 7.6.1 Permissible transfer functions for Class 1B filters.

	$c_{30} = c_{51} = 0$	$c_{50} = c_{31} = 0$	$c_{30} = c_{31} = 0$	$c_{50} = c_{51} = 0$
T_{45}	$\dfrac{c_{50}}{a_{50} + a_{51}s}$	$\dfrac{c_{51}s}{a_{50} + a_{51}s}$	$\dfrac{c_{50} + c_{51}s}{a_{50} + a_{51}s}$	0
T_{63}	$\dfrac{c_{31}s}{a_{30} + a_{31}s}$	$\dfrac{c_{30}}{a_{30} + a_{31}s}$	0	$\dfrac{c_{30} + c_{31}s}{a_{30} + a_{31}s}$

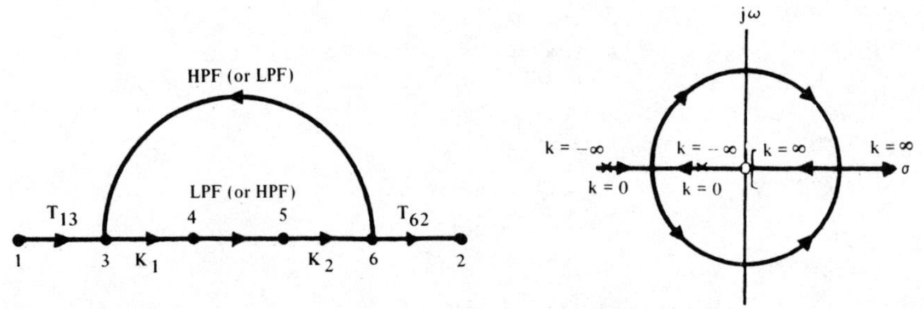

Fig. 7.6.1 Flow graph and root locus for Class 1B filters.

$$k = \frac{a_{30}a_{51} + a_{31}a_{50}}{a_{30}a_{51}}\left(K_1K_2\frac{c_{30}c_{51} + c_{31}c_{50}}{a_{30}a_{51} + a_{31}a_{50}}\right) \tag{7.6.6}$$

k equals the loop gain, $K_1K_2T_{43}T_{65}$, at the center frequency of the filter scaled by $(a_1 + a_2)/a_1$. The root locus for the poles of Class 1B filters is shown in Fig. 7.6.1. This root locus was also considered in Example 1.16.2. The root locus behavior due to k increasing from $-\infty$ to $+\infty$ is as follows: the system poles originate at $s = 0$ and $s = -\infty$ and travel along the negative real axis passing through $s = -a_1, -a_2$ for $k = 0$; they break away from the negative real axis, travel around a circle of radius $\sqrt{a_1a_2}$ centered at the origin and break onto the positive real axis; they travel to $s = 0$ and $s = +\infty$ where they terminate. The poles lie on the negative real axis for $k \leqslant 0$ and migrate into the right-half-plane for large values of $k > 0$. Thus, Class 1B filters are conditionally stable for negative k and potentially unstable for positive k. The amplifiers must have gains of the same sign to produce complex poles.

Since the Class 1B filter determinant is given by Eq. 7.6.5, the filter poles are characterized by

$$\omega_o = (a_1a_2)^{1/2}, \qquad Q = (a_1a_2)^{1/2}/(a_1 + a_2 - ka_1) \tag{7.6.7}$$

Therefore, the various sensitivities equal

$$S_k^{\omega_o} = 0, \qquad S_{a_1}^{\omega_o} = S_{a_2}^{\omega_o} = 1/2$$

$$S_k^Q = ka_1/[ka_1 - (a_1 + a_2)] = Q(a_1 + a_2)/(a_1a_2)^{1/2} - 1 \geqslant 2Q - 1 \tag{7.6.8}$$

$$-S_{a_1}^Q = S_{a_2}^Q = (1 - k)a_1/[(1 - k)a_1 + a_2] - 1/2 = Q(a_2/a_1)^{1/2} - 1/2$$

where for complex poles, the gain equals

$$k = [(a_1 + a_2)/a_1]\,[1 - (a_1a_2)^{1/2}/Q(a_1 + a_2)] \geqslant (1 + a_2/a_1)(1 - 1/2Q) \tag{7.6.9}$$

from Eq. 7.6.7b.

Since ω_o is independent of gain k, the active sensitivity, $S_k^{\omega_o}$, is zero. To minimize the active Q sensitivity, S_k^Q, we set $a_1 = a_2$ from Eq. 7.6.8c. Then S_k^Q equals $(2Q - 1)$ which is large (for high Q) but the gain required is only $(2 - 1/Q)$ which is small.

However, if we wish to minimize the gain k, it is easily shown from Eq. 7.6.9 that we must maximize the separation between a_1 and a_2 where $a_1/a_2 = 4Q^2$. This reduces the gain k to $(1 - 1/4Q^2)$ but the active Q sensitivities increase to $(2Q^2 - 1/2)$.

The passive ω_o sensitivity, $S_{a_i}^{\omega_o}$, is equal to 1/2. From Eq. 7.6.8d, the passive Q sensitivity, $S_{a_i}^Q$, is dependent upon the a_1/a_2 ratio. Under the minimum active Q sensitivity condition when $a_1/a_2 = 1$, then $\pm S_{a_i}^Q$ equals $(Q - 1/2)$ which is half the S_k^Q value. Under the minimum gain condition where $a_1/a_2 = 4Q^2$, then the $S_{a_i}^Q$'s reduce to zero but S_k^Q increases to $(2Q^2 - 1/2)$. Reducing a_1/a_2 from unity improves neither sensitivity and increases the required gain. These results are tabulated in Table 7.19.1.

Thus, unlike Class 1A and $1\overline{A}$ filters, a gain-sensitivity design compromise must be made. Thus, we see that although Class 1B filters require low gains of about 2 and have zero $S_k^{\omega_o}$ sensitivities, they have large S_k^Q sensitivities of $(2Q - 1)$ and $S_{a_i}^Q$ sensitivities of $(Q - 1/2)$. Since the sensitivities increase by Q when gain is reduced towards its minimum of $(1 - 1/4Q^2)$, this is an undesirable gain-sensitivity tradeoff in most applications.

EXAMPLE 7.6.1 Derive the flow graph and transfer function for the active filter shown in Fig. 7.6.2. Verify that it is a Class 1B filter.

Solution The various node voltages of the filter are labelled to correspond with those of the flow graph. The branch gains are easily calculated as follows:

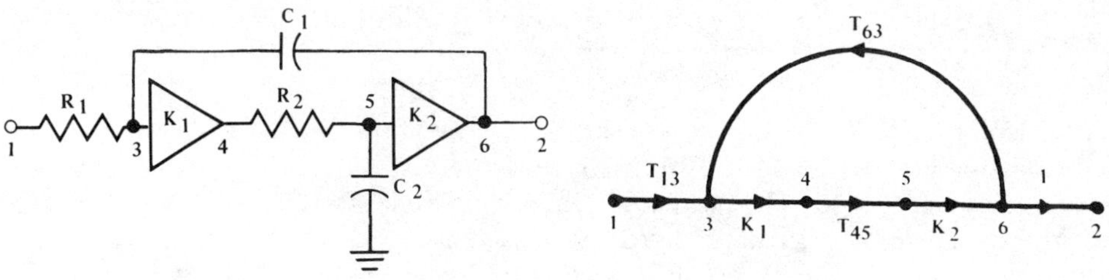

Fig. 7.6.2 Class 1B filter and its flow graph.

$$T_{13}=\frac{1}{1+sR_1C_1} \qquad T_{43}=0 \qquad T_{63}=\frac{sR_1C_1}{1+sR_1C_1}$$

$$T_{15}=0 \qquad T_{45}=\frac{1}{1+sR_2C_2} \qquad T_{65}=0 \tag{7.6.10}$$

$$T_{12}=0 \qquad T_{42}=0 \qquad T_{62}=1$$

This filter has low-pass coupling from K_1 to K_2 and high-pass coupling from K_2 to K_1. Neither amplifier has local feedback. Inspection of Table 7.19.1 shows that this is a Class 1B filter. Its gain equals

$$H(s)=\frac{K_1K_2T_{13}T_{45}}{1-K_1K_2T_{45}T_{63}}=\frac{K_1K_2}{(1+sR_1C_1)(1+sR_2C_2)-K_1K_2sR_1C_1}$$

$$=\frac{K_1K_2}{s^2R_1C_1R_2C_2+s[R_1C_1(1-K_1K_2)+R_2C_2]\ s+1} \tag{7.6.11}$$

so the filter is a low-pass type.

7.7 CLASS 1C FILTERS

Class 1C filters have active portions which vary with s^2 and s^1 only. This requires

$$b_{30}=b_{50}=d_0=0 \tag{7.7.1}$$

where $d_0=0$ requires

$$c_{30}c_{50}=0 \tag{7.7.2}$$

The local feedback has transfer functions

$$T_{43}=\frac{b_{31}s}{a_{30}+a_{31}s}, \qquad T_{63}=\frac{b_{51}s}{a_{50}+a_{51}s} \tag{7.7.3}$$

which is high-pass. It is interesting to note that Class 1C filters may possess local feedback about the K_1 and K_2 amplifiers as do Class $\overline{1C}$ and 1E filters as we shall see. The cross-coupling has the form listed in Table 7.7.1. The cross-coupling networks are high-pass and quasi-high-pass, or alternatively, both high-pass. Here we use the term quasi-high-pass to mean a high-pass filter which has finite (rather than zero) gain at s = 0. The various transfer functions for Class 1C filters are listed in Table 7.19.1. It is interesting to note that there must be local feedback (T_{43} and/or T_{65}) whenever T_{45} and T_{63} are high-pass. Otherwise, when T_{45} or T_{63} are quasi-high-pass then there need be no local feedback (see Eq. 7.7.4).

The system determinant for Class 1C filters equals

Table 7.7.1 Permissible transfer functions for Class 1C filters.

	$c_{30} = 0$	$c_{50} = 0$	$c_{30} = c_{50} = 0$
T_{45}	$\dfrac{c_{50} + c_{51}s}{a_{50} + a_{51}s}$	$\dfrac{c_{51}s}{a_{50} + a_{51}s}$	$\dfrac{c_{51}s}{a_{50} + a_{51}s}$
T_{63}	$\dfrac{c_{31}s}{a_{30} + a_{31}s}$	$\dfrac{c_{30} + c_{31}s}{a_{30} + a_{31}s}$	$\dfrac{c_{31}s}{a_{30} + a_{31}s}$

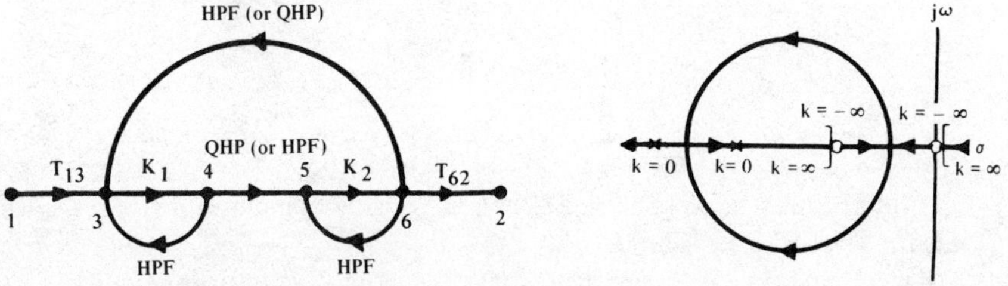

Fig. 7.7.1 Flow graph and root locus for Class 1C filters.

$$\Delta(s) = (a_{31}a_{51} - K_1a_{51}b_{31} - K_2a_{31}b_{51} + K_1K_2d_2)s^2 + (a_{30}a_{51} + a_{31}a_{50} - K_1a_{50}b_{31} - K_2a_{30}b_{51} + K_1K_2d_1)s + a_{30}a_{50} \quad (7.7.4)$$

where $d_1 = -c_{30}c_{51} - c_{31}c_{50}$ and $d_2 = b_{31}b_{51} - c_{31}c_{51}$. $\Delta(s)$ involves not only K_1K_2 products as before, but individual K_1 and K_2 terms also. In order to draw the root locus of the system poles, due to the variation of a single parameter, we must therefore fix either K_1 or K_2. Then $\Delta(s)$ may be expressed as

$$\Delta(s) = (s + a_1)(s + a_2) - ks(s + a_4) \quad (7.7.5)$$

where a_1 and a_2 may be complex and lie anywhere in the s-plane. a_4 must be real and can lie anywhere on the real axis. k equals the high-frequency loop gain, (K_1T_{43} or K_2T_{65}) + $K_1K_2T_{45}T_{63}$, of the filter. Suppose a_1, a_2, and a_4 are chosen as shown in Fig. 7.7.1. The behavior of the poles as k varies from $-\infty$ to $+\infty$ is as follows: the poles originate at $s = 0, -a_4$; they travel along the real axis and break away at (use minus sign)

$$s = -[a_1a_2/(a_1 + a_2 - a_4)]\left\{1 \mp [(1 - a_4/a_1)(1 - a_4/a_2)]^{1/2}\right\} \quad (7.7.6)$$

they travel around a circle and break onto the real axis at s given by Eq. 7.7.6 (use plus sign); they travel in opposite directions through the poles at $s = -a_1, -a_2$ for $k = 0$; the pole at $s = -a_2$ travels towards $-\infty$, reappears at $+\infty$, travels back along the positive real axis, and terminates at the origin; the other pole at $s = -a_1$ travels to $s = -a_4$ along the real axis. In general, Class 1C filters are potentially unstable for positive and negative K_1 and K_2.

Setting $a_4 = a_1a_3$ in Eq. 7.7.5, the filter poles are characterized by

$$\omega_o = [a_1a_2/(1 - k)]^{1/2}, \qquad Q = [a_1a_2(1 - k)]^{1/2}/(a_1 + a_2 - ka_1a_3) \quad (7.7.7)$$

Therefore, the various sensitivities equal

$$-S_k^{\omega_o} = -k/2(1 - k), \qquad S_{a_1}^{\omega_o} = S_{a_2}^{\omega_o} = 1/2$$

$$S_k^Q = [-k/2(1 - k)] - [-ka_1a_3/(a_1 + a_2 - ka_1a_3)] \quad (7.7.8a, b, c)$$

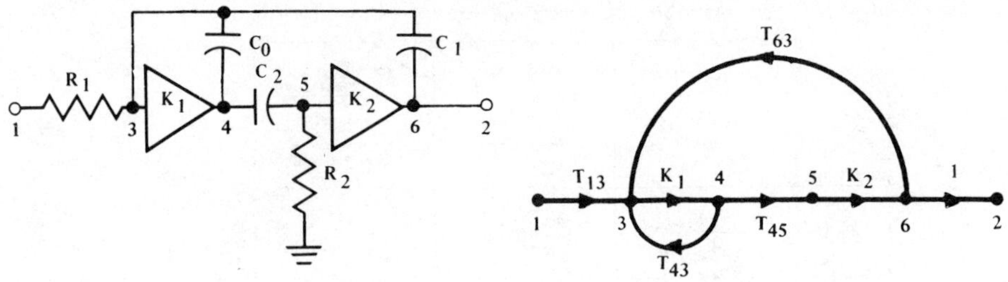

Fig. 7.7.2 Class 1C filter and its flow graph.

$$-S^Q_{a_1} = S^Q_{a_2} = (a_1 - ka_1a_3)/(a_1 + a_2 - ka_1a_3) - \tfrac{1}{2}$$

$$= (a_1 - a_2 - ka_1a_3)/(a_1 + a_2 - ka_1a_3), \qquad -S^Q_{a_3} = S^{\omega_o}_k + S^Q_k \qquad (7.7.8d, e)$$

Although it is tedious to establish the gain/sensitivity bounds, it can be shown that the general results for Class 1C filters are:[6]

1. Higher loop gain but lower sensitivities can be obtained over those of Class 1A filters.
2. Lower loop gain but higher sensitivities can be obtained over those of Class 1B filters.
3. Intermediate loop gain and sensitivities between those of Class 1A and Class 1B filters can be obtained.

Therefore, considerable design tradeoffs are available to the designer using Class 1C filters.

Let us justify these results in terms of root locus. Let $-a_4 = +\infty$ in the root locus of Fig. 7.7.1 and Eq. 7.7.5. Then the locus is that of the Class 1B filter. The Class 1C filter (negative) gain-sensitivity limits are those for the Class 1B filter. Next, let $-a_4 \to 0$ and the root locus becomes that of a Class 1A filter. Between these two loci, we have intermediate (negative) gain-sensitivity relations. Then, let $-a_4 \to -a_1$ in which case we reduce the sensitivity (increase the gain) limitations for Class 1A filters. Note that $-a_4 \in (-a_2, -a_1)$ is not a useful case since complex poles cannot be obtained. However, $-a_4 \to (-\infty, -a_2)$ can be used since complex poles can again be obtained. In this case, the sensitivity limits of the Class 1B filter are exceeded (although gain is reduced) so this is not a practical mode of operation.

EXAMPLE 7.7.1 Derive the flow graph and transfer function for the filter shown in Fig. 7.7.2. Verify that it is a Class 1C filter.

Solution The various node voltages of the filter are labelled to correspond with those of the flow graph. The branch gains are easily calculated as follows:

$$T_{13} = \frac{1}{1 + sR_1(C_0 + C_1)} \qquad T_{43} = \frac{sR_1C_0}{1 + sR_1(C_0 + C_1)} \qquad T_{63} = \frac{sR_1C_1}{1 + sR_1(C_0 + C_1)}$$

$$T_{15} = 0 \qquad T_{45} = \frac{sR_2C_2}{1 + sR_2C_2} \qquad T_{65} = 0 \qquad (7.7.9)$$

$$T_{12} = 0 \qquad T_{42} = 0 \qquad T_{62} = 1$$

From the flow graph, we see that the K_1 amplifier now has local feedback while K_2 has none. The cross-coupling from K_1 to K_2 is high-pass, as is that from K_2 to K_1. Inspecting Table 7.19.1, we see this is a Class 1C filter having $b_{51} = 0$. The gain of the active filter equals

$$H(s) = \frac{K_1K_2T_{13}T_{45}}{1 - K_1T_{43} - K_1K_2T_{45}T_{63}}$$

$$= \frac{K_1K_2sR_1C_0}{[1 + sR_1(C_0 + C_1)]\,[1 + sR_1C_1] - K_1sR_1C_0(1 + sR_1C_1) - K_1K_2s^2R_1{}^2C_1{}^2}$$

$$= \frac{K_1K_2sR_2C_2}{s^2[1 + \rho(1 - K_1) - K_1K_2]R_1C_1R_2C_2 + s[R_1C_1(1 + \rho(1 - K_1)) + R_2C_2] + 1} \tag{7.7.10}$$

where $\rho = C_0/C_1$. We see that the filter is a band-pass type.

7.8 CLASS $1\overline{C}$ FILTERS

Class $1\overline{C}$ filters have active portions which involve s^1 and s^0 only. This requires

$$b_{31} = b_{51} = d_2 = 0 \tag{7.8.1}$$

where $d_2 = 0$ requires

$$c_{31}c_{51} = 0 \tag{7.8.2}$$

The local feedback has the form

$$T_{43} = \frac{b_{30}}{a_{30} + a_{31}s}, \qquad T_{65} = \frac{b_{50}}{a_{50} + a_{51}s} \tag{7.8.3}$$

which is low-pass. The cross-coupling has the form listed in Table 7.8.1. The cross-coupling is low-pass or quasi-low-pass in form. Thus, Class $1\overline{C}$ differ from Class 1C filters only in that all local feedback is low-pass rather than high-pass. The various transfer functions are listed in Table 7.19.1. Again, there must be local feedback whenever T_{45} and T_{65} are low-pass. When T_{45} or T_{63} are quasi-low-pass, then there need be no local feedback.

The system determinant for Class $1\overline{C}$ filters equals

Table 7.8.1 Permissible transfer functions for Class $1\overline{C}$ filters.

	$c_{31} = 0$	$c_{51} = 0$	$c_{31} = c_{51} = 0$
T_{45}	$\frac{c_{50} + c_{51}s}{a_{50} + a_{51}s}$	$\frac{c_{50}}{a_{50} + a_{51}s}$	$\frac{c_{50}}{a_{50} + a_{51}s}$
T_{63}	$\frac{c_{30}}{a_{30} + a_{31}s}$	$\frac{c_{30} + c_{31}s}{a_{30} + a_{31}s}$	$\frac{c_{30}}{a_{30} + a_{31}s}$

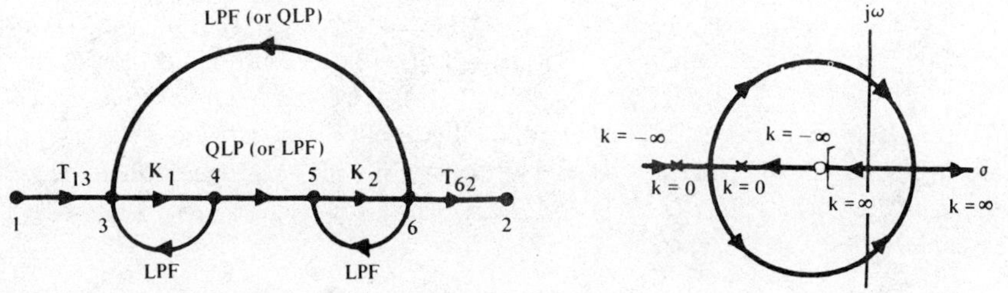

Fig. 7.8.1 Flow graph and root locus for Class $1\overline{C}$ filters.

$$\Delta(s) = a_{31}a_{51}s^2 + (a_{30}a_{51} + a_{31}a_{50} - K_1a_{51}b_{30} - K_2a_{31}b_{50} + K_1K_2d_1)s + (a_{30}a_{50} - K_1a_{50}b_{30} - K_2a_{30}b_{50} + K_1K_2d_0) \quad (7.8.4)$$

where $d_0 = b_{30}b_{50} - c_{30}c_{50}$ and $d_1 = -c_{30}c_{51} - c_{31}c_{50}$. Just as in Class 1C filters, $\Delta(s)$ involves not only K_1K_2 products as before, but individual K_1 and K_2 terms also. In order to draw the root locus of the system poles, we therefore fix either K_1 or K_2 which forces $\Delta(s)$ to involve one variable gain only. Then $\Delta(s)$ may be expressed as

$$\Delta(s) = (s + a_1)(s + a_2) - k(s + a_4) \quad (7.8.5)$$

where a_1 and a_2 may be complex and lie anywhere in the s-plane. a_4 must be real and can lie anywhere on the real axis. k is proportional to the low-frequency loop gain, $(K_1T_{43}$ or $K_2T_{65}) + K_1K_2T_{45}T_{63}$, of the filter. Suppose a_1, a_2, and a_4 are chosen as shown in Fig. 7.8.1. Then the behavior of the poles are as follows as k varies from $-\infty$ to $+\infty$: the poles originate at $s = -a_4, -\infty$; they travel along the negative real axis passing through $s = -a_1, -a_2$ for $k = 0$; they break away from the negative real axis, travel around a circle of radius $[(a_1 - a_4)(a_2 - a_4)]^{1/2}$ centered at $s = -a_4$ and break onto the positive real axis; they travel in opposite directions to $s = -a_4$ and $s = +\infty$ where they terminate. In general, Class $1\overline{C}$ filters are potentially unstable for positive and negative K_1 and K_2.

For convenience, let us re-express the filter determinant given by Eq. 7.8.5 as

$$\Delta(s) = (s + a_1)(s + a_2) - ka_1(a_3s + a_2) \quad (7.8.6)$$

Then the poles are characterized by

$$\omega_o = [a_1a_2(1 - k)]^{1/2}, \qquad Q = [a_1a_2(1 - k)]^{1/2}/(a_1 + a_2 - ka_1a_3) \quad (7.8.7)$$

The ω_o sensitivities equal

$$S_k^{\omega_o} = -k/2(1 - k), \qquad S_{a_1}^{\omega_o} = S_{a_2}^{\omega_o} = 1/2 \quad (7.8.8)$$

which are identical to those in Eq. 7.7.8 except for the sign of $S_k^{\omega_o}$ due to the ω_o expression. Comparing the Q expression with that of the Class 1C filter given by Eq. 7.7.7, we see that they are identical. Therefore, the Q sensitivities of Class $1\overline{C}$ filters are also given by Eq. 7.7.8. Thus, we see that Class $1\overline{C}$ filters have the same gain-sensitivity tradeoffs as Class 1C filters. The general gain and sensitivity bounds for Class $1\overline{C}$ filters are:

1. Higher loop gain but lower sensitivities can be obtained over those of Class $1\overline{A}$ filters.
2. Lower loop gain but higher sensitivities can be obtained over those of Class 1B filters.
3. Intermediate loop gain and sensitivities between those of Class $1\overline{A}$ and Class 1B filters can be obtained.

Again, many design tradeoffs can be made by the engineer using Class $1\overline{C}$ filters.

Let us justify these results from a root locus standpoint. Letting $-a_4 = 0$ in the root locus of Fig. 7.8.1 and Eq. 7.8.5, then the locus is that of a Class 1B filter and the gain-sensitivity limits are those for the Class 1B filter. Then as $-a_4 \to +\infty$, the locus becomes that of a Class $1\overline{A}$ filter with the corresponding gain-sensitivity limits. Between these two loci, we have intermediate gain-sensitivity relations. Then let $-a_4 \in (-\infty, -a_2)$ in which case we reduce the sensitivity (increase the gain) limitations for the Class $1\overline{C}$ filters. Note for $-a_4 \in (-a_1, 0)$, complex poles cannot be obtained.

EXAMPLE 7.8.1 Derive the flow graph and transfer function for the filter shown in Fig. 7.8.2. Verify that it is a Class $1\overline{C}$ filter.

Solution The various node voltages of the filter are labelled to correspond with those of the flow

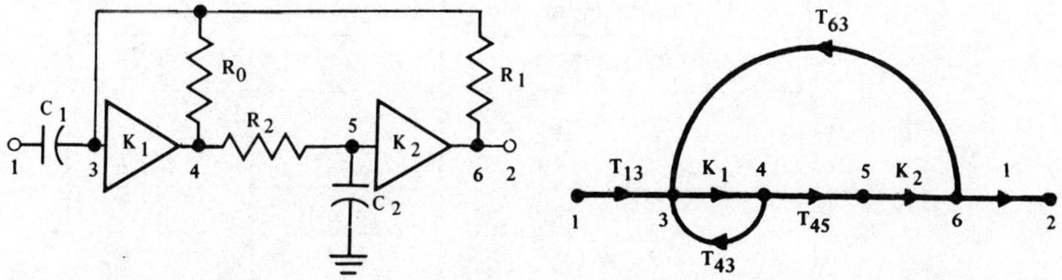

Fig. 7.8.2 Class $1\overline{C}$ filter and its flow graph.

graph. The branch gains are easily calculated as follows:

$$T_{13} = \frac{sC_1R_0R_1/(R_0+R_1)}{1+sC_1R_0R_1/(R_0+R_1)} \qquad T_{43} = \frac{R_1/(R_0+R_1)}{1+sC_1R_0R_1/(R_0+R_1)}$$

$$T_{15} = 0 \qquad T_{45} = \frac{1}{1+sR_2C_2}$$

$$T_{12} = 0 \qquad T_{42} = 0$$

$$T_{63} = \frac{R_0/(R_0+R_1)}{1+sC_1R_0R_1/(R_0+R_1)}$$

$$T_{65} = 0 \tag{7.8.9}$$

$$T_{62} = 1$$

Now we see that K_1 has local low-pass feedback while K_2 has none. The cross-coupling from K_1 to K_2 is low-pass; that from K_2 to K_1 is also low-pass. Inspection of Table 7.19.1 shows this is a Class $1\overline{C}$ filter having $b_{50} = 0$. Its gain equals

$$H(s) = \frac{K_1K_2T_{13}T_{45}}{1 - K_1T_{43} - K_1K_2T_{45}T_{63}}$$

$$= \frac{K_1K_2sC_1R_0R_1/(R_0+R_1)}{(1+sR_2C_2)[1+sC_1R_0R_1/(R_0+R_1) - K_1R_1/(R_0+R_1)] - K_1K_2R_0/(R_0+R1)}$$

$$= \frac{K_1K_2sR_1C_1}{[(R_0+R_1)/R_0](1+sR_2C_2)[1+sC_1R_0R_1/(R_0+R_1)] - (K_1R_1/R_0)(1+sR_2C_2) - K_1K_2}$$

$$= \frac{K_1K_2sR_1C_1}{s^2R_1C_1R_2C_2 + s[R_1C_1 + R_2C_2(1+\rho(1-K_1))] + [1+\rho(1-K_1) - K_1K_2]} \tag{7.8.10}$$

where $\rho = R_1/R_0$. Therefore, the filter is a band-pass type.

7.9 CLASS 1D FILTERS

In Class 1D filters, the active portion of $\Delta(s)$ varies with both s^2 and s^0. Therefore

$$b_{30} = b_{31} = b_{50} = b_{51} = d_1 = 0 \tag{7.9.1}$$

where $d_1 = 0$ requires

$$c_{30}c_{51} = 0, \qquad c_{31}c_{50} = 0 \tag{7.9.2}$$

The permissible transfer functions for the cross-coupling terms are given in Table 7.9.1. We

Table 7.9.1 Permissible transfer functions for Class 1D filters.

	$c_{30} = c_{31} = 0$	$c_{50} = c_{51} = 0$	$c_{30} = c_{50} = 0$	$c_{31} = c_{51} = 0$
T_{45}	$\dfrac{c_{50} + c_{51}s}{a_{50} + a_{51}s}$	0	$\dfrac{c_{51}s}{a_{50} + a_{51}s}$	$\dfrac{c_{50}}{a_{50} + a_{51}s}$
T_{63}	0	$\dfrac{c_{30} + c_{31}s}{a_{30} + a_{31}s}$	$\dfrac{c_{31}s}{a_{30} + a_{31}s}$	$\dfrac{c_{30}}{a_{30} + a_{31}s}$

can now show that Class 1D filters do not exist because of these conditions.

The system determinant for Class 1D filters equals

$$\Delta(s) = (a_{31}a_{51} + K_1K_2d_2)s^2 + (a_{30}a_{51} + a_{31}a_{50})s + (a_{30}a_{50} + K_1K_2d_0) \tag{7.9.3}$$

where $d_0 = -c_{30}c_{50}$ and $d_2 = -c_{31}c_{51}$. For nonzero d_0 and d_2, none of the coefficient conditions listed in Table 7.9.1 can be satisfied. Therefore, no Class 1D filters exist.

7.10 CLASS 1E FILTERS

In Class 1E filters, the active portion of $\Delta(s)$ varies with s^2, s^1, and s^0. This is the most general case having transfer functions

$$T_{43} = \frac{b_{30} + b_{31}s}{a_{30} + a_{31}s}, \quad T_{63} = \frac{c_{30} + c_{31}s}{a_{30} + a_{31}s}, \quad T_{65} = \frac{b_{50} + b_{51}s}{a_{50} + a_{51}s}, \quad T_{45} = \frac{c_{50} + c_{51}s}{a_{50} + a_{51}s} \tag{7.10.1}$$

all of which have first-order numerators as listed in Table 7.19.1. Analog computer or state-variable feedback filters fall in this category.

The system determinant for Class 1E filters is given by Eq. 7.3.3 and has the most general form involving K_1, K_2, and K_1K_2 products. We therefore fix K_1 or K_2 which forces $\Delta(s)$ to involve one variable gain only. In either case, expressing $\Delta(s)$ as

$$\Delta(s) = (s + a_1)(s + a_2) - k(s + a_3)(s + a_4) \tag{7.10.2}$$

then a_1, a_2, a_3, and a_4 may be complex and lie anywhere in the s-plane. Suppose the a_i's are chosen as shown in Fig. 7.10.1. Then the root locus can be easily drawn as shown. In general, Class 1E filters are potentially unstable for positive and negative K_1 and K_2.

From Eq. 7.10.2, the poles of the Class 1E filter are characterized by

$$\begin{aligned} \omega_o &= [(a_1a_2 - ka_3a_4)/(1 - k)]^{1/2} \\ Q &= [(a_1a_2 - ka_3a_4)(1 - k)]^{1/2}/[a_1 + a_2 - k(a_3 + a_4)] \end{aligned} \tag{7.10.3}$$

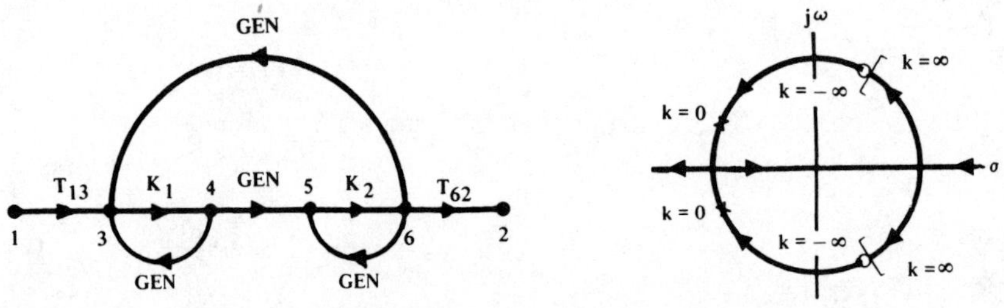

Fig. 7.10.1 Flow graph and root locus for Class 1E filters.

The various sensitivities therefore equal

$$S_k^{\omega_o} = \tfrac{1}{2}[-k\alpha_3\alpha_4/(\alpha_1\alpha_2 - k\alpha_3\alpha_4) - (-k)/(1-k)]$$
$$= \tfrac{1}{2}[k(\alpha_1\alpha_2 - \alpha_3\alpha_4)/(1-k)(\alpha_1\alpha_2 - k\alpha_3\alpha_4)]$$

$$S_{\alpha_1}^{\omega_o} = S_{\alpha_2}^{\omega_o} = \tfrac{1}{2}[\alpha_1\alpha_2/(\alpha_1\alpha_2 - k\alpha_3\alpha_4)], \qquad S_{\alpha_3}^{\omega_o} = S_{\alpha_4}^{\omega_o} = \tfrac{1}{2}[-k\alpha_3\alpha_4/(\alpha_1\alpha_2 - k\alpha_3\alpha_4)]$$

$$S_k^Q = \tfrac{1}{2}[-k/(1-k) + (-k\alpha_3\alpha_4)/(\alpha_1\alpha_2 - k\alpha_3\alpha_4)] - k(\alpha_3+\alpha_4)/[\alpha_1+\alpha_2-k(\alpha_3+\alpha_4)]$$

$$S_{\alpha_1}^Q = \tfrac{1}{2}[\alpha_1\alpha_2/(\alpha_1\alpha_2 - k\alpha_3\alpha_4)] - \alpha_1/[\alpha_1+\alpha_2-k(\alpha_3+\alpha_4)] \tag{7.10.4}$$
$$S_{\alpha_2}^Q = \tfrac{1}{2}[\alpha_1\alpha_2/(\alpha_1\alpha_2 - k\alpha_3\alpha_4)] - \alpha_2/[\alpha_1+\alpha_2-k(\alpha_3+\alpha_4)]$$
$$S_{\alpha_3}^Q = \tfrac{1}{2}[-k\alpha_3\alpha_4/(\alpha_1\alpha_2 - k\alpha_3\alpha_4)] - k\alpha_3/[\alpha_1+\alpha_2-k(\alpha_3+\alpha_4)]$$
$$S_{\alpha_4}^Q = \tfrac{1}{2}[-k\alpha_3\alpha_4/(\alpha_1\alpha_2 - k\alpha_3\alpha_4)] - k\alpha_4/[\alpha_1+\alpha_2-k(\alpha_3+\alpha_4)]$$

Since these sensitivities have a more general form than those of Class 1C and 1C filters, they have more general gain-sensitivity tradeoffs.

The situation becomes simplified when one or both of the amplifiers assumes infinite gain. Such first-order decomposition filters must be Class 1E types. This is required if a second-order gain function is to be obtained. Since Class 1E filters have the gains appearing in each denominator term, the gains may be factored out and cancelled with numerator terms when $k \to \infty$. As gain $k \to \infty$, we see that the sensitivities of Eq. 7.10.4 reduce to

$$S_k^{\omega_o} = S_{\alpha_1}^{\omega_o} = S_{\alpha_2}^{\omega_o} = 0, \quad S_k^Q = S_{\alpha_1}^Q = S_{\alpha_2}^Q = 0, \quad S_{\alpha_3}^{\omega_o} = S_{\alpha_4}^{\omega_o} = -S_{\alpha_3}^Q = -S_{\alpha_4}^Q = \tfrac{1}{2} \tag{7.10.5}$$

Therefore, the active and several passive sensitivities approach zero. The passive α_3 and α_4 sensitivities approach $\pm\frac{1}{2}$. Therefore, this is the best of all filter classes in terms of sensitivity. Thus, we can reduce both active and passive sensitivities to zero at the expense of providing infinite gain. Since we use operational amplifiers having gains of 80–120 dB (i.e., $10^4 - 10^6$), virtually infinite gain can be provided for many applications. Therefore, Class 1E infinite gain filters can be used to great advantage.

EXAMPLE 7.10.1 Derive the flow graph and transfer function for the filter shown in Fig. 7.10.2. Treat the input amplifier as an ideal summer having gain $K \to \infty$. Verify that this is a Class 1E filter.

Solution The various node voltages of the filter are labelled to correspond with those of the flow graph. Notice that we include one additional node in the standard graph to represent the summer. The branch gains are easily written as:

$$T_{13'} = \frac{R_4}{R_3+R_4}(1 + R_6/R_5) \qquad T'_{43'} = \frac{R_3}{R_3+R_4}(1 + R_6/R_5) \qquad T_{63'} = -R_6/R_5$$

$$T_{15} = 0 \qquad T_{45} = \frac{1}{1+sR_2C_2} \qquad T_{65} = \frac{sR_2C_2}{1+sR_2C_2}$$

$$T_{12} = 0 \qquad T_{42} = 0 \qquad T_{62} = 1$$

$$T_{3'3} = \frac{1}{1+sR_1C_1} \qquad T_{43} = \frac{sR_1C_1}{1+sR_1C_1} \tag{7.10.6}$$

where the gains of the branches terminating at the summing node 3′ are written using the results of Examples 7.1.2 and 7.1.3. Eliminating node 3 results in the same graph except that gain T_{43}' becomes

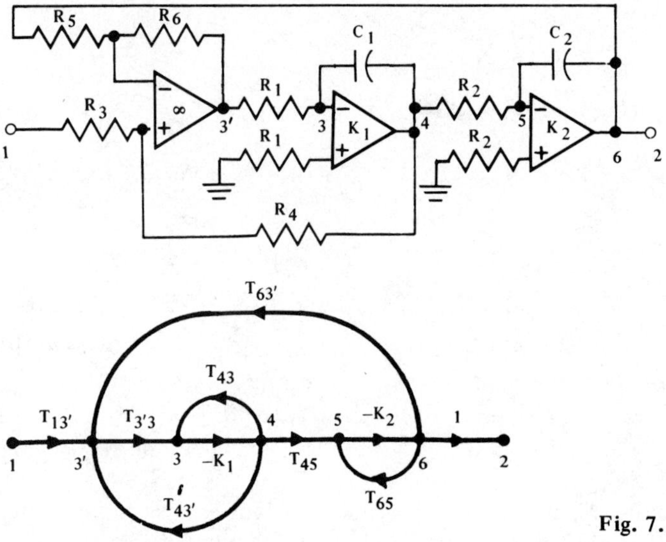

Fig. 7.10.2 Class 1E and its flow graph.

$$T_{43'} = T'_{43'} + T_{43}/T_{3'3} = \frac{R_3}{R_3 + R_4}(1 + R_6/R_5) + sR_1C_1 = b_{30} + b_{31}s \tag{7.10.7}$$

Therefore, we see that local feedback $T_{43'}$ is quasi-high-pass while T_{65} is high-pass. The cross-coupling T_{45} and $T_{63'}$ is constant. Thus, we see from Table 7.19.1 that this is a Class 1E filter. The gain of the filter equals

$$H(s) = \frac{K_1K_2T_{13'}T_{3'3}T_{45}}{1 + K_1T_{3'3}T_{43'} + K_2T_{65} + K_1K_2T_{3'3}T_{43'}T_{65}} \tag{7.10.8}$$

which results in a complicated expression. However, letting the amplifier gains K_1 and $K_2 \to \infty$, then the flow graph simplifies to that shown in Fig. 7.10.3. The gain of the filter is easily written from this graph as

$$H(s) = \frac{\dfrac{1}{s^2R_1C_1R_2C_2}\dfrac{1 + R_6/R_5}{1 + R_3/R_4}}{1 + \dfrac{1}{sR_1C_1}\dfrac{1 + R_6/R_5}{1 + R_4/R_3} + \dfrac{1}{s^2R_1C_1R_2C_2}\dfrac{R_6}{R_5}}$$

$$= \frac{1 + R_6/R_5}{1 + R_3/R_4}\,\frac{1}{s^2R_1C_1R_2C_2 + sR_2C_2\dfrac{1 + R_6/R_5}{1 + R_4/R_3} + \dfrac{R_6}{R_5}} \tag{7.10.9}$$

so the filter is a low-pass type.

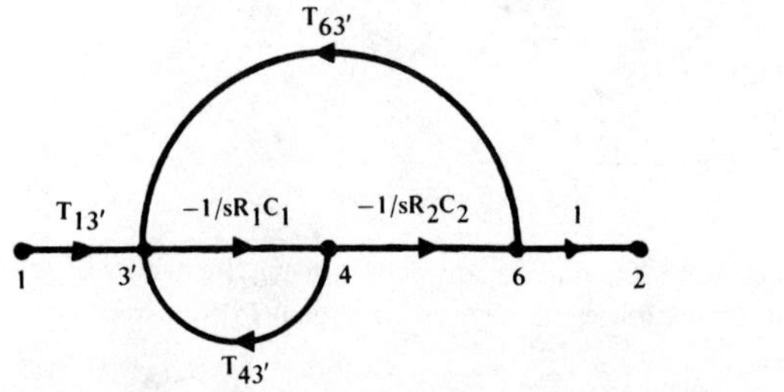

Fig. 7.10.3 Simplified flow graph under limiting gain conditions.

7.11 SECOND-ORDER DECOMPOSITION FILTERS

In second-order decomposition filters, D_{43} is a second-order polynomial and D_{65} is a zero-order polynomial, or vice versa. Without loss of generality, we set

$$\begin{aligned} &D_{13} = D_{43} = D_{63} = a_{30} + a_{31}s + a_{32}s^2 && D_{15} = D_{45} = D_{65} = a_{50} \\ &N_{43} = b_{30} + b_{31}s + b_{32}s^2 && N_{65} = b_{50} \\ &N_{63} = c_{30} + c_{31}s + c_{32}s^2 && N_{45} = c_{50} \\ &N_{43}N_{65} - N_{45}N_{63} = d_2s^2 + d_1s + d_0 \end{aligned} \tag{7.11.1}$$

The difference equation is used for notational brevity and equals

$$\begin{aligned} N_{43}N_{65} - N_{45}N_{63} &= b_{50}(b_{30} + b_{31}s + b_{32}s^2) - c_{50}(c_{30} + c_{31}s + c_{32}s^2) \\ &= (b_{32}b_{50} - c_{32}c_{50})s^2 + (b_{31}b_{50} - c_{31}c_{50})s + (b_{30}b_{50} - c_{30}c_{50}) = d_2s^2 + d_1s + d_0 \end{aligned} \tag{7.11.2}$$

Substituting these polynomials into the system determinant and collecting like powers of s yields

$$\begin{aligned} \Delta(s) &= a_{50}D_{43} - K_1a_{50}N_{43} - K_2b_{50}D_{43} + K_1K_2(d_2s^2 + d_1s + d_0) \\ &= (a_{32}a_{50} - K_1a_{50}b_{32} - K_2a_{32}b_{50} + K_1K_2d_2)s^2 \\ &\quad + (a_{31}a_{50} - K_1a_{50}b_{31} - K_2a_{31}b_{50} + K_1K_2d_1)s \\ &\quad + (a_{30}a_{50} - K_1a_{50}b_{30} - K_2a_{30}b_{50} + K_1K_2d_0) \end{aligned} \tag{7.11.3}$$

Now we determine the a_{ij}, b_{ij}, c_{ij}, and d_j coefficient conditions which are required to produce the various classes of filters. Note that the Fialkow-Gerst conditions require

$$\begin{aligned} &0 \leqslant b_{32} \leqslant a_{32}, \quad 0 \leqslant c_{32} \leqslant a_{32}, \quad 0 \leqslant b_{50} \leqslant a_{50} \\ &0 \leqslant b_{31} \leqslant a_{31}, \quad 0 \leqslant c_{31} \leqslant a_{31}, \quad 0 \leqslant c_{50} \leqslant a_{50} \\ &0 \leqslant b_{30} \leqslant a_{30}, \quad 0 \leqslant c_{30} \leqslant a_{30} \end{aligned} \tag{7.11.4}$$

Since the d_j coefficients satisfy

$$d_2 = b_{32}b_{50} - c_{32}c_{50}, \qquad d_1 = b_{31}b_{50} - c_{31}c_{50}, \qquad d_0 = b_{30}b_{50} - c_{30}c_{50} \tag{7.11.5}$$

these coefficients may be positive, negative, or zero depending upon the b_{ij}'s and c_{ij}'s.

The general flow graph for second-order decomposition filters is shown in Fig. 7.11.1. In this decomposition class, the K_2 amplifier (if present) has constant (frequency-independent)

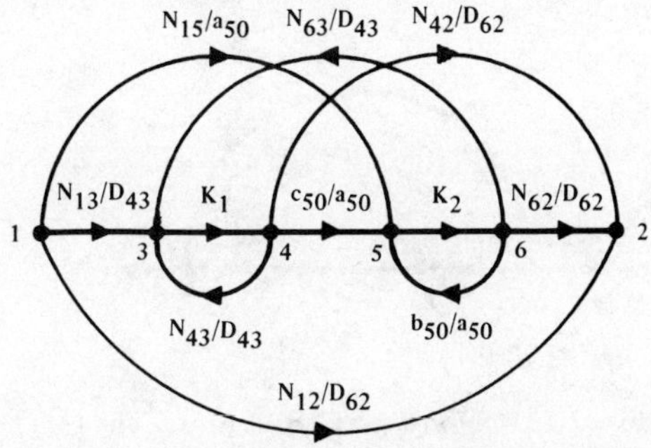

Fig. 7.11.1 General flow graph of second-order decomposition filters.

local feedback and constant cross-coupling. Thus, the second-order decomposition classification depends primarily upon the type of local feedback and cross-coupling of the K_1 amplifier. We shall see that all second-order decomposition filters can be realized with a single amplifier which is advantageous from a parts count viewpoint. This is quite different than first-order decomposition filters which always required two amplifiers.

As with the first-order decompositions, *we will omit the T_{12}, T_{15}, and T_{42} branches from the flow graphs to give them maximum simplicity.* The engineer should again draw in these branches after he grasps the basic concepts of this chapter.

7.12 CLASS 2A FILTERS

In Class 2A filters, the active portion of $\Delta(s)$ varies with s^2 only. This requires

$$b_{30} = b_{31} = b_{50} = d_0 = d_1 = 0 \tag{7.12.1}$$

where $d_0 = d_1 = 0$ further requires

$$c_{30}c_{50} = 0, \qquad c_{31}c_{50} = 0 \tag{7.12.2}$$

The combinations of c_{30}, c_{31}, and c_{50} which allow these equations to be satisfied are listed in Table 7.12.1. The various transfer functions for Class 2A filters equal (for $c_{50} \neq 0$),

$$T_{43} = \frac{b_{32}s^2}{a_{30} + a_{31}s + a_{32}s^2} \qquad T_{63} = \frac{c_{32}s^2}{a_{30} + a_{31}s + a_{32}s^2}$$
$$T_{65} = 0 \qquad T_{45} = c_{50}/a_{50} \tag{7.12.3}$$

Thus, Class 2A filters have high-pass local feedback and high-pass cross-coupling to the K_1 amplifier. The K_2 amplifier has no local feedback but constant cross-coupling. When $c_{50} = 0$, this is equivalent to $K_2 = 0$ or the single-amplifier filter. In this case, $T_{63} = 0$. This is summarized in Table 7.19.2.

Table 7.12.1 Permissible transfer functions for Class 2A filters.

	$c_{30} = c_{31} = 0$	$c_{50} = 0$
T_{43}	$\dfrac{b_{32}s^2}{a_{30} + a_{31}s + a_{32}s^2}$	$\dfrac{b_{32}s^2}{a_{30} + a_{31}s + a_{32}s^2}$
T_{63}	$\dfrac{c_{32}s^2}{a_{30} + a_{31}s + a_{32}s^2}$	0

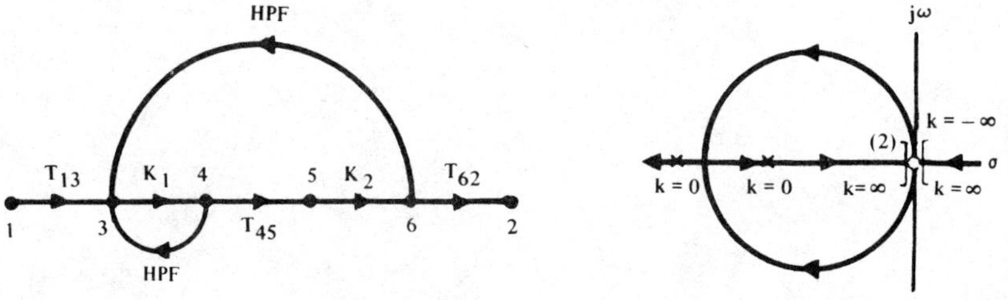

Fig. 7.12.1 Flow graph and root locus for Class 2A filters.

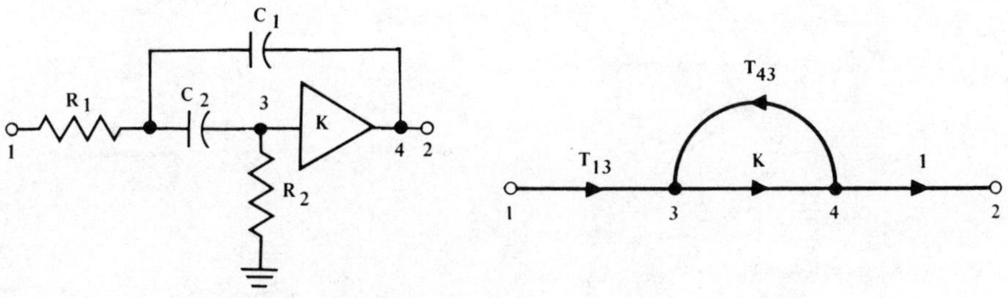

Fig. 7.12.2 Class 2A filter and its flow graph.

The system determinant for Class 2A filters equals

$$\Delta(s) = (a_{32}a_{50} - K_1 a_{50} b_{32} + K_1 K_2 d_2)s^2 + a_{31}a_{50}s + a_{30}a_{50} \tag{7.12.4}$$

where $d_2 = -c_{32}c_{50}$. The system determinant may be expressed as

$$\Delta(s) = (s + a_1)(s + a_2) - ks^2 \tag{7.12.5}$$

where k equals

$$k = K_1 b_{32}/a_{32} + K_1 K_2 c_{32} c_{50}/a_{32}a_{50} \tag{7.12.6}$$

Note that k equals the high-frequency loop gain, $K_1 T_{43} + K_1 K_2 T_{45} T_{63}$, of the filter. Fixing either K_1 or K_2, a_1 and a_2 may lie anywhere in the s-plane and are conjugates if complex. The root locus of the system poles may be drawn as shown in Fig. 7.12.1. It is identical to that for Class 1A filters where a_1 and a_2 were negative real. In general, Class 2A filters are potentially unstable for both positive and negative K_1 and K_2. When a_1 and a_2 are negative real, complex poles are produced for negative k so at least one of the amplifier gains must be negative. In the single amplifier case, K_1 is negative.

The system determinant is given by Eq. 7.12.5. Since it is identical to that for Class 1A filters, given by Eq. 7.4.6, the gain-sensitivity limits are identical with a minor change. In second-order decompositions, second-order RC networks are used. Since the poles of such networks are negative real and can never be equal, $Q < ½$. Thus, the equality condition can never be obtained as in first-order decompositions where $Q \leqslant ½$. It can only be approached by making $a_1 \cong a_2$. This is the minor change which was just mentioned. The same gain-sensitivity observations made for the Class 1A filter (Eq. 14.4.9–14.4.11) apply here and are listed in Table 7.19.3. Thus, Class 2A filters will always have low sensitivities (the order of ±½) but will require a high amplifier gain of at least $-(4Q^2 - 1)$.

EXAMPLE 7.12.1 Derive the flow graph and transfer function for the active filter shown in Fig. 7.12.2 Verify that it is a Class 2A filter.

Solution The various node voltages of the filter are labelled to correspond with those of the flow graph. However, there is one additional node not contained in the flow graph and this makes the calculation of the branch gains more involved as we shall now see. The two ladder networks having gains T_{13} and T_{43} which must be calculated are shown in Fig. 7.12.3 with their flow graph descriptions discussed in Chap. 1. We follow the approach discussed in Example 1.14.3. To eliminate confusion in labelling, we use the notation E for voltage, and J for current for any internal node voltages or branch currents. Gain T_{13} equals

$$T_{13} = \frac{R_2C_2/R_1C_1}{1 + 1/sR_1C_1 + C_2/C_1 + sR_2C_2 + R_2C_2/R_1C_1}$$

$$= \frac{R_2C_2/R_1C_1}{sR_2C_2 + (1 + C_2/C_1 + R_2C_2/R_1C_1) + 1/sR_1C_1}$$

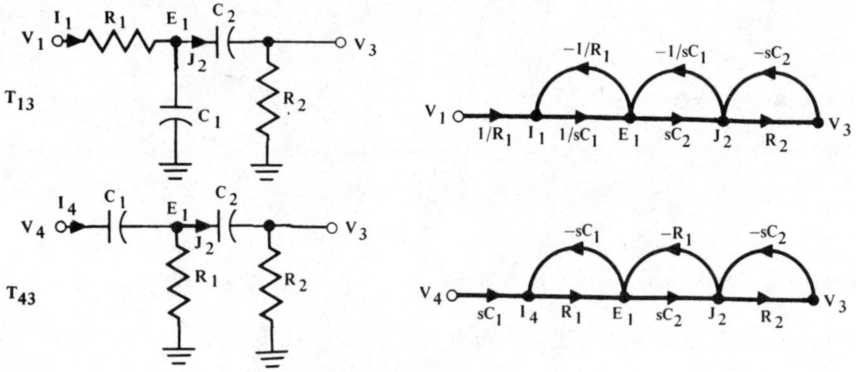

Fig. 7.12.3 T_{13} and T_{43} networks and their flow graphs.

$$= \frac{sR_2C_2}{s^2R_1C_1R_2C_2 + s[R_1C_1(1 + C_2/C_1) + R_2C_2] + 1} \tag{7.12.7}$$

and T_{43} equals

$$T_{43} = \frac{s^2R_1C_1R_2C_2}{s^2R_1C_1R_2C_2 + s[R_1C_1(1 + C_2/C_1) + R_2C_2] + 1} \tag{7.12.8}$$

Since T_{43} is a high-pass network of second-order, we see from Table 7.19.2 that this is a Class 2A single-amplifier filter. The gain of the filter equals

$$H(s) = \frac{KT_{13}}{1 - KT_{43}} = \frac{KsR_2C_2}{s^2(1 - K)R_1C_1R_2C_2 + s[R_1C_1(1 + C_2/C_1) + R_2C_2] + 1} \tag{7.12.9}$$

so the filter is a band-pass type.

7.13 CLASS $2\overline{A}$ FILTERS

In Class $2\overline{A}$ filters, the active portion of $\Delta(s)$ varies with s^0 only. This requires

$$b_{31} = b_{32} = b_{50} = d_2 = d_1 = 0 \tag{7.13.1}$$

where $d_1 = d_2 = 0$ requires additionally that

$$c_{32}c_{50} = 0, \qquad c_{31}c_{50} = 0 \tag{7.13.2}$$

The combinations of c_{31}, c_{32}, and c_{50} which allow these equations to be satisfied are listed in Table 7.13.1. Class $2\overline{A}$ filters have transfer functions which equal

$$T_{43} = \frac{b_{30}}{a_{30} + a_{31}s + a_{32}s^2} \qquad T_{63} = \frac{c_{30}}{a_{30} + a_{31}s + a_{32}s^2} \tag{7.13.3}$$

$$T_{65} = 0 \qquad T_{45} = c_{50}/a_{50}$$

Thus, Class $2\overline{A}$ filters have low-pass local feedback and low-pass cross-coupling to the K_1 amplifier. Class $2\overline{A}$ filters differ from Class 2A filters only in that the local feedback and cross-coupling is low-pass rather than high-pass. The single-amplifier filter results when $K_2 = 0$, or equivalently $c_{50} = 0$, in which case $T_{63} = 0$. This is summarized in Table 7.19.2.

Table 7.13.1 Permissible transfer functions for Class $2\bar{A}$ filters.

	$c_{31} = c_{32} = 0$	$c_{50} = 0$
T_{43}	$\dfrac{b_{30}}{a_{30} + a_{31}s + a_{32}s^2}$	$\dfrac{b_{30}}{a_{30} + a_{31}s + a_{32}s^2}$
T_{63}	$\dfrac{c_{30}}{a_{30} + a_{31}s + a_{32}s^2}$	0

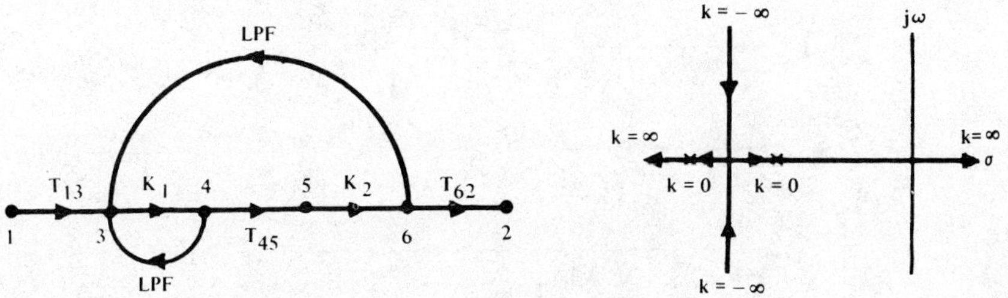

Fig. 7.13.1 Flow graph and root locus for Class $2\bar{A}$ filters.

The system determinant for Class $2\bar{A}$ filters equals

$$\Delta(s) = a_{32}a_{50}s^2 + a_{31}a_{50}s + (a_{30}a_{50} - K_1a_{50}b_{30} + K_1K_2d_0) \tag{7.13.4}$$

where $d_0 = -c_{30}c_{50}$. The system determinant may be expressed as

$$\Delta(s) = (s + a_1)(s + a_2) - ka_1a_2 \tag{7.13.5}$$

where k equals

$$k = K_1b_{30}/a_{30} + K_1K_2c_{30}c_{50}/a_{30}a_{50} \tag{7.13.6}$$

In Class $2\bar{A}$ filters, k equals the low-frequency loop gain, $K_1T_{43} + K_1K_2T_{45}T_{63}$, of the filter. Fixing K_1 or K_2, a_1 and a_2 may lie anywhere in the s-plane and are conjugates if complex. The root locus is shown in Fig. 7.13.1. It is identical to that for Class $1\bar{A}$ filters where a_1 and a_2 were negative real. Generally, Class $2\bar{A}$ filters are potentially unstable for positive and negative K_1 and K_2. When a_1 and a_2 are negative real, at least one of the amplifiers must have negative gain to produce complex poles. In the single amplifier case, K_1 is negative.

The system determinant is given by Eq. 7.13.5. Since it is identical to that for Class $1\bar{A}$ filter given by Eq. 7.5.6, identical gain-sensitivity limits exist (Eqs. 7.5.8–7.5.10) except the equality conditions can never be obtained. They are identical to those for Class 2A filters (except for the sign of $S_k^{\omega_o}$). Thus, Class $2\bar{A}$ filters will always have low sensitivities (the order of ½) but will require a high amplifier gain of at least $-(4Q^2 - 1)$.

EXAMPLE 7.13.1 Derive the flow graph and transfer function for the active filter shown in Fig. 7.13.2. Verify that it is a Class $2\bar{A}$ filter.

Solution The various node voltages of the filter are labelled to correspond with those of the flow graph. Again, there is one additional node which is not contained in the flow graph. This makes the branch gains more difficult to determine. The two ladder networks whose gains must be calculated are shown in Fig. 7.13.3 along with their flow graphs. Note that we have used the convention introduced earlier where E is voltage and J is current for internal nodes and branches in the ladder. Gain T_{13} equals

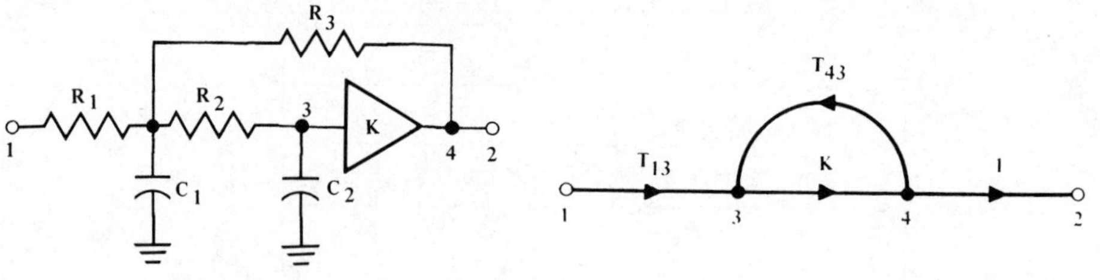

Fig. 7.13.2 Class $2\overline{A}$ filter and its flow graph.

$$T_{13} = \frac{R_3/R_1 sR_2C_2(1 + sR_3C_1)}{1 + R_3/R_1(1 + sR_3C_1) + R_3/R_2(1 + sR_3C_1) + 1/sR_2C_2 + R_3/R_1 sR_2C_2(1 + sR_3C_1)}$$

$$= \frac{R_3/R_1}{s^2R_2C_2R_3C_1 + s(R_2C_2[1 + R_3(1/R_1 + 1/R_2)] + R_3C_1) + (1 + R_3/R_1)}$$

$$= \frac{1}{s^2R_1C_1R_2C_2 + s[R_1C_1(1 + C_2/C_1) + R_2C_2(1 + R_1/R_3)] + (1 + R_1/R_3)} \tag{7.13.7}$$

From the ladder networks of Fig. 7.13.3, we see that the gain T_{43} is equal to T_{13} where R_1 and R_3 are interchanged. Thus,

$$T_{43} = \frac{1}{s^2R_3C_1R_2C_2 + s(R_3C_1 + R_2C_2[1 + R_3(1/R_1 + 1/R_2)]) + (1 + R_1/R_3)}$$

$$= \frac{R_1/R_3}{s^2R_1C_1R_2C_2 + s[R_1C_1(1 + C_2/C_1) + R_2C_2(1 + R_1/R_3)] + (1 + R_1/R_3)} \tag{7.13.8}$$

Since T_{43} is low-pass network of second-order, we see from Table 7.19.2 that this is a Class $2\overline{A}$ single-amplifier filter. The gain of the filter equals

$$H(s) = \frac{KT_{13}}{1 - KT_{43}} \tag{7.13.9}$$

$$= \frac{K}{s^2R_1C_1R_2C_2 + s[R_1C_1(1 + C_2/C_1) + R_2C_2(1 + R_1/R_3)] + [1 + (1 - K)R_1/R_3]}$$

so the filter is a low-pass type.

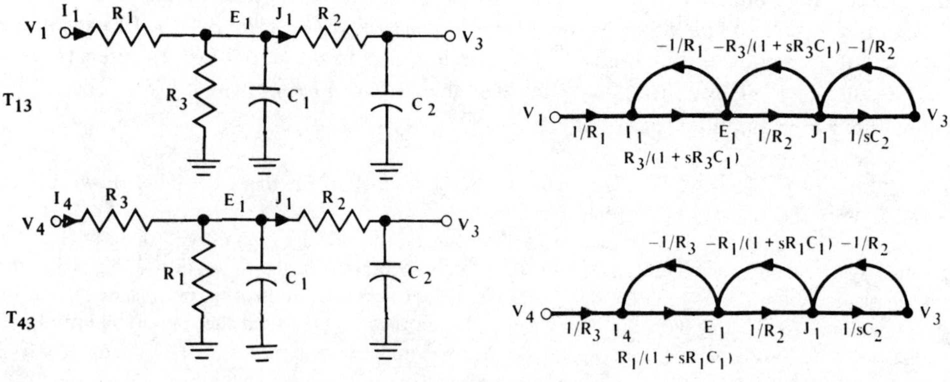

Fig. 7.13.3 T_{13} and T_{43} networks and their flow graphs.

7.14 CLASS 2B FILTERS

In Class 2B filters, the active portion of $\Delta(s)$ varies with s^1 only which requires

$$b_{30} = b_{32} = b_{50} = d_0 = d_2 = 0 \tag{7.14.1}$$

where $d_0 = d_2 = 0$ further requires

$$c_{30}c_{50} = 0, \qquad c_{32}c_{50} = 0 \tag{7.14.2}$$

The combinations of c_{30}, c_{32}, and c_{50} which are allowed are listed in Table 7.14.1. The various transfer functions equal (for $c_{50} \neq 0$)

$$T_{43} = \frac{b_{31}s}{a_{30} + a_{31}s + a_{32}s^2} \qquad T_{63} = \frac{c_{31}s}{a_{30} + a_{31}s + a_{32}s^2} \tag{7.14.3}$$

$$T_{65} = 0 \qquad T_{45} = c_{50}/a_{50}$$

Therefore, Class 2B filters have band-pass local feedback and band-pass cross-coupling to the K_1 amplifier. The K_2 amplifier again has no local feedback but constant cross-coupling. In the single amplifier case when $K_2 = 0$, or equivalently $c_{50} = 0$, the gain $T_{63} = 0$. This is listed in Table 7.19.2.

The system determinant for Class 2B filters equals

$$\Delta(s) = a_{32}a_{50}s^2 + (a_{31}a_{50} - K_1a_{50}b_{31} + K_1K_2d_1)s + a_{30}a_{50} \tag{7.14.4}$$

where $d_1 = -c_{31}c_{50}$. The system determinant can be expressed as

$$\Delta(s) = (s + a_1)(s + a_2) - ka_1s \tag{7.14.5}$$

where

$$k = [(a_1 + a_2)/a_1]\,[K_1b_{31}/a_{31} + K_1K_2c_{31}c_{50}/a_{31}a_{50}] \tag{7.14.6}$$

Table 7.14.1 Permissible transfer functions for Class 2B filters.

	$c_{30} = c_{32} = 0$	$c_{50} = 0$
T_{43}	$\dfrac{b_{31}s}{a_{30} + a_{31}s + a_{32}s^2}$	$\dfrac{b_{31}s}{a_{30} + a_{31}s + a_{32}s^2}$
T_{63}	$\dfrac{c_{31}s}{a_{30} + a_{31}s + a_{32}s^2}$	0

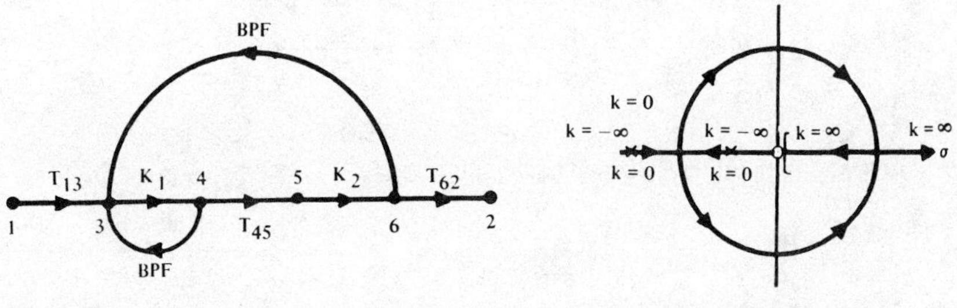

Fig. 7.14.1 Flow graph and root locus for Class 2B filters.

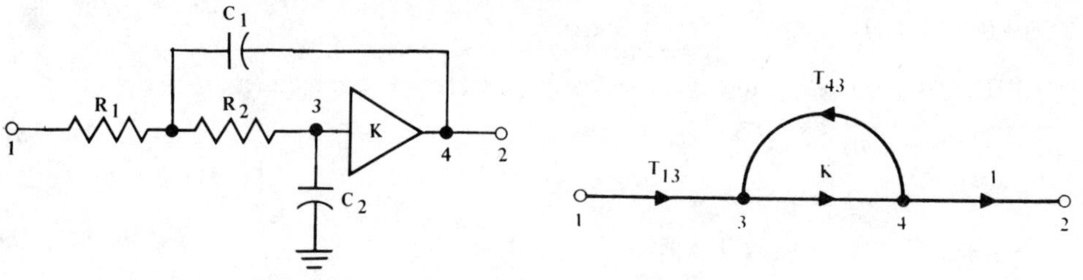

Fig. 7.14.2 Class 2B filter and its flow graph.

k equals the loop gain, $K_1T_{43} + K_1K_2T_{45}T_{63}$, at the center frequency of the filter scaled by $(a_1 + a_2)/a_1$. Fixing either K_1 or K_2, a_1 and a_2 may lie anywhere in the s-plane and are conjugates if complex. The root locus of the system poles is drawn in Fig. 7.14.1. It is identical to that for Class 1B filters where a_1 and a_2 were negative real. Class 2B filters are potentially unstable for positive and negative K_1 and K_2 in general. When a_1 and a_2 are negative real, the amplifiers must have the same signs to produce complex poles. In the single-amplifier case, K_1 is positive.

The system determinant is given by Eq. 7.14.5. Since it is identical to that for Class 1B filters given by Eq. 7.6.5, the gain-sensitivity limits (Eq. 7.6.7–7.6.9) are identical excluding the equality signs. These are listed in Table 7.19.3.

By analogy with the Class 1B filter results, we see that minimizing the separation between a_1 and a_2 forces $S_k^Q \to (2Q - 1)$ and $\pm S_{a_i}^Q \to (Q - \frac{1}{2})$ for gain $k \to (2 - 1/Q)$. This is the usual mode of operation. Although we can reduce the gain S to $k \to (1 - 1/4Q^2)$ by maximizing the separation between a_1 and a_2 as $a_1/a_2 = 4Q^2$, we see S_k^Q and $\pm S_{a_i}^Q \to (2Q^2 - \frac{1}{2})$ which is undesirable.

EXAMPLE 7.14.1 Derive the flow graph and transfer function for the active filter shown in Fig. 7.14.2. Verify that it is a Class 2B filter.

Solution The various node voltages of the filter are labelled to correspond with those of the flow graph. The two ladder networks whose gains T_{13} and T_{43} must be calculated are shown in Fig. 7.14.3 with their associated flow graphs.

T_{13} is the gain of a low-pass filter as contrasted to the high-pass filter ladder in Example 7.12.1. Using Mason's gain formula, T_{13} equals

$$T_{13} = \frac{1/s^2R_1C_1R_2C_2}{1 + 1/sR_1C_1 + 1/sR_2C_1 + 1/sR_2C_2 + 1/s^2R_1C_1R_2C_2}$$

$$= \frac{1}{s^2R_1C_1R_2C_2 + s[R_1(C_1 + C_2) + R_2C_2] + 1} \qquad (7.14.7)$$

and T_{43} equals

$$T_{43} = \frac{R_1C_1/R_2C_2}{1 + R_1/R_2 + R_1C_1/R_2C_2 + sR_1C_1 + 1/sR_2C_2}$$

$$= \frac{sR_1C_1}{s^2R_1C_1R_2C_2 + s[R_1(C_1 + C_2) + R_2C_2] + 1} \qquad (7.14.8)$$

We see that T_{43} is a band-pass filter of second-order so from Table 7.19.2, this must be a Class 2B single-amplifier filter. The gain of the filter equals

$$H(s) = \frac{KT_{13}}{1 - KT_{43}} = \frac{K}{s^2R_1C_1R_2C_2 + s[R_1C_1(1 - K + C_2/C_1) + R_2C_2] + 1} \qquad (7.14.9)$$

so the filter is a low-pass type.

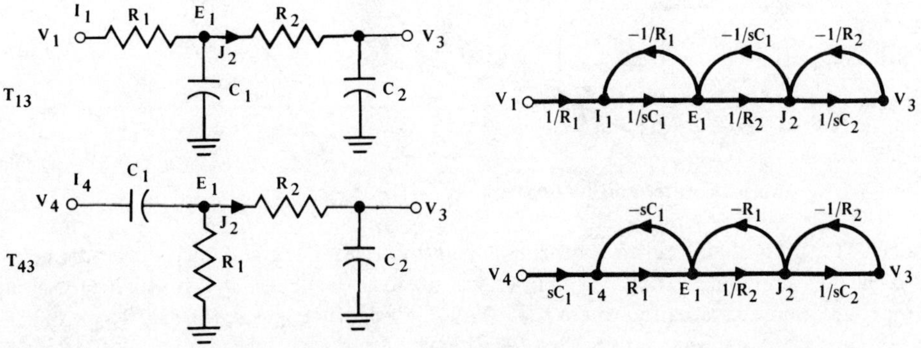

Fig. 7.14.3 T_{13} and T_{43} networks and their flow graphs.

7.15 CLASS 2C FILTERS

In Class 2C filters, the active portion of $\Delta(s)$ varies with s^2 and s^1. This requires

$$b_{30} = b_{50} = d_0 = 0 \tag{7.15.1}$$

where $d_0 = 0$ requires

$$c_{30}c_{50} = 0 \tag{7.15.2}$$

Therefore, $c_{30} = 0$ or $c_{50} = 0$ as listed in Table 7.15.1. The transfer functions equal (for $c_{50} \neq 0$)

$$T_{43} = \frac{b_{31}s + b_{32}s^2}{a_{30} + a_{31}s + a_{32}s^2} \qquad T_{63} = \frac{c_{31}s + c_{32}s^2}{a_{30} + a_{31}s + a_{32}s^2} \tag{7.15.3}$$

$$T_{65} = 0 \qquad T_{45} = c_{50}/a_{50}$$

Table 7.15.1 Permissible transfer functions for Class 2C filters.

	$c_{30} = 0$	$c_{50} = 0$
T_{43}	$\dfrac{b_{31}s + b_{32}s^2}{a_{30} + a_{31}s + a_{32}s^2}$	$\dfrac{b_{31}s + b_{32}s^2}{a_{30} + a_{31}s + a_{32}s^2}$
T_{63}	$\dfrac{c_{31}s + c_{32}s^2}{a_{30} + a_{31}s + a_{32}s^2}$	0

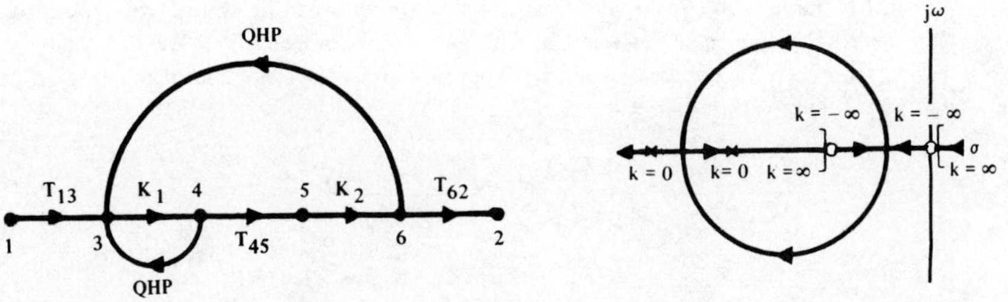

Fig. 7.15.1 Flow graph and root locus for Class 2C filters.

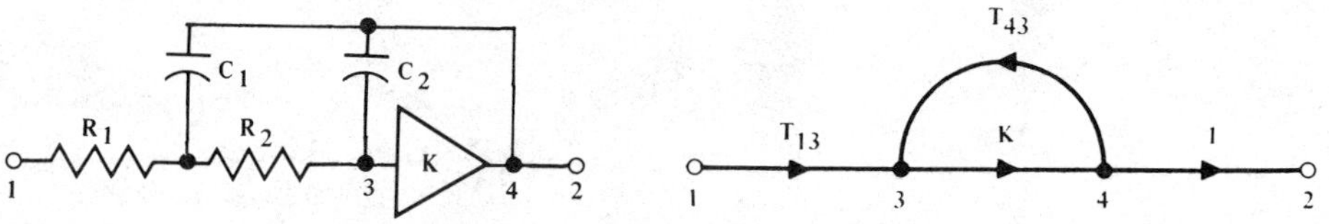

Fig. 7.15.2 Class 2C filter and its flow graph.

Class 2C filters therefore have quasi-high-pass local feedback and quasi-high-pass cross-coupling to the K_1 amplifier. The K_2 amplifier has no local feedback and constant cross-coupling. In the single amplifier situation where $K_2 = 0$, or equivalently $c_{50} = 0$, the gain $T_{63} = 0$.

The system determinant for Class 2C filters equals

$$\Delta(s) = (a_{32}a_{50} - K_1 a_{50} b_{32} + K_1 K_2 d_2)s^2 + (a_{31}a_{50} - K_1 a_{50} b_{31} + K_1 K_2 d_1)s + a_{30}a_{50} \tag{7.15.4}$$

where $d_2 = -c_{32}c_{50}$ and $d_1 = -c_{31}c_{50}$. Fixing either K_1 or K_2, then the system determinant has the form

$$\Delta(s) = (s + \alpha_1)(s + \alpha_2) - ks(s + \alpha_4) \tag{7.15.5}$$

k equals the high-frequency loop gain, $K_1 T_{43} + K_1 K_2 T_{45} T_{63}$, of the filter. α_1 and α_2 may lie anywhere in the s-plane and are conjugates if complex. The root locus of the system poles for Class 2C filters is shown in Fig. 7.15.1. It is identical to that for Class 1C filters. Generally, Class 2C filters are potentially unstable for positive and negative K_1 and K_2.

Comparing the system determinant of Class 2C filters (Eq. 7.15.5) with that of Class 1C filters given by Eq. 7.7.5, we see that they are identical. Thus, the gain-sensitivity tradeoffs found for Class 1C filters apply to Class 2C filters. Therefore, we can say:

1. Higher loop gain but lower sensitivities can be obtained over those of Class 2A filters.
2. Lower loop gain but higher sensitivities can be obtained over those of Class 2B filters.
3. Intermediate loop gain and sensitivities between those of Class 2A and Class 2B filters can be obtained.

Thus, these design tradeoffs can be used to advantage by the engineer in designing Class 2C filters.

EXAMPLE 7.15.1 Derive the flow graph and transfer function for the active filter shown in Fig. 7.15.2. Verify that it is a Class 2C filter.

Solution The transfer functions T_{13} and T_{43} of the two networks shown in Fig. 7.15.3 must be determined. The gain T_{13} of the low-pass ladder can be immediately written from the results of Example 7.14.1 as

$$T_{13} = \frac{1}{s^2 R_1 C_1 R_2 C_2 + s[R_1 C_1(1 + C_2/C_1) + R_2 C_2] + 1} \tag{7.15.6}$$

The gain T_{43} of the second network is more complicated to determine. Although a flow graph can be drawn for the network from which its transfer function can be found, we choose to use an alternative approach. Here we shall make use of Thevenin equivalent circuits. We first view the network as being driven from two V_4 sources. Then we Thevenize the R_1C_1 portion of the network, afterwhich we can write by superposition that

$$V_3 = \left(\frac{Z_1}{Z_1 + Z_2} + \frac{kZ_2}{Z_1 + Z_2}\right)V_4 = \left(\frac{Z_1 + kZ_2}{Z_1 + Z_2}\right)V_4 \tag{7.15.7}$$

so that the gain $T_{43} = V_3/V_4 = (Z_1 + kZ_2)/(Z_1 + Z_2)$ where

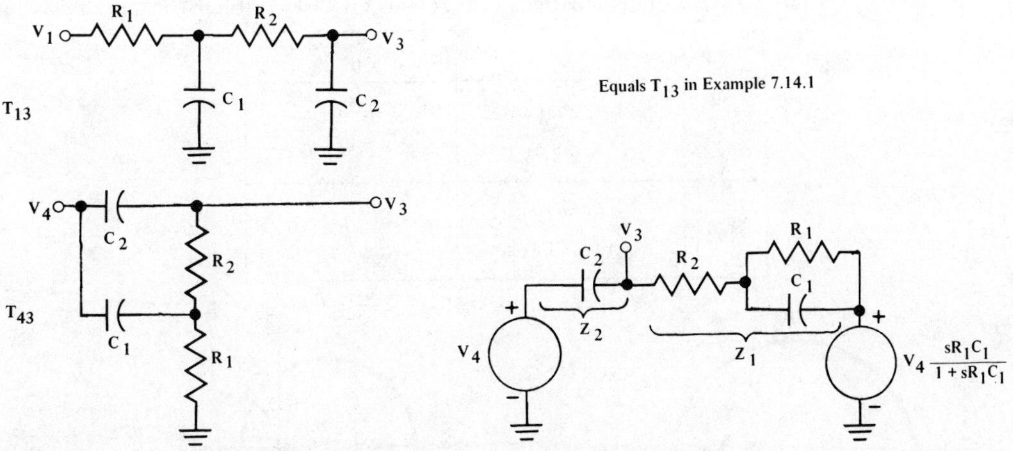

Fig. 7.15.3 T_{13} and T_{43} networks and a convenient equivalent circuit.

$$T_{43} = \frac{\left(R_2 + \dfrac{R_1}{1 + sR_1C_1}\right) + \left(\dfrac{sR_1C_1}{1 + sR_1C_1}\right)\dfrac{1}{sC_2}}{R_2 + R_1/(1 + sR_1C_1) + 1/sC_2} = \frac{sR_2C_2(1 + sR_1C_1) + sR_1C_2 + sR_1C_1}{sR_2C_2(1 + sR_1C_1) + sR_1C_2 + (1 + sR_1C_1)}$$

$$= \frac{s^2R_1C_1R_2C_2 + s[R_1C_1(1 + C_2/C_1) + R_2C_2]}{s^2R_1C_1R_2C_2 + s[R_1C_1(1 + C_2/C_1) + R_2C_2] + 1} \tag{7.15.8}$$

This is a quasi-high-pass transfer function. From Table 7.19.2, we see that it must be a Class 2C single-amplifier filter. Its gain equals

$$H(s) = \frac{KT_{13}}{1 - KT_{43}} = \frac{K}{s^2(1 - K)R_1C_1R_2C_2 + s(1 - K)[R_1C_1(1 + C_2/C_1) + R_2C_2] + 1} \tag{7.15.9}$$

so the filter is a low-pass type.

7.16 CLASS $2\overline{C}$ FILTERS

In Class $2\overline{C}$ filters, the active portion of $\Delta(s)$ varies with s^1 and s^0. This requires

$$b_{32} = b_{50} = d_2 = 0 \tag{7.16.1}$$

where $d_2 = 0$ also requires

$$c_{32}c_{50} = 0 \tag{7.16.2}$$

Therefore, $c_{32} = 0$ or $c_{50} = 0$ as listed in Table 7.16.1. Their transfer functions equal (for $c_{50} \neq 0$)

$$T_{43} = \frac{b_{30} + b_{31}s}{a_{30} + a_{31}s + a_{32}s^2} \qquad T_{63} = \frac{c_{30} + c_{31}s}{a_{30} + a_{31}s + a_{32}s^2} \tag{7.16.3}$$

$$T_{65} = 0 \qquad T_{45} = c_{50}/a_{50}$$

Class $2\overline{C}$ filters have quasi-low-pass local feedback and quasi-low pass cross-coupling to the K_1 amplifier. The K_2 amplifier has no local feedback but constant cross-coupling. Class $2\overline{C}$ filters differ from Class 2C filters only in that the feedback networks are quasi-low-pass rather than

Table 7.16.1 Permissible transfer functions for Class $2\overline{C}$ filters.

	$c_{32} = 0$	$c_{50} = 0$
T_{43}	$\dfrac{b_{30} + b_{31}s}{a_{30} + a_{31}s + a_{32}s^2}$	$\dfrac{b_{30} + b_{31}s}{a_{30} + a_{31}s + a_{32}s^2}$
T_{63}	$\dfrac{c_{30} + c_{31}s}{a_{30} + a_{31}s + a_{32}s^2}$	0

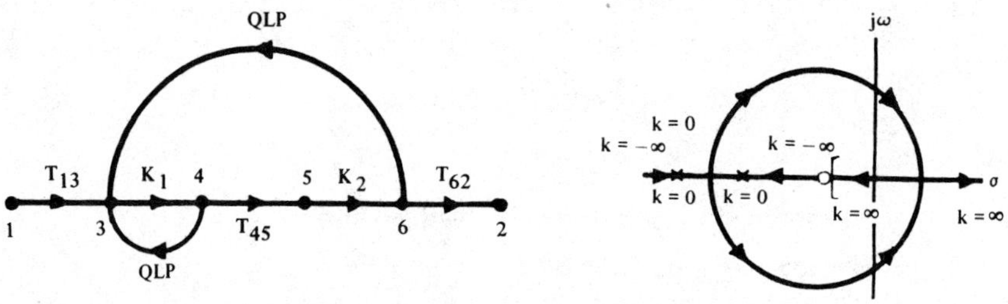

Fig. 7.16.1 Flow graph and root locus for Class $2\overline{C}$ filters.

quasi-high-pass. In the single amplifier situation when $K_2 = 0$, or equivalently $c_{50} = 0$, the gain $T_{63} = 0$.

Class $2\overline{C}$ filters have a system determinant which equals

$$\Delta(s) = a_{32}a_{50}s^2 + (a_{31}a_{50} - K_1a_{50}b_{31} + K_1K_2d_1)s + (a_{30}a_{50} - K_1a_{50}b_{30} + K_1K_2d_0) \tag{7.16.4}$$

where $d_1 = -c_{31}c_{50}$, and $d_0 = -c_{30}c_{50}$. Fixing either K_1 or K_2, then the system determinant has the form

$$\Delta(s) = (s + \alpha_1)(s + \alpha_2) - k(s + \alpha_4) \tag{7.16.5}$$

k is proportional to the low-frequency loop gain, $K_1T_{43} + K_1K_2T_{45}T_{63}$, of the filter. The root locus of the system poles for Class $2\overline{C}$ filters is shown in Fig. 7.16.1. It is identical to that for Class $1\overline{C}$ filters. Class $2\overline{C}$ filters are potentially unstable for both positive and negative K_1 and K_2.

Comparing the system determinant of Class $2\overline{C}$ filters (Eq. 7.16.5) with that of Class $1\overline{C}$ filters given by Eq. 7.8.6, we see they are analogous. Thus, the gain-sensitivity tradeoff found for Class $1\overline{C}$ filters apply to Class $2\overline{C}$ filters. Therefore, we can say:

1. Higher loop gain but lower sensitivities can be obtained over those of Class $2\overline{A}$ filters.
2. Lower loop gain but higher sensitivities can be obtained over those of Class 2B filters.
3. Intermediate loop gain and sensitivities between those of Class $2\overline{A}$ and 2B filters can be obtained.

Again, great design flexibility is available in Class $2\overline{C}$ filters.

EXAMPLE 7.16.1 Derive the flow graph and transfer function for the active filter shown in Fig. 7.16.2. Verify that it is a Class $2\overline{C}$ filter.

Solution The various node voltages of the filter are labelled to correspond with those of the flow graph. The three ladder networks whose gains T_{13}, T_{43}, and T_{63} must be calculated are shown in Fig. 7.16.3 with their associated flow graphs.

T_{13} can be calculated from the flow graph. T_{13} may also be calculated by replacing R_1 by $R_1/(1 + sR_1C_3)$ in the T_{43} expression of Example 7.14.1. Alternatively, the Thevenin equivalent circuit

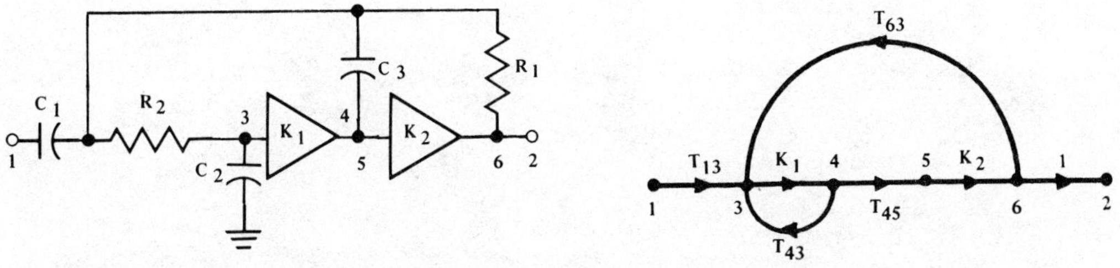

Fig. 7.16.2 Class 2$\overline{C}$ filter and its flow graph.

of the C_1 and C_3 divider may be used, in which case the T_{43} expression of Example 7.14.1 is utilized where C_1 is replaced by $(C_1 + C_3)$ and multiplied by $C_1/(C_1 + C_3)$. Following this procedure,

$$T_{13} = \frac{C_1}{C_1 + C_3} \frac{sR_1(C_1 + C_3)}{s^2R_1(C_1 + C_3)R_2C_2 + s[R_1(C_1 + C_3)R_2C_2 + R_1C_2 + R_2C_2] + 1}$$

$$= \frac{sR_1C_1}{s^2R_1(C_1 + C_3)R_2C_2 + s[R_1(C_1 + C_2 + C_3) + R_2C_2] + 1} \qquad (7.16.6)$$

T_{43} is identical to T_{13} when C_1 and C_3 are interchanged. Thus,

$$T_{43} = \frac{sR_1C_3}{s^2R_1(C_1 + C_3)R_2C_2 + s[R_1(C_1 + C_2 + C_3) + R_2C_2] + 1} \qquad (7.16.7)$$

directly from the T_{13} expression. T_{63} equals

$$T_{63} = \frac{1}{s^2R_1(C_1 + C_3)R_2C_2 + s[R_1(C_1 + C_2 + C_3) + R_2C_2] + 1} \qquad (7.16.8)$$

using the T_{13} gain expression in Example 7.14.1 where C_1 is replaced by $(C_1 + C_3)$. We see that T_{43} is band-pass and T_{63} is low-pass. Thus, from Table 7.19.2, this must be a Class 2$\overline{C}$ filter. Its gain equals

$$H(s) = \frac{K_1K_2T_{13}T_{45}}{1 - K_1T_{43} - K_1K_2T_{63}T_{45}}$$

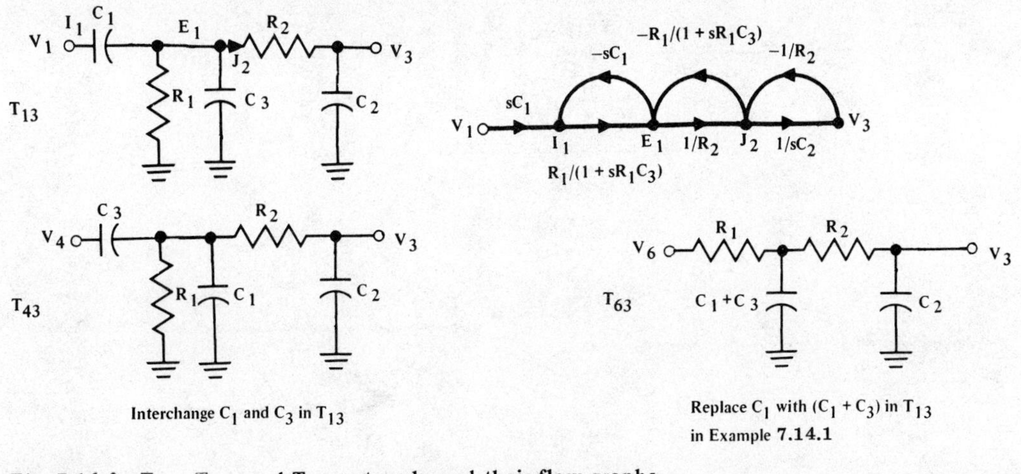

Fig. 7.16.3 T_{13}, T_{43}, and T_{63} networks and their flow graphs.

$$= \frac{K_1K_2sR_1C_1}{s^2R_1(C_1+C_3)R_2C_2 + s[R_1(C_1+C_2+(1-K_1)C_3)+R_2C_2] + (1-K_1K_2)} \tag{7.16.9}$$

so the filter is a band-pass type.

7.17 CLASS 2D FILTERS

In Class 2D filters, the active portion of $\Delta(s)$ varies with s^2 and s^0 which requires

$$b_{31} = b_{50} = d_1 = 0 \tag{7.17.1}$$

where $d_1 = 0$ requires

$$c_{31}c_{50} = 0 \tag{7.17.2}$$

Therefore, $c_{31} = 0$ or $c_{50} = 0$ as listed in Table 7.17.1. The Class 2D filter transfer functions equal (for $c_{50} \neq 0$)

$$T_{43} = \frac{b_{30}+b_{32}s^2}{a_{30}+a_{31}s+a_{32}s^2} \qquad T_{63} = \frac{c_{30}+c_{32}s^2}{a_{30}+a_{31}s+a_{32}s^2}$$
$$T_{65} = 0 \qquad T_{45} = c_{50}/a_{50} \tag{7.17.3}$$

Class 2D filters have band-stop local feedback and band-stop cross-coupling to the K_1 amplifier. The K_2 amplifier has no local feedback but constant cross-coupling. In the single amplifier situation when $K_2 = 0$, or equivalently $c_{50} = 0$, the gain $T_{63} = 0$.

Class 2D filters have system determinants which equal

$$\Delta(s) = (a_{32}a_{50} - K_1a_{50}b_{32} + K_1K_2d_2)s^2 + a_{31}a_{50}s + (a_{30}a_{50} - K_1a_{50}b_{30} + K_1K_2d_0) \tag{7.17.4}$$

Table 7.17.1 Permissible transfer functions for Class 2D filters.

	$c_{31} = 0$	$c_{50} = 0$
T_{43}	$\frac{b_{30}+b_{32}s^2}{a_{30}+a_{31}s+a_{32}s^2}$	$\frac{b_{30}+b_{32}s^2}{a_{30}+a_{31}s+a_{32}s^2}$
T_{63}	$\frac{c_{30}+c_{32}s^2}{a_{30}+a_{31}s+a_{32}s^2}$	0

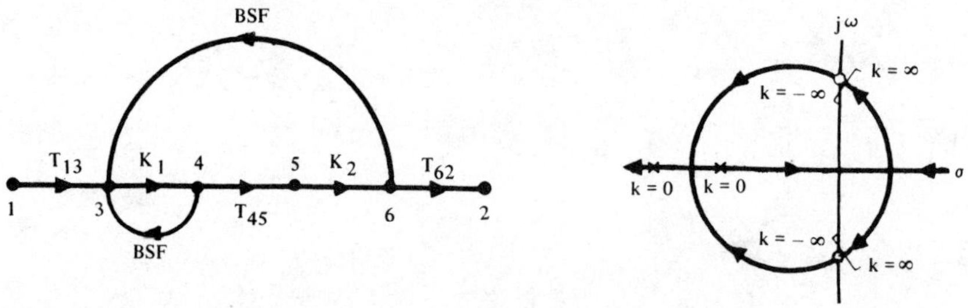

Fig. 7.17.1 Flow graph and root locus for Class 2D filters.

where $d_2 = -c_{32}c_{50}$ and $d_o = -c_{30}c_{50}$. The system determinant has the form

$$\Delta(s) = (s + a_1)(s + a_2) - k(s^2 + a_1 a_2 a_3^2) \tag{7.17.5}$$

where

$$k = K_1 b_{32}/c_{32} + K_1 K_2 c_{32} c_{50}/a_{32} a_{50} \tag{7.17.6}$$

k equals the high-frequency loop gain, $K_1 T_{43} + K_1 K_2 T_{45} T_{63}$, for the filter. Fixing either K_1 or K_2, the root locus of the filter poles is shown in Fig. 7.17.1. Generally, Class 2D filters are potentially unstable for positive and negative K_1 and K_2.

From the system determinant of Eq. 7.17.5, the filter poles are characterized by

$$\omega_o = [a_1 a_2(1 - ka_3^2)/(1 - k)]^{1/2}, \qquad Q = [(a_1 a_2)^{1/2}/(a_1 + a_2)]\,[(1 - ka_3^2)(1 - k)]^{1/2} \tag{7.17.7}$$

Therefore, the various sensitivities equal

$$-\tfrac{1}{2} < S_k^{\omega_o} = \tfrac{1}{2}[(-ka_3^2)/(1 - ka_3^2) - (-k)/(1 - k)]$$
$$= \tfrac{1}{2}[k/(1 - k)]\,[(1 - a_3^2)/(1 - ka_3^2)] < \tfrac{1}{2}$$

$$S_{a_1}^{\omega_o} = S_{a_2}^{\omega_o} = \tfrac{1}{2}, \qquad 0 \leqslant S_k^Q = \tfrac{1}{2}[(-ka_3^2)/(1 - ka_3^2) + (-k)/(1 - k)] < 1 \tag{7.17.8}$$

$$0 \leqslant S_{a_3}^{\omega_o} = S_{a_3}^Q = (-ka_3^2)/(1 - ka_3^2) < 1$$

$$-1 < S_{a_1}^Q = -S_{a_2}^Q = (a_1 - a_2)/(a_1 + a_2) < 1$$

Previously we found that Class 1D filters were nonexistent. Therefore, we must determine new gain-sensitivity limits for Class 2D filters. The gain k required to obtain a given Q is found by solving

$$a_3^2 k^2 - k(1 + a_3^2) + (1 - a^2 Q^2) = 0 \tag{7.17.9}$$

which is Eq. 7.17.7b in rearranged form and $a = (a_1 + a_2)/\sqrt{a_1 a_2} \geqslant 2$. Using the quadratic formula and solving for k in Eq. 7.17.9 gives

$$-k = (a^2Q^2 - 1)^{1/2}\left\{[1 - (1 + a_3^2)^2/(a^2Q^2 - 1)]^{1/2} - (1 + a_3^2)/2(a^2Q^2 - 1)^{1/2}\right\} \tag{7.17.10}$$

To determine the minimum k value, we set $dk/da_3 = 0$ and evaluate $a_3 = 1$. Substituting a_3 into Eq. 7.17.10, yields the minimum gain as

$$-k = aQ - 1 = (a_1 + a_2)Q/(a_1 a_2)^{1/2} - 1 > 2Q - 1 \tag{7.17.11}$$

The active ω_o sensitivity, $S_k^{\omega_o}$, never exceeds ±½ while the active Q sensitivity, S_k^Q, never exceeds ±1. To minimize $|S_k^{\omega_o}|$, we set $a_3 = 1$ which yields $S_k^{\omega_o} = 0$. Then $S_k^Q = -k/(1 - k) = (1 - 1/2Q)$. S_k^Q can be reduced to half this value by setting $a_3 = 0$, but this increases $S_k^{\omega_o}$ so that $S_k^{\omega_o} = -S_k^Q \cong (1 - 1/2Q)/2$.

The passive sensitivities $S_{a_i}^Q$ are zero when $a_1 = a_2$. The passive sensitivities $S_{a_3}^{\omega_o} = S_{a_3}^Q$ are reduced to zero by making $a_3 = 0$. However, this increases the gain required.

The gain k is minimized when $a_3 = 1$ and the time constants $a_1 = a_2$. Then $-k > (2Q - 1) \cong 2Q$. Thus, the approximate gain required for Class 2D filters is the square root of that (or half the number of dB) required for Class 2A and $2\overline{A}$ filters.

Thus, we see Class 2D filters require design tradeoffs to be made. Their gains will be smaller than those for Class 2A and $2\overline{A}$ filters, but several of their sensitivities will be slightly larger.

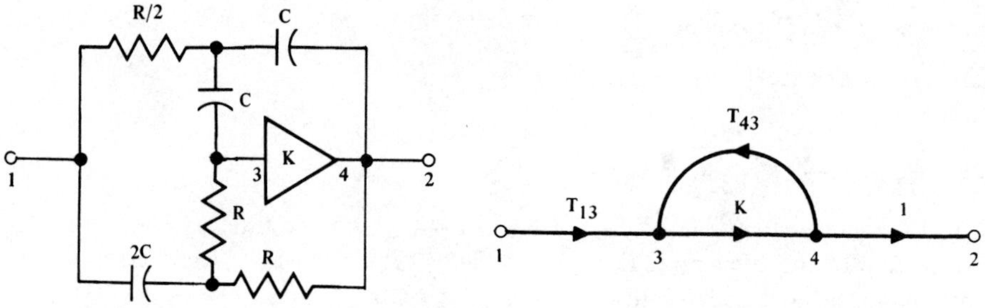

Fig. 7.17.2 Class 2D filter and its flow graph.

EXAMPLE 7.17.1 Derive the flow graph and transfer function for the active filter shown in Fig. 7.17.2. Verify that it is a Class 2D filter.

Solution The various node voltages of the filter are labelled to correspond to those of the flow graph. The twin-T networks whose gains T_{13} and T_{43} must be calculated are shown in Fig. 7.17.3. Using matrix methods, these gains are easily calculated. T_{43} was calculated in Example 1.11.5 as

$$T_{43} = \frac{(sRC)^2 + 1}{(sRC)^2 + 4sRC + 1} \tag{7.17.12}$$

Using a similar method to calculate T_{13} yields

$$T_{13} = \frac{4sRC}{(sRC)^2 + 4sRC + 1} \tag{7.17.13}$$

Since T_{43} is a notch network, we see from Table 7.19.2 that this is a Class 2D single-amplifier filter. The gain of the filter equals

$$H(s) = \frac{KT_{13}}{1 - KT_{43}} = \frac{4KsRC}{(sRC)^2(1-K) + 4sRC + (1-K)} \tag{7.17.14}$$

so the filter is a band-pass type.

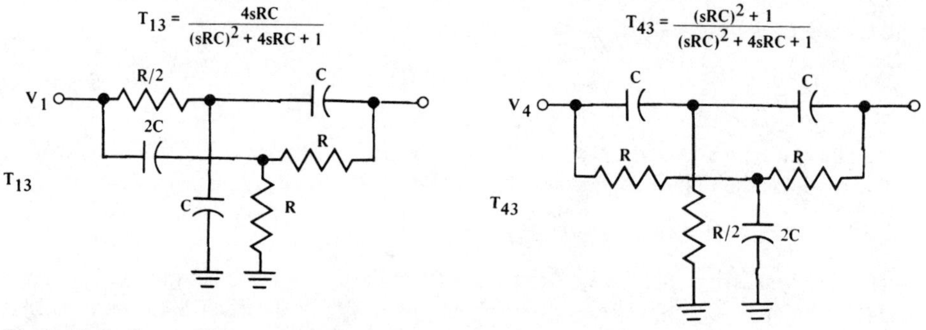

Fig. 7.17.3 T_{13} and T_{43} networks and transfer functions.

7.18 CLASS 2E FILTERS

In Class 2E filters, the active portion of $\Delta(s)$ varies with s^2, s^1, and s^0. This is the most general case where

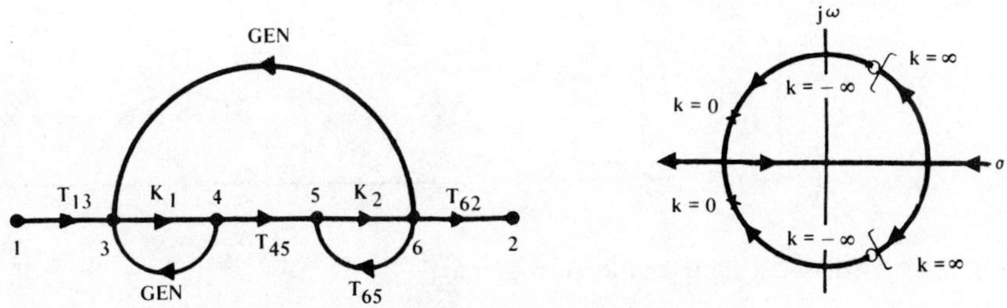

Fig. 7.18.1 Flow graph and root locus for Class 2E filters.

$$T_{43} = \frac{b_{30} + b_{31}s + b_{32}s^2}{a_{30} + a_{31}s + a_{32}s^2} \qquad T_{63} = \frac{c_{30} + c_{31}s + c_{32}s^2}{a_{30} + a_{31}s + a_{32}s^2} \tag{7.18.1}$$

$$T_{65} = b_{50}/a_{50} \qquad T_{45} = c_{50}/a_{50}$$

The system determinant has the form

$$\Delta(s) = (s + a_1)(s + a_2) - k(s + a_3)(s + a_4) \tag{7.18.2}$$

Fixing either K_1 or K_2, the root locus of the system poles is shown in Fig. 7.18.1. It is identical to that for Class 1E filters. In general, Class 2E filters are potentially unstable for positive and negative K_1 and K_2.

Since the system determinant for Class 2E filters is identical to that for Class 1E filters given by Eq. 7.10.2, identical gain-sensitivity equations exist. Therefore, Class 2E filters have parameters given by Eq. 7.10.3 and sensitivities given by Eq. 7.10.4. They have the same gain-sensitivity tradeoffs as Class 1E filters.

The situation simplifies when one or both of the amplifiers assume infinite gain. Such second-order decomposition filters must be Class 2E types. The limiting sensitivity relations are given by Eq. 7.10.5. Again, active sensitivities can be reduced to zero at the expense of providing infinite gain. Thus, we can use Class 2E infinite gain filters to great advantage. In general, they have the lowest sensitivities of all second-order decomposition filters.

EXAMPLE 7.18.1 Derive the flow graph and transfer function for the active filter shown in Fig. 7.18.2. Verify that it is a Class 2E filter.

Solution The various node voltages of the filter are labelled to correspond with those of the flow graph. The gains T_{13} and T_{43} are easily written using impedance ratios. T_{13} equals

$$T_{13} = \frac{Z_2}{Z_1 + Z_2} = \frac{sR_2C_1}{(1 + sR_1C_1)(1 + sR_2C_2) + sR_2C_1}$$
$$= \frac{sR_2C_1}{s^2R_1C_1R_2C_2 + s[R_1C_1 + R_2C_1 + R_2C_2] + 1} \tag{7.18.3}$$

while T_{43} equals

$$T_{43} = \frac{Z_1}{Z_1 + Z_2} = \frac{(1 + sR_1C_1)(1 + sR_2C_2)}{s^2R_1C_1R_2C_2 + s[R_1C_1 + R_2C_1 + R_2C_2] + 1}$$
$$= \frac{s^2R_1C_1R_2C_2 + s[R_1C_1 + R_2C_2] + 1}{s^2R_1C_1R_2C_2 + s[R_1C_1 + R_2C_1 + R_2C_2] + 1} \tag{7.18.4}$$

T_{43} is a general biquadratic function. Thus, from Table 7.19.2, this must be a Class 2E single-amplifier

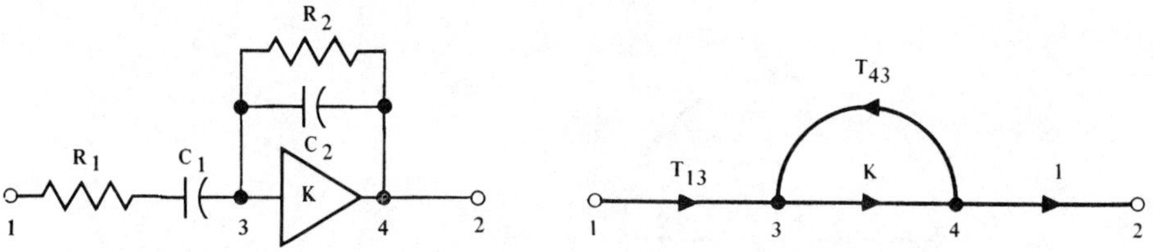

Fig. 7.18.2 Class 2E filter and its flow graph.

filter. The gain of the filter equals

$$H(s) = \frac{KT_{13}}{1 - KT_{43}} = \frac{KsR_2C_1}{(1-K)(1+sR_1C_1)(1+sR_2C_2) + sR_2C_1}$$

$$= \frac{KsR_2C_1}{s^2(1-K)R_1C_1R_2C_2 + s[(R_1C_1 + R_2C_2)(1-K) + R_2C_1] + (1-K)} \tag{7.18.5}$$

so the filter is a band-pass type.

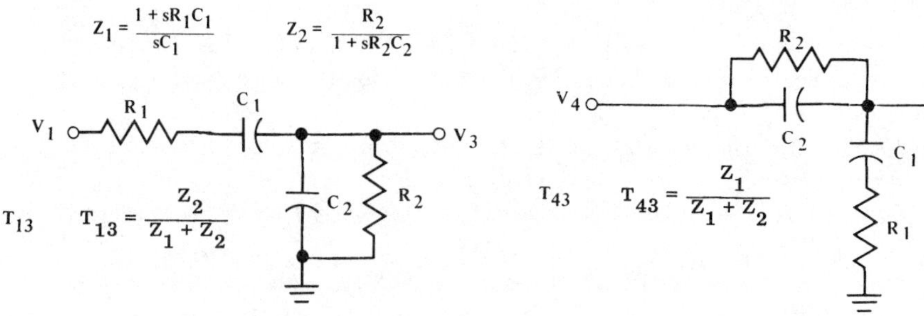

Fig. 7.18.3 T_{13} and T_{43} networks and their transfer functions.

7.19 ACTIVE FILTER CLASSIFICATION IN RETROSPECT

We have shown in this chapter that any RC active filter composed of one or two operational amplifiers and having a first or second-order transfer function can be categorized into one of 13 classes. We have seen that each class within a decomposition group has its own particular determinant and root locus of system poles as shown in Fig. 7.19.1. The classification can often be carried out through inspection by categorizing the feedback network types as listed in Tables 7.19.1 and 7.19.2.

The summary of the sensitivities of ω_o and Q with respect to both the active and passive parameters determined for the various classes are listed in Table 7.19.3. It shows that, in general, Class 1X and 2X active filters have analogous relations (X = A–E). For example, Class 1A and 2A filters have $S_k^{\omega_o}$ and S_k^Q bounded by ½, low passive sensitivities, and large closed-loop gain requirements bounded by $-(4Q^2 - 1)$. Generally, Class C, D, and E filters have characteristics which may either fall between those for Class A and Class B filters, or exceed them.

Active filter design philosophy basically depends upon root locus. Say for example we wish to minimize variations in Q (or ζ) with respect to gain k. In Class A, $\overline{\text{A}}$, and B filters, we do this by making gain k as small as possible for any given Q. Minimizing gain requires minimizing the separation between a_1 and a_2 (the passive corner frequencies) in the root loci of Fig. 7.19.1.

Alternatively, if we wish to minimize the gain k required to obtain a given Q or ζ, then we also minimize the passive time constants in Class A and $\overline{\text{A}}$ filters. However, we maximize the

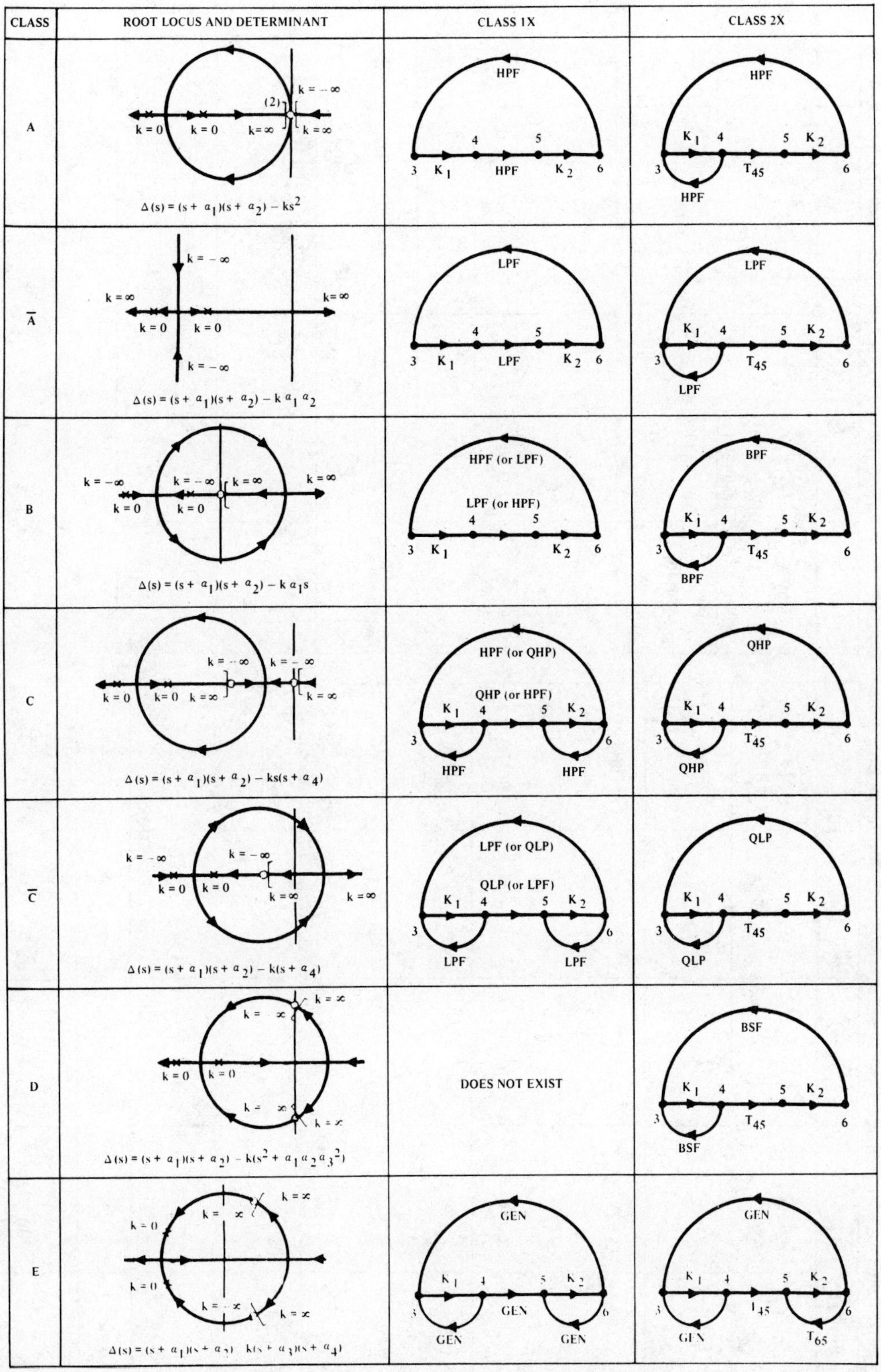

Fig. 7.19.1 Summary of root loci and flow graphs.

Table 7.19.1 Summary of transfer functions (first-order decomposition).

Filter Class	T_{43}	T_{63}	T_{65}	T_{45}
Class 1A	0	$\frac{c_{31}s}{a_{30}+a_{31}s}$ HP	0	$\frac{c_{51}s}{a_{50}+a_{51}s}$ HP
Class $1\overline{A}$	0	$\frac{c_{30}}{a_{30}+a_{31}s}$ LP	0	$\frac{c_{50}}{a_{50}+a_{51}s}$ LP
Class 1B	0	$\frac{c_{31}s}{a_{30}+a_{31}s}$ HP $\frac{c_{30}}{a_{30}+a_{31}s}$ LP	0	$\frac{c_{50}}{a_{50}+a_{51}s}$ LP $\frac{c_{51}s}{a_{50}+a_{51}s}$ HP
Class 1C	$\frac{b_{31}s}{a_{30}+a_{31}s}$ HP	$\frac{c_{31}s}{a_{30}+a_{31}s}$ HP $\frac{c_{30}+c_{31}s}{a_{30}+a_{31}s}$ QHP	$\frac{b_{51}s}{a_{50}+a_{51}s}$ HP	$\frac{c_{50}+c_{51}s}{a_{50}+a_{51}s}$ QHP $\frac{c_{51}s}{a_{50}+a_{51}s}$ HP
Class $1\overline{C}$	$\frac{b_{30}}{a_{30}+a_{31}s}$ LP	$\frac{c_{30}}{a_{30}+a_{31}s}$ LP $\frac{c_{30}+c_{31}s}{a_{30}+a_{31}s}$ QLP	$\frac{b_{50}}{a_{50}+a_{51}s}$ LP	$\frac{c_{50}+c_{51}s}{a_{50}+a_{51}s}$ QLP $\frac{c_{50}}{a_{50}+a_{51}s}$ LP
Class 1D	Does Not Exist			
Class 1E	$\frac{b_{30}+b_{31}s}{a_{30}+a_{31}s}$ GEN	$\frac{c_{30}+c_{31}s}{a_{30}+a_{31}s}$ GEN	$\frac{b_{50}+b_{51}s}{a_{50}+a_{51}s}$ GEN	$\frac{c_{50}+c_{51}s}{a_{50}+a_{51}s}$ GEN

Table 7.19.2 Summary of transfer functions (second-order decomposition).

Filter Class	T_{43}	T_{63}	T_{65}	T_{45}
Class 2A	$\frac{b_{32}s^2}{a_{30}+a_{31}s+a_{32}s^2}$ HP	$\frac{c_{32}s^2}{a_{30}+a_{31}s+a_{32}s^2}$ HP	0	$\frac{c_{50}}{a_{50}}$
Class $2\overline{A}$	$\frac{b_{30}}{a_{30}+a_{31}s+a_{32}s^2}$ LP	$\frac{c_{30}}{a_{30}+a_{31}s+a_{32}s^2}$ LP	0	$\frac{c_{50}}{a_{50}}$
Class 2B	$\frac{b_{31}s}{a_{30}+a_{31}s+a_{32}s^2}$ BP	$\frac{c_{31}s}{a_{30}+a_{31}s+a_{32}s^2}$ BP	0	$\frac{c_{50}}{a_{50}}$
Class 2C	$\frac{b_{31}s+b_{32}s^2}{a_{30}+a_{31}s+a_{32}s^2}$ QHP	$\frac{c_{31}s+c_{32}s^2}{a_{30}+a_{31}s+a_{32}s^2}$ QHP	0	$\frac{c_{50}}{a_{50}}$
Class $2\overline{C}$	$\frac{b_{30}+b_{31}s}{a_{30}+a_{31}s+a_{32}s^2}$ QLP	$\frac{c_{30}+c_{31}s}{a_{30}+a_{31}s+a_{32}s^2}$ QLP	0	$\frac{a_{50}}{a_{50}}$
Class 2D	$\frac{b_{30}+b_{32}s^2}{a_{30}+a_{31}s+a_{32}s^2}$ BS	$\frac{c_{30}+c_{32}s^2}{a_{30}+a_{31}s+a_{32}s^2}$ BS	0	$\frac{c_{50}}{a_{50}}$
Class 2E	$\frac{b_{30}+b_{31}s+b_{32}s^2}{a_{30}+a_{31}s+a_{32}s^2}$ GEN	$\frac{c_{30}+c_{31}s+c_{32}s^2}{a_{30}+a_{31}s+a_{32}s^2}$ GEN	$\frac{b_{50}}{a_{50}}$	$\frac{c_{50}}{a_{50}}$

Table 7.19.3 Summary of gain-sensitivity relations for Class 2X filters. For Class 1X filters, add equality signs to the inequalities. (All passive ω_o sensitivities equal ½.)

Class	Loop Gain K	Active Q Sensitivity	Active ω_o Sensitivity	Passive Q Sensitivity
A	$-K > 4Q^2 - 1$	$S > ½(1 - 1/4Q^2)$	$-S > ½(1 - 1/4Q^2)$	$\|S\| < 1$
$\overline{A}$	$-K > 4Q^2 - 1$	$S > ½(1 - 1/4Q^2)$	$S > ½(1 - 1/4Q^2)$	$\|S\| < 1$
B	$K > 1 - 1/2Q$	$S > 4Q^2 - 1$	0	$\|S\| > (Q - ½)$
C	Tradeoff			
$\overline{C}$	Tradeoff			
2D (only)	$K > 2Q - 1$	1	0	$\|S\| < 1$
E	Tradeoff			

separation to $a_1/a_2 = 4Q^2$ in Class B filters. We see that Class A and $\overline{A}$ filters will always have small variations in ω_o and Q due to variations in a_1, a_2, and k. However, Class B filters will have large variations in Q. Of course, ω_o is independent of k in Class B filters. In all filters, increasing Q requires increasing gain $|k|$.

Another very useful design fact concerns the resonant frequency ω_o of the filter. Although it is independent of gain k in Class B filters, it can be used to control ω_o in Class A and $\overline{A}$ filters. In Class B filters, ω_o equals the geometric means of the passive corner frequencies ($\omega_o = \sqrt{a_1 a_2}$). In Class A filters, ω_o is increased (or up-scaled) by a factor $\sqrt{1-k}$. In Class $\overline{A}$ filters, ω_o is decreased (or down-scaled) by a factor $\sqrt{1-k}$. This fact allows us to very often obtain more satisfactory designs using Class A (or C) for lower-frequency filters (below 100 Hz) and Class $\overline{A}$ (or $\overline{C}$) for higher-frequency filters (above 10 KHz) due to the passive component values.

Class C and $\overline{C}$ filters are generalized combinations of Class A, $\overline{A}$, and B filters. Their root loci are shown in Fig. 7.19.2. Class C ($\overline{C}$) filters having a locus lying between the Class A and B ($\overline{A}$ and B) filter loci have intermediate gain-sensitivity values. However, when the locus lies inside (outside) this region, the sensitivity values are reduced but the gains are increased. But when the locus lies outside (inside) this region, the gains are reduced but the sensitivities are increased. This is usually a poor mode of operation. In both cases, when the origin is not encircled, there are maximum Q values that can be obtained. Thus, Class C and $\overline{C}$ filters are very flexible.

Class 2D filters have a more general root locus than Class A and $\overline{A}$ filters as shown in Fig. 7.19.3. In A and $\overline{A}$ filters, the root locus terminated on the zeros which lay at either the origin or infinity. However, the zeros of Class D filters usually lie on the jω-axis although they can

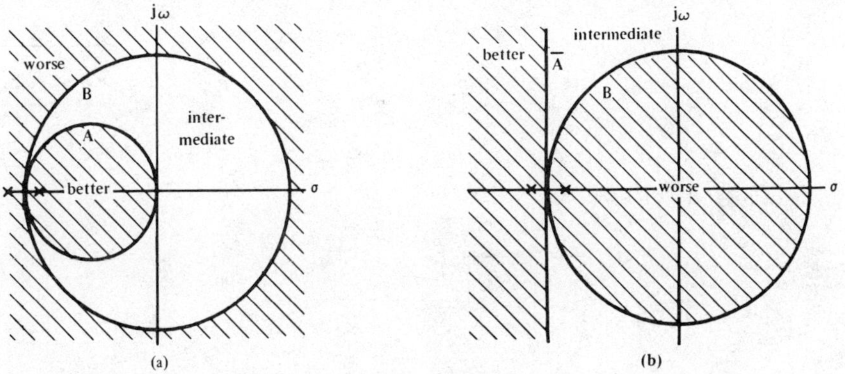

Fig. 7.19.2 Root loci for (a) Class C and (b) $\overline{C}$ filters.

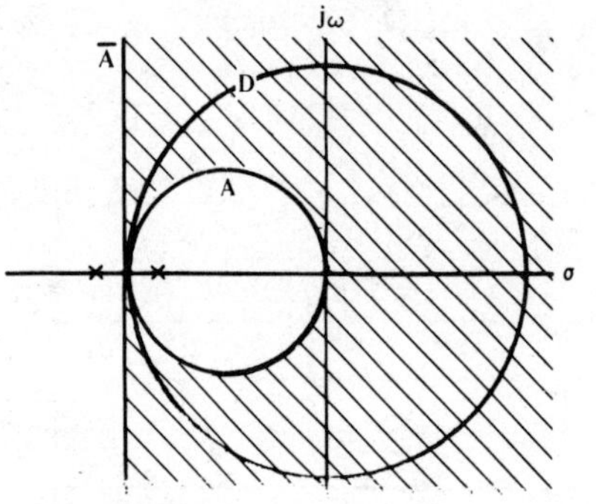

Fig. 7.19.3 Root loci for Class A, $\overline{A}$, and D filters.

lie on the σ-axis. They have gain-sensitivity tradeoffs which lie between those of Class A or $\overline{A}$ filters and B filters.

Class E filters have complex conjugate zeros that lie anywhere in the s-plane. Therefore, they are the most general of all filter classes.

When small $S_k^{\omega_o}$ sensitivities are required and small gain is available, Class B filters are utilized; however, large S_k^Q and passive sensitivities must be tolerated. When both small $S_k^{\omega_o}$ and S_k^Q sensitivities are required, Class A and $\overline{A}$ filters are utilized; although small passive sensitivities are simultaneously obtained, large gains are required. When a tradeoff between $S_k^{\omega_o}$ and S_k^Q sensitivities and gain is desired, then Class C, D, or E filters are utilized. Class E infinite gain filters can be used to obtain zero active sensitivities and low passive sensitivities. Class A and C filters are especially useful at lower frequencies and Class $\overline{A}$ and $\overline{C}$ filters at higher frequencies.

The importance of both the classification and bounds should now be appreciated by the design engineer. Their value will become even more clear in the following chapters in which various types of filters are tabulated and discussed.

Now that we have established a general classification system, we shall proceed to investigate low-pass, high-pass, band-pass, band-stop, and all-pass filters. We shall thus classify the numerators of the gain functions in addition to their denominators as we have done here. These chapters will be especially useful to engineers in rapidly choosing filters and formulating designs.

PROBLEMS

Unless asked otherwise, derive the flow graph and transfer function for the RC active filter shown below. Classify the filter directly from the flow graph. Verify the classification from the transfer function. Is the filter low-pass, high-pass, band-pass, band-stop, all-pass, or a quasi- variety?

7.1

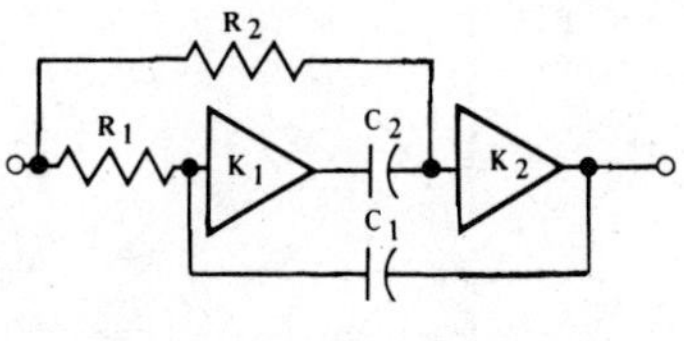

7.3

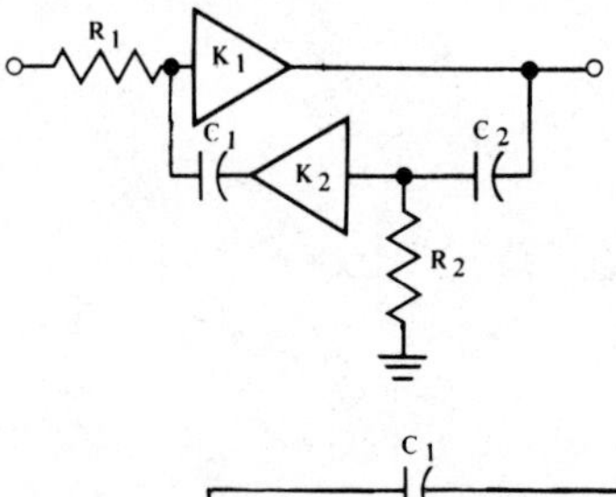

7.2

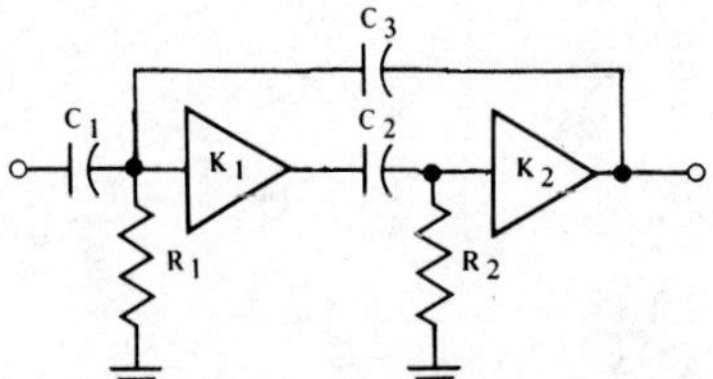

7.4

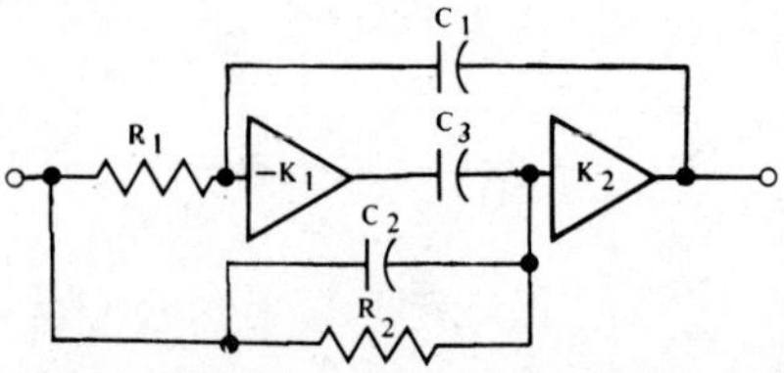

7.5 A Class 1A band-pass filter is shown in Fig. 7.4.2. How must the parameters be chosen to obtain (a) minimum sensitivities and (b) minimum gain? What are the gain-sensitivity values using these parameters? (c) Which set of parameters is best? Justify. (d) Replace amplifier K_1 with a short to produce a Class 2A band-pass filter. Repeat parts (a) and (b).

7.6 We have seen that Class 1X and 2X filters are closely related. For instance, the Class 1B band-pass filter of Example 7.6.1 can be drawn by careful inspection of the Class 2B band-pass filter of Example 7.14.1 and use of Table 7.19.1. Obtain a Class $1\overline{A}$ low-pass filter from the Class $2\overline{A}$ filter of Example 7.13.1. Draw the flow graph for the Class $1\overline{A}$ filter and derive its transfer function.

7.7

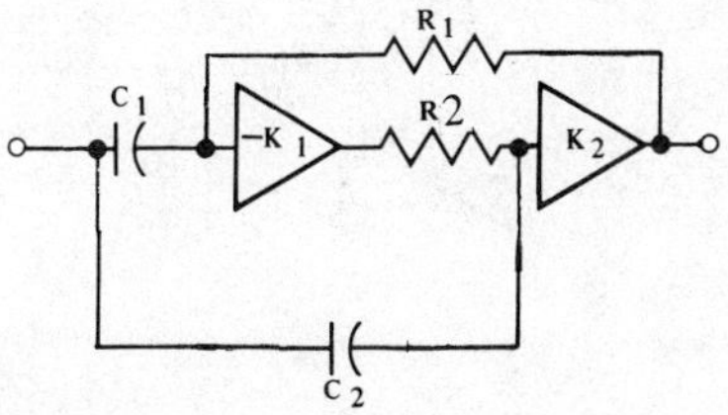

7.8

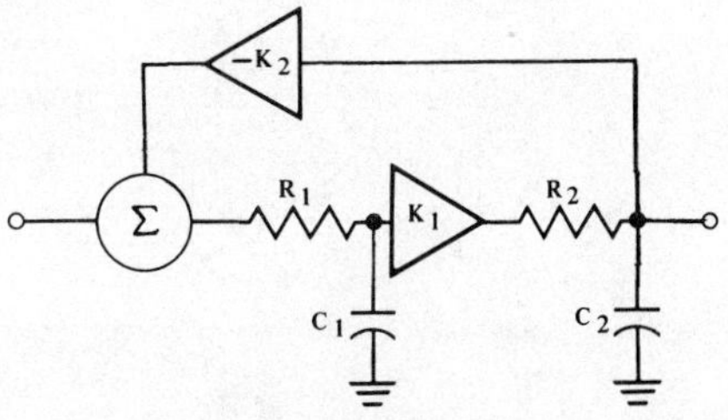

7.9

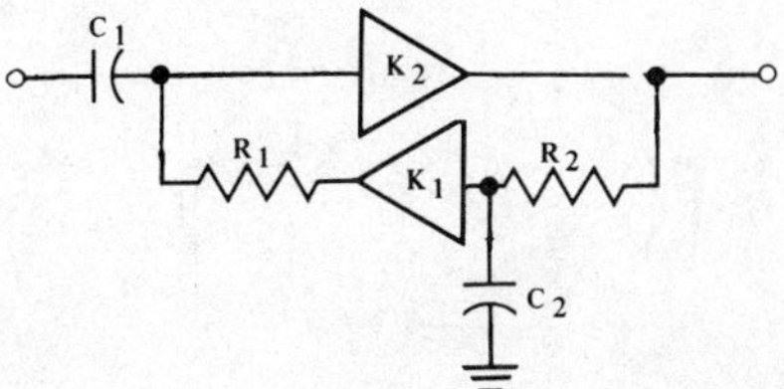

7.10

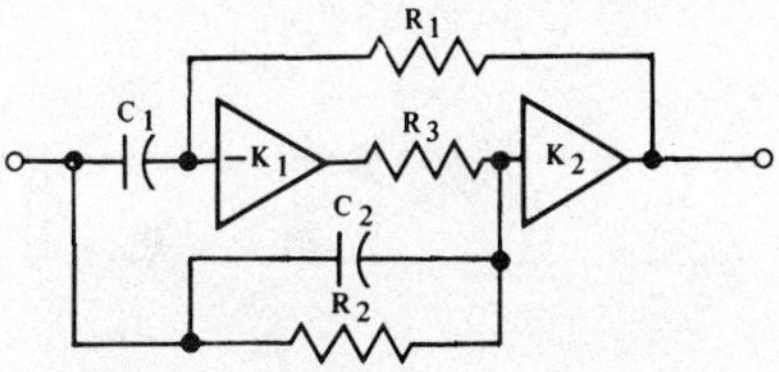

7.11

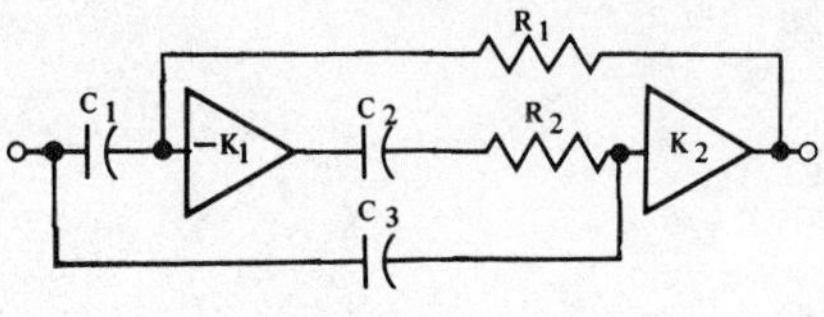

7.12

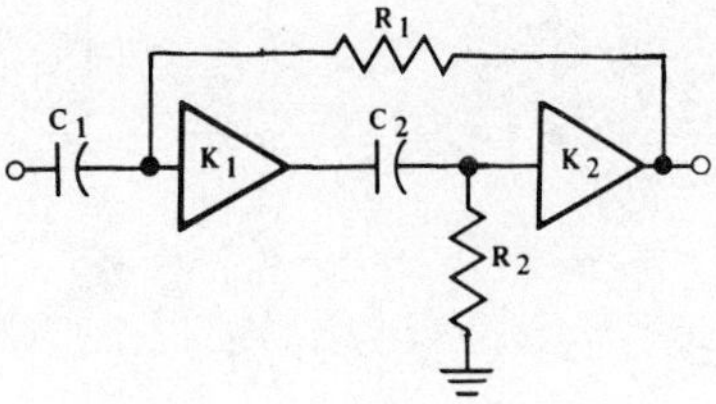

7.13

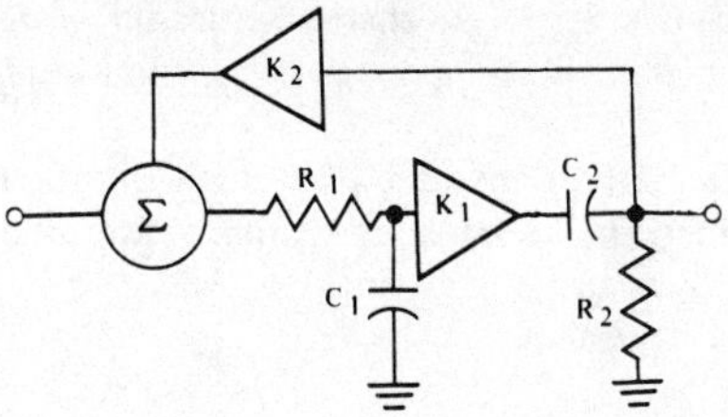

7.14

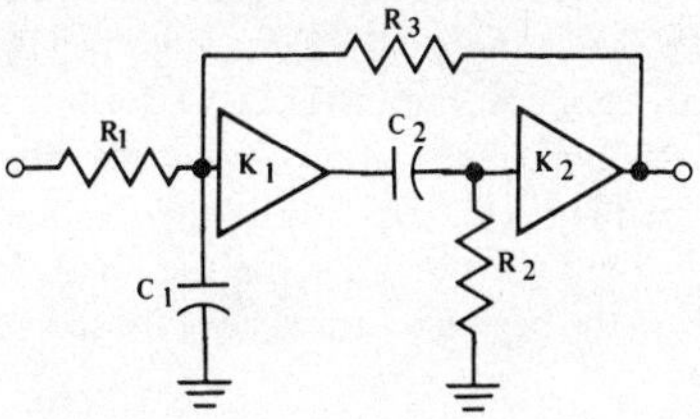

7.15

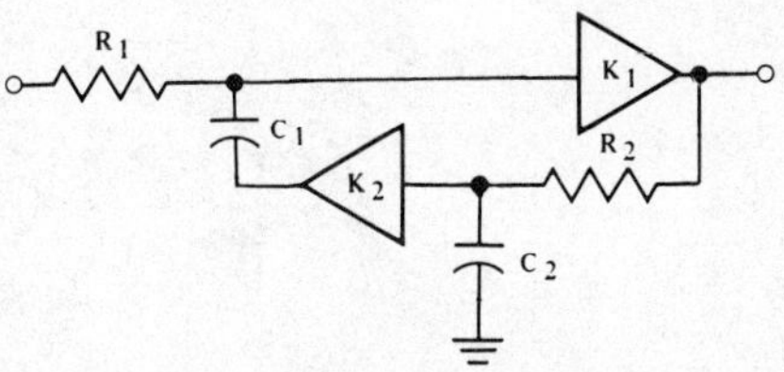

7.16

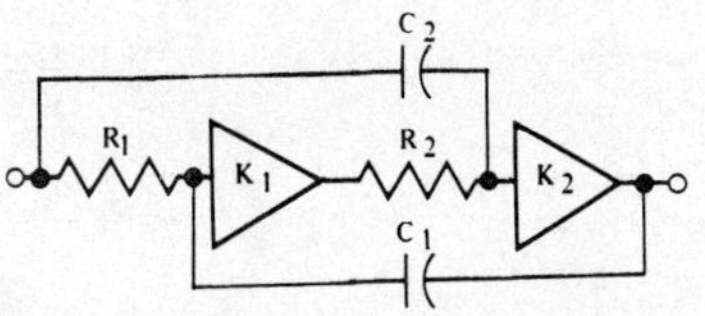

7.17

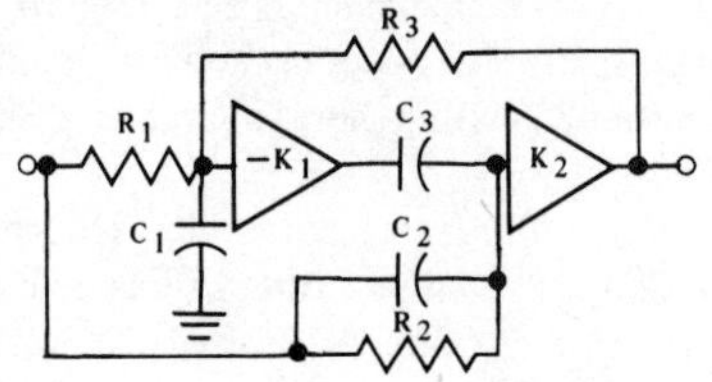

7.18

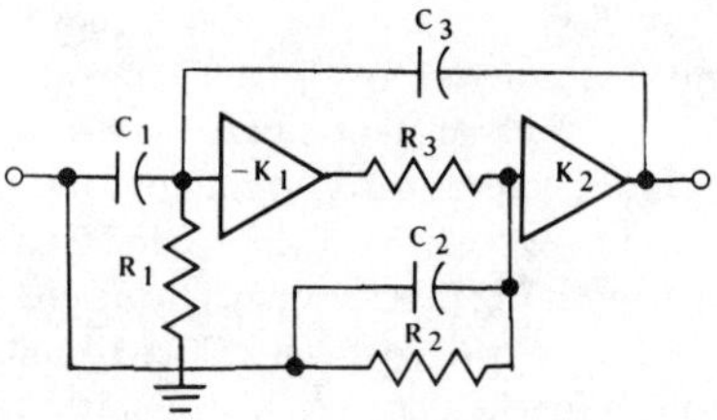

7.19

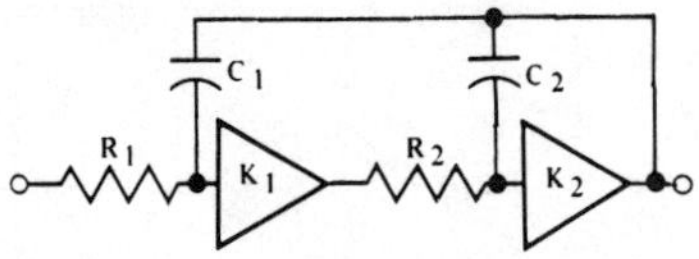

7.20

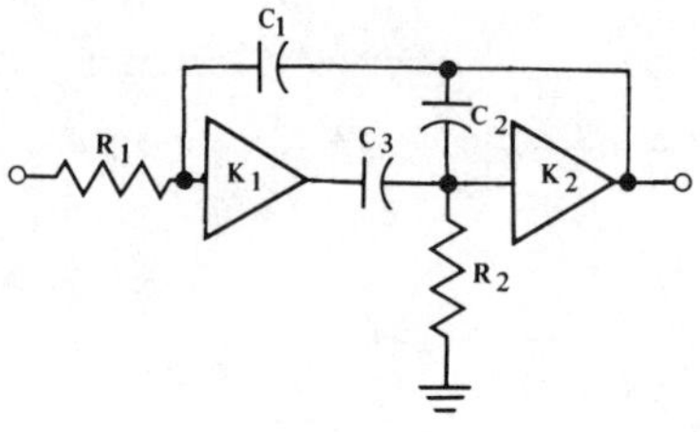

7.21

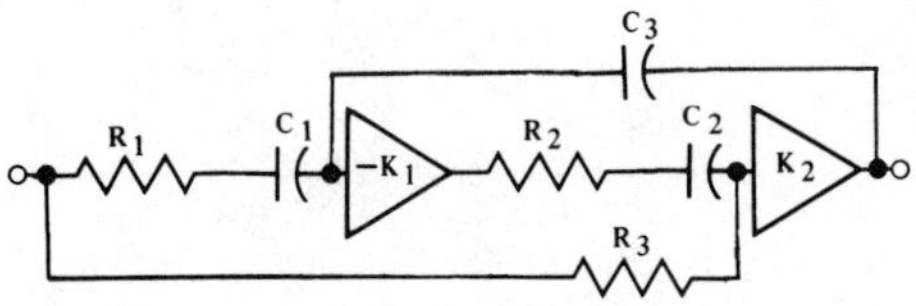

7.22

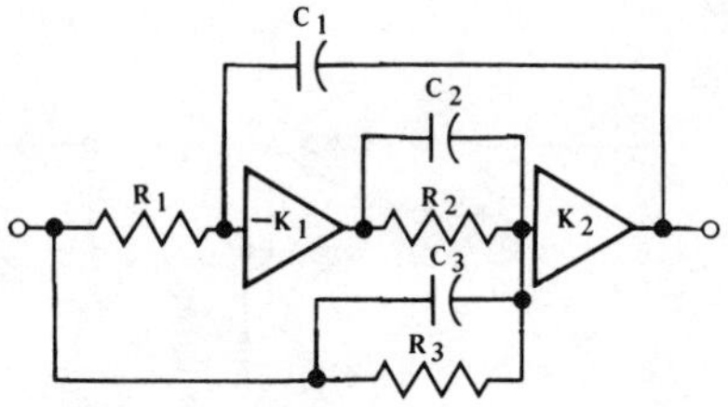

7.23

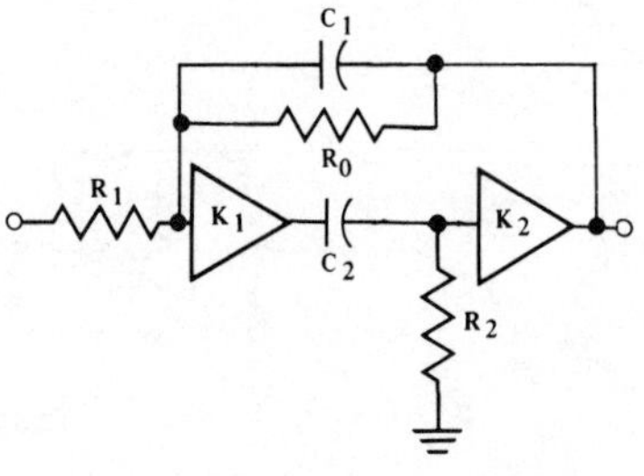

7.24 A Class 1C band-pass filter was analyzed in Example 7.7.1. Its characteristics therefore lie between (or exceed) those of a Class 1A and 1B filter. Determine which components to vary to force it to approach a (a) Class 1A filter, (b) Class 1B filter.

7.25 Suppose we remove R_2 in the filter of Example 7.7.1. Derive the flow graph and the transfer function for the filter. Determine the parameters of the filter. Is the transfer function still second-order?

7.26 Repeat Prob. 7.24 for the Class $1\overline{C}$ band-pass filter analyzed in Example 7.8.1. Note that its characteristics lie between (or exceed) those of a Class $1\overline{A}$ and 1B filter.

7.27

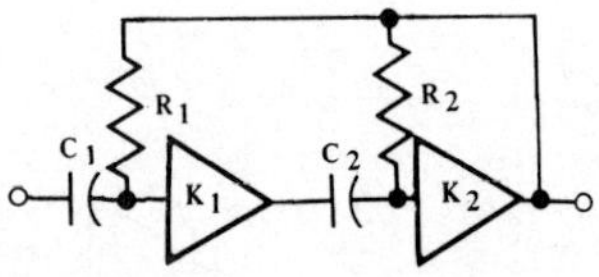

7.28

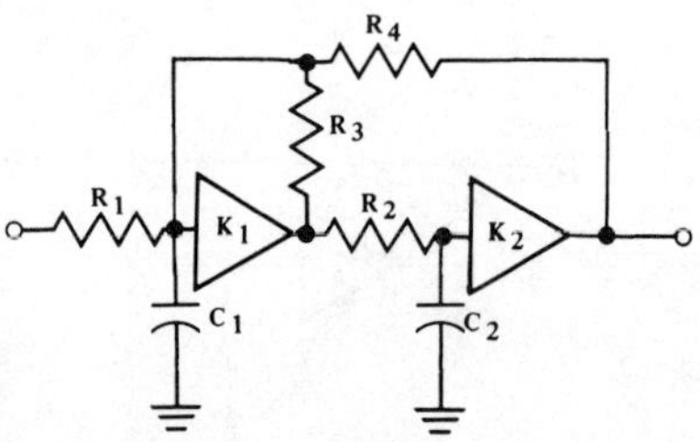

7.29

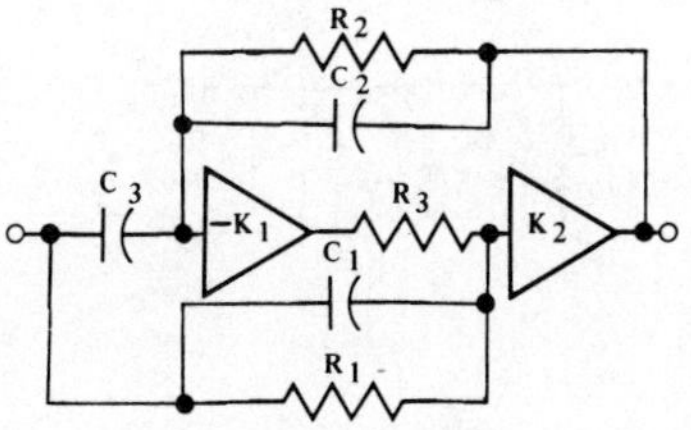

7.30

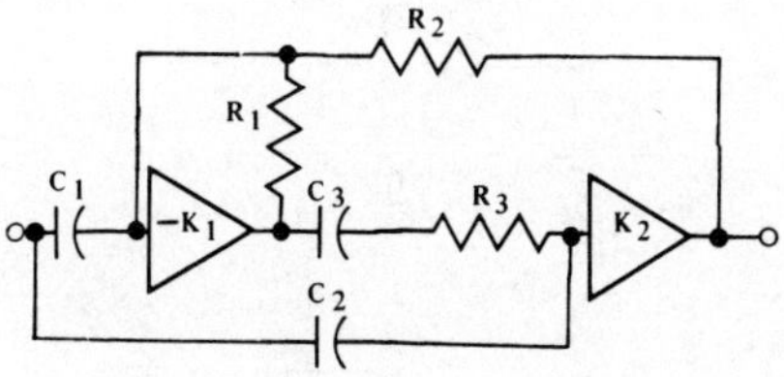

7.31

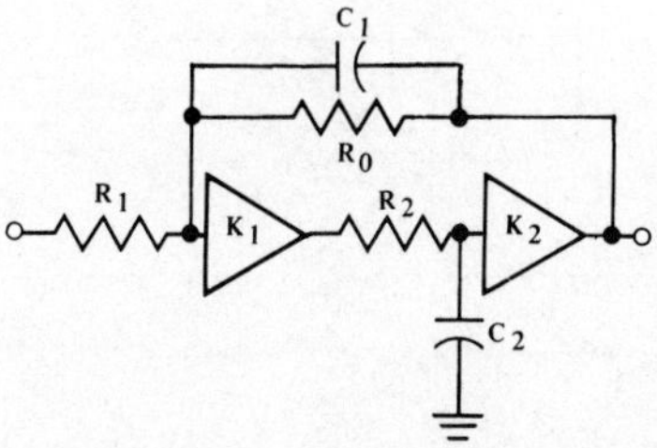

7.32

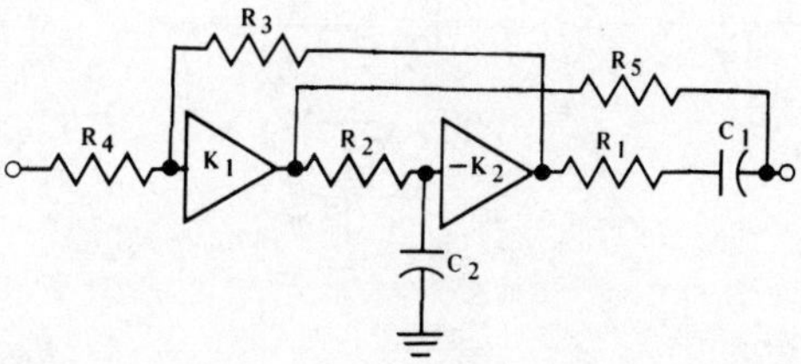

7.33

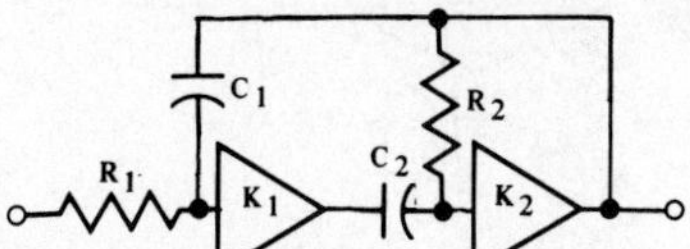

7.34

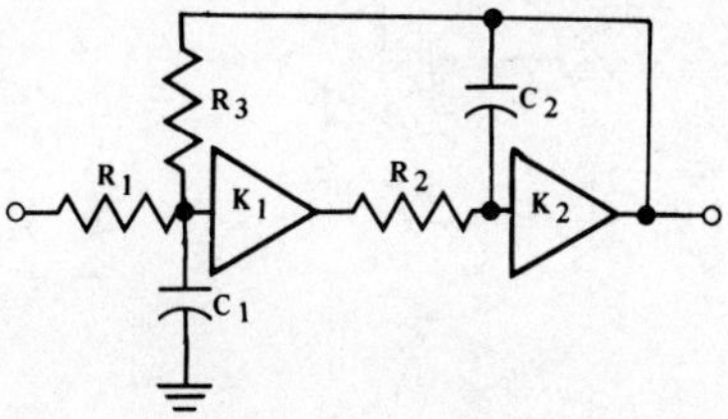

7.35

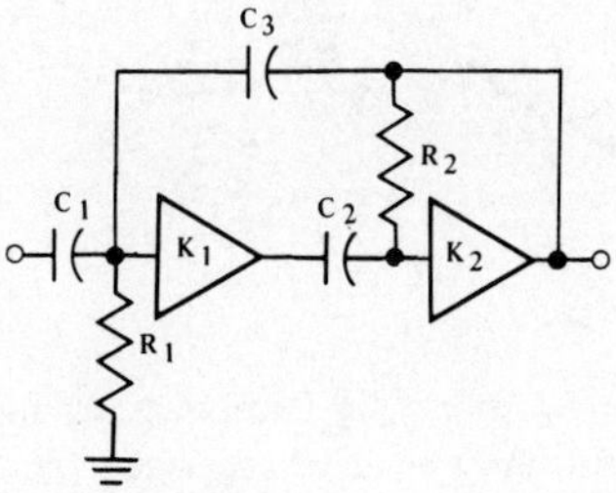

7.36

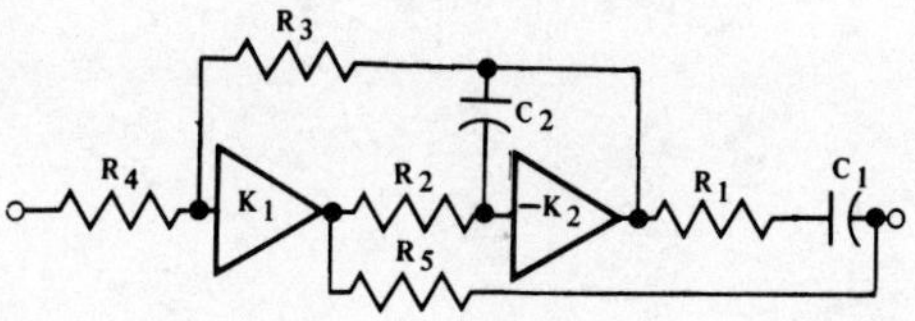

7.37

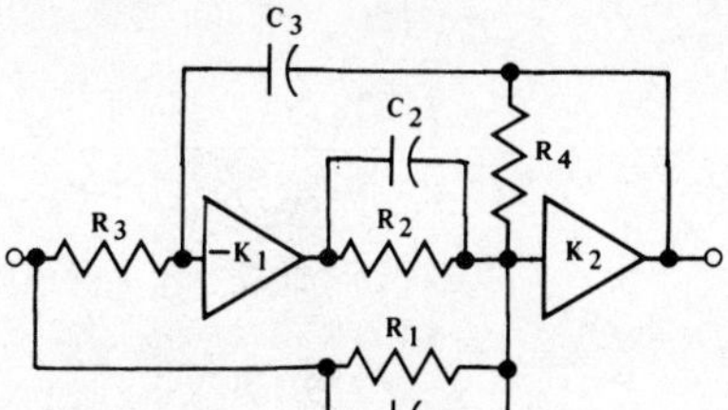

7.38

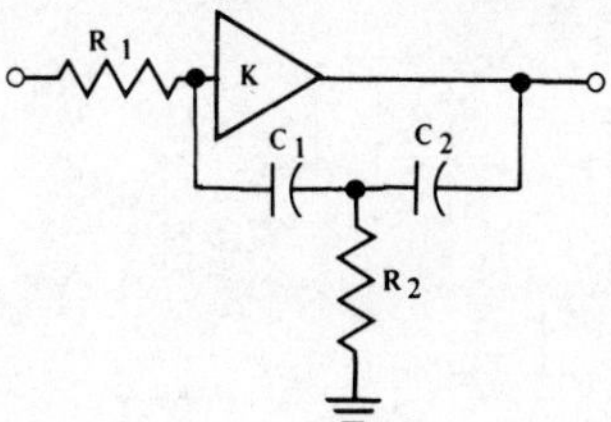

7.39

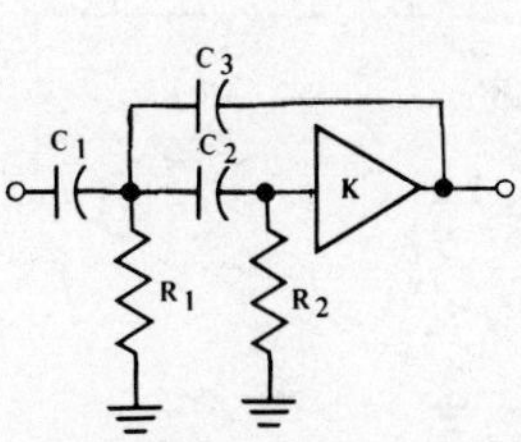

7.40

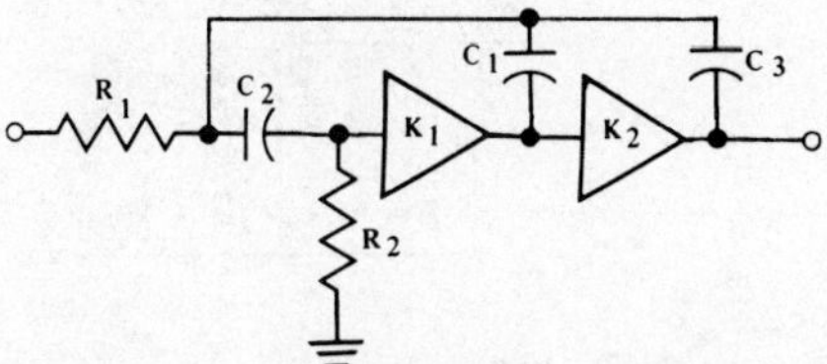

7.41

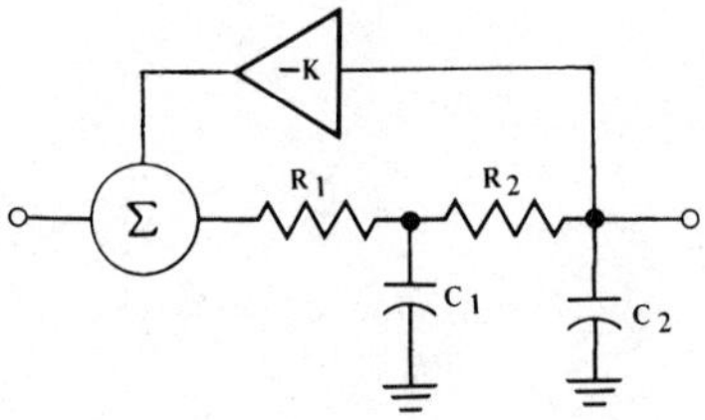

7.42

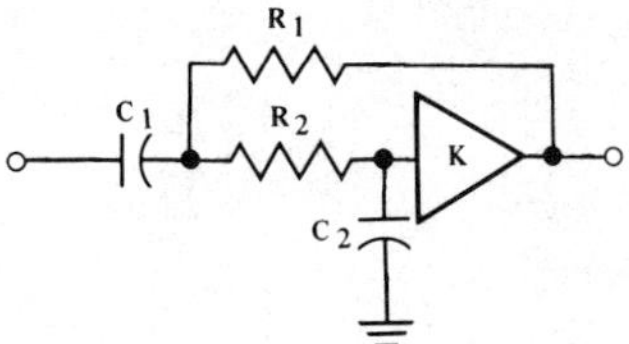

7.43

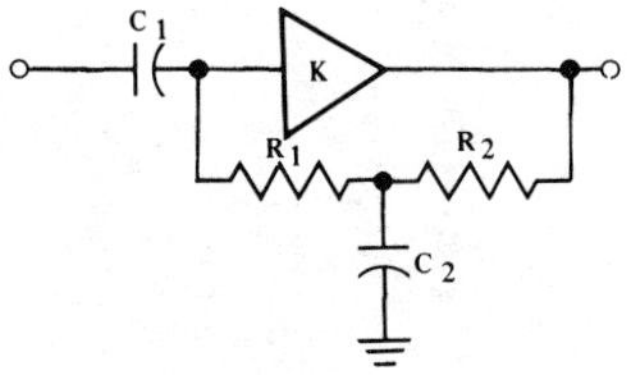

7.44

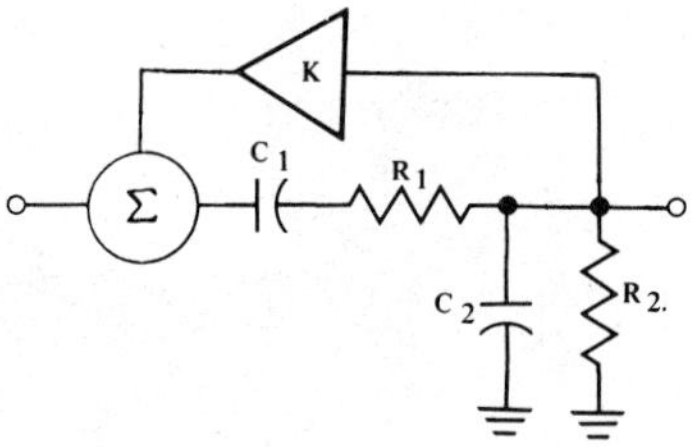

7.45

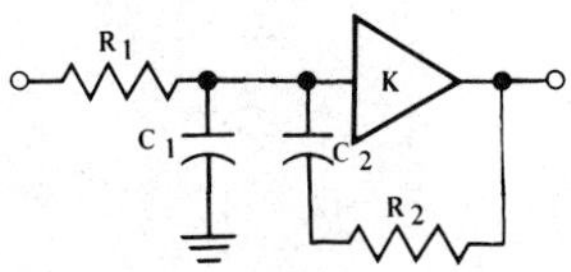

7.46

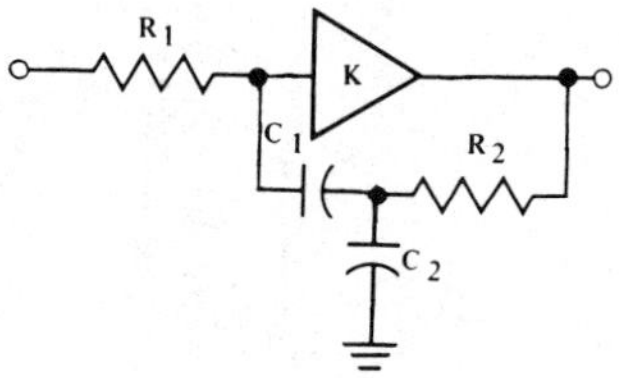

7.47

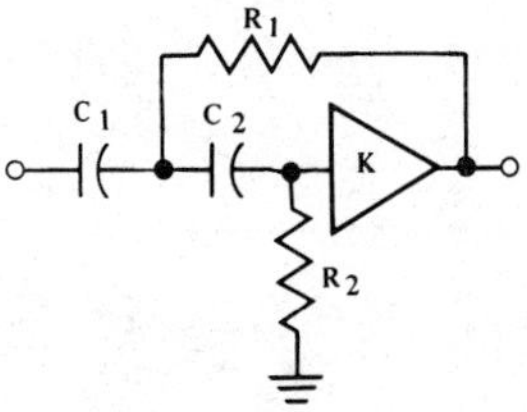

7.48

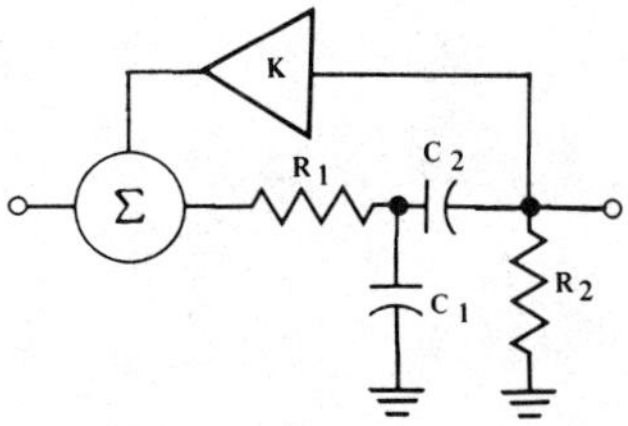

7.49 A Class 2B filter is shown in Fig. P7.49 with its transfer function. (a) Determine ω_o and Q of the filter. (b) To minimize the sensitivities, the passive time constants must be matched. What component relations are required under this condition? (c) How should R_1 and R_3 be chosen to minimize the gain under the minimum sensitivity conditions of part (b)?

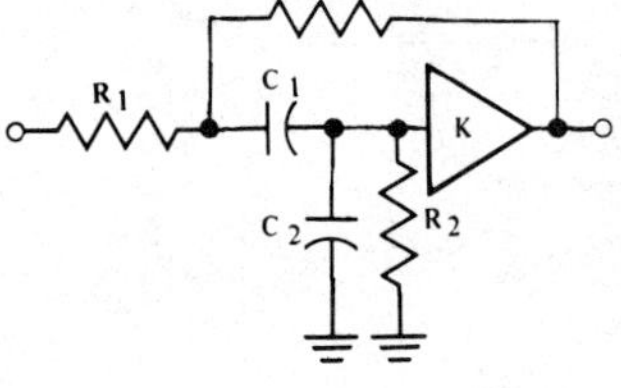

$$H(s) = \frac{\rho K s T_1}{s^2 T_1 T_2 + s[T_1(1 + \rho + (1 - K)R_2/R_3) + T_2(1 + R_1/R_3)] + (1 + R_1/R_3)}$$

$$T_1 = R_1 C_1, \qquad T_2 = R_2 C_2, \qquad \rho = R_2/R_1$$

Fig. P7.49

7.50

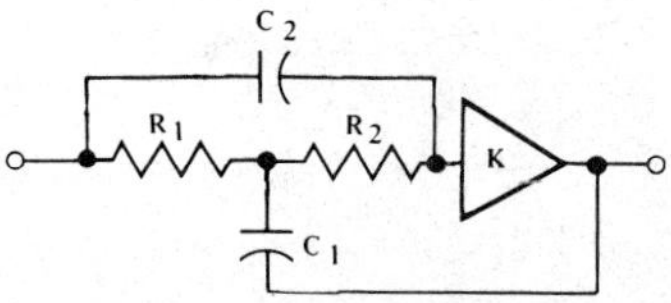

7.51

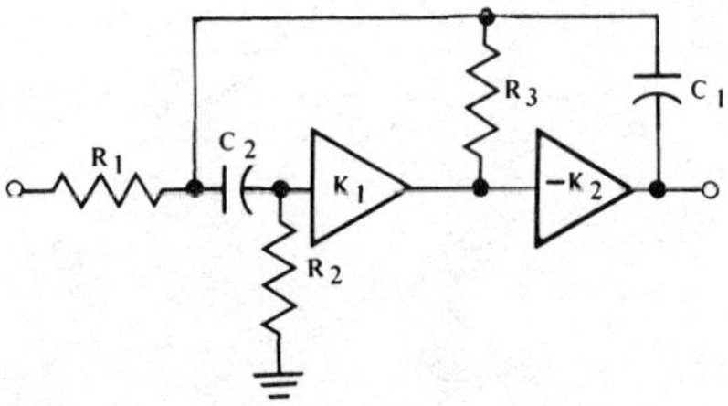

7.52

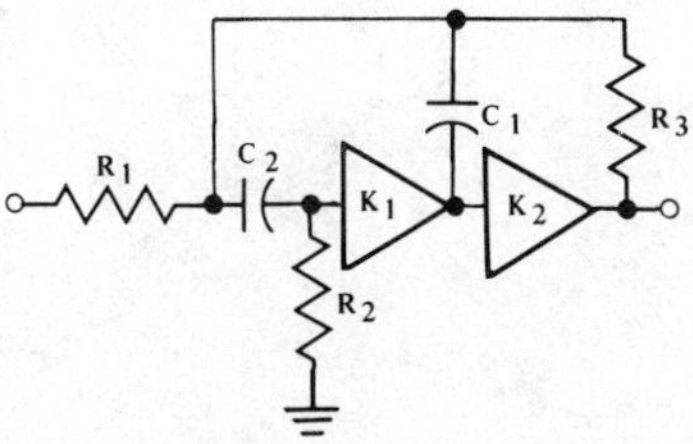

7.53

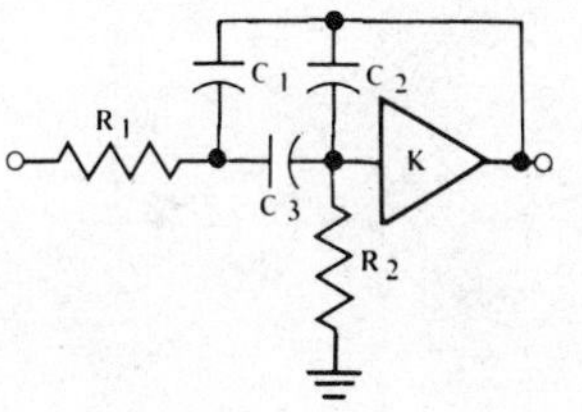

7.54

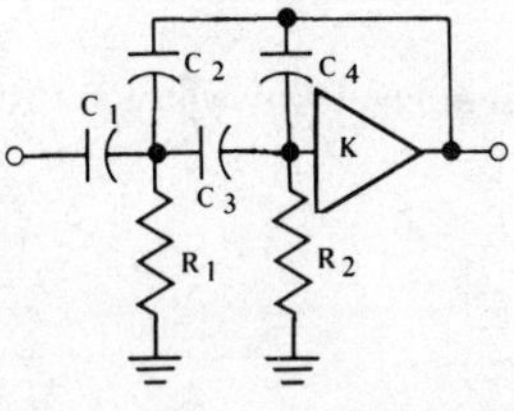

7.55

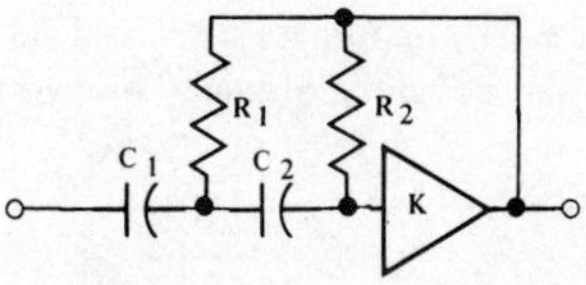

7.56 Repeat Prob. 7.24 for the Class 2C low-pass filter analyzed in Example 7.15.1. Note that its characteristics lie between (or exceed) those of a Class 2A and 2B filter.

7.57 Repeat Prob. 7.24 for the Class $2\overline{C}$ band-pass filter analyzed in Example 7.16.1. Note that its characteristics lie between (or exceed) those of a Class $2\overline{A}$ and 2B filter.

7.58

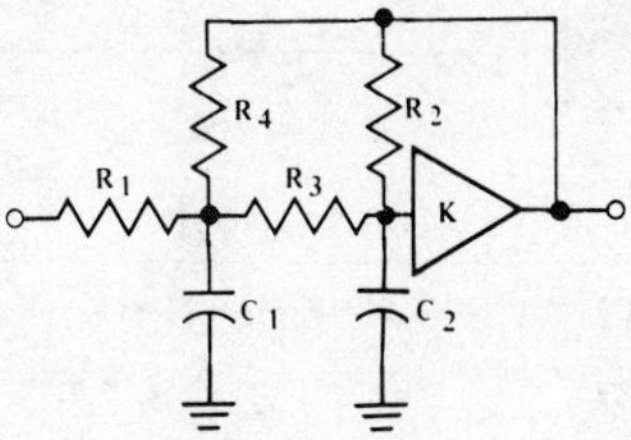

7.59

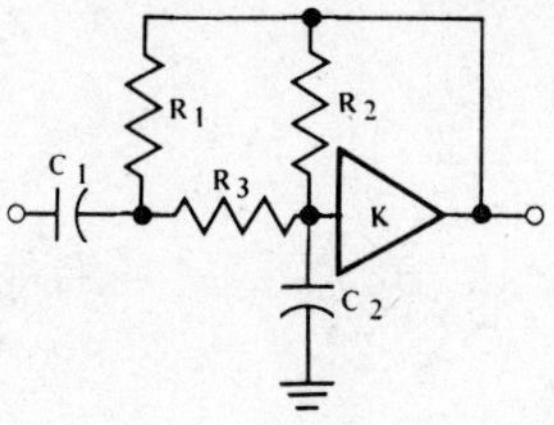

7.60

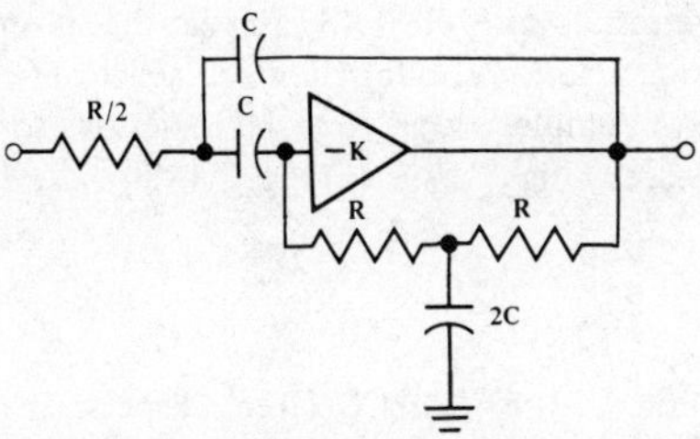

Note: Do not derive the transfer function since T_{13} is involved. (Hint: The transfer function for a symmetrical twin-T is given by Eq. 1.11.37.)

7.61

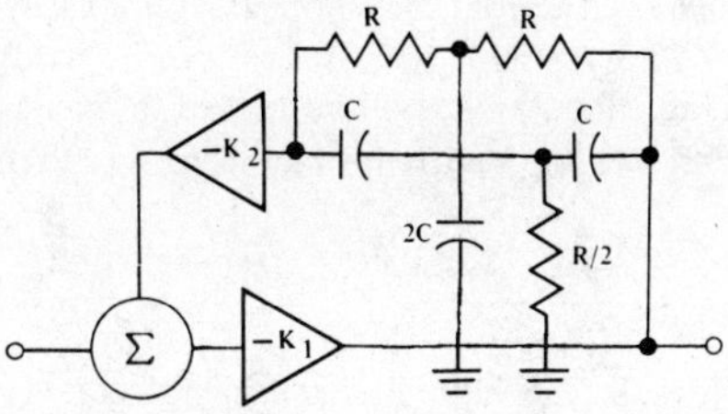

(Hint: The transfer function for a symmetrical twin-T is given by Eq. 1.11.37.)

7.62

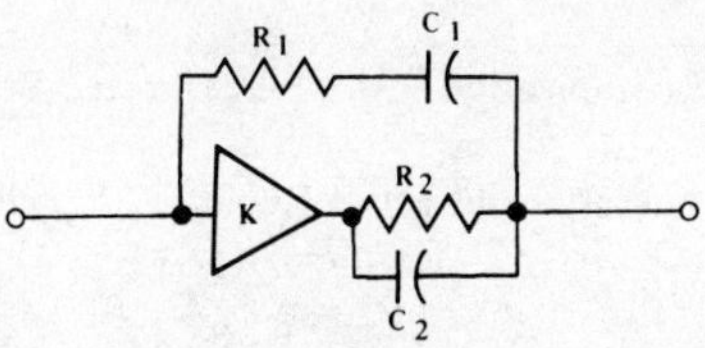

7.63

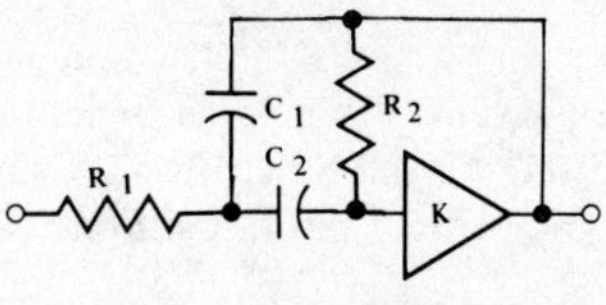

7.64

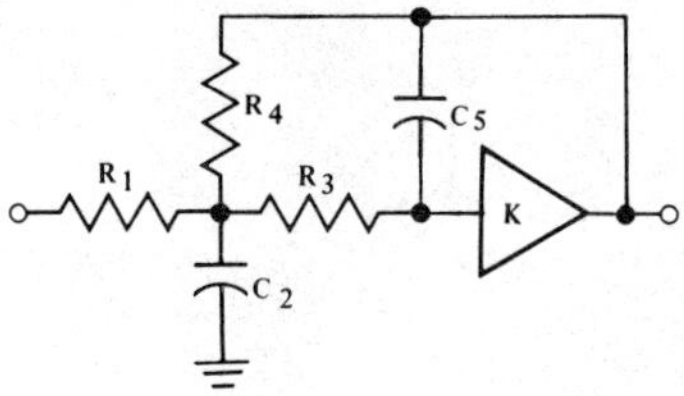

7.65

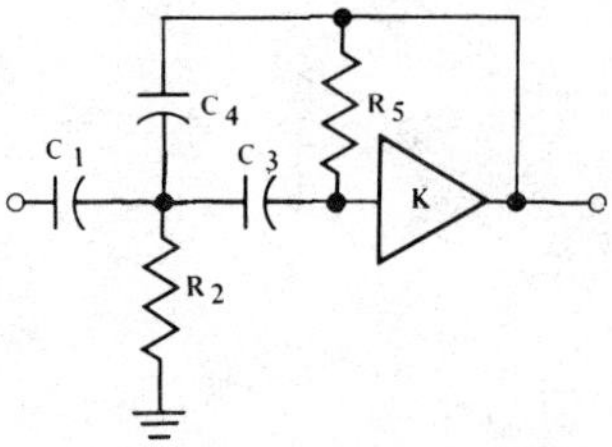

7.66 A Class 2E band-pass filter was analyzed in Example 7.18.1. Determine which components to vary to force it to approach a Class 2D filter.

7.67 A Class 2E band-pass filter and its transfer function are shown in Fig. P7.67 where T = RC. Discuss what other classes can be obtained by varying parameter values.

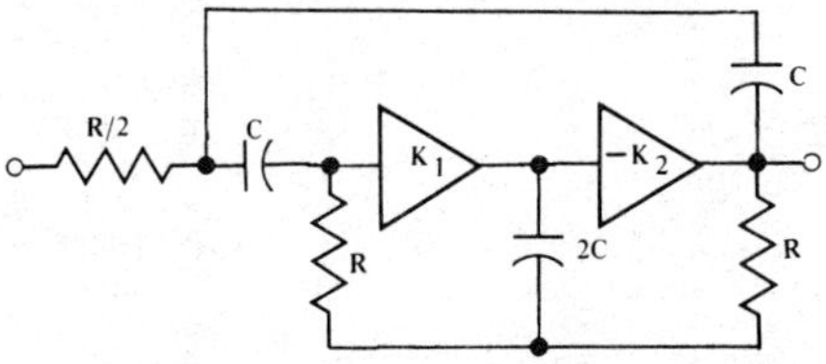

$$H(s) = \frac{-2K_1K_2sT}{s^2(1 + K_1K_2)T^2 + s2(2 - K_1)T + (1 + K_1K_2)}$$

Fig. P7.67

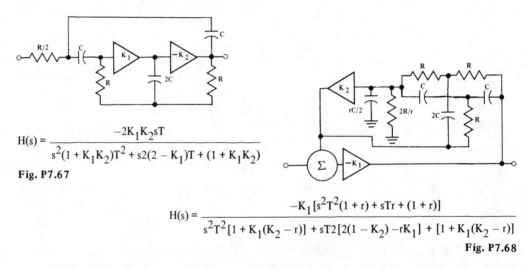

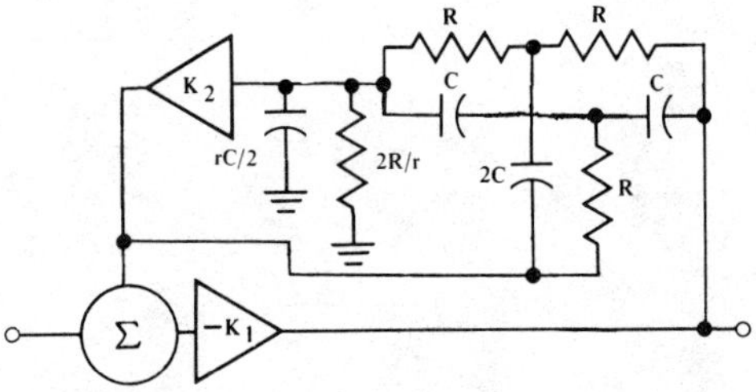

$$H(s) = \frac{-K_1[s^2T^2(1 + r) + sTr + (1 + r)]}{s^2T^2[1 + K_1(K_2 - r)] + sT2[2(1 - K_2) - rK_1] + [1 + K_1(K_2 - r)]}$$

Fig. P7.68

7.68 A Class 2E biquadratic filter and its transfer function are shown in Fig. P7.68 where T = RC. Discuss what other classes can be obtained by varying parameter values.

7.69 The root loci of Chap. 7 are easily drawn using the results of Prob. 1.43. Repeat that problem.

7.70 A useful analysis tool can be used to find the transfer functions of ungrounded passive networks (see Fig. 9.6.2). As will be proved in Sec. 9.6, the inputs have complementary transfer functions so that $T_{23} = 1 - T_{13}$. Verify this fact using the filters in (a) Fig. 7.15.2, (b) Fig. 7.17.2, (c) Fig. 7.18.3.

REFERENCES

1. Mitra, S. K., "Filter design using integrated operational amplifiers," 1969 WESCON Tech. Papers. Soderstrand, M. A., and S. K. Mitra, "Gain and sensitivity limitations of active RC filters," IEEE Trans. Circuit Theory, vol. CT-18, pp. 600–609, Nov., 1971.
2. Ta, F. C., "Theory of topological signal flow graphs," M.S.E.E. Directed Research, California State Univ., Long Beach, June, 1974.
3. Van Valkenburg, M. E., *Introduction to Modern Network Synthesis,* Chap. 10, Wiley, NY, 1960.
4. Mitra, S. K., "A network transformation for active RC networks," Proc. IEEE, vol. 55, pp. 2021–2022, Nov., 1967.
5. Ishikawa, K. Y., "Active RC filter gain and gain sensitivity optimization," M.S.E.E. Directed Research, California State Univ., Long Beach, June, 1973.
6. Soderstrand, M. A., and S. K. Mitra, "Gain and sensitivity limitations of active RC filters," Tech. Rep., NSF Grant GK 14736, Univ. of California, Davis, 1971.

8 LOW-PASS FILTERS

"Much is new but much has been forgotten"

Now that we have classified filters in general and determined their gain and sensitivity bounds, we wish to utilize these results in actual filter design. Since we classified filters by the denominators of their gain expressions, we now further classify them by their numerator forms as low-pass, high-pass, band-pass, band-stop, or all-pass filters. This chapter is concerned exclusively with low-pass filters. In later chapters, the other types will be investigated.

We will first discuss low-pass filters from the classification viewpoint of Chap. 7. We then investigate a variety of low-pass filters which are known, after which a compilation of filter types will be prepared and tabulated. Each filter will be described by its own design sheet developed from the viewpoint of design usefulness. These sheets will form the basis for our actual filter design, and will be invaluable to the design engineer. We will compare the gains and sensitivity bounds for the various classes with the limits established in the last chapter. These are important since the gains determine the usable frequency range of a filter and the sensitivities determine its maximum selectivity. We will make qualitative evaluations of the filters, and describe situations in which their use is appropriate. A variety of practical examples will be discussed to illustrate the design tradeoffs.

We shall also consider gain-tuned and passive-tuned low-pass filters. These are constant-ζ filters whose corner frequency ω_o may be varied using gain or a passive parameter. We shall discuss immittance calculations which include, for example, the input impedance of a filter which is an important design consideration. High-frequency active filters will also be considered. Then we shall conclude with a discussion of alternative methods to cascade design. Although these methods yield lower sensitivity designs, they are generally more complicated and are more difficult to tune.

This and the following chapters will draw together all of the material of the previous chapters. The engineer may find it surprising that active filter design can become simple and routine when properly executed. We shall be using some component information involving resistors, capacitors, and operational amplifiers from Chap. 14. This will include such matters as standard values and tolerances which we will briefly review. If filter designs are to be practical, such information must be incorporated into their formulation.

8.1 LOW-PASS FILTER CLASSES

Low-pass filters of second-order have gains given by

$$H(s) = \frac{H_o}{(s/\omega_o)^2 + 2\zeta(s/\omega_o) + 1} \qquad (8.1.1)$$

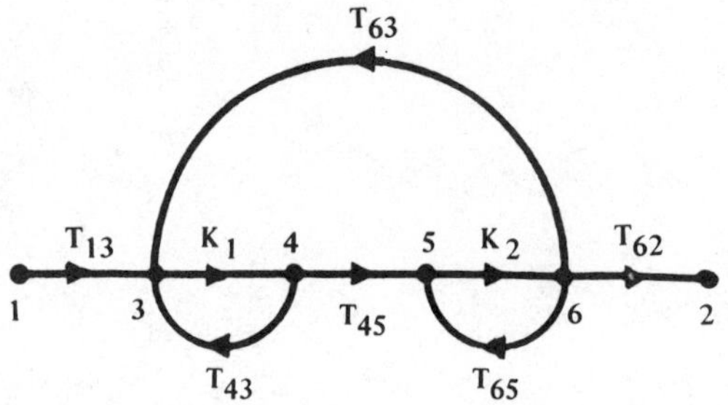

Fig. 8.1.1 Flow graph of simplest active filter having single forward branch.

If a finite zero is present, then the gain equals

$$H(s) = H_o \frac{1 + s/z}{(s/\omega_o)^2 + 2\zeta(s/\omega_o) + 1} \tag{8.1.2}$$

Quasi-low-pass filters fail to have zero gain at infinite frequency. Their gains equal

$$H(s) = H_o \frac{(s/\omega_{oz})^2 + 2\zeta_z(s/\omega_{oz}) + 1}{(s/\omega_{op})^2 + 2\zeta_p(s/\omega_{op}) + 1} \tag{8.1.3}$$

Such band-stop filters are necessary when designing elliptic filters. In general, we shall be concerned with only the second-order low-pass filter. When a band-stop filter stage is required, we shall simply utilize a filter from Chap. 11 and reserve its discussion for that chapter. A second-order low-pass filter is completely characterized by its resonant frequency ω_o, damping factor ζ (or $Q = 1/2\zeta$), and low-frequency (i.e., dc) gain H_o. In the filter designs of Chaps. 2–6, we summarized this information in a low-pass filter (LPF) block. We now want to implement such blocks with actual hardware.

We must first select the class of low-pass filter which we want to utilize. In the previous chapter, we discussed the gain requirements and sensitivity bounds for the various classes. In general, we saw the necessity of making a design tradeoff between the amplifier gain and the active and passive sensitivities of the filter. However, this assumes that low-pass filters can be realized in any class. Indeed such is the case, as we shall now prove.

We begin by considering the active filter which has the simplest topology. Such filters have flow graphs with a single forward branch as shown in Fig. 8.1.1. These active filters satisfy:

1. The amplifiers are ideal in the sense that they have zero output impedance.
2. The active filter output corresponds to the output of the second amplifier having gain K_2.
3. The active filter input is applied only to the first amplifier having gain K_1.

The requirements of 1 and 2 constrain the flow graph to have $T_{62} = 1$ (direct coupling from K_2 to output). They also require $T_{12} = 0$ since T_{12} is calculated by setting $K_1 = K_2 = 0$. But since $K_2 = 0$, then the filter output V_2 must equal zero. The third requirement forces $T_{15} = 0$. In effect, then, these filters must have the flow graphs drawn for each filter class in Chap. 7.

The transfer function of these filters equals

$$\begin{aligned} H(s) &= \frac{K_1K_2T_{13}T_{45}}{1 - K_1T_{43} - K_2T_{65} + K_1K_2(T_{43}T_{65} - T_{45}T_{63})} \\ &= \frac{K_1K_2N_{13}N_{45}}{D_{13}D_{45} - K_1N_{43}D_{45} - K_2N_{65}D_{13} + K_1K_2(N_{43}N_{65} - N_{45}N_{63})} \end{aligned} \tag{8.1.4}$$

from Eqs. 7.2.2 and 7.2.8. Thus, the form of the numerators of T_{13} and T_{45} determine the filter type. If a low-pass filter is required, then T_{13} and T_{45} must be low-pass filters. If a quasi-low-pass filter is needed, then either T_{13} or T_{45} must be quasi-low-pass (while the other remains low-pass).

Let us look in more detail at how this allows low-pass filters to be actually formulated. Since we will now be analyzing the numerator of the transfer function, we must introduce several additional terms to the basic equations given by Eqs. 7.3.1, 7.3.5, 7.11.1, and 7.11.5. These terms are N_{13}, N_{15}, N_{42}, and N_{62}. For first-order decomposition filters the general equations become

$$D_{13} = D_{43} = D_{63} = a_{30} + a_{31}s$$

$$D_{15} = D_{45} = D_{65} = a_{50} + a_{51}s$$

$$D_{12} = D_{42} = D_{62} = a_{20} + a_{21}s$$

$$N_{43} = b_{30} + b_{31}s \qquad N_{65} = b_{50} + b_{51}s \qquad N_{13} = d_{30} + d_{31}s$$

$$N_{63} = c_{30} + c_{31}s \qquad N_{45} = c_{50} + c_{51}s \qquad N_{15} = d_{50} + d_{51}s \tag{8.1.5}$$

$$N_{42} = c_{20} + c_{21}s \qquad N_{62} = b_{20} + b_{21}s \qquad N_{12} = 0$$

$$(N_{43}N_{65} - N_{45}N_{63}) = d_2s^2 + d_1s + d_0$$

$$d_2 = (b_{31}b_{51} - c_{31}c_{51}) \qquad d_1 = (b_{30}b_{51} + b_{31}b_{50} - c_{30}c_{51} - c_{31}c_{50})$$

$$d_0 = (b_{30}b_{50} - c_{30}c_{50})$$

The Fialkow-Gerst conditions, given by Eq. 7.3.4, generalize to

$$0 \leqslant b_{20}, c_{20} \leqslant a_{20} \qquad 0 \leqslant b_{21}, c_{21} \leqslant a_{21} \qquad 0 \leqslant b_{30}, c_{30}, d_{30} \leqslant a_{30}$$

$$0 \leqslant b_{31}, c_{31}, d_{31} \leqslant a_{31} \qquad 0 \leqslant b_{50}, c_{50}, d_{50} \leqslant a_{50} \qquad 0 \leqslant b_{51}, c_{51}, d_{51} \leqslant a_{51} \tag{8.1.6}$$

For second-order decomposition filters, the general equations become

$$D_{13} = D_{43} = D_{63} = a_{30} + a_{31}s + a_{32}s^2$$

$$D_{15} = D_{45} = D_{65} = a_{50} \qquad D_{12} = D_{42} = D_{62} = 1$$

$$N_{13} = d_{30} + d_{31}s + d_{32}s^2, \qquad N_{63} = c_{30} + c_{31}s + c_{32}s^2, \qquad N_{43} = b_{30} + b_{31}s + b_{32}s^2$$

$$N_{65} = b_{50}, \qquad N_{45} = c_{50}, \qquad N_{62} = 1, \qquad N_{15} = N_{42} = N_{12} = 0 \tag{8.1.7}$$

$$(N_{43}N_{65} - N_{45}N_{63}) = d_2s^2 + d_1s + d_0$$

$$d_2 = (b_{32}b_{50} - c_{32}c_{50}) \qquad d_1 = (b_{31}b_{50} - c_{31}c_{50}) \qquad d_0 = (b_{30}b_{50} - c_{30}c_{50})$$

where Eq. 7.11.4 is

$$0 \leqslant b_{30}, c_{30}, d_{30} \leqslant a_{30} \qquad 0 \leqslant b_{31}, c_{31}, d_{31} \leqslant a_{31} \qquad 0 \leqslant b_{32}, c_{32}, d_{32} \leqslant a_{32}$$

$$0 \leqslant b_{50}, c_{50} \leqslant a_{50} \tag{8.1.8}$$

With these additions, we can now easily extend the analysis of Chap. 7 to obtain a wide variety of low-pass filters.

The denominator of the gain function is given by Eq. 8.1.4. It involves the transfer functions of the feedback branches listed in Tables 7.19.1 and 7.19.2. The numerator of the transfer func-

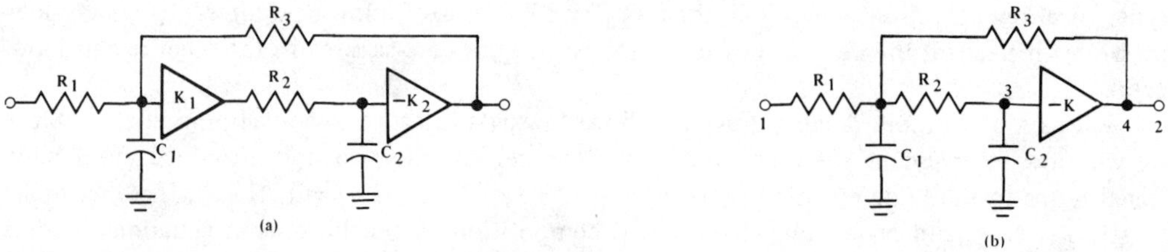

Fig. 8.1.2 (a) Class $1\bar{A}$ and (b) Class $2\bar{A}$ low-pass filters.

tion for first-order decomposition filters equals

$$\text{Num } H(s) = K_1K_2(c_{50} + c_{51}s)(d_{30} + d_{31}s) \tag{8.1.9}$$

from Eqs. 8.1.4 and 8.1.5. To force H(s) to be low-pass, we must set the s^1 and s^2 coefficients of Num H to equal zero. This requires $c_{51} = d_{31} = 0$ so that

$$T_{13} = \frac{d_{30}}{a_{30} + a_{31}s} \quad \text{(LPF)}, \qquad T_{45} = \frac{c_{50}}{a_{50} + a_{51}s} \quad \text{(LPF)} \tag{8.1.10}$$

Alternatively, the numerator of the transfer function for second-order decomposition filters equals

$$\text{Num } H(s) = K_1K_2c_{50}(d_{30} + d_{31}s + d_{32}s^2) \tag{8.1.11}$$

from Eqs. 8.1.4 and 8.1.7. For H(s) to be low-pass, $d_{31} = d_{32} = 0$ so that

$$T_{13} = \frac{d_{30}}{a_{30} + a_{31}s + a_{32}s^2} \quad \text{(LPF)}, \qquad T_{45} = \frac{c_{50}}{a_{50}} \quad \text{(constant)} \tag{8.1.12}$$

By simply investigating the form of T_{45} from Tables 7.19.1 and 7.19.2, we can immediately exclude any classes in which T_{45} fails to be a low-pass type. From Table 7.19.1, we see that Class 1A has a high-pass T_{45}. Thus, Class 1A low-pass filters having the topological constraints listed previously cannot exist. All other types of Class 1X filters are realizable in low-pass form, assuming that T_{13} is low-pass. In Class 2X filters, T_{45} is constant. Thus, low-pass filters result whenever T_{13} is low-pass. We may conclude then, that generally, low-pass filters of every class are realizable except Class 1A. If we remove the restriction of $T_{15} = 0$ or $T_{12} = 0$, then low-pass filters of every class can be realized and we have free rein to choose the filter best suited to the application.

To illustrate the use of these results, let us formulate a Class $1\bar{A}$ low-pass filter having the topological constraints of Fig. 8.1.1. From Table 7.19.1 and Eq. 8.1.10, such filters must have branch transfer functions of

$$T_{13} \text{ (LPF)}, \qquad T_{63} = \frac{c_{30}}{a_{30} + a_{31}s} \text{ (LPF)}, \qquad T_{45} \text{ (LPF)} \tag{8.1.13}$$

which are all low-pass. What remains is simply to arrange RC networks having these first-order transfer functions to fit the topology of Fig. 8.1.1. One such resulting filter is shown in Fig. 8.1.2a. With practice, the design engineer can generate his own filters.

A Class 2A low-pass filter is obtained in a similar manner. From Table 7.19.2 and Eq. 8.1.12,

$$T_{13} \text{ (LPF)}, \qquad T_{63} = \frac{c_{30}}{a_{30} + a_{31}s + a_{32}s^2} \text{ (LPF)}, \qquad T_{45} \text{ (constant)} \tag{8.1.14}$$

A single-amplifier realization is shown in Fig. 8.1.2b. In many cases, simply replacing K_1 in the Class 1X filter with a short circuit produces a Class 2X filter.

8.2 FILTER DESIGN SHEETS

Using this technique, a variety of active filters can be formulated. Most presently known filters have evolved from the past. The majority of these filters were designed from experience and intuition; a few were designed using formal synthesis methods. In the next section, a representative group of filters is tabulated. Now let us see how to facilitate use of these filters in actual design.

This is accomplished by preparing a design sheet which summarizes the primary design information for the filter. A sample design sheet for a Class 1B low-pass filter is shown in Table 8.2.1. The sheet lists: (a) filter class: filter type, (2) transfer function, (3) parameters: ω_o, ζ, H_o; (4) design equations, (5) sensitivities, (6) schematic, and (7) references. These are the most important design parameters of the filter. Note that we arbitrarily choose to use $\zeta = 1/2Q$ to describe low-pass filters rather than Q. We shall use Q when we later investigate band-pass and band-stop filters. References are sometimes included which give useful design information or which indicate the historical development of the filter.

Once a filter topology has been selected, the filter classication and type is established using the flow graph techniques of the last chapter. The gain equation is then calculated from the flow graph. For example, the Class 1B low-pass filter has the flow graph shown in Fig. 7.6.2 and a gain equation given by Eq. 7.6.11 of

$$H(s) = \frac{K_1K_2}{s^2R_1C_1R_2C_2 + s[R_1C_1(1 - K_1K_2) + R_2C_2] + 1} \tag{8.2.1}$$

Expressing the gain equation in the standard form of Eq. 8.1.1, we now write parameters ω_o, ζ, and H_o directly from the gain equation. We denote the resonant frequency ω_o, rather than ω_n, to be consistent with the transformation notation of Chap. 6. ζ is the damping factor of the poles. H_o is equal to the dc gain of the filter. These parameters are equal to

$$\omega_o = 1/(R_1C_1R_2C_2)^{1/2}, \qquad \zeta = \frac{R_1C_1(1 - K_1K_2) + R_2C_2}{2(R_1C_1R_2C_2)^{1/2}}, \qquad H_o = K_1K_2 \tag{8.2.2}$$

Now we determine the design equations for the filter. We must design the filter to meet its required ω_o, ζ, and H_o. As discussed in Chap. 7, it is important to choose the parameters to obtain the desired gain-sensitivity tradeoff. Recall that this tradeoff depends on the ratio of the passive time constants which is selected. We shall illustrate this selection in a moment. Algebraically, we in general have p parameters or component values to calculate and q equations to satisfy. This gives us (p – q) degrees of freedom with which to select component values. Generally, increasing the degrees of freedom introduces more design flexibility and improves filter performance at the expense of complicating the design equations. Experience generally indicates the most practical number of degrees of freedom to use.

For example, the Class 1B low-pass filter has $p = 6$ parameters: R_1, C_1, R_2, C_2, K_1, and K_2. If we have to obtain the required ω_o and ζ, then $q = 2$. Thus, we have $p - q = 6 - 2 = 4$ degrees of freedom. However, to simplify design, suppose we choose or set $R_1 = R_2 = R$, $C_1 = C_2 = C$, and $K_1 = K_2 = K$. This increases q to $q = 2 + 3 = 5$. Since $(p - q) = 6 - 5 = 1$, we now have a single degree-of-freedom with which to design the filter. Under these conditions, the parameter equations in Eq. 8.2.2 become

$$\omega_o = 1/RC, \qquad \zeta = 1 - K^2/2, \qquad H_o = K^2 \tag{8.2.3}$$

Table 8.2.1 Sample filter design sheet.

CLASS 1B: LOW-PASS

Transfer Function:

$$H(s) = \frac{K_1K_2}{s^2R_1C_1R_2C_2 + s[R_1C_1(1 - K_1K_2) + R_2C_2] + 1}$$

Parameters:

$$\omega_o = \frac{1}{(R_1C_1R_2C_2)^{1/2}} \qquad H_o = K_1K_2$$

$$\zeta = \frac{R_1C_1(1 - K_1K_2) + R_2C_2}{2(R_1C_1R_2C_2)^{1/2}}$$

Design Equations: Set $R_2C_2 = k^2R_1C_1$

Given: ω_o, ζ, H_o

Choose: C_1, C_2

Calculate: $k = \zeta \pm [\zeta^2 - (1 - H_o)]^{1/2}$

$R_1 = 1/k\omega_oC_1$

$R_2 = k/\omega_oC_2$

$K_1K_2 = H_o$

Sensitivities:

$$S_{R_1}^{\omega_o} = S_{R_2}^{\omega_o} = S_{C_1}^{\omega_o} = S_{C_2}^{\omega_o} = -\tfrac{1}{2} \qquad S_{K_1}^{H_o} = S_{K_2}^{H_o} = 1$$

$$S_{R_1}^{\zeta} = -S_{R_2}^{\zeta} = S_{C_1}^{\zeta} = -S_{C_2}^{\zeta} = \tfrac{1}{2}(1 - k/\zeta)$$

$$S_{K_1}^{\zeta} = S_{K_2}^{\zeta} = 1 - (k + 1/k)/2\zeta$$

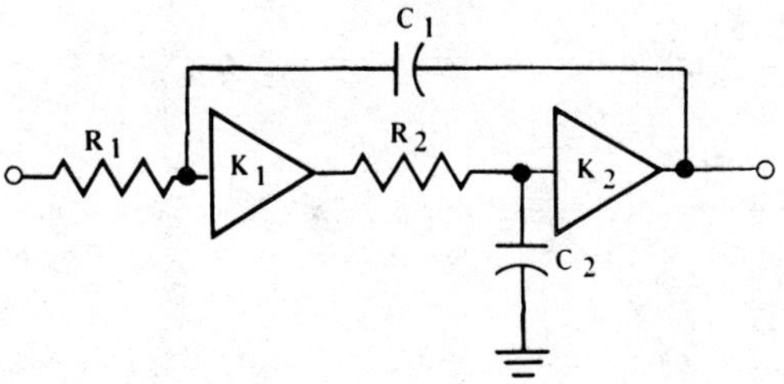

R. P. Sallen and E. L. Key, "A practical method for designing RC active filters," IRE Trans. Circuit Theory, vol. CT-2, pp. 74–85, March, 1955; and R. E. Bach, "Selecting RC values for active filters," Electronics, pp. 82–85, May 13, 1960.

Thus, K is determined by ζ. In turn, H_o is determined by K. Thus, our single degree-of-freedom is R or C. Now the question is, which component should we select? Generally, we want to select the component having the most restricted range or number of available (i.e., standard) values. Since capacitors have the fewest standard values, we shall generally select C values and then calculate $R = 1/\omega_o C$.

Suppose that we instead set $K_1 = K_2 = K$ and $R_2C_2 = k^2R_1C_1$ so that the time constant of the R_2C_2 network is k^2 times that of the R_1C_1 network. Substituting the time constant constraint into the parameter equations of Eq. 8.2.2 gives

$$\omega_o = 1/kT, \qquad \zeta = (1 - H_o + k^2)/2k \tag{8.2.4}$$

where $T_1 = R_1C_1$ and $K = H_o$. We see that ζ requires k be chosen so that

$$k = \zeta \pm [\zeta^2 - (1 - H_o)]^{1/2} \tag{8.2.5}$$

Then solving for R_1 and R_2 from the ω_o equation gives

$$R_1 = 1/k\omega_o C_1, \qquad R_2 = k/\omega_o C_2 \tag{8.2.6}$$

Therefore, choosing C_1 and C_2, we then calculate R_1 and R_2. From a more general standpoint, given ω_o, ζ, H_o, we have q = 4. Since p = 6, we have (p – q) = (6 – 4) = 2 degrees of freedom. We use them in choosing C_1 and C_2. The design equations are listed in Table 8.2.1.

Very often, we will find implicit constraints in the parameter equations and design equations. When these constraints are obvious, they are not entered on the design sheet. For the filter being considered, since $0 \leqslant \zeta \leqslant 1$ for complex poles, then it is easy to show from Eq. 8.2.5 that $(k - 1)^2 \leqslant H_o \leqslant (1 + k^2)$. Therefore, the dc gain must be positive but cannot exceed $(1 + k^2)$. If H_o exceeds $(1 + k^2)$, then $\zeta < 0$ and cannot be realized. Thus, a gain block following the filter is necessary if greater than $(1 + k^2)$ dc gain is to be obtained.

Now that we have calculated the required parameter values, we want to consider drifts in ω_o, ζ, and H_o due to drifts (i.e., initial tolerance error; and temperature, aging, and other drifts due to environmental effects) in the parameter values R_1, C_1, R_2, C_2, K_1, and K_2. If the component drifts are small so that first-order sensitivity analysis can be used, then we wish to know the sensitivity coefficients. Sensitivity was discussed in Sec. 1.15. These are also listed on the design sheet for ready reference and are calculated directly from the parameter equations for ω_o, ζ, and H_o. For example, we see that the active sensitivities

$$S_{K_1}^{\omega_o} = S_{K_2}^{\omega_o} = 0 \tag{8.2.7}$$

since ω_o is independent of K_1 and K_2. The passive sensitivities of ω_o equal

$$S_{R_1}^{\omega_o} = S_{C_1}^{\omega_o} = S_{R_2}^{\omega_o} = S_{C_2}^{\omega_o} = -1/2 \tag{8.2.8}$$

which shows that a 1% drift in any of the passive parameters produces about a ½% drift in ω_o. The active ζ sensitivities equal

$$S_{K_1}^{\zeta} = S_{K_2}^{\zeta} = -\frac{K_1K_2}{1 - K_1K_2}\,\frac{R_1C_1(1 - K_1K_2)}{R_1C_1(1 - K_1K_2) + R_2C_2} = -\frac{K_1K_2}{1 + k^2 - K_1K_2} \tag{8.2.9}$$

but since from Eq. 8.2.4, $\zeta = (1 + k^2 - K_1K_2)/2k$, then

$$S_{K_1}^{\zeta} = S_{K_2}^{\zeta} = \frac{2k\zeta - (1 + k^2)}{2k\zeta} = 1 - \frac{1 + k^2}{2k\zeta} \tag{8.2.10}$$

In like manner, the passive ζ sensitivities equal

$$S_{R_1}^{\zeta} = S_{C_1}^{\zeta} = -S_{R_2}^{\zeta} = -S_{C_2}^{\zeta} = \tfrac{1}{2}(1 - k/\zeta) \tag{8.2.11}$$

The H_o sensitivities equal

$$S_{R_1}^{H_o} = S_{C_1}^{H_o} = S_{R_2}^{H_o} = S_{C_2}^{H_o} = 0, \qquad S_{K_1}^{H_o} = S_{K_2}^{H_o} = 1 \tag{8.2.12}$$

so drift in H_o occurs only for drifts in gains K_1 and K_2.

Now let us utilize these results. Although the drifts in ω_o and H_o are small, the drifts in ζ due to drifts in R_1, C_1, R_2, C_2, K_1, and K_2 depend upon k and ζ. Most often we wish to minimize these sensitivities to obtain the lowest drift design. For example, if we choose k so $k = \zeta$, then we obtain ζ sensitivities of

$$S_{K_1}^{\zeta} = S_{K_2}^{\zeta} = \tfrac{1}{2}(1 - 1/\zeta^2), \qquad S_{R_1}^{\zeta} = S_{C_1}^{\zeta} = -S_{R_2}^{\zeta} = -S_{C_2}^{\zeta} = 0 \tag{8.2.13}$$

They are zero except for S_K^{ζ} which is extremely large for small ζ. Alternatively, we could set $k = 1$ so that

$$S_{K_1}^{\zeta} = S_{K_2}^{\zeta} = 1 - 1/\zeta, \qquad S_{R_1}^{\zeta} = S_{C_1}^{\zeta} = -S_{R_2}^{\zeta} = -S_{C_2}^{\zeta} = \tfrac{1}{2}(1 - 1/\zeta) \tag{8.2.14}$$

which are large for small ζ. Thus, there are many ways in which we can select k. Improperly choosing k produces large sensitivities. This important but subtle fact is often overlooked by filter designers. It is the cause of the downfall of many filters in practice. Not only must the filter classes be properly chosen, but so also must the design equations.

It is important to choose the passive time constants to obtain the desired gain-sensitivity tradeoff as summarized in Sec. 7.19. Before proceeding, the engineer should now reread that section. To obtain minimum sensitivity designs in Class A, $\overline{\text{A}}$, and B filters, the passive time constants must be matched. This produces minimum gain Class A and $\overline{\text{A}}$ filters, and Class B filters having gains of about two. In Class B filters, these gains may be reduced towards unity by separating the time constants by $4Q^2$ but the sensitivities increase by Q which is undesirable.

Class C and $\overline{\text{C}}$ filters have real pole a_4 associated with the active portion of their denominators. When a_4 is chosen to produce one set of root loci shown in Fig. 7.19.2, their sensitivities are lower than those of Class A and $\overline{\text{A}}$ filters, but the gain required is larger. For another set of a_4, the situation is reversed.

Class D filters usually have an imaginary pole pair on the $j\omega$-axis associated with the active portion of their denominators. When this pole is equal to the geometric mean of the passive corner frequencies, lower gain but higher passive sensitivity filters are obtained; otherwise the Class D filter approaches a Class A or $\overline{\text{A}}$ filter.

Class E filters are the most general with the greatest gain-sensitivity tradeoffs. Generally, as their gain is increased, their active sensitivities become smaller. In the limit as gain approaches infinity, their active sensitivities approach zero.

Thus, we see that gain-sensitivity compromises are necessary in the design equations for Class C, $\overline{\text{C}}$, D, and E filters. In many of our design equations, we choose parameters to obtain H_o as well as ω_o and ζ. This further constraint very often fixes gains K_1 and K_2 and prevents us from obtaining minimum sensitivity designs. If we instead allow H_o to be unspecified, so that minimum sensitivity designs can be obtained, a gain block is often needed following the filter. With experience, the design engineer will know when this is a good alternative.

EXAMPLE 8.2.1 Obtain the minimum active Q sensitivity designs for the Class 1B low-pass filter of Table 8.2.1.

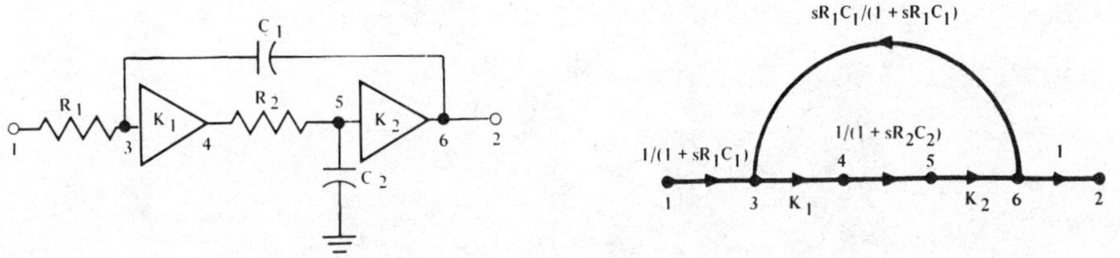

Fig. 8.2.1 Class 1B low-pass filter and its flow graph.

Solution The flow graph for this filter was determined in Example 7.6.1 and is shown below. The cross-coupling equalled

$$T_{45} = \frac{1}{1 + sR_2C_2}, \qquad T_{63} = \frac{sR_1C_1}{1 + sR_1C_1} \tag{8.2.15}$$

and there is no local feedback. The filter determinant is equal to

$$\Delta(s) = 1 - \frac{K_1K_2sR_1C_1}{(1 + sR_1C_1)(1 + sR_2C_2)} \tag{8.2.16}$$

which can be manipulated into the form

$$\Delta'(s) = \Delta(s)/R_1C_1R_2C_2 = (s + 1/R_1C_1)(s + 1/R_2C_2) - sK_1K_2/R_2C_2 \tag{8.2.17}$$

Comparing Δ' with the Class 1B standard form of Eq. 7.6.5, then the passive corner frequencies equal

$$a_1 = 1/R_2C_2, \qquad a_2 = 1/R_1C_1 \tag{8.2.18}$$

For a minimum Q sensitivity design, we set the passive corner frequency ratio equal to unity as

$$a_1/a_2 = R_1C_1/R_2C_2 = 1 \tag{8.2.19}$$

For a minimum gain design, we set this ratio equal to $4Q^2$ as

$$a_1/a_2 = R_1C_1/R_2C_2 = 4Q^2 = 1/\zeta^2 \tag{8.2.20}$$

Thus, the only difference in the design is the choice of the passive corner frequency or time constant ratio a_1/a_2.

EXAMPLE 8.2.2 Prepare the design sheets for the minimum gain and minimum active Q sensitivity realizations determined in the previous example.

Solution The parameters of the filter are given by Eq. 8.2.2. Now let us determine the design equations and sensitivities. From Example 8.2.1, for minimum sensitivity, we set $R_1C_1 = R_2C_2$. Then ω_o is fixed by choosing the proper K_1K_2 value, and H_o becomes a dependent variable. The design equations and sensitivities are listed on the design sheet of Table 8.2.2. Note that the gain and active Q sensitivities are those found previously in Eq. 8.2.14.

For minimum gain, we must instead set $R_1C_1 = 4Q^2R_2C_2$. This yields the second set of design equations listed in Table 8.2.2. The sensitivities were found in Eq. 8.2.13. We see that less gain is required at the expense of greatly increased sensitivities.

This example re-emphasizes the fact that to obtain minimum sensitivity and/or minimum gain designs, parameter H_o often cannot be specified. This is not usually a problem since gain levels elsewhere in the system can often be adjusted. At worse, a gain buffer may be necessary.

Now that we have reviewed the various ways in which design equations can be formed, let us introduce a collection of active filter designs.

Table 8.2.2 Continuation of sample filter design sheet of Table 8.2.1.

CLASS 1B: LOW-PASS (Continued)

Design Equations: Set k = 1, $R_1 = R_2 = R$, $C_1 = C_2 = C$ (For Minimum Sensitivity)

Given: ω_o, ζ

Choose: C

Calculate: $R = 1/\omega_o C$

$K_1 K_2 = 2(1 - \zeta)$

$H_o = K_1 K_2$

Sensitivities:

$$S_{R_1}^{\omega_o} = S_{R_2}^{\omega_o} = S_{C_1}^{\omega_o} = S_{C_2}^{\omega_o} = -\tfrac{1}{2} \qquad S_{K_1}^{\zeta} = S_{K_2}^{\zeta} = 1 - 1/\zeta$$

$$S_{R_1}^{\zeta} = -S_{R_2}^{\zeta} = S_{C_1}^{\zeta} = -S_{C_2}^{\zeta} = \tfrac{1}{2}(1 - 1/\zeta) \qquad S_{K_1}^{H_o} = S_{K_2}^{H_o} = 1$$

Design Equations: Set $R_2 C_2 = R_1 C_1 / 4Q^2 = \zeta^2 R_1 C_1$ (For Minimum Gain)

Given: ω_o, ζ

Choose; C_1, C_2

Calculate: $R_1 = 1/\zeta\omega_o C_1$ $\qquad K_1 K_2 = 1 - \zeta^2$

$R_2 = \zeta/\omega_o C_2$ $\qquad H_o = K_1 K_2$

Sensitivities:

$$S_{R_1}^{\omega_o} = S_{R_2}^{\omega_o} = S_{C_1}^{\omega_o} = S_{C_2}^{\omega_o} = -\tfrac{1}{2} \qquad S_{K_1}^{\zeta} = S_{K_2}^{\zeta} = \tfrac{1}{2}(1 - 1/\zeta^2)$$

$$S_{R_1}^{\zeta} = -S_{R_2}^{\zeta} = S_{C_1}^{\zeta} = -S_{C_2}^{\zeta} = 0 \qquad S_{K_1}^{H_o} = S_{K_2}^{H_o} = 1$$

8.3 LOW-PASS FILTER COMPILATIONS

For rapid and efficient designs of active filters, we require a set of well-defined and readily available filter designs. A number of these design sheets are compiled in this section.[1] Although the filters which have been selected are by no means exhaustive of those available, they are representative of those which exist and have been found useful in actual design work. The engineer may find other forms which he may prefer for a specific application; nevertheless, these compiled filters can be used in almost all applications. These design sheets have been prepared as discussed in the previous section. For simplicity, sensitivities which equal zero are not entered on the sheets.

CLASS 1A: LOW-PASS

Transfer Function:

$$H(s) = \frac{K_1K_2}{s^2(1 + K_1K_2)R_1C_1R_2C_2 + s(R_1C_1 + R_2C_2) + 1}$$

Parameters:

$$\omega_o = \frac{1}{[(1 + K_1K_2)R_1C_1R_2C_2]^{1/2}} \qquad H_o = K_1K_2$$

$$\zeta = \frac{(R_1C_1/R_2C_2)^{1/2} + (R_2C_2/R_1C_1)^{1/2}}{2(1 + K_1K_2)^{1/2}}$$

Design Equations: Set $R_1 = R_2 = R$, $C_1 = C_2 = C$ (For Minimum Gain and Minimum Sensitivity)

Given: ω_o, ζ

Choose: C

Calculate: $R = \zeta/\omega_o C$

$K_1K_2 = 1/\zeta^2 - 1$

$H_o = K_1K_2$

Sensitivities:

$$S_{R_1}^{\omega_o} = S_{R_2}^{\omega_o} = S_{C_1}^{\omega_o} = S_{C_2}^{\omega_o} = -\tfrac{1}{2}$$

$$S_{K_1}^{\omega_o} = S_{K_2}^{\omega_o} = S_{K_1}^{\zeta} = S_{K_2}^{\zeta} = -\tfrac{1}{2}(1 - \zeta^2)$$

$$S_{K_1}^{H_o} = S_{K_2}^{H_o} = 1$$

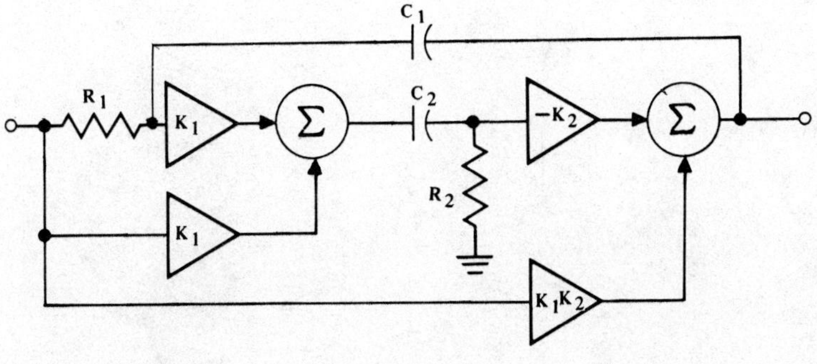

M. A. Soderstrand and S. K. Mitra, "Gain and sensitivity limitations of active RC filters," Tech. Rep., NSF Grant GK 14736, Univ. of California, Davis, 1971.

CLASS $1\overline{A}$: LOW-PASS

Transfer Function:

$$H(s) = \frac{-K_1K_2}{s^2R_1C_1R_2C_2 + s[R_1C_1 + R_2C_2(1 + R_1/R_3)] + [1 + (1 + K_1K_2)R_1/R_3]}$$

Parameters:

$$\omega_o = \left[\frac{1 + (1 + K_1K_2)R_1/R_3}{R_1C_1R_2C_2}\right]^{1/2} \qquad H_o = \frac{-K_1K_2}{1 + (1 + K_1K_2)R_1/R_3}$$

$$\zeta = \frac{(R_1C_1/R_2C_2)^{1/2} + (R_2C_2/R_1C_1)^{1/2}(1 + R_1/R_3)}{2[1 + (1 + K_1K_2)R_1/R_3]^{1/2}}$$

Design Equations: Set $\rho = R_3/R_1$, $C_1R_1R_3/(R_1 + R_3) = R_2C_2$ (For Minimum Gain and Minimum Sensitivity)

Given: ω_o, ζ

Choose: C_1, C_2, ρ

Calculate: $R_2 = 1/\zeta\omega_oC_2$ $\qquad R_1 = R_3/\rho$

$R_3 = (1 + \rho)/\zeta\omega_oC_1$ $\qquad K_1K_2 = (1 + \rho)(1/\zeta^2 - 1)$

$H_o = -\rho K_1K_2/(1 + \rho + K_1K_2)$

Sensitivities:

$S_{K_1}^{\omega_o} = S_{K_2}^{\omega_o} = -\rho\zeta^2/2(1 + \rho)$ $\qquad S_{K_1}^{\zeta} = S_{K_2}^{\zeta} = (\zeta^2 - 1)/2$

$S_{R_2}^{\omega_o} = S_{C_1}^{\omega_o} = S_{C_2}^{\omega_o} = -1/2$ $\qquad S_{R_1}^{\zeta} = -S_{R_3}^{\zeta} = \rho(\zeta^2 - 1)/2(1 + \rho)$

$S_{R_1}^{\omega_o} = \rho(\zeta^2 - 1)/2(1 + \rho)$ $\qquad S_{K_1}^{H_o} = S_{K_2}^{H_o} = -\zeta^2$

$S_{R_3}^{\omega_o} = [\rho(\zeta^2 - 1) - 1]/2(1 + \rho)$ $\qquad S_{R_1}^{H_o} = -S_{R_3}^{H_o} = \rho(1 - \zeta^2)/(1 + \rho)$

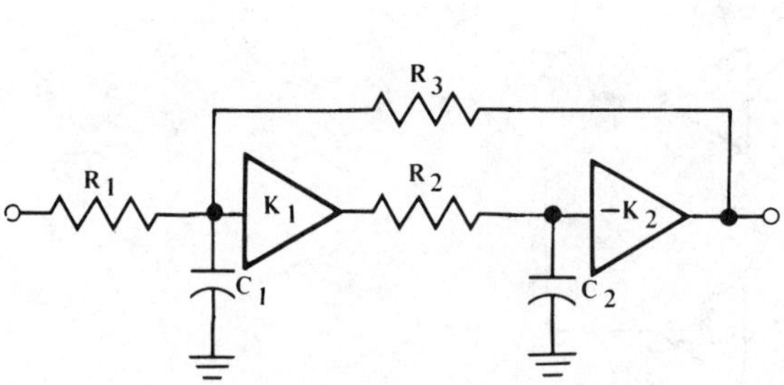

T. Deliyannis, "A low-pass filter with extremely low sensitivity," Proc. IEEE, vol. 58, pp. 1366–1367, Sept., 1970.

CLASS 1B: LOW-PASS

Transfer Function:

$$H(s) = \frac{K_1K_2}{s^2R_1C_1R_2C_2 + s[R_1C_1(1 - K_1K_2) + R_2C_2] + 1}$$

Parameters:

$$\omega_o = \frac{1}{(R_1C_1R_2C_2)^{1/2}} \qquad H_o = K_1K_2$$

$$\zeta = \tfrac{1}{2}\,[(R_1C_1/R_2C_2)^{1/2}(1 - K_1K_2) + (R_2C_2/R_1C_1)^{1/2}]$$

Design Equations: Set $R_1 = R_2 = R$, $C_1 = C_2 = C$ (For Minimum Active Sensitivity)

Given: ω_o, ζ

Choose: C

Calculate: $R = 1/\omega_o C$

$K_1K_2 = 2(1 - \zeta)$

$H_o = K_1K_2$

Sensitivities:

$$S_{R_1}^{\omega_o} = S_{R_2}^{\omega_o} = S_{C_1}^{\omega_o} = S_{C_2}^{\omega_o} = -\tfrac{1}{2}$$

$$S_{K_1}^{\zeta} = S_{K_2}^{\zeta} = 1 - 1/\zeta$$

$$S_{R_1}^{\zeta} = -S_{R_2}^{\zeta} = S_{C_1}^{\zeta} = -S_{C_2}^{\zeta} = \tfrac{1}{2}(1 - 1/\zeta)$$

$$S_{K_1}^{H_o} = S_{K_2}^{H_o} = 1$$

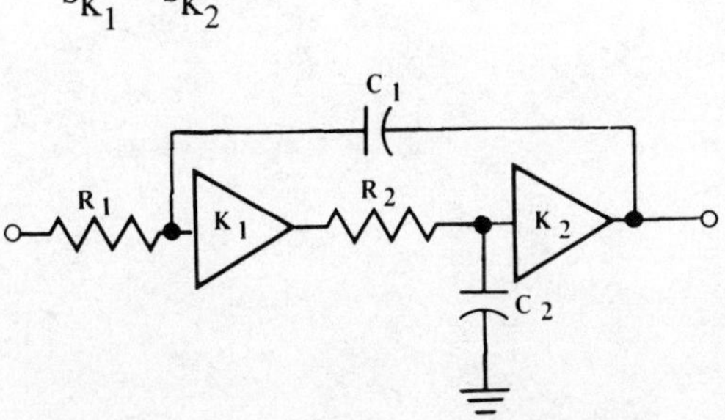

R. P. Sallen and E. L. Key, "A practical method for designing RC active filters," IRE Trans. Circuit Theory, vol. CT-2, pp. 74–85, March, 1955; and R. E. Bach, "Selecting RC values for active filters," Electronics, pp. 82–85, May 13, 1960.

CLASS 1C: LOW-PASS

Transfer Function:

$$H(s) = \frac{K_1K_2}{s^2(1+K_2)R_1C_1R_2C_2 + s[R_1C_1(1-K_1K_2)+R_2C_2(1+K_2)] + 1}$$

Parameters:

$$\omega_o = \frac{1}{[(1+K_2)R_1C_1R_2C_2]^{1/2}} \qquad H_o = K_1K_2$$

$$\zeta = \frac{(R_1C_1/R_2C_2)^{1/2}(1-K_1K_2) + (R_2C_2/R_1C_1)^{1/2}(1+K_2)}{2(1+K_2)^{1/2}}$$

Design Equations: Set $R_1 = \rho R_2, \quad C_1 = \rho C_2, \quad R_1C_1 = \rho^2 R_2C_2$

Given: ω_o, ζ, H_o

Choose: C_1, ρ

Calculate: $K_2 = -1 + \rho^2[-1 + 2\zeta^2 + H_o \pm 2\zeta(\zeta^2 + H_o - 1)^{1/2}]$

$K_1 = H_o/K_2$

$R_1 = \rho/\omega_o C_1(1+K_2)^{1/2}$

Sensitivities:

$$S_{K_2}^{\omega_o} = -K_2/2(1+K_2)$$

$$S_{R_1}^{\omega_o} = S_{R_2}^{\omega_o} = S_{C_1}^{\omega_o} = S_{C_2}^{\omega_o} = -\tfrac{1}{2}$$

$$S_{K_1}^{\zeta} = \frac{-\rho^2 H_o}{\rho^2(1-H_o)+1+K_2}$$

$$S_{K_2}^{\zeta} = \frac{(1+K_2-\rho^2)K_2 - \rho^2H_o(2+K_2)}{2[\rho^2(1-H_o)+1+K_2](1+K_2)}$$

$$S_{R_1}^{\zeta} = -S_{R_2}^{\zeta} = S_{C_1}^{\zeta} = -S_{C_2}^{\zeta} = \frac{\rho^2(1-H_o)-(1+K_2)}{2[\rho^2(1-H_o)+1+K_2]}$$

$$S_{K_1}^{H_o} = S_{K_2}^{H_o} = 1$$

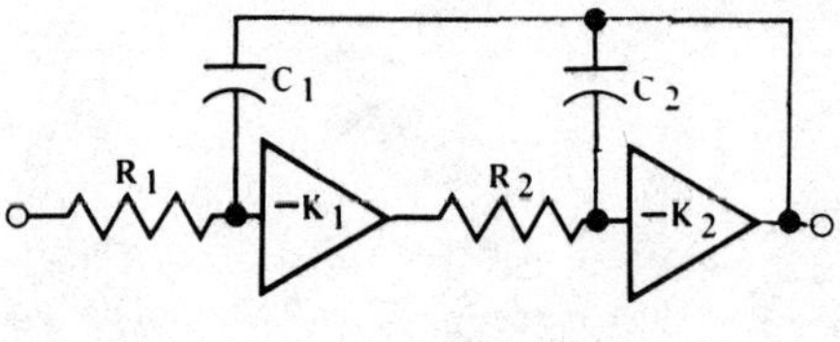

CLASS $1\overline{C}$: LOW-PASS

Transfer Function:

$$H(s) = \frac{-K_1K_2R_3R_4}{s^2R_1C_1R_2C_2R_3R_4 + s[R_1C_1R_3R_4 + R_2C_2(R_1R_3 + R_1R_4 + R_3R_4) + K_1R_1R_2C_2R_4] + [R_1R_3 + R_1R_4 + R_3R_4 + K_1R_1(K_2R_3 + R_4)]}$$

Parameters:

$$\omega_o = \left[\frac{1 + R_1[(R_3 + R_4)/R_3R_4] + K_1(K_2 + R_4/R_3)}{R_1C_1R_2C_2}\right]^{1/2} \qquad H_o = \frac{-K_1K_2R_3R_4}{R_1R_3 + R_1R_4 + R_3R_4 + K_1R_1(K_2R_3 + R_4)}$$

$$\zeta = \frac{R_1C_1R_3R_4 + R_2C_2(R_1R_3 + R_1R_4 + R_3R_4) + K_1R_1R_2C_2R_4}{2\left\{R_1C_1R_2C_2R_3R_4[R_1R_3 + R_1R_4 + R_3R_4 + K_1R_1(K_2R_3 + R_4)]\right\}^{1/2}}$$

Design Equations: Set $R_1 = R_2 = R_3/\rho = R_4 = R$, $C_1 = C_2 = C$

Given: ω_o, ζ

Choose: C, K_2, ρ

Calculate: $K_1 = -(1 + 3\rho) + 2\zeta^2\rho(1 + \rho K_2) - 2\zeta[-\rho(1 + 3\rho)(1 + \rho K_2) + \zeta^2\rho^2(1 + \rho K_2) + \rho(1 + 2\rho)]^{1/2}$

$$R = \frac{1}{\omega_o C}\,\frac{[1 + 2\rho + K_1(1 + \rho K_2)]^{1/2}}{\rho^{1/2}}, \qquad H_o = -\rho K_1K_2/[1 + 2\rho + K_1(1 + \rho K_2)]$$

Sensitivities: (For $\rho = 1$ and $K_2 = 3$) Set $a = 4K_1 + 3$, $b = 8K_1^2 + 38K_1 + 24$

$S_{K_1}^{\omega_o} = 2K_1/a$

$S_{K_2}^{\omega_o} = 3K_1/2a$

$S_{R_1}^{\omega_o} = (1 + 4K_1)/2a$

$S_{R_2}^{\omega_o} = S_{C_1}^{\omega_o} = S_{C_2}^{\omega_o} = -1/2$

$S_{R_3}^{\omega_o} = -(1 + K_1)/2a$

$S_{R_4}^{\omega_o} = -(1 + 3K_1)/2a$

$S_{K_1}^{\zeta} = (2K_1^2 + 5K_1)/4(K_1^2 + 4K_1 + 3)$

$S_{K_2}^{\zeta} = 3K_1/2a$

$S_{R_1}^{\zeta} = (31K_1 + 4)/b$

$S_{R_2}^{\zeta} = (2 + K_1)/2(4 + K_1)$

$S_{R_3}^{\zeta} = (7K_1^2 + 36K_1 + 38)/b$

$S_{R_4}^{\zeta} = (13K_1^2 + 39K_1 + 38)/b$

$S_{C_1}^{\zeta} = -(2 + K_1)/2(4 + K_1)$

$S_{C_2}^{\zeta} = (2 + K_1)/2(4 - K_1)$

$S_{K_1}^{H_o} = -1/(1 + 2K_1)$

$S_{K_2}^{H_o} = -(2 + K_1)/(2 + 4K_1)$

$S_{R_1}^{H_o} = 1$

$S_{R_3}^{H_o} = K_1/(2 + 4K_1)$

$S_{R_4}^{H_o} = 3K_1/(2 + 4K_1)$

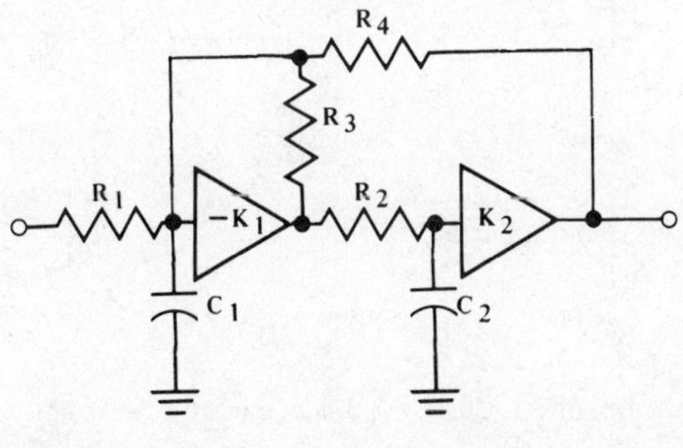

CLASS 1E: LOW-PASS

Transfer Function:

$$H(s) = \frac{(1 + R_6/R_5)/(1 + R_3/R_4)}{s^2R_1C_1R_2C_2 + sR_2C_2[(1 + R_6/R_5)/(1 + R_4/R_3)] + R_6/R_5}$$

Parameters:

$$\omega_o = \left[\frac{R_6/R_5}{R_1C_1R_2C_2}\right]^{1/2} \qquad H_o = \frac{1 + R_5/R_6}{1 + R_3/R_4}$$

$$\zeta = \frac{1}{2}\,\frac{1 + R_6/R_5}{1 + R_4/R_3}\left[\frac{R_5}{R_6}\,\frac{R_2C_2}{R_1C_1}\right]^{1/2}$$

Design Equations: Set $R_1 = R_2 = R$, $C_1 = C_2 = C$, $R_3 = R_5 = R_6$

Given: ω_o, ζ

Choose: C, R_3

Calculate: $R = 1/\omega_o C$

$R_4 = (1/\zeta - 1)R_3$

$H_o = 2(1 - \zeta)$

Sensitivities:

$$S_{R_1}^{\omega_o} = S_{R_2}^{\omega_o} = S_{R_5}^{\omega_o} = -S_{R_6}^{\omega_o} = S_{C_1}^{\omega_o} = S_{C_2}^{\omega_o} = -\tfrac{1}{2} \qquad S_{R_3}^{H_o} = -S_{R_4}^{H_o} = -\zeta$$

$$S_{R_1}^{\zeta} = -S_{R_2}^{\zeta} = S_{C_1}^{\zeta} = -S_{C_2}^{\zeta} = -\tfrac{1}{2} \qquad S_{R_5}^{H_o} = -S_{R_6}^{H_o} = \tfrac{1}{2}$$

$$S_{R_3}^{\zeta} = -S_{R_4}^{\zeta} = \zeta$$

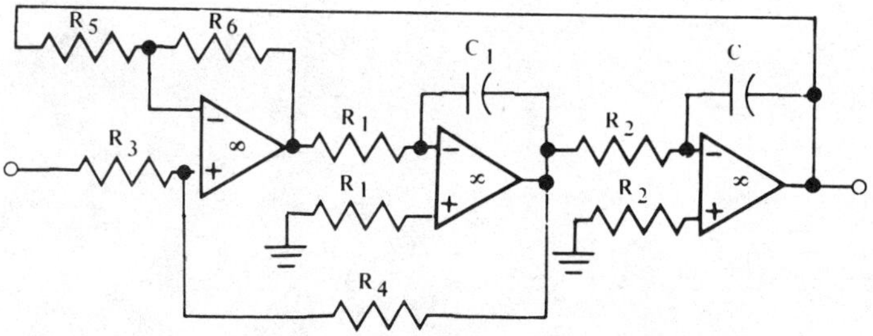

L. P. Huelsman, J. G. Graeme, and G. E. Tobey, *Operational Amplifiers,* Chap. 8.3.3, McGraw-Hill, NY, 1971.

CLASS 2A: LOW-PASS

Transfer Function:

$$H(s) = \frac{K/2}{s^2(1+K)R_1C_1R_2C_2 + s[R_1C_1(1+C_2/C_1) + R_2C_2] + 1}$$

Parameters;

$$\omega_o = \frac{1}{[(1+K)R_1C_1R_2C_2]^{1/2}} \qquad H_o = K/2$$

$$\zeta = \frac{(R_1C_1/R_2C_2)^{1/2}(1 + C_2/C_1) + (R_2C_2/R_1C_1)^{1/2}}{2(1+K)^{1/2}}$$

Design Equations: Set $R_1 = R_2 = R$, $C_1 = C_2 = C$

Given: ω_o, ζ

Choose: C

Calculate: $R = 2\zeta/3\omega_o C$

$K = 9/4\zeta^2 - 1$

$H_o = K/2$

Sensitivities:

$$S_{R_1}^{\omega_o} = S_{R_2}^{\omega_o} = S_{C_1}^{\omega_o} = S_{C_2}^{\omega_o} = -\tfrac{1}{2}$$

$$S_K^{\omega_o} = S_K^{\zeta} = -\tfrac{1}{2}(1 - 4\zeta^2/9)$$

$$S_{R_1}^{\zeta} = -S_{R_2}^{\zeta} = -S_{C_1}^{\zeta} = S_{C_2}^{\zeta} = 1/6$$

$$S_K^{H_o} = 1$$

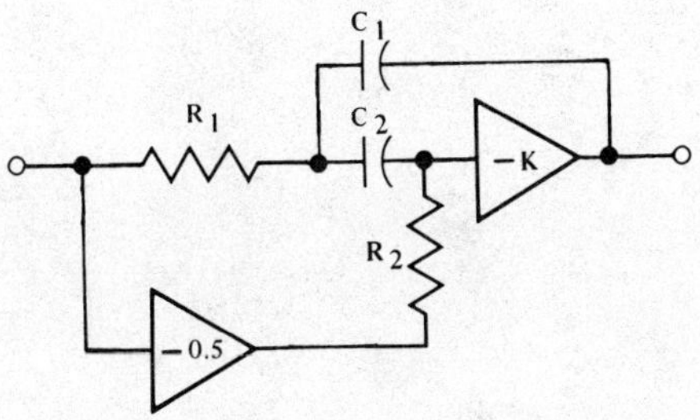

M. A. Soderstrand and S. K. Mitra, loc. cit.

CLASS $2\bar{A}$: LOW-PASS

Transfer Function:

$$H(s) = \frac{-K}{s^2R_1C_1R_2C_2 + s[R_1C_1(1 + C_2/C_1) + R_2C_2(1 + R_1/R_3)] + [1 + (1 + K)R_1/R_3]}$$

Parameters:

$$\omega_o = \left[\frac{1 + (1 + K)R_1/R_3}{R_1C_1R_2C_2}\right]^{1/2} \qquad H_o = \frac{-K}{1 + (1 + K)R_1/R_3}$$

$$\zeta = \frac{(R_1C_1/R_2C_2)^{1/2}(1 + C_2/C_1) + (R_2C_2/R_1C_1)^{1/2}(1 + R_1/R_3)}{2[1 + (1 + K)R_1/R_3]^{1/2}}$$

Design Equations: Set $\rho = R_3/R_1 \ll 1$, $R_1' = R_1R_3/(R_1 + R_3)$, $R_2C_2 = R_1'C_1$

(Towards Minimum Gain and Minimum Sensitivity)

Given: ω_o, ζ

Choose: C_1, C_2, ρ

Calculate: $R_2 = \dfrac{1 + \rho + C_2/C_1}{\zeta\omega_o C_2}$ $\qquad R_3 = \rho R_1$

$R_1' = R_2C_2/C_1$ $\qquad K = (1 + \rho)[(1 + C_2/2C_1)^2/\zeta^2 - 1]$

$R_1 = R_1'(1 + \rho)/\rho$ $\qquad H_o = -\rho K/(1 + \rho + K)$

Sensitivities:

$S_K^{\omega_o} = -S_K^{\zeta} = K/2(1 + \rho + K)$ $\qquad S_{R_1}^{\zeta} = \frac{1}{2}[(1 + \rho)^3/\zeta\rho^2 - \rho]$

$S_{R_1}^{\omega_o} = -\rho/2(1 + \rho + K)$ $\qquad S_{R_2}^{\zeta} = -[(1 + \rho)/\rho](C_2/C_1)^{1/2}(1 + C_2/C_1)$

$S_{R_2}^{\omega_o} = S_{C_1}^{\omega_o} = S_{C_2}^{\omega_o} = -\frac{1}{2}$ $\qquad S_{R_3}^{\zeta} = -\frac{1}{2}[(1 + K)/(1 + \rho + K) + (1 + \rho)/2\rho]$

$S_{R_3}^{\omega_o} = -(1 + K)/2(1 + \rho + K)$ $\qquad S_{C_1}^{\zeta} = -S_{C_2}^{\zeta} = -\rho/2(1 + \rho)$

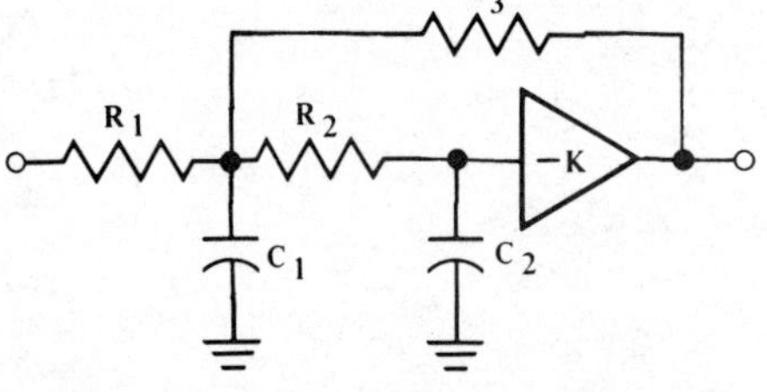

$S_K^{H_o} = (1 + \rho)/(1 + \rho + K)$

$S_{R_1}^{H_o} = -S_{R_3}^{H_o} = (1 + K)/(1 + \rho + K)$

R. P. Sallen and E. L. Key, loc. cit.

CLASS 2B: LOW-PASS

Transfer Function:

$$H(s) = \frac{K}{s^2 R_1 C_1 R_2 C_2 + s[R_1 C_1(1 + C_2/C_1 - K) + R_2 C_2] + 1}$$

Parameters:

$$\omega_o = \frac{1}{(R_1 C_1 R_2 C_2)^{1/2}} \qquad H_o = K$$

$$\zeta = \tfrac{1}{2}\,[(R_1C_1/R_2C_2)^{1/2}(1 + C_2/C_1 - K) + (R_2C_2/R_1C_1)^{1/2}]$$

Design Equations: Set $\rho = C_2/C_1 \ll 1$, $R_1C_1 = R_2C_2$ (Towards Minimum Active Sensitivity)

Given: ω_o, ζ

Choose: C_1, ρ

Calculate: $R_1 = 1/\omega_o C_1$ $\qquad K = 2(1 - \zeta) + \rho$

$R_2 = R_1/\rho$ $\qquad H_o = K$

$C_2 = \rho C_1$

Sensitivities:

$$S_{R_1}^{\omega_o} = S_{R_2}^{\omega_o} = S_{C_1}^{\omega_o} = S_{C_2}^{\omega_o} = -\tfrac{1}{2} \qquad S_K^{H_o} = 1$$

$$S_K^{\zeta} = [1 - (2 + \rho)/2\zeta]$$

$$S_{R_1}^{\zeta} = -S_{R_2}^{\zeta} = \tfrac{1}{2}(1 - 1/\zeta)$$

$$S_{C_1}^{\zeta} = -S_{C_2}^{\zeta} = \tfrac{1}{2}[1 - (1 + \rho)/\zeta]$$

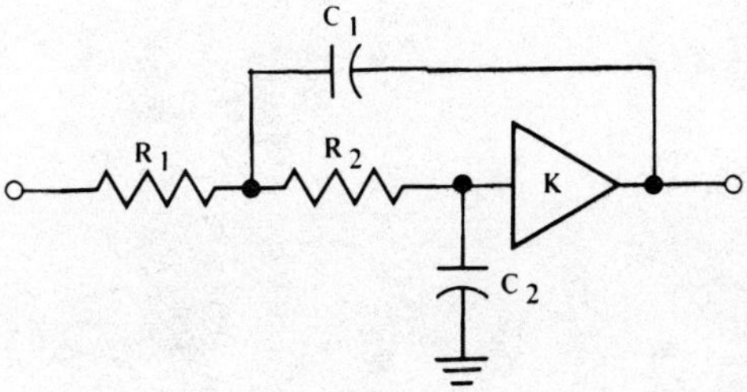

R. P. Sallen and E. L. Key, loc. cit.; and J. L. Hilburn and D. E. Johnson, *Manual of Active Filter Design*, Chap. 2, McGraw-Hill, NY, 1973.

CLASS 2C: LOW-PASS

Transfer Function:

$$H(s) = \frac{K}{s^2(1-K)R_1C_1R_2C_2 + s(1-K)[R_1C_1(1+C_2/C_1)+R_2C_2] + 1}$$

Parameters:

$$\omega_o = \frac{1}{[(1-K)R_1C_1R_2C_2]^{1/2}} \qquad H_o = K$$

$$\zeta = ½\,(1-K)^{1/2}[(R_1C_1/R_2C_2)^{1/2}(1+C_2/C_1) + (R_2C_2/R_1C_1)^{1/2}]$$

Design Equations: Set $C_1 = C_2 = C$

Given: ω_o, ζ, H_o

Choose: C

Calculate: $R_1 = \dfrac{\zeta \pm [\zeta^2 - 2(1-H_o)]^{1/2}}{2(1-H_o)} \dfrac{1}{\omega_o C} = \dfrac{F}{\omega_o C}$ $\qquad K = H_o$

$$R_2 = \frac{1}{F(1-H_o)\omega_o C}$$

Sensitivities:

$$S_{R_1}^{\omega_o} = S_{R_2}^{\omega_o} = S_{C_1}^{\omega_o} = S_{C_2}^{\omega_o} = -½ \qquad S_K^{H_o} = 1$$

$$S_K^{\omega_o} = -S_K^{\zeta} = H_o/2(1-H_o)$$

$$S_{R_1}^{\zeta} = -S_{R_2}^{\zeta} = ½ - 1/\zeta F$$

$$S_{C_1}^{\zeta} = -S_{C_2}^{\zeta} = -½ + F(1-H_o)/\zeta$$

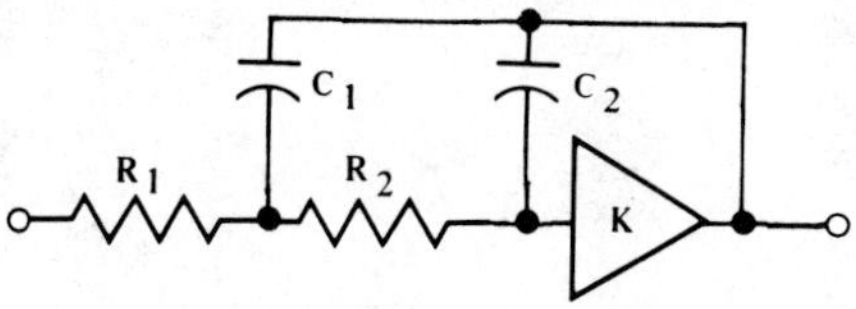

R. M. Inigo, "Active filter realization using finite-gain voltage amplifiers," IEEE Trans. Circuit Theory, vol. CT-17, pp. 445–448, Aug., 1970.

CLASS $2\overline{C}$: LOW-PASS

Transfer Function:

$$H(s) = \frac{-KR_2R_4}{s^2R_1C_1R_2C_2R_3R_4 + s\left\{R_1C_1[R_3R_4(1+K) + R_2R_4] + R_2C_2[R_3(R_1+R_4) + R_1R_4]\right\} + \left\{(R_1+R_4)[R_2+R_3(1+K)] + KR_1(R_2+R_4) + R_1R_4\right\}}$$

Parameters:

$$\omega_o = \left[\frac{(R_1+R_4)[R_2+R_3(1+K)] + KR_1(R_2+R_4) + R_1R_4}{R_1C_1R_2C_2R_3R_4}\right]^{1/2}$$

$$\zeta = \frac{R_1C_1[R_3R_4(1+K) + R_2R_4] + R_2C_2[R_3(R_1+R_4) + R_1R_4]}{2(R_1C_1R_2C_2R_3R_4)^{1/2}\left\{(R_1+R_4)[R_2+R_3(1+K)] + KR_1(R_2+R_4) + R_1R_4\right\}^{1/2}}$$

$$H_o = \frac{-KR_2R_4}{(R_1+R_4)[R_2+R_3(1+K)] + KR_1(R_2+R_4) + R_1R_4}$$

Design Equations: Set $R_1 = R_2 = R_3 = R_4 = R$, $C_1 = C_2 = C$

Given: ω_o, ζ

Choose: C

Calculate: $K = -5 + 8\zeta^2 \pm 2\zeta(16\zeta^2 - 15)^{1/2}$, $R = (4K+5)^{1/2}/\omega_o C$, $H_o = -K/(5+4K)$

Sensitivities: Set $a = 4K + 5$, $b = 4K^2 + 25K + 25$

$S_K^{\omega_o} = (2K+1)/a$

$S_{R_1}^{\omega_o} = -(K+2)/2a$

$S_{R_2}^{\omega_o} = -3(K+1)/2a$

$S_{R_3}^{\omega_o} = -(2K+3)/2a$

$S_{R_4}^{\omega_o} = -(K+1)/a$

$S_{C_1}^{\omega_o} = S_{C_2}^{\omega_o} = -1/2$

$S_K^{\zeta} = (2K^2 - 5K)/b$

$S_{R_1}^{\zeta} = (K^2 - 9K - 10)/2b$

$S_{R_2}^{\zeta} = (-2K^2 + 17K + 15)/2b$

$S_{R_3}^{\zeta} = (2K^2 - 3K - 5)/2b$

$S_{R_4}^{\zeta} = (K^2 + K)/b$

$S_{C_1}^{\zeta} = -S_{C_2}^{\zeta} = (K-1)/2(K+5)$

$S_K^{H_o} = -(2K+5)/a$

$S_{R_1}^{H_o} = (3K+3)/a$

$S_{R_2}^{H_o} = -3(K+1)/a$

$S_{R_3}^{H_o} = -S_{R_4}^{H_o} = 2(K+1)/a$

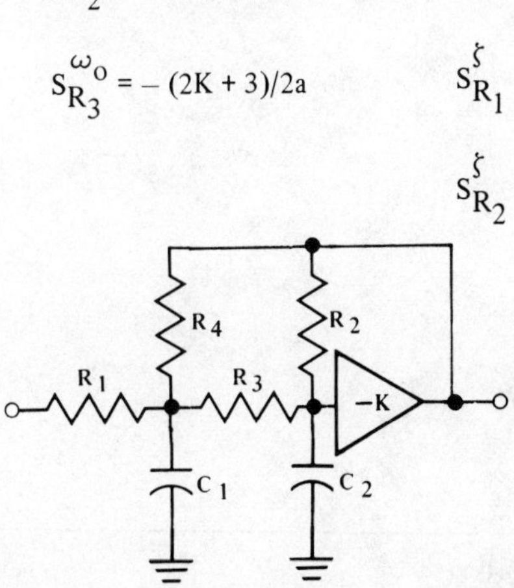

CLASS 2E: LOW-PASS

Transfer Function:

$$H(s) = \frac{-R_4/R_1}{s^2R_3C_2R_4C_5 + sC_5[R_3(1 + R_4/R_1) + R_4] + 1}$$

Parameters:

$$\omega_o = \frac{1}{(R_3C_2R_4C_5)^{1/2}} \qquad H_o = -R_4/R_1$$

$$\zeta = \tfrac{1}{2}(C_5/C_2)^{1/2}\,[(R_3/R_4)^{1/2}(1 + R_4/R_1) + (R_4/R_3)^{1/2}]$$

Design Equations: Set $C_5 = KC_2$

Given: ω_o, ζ, $-H_o$

Choose: C_2, K

Calculate: $C_5 = KC_2$ $\qquad R_1 = R_4/(-H_o)$

$$R_4 = \frac{\zeta \pm [\zeta^2 - K(1 - H_o)]^{1/2}}{\omega_o C_5} = \frac{F}{\omega_o C_5} \qquad R_3 = \frac{1}{F\omega_o C_2}$$

Sensitivities:

$$S_{R_3}^{\omega_o} = S_{R_4}^{\omega_o} = S_{C_2}^{\omega_o} = S_{C_4}^{\omega_o} = -\tfrac{1}{2} \qquad S_{R_4}^{H_o} = -S_{R_1}^{H_o} = 1$$

$$S_{R_1}^{\zeta} = -H_oK/2\zeta F$$

$$S_{R_3}^{\zeta} = \tfrac{1}{2} - F/\zeta$$

$$S_{R_4}^{\zeta} = \tfrac{1}{2} - K/2\zeta F$$

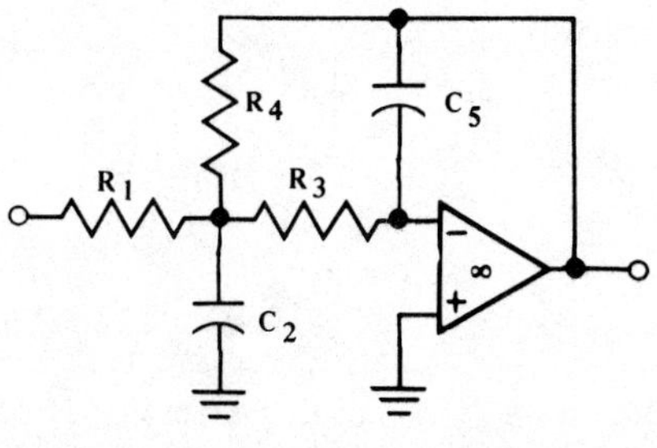

L. P. Huelsman, J. G. Graeme, and G. E. Tobey, op. cit., Chap. 8.3.1.

8.4 COMPONENT SELECTION

In designing active filters, we need to calculate and select the proper component values. These include resistors, capacitors, operational amplifiers, and potentiometers. Although we discuss this selection in great detail in Chap. 14, we need to make use of a few of the basic results as we proceed with the filter designs of the following chapters. These results are simply the standard values and tolerances of R's, C's, and pots, impedance paper, and the gains and impedances of operational amplifiers.

Commercially available resistors have tolerances of ¼, ½, 1, 5, 10, and 20%. Their values range from 1 Ω to 22 MΩ for the 5, 10, and 20% values, and from 10.0 Ω to 1 MΩ for the ¼, ½, and 1% values. The standard values are listed in Tables 14.1.2 and 14.1.3 (mark these pages now for easy reference later). In designs, we will generally use 1% values.

In many filter designs, we use potentiometers for tuning ω_o, ζ, and/or H_o. Pots have values ranging from 100 Ω to 1 MΩ with standard values of 1, 2, and 5. Their standard tolerances are 5, 10, and 20%.

Capacitors have tolerances of 5, 10, and 20%. Their values range from 10 pF to 1 μF in the types suitable for active filter applications. Their standard values coincide with those of resistors and are listed in Table 14.1.3. Although we usually use 5% capacitors, we shall generally select from the limited range of the 20% values. These values have the greatest commercial volume and are sometimes available at a reduced cost. Also, many companies produce 5% capacitors having only values in the 20% range.

There are several selection rules which we shall generally observe in our designs. Resistors less than 100 KΩ will be used when possible. This insures the parasitic resistances of op amps and the worse case leakage resistance of printed circuit boards will be negligible. Small resistance values will be avoided when their power dissipation becomes excessive. For example, if a ¼ W resistor is to withstand a 10 V rms signal, it must be greater than 400 Ω. Capacitors less than 1 μF (and 0.1 μF when possible) will be used due to their wide availability. Capacitors greater than 100 pF will generally be used which again insures that parasitic capacitance will be negligible. In Chap. 14, we will establish much more precise results; however, these guidelines will suffice for now.

One design aid which we shall use extensively is that of the impedance paper. *Impedance paper* is a collection of Bode magnitude plots showing the impedance of resistors, capacitors, and inductors versus frequency. Since the impedance of an R, L, and C equals

$$|Z_R(jf)| = R, \qquad |Z_L(jf)| = 2\pi fL, \qquad |Z_C(jf)| = 1/2\pi fC \tag{8.4.1}$$

their Bode magnitude plots consist of straight lines having slopes 0, +20, and −20 dB/dec, respectively. These plots are shown on the impedance paper of Figs. 14.1.9 and 14.1.10 (mark these pages now also). Resistors have constant impedances which are invariant with frequency; the R values (in Ω) are labelled along the left-hand edge of the graph. Inductors have impedance given by the diagonal lines of slope +20 dB/dec; the L values (in μH and H) are labelled along the top and right-hand edge of the graph. Capacitors have impedances given by the diagonal lines of slope −20 dB/dec; the C values (in pF and μF) are labelled along the right-hand edge of the graph. Frequency varies from 10 Hz to 5 MHz along the bottom of the graph.

For example, a 0.1 μF capacitance has an impedance magnitude of 15.9 KΩ at 100 Hz and 318 Ω at 5 KHz. These results are obtained by identifying the 0.1 μF line, and reading off the impedance magnitude at f = 100 Hz and 5 KHz as shown in Fig. 8.4.1a. We first find the approximate impedance value from Fig. 14.1.9, and then the exact value from Fig. 14.1.10. The advantage of using impedance paper rather than equations is the great insight the designer has in the initial selection of capacitor values in filter design. He can immediately see the resistor-capacitor tradeoffs in his design, and is freed from the trial-and-error drudgery of calculator or slide rule operations.

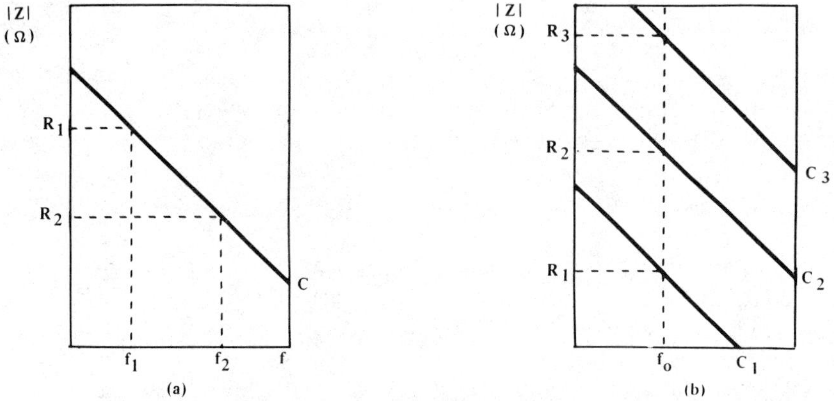

Fig. 8.4.1 (a) Determination of capacitor impedance at various frequencies and (b) tradeoff in R and C for constant RC product or constant corner frequency f_o.

We will often encounter design equations having the form $\omega_o = 1/RC$ or

$$R = 1/\omega_o C = 1/2\pi f_o C \tag{8.4.2}$$

Comparing this equation with Eq. 8.4.1, we see that it simply gives the impedance R of a capacitor C at frequency f_o. Thus, we can use impedance paper to show the tradeoffs in R for various C's when f_o is specified. Three (R, C) combinations are shown in Fig. 8.4.1b which all satisfy this equation. Thus, we can choose the best (R, C) combination by simple inspection of impedance paper. Note here that we will always express such time constant equations in radian frequency form to simplify their appearance; however, we shall always use impedance paper and Hertzian frequency f_o in solving design problems.

We shall often encounter more involved time constant equations such as

$$R = \left\{\zeta \pm [\zeta^2 - K(1 + H_o)]^{1/2}\right\}/\omega_o C = F/\omega_o C = 1/\omega_o' C \tag{8.4.3}$$

The filter design requirements generally fix K, ζ, and H_o. We can express this equation as $R = 1/\omega_o' C$ where $\omega_o' = \omega_o/\zeta F$. F can be considered as a correction factor and ζF as a frequency scaling constant. Thus, by determining the ζF and ω_o required by the design, we can enter $f_o' = \omega_o'/2\pi$ on impedance paper. Then we can find the (R, C) combinations required as before. This is an especially useful technique as we shall see.

Operational amplifiers (or simply op amps) are used to realize the gain blocks (i.e., amplifiers) in filter designs. When operated in an open-loop mode, op amps have gains of 80–100 dB (10^4–10^5). They have input impedances of typically 1 MΩ and output impedances less than 100 Ω. The input and output parasitic capacitances are less than 10 pF. When operated in a closed-loop mode, we will generally use the arrangements shown in Examples 7.1.2 and 7.1.3. There the closed-loop gain can be reduced from the open-loop value to zero depending upon the resistor ratio used. In the inverting mode of Example 7.1.2, the input impedance equals R_1 and the output impedance approaches zero. In the noninverting mode of Example 7.1.3, the input impedance equals $R_2 + R_3$ and the output impedance approaches zero. This information is summarized on the amplifier design sheets of Tables 8.4.1 and 8.4.2. These tables are very important since they will be used for the design of all the gain blocks in the rest of the book (mark these tables too). It should also be noted that the design equations insure that the dc resistance seen from both inputs of the op amp are equal. Matching of these resistances minimizes voltage offsets due to bias currents into the op amp as shall be discussed in Chap. 14. We will now illustrate the use of the amplifier design sheets with several examples.

Table 8.4.1 Design of noninverting amplifier. (For gain less than unity, see Eq. 8.5.26.)

Transfer Function: $K = \dfrac{1 + R_f/R_1}{1 + R_2/R_3}$ (Eq. 7.1.10)

Input Impedance: $Z_{in} = R_2 + R_3$

Design Equations ($K \geqslant 1$): Set $R_3 = \infty$, $R_2 = R_1 \| R_f$ (For Minimum Offset)

Given: K, R_2

Calculate: $R_f = KR_2$, $R_1 = R_f/(K-1) = R_2K/(K-1)$

Sensitivities: $S^K_{R_f} = -S^K_{R_1} = 1/(1 + R_1/R_f)$, $S^K_{R_3} = -S^K_{R_2} = 1/(1 + R_3/R_2)$

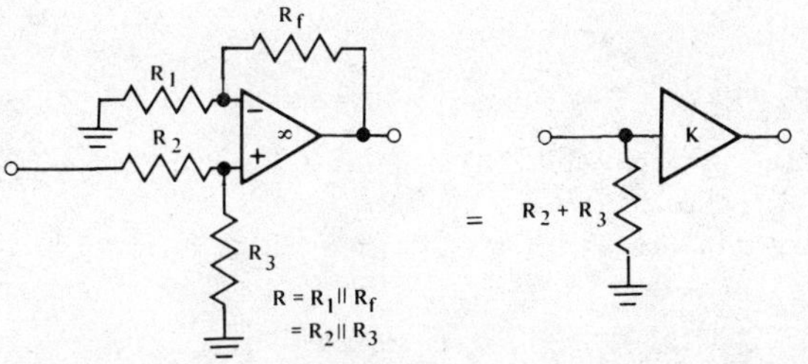

Table 8.4.2 Design of inverting amplifier. (For high input impedance version, see Fig. 8.5.4a and Prob. 8.3.)

Transfer Function: $-K = R_f/R_1$ (Eq. 7.1.7)

Input Impedance: $Z_{in} = R_1$

Design Equations: Set $R_o = R_1 \| R_f$ (For Minimum Offset)

Given: K, R_1

Calculate: $R_f = -KR_1$, $R_o = R_f/(1-K) = -R_1K/(1-K)$

Sensitivities: $S^K_{R_f} = -S^K_{R_1} = 1$

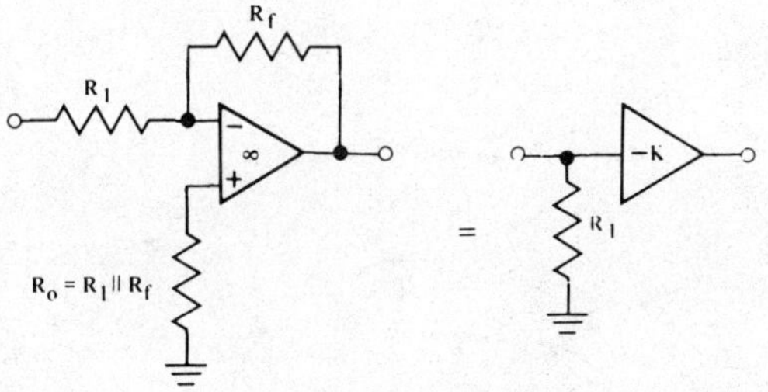

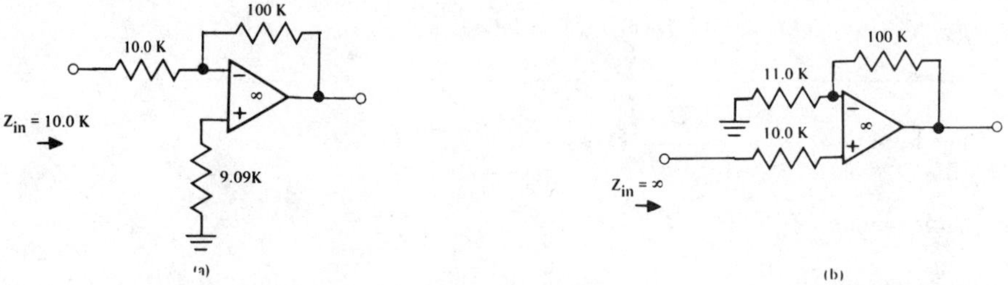

Fig. 8.4.2 Realization of gain blocks having gains (a) −10 and (b) +10 in Example 8.4.1.

EXAMPLE 8.4.1 Design gain blocks of ±10. Use the inverting and noninverting amplifiers of Tables 8.4.1 and 8.4.2. Determine the input impedance of each gain block.
Solution Let us first design the inverting amplifier. From Table 8.4.2, $-K = 10$ and R_1 must be selected. Selecting $R_1 = 10$ K, then

$$R_f = -KR_1 = 10(10\ \text{K}) = 100\ \text{K} \tag{8.4.4}$$

To minimize bias current effects, we insert a resistance R_o of value

$$R_o = R_1 || R_f = R_f/(1 - K) = 100\ \text{K}/(1 + 10) = 9.09\ \text{K} \tag{8.4.5}$$

in the noninverting lead of the op amp. The amplifier is shown in Fig. 8.4.2a. The input impedance Z_{in} of the noninverting gain block equals $R_1 = 10.0$ K.

The noninverting amplifier is also easily designed. From Table 8.4.1, $K = 10$ and R_2 must be selected. Selecting $R_2 = 10$ K, then

$$\begin{aligned} R_f &= KR_2 = 10(10\ \text{K}) = 100\ \text{K} \\ R_1 &= R_f/(K - 1) = 100\ \text{K}/(10 - 1) = 11.1\ \text{K}\ \ (\text{use } 11.0\ \text{K}) \end{aligned} \tag{8.4.6}$$

To minimize bias current effects, the design equations have been derived so that $R_2 = R_1 || R_f$ when $R_3 = \infty$ while simultaneously realizing a gain K. The input impedance is infinite since $R_3 = \infty$. Note that all resistors are 1% standard values from Table 14.1.2. If the component values calculated are not standard values, we select *standard values* and enter them in *parentheses*. This will be our notation method for specifying components.

This example illustrates the design procedure for realizing inverting and noninverting gain blocks. Now let us go one step further and design first-order low-pass filters using these gain blocks. These first-order stages will be used in most of our later designs of odd-order low-pass filters.

EXAMPLE 8.4.2 Design a first-order low-pass filter having a corner frequency of 10 KHz and dc gain of 10. Use the noninverting operational amplifier form shown in Fig. 8.4.3.
Solution In the noninverting mode, the gain of the low-pass filter equals

$$H(s) = \frac{Z_3}{Z_2 + Z_3}(1 + R_f/R_1) = K\frac{1/sC}{R + 1/sC} \tag{8.4.7}$$

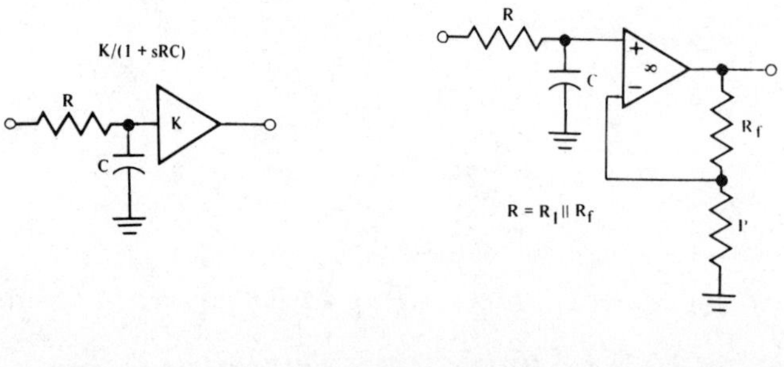

Fig. 8.4.3 First-order low-pass filter (noninverting).

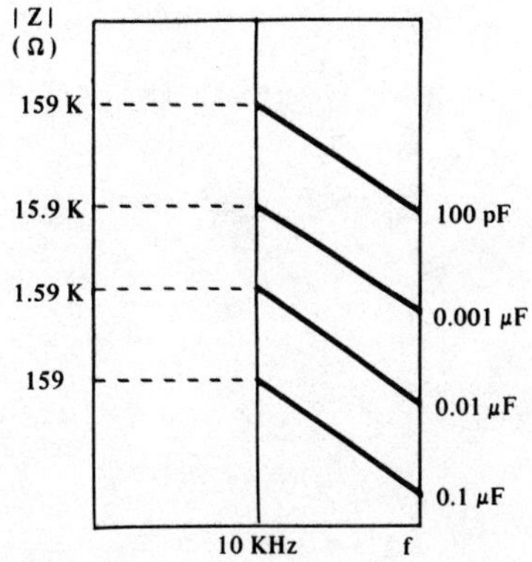

Fig. 8.4.4 Selection of C and R in Examples 8.4.2 and 8.4.3.

using Table 8.4.1 and/or Eq. 7.1.10. Therefore, we can write that

$$H_o = K, \qquad \omega_o = 1/RC, \qquad f_o = 1/2\pi RC \tag{8.4.8}$$

The amplifier gain K equals $K = 1 + R_f/R_1$ when $R_3 = \infty$ from Table 8.4.1.

Let us begin our design by selecting C. The choice involves choosing a standard C value which will result in an R which is not too large or too small. Here $R < 20\ K\Omega$ to reduce bias current effects, but $R > 400\ \Omega$ because of excessive high-frequency power dissipation (note that R_2 equals the input impedance of the filter when $f \gg f_o$). We use trial-and-error techniques for selecting C and R; however, rather than using the algebraic equation $R = 1/2\pi f_o C$, we use impedance paper to gain the greatest insight to (R, C) tradeoffs.

A variety of (R, C) combinations are shown in Fig. 8.4.4. Let us choose $C = 0.001\ \mu F = 1000$ pF which is a (20% tolerance) standard value from Table 14.1.3. Since R = 15.9 K is required, we use a 16.2 K (1% tolerance) or 16 K (5% tolerance) resistor from Tables 14.1.2 and 14.1.3. We shall use R = 16 K.

Now we design the amplifier and calculate the required (R_1, R_f) combination. To minimize offset current effects, we must set $R_1 \| R_f$ equal to R so that $R = R_1R_f/(R_1 + R_f) = 16$ K. To obtain the proper gain, $K = (R_1 + R_f)/R_f = 10$. Therefore, using the design equations of Table 8.4.1, the required resistor values therefore equal

$$\begin{aligned} R_f &= KR = 10(16\ K) = 160\ K \\ R_1 &= [K/(K-1)]R = (10/9)(16\ K) = 17.8\ K \quad \text{(use 18 K)} \end{aligned} \tag{8.4.9}$$

The completed design is shown in Fig. 8.4.5a.

EXAMPLE 8.4.3 Redesign the first-order low-pass filter having a corner frequency of 10 KHz and dc gain of 10 of Example 8.4.2. Use the inverting operational amplifier form shown in Fig. 8.4.6.

Solution In the inverting mode, the gain equals $H(s) = -Z_f/Z_1$ using Eq. 7.1.7. Substituting the component values into H(s), we obtain

Fig. 8.4.5 Realization of low-pass filters of (a) Example 8.4.2 and (b) Example 8.4.3.

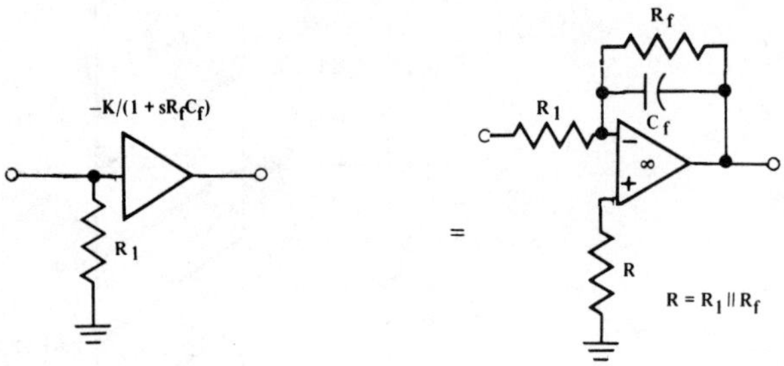

Fig. 8.4.6 First-order low-pass filter (inverting).

$$H(s) = -\frac{1}{R_1}\frac{R_f}{1 + sR_fC_f} = -\frac{R_f}{R_1}\frac{1}{1 + sR_fC_f} = \frac{K}{1 + sR_fC_f} \tag{8.4.10}$$

so that

$$H_o = K, \qquad \omega_o = 1/R_fC_f, \qquad K = -R_f/R_1 \tag{8.4.11}$$

Since the dc gain H_o equals -10, then $R_f = 10R_1$ from K. Since the input impedance equals R_1, we must choose R_1 large enough so the power dissipation does not become excessive. The (R_f, C_f) combinations which can be used are shown in Fig. 8.4.4. Since $R_1 = R_f/10$, we can immediately select

$$R_1 = 15.9\text{ K (use 16 K)}, \qquad R_f = 159\text{ K (use 160 K)}, \qquad C_f = 100\text{ pF} \tag{8.4.12}$$

Since R_o is set equal to $R_1 \| R_f$ to minimize bias current effects, then from Table 8.4.2,

$$R_o = R_1R_f/(R_1 + R_f) = [-H_o/(1 - H_o)]\,R_1 = R_f/(1 - H_o) \tag{8.4.13}$$

Therefore, $R_o = 160\text{ K}/(1 + 10) = 14.5$ K (use 15 K). The complete design is shown in Fig. 8.4.5b.

These examples show the relative ease with which active filters can be designed. Although we will be designing more complicated filters, the basic approach is the same.

8.5 LOW-PASS FILTER DESIGN EXAMPLES

Now that we have reviewed basic component ranges, tolerances, and drifts, and the basic low-pass filter forms, let us proceed to design a variety of low-pass filters. We will use some of the low-pass filter stages compiled in Chap. 8.3.

In Chaps. 2 (Frequency Domain Analysis) and 3 (Time Domain Analysis), we designed filters in block diagram form using trial-and-error design techniques. In Chaps. 4 (Classical Filter Response) and 5 (Optimum Filter Response), we designed low-pass filters using tabulated results. In Chap. 7 (Active Filter Classification), we developed an orderly system with which to classify and analyze filters. We now proceed to realize the low-pass filter blocks with hardware. The engineer may wish to skim over these chapters to refresh his memory regarding the block diagrams obtained earlier. We will now simply utilize these blocks directly for our filter designs.

EXAMPLE 8.5.1 A third-order Butterworth filter must be designed with $H_o = 10$ and $f_o = 1$ KHz. Draw a block diagram for the filter using a first- and second-order stage. Design the required active filter using the Class 1B filter for the second stage, and the passive first-order low-pass filter and gain buffer for the first stage as shown in Fig. 8.5.1. Draw the completed filter.

Solution The normalized poles for the third-order Butterworth filter are obtained from Table 4.3.1 which lists the Butterworth poles. The block diagram for the entire filter is shown in Fig. 8.5.1. The gain of the second stage is arbitrary because of the gain buffer of the first stage. The design equations for the Class 1B filter of the second stage are:

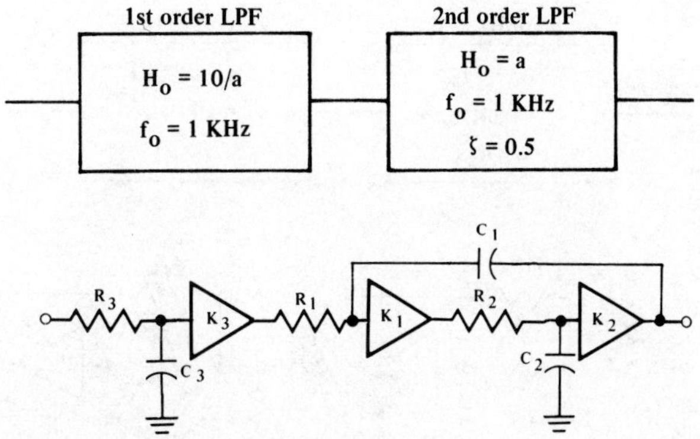

Fig. 8.5.1 Block diagram of third-order Butterworth low-pass filter and its realization form.

Set: $R_1 = R_2 = R, \quad C_1 = C_2 = C$ (For Minimum Sensitivity)

Given: ω_o, ζ

Choose: C (use 20% standard value)

Calculate: $R = 1/\omega_o C, \quad K_1K_2 = 2(1 - \zeta), \quad H_o = K_1K_2$

Since $f_o = 1$ KHz, we can immediately write using impedance paper that

$$C = 0.01\ \mu F, \qquad R = 15.9\ K\ \text{(use 16.2 K)} \tag{8.5.1}$$

By inspection, $K_1K_2 = 2(1 - 0.5) = 1$ and $H_o = 1$. K_1 and K_2 are easily realized using voltage followers with unity gain from Table 8.4.1.

The first stage was discussed in Example 8.4.2. For this application, we choose $C = 0.01\ \mu F$ so R = 15.9 K (use 16.2 K). For the gain buffer, since the overall gain equals 10, then $K_3 = 10$. Using a voltage follower requires $R_f/R_1 = 9$. Choosing $R_1 = 16.2$ K to maximize resistor commonality, then $R_f = 9R_1 =$ 146 K (use 147 K). The complete filter is shown in Fig. 8.5.2.

EXAMPLE 8.5.2 Design a fourth-order Butterworth filter having $H_o = 1$ and $f_o = 10$ KHz. Use the Class $2\overline{A}$ filter shown in Fig. 8.5.3.

Solution The block diagram for the filter is shown in Fig. 8.5.3. The design equations for the Class $2\overline{A}$ filter are:

Set: $\rho = R_3/R_1 \ll 1, \quad R_1' = R_1R_3/(R_1 + R_3), \quad R_2C_2 = R_1'C_1$

Given: ω_o, ζ

Choose: C_1, C_2, ρ

Calculate: $R_2 = \dfrac{1 + \rho + C_2/C_1}{\zeta\omega_o C_2}, \quad R_1' = R_2C_2/C_1, \quad R_1 = \dfrac{1 + \rho}{\rho} R_1'$

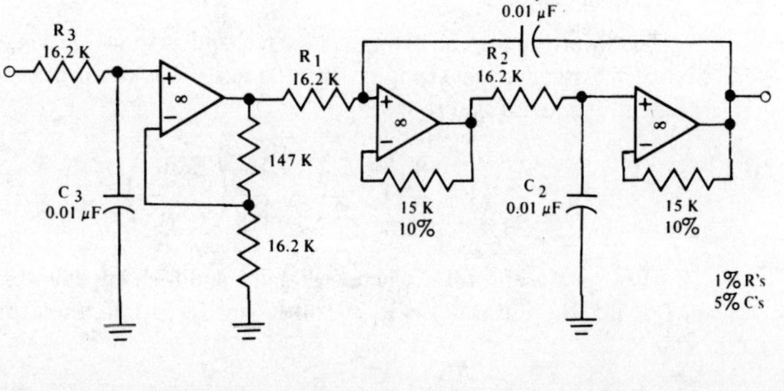

Fig. 8.5.2 Realization of third-order Butterworth low-pass filter.

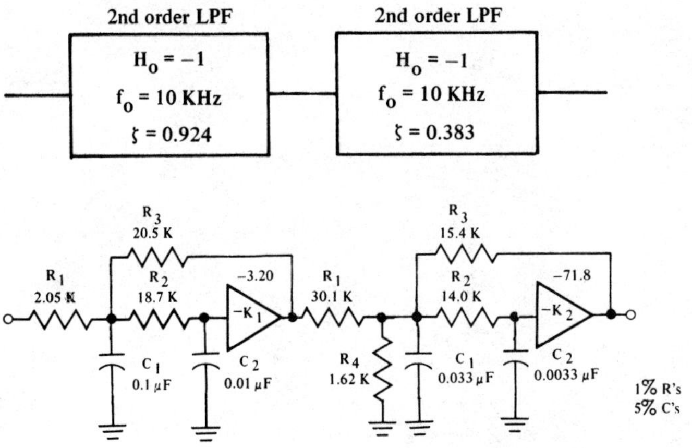

Fig. 8.5.3 Block diagram of fourth-order Butterworth low-pass filter and its realization form.

$$R_3 = \rho R_1, \quad K = (1+\rho)\left[\left(\frac{1 + C_2/2C_1}{\zeta}\right)^2 - 1\right], \quad H_o = -\frac{\rho K}{1+\rho+K}$$

The first stage is easily designed as:

$$\begin{aligned}
&\rho = R_3/R_1 = 10, \quad C_2/C_1 = 0.1, \quad R_1' = 0.91R_1 \\
&1/R_2C_2 = 0.924\omega_o/(1 + 10 + 0.1) = 0.0832\omega_o = 2\pi(832 \text{ Hz}) \\
&C_1 = 0.1\ \mu\text{F}, \quad C_2 = 0.01\ \mu\text{F}, \quad R_2 = 19.1 \text{ K (use 18.7 K)}, \quad R_1' = 0.1R_2 = 1.87 \text{ K} \\
&R_1 = R_1'(1 + 10)/10 = 1.1R_1' = 2.06 \text{ K (use 2.05 K)}, \quad R_3 = 10R_1 = 20.5 \text{ K} \\
&K_1 = (1 + 10)[((1 + 0.1/2)/0.924)^2 - 1] = 3.2, \quad H_o = -10(3.2)/(1 + 10 + 3.2) = -2.25
\end{aligned} \tag{8.5.2}$$

The second stage is designed in the same fashion. Using the same ρ, C_2/C_1, and R_1' as before, then:

$$\begin{aligned}
&1/R_2C_2 = 0.383\omega_o/11.1 = 0.0345\omega_o = 2\pi(345 \text{ Hz}) \\
&C_1 = 0.033\ \mu\text{F}, \quad C_2 = 0.0033\ \mu\text{F}, \quad R_2 = 14.0 \text{ K}, \quad R_1' = 0.1R_2 = 1.40 \text{ K} \\
&R_1 = 1.1R_1' = 1.51 \text{ K (use 1.54 K)}, \quad R_3 = 10R_1 = 15.4 \text{ K} \\
&K_2 = (1 + 10)[((1 + 0.1/2)/0.383)^2 - 1] = 71.8, \quad H_o = -10(71.8)/(1 + 10 + 71.8) = -8.67
\end{aligned} \tag{8.5.3}$$

The basic filter design is shown in Fig. 8.5.3. Since the overall gain equals (−2.25)(−8.67) = 19.5, we insert a 19.5:1 voltage divider between the two stages. To minimize the parts count, we include R_1 in the voltage divider. As will be shown in Example 8.5.6, the resistors in the voltage divider equal

$$\begin{aligned}
&R_1 = R_o/K = 19.5R_o = 19.5(1.54 \text{ K}) = 30.0 \text{ K (use 30.1 K)} \\
&R_4 = R_1/(1/K - 1) = 30.1 \text{ K}/(19.5 - 1) = 1.63 \text{ K (use 1.62 K)}
\end{aligned} \tag{8.5.4}$$

The inverting gain blocks are easily realized as shown in Fig. 8.5.4a. This circuit is a slight modification of the standard inverting op amp circuit. It is often designed so that $R_3 \ll R_2 \ll R_f$ in which case the gain H_o equals (see Prob. 8.3)

$$-H_o = \frac{R_f}{R_1}\left(1 + \frac{R_2}{R_3}\right) + \frac{R_2}{R_1} \cong \frac{R_f}{R_1}\left(1 + \frac{R_2}{R_3}\right) \cong \frac{R_f}{R_1}\frac{R_2}{R_3} \tag{8.5.5}$$

This is a very useful form when high gains and high impedances are required simultaneously. As shown in Fig. 8.5.4b, letting $R_1 = R_f = 100$ K and $R_3 = 1$ K, then for the first stage where $K_1 = 3.20$, we set

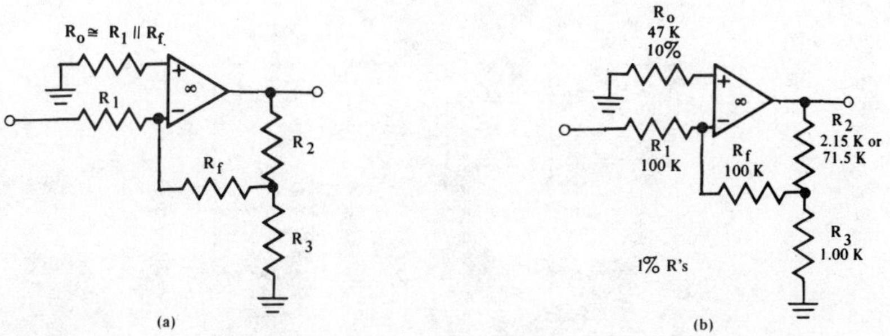

Fig. 8.5.4 (a) High impedance inverting gain block and (b) realization of gain blocks in Fig. 8.5.3.

R_2 = 2.15 K. For the second stage where K_2 = 71.8 we set R_2 = 71.5 K. Since the input impedance to this gain block is R_1, it will slightly load the filter circuit and cause slight detuning. Detuning is minimized by making the filter resistor values small compared with R_1 of the gain block. However, the best solution is to add another resistor R_5 in parallel with C_2 in the basic Class $2\bar{A}$ filter of Fig. 8.5.3. The transfer function is then recalculated and a new set of design equations formulated. By this means, R_5 can then be used to account for the impedance loading of the gain block, and no detuning occurs.

EXAMPLE 8.5.3 Design a fourth-order Bessel filter having a 3 dB cutoff frequency equalling 1000 Hz and unity dc gain. Use a Class 2B realization. The block diagram and Class 2B realization form are shown in Fig. 8.5.5.

Solution One set of Class 2B filter design equations are:

Set: $\rho = C_2/C_1 \ll 1, \quad R_1C_1 = R_2C_2$ (Towards Minimum Active Sensitivity)

Given: ω_o, ζ

Choose: C_1, ρ

Calculate: $R_1 = 1/\omega_o C_1, \quad R_2 = R_1/\rho, \quad C_2 = \rho C_1, \quad K = 2(1-\zeta)+\rho, \quad H_o = K$

For the first stage, we choose $\rho = 0.1$. Then:

$$\begin{aligned} &1/R_1C_1 = 2\pi(1.43\text{ KHz}), \quad C_1 = 0.1\ \mu\text{F}, \quad C_2 = 0.1C_1 = 0.01\ \mu\text{F} \\ &R_1 = 1.11\text{ K (use 1.10 K)}, \quad R_2 = 1.11\text{ K}/0.1 = 11.1\text{ K (use 11.0 K)} \\ &K_1 = 2(1-0.958)+0.1 = 0.182, \quad H_o = 0.182 \end{aligned} \tag{8.5.6}$$

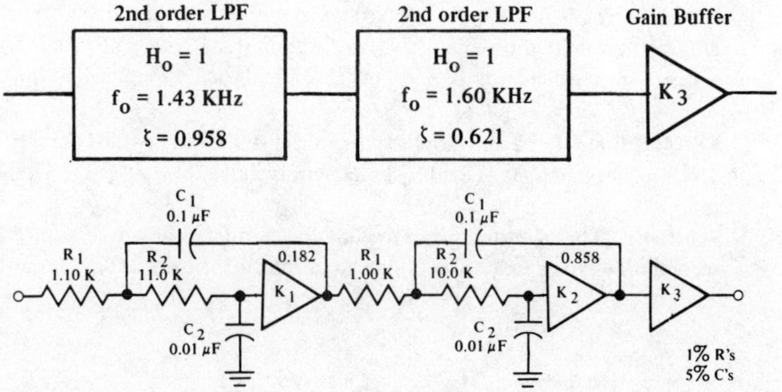

Fig. 8.5.5 Block diagram of fourth-order Bessel low-pass filter and its realization form.

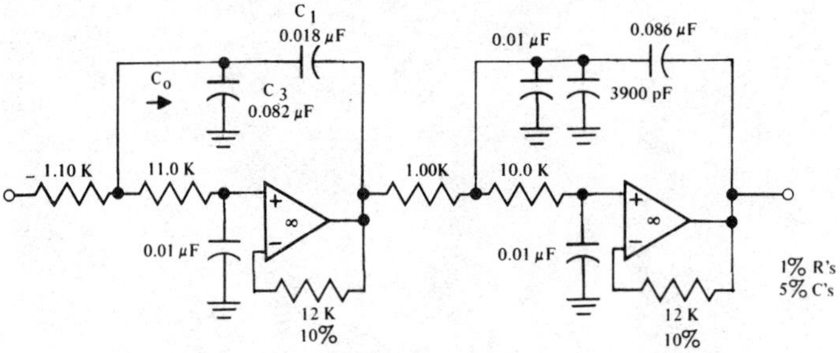

Fig. 8.5.6 Realization of fourth-order Bessel low-pass filter.

For the second stage, we also choose $\rho = 0.1$. Then:

$$1/R_1C_1 = 2\pi(1.60 \text{ KHz}), \quad C_1 = 0.1\ \mu F, \quad C_2 = 0.1C_1 = 0.01\ \mu F$$
$$R_1 = 995\ \Omega \text{ (use 1.00 K)}, \quad R_2 = 995/0.1 = 9.95 \text{ K (use 10.0 K)} \tag{8.5.7}$$
$$K_2 = 2(1 - 0.621) + 0.1 = 0.858, \quad H_o = 0.858$$

The preliminary design is shown in Fig. 8.5.5. Let us complete the design using a slightly different approach. We shall eliminate the need for gain block K_3 and also eliminate detuning effects. We do this by setting $K_1 = K_2 = 1$ and using (C_1, C_3) voltage dividers of gain K in the feedback loops as shown in Fig. 8.5.6. Note that in general,

$$C_o = C_1 + C_3, \quad K = C_1/(C_1 + C_3) \tag{8.5.8}$$

In the first stage, $C_o = 0.1\ \mu F$ from Eq. 8.5.6 so that the capacitors equal

$$C_1 = KC_o = 0.182(0.1\ \mu F) = 0.0182\ \mu F \text{ (use 0.018 } \mu F)$$
$$C_3 = (1 - K)C_o = (1 - 0.182)(0.1\ \mu F) = 0.0818\ \mu F \text{ (use 0.082 } \mu F) \tag{8.5.9}$$

Repeating these calculations in the second stage using Eq. 8.5.7, the capacitors equal

$$C_1 = 0.858(0.1\ \mu F) = 0.0858\ \mu F \text{ (use 0.086 } \mu F)$$
$$C_3 = (1 - 0.858)(0.1\ \mu F) = 0.0141\ \mu F \text{ (use 0.01 } \mu F \text{ || 3900 pF)} \tag{8.5.10}$$

The resistor values are unchanged from those given by Eqs. 8.5.6 and 8.5.7 and the final design is shown in Fig. 8.5.6. The design equations for the capacitor attenuator of gain K given by Eq. 8.5.8 are important and will be used often in filter designs.

It should be noted that this approach usually produces capacitor values that are nonstandard. Some trial-and-error is necessary to determine the most suitable capacitor values. We could eliminate the padding capacitor in the second stage by scaling (C_1, C_3, C_2) to (0.068 μF, 0.011 μF, 0.0082 μF). This necessitates recalculating (R_1, R_2) as (1.27 K, 12.7 K) to maintain the corner frequency at 1.6 KHz.

EXAMPLE 8.5.4 A third-order parabolic filter having a 3 dB corner frequency of 1000 Hz and dc gain of 10 must be designed. Its block diagram is shown in Fig. 8.5.7. Design the filter using a Class 2C realization.

Solution The required filter realization form is shown in Fig. 8.5.7. We begin by designing the second-order stage first. The design equations for the Class 2C filter are:

Set: $C_1 = C_2 = C$

Given: ω_o, ζ, H_o

Choose: C

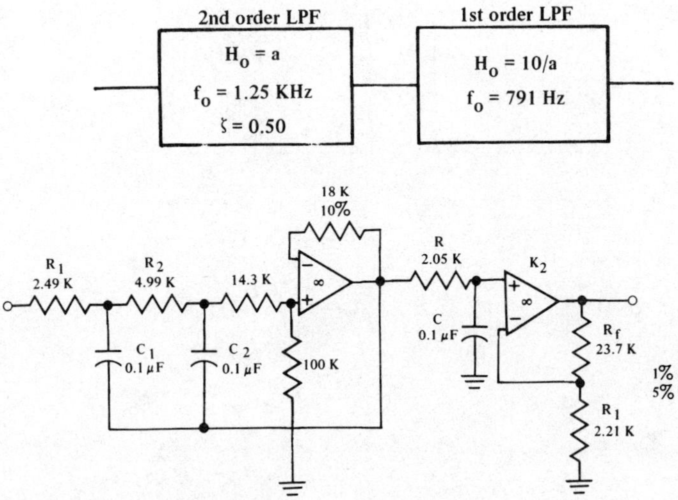

Fig. 8.5.7 Block diagram of third-order parabolic low-pass filter and its realization.

$$\text{Calculate: } R_1 = \frac{\zeta \pm [\zeta^2 - 2(1-H_o)]^{1/2}}{2(1-H_o)} \frac{1}{\omega_o C} = \frac{F}{\omega_o C}, \quad R_2 = \frac{1}{F(1-H_o)\omega_o C}, \quad K = H_o$$

We see that for the filter to be realizable,

$$(1 - \zeta^2/2) \leqslant H_o \leqslant 1 \tag{8.5.11}$$

from the R_1 and R_2 equations. Therefore, since $\zeta = 0.5$ and $(1 - 0.5^2/2) = 0.875$, then $0.875 \leqslant H_o \leqslant 1$. Letting $H_o = 0.875$, then the first stage is easily designed as:

$$F = \zeta/2(1-H_o) = 1/\zeta = 1/0.5 = 2$$

$$1/R_1C = \zeta\omega_o = 2\pi[0.5(1.25\text{ KHz})] = 2\pi(625\text{ Hz}) \tag{8.5.12}$$

$$1/R_2C = \zeta\omega_o/2 = 2\pi(625\text{ Hz}/2) = 2\pi(313\text{ Hz}), \qquad C = 0.1\ \mu F$$

$$R_1 = 2.55\text{ K (use 2.49 K)}, \qquad R_2 = 5.10\text{ K (use 4.99 K)}, \qquad K_1 = 0.875 = 1/1.143$$

The second stage design is:

$$1/RC = 2\pi(791\text{ Hz}), \qquad C = 0.1\ \mu F, \qquad R = 2.01\text{ K (use 2.05 K)}$$

$$K_2 = 10/K_1 = 10/0.875 = 11.4, \qquad R_f = K_2R = 11.4(2.05\text{ K}) = 23.4\text{ K (use 23.7 K)} \tag{8.5.13}$$

$$R_1 = R_f/(K_2 - 1) = 23.7\text{ K}/(11.4 - 1) = 2.25\text{ K (use 2.21 K)}$$

The complete filter is shown in Fig. 8.5.7. The gain block K_1 is realized using a voltage follower with an input divider as shown. The same loading problem exists here as in Fig. 8.5.3. By adding a third resistor R_3 from the K_1 input to ground in the basic Class 2C filter, the equations can be reformulated to account for amplifier loading effects.

EXAMPLE 8.5.5 Design a fourth-order Chebyshev low-pass filter having a 3 dB passband ripple, a maximum passband gain of unity, and a 3 dB cutoff frequency of 1000 Hz. Use a Class 2E filter realization.
Solution The block diagram for the filter was discussed in Example 6.3.2 and is shown in Fig. 8.5.8. The Class 2E filter realization form is also shown. The design procedure for this filter is:

Set: $C_5 = KC_2$

Given: $\omega_o, \zeta, -H_o$

Choose: C_2, K

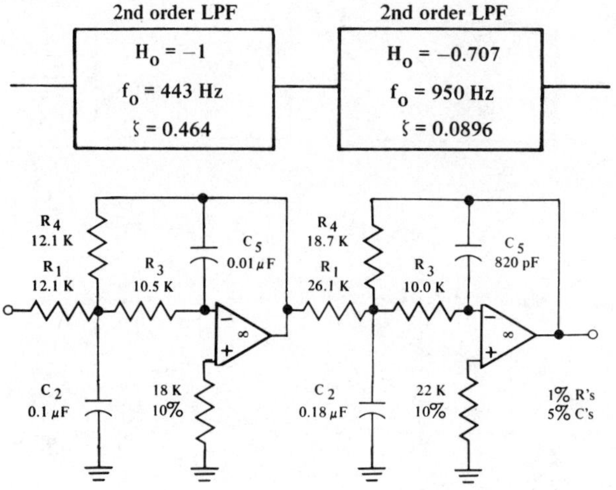

Fig. 8.5.8 Block diagram of fourth-order Chebyshev low-pass filter and its realization.

$$\text{Calculate: } C_5 = KC_2, \quad R_4 = \frac{\zeta \pm [\zeta^2 - K(1 - H_o)]^{1/2}}{\omega_o C_5} = \frac{F}{\omega_o C_5}$$

$$R_3 = \frac{1}{F\omega_o C_2}, \quad R_1 = \frac{R_4}{-H_o}$$

The maximum K values are determined from the R_4 equation to equal $K \leqslant \zeta^2/(1 - H_o)$ so that

$$K_1 \leqslant 0.464^2/2 = 0.108, \qquad K_2 \leqslant 0.0896^2/1.707 = 0.0047 \tag{8.5.14}$$

To obtain standard C values for the first stage, we let:

$$C_2 = 0.1\ \mu F, \quad K_1 = 0.1, \quad C_5 = 0.1(0.1\ \mu F) = 0.01\ \mu F$$

$$\begin{aligned} &F = 0.464 \pm [0.464^2 - 0.1(1 - (-1))]^{1/2} = 0.464 \pm 0.124 = 0.340,\ 0.588 \ \text{(use 0.340)} \\ &1/R_4C_5 = 2\pi(443\ \text{Hz}/0.340) = 2\pi(1.30\ \text{KHz}), \quad R_4 = R_1 = 12.3\ \text{K (use 12.1 K)} \\ &1/R_3C_2 = 2\pi[0.340(443\ \text{Hz})] = 2\pi(151\ \text{Hz}), \quad R_3 = 10.6\ \text{K (use 10.5 K)} \end{aligned} \tag{8.5.15}$$

For the second stage, choose:

$$C_2 = 0.18\ \mu F, \quad K_2 = 0.0047, \quad C_5 = 0.0047(0.18\ \mu F) = 820\ \text{pF}$$

$$F = 0.0896 \pm [0.0896^2 - 0.0047(1 - (-0.707))]^{1/2} = 0.0896 \pm 0.002 = 0.0876,\ 0.0916 \quad \text{(use 0.0916)}$$

$$1/R_4C_5 = 2\pi(950/0.916) = 2\pi(10.4\ \text{KHz}), \quad R_4 = 18.7\ \text{K} \tag{8.5.16}$$

$$R_1 = 18.7\ \text{K}/0.707 = 26.4\ \text{K (use 26.1 K)}$$

$$1/R_3C_2 = 2\pi[0.0916(950\ \text{Hz})] = 2\pi(87.0\ \text{Hz}), \quad R_3 = 10.2\ \text{K (use 10.0 K)}$$

The complete filter is shown in Fig. 8.5.8.

EXAMPLE 8.5.6 A third-order elliptic filter must be designed which has 1.25 dB in-band ripple with a −1.25 dB frequency of 1000 Hz. The maximum in-band gain equals 0 dB. The stopband frequency equals 2000 Hz with a minimum stopband attenuation of 35 dB. Design the filter using a Class 2B band-stop filter as shown in Fig. 8.5.9. Begin by verifying the block diagram of the filter given in Fig. 8.5.9.

Solution From Table 4.8.2, the required normalized transfer function equals

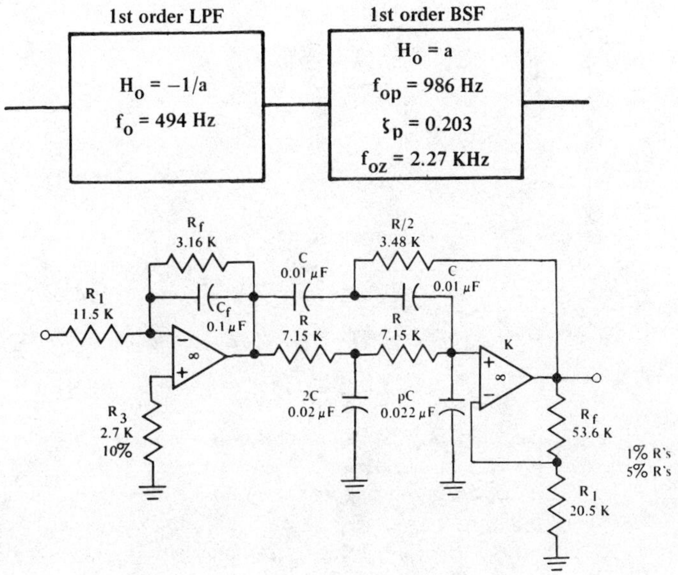

Fig. 8.5.9 Block diagram of third-order elliptic low-pass filter and its realization.

$$H(s) = \frac{0.986^2}{2.27^2}\,\frac{0.494}{s + 0.494}\,\frac{s^2 + 2.27^2}{(s + 0.2)^2 + 0.966^2} \tag{8.5.17}$$

where the complex pole parameters equal

$$\omega_{op} = [0.2^2 + 0.966^2]^{1/2} = 0.986, \qquad \zeta_p = 0.2/0.986 = 0.203 \tag{8.5.18}$$

Therefore, a first-order low-pass filter must be cascaded with a first-order band-stop filter to obtain the elliptic filter response. The filter parameters are given in the blocks of Fig. 8.5.9.

The design equations for the Class 2B band-stop filter where $\omega_{oz} > \omega_{op}$ are found in Sec. 11.3. Let us begin by designing this stage. The design procedure is:

Given: $\omega_{op}, \zeta_p, \omega_{oz}$

Choose: C

Calculate: $R = 1/\omega_{oz}C$, $\quad p = 0.5[(\omega_{oz}/\omega_{op})^2 - 1]$, $\quad K = 2 + p - \zeta_p\omega_{oz}/\omega_{op}$, $\quad H_o = K$

Since the design constant p equals

$$p = 0.5[(2.27/0.986)^2 - 1] = 0.5(2.3^2 - 1) = 2.15 \tag{8.5.19}$$

let us select the capacitors so

$$C = 0.01\ \mu F, \qquad 2C = 0.0\,2\ \mu F, \qquad pC = 0.0215\ \mu F \text{ (use } 0.022\ \mu F) \tag{8.5.20}$$

Then from impedance paper,

$$1/RC = 2\pi(2270 \text{ Hz}), \qquad R = 7.01 \text{ K (use 7.15 K)}, \qquad R/2 = 3.51 \text{ K (use 3.48 K)} \tag{8.5.21}$$

Amplifier gain K equals

$$K = 2 + 2.15 - 0.203(2.27/0.986) = 4.15 - 0.47 = 3.68 \tag{8.5.22}$$

Using a noninverting amplifier for K, then from Table 8.4.1, the resistors equal

$$\begin{aligned} R_f &= K(2R) = 3.68(2)(7.15 \text{ K}) = 52.6 \text{ K (use 53.6 K)} \\ R_1 &= R_f/(K - 1) = 53.6 \text{ K}/(3.68 - 1) = 20.0 \text{ K (use 20.5 K)} \end{aligned} \tag{8.5.23}$$

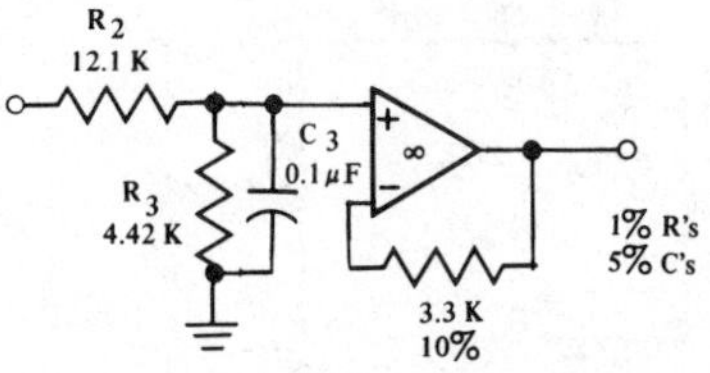

Fig. 8.5.10 Alternative first stage of elliptic low-pass filter in Fig. 8.5.9.

This completes the design of the second stage.

Since the low-frequency gain of the second stage equals $H_o = K = 3.68$, the first stage must have gain $-H_o = 1/3.69 = 0.272$. Choosing $C_f = 0.1\ \mu F$, then from impedance paper and Table 8.4.2,

$$1/R_fC_f = 2\pi(494\ Hz), \qquad R_f = 3.22\ K\ \text{(use 3.16 K)}$$
$$R_1 = R_f/(-K) = 3.16\ K/0.272 = 11.6\ K\ \text{(use 11.5 K)} \tag{8.5.24}$$

The complete third-order elliptic filter is shown in Fig. 8.5.9. Note that since an inverting first stage was used, the overall gain is negative.

We can use a noninverting first stage for a positive gain if required. In this case, we operate the operational amplifier as a voltage follower with a voltage divider of gain K at its input. If we select $C_3 = 0.1\ \mu F$, then $R = R_2||R_3 = 3.22$ K using impedance paper for a 494 Hz cutoff frequency. From Table 8.4.1, since

$$R = R_2||R_3 = R_2R_3/(R_2 + R_3) = R_2K \tag{8.5.25}$$

where $K = 1/3.68$, then the resistors equal

$$R_2 = R/K = 3.68(3.22\ K) = 11.8\ K\ \text{(use 12.1 K)}$$
$$R_3 = R_2/(1/K - 1) = 12.1\ K/(3.68 - 1) = 4.51\ K\ \text{(use 4.42 K)} \tag{8.5.26}$$

The complete first stage is shown in Fig. 8.5.10. The design equations for the resistor attenuator of gain K given by Eq. 8.5.26 are important and will be used often in filter designs.

Before proceeding, let us investigate the effects of using imprecise component values in filter designs. For illustrative purposes, let us consider Example 8.4.3. From Eq. 8.4.11, we have a low frequency gain H_o and corner frequency f_o which equal

$$H_o = -R_f/R_1, \qquad f_o = 1/2\pi R_fC_f \tag{8.5.27}$$

The tolerances on H_o and f_o, denoted by T_{H_o} and T_{f_o} respectively, can be determined by expressing H_o and f_o as

$$H_o(1 + T_{H_o}) = -\frac{R_f(1 + T_{R_f})}{R_1(1 + T_{R_1})}, \qquad f_o(1 + T_{f_o}) = \frac{1}{2\pi R_f(1 + T_{R_f})C_f(1 + T_{C_f})} \tag{8.5.28}$$

where T_R and T_C are the tolerances of the respective resistors and capacitors. Combining Eqs. 8.5.27 and 8.5.28, we can write

$$1 + T_{H_o} = (1 + T_{R_f})/(1 + T_{R_1}), \qquad 1 + T_{f_o} = 1/(1 + T_{R_f})(1 + T_{C_f}) \tag{8.5.29}$$

so that solving for the gain and corner frequency tolerances gives

$$T_{H_o} = (1 + T_{R_f})/(1 + T_{R_1}) - 1, \qquad T_{f_o} = 1/(1 + T_{R_f})(1 + T_{C_f}) - 1 \tag{8.5.30}$$

In general, we want to estimate the total drift in H_o and f_o due to initial tolerance error and drifts in R_1, R_f, and C_f. We see from these equations that the drifts in H_o and f_o can be calculated from the drifts in R_1, R_f, and C_f.

Let us assume the following: all components can have 5% initial tolerance error and drift 5%. We shall also use different resistor ratios from those of Eq. 8.4.12 to illustrate an important point. Let us select

$$R_1 = 15\text{ K} \pm 10\%, \qquad R_f = 150\text{ K} \pm 10\%, \qquad C_f = 100\text{ pF} \pm 10\% \tag{8.5.31}$$

Therefore, for the corner frequency tolerance, we use component tolerances of

$$T_{C_f} = \pm 10\%, \qquad T_{R_f} = \pm 10\% - 5.7\% = 4.3\%,\ -15.7\% \tag{8.5.32}$$

The −5.7% arises because 159 K was required but we used 150 K. If we used 150 K in Eq. 8.5.27, this error would be negligible; however, we want to illustrate the effects of this error. Substituting Eq. 8.5.32 into Eq. 8.5.30, the worst-case T_{f_o} equals

$$\begin{aligned} T_{f_{o\,min}} &= 1/(1.1)(1.043) - 1 = 0.87 - 1 = -13\% \\ T_{f_{o\,max}} &= 1/(0.9)(0.843) - 1 = 1.32 - 1 = 32\% \end{aligned} \tag{8.5.33}$$

If we use a variable R_f and tune for f_o = 10 KHz, then the drifts are due to temperature only and equal

$$T_{C_f} = \pm 5\%, \qquad T_{R_f} = \pm 5\% \tag{8.5.34}$$

Substituting Eq. 8.5.34 into Eq. 8.5.30 gives

$$\begin{aligned} T_{f_{o\,min}} &= 1/(1.05)(1.05) - 1 = 0.91 - 1 = -9\% \\ T_{f_{o\,max}} &= 1/(0.95)(0.95) - 1 = 1.11 - 1 = 11\% \end{aligned} \tag{8.5.35}$$

Therefore, we can reduce the worst-case drifts appreciably. Admittedly, the worst-case combination of elements seldom occurs. Nevertheless, most engineers want to assure themselves of the drifts which could occur and reduce component tolerances if they deem it desirable.

For the gain tolerance, we use component tolerances of

$$T_{R_f} = \pm 10\%, \qquad T_{R_1} = \pm 10\% \tag{8.5.36}$$

Substituting Eq. 8.5.36 into Eq. 8.5.30, the worst-case T_{H_o} equals

$$\begin{aligned} T_{H_{o\,min}} &= (1 - 0.1)/(1 + 0.1) - 1 = 0.82 - 1 = -18\% \\ T_{H_{o\,max}} &= (1 + 0.1)/(1 - 0.1) - 1 = 1.22 - 1 = 22\% \end{aligned} \tag{8.5.37}$$

If we use a variable R_1 or R_f and adjust for the proper dc gain, then the component tolerances equal

$$T_{R_f} = \pm 5\%, \qquad T_{R_1} = \pm 5\% \tag{8.5.38}$$

due to temperature drift alone. Therefore, the gain tolerances equal

$$\begin{aligned} T_{H_{o\,min}} &= (1 - 0.05)/(1 + 0.05) - 1 = 0.90 - 1 = -10\% \\ T_{H_{o\,max}} &= (1 + 0.05)/(1 - 0.05) - 1 = 1.11 - 1 = 11\% \end{aligned} \tag{8.5.39}$$

so we can reduce the tolerances by half.

If the minimum and maximum worst-case tolerances are excessive for the design, then we specify tighter tolerance and smaller drift components. Because capacitors having a tolerance less than 5% are expensive, we prefer to use tuning or trimming techniques to account for initial errors. We then specify low drift components which can be done relatively inexpensively. In this situation, if we use resistor tuning, and choose components having temperature drifts of

$$T_{R_f} = \pm 0.5\%, \qquad T_{R_1} = \pm 0.5\%, \qquad T_{C_f} = \pm 1\% \tag{8.5.40}$$

then substituting Eq. 8.5.40 into Eq. 8.5.30 gives

$$T_{f_{o\,min}} = T_{f_{o\,max}} = \pm 1.5\%, \qquad T_{H_{o\,min}} = T_{H_{o\,max}} = \pm 1\% \tag{8.5.41}$$

which is an order of magnitude less than the previous values found in Eqs. 8.5.35 and 8.5.39. These components are fairly inexpensive and widely available as we shall discuss in Chap. 14.

When the drifts are small, then we can simplify drift analysis by using sensitivity expressions. From Eq. 8.4.11, we can express the various sensitivities as

$$S_{R_f}^{f_o} = S_{C_f}^{f_o} = -1, \qquad S_{R_f}^{H_o} = -S_{R_1}^{H_o} = 1, \qquad S_{R_1}^{f_o} = S_{C_f}^{H_o} = 0 \tag{8.5.42}$$

Using the first-order sensitivity results of Sec. 1.15, then the corner frequency and gain tolerances equal to

$$T_{f_o} = S_{R_f}^{f_o} T_{R_f} + S_{C_f}^{f_o} T_{C_f}, \qquad T_{H_o} = S_{R_f}^{H_o} T_{R_f} + S_{R_1}^{H_o} T_{R_1} \tag{8.5.43}$$

If we repeat the worst-case analysis using the wide component tolerances of Eqs. 8.5.32 and 8.5.36 in Eq. 8.5.43, we obtain

$$\begin{aligned} T_{f_{o\,min}} &= -1(4.3\%) - 1(10\%) = -14.3\%, & T_{H_{o\,min}} &= -1(10\%) + 1(-10\%) = -20\% \\ T_{f_{o\,max}} &= -1(-15.1\%) - 1(-10\%) = 25.7\%, & T_{H_{o\,max}} &= -1(-10\%) + 1(10\%) = 20\% \end{aligned} \tag{8.5.44}$$

These results are fairly close to the exact values given by Eqs. 8.5.33 and 8.5.37. Under the reduced drift condition of Eq. 8.5.40, then the corner frequency and gain tolerances reduce to

$$\begin{aligned} T_{f_{o\,min}} &= T_{f_{o\,max}} = -1(\pm 1\%) - 1(\pm 0.5\%) = \pm 1.5\% \\ T_{H_{o\,min}} &= T_{H_{o\,max}} = -1(\pm 0.5\%) + 1(\mp 0.5\%) = \pm 1\% \end{aligned} \tag{8.5.45}$$

which agree exactly with Eq. 8.5.41. Thus, under small drifts, we will rely primarily upon sensitivity results. Note that if R_1 and R_f have *correlated drifts* in the same direction (i.e. $T_{R_1} = T_{R_f}$), then from both Eqs. 8.5.30 and 8.5.43 the gain tolerance equals

$$T_{H_{o\,min}} = T_{H_{o\,max}} = 0\% \tag{8.5.46}$$

This is very often the case so that the worst-case gain tolerances will generally be very small. However, drifts in resistor and capacitor values are generally *uncorrelated* so this fortuitous situation does not occur for corner frequency f_o. In the special situation where R_f and C_f have correlated

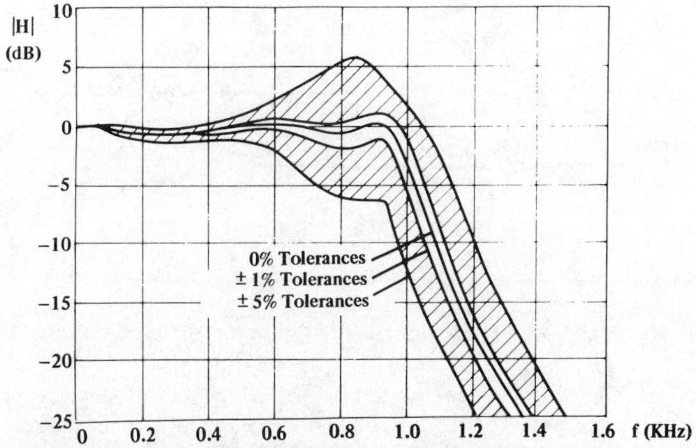

Fig. 8.5.11 Worst-case frequency responses of fifth-order Chebyshev low-pass filter.[2]

drifts in the opposite directions, then from both Eq. 8.5.30 and Eq. 8.5.43 the corner frequency tolerance equals

$$T_{f_{o\,min}} = T_{f_{o\,max}} = 0\% \tag{8.5.47}$$

We see that the effects of component tolerances and drifts can be easily calculated. This is the basic approach we use when specifying the type of resistors, capacitors, and op amps to be used in our filter designs. Component types will be discussed thoroughly in Chap. 14.

Now the question is, how do we estimate the variation in parameters of more complicated higher-order filters? The mathematics become too involved to analytically predict parameter variations so that the computer solutions are required. Generally either *worst-case* or *Monte Carlo analysis* is used. Worst-case analysis is illustrated in Fig. 8.5.11 which shows the response of a fifth-order Chebyshev filter having 1 dB ripple, a 1 dB corner frequency of 1 KHz, and a dc unity gain. The filter was designed using Class 2B filter stages and the realization form of Prob. 9.8. The nominal response is calculated by the computer using exact resistor values. Then each component is varied between its minimum and maximum values (i.e., its tolerances) and the responses are recalculated. This requires 2^N iterations where N equals the number of filter components. Here the gain is fixed and $N = 10$ so $2^{10} = 1024$ iterations are required. The computer stores the minimum and maximum response values at each frequency used. These values then form the worst-case response bounds in 8.5.11. This results in the unshaded area for ± 1% component tolerances and the shaded area for ± 5% component tolerances. We see by inspection that the ripple and ripple frequencies equal

$$\begin{aligned} T_R = T_C = \pm 1\%, &\quad \epsilon = -2 \rightarrow 1 \text{ dB}, \quad f_o = 95 \rightarrow 101 \text{ Hz} \\ T_R = T_C = \pm 5\%, &\quad \epsilon = -7 \rightarrow 6 \text{ dB}, \quad f_o = 95 \rightarrow 115 \text{ Hz} \end{aligned} \tag{8.5.48}$$

Thus, the worst-case ripple becomes 3 dB and the worst-case ripple frequency lies between 95 and 101 Hz for only ± 1% variation in component values. The situation becomes disastrous when we allow ± 5% component tolerances. Of course, these are worst-case situations where we determine the worst set of circumstances to degrade filter performance.

A more realistic approach uses Monte Carlo analysis. Here the component values used are selected according to their distributions, which for example, may be Gaussian or normal with some mean (nominal value) and standard deviation (one to three standard deviations are generally equal

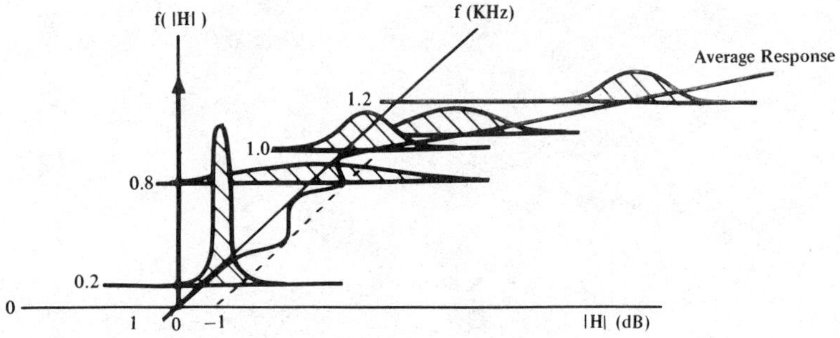

Fig. 8.5.12 Monte Carlo analysis of fifth-order Chebyshev low-pass filter response.

to the tolerance). Then the response is calculated, the results stored, and the process repeated. After as many iterations as desired are made, histograms of the response are formed at various frequencies as shown in Fig. 8.5.12. If enough iterations are used, the histograms become probability density functions. These functions allow the engineer to estimate the probability of not exceeding arbitrary response bounds at every frequency. In a sense, they allow him to estimate what percentage of active filters he would have to reject which did not meet his response requirements. Monte Carlo analysis gives him more realistic results than worst-case analysis; of course, it requires more computer time since all the component values must be selected before each iteration. With the gain-sensitivity approach we have used for filter design, the engineer can select alternate filter classes or design equations to improve sensitivities which will reduce response tolerances. Nevertheless, he must still resort to the computer to assess improvement.

Monte Carlo analysis is general and can be applied to other responses such as the delay or step responses. Later in this chapter, we will consider alternative approaches to cascade design which improves sensitivities and reduces drifts. However, the tuning becomes very involved.

8.6 GAIN-TUNED LOW-PASS FILTERS

There are a broad group of applications which require filters having variable corner frequency ω_o or damping factor ζ. Such filters are said to be tunable. The root loci for tunable ω_o and ζ filters are shown in Fig. 8.6.1. When amplifier gains K_1 and K_2 are used to control either ω_o or ζ they are said to be *gain-tuned.* Alternatively, when passive components are used, they are said to be *passive-tuned.* Both active and passive tuning are used in practice. Let us first consider gain-tuning.

From a root locus standpoint, we can easily determine which classes can be used to construct tunable filters. Comparing the root loci of Fig. 8.6.1 with those of Chap. 7 in Fig. 7.19.1, we observe that for gain-tuning:

Class A: Not useful
Class $\overline{A}$: Inherently constant $a = \zeta\omega_o$/tunable ω_o
Class B: Inherently constant ω_o/tunable ζ
Class C, $\overline{C}$, E: Can be adjusted to be close to any of these
Class D: Can be adjusted to be constant ω_o/tunable ζ or close to any of the others

It is important to note that filters are said to be tunable when their root loci approximate those shown in Fig. 8.6.1 over a *finite* range in the parameter being tuned. This is illustrated in Fig. 8.6.2 where we have placed tolerances on the parameters to be held constant which are ζ, a, and ω_o, respectively. The required tuning range is from ω_o to $(\omega_o + \Delta\omega)$ and Q_o to $(Q_o + \Delta Q)$, respectively. As long as the actual root locus for a filter falls inside the shaded region so defined, they are considered to be tunable. The Class C, $\overline{C}$, D, and E root loci shown have this property.

Therefore, Class $\overline{A}$ filters can be used as gain-tunable-ω_o filters with constant a (or adjust Class C–E filters for almost constant a). Class B and D filters can be used as gain-tunable-ζ filters

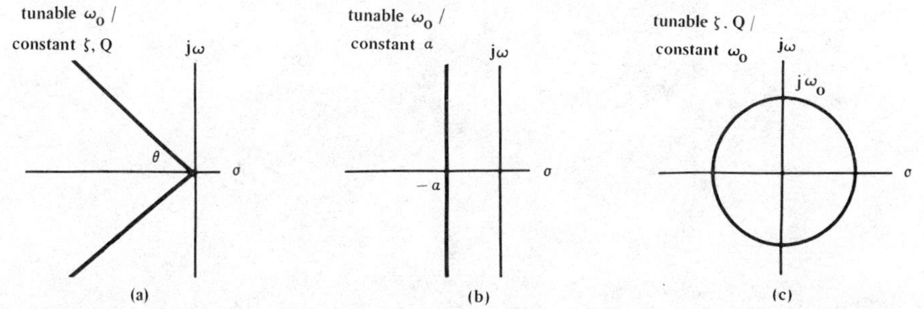

Fig. 8.6.1 Root loci for (a) tunable ω_o/constant ζ, (b) tunable ω_o/constant a, and (c) tunable ζ/constant ω_o filters.

with constant ω_o (or adjust Class C, $\overline{C}$, or E filters for almost constant ω_o). Class C, $\overline{C}$ and E filters can be used for gain-tuning of ω_o with almost constant ζ. The only class which is not useful for tuning is Class A. In low-pass filter applications, we generally require only filters with constant ζ and tunable ω_o. Thus, Class C, $\overline{C}$, D, and E filters are necessary.

For obtaining a gain-tuned low-pass filter, it must have a transfer function

$$H(s) = \frac{H_o K^2 b^2}{s^2 + aKs + K^2 b^2} \tag{8.6.1}$$

where a and b are constant. The filter parameters are $\omega_o = bK$ and $\zeta = a/2b$. We see that ω_o can be varied with K and that ζ remains constant. However, a Class $\overline{C}$ filter has a transfer function determinant given by Eq. 7.8.6 and a ω_o and ζ given by Eq. 7.8.7. ω_o is not exactly linear in K and ζ varies slightly with K. Class D and E filters have more general expressions. Therefore, gain tunable low-pass filters are realized approximately using Class $\overline{C}$, D, or E filters. Because the coefficient of s^0 involved $K^2 \sim K_1 K_2$, only two-amplifier forms are suitable. Due to the stringent coefficient conditions on both s^1 and s^0, Bruminhent and Su have shown that only six filters having the minimum number of nodes (i.e., six) are possible.[3] These canonical gain-tuned filters are shown in Fig. 8.6.3. To introduce these filters, consider the following example.

EXAMPLE 8.6.1 Obtain the flow graph and gain for the third gain-tuned filter of Fig. 8.6.3.
Solution The flow graph is easily obtained for this filter. Labelling the filter nodes, the flow graph is drawn in Fig. 8.6.4. The branch gains can be written by inspection as

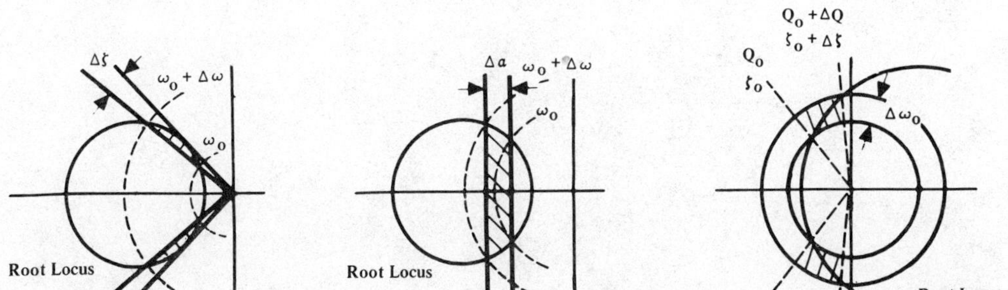

Fig. 8.6.2 Tolerance on root loci for (a) tunable ω_o/constant ζ, (b) tunable ω_o/constant a, and (c) tunable ζ/constant ω_o filters.

$2\overline{C}$

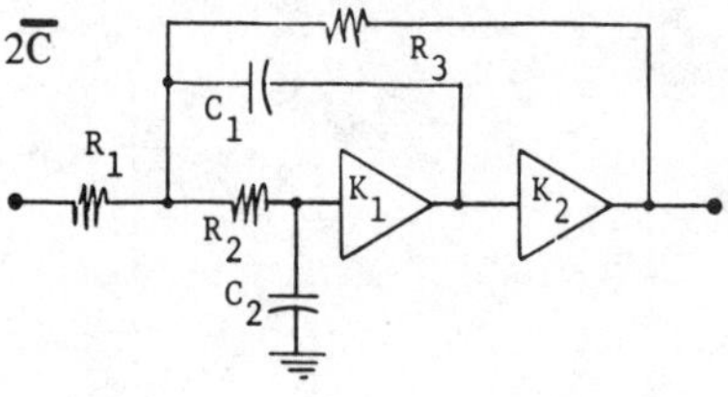

$$K_1=-K_2=-K_0<0$$
$$G_1=G>0,\ G_2=\alpha G,\ G_3=\beta G$$
$$\beta C_2=\gamma^2 C_1\alpha,\ \gamma>0,\ \beta>>\alpha$$
$$Q_0=\frac{\gamma}{(1+A)}$$
$$\omega_0=\frac{\beta}{\gamma C_1}GK_0$$
$$K_{0_{min}}=\frac{1+\gamma^2(1+\frac{1}{\beta})}{\gamma}Q_0\frac{1+A}{A}$$
$$\text{DC gain}=-\frac{1}{\beta}$$

$2\overline{C}$

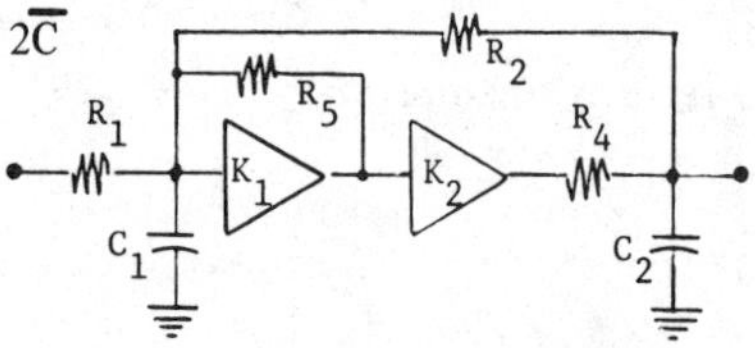

$$K_1=-K_2=-K_0<0$$
$$G_1=G>0,\ G_2=\alpha G,\ G_4=\beta G$$
$$G_5=\gamma G$$
$$\beta C_1=\alpha C_2,\ \alpha>>1+\gamma$$
$$Q_0=\frac{\beta}{\gamma(1+A)}$$
$$\omega_0=\frac{\beta GK_0}{C_2}$$
$$K_{0_{min}}=(2+\frac{\alpha}{\beta})Q_0\frac{1+A}{A}$$
$$\text{DC gain}=-\frac{1}{\alpha}$$

$1\overline{C}$

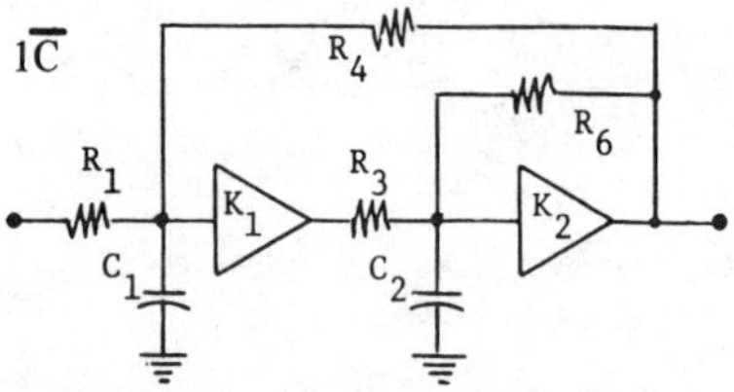

$$K_1=-K_2=K_0>0$$
$$G_1=G>0,\ G_3=\alpha G,\ G_4=\beta G$$
$$G_6=\gamma G$$
$$\alpha C_1=\beta C_2,\ \beta>>1$$
$$Q_0=\frac{\alpha}{\gamma(1+A)}$$
$$\omega_0=\frac{\beta GK_0}{C_1}$$
$$K_{0_{min}}=2Q_0\frac{1+A}{A}+\frac{1}{A}$$
$$\text{DC gain}=-\frac{1}{\beta}$$

$1\overline{C}$

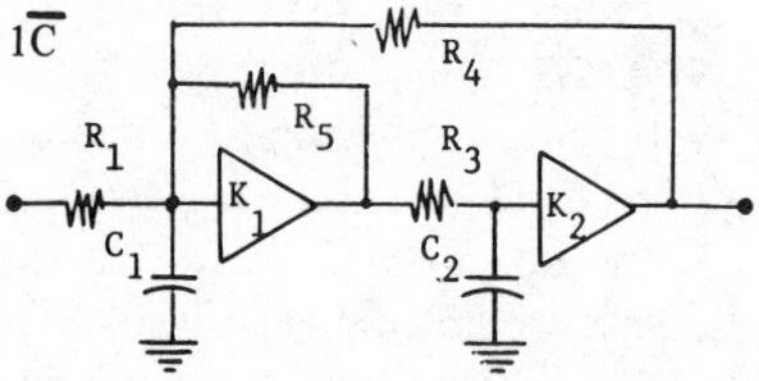

$$K_1=-K_2=-K_0<0$$
$$G_1=G>0,\ G_3=\alpha G,\ G_4=\beta G$$
$$G_5=\gamma G$$
$$\alpha C_1=\beta C_2,\ \beta>>1$$
$$Q_0=\frac{\beta}{\gamma(1+A)}$$
$$\omega_0=\frac{\beta GK_0}{C_1}$$
$$K_{0_{min}}=2Q_0\frac{1+A}{A}+\frac{1}{A}$$
$$\text{DC gain}=-\frac{1}{\beta}$$

2E

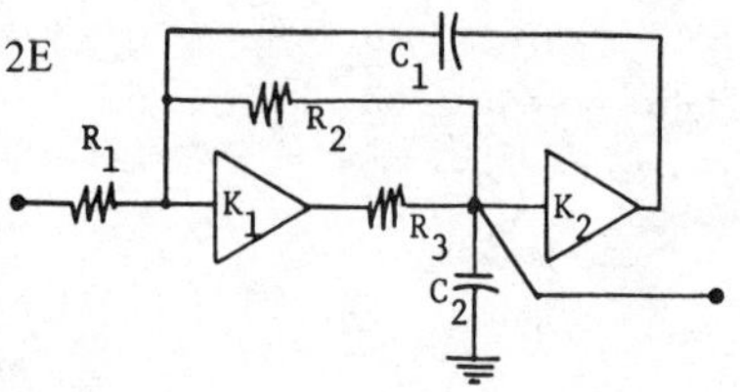

$$K_1=-K_0^2,\ K_2=\frac{1}{K_0},\ K_0>0$$
$$G_1=G>0,\ G_2=\alpha G,\ G_3=\beta G$$
$$\alpha C_2=\beta\gamma^2 C_1,\ \gamma>0,\ \beta>>\alpha>>1$$
$$Q_0=\frac{\gamma}{1+A}$$
$$\omega_0=\frac{\alpha GK_0}{\gamma C_1}$$
$$K_{0_{min}}=\frac{1+\gamma^2}{\gamma}Q_0\frac{1+A}{A}$$
$$\text{DC gain}=-\frac{1}{\alpha}$$

2E

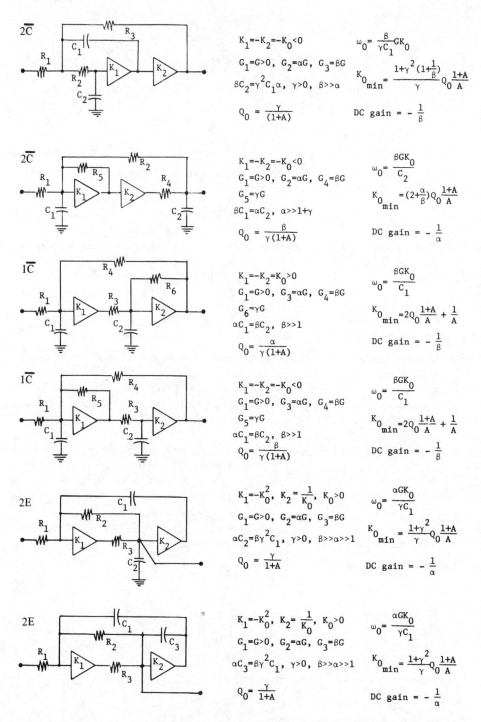

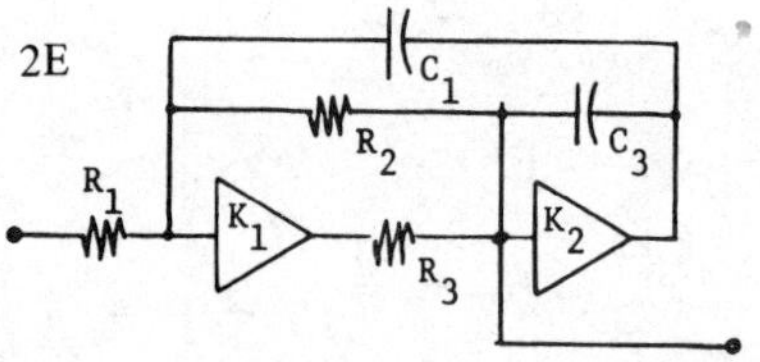

$$K_1=-K_0^2,\ K_2=\frac{1}{K_0},\ K_0>0$$
$$G_1=G>0,\ G_2=\alpha G,\ G_3=\beta G$$
$$\alpha C_3=\beta\gamma^2 C_1,\ \gamma>0,\ \beta>>\alpha>>1$$
$$Q_0=\frac{\gamma}{1+A}$$
$$\omega_0=\frac{\alpha GK_0}{\gamma C_1}$$
$$K_{0_{min}}=\frac{1+\gamma^2}{\gamma}Q_0\frac{1+A}{A}$$
$$\text{DC gain}=-\frac{1}{\alpha}$$

Fig. 8.6.3 Canonical gain-tunable low-pass filters. (Note that $\Delta Q_o/Q_o = \Delta A_o/A_o = A(N-1)/(N+A)$ for all filters.) (From S. Bruminhent and K. L. Su, "Gain-tuned active filters," Proc. Intl. Symp. on Circuits and Systems, pp. 443–447, April, 1974.)

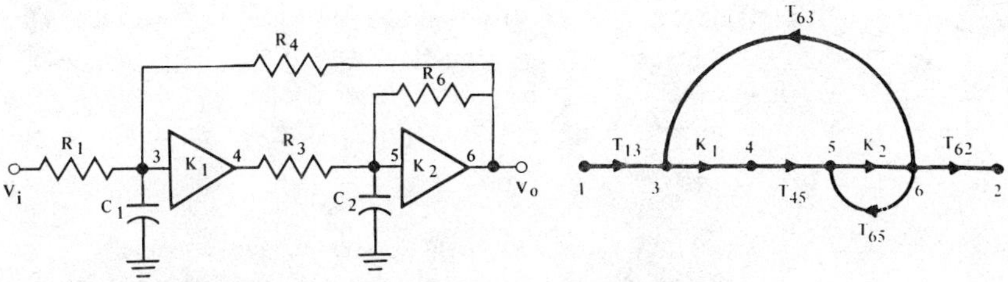

Fig. 8.6.4 Flow graph of gain-tuned filter of Example 8.6.1.

$$T_{13} = \frac{R_4}{R_1 + R_4} \frac{1}{1 + sC_1R_1R_4/(R_1 + R_4)} = \frac{R_4}{R_1 + R_4 + sC_1R_1R_4}$$

$$T_{45} = \frac{R_6}{R_3 + R_6} \frac{1}{1 + sC_2R_3R_6/(R_3 + R_6)} = \frac{R_6}{R_3 + R_6 + sC_2R_3R_6} \tag{8.6.2}$$

$$T_{63} = T_{13}R_1/R_4, \qquad T_{65} = T_{45}R_3/R_6$$

The transfer function of the filter equals

$$H(s) = \frac{K_1K_2T_{13}T_{45}}{1 - K_2T_{65} - K_1K_2T_{45}T_{63}}$$

$$= \frac{K_1K_2R_4R_6}{(R_1 + R_4 + sC_1R_1R_4)(R_3 + R_6 + sC_2R_3R_6) - K_2R_3(R_1 + R_4 + sC_1R_1R_4) - K_1K_2R_1R_6}$$

$$= \frac{K_1K_2R_4R_6}{s^2R_1C_1R_3C_2R_4R_6 + s[C_1R_1R_4(R_3 + R_6) + C_2R_3R_6(R_1 + R_4) - K_2C_1R_1R_3R_4] + [((1 - K_2)R_3 + R_6)(R_1 + R_4) - K_1K_2R_1R_6]} \tag{8.6.3}$$

Introducing the notation that

$$R_1 = R, \quad R_3 = R/a, \quad R_4 = R/\beta, \quad R_6 = R/\gamma, \quad aC_1 = \beta C_2, \quad K_1 = -K_2 = K_0 \tag{8.6.4}$$

then the gain given by Eq. 8.6.3 can be expressed as

$$H(s) = \frac{-K_0{}^2\beta/(R_1C_1)^2}{s^2 + s(\gamma\beta K_0/aR_1C_1)(1 + A) + (\beta K_0/R_1C_1)^2(1 + B)} \tag{8.6.5}$$

where the constants A and B equal

$$A = (-1/K_2)[(1 + R_6/R_3) + (1 + R_4/R_1)R_6C_2/R_4C_1] = (1/K_0)[1 + (2 + 1/\beta)a/\gamma]$$
$$B = (-1/K_1K_2)[1 + (1 - K_2)R_3/R_6][1 + R_4/R_1] = (1/K_0{}^2)(1 + 1/\beta)[1 + (1 + K_0)\gamma/a] \tag{8.6.6}$$

Therefore, the filter parameters equal

$$\omega_o = (\beta K_0/R_1C_1)(1 + B)^{1/2} \cong \beta K_0/R_1C_1, \qquad Q_o = a(1 + B)^{1/2}/\gamma(1 + A) \cong a/\gamma(1 + A)$$
$$H_o = -1/\beta(1 + B) \cong -1/\beta \tag{8.6.7}$$

In order that ω_o varies with K_0 and the Q_o is constant, we require A and B $\ll 1$. The filter parameters for the various tunable filters are listed in Fig. 8.6.3.

Gain-tuned filters have Q's which vary slightly. However, filters are considered to be constant Q if their tolerance on Q is sufficiently low. To relate the Q tolerance to other parameters, suppose the tuning range is $\Delta\omega_o$ so that the corner frequency lies between ω_o and $\omega_o + \Delta\omega_o$ for gain changes from K_o to $K_o + \Delta K_o$. Defining the normalized tuning range N as

$$N = (\omega_o + \Delta\omega_o)/\omega_o = 1 + \Delta\omega_o/\omega_o = \omega_{o\,max}/\omega_{o\,min} \tag{8.6.8}$$

then for the filter described by Eq. 8.6.1 having constant Q and tunable ω_o,

$$N = (K_o + \Delta K_o)/K_o = 1 + \Delta K_o/K_o = K_{o\,max}/K_{o\,min} \tag{8.6.9}$$

Therefore, the normalized variation ΔK_o in K_o equals $\Delta K_o/K_o = \Delta\omega_o/\omega_o = N - 1$. The normalized variation ΔQ_o in Q_o equals

$$T_Q = \Delta Q_o/Q_o = \frac{\Delta K_o/K_o}{1 + K_o + \Delta K_o} = \frac{(1 - N)A}{1 + NA} \tag{8.6.10}$$

from Eq. 8.6.7b. This holds true for all the filters in Fig. 8.6.3. Solving Eq. 8.6.10 for A gives

$$A = T_Q/[1 - N(1 + T_Q)] \tag{8.6.11}$$

Thus, when the tuning range N and tolerance on Q_o are specified, then the maximum value of A can be determined. For example, for a tuning range of 2:1, N = 1 + 1 = 2. If we require the Q_o tolerance T_Q not to exceed ± 5%, Eq. 8.6.11 gives a maximum value of A as

$$A = 0.05/|1 - 2(1 + 0.05)| = 0.05/|1 - 2.1| = 0.045 \tag{8.6.12}$$

Therefore, $A \leqslant 0.045$ if our Q variation is to be less than ± 5% over this tuning range.

Since A and Q_o can be related to the amplifier gains K_o required to produce the frequency change, we can complete the design by expressing this dependency. Combining the expressions for A and Q given by Eqs. 8.6.6 and 8.6.7 and solving for α/γ, it is easy to show that

$$A = [1 + Q_o(1 + A)(2 + 1/\beta)]/K_o \tag{8.6.13}$$

assuming $B \ll 1$. Solving for the required amplifier gains,

$$K_o = [1 + 2Q_o(1 + A)(1 + 1/2\beta)]/A \tag{8.6.14}$$

The required gain is minimum when β is selected so $\beta \gg 1$ in which case the gain $K_{omin} \cong [1 + 2Q_o(1 + A)]/A \cong (1 + 2Q_o)/A$. Thus, when A and Q_o are specified, the minimum amplifier gains K_{omin} can be determined. If $Q_o = 0.707$ or $\zeta = 0.707$ for a second-order tunable Butterworth filter, then using Eq. 8.6.12, the minimum gain required is

$$K_{o\,min} \cong [1 + 2(0.707)(1 + 0.045)]/0.045 = (1 + 1.48)/0.045 \cong 55 \tag{8.6.15}$$

for a tuning range of 200%. Since $\Delta K_o/K_o = N - 1 = 2 - 1 = 1$, then the gain change required equals $\Delta K_o = K_o \cong 55$. Therefore, the maximum amplifier gains must equal $K_{omax} \cong K_o + \Delta K_o = 110$. The expressions for K_{omin} and the parameter requirements to achieve these minimum values are listed in Fig. 8.6.3. The dc filter gains $|H(j0)|$ are also listed.

EXAMPLE 8.6.2 Design the gain-tuned filter of Example 8.6.1 to have a lower corner frequency of 10 KHz, a 2:1 tuning range, a Q of 0.707 (a Butterworth characteristic), and a Q tolerance of ± 5%.

Solution We determined earlier in Eq. 8.6.12 that $A \leqslant 0.045$. We also determined in Eq. 8.6.15 that the gain was minimum if $\beta \gg 1$ and equalled 55. The parameters of the filters are

$$\omega_o = \beta K_o/R_1C_1, \qquad Q_o = \alpha/\gamma(1 + A), \qquad H(0) = -1/\beta \tag{8.6.16}$$

from Fig. 8.6.3. Choosing H(0) = –1, then $\beta = 1$. Recalculating the gain using Eq. 8.6.14 yields

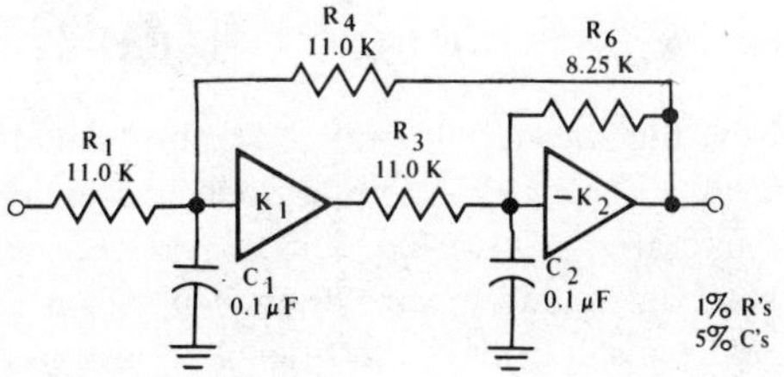

Fig. 8.6.5 Gain-tuned low-pass filter realization of Example 8.6.2.

$$K_o\,\text{min} = [1 + 2(0.707)(1.045)(1 + 0.5)]/0.045 = 71 \tag{8.6.17}$$

which is slightly larger than the earlier value of 55. Letting $\alpha = \beta$, then solving Eq. 8.6.16b for γ gives

$$\gamma = \alpha/(1 + A)Q_o = 1/(1 + 0.045)(0.707) = 1.35 \tag{8.6.18}$$

Since Eq. 8.6.16a requires that

$$1/R_1C_1 = \omega_o/\beta K_0 = 2\pi(10\text{ KHz})/71 = 2\pi(141\text{ Hz}) \tag{8.6.19}$$

then we can choose R_1 and C_1 to be convenient values. Selecting $C_1 = 0.1\ \mu F$, then $R_1 = 11.3$ K (use 11.0 K) from Fig. 14.1.9. The other component values equal

$$R_3 = R_4 = R_1/\beta = 11.0\text{ K}/1 = 11.0\text{ K}, \qquad R_6 = R_1/\gamma = 11.0\text{ K}/1.35 = 8.15\text{ K (use 8.25 K)}$$
$$C_2 = \alpha C_1/\beta = 0.1\ \mu F, \qquad K_1 = -K_2 = 71 \rightarrow 142 \tag{8.6.20}$$

If G_1 equals the minimum amplifier gain and G_2 the maximum amplifier gain required with resistors R_a, R_b, and R_c forming the voltage divider, then it is easy to show that the resistor ratios must equal (see Prob. 8.3) (when $R_f = R_1$)

$$R_a/R_b \cong G_1G_2/(G_2 - G_1) \cong G_1, \qquad R_c/R_b \cong G_1/(G_2 - G_1) \cong (R_a/R_b)/G_2; \qquad G_2 \gg G_1 \tag{8.6.21}$$

The complete gain-tuned filter is shown in Fig. 8.6.5 exclusive of the amplifier gain controls. Now let us add these. K_1 is realized by an op amp connected in a noninverting mode as shown in Fig. 8.6.6 where a 1 K pot is used to adjust gain. K_2 is realized by another op amp connected in an inverting mode; the same 1 K pot arrangement is used to adjust gain. The pots are mechanically connected together (a dual pot) so that the gains track one another. A 10 K resistor is used at the inverting terminal of K_2 to maintain low offset voltage.

It is important to remember that since the gain-tuned filters of Fig. 8.6.3 are operated as Class $\overline{C}$ (see Eq. 8.6.1), frequency ω_o is down-scaled by gain K. Thus, these gain-tuned filters are primarily useful for higher-frequency applications.

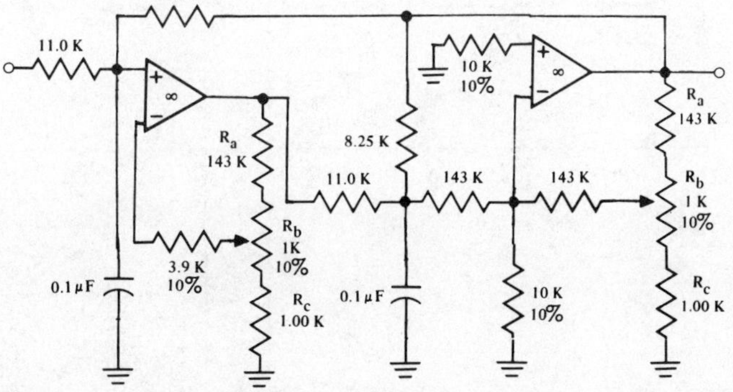

Fig. 8.6.6 Resistor gain controls in Example 8.6.2.

8.7 PASSIVE-TUNED LOW-PASS FILTERS

Now that we have considered gain-tuned low-pass filters, let us briefly review passive-tuned filters. We shall begin by determining the system determinants for the various classes of filters in Chap. 7. These are listed in Fig. 7.19.1. Passive-tuned filters are tuned by varying the passive corner frequencies a_1 and/or a_2 rather than gain K as in gain-tuned filters. Suppose a_1 is varied and a_2 is held constant; then, the filter determinants are easily expressed in terms of a_1 as listed in Table 8.7.1. The root loci of the various classes are also shown. We see that they all have the same circular form which is the same as that for the gain-tuned filters just discussed. Thus, the design considerations are virtually identical. We now see that filters of every class (rather than just Class C, $\overline{C}$, D, and E) can be passive-tuned.

The situation is improved even more when we consider the double-tuned case where both a_1 and a_2 are varied. For convenience we shall take $a = a_1 = a_2$, but the results will still apply if they are proportional. Under this condition, the determinants listed in Table 8.7.1 reduce to those listed in Table 8.7.2. The root loci of the various classes are also shown. We see that they have

Table 8.7.1   Root loci for passive-tuned filters (single-tuned using a_1).*

A $\Delta(s) = s[s(1-k)+a_2] + a_1(s+a_2)$

C $\Delta(s) = s[s(1-k)+a_2] + a_1[s(1-ka_3)+a_2]$

$\overline{A}$ $\Delta(s) = s(s+a_2) + a_1[s+a_2(1-k)]$

$\overline{C}$ $\Delta(s) = s(s+a_2) + a_1[s(1-ka_3)+a_2(1-k)]$

B $\Delta(s) = s(s+a_2) + a_1[s(1-k)+a_2]$

D $\Delta(s) = s[s(1-k)+a_2] + a_1[s+a_2(1-ka_3^2)]$

*The lower-half s-plane is not shown.

E $\Delta(s) = s[s(1-k)+a_2(1-ka_4)] +$
$a_1[s(1-ka_3)+a_2(1-ka_3a_4)]$

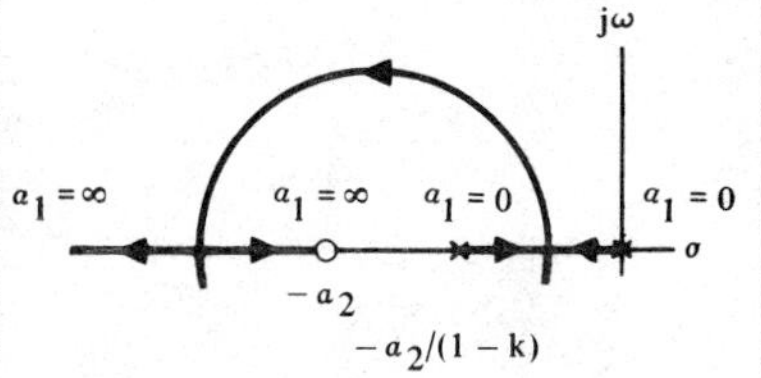

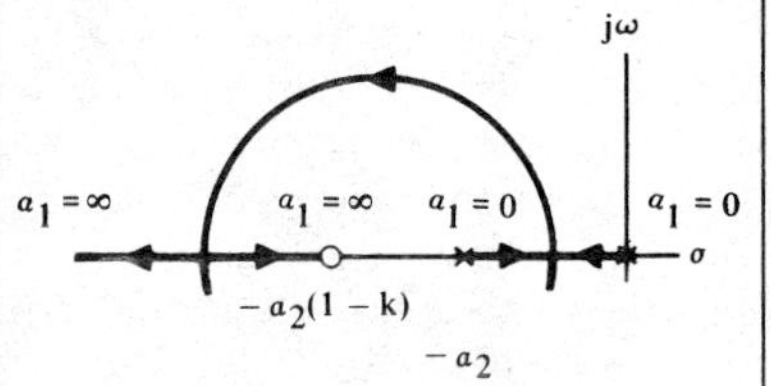

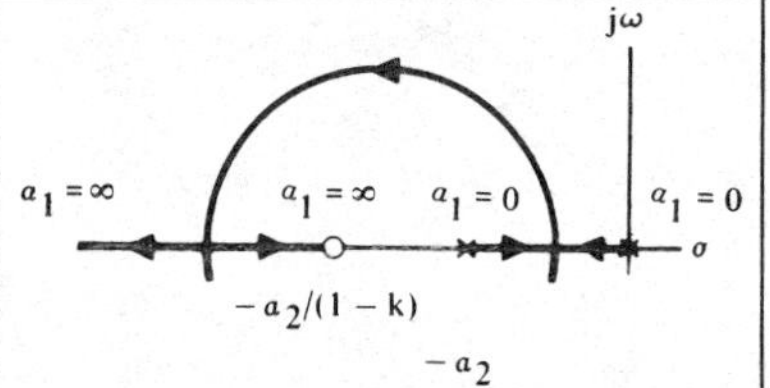

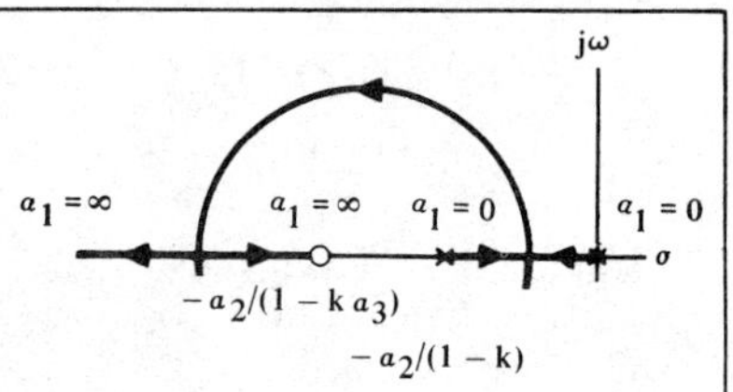

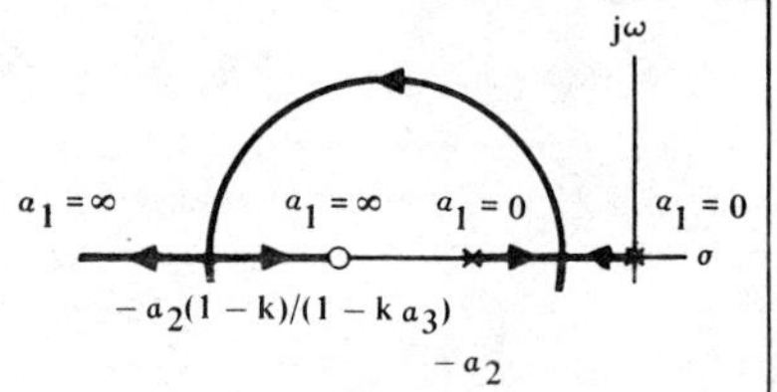

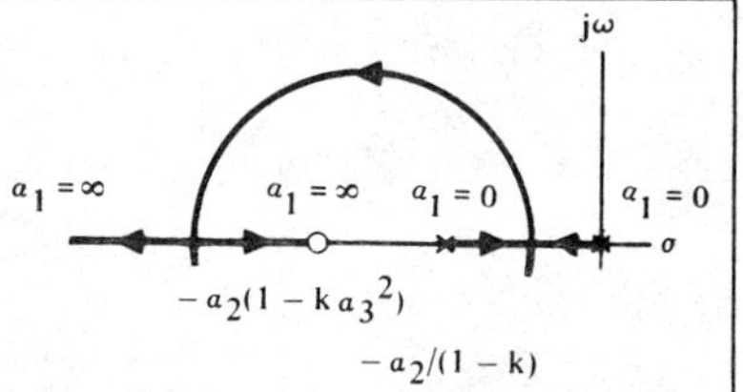

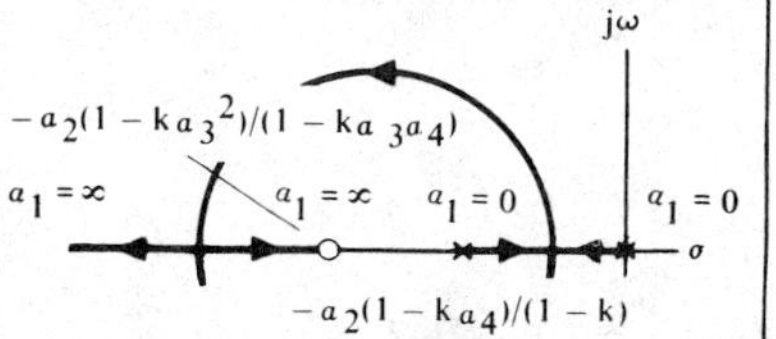

ideal form shown in Fig. 8.6.1a for tunable ω_o/constant ζ filters. They differ only in their damping factors as shown. Thus, such passive-tuned filters can be realized exactly using double-tuning or approximately using single-tuning of the time constants. These factors give us great latitude in designing passive-tuned filters.

In general, designing passive-tuned filters is much simpler than designing gain-tuned filters. Since the passive corner frequencies equal

$$a_i = 1/R_iC_i \tag{8.7.1}$$

in most cases, we could use either resistor- or capacitor-tuning to control a_i. However, as a practical matter, variable capacitors have too small a value (10-100 pF) to be generally useful in tuning active filters. Thus, resistor tuning is always used. In double-tuning, $\omega_o \sim a$. If the required corner frequency lies between ω_{omin} and ω_{omax} where the tuning range is $N = \omega_{omax}/\omega_{omin}$, then Eq. 8.7.1 can be used to show that

$$CR_{max} = 1/\omega_{o\,min}, \qquad CR_{min} = 1/\omega_{o\,max} \tag{8.7.2}$$

Table 8.7.2 Root loci for passive-tuned filters (double-tuned where $a_1 = a_2 = a$).*

Type	ζ	Root locus	$\Delta(s)$
A	$\zeta = 1/(1-k)^{1/2}$	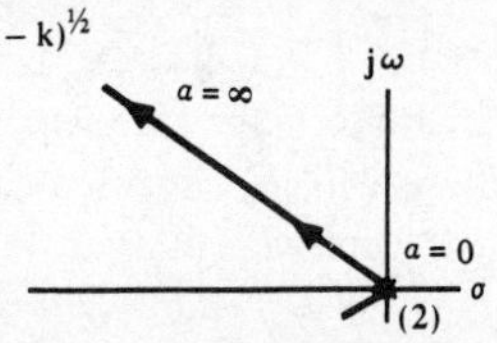	$\Delta(s) = s^2(1-k) + 2as + a^2$
$\overline{A}$	$\zeta = 1/(1-k)^{1/2}$	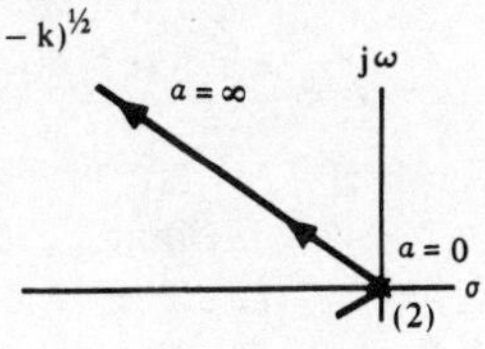	$\Delta(s) = s^2 + 2as + (1-k)a^2$
B	$\zeta = 1 - k/2$	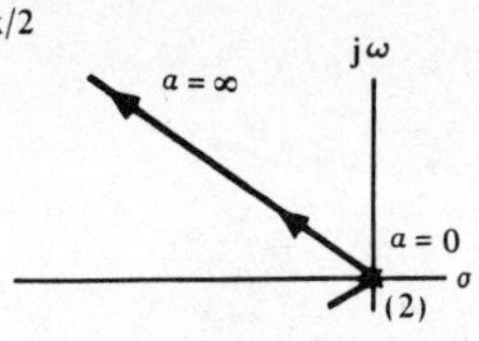	$\Delta(s) = s^2(1-k) + (2-k)s + a^2$
C	$\zeta = (1 - ka_3/2)/(1-k)^{1/2}$	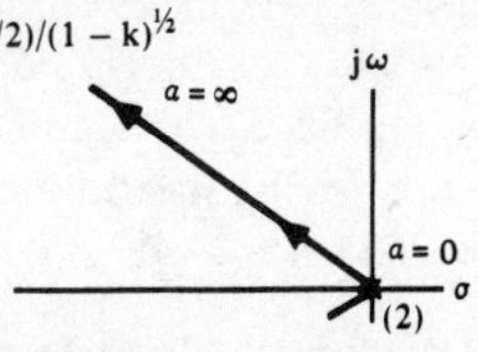	$\Delta(s) = s^2(1-k) + (2-ka_3)as + a^2$
$\overline{C}$	$\zeta = (1 - ka_3/2)/(1-k)^{1/2}$	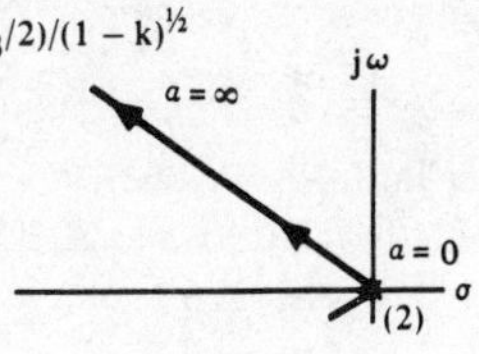	$\Delta(s) = s^2 + (2-ka_3)as + (1-k)a^2$
D	$\zeta = [(1-k)(1-ka_3^2)]^{1/2}$	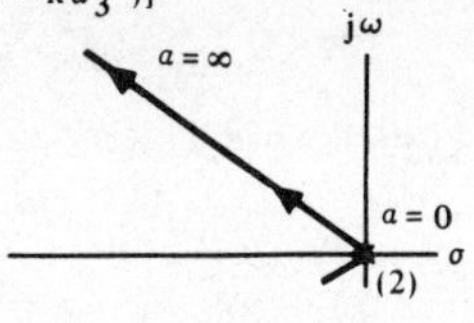	$\Delta(s) = s^2(1-k) + 2as + (1-ka_3^2)a^2$
E	$\zeta = [1 - k(a_3 + a_4)/2)]/[(1-k)(1-ka_3^2)]^{1/2}$	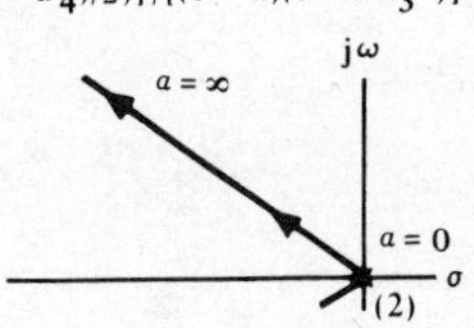	$\Delta(s) = (s+a)^2 - k(s+a_3a)(s+a_4a)$

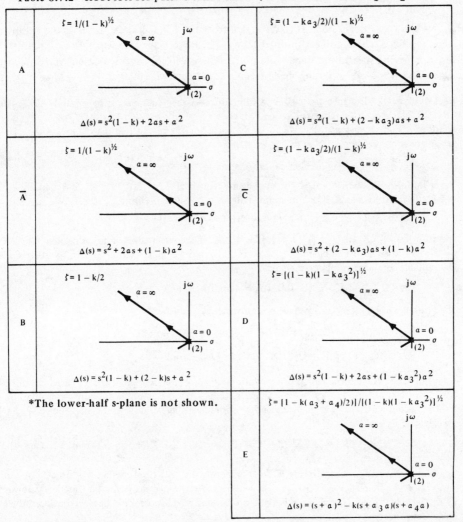

*The lower-half s-plane is not shown.

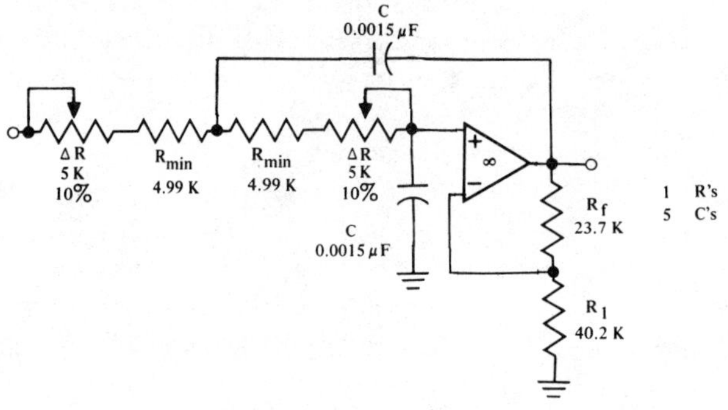

Fig. 8.7.1 Passive-tuned low-pass filter realization of Example 8.7.1.

Therefore, the required tuning range $\Delta R = R_{max} - R_{min}$ in R is determined from Eq. 8.7.2 to be

$$C\Delta R = C(R_{max} - R_{min}) = (N-1)/\omega_{o\,max} \tag{8.7.3}$$

Combining Eqs. 8.7.2 and 8.7.3 shows that R_{min} and R_{max} can be re-expressed in terms of ΔR as

$$R_{min} = [1/(N-1)]\Delta R, \qquad R_{max} = [N/(N-1)]\Delta R \tag{8.7.4}$$

so $R_{max} = NR_{min}$. It is important to recognize from Eq. 8.7.1 that ω_o varies as the reciprocal of R rather than R. To obtain linear tuning over a logarithmic range (the usual case of interest), variable resistors having logarithmic tapers are used. These will be discussed extensively in Sec. 14.2. Also note that since $\omega_o \sim \sqrt{a}$ using single-tuning, ω_o is nonlinear in a.

EXAMPLE 8.7.1 Design a passive-tuned filter to meet the requirements of Example 8.6.2. Use the Class 2B filter realization tabulated in Sec. 8.3.

Solution For convenience, let us choose the capacitors to be equal so that $C = C_1 = C_2$. Then the design equations become

$$K = 3 - 2\zeta, \qquad R = 1/\omega_o C \tag{8.7.5}$$

For a Butterworth filter, $\zeta = 0.707$ so that gain K equals $K = 3 - 2(0.707) = 1.586$. Since the filter is tunable from 10 KHz to 20 KHz, the tuning range N = 2. Therefore from Eq. 8.7.3,

$$C\Delta R = C(R_{max} - R_{min}) = 1/2\pi(20\text{ KHz}) \tag{8.7.6}$$

and from Eq. 8.7.4, $R_{min} = [1/(2-1)]\Delta R = \Delta R$. If the exact tuning range is desired, then ΔR must be selected to equal the standard pot values of 1, 2, or 5. C must then be chosen to satisfy Eq. 8.7.5. One suitable combination of components is

$$\Delta R = R_{min} = 5\text{ K}, \qquad C = 0.0016\ \mu\text{F (use } 0.0015\ \mu\text{F)} \tag{8.7.7}$$

The (arithmetic and geometric) average pot resistance R_{av} satisfies

$$\begin{aligned} R_{av} &= 0.5(R_{min} + R_{max}) = 0.5[(N+1)/(N-1)]\Delta R \quad \text{(arithmetic)} \\ R_{av} &= (R_{min}R_{max})^{1/2} = [N^{1/2}/(N-1)]\Delta R \quad \text{(geometric)} \end{aligned} \tag{8.7.8}$$

from Eq. 8.7.4. R_{av} depends upon whether arithmetic or geometric tuning of ω_o is used. In this design, N = 2 which is not too large so we use linear tuning. Now the amplifier is easily designed using Table 8.4.1. Since the average dc resistance seen by the noninverting input of the op amp equals $2R_{av} = 15$ K, we calculate R_1 and R_f as

$$R_f = 1.586(15\text{ K}) = 23.8\text{ K (use 23.7 K)}, \qquad R_1 = 23.7\text{ K}/(1.586-1) = 40.4\text{ K (use 40.2 K)} \tag{8.7.9}$$

The complete filter is shown in Fig. 8.7.1. Trimming the pots for a minimum resistance of zero produces a corner frequency of 20 KHz. Increasing the resistance decreases the frequency towards 10 KHz. Note that if the tuning range was not critical, single 10 K pots could be used; however, the tuning range would become very large since $R_{min} \cong 0$ and $\omega_o = 1/RC$.

This example shows that passive-tuned filters are easily designed. Since any of the filter classes may be used, any of the low-pass filters in Sec. 8.3 can be utilized.[4] The design procedure follows that of Example 8.7.1.

8.8 IMMITTANCE CALCULATIONS

An important design consideration is the immittance characteristic of a filter. For example, if the input impedance is too small or the input admittance too large, then excessive drive current is required from the preceding stage which is undesirable. As discussed in Sec. 1.10, Blackman's immittance relations provide a convenient analytical means by which such input immittances may be determined. These relations are

$$Z^{(k)} = Z^{(0)}\frac{1 - T_s}{1 - T_\infty}, \qquad Y^{(k)} = Y^{(0)}\frac{1 - T_\infty}{1 - T_s} \tag{8.8.1}$$

from Eq. 1.10.18 where $Z^{(k)}$ and $Y^{(k)}$ are the input immittances; $Z^{(0)}$ and $Y^{(0)}$ are these immittances for $k = 0$; and T_s and T_∞ are the return ratios for k under short-circuit and open-circuit conditions at the port at which $Z^{(k)}$ or $Y^{(k)}$ is being measured. Recall that k is the source strength of one controlled source $y = kx$ in the filter. Since these equations were thoroughly discussed and their use illustrated in Sec. 1.10, we shall now simply utilize them. The engineer may wish to briefly review that section before proceeding further.

EXAMPLE 8.8.1 A Class 1B low-pass filter was examined in the earlier part of the chapter. Its design sheet was given in Table 8.2.1; its minimum gain and sensitivity designs were discussed in Examples 8.2.1 and 8.2.2, and the results tabulated in Table 8.2.2. A design example was given in Example 8.5.1. Now determine the input impedance of the Class 1B low-pass filter.

Solution The Class 1B filter is shown in Fig. 8.8.1a. We want to calculate the input impedance Z_{in}. We will use Blackman's impedance relation given by Eq. 8.8.1a where $Z_{in} = Z^{(k)}$. k is the strength of one of the controlled sources, K_1 or K_2, in the filter. Let us choose K_1 to be the controlled source of interest. K_2 shall operate normally and will not be manipulated. Now we calculate $Z^{(0)}$, T_s, and T_∞.

To calculate $Z^{(0)}$, we set $K_1 = 0$ and determine Z_{in} as shown in Fig. 8.8.1b. Therefore,

$$Z^{(0)} = R_1 + 1/sC_1 = (1 + sR_1C_1)/sC_1 \tag{8.8.2}$$

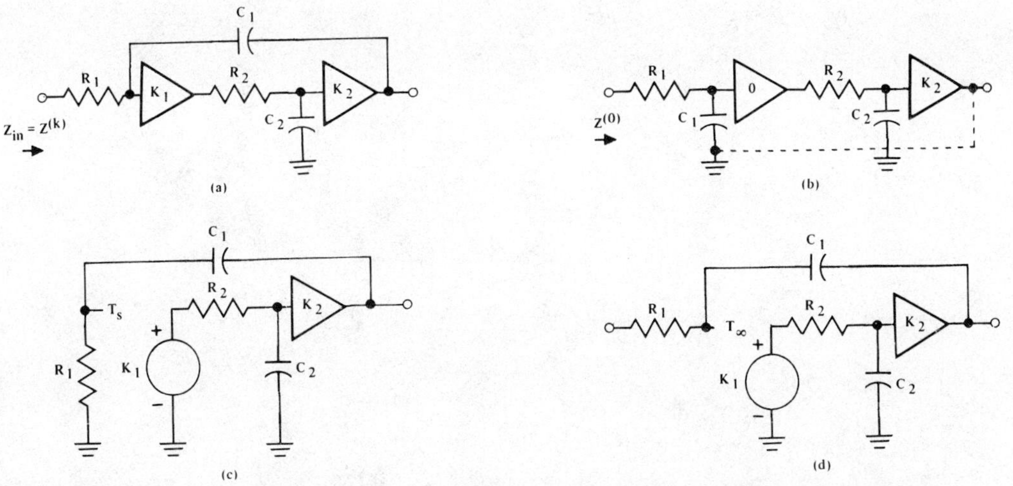

Fig. 8.8.1 (a) Class 1B low-pass filter and its form for calculating (b) $Z^{(0)}$, (c) T_s, and (d) T_∞.

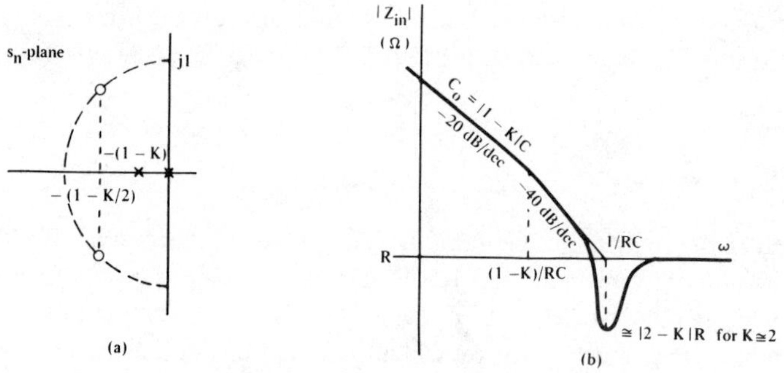

Fig. 8.8.2 (a) Pole-zero pattern and (b) Bode magnitude characteristic for Z_{in} of Class 1B low-pass filter.

To calculate T_s, we replace the K_1 controlled source having $V_4 = K_1V_3$ by an independent source of strength K_1. Then T_s is equal to V_3 where the input port is short-circuited as shown in Fig. 8.8.1c. Thus,

$$T_s = K_1K_2sR_1C_1/[(1 + sR_1C_1)(1 + sR_2C_2)] \tag{8.8.3}$$

To calculate T_∞, we open-circuit the input port and determine V_3 as shown in Fig. 8.8.1d where

$$T_\infty = K_1K_2/(1 + sR_2C_2) \tag{8.8.4}$$

Substituting Eqs. 8.8.2–8.8.4 into Eq. 8.8.1, then the input impedance equals

$$Z_{in} = \frac{1}{sC_1}\,\frac{s^2R_1C_1R_2C_2 + s[R_1C_1(1 - K_1K_2) + R_2C_2] + 1}{sR_2C_2 + (1 - K_1K_2)} \tag{8.8.5}$$

From Eq. 8.2.1, we see that the zeros of Z_{in} are the poles of the gain function H(s). Z_{in} has one pole at the origin and the other depends upon K_1K_2. For $K_1K_2 > 1$ or high-Q designs, it lies on the positive real axis; otherwise, it lies on the negative real axis. For complex poles, $0 < K_1K_2 < 2$ is the usual mode of operation. It is rather remarkable that immittance calculations can be made so easily using Blackman's immittance relations.

EXAMPLE 8.8.2 A minimum active sensitivity design is obtained by setting $R_1 = R_2 = R$ and $C_1 = C_2 = C$. Determine the input impedance under this condition and interpret the results.

Solution Equating R's and C's in Eq. 8.8.5 and setting $K = K_1K_2$ reduces Z_{in} to

$$Z_{in} = \frac{1}{sC(1 - K)}\,\frac{(sRC)^2 + sRC(2 - K) + 1}{1 + sRC/(1 - K)} \tag{8.8.6}$$

Introducing normalized frequency $s_n = sRC$, then

$$Z_{in} = \frac{R}{s_n(1 - K)}\,\frac{s_n^2 + (2 - K)s_n + 1}{1 + s_n/(1 - K)} \tag{8.8.7}$$

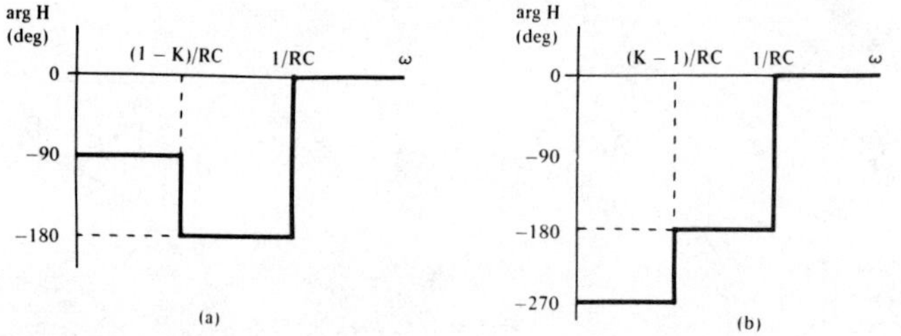

Fig. 8.8.3 Phase characteristic for Z_{in} of Class 1B low-pass filter for (a) $0 < K < 1$ and (b) $1 < K < 2$.

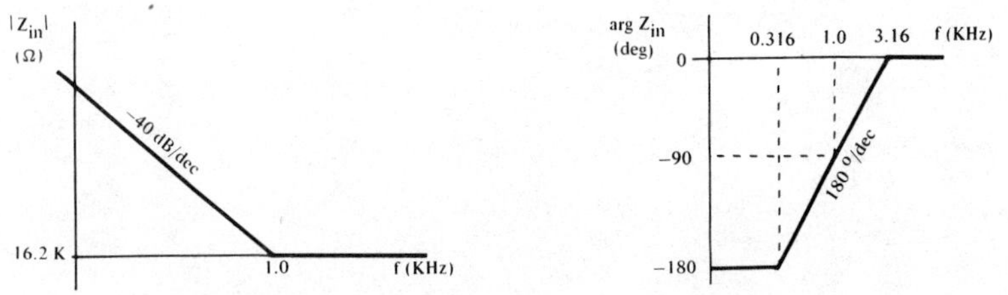

Fig. 8.8.4 Magnitude and phase characteristics of Z_{in} for Example 8.5.1.

The pole-zero pattern is shown in Fig. 8.8.2a. The Bode magnitude response is shown in Fig. 8.8.2b. At low frequencies, the input appears to be capacitive with value $C_o = |1 - K|C$.

At high frequencies, the input impedance is resistive and approaches R. Near the corner frequency 1/RC of the filter, the magnitude response exhibits $1/2|\zeta|$ of normalized peaking from Eq. 2.4.8 when $|\zeta| \ll 1$. The impedance characteristic has almost the same amount of negative peaking. Since $\zeta = 1 - K/2$ in the minimum sensitivity filter design of Table 8.2.2, then $|Z_{in}|_{min} \cong 2R|1 - K/2| = R|2 - K|$ for $K \cong 2$. It is much smaller than R for high-Q filters which have large peaking in their magnitude response. In many cases, it is convenient to plot the magnitude characteristic on impedance paper.

Phase is also very important. This is shown in Fig. 8.8.3, where we have used abrupt phase approximations (rather than the linear phase approximations ±45 °/dec or ±90/ζ °/dec of Chap. 2) to simplify the appearance of the plots. We see that at low frequencies, the input impedance of high-Q filters is that of a negative C. It becomes resistive in the vicinity of the corner frequency of the filter.

EXAMPLE 8.8.3 Determine the input impedance response of the Class 1B filter in Example 8.5.1.
Solution Using Eq. 8.8.6 and the component values calculated in Eq. 8.5.1 gives

$$Z_{in} = R(s_n^2 + s_n + 1)/s_n^2 \tag{8.8.8}$$

where R = 16.2 K and $s_n = s/2\pi(1\text{ KHz})$. The magnitude and phase of Z_{in} are shown in Fig. 8.8.4. Since $\zeta = 0.5$, the actual response is almost that of the approximation. At frequencies above approximately 3.2 KHz, the input is resistive with a value of 16.2 K.

These examples have illustrated the relative ease with which immittance calculations may be made. We see that input impedances are important when calculating the drive current requirements for active filters. If the impedances become too small so that the drive required is excessive, then the impedance characteristic must be increased or scaled up to the proper level. Of course, we can also calculate output impedances using this approach. When output impedances become too large, the op amps no longer appear to be ideal voltage sources. This results in transfer function errors.

8.9 HIGH-FREQUENCY FILTERS

The bandwidths of the amplifiers used in active filters determine their useful frequency range. As will be discussed in Sec. 14.4, their gain G is constant (usually about 10^5–10^6) up to the 3 dB frequency B (Hz) and then rolls off at −20 dB/dec (see Fig. 14.4.2). The gain-bandwidth product, denoted as GB, is constant for fixed-compensation op amps. The GB typically equals 10^6 for many such op amps but can be several orders of magnitude larger for wide bandwidth types. When designing amplifier blocks such as was done in Sec. 8.5, we generally determine the product of amplifier gain K and corner frequency f_o. Then we select an op amp which has $GB \gg Kf_o$ when designing the amplifier. For instance in Example 8.5.2, K = 71.8 and f_o = 10 KHz so that Kf_o = 0.718 MHz. Thus, an ordinary op amp having GB = 1 MHz is adequate to use in the amplifier. However, if the filter was required to operate at 100 KHz so that Kf_o = 7.18 MHz, a wide-bandwidth type op amp must be used.

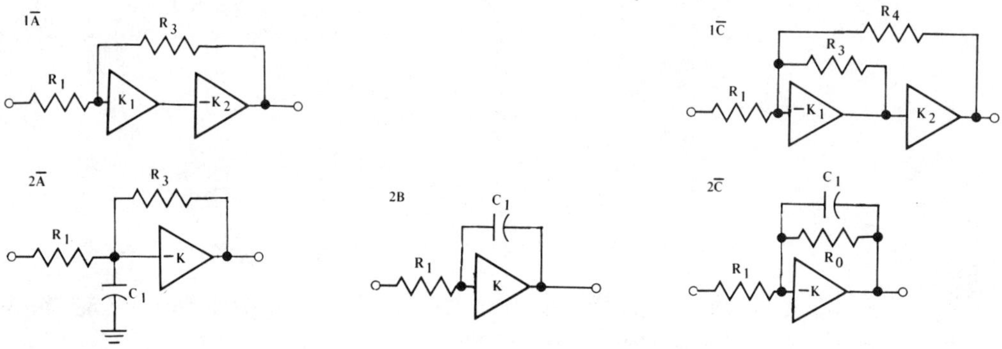

Fig. 8.9.1 Some high-frequency filters.

An alternative design approach can be used however in designing active filters which operate to frequencies of 1 MHz and beyond. This approach *utilizes* the inherent low-pass characteristic of the op amp in design. The op amp itself behaves as a first-order low-pass filter (having a buffered input) with bandwidth B followed by an ideal gain block having infinite bandwidth and gain ±G as shown in Fig. 8.4.3a. Therefore, the op amp contains an equivalent RC network. In appropriate filter classes, we can utilize this network directly in design rather than adding an additional external R_eC_e network (while insuring $1/RC \gg 1/R_eC_e$). Since we now utilize the inherent gain characteristic of the op amp, we can therefore operate the filter at much higher frequencies. Op amps having external compensations are often used with this approach and shall be discussed extensively in Sec. 14.4. For our present purposes, we will simply recognize that we can specify the gain K and bandwidth B of each op amp independently.[5]

Now the question is, what classes can be utilized to produce these high-frequency filters? Following the same reasoning that was used for the single-forward-branch filters discussed in Fig. 8.1.1, we can make basically two observations: (1) Class 1X filters utilize two amplifiers and require no capacitors. Since all feedback must be low-pass, Class $1\bar{A}$ and $1\bar{C}$ filters can be used. (2) Class 2X filters utilize single amplifiers and require one capacitor. Since all feedback must be low-pass or band-pass, Class $2\bar{A}$, 2B, and $2\bar{C}$ filters can be used. Examples of these filters are shown in Fig. 8.9.1. By inserting the op amp representation of Fig. 8.4.3a into these filters, the filters listed in Sec. 8.3 are obtained. Since there are no gain-sensitivity advantages between these Class 1X and Class 2X filters (because the buffered input to the RC network in Fig. 8.4.3a gives time constant isolation), the basic design consideration is whether or not a capacitor shall be used in place of an op amp. It should be remembered when making the choice that tuning is slightly simpler in Class 1X filters.

EXAMPLE 8.9.1 FDM communication systems process signals in the 60–108 KHz range as discussed in Prob. 6.27. Design a fourth-order Butterworth low-pass filter having a gain of 100 and a corner frequency of 108 KHz. Use the Class $1\bar{A}$ realization shown in Fig. 8.9.1.[6]

Solution The block diagram of the filter is similar to that shown in Fig. 8.5.3 where $H_o = -\sqrt{100} = -10$ and f_o = 108 KHz. It is easily shown that the filter gain is identical to that of the Class $1\bar{A}$ filter tabulated in Sec. 8.3 when R_1/R_3 is omitted from the s^1 term. Modifying the design equations accordingly as shown in the next equation, the first stage has parameters:

$$\begin{aligned} \rho &= -H_o/(1-\zeta^2) = -10/(1-0.924^2) = 10/0.146 = 6.84 \\ K_1K_2 &= (1/\zeta^2 - 1)(1+\rho) = (1/0.924^2 - 1)(1+6.84) = 1.34 \qquad (8.9.1) \\ 1/T &= \zeta\omega_o = 2\pi(0.924)(108\text{ KHz}) = 2\pi(99.8\text{ KHz}) \end{aligned}$$

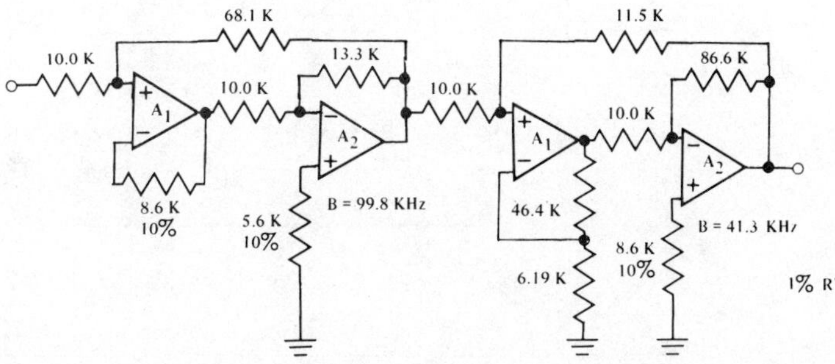

Fig. 8.9.2 High-frequency low-pass filter realization of Example 8.9.1.

where the amplifier time constants $T_1 = T_2 = T$. The second stage has parameters

$$\rho = -10/(1 - 0.382^2) = 10/0.854 = 11.7, \qquad K_1K_2 = (1/0.382^2 - 1)(1 + 11.7) = 74.3$$
$$1/T = 2\pi(0.382)(108 \text{ KHz}) = 2\pi(41.3 \text{ KHz}) \tag{8.9.2}$$

Now the gain blocks are designed. In the first stage, we select $K_1 = 1$ and $K_2 = 1.34$. In the second stage, we select $K_1 = K_2 = \sqrt{74.3} = 8.62$. The resistors are calculated as shown in Fig. 8.9.2. The last step is to adjust the external compensation of the op amps to produce bandwidths of 99.8 KHz and 41.3 KHz, respectively, in each stage. The type of compensation required depends upon the op amp selected. Usually one resistor and one capacitor is required. The resistor is often tuned to obtain the proper bandwidth. We will leave this design detail for Sec. 14.4.

We should make two other important observations. First, the stability of the op amp bandwidths determines the stability of ω_o and ζ which can be obtained. Since this stability depends upon the op amp type and manufacturer, the engineer must be careful to investigate this area before finalizing design. Second, since inverting and noninverting gain blocks can be interchanged, most high-frequency filters have two forms.

8.10 ALTERNATIVES TO CASCADE FILTER DESIGN

Thus far, we have utilized cascade design to implement active filters. The primary reason was the ease of design and the simple tuning of each block. Now we wish to discuss alternative implementations which are desirable in situations requiring high-Q, low-drift filters.

Unfortunately, cascade design suffers from poor sensitivity. This is due to the isolation between blocks so that drifts in the ω_o and Q of one stage produces no drifts in the ω_o's and Q's of the other stages. Thus, there is no interaction between stages as in passive networks where component drifts tend to compensate one another. This results in responses which rapidly degrade as component tolerances are increased as shown in Fig. 8.5.11. To improve the responses, filter topologies need to be used which exhibit interaction between stages.

Several approaches have been introduced and used with success. These include:[7]

1. Follow-the-leader (FL) design
2. Leapfrog (LF) design
3. Simulated LC ladder design

The block diagrams for these various approaches are shown in Fig. 8.10.1. It is evident that the FL and LF approaches differ from cascade design by the presence of external feedback paths. This introduces the interaction between stages which is needed to obtain lower overall sensitivity. Of course, this also complicates the design equations and the tuning of the filter. The third method simulates passive LC ladders using active components to implement inductors.

Follow-the-leader design is also referred to as *multiloop* or *multiple-feedback, coupled-biquad,* or *state-variable* design. The blocks are the second-order low-pass, high-pass, or band-pass filters

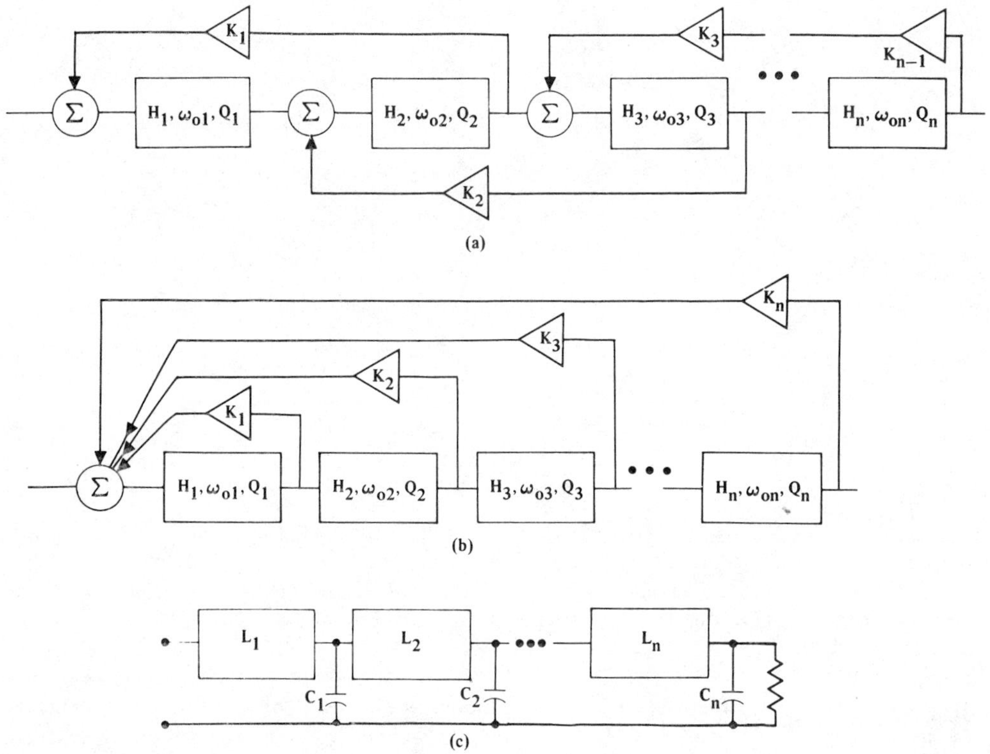

Fig. 8.10.1 Alternative design approaches including (a) follow-the-leader, (b) leapfrog, and (c) simulated LC (low-pass) ladder design.

(as appropriate to obtain the overall transfer function) that we have used in cascade design. (Transmission zeros are obtained using band-stop filters or feed-forward paths and a summer.) Their parameters are determined using the computer to solve a system of linear but underconstrained equations. Due to the degrees of freedom available to the designer, optimization methods can be used to reduce overall sensitivities by optimally selecting the block parameters. A variation of the FL design approach is called the *primary resonator block* (PRB) method. Here, all of the blocks are constrained to be identical. This simplifies the tuning since once the individual blocks have been adjusted to the same set of parameters, overall tuning is accomplished by adjusting only the individual amplifier gains K_i. However, only suboptimal sensitivities can be obtained compared with those obtained using the FL design approach.

Leapfrog design also utilizes second-order blocks.[8] The internal blocks have $Q = \infty$. Their other parameters are determined by solving a system of linear, underconstrained equations which become nonlinear (with respect to the loop gains) for $n > 3$ unlike the FL case. The block parameters can again be optimized to yield minimum overall sensitivity.

Simulated LC ladder design uses active networks to replace inductors in standard passive LC ladders.[9] Networks such as gyrators, NIC's, or operational amplifiers may be used.

A comparison of these various design approaches is difficult. Laker and Ghausi have performed sensitivity comparisons for third-order band-pass filters of different types (e.g., Butterworth, Chebyshev, Bessel, etc.).[7] The Butterworth filter parameters are listed in Table 8.10.1. They conclude that the leapfrog design approach using optimum block parameters yields the best sensitivities in most cases. However, the improvement is modest (5–10%) and the optimum is rather broad (as for the ISE criterion in Fig. 5.1.3). Thus, for ease of design and tunability, the engineer may wish to use one of the other methods.

Table 8.10.1 Optimum parameters for third-order Butterworth band-pass filters having $\omega_o = 1$ and Q = 25.[7] (All blocks have $\omega_{oi} = 1$ except in cascade design.)

	FL	PRB	LF	Opt. LF	Cascade
Q_1	44.1538	37.5000	26.3158	47.1698	50.0075
Q_2	44.1532	37.5000	∞	69.4444	50.0075
Q_3	28.8155	37.5000	23.8095	22.5225	12.5000
k_1	0.6969	0.6667	0.5147	0.6085	0
k_2	0.1172	0.2593	0.4784	0.2128	0
S	0.01241	0.001191	0.01164	0.01152	0.01857

Although these alternative design methods are of paramount importance to the engineer, they have not yet been fully explored and described. They are also mathematically complicated especially when optimization is used. Thus, we choose not to go into the intricate details of this topic but simply urge the engineer to study the current results in this emerging field before completing his critical high-Q active filter designs.

PROBLEMS

8.1 Low-pass filters have the typical frequency response shown in Prob. 6.1. Describe the parameters required to specify the response.

8.2 The importance of compiling complete filter specifications cannot be overemphasized. A typical specification sheet was shown in Prob. 6.2. Briefly list the reasons for providing each data entry listed on that sheet.

8.3 (a) To obtain an amplifier having a large negative gain K, we use an op amp in the inverting mode. Since $K = -R_f/R_1$, R_1 must be small and R_f large. Small R_1 loads the preceding stage and/or consumes excessive power; large R_f gives rise to current leakage effects. A modified inverting amplifier arrangement is shown in Fig. 8.5.4a which alleviates these problems. Show that its gain is given by Eq. 8.5.5. Derive the value of the offset resistor R_o. Obtain the design equations for the amplifier. (Hint: Use a Y-Δ transformation). (b) The amplifier arrangement in Fig. 8.5.4a is useful for gain-tuning purposes as shown in Fig. 8.6.6. If G_1 (G_2) equals the minimum (maximum) gain required and (R_a, R_b, R_c) form the voltage divider at the amplifier output, show that the resistor ratios R_a/R_b and R_c/R_b are given by Eq. 8.6.21. (Hint: Use the results of part (a).)

8.4 Several amplitude equalizers were analyzed in Chap. 2. Their transfer functions are listed below. Design these filters using the realization form of Fig. P8.5. Which filters are undesirable and why?
(a) In Prob. 2.2, $H(s) = (s + 2\pi(3000\text{ Hz}))/(s + 2\pi(70\text{ Hz}))$.
(b) In Prob. 2.7, $H(s) = [(s + 2\pi(0.1\text{ Hz}))/(s + 2\pi(0.01\text{ Hz}))]^3$.
(c) In Prob. 2.8, $H_1(s) = 14.28(s + 2\pi(2.1\text{ KHz}))/(s + 2\pi(30\text{ KHz}))$ and $H_2(s) = 1/(s + 2\pi(2.1\text{ KHz}))$.

8.5 A common industrial filter is shown in Fig. P8.5. It uses two RC networks (characterized by admittance matrices y^a and y^b) and an infinite gain op amp. (a) Write the two-port equations for the two RC networks. (b) Since the op amp has infinite gain, it will produce whatever V_3 is needed to maintain its input voltage difference at zero ($V_2 = 0$). What are the two-port equations of part (a) under this condition? (c) Since the op amp draws no current, $-I_2{}^a = I_1{}^b$. What is the voltage gain of the filter under this condition from part (b)? (d) Since the y_{ij}'s are RC networks, where must their poles and zeros lie? (e) Suppose a voltage gain $H(s) = -s/(s + 1)(s + 10)$ is needed. Derive the two RC networks which will produce this gain using part (c). (Hint: Remember that part (c) must yield $H(s) = -Z_f/Z_1$, equivalently.)

8.6 A quasi-low-pass filter is shown in Fig. P8.6. Determine the transfer function of the filter and plot its magnitude response.

8.7 A Class $1\overline{A}$ low-pass filter is shown in Sec. 8.3. (a) Draw the flow graph for the filter. (b) What are the parameter relations if a minimum sensitivity realization is required? (c) Under these constraints, what parameters would you set equal in deriving design equations? (d) Now consider the corresponding

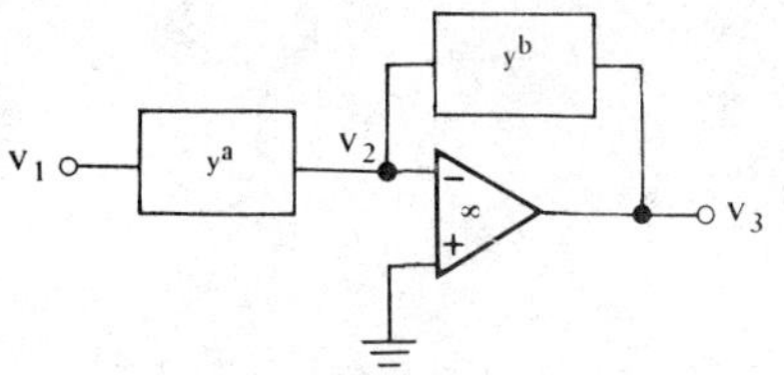

Fig. P8.5

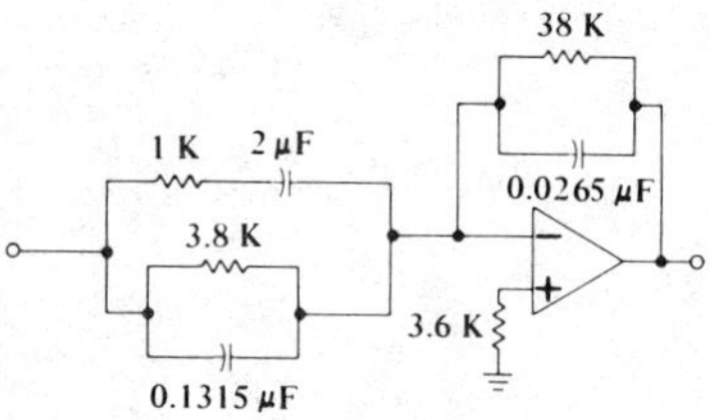

Fig. P8.6 (Courtesy of Motorola[10])

Class $2\bar{A}$ low-pass filter. Obtain an alternative set of design equations to obtain low sensitivities. (Hint: If $R_2 = 10R_1$ and $C_2 = 0.1C_1$, then $R_1C_1 = R_2C_2$ and the passive time constants are about equal.)

8.8 A commercial low-pass filter is shown in Fig. P8.8. In the balanced form, $R_1C_1 = R_2C_2$. An unbalanced form can be used to reduce the required gain. (a) Classify the filter. (b) What advantage is there in using the amplifier with gain G? (c) Discuss the effects of unbalancing the time constants in terms of the gain required and the sensitivity obtained.

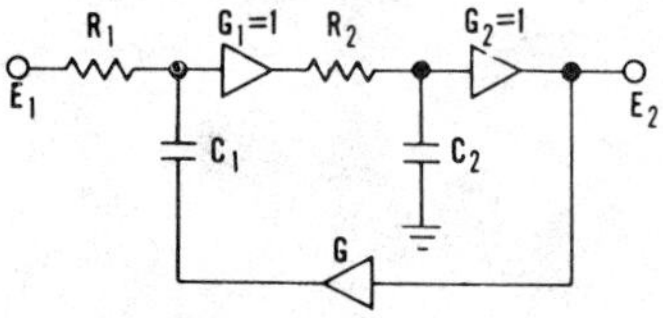

Fig. P8.8 (Courtesy of Krohn-Hite Corp.[11])

8.9 A Class 1B low-pass filter is shown in Sec. 8.3. (a) Determine the parameters of the filter. (b) Can this filter be easily tuned to obtain the proper f_o and Q? What parameters vary when the amplifier gains are varied and can this be used to advantage? (c) Design a filter having $f_o = 1$ KHz and $Q = 10$.

8.10 (a) A third-order Butterworth low-pass filter was designed in Example 8.5.1 using a Class 1B second-order stage. Calculate the active and passive sensitivities of ω_o, Q, and H_o for both stages. Compute the total drift in these parameters assuming resistor and capacitor tolerances of ± 1% ± ½%. (b) If the drifts in ω_o, Q, and H_o are to be limited to ± 1%, show how pots should be used for initial tuning. What must the TC of the resistors and capacitors then equal?

8.11 A wideband voice filter is required. Design it to be fourth-order Chebyshev having 3 dB in-band ripple, a 3 dB bandwidth of 20 KHz, and a maximum low-frequency gain of unity. Use a Class 1B realization. (a) Obtain a minimum gain design. (b) Obtain a minimum sensitivity design.

8.12 (a) A 1000 Bps noise suppression (i.e., data smoothing) filter was analyzed in Example 3.8.1. Design it to be fourth-order Bessel having a 3 dB bandwidth of 1 KHz and unity dc gain. Use a Class 1B realization. (b) Describe how you would tune or align the completed filter to insure the parameters of each block. Assume that the C's are 20% components and the R's are 1% components.

8.13 A Class 1C low-pass filter is shown in Sec. 8.3. From the design sheet for this filter, describe what components to vary to force it to approach (a) a Class 1B filter and (b) a Class 1A filter. (c) Under these constraints, can we obtain the gain-sensitivity bounds in both classes?

8.14 A 3.5 Hz Delta wave filter for EEG measurements was analyzed in Prob. 4.19. (a) Explain why a Class A or C filter is more appropriate to use than a Class $\bar{A}$ or $\bar{C}$ filter. (b) Design the filter to be fourth-order Chebyshev having 0.5 dB in-band ripple and a 3 dB bandwidth of 3.5 Hz. Use a Class 1C realization. (Hint: A better set of design equations here is to set $R_1C_1 = R_2C_2$ and solve $(1 + K_2)^{1/2} = 1/\omega_o RC$ and $\zeta = [2 + K_2(1 - K_1)]/2(1 + K_2)^{1/2}$ for K_1 and K_2.)

8.15 A 1 Hz phase detection filter was analyzed in Prob. 4.20. Repeat Prob. 8.14 assuming the in-band ripple is 1 dB and the 3 dB bandwidth is 1 Hz.

8.16 A 300 Hz band-limiting sonar filter was analyzed in Example 2.4.3. Design it to be fourth-order Papoulis having a 3 dB bandwidth of 300 Hz and a dc gain of 10. Use a Class 1C realization.

8.17 Class 1E filters are among the most stable of all the filter types. Many are commercially available in hybrid form. One such filter, which may be operated in low-pass, high-pass, or band-pass modes, is shown in Fig. P8.17. The general transfer functions are either inverting ($R_8 = \infty$) or noninverting ($R_3 = \infty$) as listed.

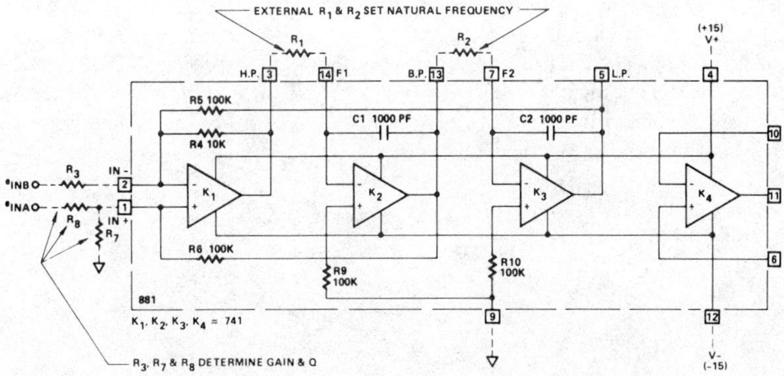

General Transfer Functions

Configurations	Non-Inverting	Inverting
Low-Pass	$\frac{e_o}{e_i} = \frac{\omega_1\omega_2 A_1(1 + A_3)}{S^2 + S\omega_1 A_2(1 + A_3) + \omega_1\omega_2 A_3}$	$\frac{e_o}{e_i} = \frac{-\omega_1\omega_2 A_4}{S^2 + S\omega_1 A_2(1 + A_4 + A_3) + \omega_1\omega_2 A_3}$
Band-Pass	$\frac{e_o}{e_i} = \frac{-S\omega_1 A_1(1 + A_3)}{S^2 + S\omega_1 A_2(1 + A_3) + \omega_1\omega_2 A_3}$	$\frac{e_o}{e_i} = \frac{S\omega_1 A_4}{S^2 + S\omega_1 A_2(1 + A_4 + A_3) + \omega_1\omega_2 A_3}$
High-Pass	$\frac{e_o}{e_i} = \frac{S^2 A_1(1 + A_3)}{S^2 + S\omega_1 A_2(1 + A_3) + \omega_1\omega_2 A_3}$	$\frac{e_o}{e_i} = \frac{-S^2 A_4}{S^2 + S\omega_1 A_2(1 + A_4 + A_3) + \omega_1\omega_2 A_3}$

$\omega_1 = \frac{1}{R_1C_1}$ $\quad \omega_2 = \frac{1}{R_2C_2}$ $\quad \omega_o = \sqrt{A_3\omega_1\omega_2}$ $\quad A_1 = \frac{1}{1 + \frac{R_8}{R_6} + \frac{R_8}{R_7}}$ $\quad A_2 = \frac{1}{1 + \frac{R_6}{R_7} + \frac{R_6}{R_8}}$ $\quad A_3 = \frac{R_4}{R_5}$ $\quad A_4 = \frac{R_4}{R_3}$

Fig. P8.17 (Courtesy of Beckman Instruments[12])

Since the noninverting gain case was described in Sec. 8.3, we shall consider only the inverting gain case. (a) Determine the parameters of the filter. (b) Verify that R_1 and R_2 determine the corner or center frequency f_o where $R_1 = R_2 = 5.03 \times 10^7/f_o$. To obtain frequencies below 50 Hz, additional external capacitors are used to shunt the internal 1000 pF capacitors. (c) Obtain a set of design equations. Verify that R_3 determines the gain of the filter. Since R_3 affects the Q of the filter, it is chosen before R_7; R_7 is then derived from Q. (d) Compare the parameters in the two (±) gain modes of operation. Is one mode more desirable than the other?

8.18 A simplified Class 1E filter is shown in Fig. P8.18 which can be operated in low-pass or band-pass modes. This filter utilizes the noninverting input of one op amp. (a) Determine the transfer function of the low-pass filter. Use a Y-Δ transformation and then assume $R_1, R_3 \ll R_4$ and $R_6, R_8 \ll R_5$. (Hint: Use the analysis technique of Example 7.10.1.) (b) Obtain a set of design equations. (c) Compare this filter with Class 1X and 2X filters of the same type in Sec. 8.3. Does it offer design advantages?

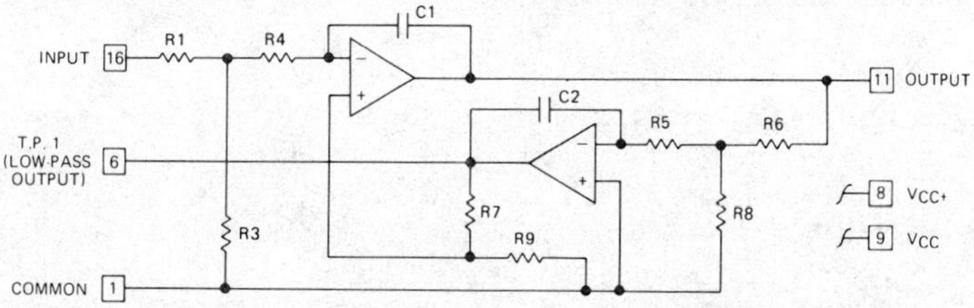

Fig. P8.18 (Courtesy of Beckman Instruments[13])

8.19 A wideband voice filter is required. Design it to be third-order Chebyshev having 3 dB in-band ripple, a 3 dB bandwidth of 20 KHz, and a dc gain of 10. Use a Class 1E realization for the second-order stage.

8.20 A 3.2 KHz band-limiting voice filter was analyzed in Prob. 4.18. Design it to be second-order Butterworth having a 3 dB bandwidth of 3.2 KHz and a dc gain of unity. Use a Class $2\bar{A}$ realization.

8.21 A 941 Hz band-splitting filter was analyzed in Example 2.6.3. Design the low-pass filter to be third-order Butterworth having a 3 dB bandwidth of 941 Hz and a dc gain of 10. Use a Class $2\bar{A}$ realization.

8.22 A commercial fourth-order low-pass filter is shown in Fig. P8.22 (cf. Prob. 8.8). Its cutoff frequency can be adjusted from a fraction of a Hertz to several tens of kilo-Hertz. (a) Classify the filter. (b) What advantage is there in using amplifiers 4 and 5? (c) Determine the transfer function and parameters for the basic second-order stage. (d) Discuss how the controls for the cutoff frequency, multiplier, response, and gain adjust the parameters.

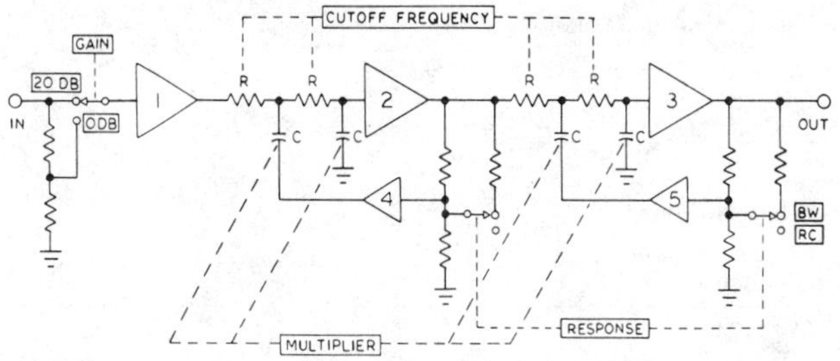

Fig. P8.22 (Courtesy of Rockland Systems Corp.[14])

8.23 The Class 1B low-pass filter in Sec. 8.3 was optimized for minimum active sensitivity and also for minimum gain. Develop analogous design equations for the Class 2B low-pass filter. Interpret the results.

8.24 Repeat Prob. 8.20 using a Class 2B realization.

8.25 A low-pass/high-pass band-splitting filter used in speech analysis was analyzed in Prob. 6.7. The filters are shown in Fig. P8.25 in block diagram form. Assume that the filters have unity gain. Design the low-pass filter using a Class 2B realization.

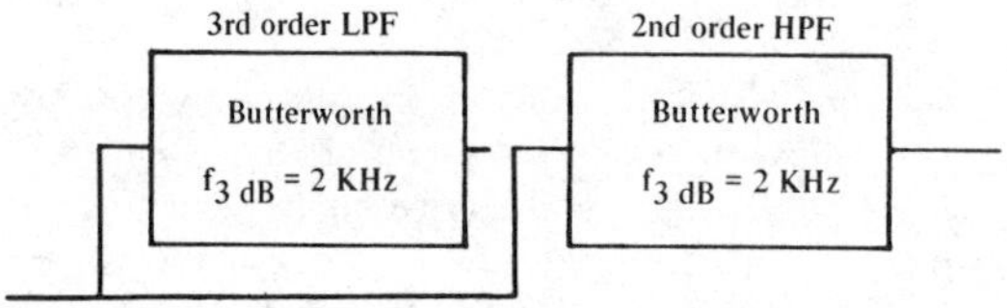

Fig. P8.25

8.26 Design a fourth-order synchronously-tuned filter having a 3 dB bandwidth of 1 KHz and unity dc gain. Use a Class 2B realization.

8.27 A generalized Class 2B low-pass filter using unity gain amplifiers is shown in Prob. 9.8. The R's are fixed and the C's are varied to obtain the required filter response (Bessel, Butterworth, or Chebyshev). The band-edge ripple frequency is unity. Is this a good method for designing these filters? Discuss.

8.28 Two band-splitting filters are shown in Fig. P8.28. One filter is low-pass and the other filter is high-pass. The bands are split at about 300 Hz. Investigate the low-pass filter on the basis of Prob. 8.27. Is it Chebyshev as indicated? Verify the corner frequency given.

8.29 A 941 Hz band-splitting filter was analyzed in Example 2.6.3. It will be designed as fourth-order elliptic having 1.25 dB of passband ripple, a 1.25 dB bandwidth of 941 Hz, a 60 dB bandwidth of 2.22 KHz, and a maximum passband gain of 20 dB. (a) Verify that the block diagram of the filter consists of a second-order LPF stage having parameters $(H_o, f_o, \zeta) = (8.66/k, 927\text{ Hz}, 0.121)$ cascaded with a first-order BSF stage having parameters $(H_o, f_{op}, Q_p, f_{oz}) = (k, 497\text{ Hz}, 0.832, 2425\text{ Hz})$. (b) Design the filter using a Class 2B realization for the BSF stage and a Class 2E filter for the LPF stage.

8.30 Consider a fifth-order low-pass elliptic filter having the following parameters:[16] $M_p = 0.28$ dB, $M_s = 50$ dB, $H_o = 20$ dB, $f_p = 1000$ Hz, and $f_s = 1556$ Hz. (a) Verify that the required transfer function equals

$$H(s) = \frac{K[s_n^2 + 1.617^2][s_n^2 + 2.438^2]}{[s_n + 0.495][(s_n + 0.097)^2 + 1.03^2][(s_n + 0.334)^2 + 0.718^2]}$$

where $s_n = s/2\pi(1000)$. (b) Realize the filter in block diagram form. (c) Design the filter using Class 2B realizations for the BSF stages.

8.31 A third-order Butterworth low-pass filter was designed in Example 8.5.1 using a Class 1B realiza-

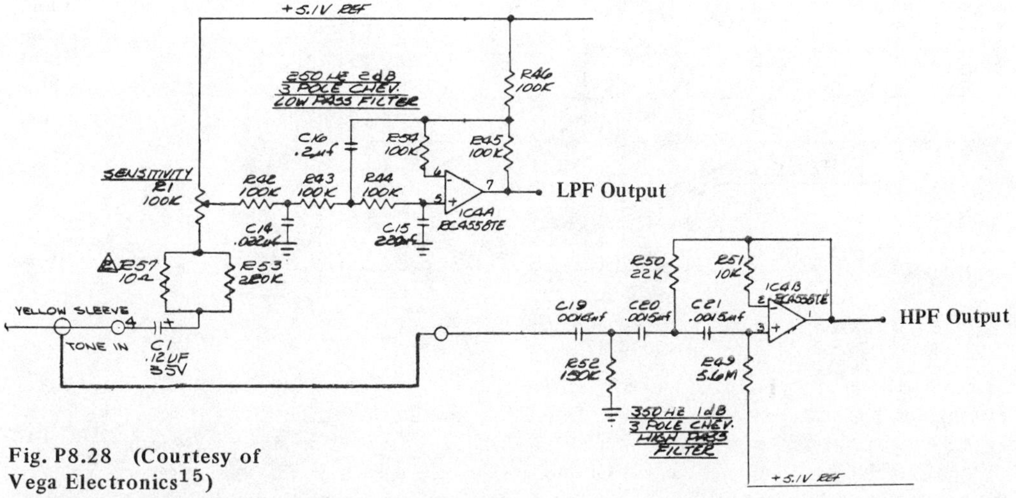

Fig. P8.28 (Courtesy of Vega Electronics[15])

tion for the second-order stage. Redesign the filter using a Class 2C realization.

8.32 Steiner found that the filter shown in Fig. P8.32 can be operated in low-pass, high-pass, or band-pass modes.[17] (a) Classify the low-pass filter. (b) What are its limiting gain-sensitivity values? (c) If Q ranges from 1 to 30, can the filter maintain constant Q based on the sensitivities in part (b)? (d) Based on the gain in part (b), can the op amp produce the gain required? (e) When operated as a tunable filter, R_1 and R_2 control frequency while Q remains constant. Do the results of part (a) confirm this?

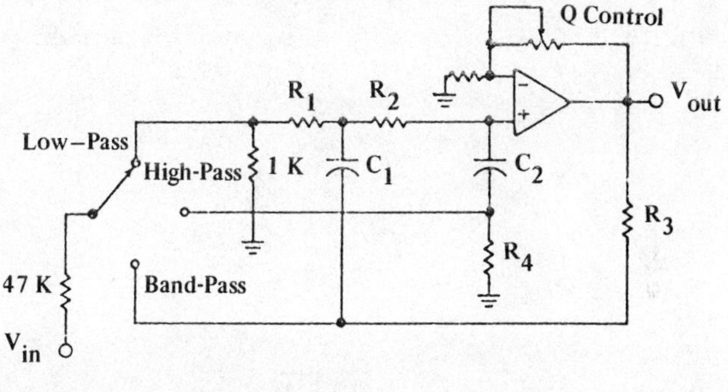

Fig. P8.32 (Courtesy of Electronic Design[17])

8.33 Low-pass pre-filtering is used in analog-to-digital (A/D) conversion to reduce sampling errors due to noise. Such filters are sometimes called anti-aliasing filters. For an 8-bit A/D converter, signals are quantized within 2^8 levels (or to about 0.1%). Thus, a noise spike which is –60 dB of the full-scale value will introduce a quantization error of a single level. For a 3 dB bandwidth of 3.2 KHz, let us require a 60 dB bandwidth of 32 KHz. For reasonable transient response, we choose the filter to be Butterworth. Then a third-order low-pass filter is required. Design the filter using a Class $2\overline{C}$ realization.

8.34 The Class 2E low-pass filter shown in Sec. 8.3 is widely used in industry. Depending upon filter requirements, different design equations are sometimes used. For example, suppose we set $R_1 = R_3$. (a) Derive the new parameter equations. Show that the dc gain depends upon the R_4/R_1 ratio and that the damping factor depends upon both the R_4/R_1 and C_2/C_5 ratios. (b) Express the C_2/C_5 ratio in terms of ζ and H_o. (c) The functional relationship determined in part (b) is plotted in Fig. P8.34. For what value of H_o is the capacitor ratio minimized?

8.35 Design a fourth-order Butterworth low-pass filter having a 3 dB bandwidth of 1 KHz and unity dc gain. Use a Class 2E realization.

8.36 Design a fourth-order Bessel low-pass filter having a 3 dB bandwidth of 1 KHz and unity dc gain. Use a Class 2E realization.

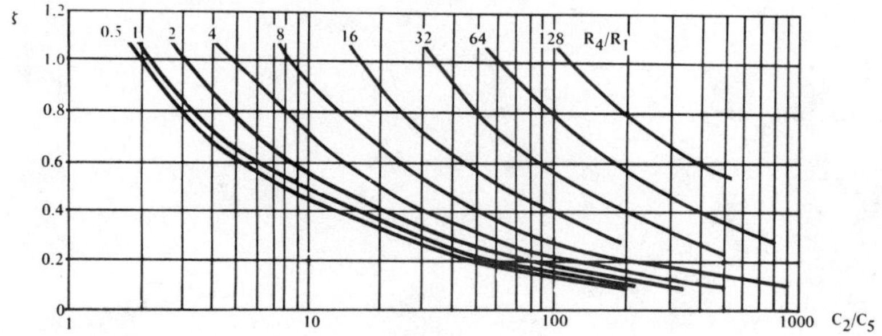

Fig P8.34 (Courtesy of Electronic Design[18]).

8.37 Design a gain-tuned Butterworth low-pass filter whose 3 dB bandwidth lies between 10–50 KHz. The variation in Q cannot exceed ± 10%. Use the first low-pass filter in Fig. 8.6.3.

8.38 Tunable filters are required in many applications. For low-Q situations, the resistor-tuned Class 2B filter is useful. (a) Determine the transfer function and parameters when the filter is operated in a unity-gain mode. (b) Write the design equations when $R_1 = R_2 = R$. Note that ζ determines the C_2/C_1 ratio in this case. (c) Design a second-order Bessel tunable filter having a 3 dB bandwidth of 100 Hz and a 10:1 tuning range.

8.39 Design a passive-tuned Class 2C filter to meet the requirements of Prob. 8.38c.

8.40 The general determinant of a second-order active filter can be expressed as $\Delta(s) = s^2 + (a_1 + a_2)s + a_1 a_2 - k(\beta_2 s^2 + \beta_1 s + \beta_0)$. The root locus of Δ for variable k is a circle having the center σ_c and radius R given in Prob. 1.43. (a) To obtain a filter design having resonant frequency ω_o and a specified Q where $S_k^Q = 0$, prove that $\sigma_c = -2Q\omega_o$ and $R = \omega_o(4Q^2 - 1)^{1/2}$.[19] (Hint: See Fig. P8.40.) (b) Prove that

$$\beta_0 = (a_1 a_2 - h\omega_o^2)/k, \qquad \beta_1 = (a_1 + a_2 - \omega_o h/Q)/k, \qquad \beta_2 = (1-h)/k$$

where $\Delta(s) = h(s^2 + s\omega_o/Q + \omega_o^2)$. h is chosen to insure realizability where $0 \leqslant \beta_0 \leqslant a_1 a_2$, $0 \leqslant \beta_1 \leqslant a_1 + a_2$, and $0 \leqslant \beta_2 \leqslant 1$.

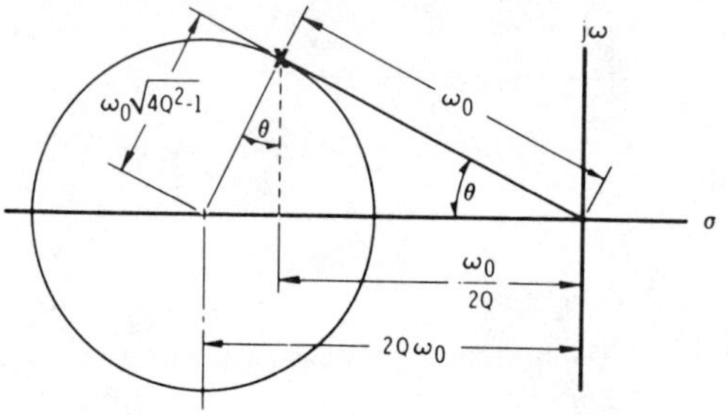

Fig. P8.40 (Courtesy of Proc. IEEE[19])

8.41 Consider the Class 2B low-pass filter of Sec. 8.3. Calculate $Z^{(0)}$, T_s, and T_∞ to use in Blackman's impedance relation. Then calculate the input impedance $Z^{(k)}$. Sketch the pole-zero pattern and the magnitude response of $Z^{(k)}$. (Hint: The gain expression is involved in $Z^{(k)}$.)

8.42 Repeat Prob. 8.41 for the Class $\overline{1A}$ low-pass filter of Sec. 8.3.

8.43 Repeat Prob. 8.41 for the Class 1C low-pass filter of Sec. 8.3.

8.44 As discussed in Prob. 2.31, low-pass filters must often be "tuned" to obtain their required parameters. Repeat that problem.

REFERENCES

1. Cole, L. G., "Practical design of active filters," M.S.E.E. Directed Research, California State Univ., Long Beach, Jan., 1975.
2. Shepard, R., "Active filters: part 12–Short cuts to network design," Electronics, pp. 82–91, Aug. 18, 1969.
3. Bruminhent, S., and K. L. Su, "Gain-tuned active filters having constant percent bandwidth," IEEE Trans. Circuits and Systems, vol. CAS-22, pp 587–594, July, 1975.

   ———, "Gain-tuned active filters," Proc. Intl. Symp. on Circuits and Systems, pp. 443–447, April, 1974.
4. Tarukachon, D., "Passive-tuned active filters," M.S.E.E. Directed Research, California State Univ., Long Beach, July, 1975.
5. Walton, J. F., "Active filters using single-pole operational amplifiers," M.S.E.E. Directed Research, California State Univ., Long Beach, June, 1976.
6. Schaumann, R., "Low-sensitivity, high-frequency tunable active filter without external capacitors," IEEE Trans. Circuits and Systems, vol. CAS-22, pp. 39–44, Jan., 1975.
7. Laker, K. R. and M. S. Ghausi, "Comparison of active multiple-loop feedback techniques for realizing high-order bandpass filters," IEEE Trans. Circuits and Systems, vol. CAS-21, pp. 774–783, Nov., 1974.
8. Geffe, P. R., "Designer's guide to: Active bandpass filters," EDN Magazine; part 1, pp. 68–73, Feb. 5, 1974; part 2, pp. 40–46, March 5, 1974; part 3, pp. 46–52, April 5, 1974; part 4, pp. 63–71, May 5, 1974; part 5, pp. 65–72, June 5, 1974; part 6, July 5, 1974.
9. Laker, K. R., M. S. Ghausi, and J. J. Kelly, "Minimum sensitivity active (leapfrog) and passive ladder bandpass filters," IEEE Trans. Circuits and Systems, vol. CAS-22, pp. 670–677, Aug., 1975.
10. Welling, B., "Analysis and design of active filters using operational amplifiers," App. Note AN-438, p. 7, Motorola, Phoenix, AZ, Nov., 1968.
11. 1974 Catalog, pp. 2–6, Krohn-Hite Corp., Cambridge, MA, 1974.
12. Model 881 Universal Active Filter, Catalog Sheet, 8 p., Publ., H72986-772-20GF, Beckman Instruments, Fullerton, CA, 7-72.
13. Series 882 Touch-Tone Band-Pass Filters, Catalog Sheet, 4 p., Publ. H74170-1073-30GF, Beckman Instruments, Fullerton, CA, 10-73.
14. The Variable Active Filter, Appl. Note AN-11, 4 p., Rockland Systems Corp., West Nyack, NY, 1970.
15. Instruction Manual Model 285 Encoder/Decoder, 2 p., Vega Electronics, El Monte, CA, March, 1973.
16. Neelakantan, M. N., "Design of elliptic function filters using a double-layer RC distributed-active circuit," IEEE Trans. Circuit Theory, vol. CT-19, pp. 403–406, July, 1972.
17. Steiner, N. A. "Voltage-tunable active filter features low, high, and bandpass modes," Electronic Design, pp. 96–98, Dec. 6, 1974, copyright Hayden Publishing, 1974.
18. Bejach, B., "Design filters in minutes," Electronic Design, pp. 86–88, May 24, 1970, copyright Hayden Publishing, 1970.
19. Soderstrand, M. A., and S. K. Mitra, "Design of RC active filters with zero gain-sensitivity product," IEEE Trans. Circuit Theory, vol. CT-20, pp. 441–445, July, 1973.

9 HIGH-PASS FILTERS

Inconspicuous molehill sometimes more important than conspicuous mountain
Oriental Proverb

Now that we have investigated the design of low-pass filters in great detail, we shall proceed to design high-pass filters. High-pass filters are first discussed from the classification viewpoint of Chap. 7. We then introduce the RC:CR transformation which allows us to construct high-pass filters directly from low-pass filters. A variety of high-pass filters will be investigated and a set of filter design sheets will be compiled. A number of high-pass filters will be designed. We will compare the gain and sensitivity bounds established in the previous chapter, and make qualitative evaluations of the designs. Tunable high-pass filters will also be considered. We will conclude with a discussion of complementary high-pass filters.

9.1 HIGH-PASS FILTER CLASSES

High-pass filters of second-order have gains which equal

$$H(s) = H_o \frac{(s/\omega_o)^2}{(s/\omega_o)^2 + 2\zeta(s/\omega_o) + 1} \tag{9.1.1}$$

If a parasitic zero is present, then the gain equals

$$H(s) = \frac{H_o}{\omega_o^2} \frac{s(s+z)}{(s/\omega_o)^2 + 2\zeta(s/\omega_o) + 1} \tag{9.1.2}$$

Quasi-high-pass filters fail to have zero gain at dc. Their gains equal

$$H(s) = H_o \left(\frac{\omega_{oz}}{\omega_{op}}\right)^2 \frac{(s/\omega_{oz})^2 + 2\zeta_z(s/\omega_{oz}) + 1}{(s/\omega_{op})^2 + 2\zeta_p(s/\omega_{op}) + 1} \tag{9.1.3}$$

Such band-stop filters are necessary when designing elliptic filters. In general, we shall be concerned with only the second-order high-pass filters. When a band-stop filter stage is required, we will simply utilize a filter from Chap. 11 and reserve its discussion for that chapter. A second-order high-pass filter is completely characterized by its resonant frequency ω_o, damping factor ζ, and high-frequency gain H_o. In the filter designs of Chaps. 2–6, this information was summarized in a high-pass filter (HPF) block. Let us now implement these blocks with hardware.

We must first select the class of high-pass filter which we want to utilize. In Chap. 7, the gain requirements and sensitivity bounds for each class were discussed. Generally, we made a tradeoff

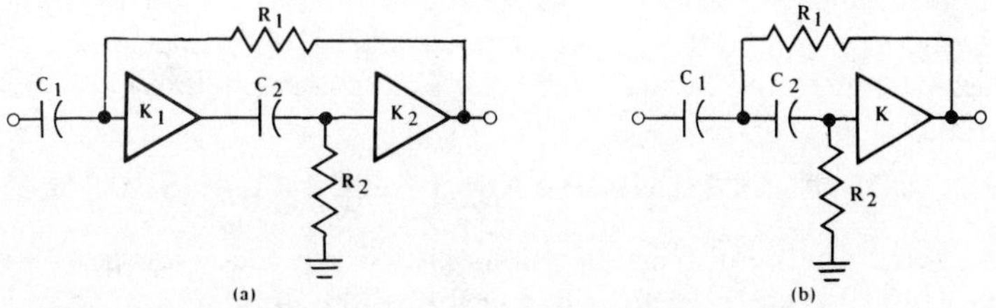

Fig. 9.1.1 (a) Class 1B and (b) Class 2B high-pass filters.

between the amplifier gain and the active and passive sensitivities of the filter. This assumes that high-pass filters can be realized in any class which is indeed the case as we shall now verify.

Consider the active filter having the simplest topology of a single forward branch using the assumptions listed in Sec. 8.1. These filters have the flow graph of Fig. 8.1.1 and a transfer function given by Eq. 8.1.4. The numerator of the gain function is equal to numerator of the forward path gain product $K_1K_2T_{13}T_{45}$; therefore, the form of the numerators of T_{13} and T_{45} determine the filter type. Using the notation of Eqs. 8.1.5–8.1.8, it was shown in Sec. 8.1 that the numerator of the transfer function H(s) for first-order decomposition filters was given by Eq. 8.1.9. For H(s) to be high-pass, we must set the s^0 and s^1 coefficients of Num H equal to zero. This requires $c_{50} = d_{30} = 0$ so that

$$T_{13} = \frac{d_{31}s}{a_{30} + a_{31}s} \text{ (HPF)}, \qquad T_{45} = \frac{c_{51}s}{a_{50} + a_{51}s} \text{ (HPF)} \tag{9.1.4}$$

Alternatively, the numerator of the transfer function H(s) for second-order decomposition filters was given by Eq. 8.1.11. For H(s) to be high-pass, this requires $d_{30} = d_{31} = 0$ so that

$$T_{13} = \frac{d_{32}s^2}{a_{30} + a_{31}s + a_{32}s^2} \text{ (HPF)}, \qquad T_{45} = \frac{c_{50}}{a_{50}} \text{ (constant)} \tag{9.1.5}$$

Again, by investigating the form of T_{45} from Tables 7.19.1 and 7.19.2, we can immediately exclude any classes where T_{45} fails to be a high-pass type. From Table 7.19.1, all Class 1X filters are realizable in high-pass form except Class $1\overline{A}$ as long as T_{13} is high-pass. From Table 7.19.12, T_{45} is always constant, so high-pass filters result whenever T_{13} is high-pass. Therefore, high-pass filters of every class are realizable except Class $1\overline{A}$. If we remove the restriction that $T_{15} = 0$ or $T_{12} = 0$, then high-pass filters of every class are realizable. Again, we have the fortuitous situation where we may choose the filter class best suited to the application.

Let us illustrate the use of these results by formulating a Class 1B high-pass filter having the topological constraints of Fig. 8.1.1. From Table 7.19.1 and Eq. 9.1.4, such filters must have branch transfer functions of

$$T_{13} \text{ (HPF)}, \qquad T_{63} = \frac{c_{30}}{a_{30} + a_{31}s} \text{ (LPF)}, \qquad T_{45} \text{ (HPF)} \tag{9.1.6}$$

Now we simply arrange RC networks having these first-order transfer functions to fit the topology of Fig. 8.1.1. One filter which results is shown in Fig. 9.1.1a.

The Class 2B high-pass filter is obtained in a similar manner. From Table 7.19.2 and Eq. 9.1.5,

$$T_{13} \text{ (HPF)}, \qquad T_{63} = \frac{c_{31}s}{a_{30} + a_{31}s + a_{32}s^2} \text{ (BPF)}, \qquad T_{45} \text{ (constant)} \tag{9.1.7}$$

A single-amplifier realization is shown in Fig. 9.1.1b. With practice, the engineer may easily generate his own filters. In the next section, a different method will be discussed which allows high-pass filters to be designed directly from low-pass filters.

9.2 LOW-PASS TO HIGH-PASS FILTER TRANSFORMATION

An extremely useful transformation exists which allows low-pass filters to be converted into high-pass filters. This is the RC:CR transformation introduced by Mitra[1], and is a direct consequence of the low-pass to high-pass transformation discussed in Chap. 6. To carry out the transformation on a low-pass filter, every resistor R_i is replaced by a capacitor $C_i = 1/R_i$, and every capacitor C_j is replaced by a resistor $R_j = 1/C_j$. All amplifiers remain intact. This transformation produces a high-pass filter whose gain equals

$$H(s) = H(p)\,\Big|_{p=1/s,\ R:1/C} \tag{9.2.1}$$

where H(p) is the gain of the low-pass filter. It is important to note that every R and C in the H(p) expression must also be replaced according to the rule of Eq. 9.2.1. Let us illustrate the RC:CR transformation with an example.

EXAMPLE 9.2.1 Convert the Class 2C low-pass filter of Sec. 8.3 to a Class $2\overline{C}$ high-pass filter using the RC:CR transformation. Determine its transfer function.

Solution The RC:CR transformation consists of replacing R's by C's and C's by R's; numerically, they assume reciprocal values. The Class 2C low-pass filter is shown in Fig. 9.2.1a. Under the transformation, the Class $2\overline{C}$ high-pass filter of Fig. 9.2.1b is produced. The low-pass filter transfer function equalled

$$H(p) = \frac{K}{p^2(1-K)R_1C_1R_2C_2 + p(1-K)[R_1C_1(1+C_2/C_1)+R_2C_2] + 1} \tag{9.2.2}$$

Therefore, under the RC:CR transformation, the high-pass filter gain equals

$$H(s) = \frac{K}{s^{-2}(1-K)(R_1C_1R_2C_2)^{-1} + s^{-1}(1-K)[(R_1C_1)^{-1}(1+R_1/R_2)+(R_2C_2)^{-1}] + 1} \tag{9.2.3}$$

Re-expressing the filter gain in standard form gives

$$H(s) = \frac{Ks^2R_1C_1R_2C_2}{s^2R_1C_1R_2C_2 + s(1-K)[R_1C_1(1+C_2/C_1)+R_2C_2] + (1-K)} \tag{9.2.4}$$

Thus, we see the great ease with which a low-pass to high-pass filter conversion may be made.

This example shows that every low-pass filter has an analogous high-pass filter. The RC:CR transformation is similar conceptually to the process of forming a complement in a digital system which was the motivation behind using the *complement sign* in our notation of classes. Physically, interchanging R's and C's converts passive low-pass filters into high-pass filters, and vice versa.

Fig. 9.2.1 Transformation of (a) Class 2C low-pass filter into a (b) Class $2\overline{C}$ high-pass filter.

Therefore, using the results in Tables 7.19.1 and 7.19.2, Class A and C filters become Class $\overline{A}$ and $\overline{C}$ filters, and vice versa, under the transformation. Passive band-pass, band-stop, and biquadratic filters *remain* band-pass, band-stop, and biquadratic filters under the transformation, respectively. Class B, D, and E filters remain in the same class under the transformation.

Now let us determine the effect that the RC:CR transformation has on the parameters of a filter. We saw in Chap. 6 that under the low-pass to high-pass transformation $p = 1/s$, the filter gain and pole Q and ζ remain invariant. However, the pole magnitude is inverted. In Example 9.2.1, since the low-pass filter has a resonant frequency of

$$\omega_o = 1/(1-K)^{1/2}(R_1C_1R_2C_2)^{1/2} \tag{9.2.5}$$

then the high-pass filter has a resonant frequency of

$$1/\omega_o = 1/(1-K)^{1/2}(R_1C_1R_2C_2)^{-1/2}, \qquad \omega_o = (1-K)^{1/2}/(R_1C_1R_2C_2)^{1/2} \tag{9.2.6}$$

This is verified by direct inspection of H(s) given by Eq. 9.2.4. The damping factor of the high-pass filter remains invariant. Thus, since the low-pass filter has

$$\zeta = \tfrac{1}{2}(1-K)^{1/2}[(R_1C_1/R_2C_2)^{1/2}(1 + C_2/C_1) + (R_2C_2/R_1C_1)^{1/2}] \tag{9.2.7}$$

then the high-pass filter has damping factor

$$\begin{aligned}\zeta &= \tfrac{1}{2}(1-K)^{1/2}[(R_2C_2/R_1C_1)^{1/2}(1 + R_1/R_2) + (R_1C_1/R_2C_2)^{1/2}] \\ &= \tfrac{1}{2}(1-K)^{1/2}[(R_1C_1/R_2C_2)^{1/2}(1 + C_2/C_1) + (R_2C_2/R_1C_1)^{1/2}]\end{aligned} \tag{9.2.8}$$

The gain of the high-pass filter also remains invariant. Since the low-pass filter has

$$H_o = K \tag{9.2.9}$$

then the high-pass filter gain equals

$$H_o = K \tag{9.2.10}$$

Therefore, it is extremely easy to convert the low-pass filter parameters into those for the analogous high-pass filter; in fact, this can often be done by inspection.

We can continue to use the RC:CR transformation in the design equations and the sensitivity equations. However, for practical considerations, this is inappropriate due to the fact that we must generally *choose* capacitor values because of their limited number of standard values. In most cases, we then *calculate* resistor values. If we were to apply the RC:CR transformation, we would choose resistor values and calculate *capacitor* values. Therefore, the values obtained would not generally be commercially available. In general, we can utilize the low-pass filters to generate high-pass filters; their gain and parameter equations are obtained using the RC:CR transformation. However, we must generate a new set of design and sensitivity equations. If we have the sensitivity equations for the general filter which have *not* been simplified (under the design equation constraints), then they *can* be used as we shall see.

To complete the discussion of the RC:CR transformation, let us continue to convert the Class 2C low-pass filter design data to indicate the proper use of the transformation. Unfortunately, the results generated will be of limited practical usefulness for the reasons just noted.

EXAMPLE 9.2.2 Convert the design and sensitivity equations for the Class 2C low-pass filter into the analogous equations for the Class $2\overline{C}$ high-pass filter.

Solution From Sec. 8.3, the Class 2C low-pass filter has the design equations:

Set: $C_1 = C_2 = C$

Choose: C (9.2.11)

Calculate: $K = H_o$, $R_1 = \dfrac{\zeta \pm [\zeta^2 - 2(1 - H_o)]^{1/2}}{2(1 - H_o)} \dfrac{1}{\omega_o C} = \dfrac{F}{\omega_o C}$, $R_2 = \dfrac{1}{F(1 - H_o)\omega_o C}$

Thus, under the transformation, the equivalent design equations for the Class $\overline{2C}$ high-pass filter are:

Set: $R_1 = R_2 = R$ (i.e., $1/R_1 = 1/R_2 = 1/R$)

Choose: R (i.e., $1/R$) (9.2.12)

Calculate: $K = H_o$, $C_1 = 1/F\omega_o R$ (i.e., $1/C_1 = F\omega_o R$),

$C_2 = F(1 - H_o)/\omega_o R$ (i.e., $1/C_2 = R\omega_o/F(1 - H_o)$)

These equations are obtained directly from the parameter set listed in Eq. 9.2.11. However, we see that calculating C values is not a desirable approach.

The sensitivity relations can also be easily written. The Class 2C low-pass filter had sensitivities (under the two design equations of Eq. 9.2.11) of

$$S_{R_1}^{\omega_o} = S_{R_2}^{\omega_o} = S_{C_1}^{\omega_o} = S_{C_2}^{\omega_o} = -½, \quad S_K^{\omega_o} = -S_K^{\zeta} = H_o/2(1 - H_o), \quad S_{R_1}^{\zeta} = -S_{R_2}^{\zeta} = ½ - 1/\zeta F$$
$$S_{C_1}^{\zeta} = -S_{C_2}^{\zeta} = -½ + F(1 - H_o)/\zeta, \quad S_K^{H_o} = 1 \qquad (9.2.13)$$

Using the sensitivity identities of Sec. 1.15 that

$$S_x^{1/y} = -S_x^y, \quad S_{1/x}^y = -S_x^y, \quad S_{1/x}^{1/y} = S_x^y \qquad (9.2.14)$$

then we can easily convert these sensitivity expressions to

$$S_{C_1}^{\omega_o} = S_{C_2}^{\omega_o} = S_{R_1}^{\omega_o} = S_{R_2}^{\omega_o} = -½, \quad S_K^{\omega_o} = S_K^{\zeta} = -H_o/2(1 - H_o), \quad S_{C_1}^{\zeta} = -S_{C_2}^{\zeta} = -½ + 1/\zeta F$$
$$S_{R_1}^{\zeta} = S_{R_2}^{\zeta} = ½ - F(1 - H_o)/\zeta, \quad S_K^{H_o} = 1 \qquad (9.2.15)$$

Thus, the sensitivities may also be easily converted under the RC:CR transformation. However, since these sensitivities were based on design equations which are inappropriate and are not used, these sensitivities cannot be used. If the sensitivities of the low-pass filter had *not* been simplified under the design equations, then they could be used. This is illustrated in the next example.

EXAMPLE 9.2.3 The Class 1B low-pass filter had a design equation in Table 8.2.1 where we set $R_2C_2 = k^2R_1C_1$. Determine the parameters and sensitivities of its analogous high-pass filter.

Solution The Class 1B low-pass filter had parameters

$$\omega_o = \frac{1}{(R_1C_1R_2C_2)^{1/2}}, \quad \zeta = \frac{R_1C_1(1 - K_1K_2) + R_2C_2}{2(R_1C_1R_2C_2)^{1/2}}, \quad H_o = K_1K_2 \qquad (9.2.16)$$

Under the condition that $R_2C_2 = k^2R_1C_1$, its sensitivities equalled

$$S_{R_1}^{\omega_o} = S_{C_1}^{\omega_o} = S_{R_2}^{\omega_o} = S_{C_2}^{\omega_o} = -½, \quad S_{R_1}^{\zeta} = S_{C_1}^{\zeta} = -S_{R_2}^{\zeta} = -S_{C_2}^{\zeta} = ½(1 - k/\zeta)$$
$$S_{K_1}^{\zeta} = S_{K_2}^{\zeta} = 1 - (k + 1/k)/2\zeta, \quad S_{K_1}^{H_o} = S_{K_2}^{H_o} = 1 \qquad (9.2.17)$$

Table 9.2.1 Conversion of parameters and sensitivity equations, when appropriate, under RC:CR transformation.

			$S_R^{\omega_o}$	↔	$S_C^{\omega_o}$
ω_o	↔	$1/\omega_o$	$S_K^{\omega_o}$	↔	$-S_K^{\omega_o}$
ζ	↔	ζ	S_R^{ζ}	↔	$-S_C^{\zeta}$
H_o	↔	H_o	S_K^{ζ}	↔	S_K^{ζ}
			$S_R^{H_o}$	↔	$-S_C^{H_o}$
			$S_K^{H_o}$	↔	$S_K^{H_o}$

Therefore, the analogous Class 1B high-pass filter has parameters

$$\omega_o = \frac{1}{(R_1C_1R_2C_2)^{1/2}}, \qquad \zeta = \frac{R_1C_1 + R_2C_2(1 - K_1K_2)}{2(R_1C_1R_2C_2)^{1/2}}, \qquad H_o = K_1K_2 \tag{9.2.18}$$

using the RC:CR transformation. Transforming the design equation to $R_1C_1 = k^2R_2C_2$, then the sensitivities of the analogous high-pass filter equal

$$S_{R_1}^{\omega_o} = S_{C_2}^{\omega_o} = S_{R_2}^{\omega_o} = S_{C_2}^{\omega_o} = -1/2, \qquad S_{R_1}^{\zeta} = S_{C_1}^{\zeta} = -S_{R_2}^{\zeta} = -S_{C_2}^{\zeta} = 1/2(k/\zeta - 1)$$
$$S_{K_1}^{\zeta} = S_{K_2}^{\zeta} = 1 - (k + 1/k)/2\zeta, \qquad S_{K_1}^{H_o} = S_{K_2}^{H_o} = 1 \tag{9.2.19}$$

Thus, in situations where time constants are related (rather than say C values), then the sensitivity results can be converted.

We can summarize the conversion of filter parameters and sensitivity equations in Table 9.2.1. The sensitivity conversions are easily proved using Eq. 9.2.14. We see that the passive ω_o, active ζ (or Q), and active H_o sensitivities are unchanged. The active ω_o, passive ζ (or Q), and passive H_o sensitivities have their signs changed.

The RC:CR transformation when applied to immittances is[2]

$$Z_{CR}(s) = s^{-1}Z_{RC}(s^{-1})\,|_{C:1/R}, \qquad Y_{CR}(s) = sY_{RC}(s^{-1})\,|_{C:1/R} \tag{9.2.20}$$

This is extremely useful because it allows low-pass filter immittance parameters such as input impedance to be converted to the equivalent high-pass filter parameters. This provides an alternative method to using Blackman's immittance relations as discussed and illustrated in Sec. 8.8.

EXAMPLE 9.2.4 The input impedance of a Class 1B low-pass filter was determined in Example 8.8.1. Determine the input impedance of the analogous Class 1B high-pass filter.

Solution The analogous Class 1B high-pass filter is shown in Fig. 9.1.1a. The input impedance to the low-pass filter equals

$$Z_{in} = \frac{1}{sC_1}\,\frac{s^2R_1C_1R_2C_2 + s[R_1C_1(1 - K_1K_2) + R_2C_2] + 1}{sR_2C_2 + (1 - K_1K_2)} \tag{9.2.21}$$

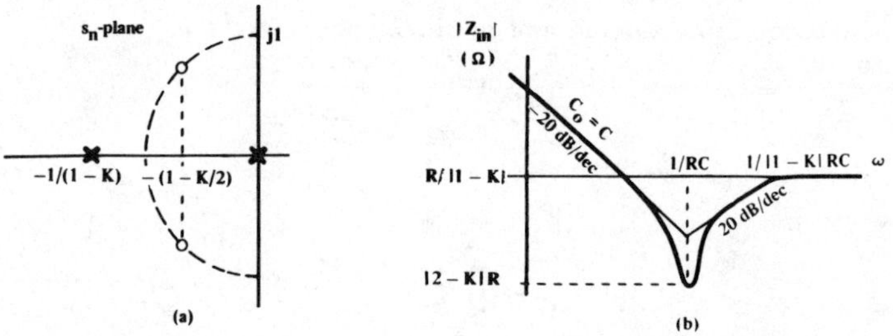

Fig. 9.2.2 (a) Pole-zero pattern and (b) Bode magnitude characteristic for Z_{in} of Class 1B high-pass filter.

from Eq. 8.8.5. Therefore, using Eq. 9.2.20, the input impedance to the high-pass filter equals

$$Z_{in} = s^{-1}(sR_1)\frac{(s^2R_1C_1R_2C_2)^{-1} + s^{-1}[(R_1C_1)^{-1}(1 - K_1K_2) + (R_2C_2)^{-1}] + 1}{(sR_2C_2)^{-1} + (1 - K_1K_2)}$$

$$= \frac{1}{sC_1}\frac{s^2R_1C_1R_2C_2 + s[R_1C_1 + R_2C_2(1 - K_1K_2)] + 1}{s(1 - K_1K_2)R_2C_2 + 1} \tag{9.2.22}$$

We see the great ease in converting immittance relations using the RC:CR transformation.

EXAMPLE 9.2.5 Determine the input impedance for the minimum active sensitivity design of Example 8.8.2.

Solution Equating R's and C's in Eq. 9.2.22 and setting $K = K_1K_2$ reduces Z_{in} to

$$Z_{in} = \frac{1}{sC}\frac{(sRC)^2 + sRC(2 - K) + 1}{s(1 - K)RC + 1} \tag{9.2.23}$$

Using normalized frequency $s_n = sRC$, then

$$Z_{in} = \frac{R}{s_n}\frac{s_n^{\ 2} + (2 - K)s_n + 1}{(1 - K)s_n + 1} \tag{9.2.24}$$

The pole-zero pattern and magnitude response of Z_{in} are shown in Fig. 9.2.2. At low frequencies, the input is capacitive with value C. At high frequencies, the input impedance is resistive and approaches $R_o = R/(1 - K)$. Near the corner frequency 1/RC of the filter, the magnitude response approaches $|Z_{in}|_{min} \cong |2 - K|R$ for $K \cong 2$ using the same reasoning as in Example 8.8.2. The phase characteristic is shown in Fig. 9.2.3. Again we have used abrupt phase approximations to simplify the appearance of the plots. At low frequencies, the input impedance is capacitive. In the vicinity of the corner frequency, the impedance becomes resistive. For high-Q filters, it is that of a negative R.

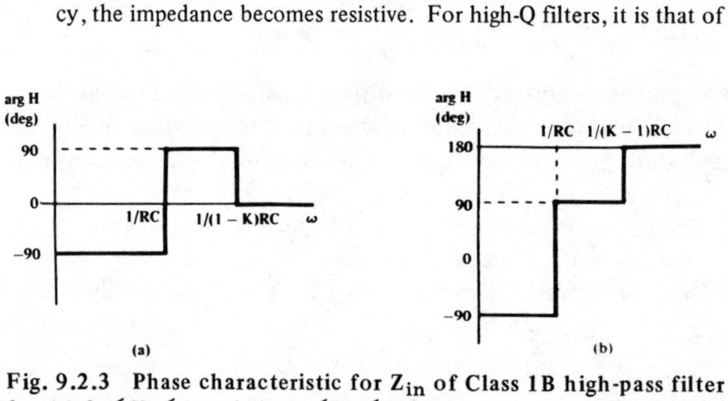

Fig. 9.2.3 Phase characteristic for Z_{in} of Class 1B high-pass filter for (a) $0 < K < 1$ and (b) $1 < K < 2$.

These Bode responses were drawn on the basis of Eq. 9.2.24. However, it should be noted that this is unnecessary. Instead, we could apply the impedance transform of Eq. 9.2.20 directly to the Bode responses of the low-pass filter shown in Figs. 8.8.2 and 8.8.3. The impedance transform given by Eq. 9.2.20 becomes

$$|Z_{CR}(j\omega)| = (j\omega)^{-1} |Z_{RC}(-j/\omega)|_{C:1/R}; \qquad \arg Z_{CR}(j\omega) = -90^{\circ} - \arg Z_{RC}(j/\omega)|_{C:1/R} \tag{9.2.25}$$

The process is the same as that discussed in Sec. 6.3.2. Magnitude responses are pivoted about $\omega = 1$ and their slopes decreased by 20 dB/dec (due to $1/s$ in Eq. 9.2.20a). Phase responses are pivoted about $\omega = 1$, inverted (signs reversed), and translated down 90°. The engineer can verify this process by comparing Figs. 9.2.2 and 9.2.3 with Figs. 8.8.2 and 8.8.3, respectively.

9.3 HIGH-PASS FILTER COMPILATIONS

We found in the previous chapter that a set of well-defined filter design sheets permitted the rapid design of active filters. A number of high-pass filters are compiled in this section.[3] Many of these high-pass filters can be obtained from the low-pass filters of the previous chapter using the RC:CR transformation. Again the high-pass filters which have been selected are representative, but by no means exhaustive, of those which exist. Although the engineer may find other forms which he may prefer for a specific application, these compiled filters can be used in almost all applications.

9.4 HIGH-PASS FILTER DESIGN EXAMPLES

With these design sheets, we are now in a position to design a variety of high-pass filters. Design of high-pass filters proceeds in the same way as that for low-pass filters with several minor changes as we shall now discuss.

In cascade design of odd-order high-pass filters, we require a first-order high-pass filter stage. Before proceeding further, let us discuss their design. The noninverting stage is shown in Fig. 9.4.1. From the RC:CR transformation viewpoint, it is the transform of the first-order low-pass filter shown in Fig. 8.4.3. Its transfer function is

$$H(s) = K\frac{sRC}{sRC + 1} \tag{9.4.1}$$

so that in terms of the parameters ω_o and H_o of the stage,

$$H_o = K, \qquad \omega_o = 1/RC \tag{9.4.2}$$

where $K = 1 + R_f/R_1$. The design of the amplifier K is the same as before as outlined in Table 8.4.1.

The inverting stage is shown in Fig. 9.4.2. Its transfer function H(s) and parameters ω_o and H_o are identical to those for the noninverting stage as given by Eqs. 9.4.1 and 9.4.2. However in this case, $K = -R_f/R$ where the design follows that outlined in Table 8.4.2. This stage is *not* the RC:CR transform of the first-order low-pass filter shown in Fig. 8.4.6. We choose to use the high-pass filter stage of Fig. 9.4.2 for two reasons: First, the op amp current required to drive C_f becomes excessive at high frequencies when R_1 is converted to C_1 (see Fig. 8.4.6). Second, resistor R can be conveniently absorbed into the amplifier in Fig. 9.4.2b. For high-gain applications, the gain block can be modified as discussed in Prob. 8.3.

CLASS 1A: HIGH-PASS

Transfer Function:

$$H(s) = \frac{-K_1K_2s^2R_1C_1R_2C_2}{s^2[1 + (C_3/C_1)(1 + K_1K_2)]R_1C_1R_2C_2 + s[R_1C_1(1 + C_3/C_1) + R_2C_2] + 1}$$

Parameters:

$$\omega_o = \frac{1}{\left\{[1 + (C_3/C_1)(1 + K_1K_2)]R_1C_1R_2C_2\right\}^{1/2}} \qquad H_o = \frac{-K_1K_2}{1 + (C_3/C_1)(1 + K_1K_2)}$$

$$\zeta = \frac{(R_1C_1/R_2C_2)^{1/2}(1 + C_3/C_1) + (R_2C_2/R_1C_1)^{1/2}}{2[1 + (C_3/C_1)(1 + K_1K_2)]^{1/2}}$$

Design Equations: Set $\rho = C_1/C_3$, $R_1(C_1 + C_3) = R_2C_2$ (For Minimum Gain and Minimum Sensitivity)

Given: ω_o, ζ

Choose: C_1, C_2, ρ

Calculate: $R_1 = \dfrac{\zeta\rho}{(1 + \rho)\omega_oC_1}$ $\qquad C_3 = C_1/\rho$

$R_2 = \zeta/\omega_oC_2$ $\qquad K_1K_2 = (1 + \rho)(1/\zeta^2 - 1)$

$H_o = -\rho K_1K_2/(1 + \rho + K_1K_2)$

Sensitivities:

$S_{K_1}^{\omega_o} = S_{K_2}^{\omega_o} = \frac{1}{2}(\zeta^2 - 1)$ $\qquad S_{K_1}^{\zeta} = S_{K_2}^{\zeta} = \frac{1}{2}(\zeta^2 - 1)$ $\qquad S_{K_1}^{H_o} = S_{K_2}^{H_o} = -\zeta^2$

$S_{R_1}^{\omega_o} = S_{R_2}^{\omega_o} = S_{C_2}^{\omega_o} = -\frac{1}{2}$ $\qquad S_{C_1}^{\zeta} = 1/2(1 + \rho)$ $\qquad S_{C_1}^{H_o} = -S_{C_2}^{H_o}$

$S_{C_1}^{\omega_o} = -\rho\zeta^2/(1 + \rho)$ $\qquad S_{C_3}^{\zeta} = -[1 + \rho(1 - \zeta^2)]/2(1 + \rho)$ $\qquad = [\rho(\zeta^2 - 1) - 1]/(1 + \rho)$

$S_{C_3}^{\omega_o} = [1 + (1 + \rho)(\zeta^2 - 1)]/(1 + \rho)(2\zeta^2 - 1)$

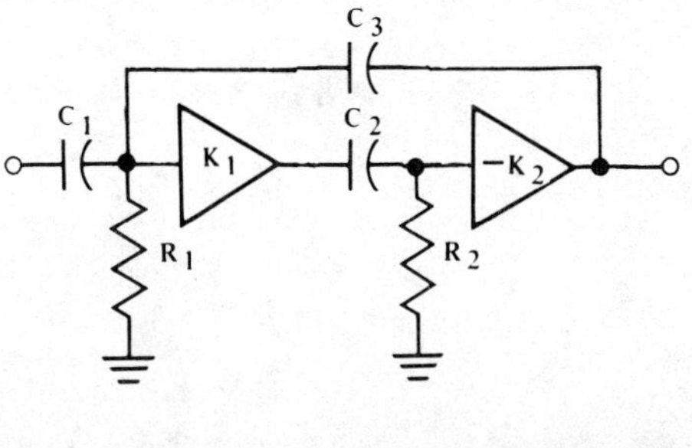

CLASS $1\overline{A}$: HIGH-PASS

Transfer Function:

$$H(s) = \frac{K_1K_2s^2R_1C_1R_2C_2}{s^2R_1C_1R_2C_2 + s(R_1C_1 + R_2C_2) + (1 + K_1K_2)}$$

Parameters:

$$\omega_o = \left[\frac{1 + K_1K_2}{R_1C_1R_2C_2}\right]^{1/2} \qquad H_o = K_1K_2$$

$$\zeta = \frac{(R_1C_1/R_2C_2)^{1/2} + (R_2C_2/R_1C_1)^{1/2}}{2(1 + K_1K_1)^{1/2}}$$

Design Equations: Set $R_1 = R_2 = R$, $C_1 = C_2 = C$ (For Minimum Gain and Minimum Sensitivity)

Given: ω_o, ζ

Choose: C

Calculate: $R = 1/\zeta\omega_oC$

$K_1K_2 = 1/\zeta^2 - 1$

$H_o = K_1K_2$

Sensitivities:

$$S_{R_1}^{\omega_o} = S_{R_2}^{\omega_o} = S_{C_1}^{\omega_o} = S_{C_2}^{\omega_o} = -\tfrac{1}{2}$$

$$S_{K_1}^{\omega_o} = S_{K_2}^{\omega_o} = -S_{K_1}^{\zeta} = -S_{K_2}^{\zeta} = \tfrac{1}{2}(1 - \zeta^2)$$

$$S_{K_1}^{H_o} = S_{K_2}^{H_o} = 1$$

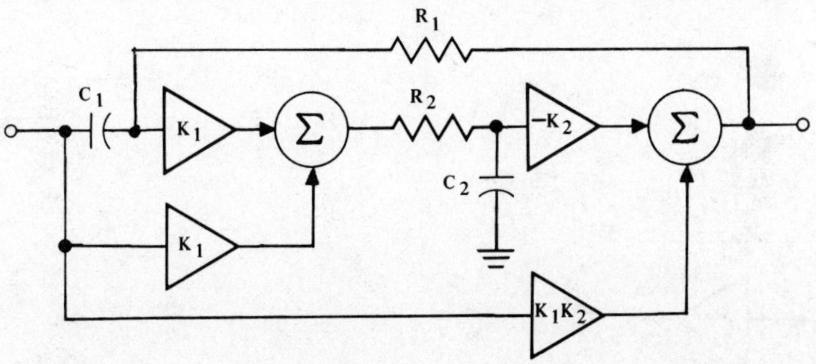

M. A. Soderstrand and S. K. Mitra, "Gain and sensitivity limitations of active RC filters," Tech. Rep., NSF Grant GK 14736, Univ. of California, Davis, 1971.

CLASS 1B: HIGH-PASS

Transfer Function:

$$H(s) = \frac{K_1K_2s^2R_1C_1R_2C_2}{s^2R_1C_1R_2C_2 + s[R_1C_1 + R_2C_2(1 - K_1K_2)] + 1}$$

Parameters:

$$\omega_o = \frac{1}{(R_1C_1R_2C_2)^{1/2}} \qquad H_o = K_1K_2$$

$$\zeta = ½\,[(R_1C_1/R_2C_2)^{1/2} + (R_2C_2/R_1C_1)^{1/2}(1 - K_1K_2)]$$

Design Equations: Set $R_1 = R_2 = R$, $C_1 = C_2 = C$ (For Minimum Active Sensitivity)

Given: ω_o, ζ

Choose: C

Calculate: $R = 1/\omega_oC$

$K_1K_2 = 2(1 - \zeta)$

$H_o = K_1K_2$

Sensitivities:

$$S_{R_1}^{\omega_o} = S_{R_2}^{\omega_o} = S_{C_1}^{\omega_o} = S_{C_2}^{\omega_o} = -½$$

$$S_{R_1}^{\zeta} = S_{C_1}^{\zeta} = -S_{R_2}^{\zeta} = -S_{C_2}^{\zeta} = ½\,(1/\zeta - 1)$$

$$S_{K_1}^{\zeta} = S_{K_2}^{\zeta} = 1 - 1/\zeta$$

$$S_{K_1}^{H_o} = S_{K_2}^{H_o} = 1$$

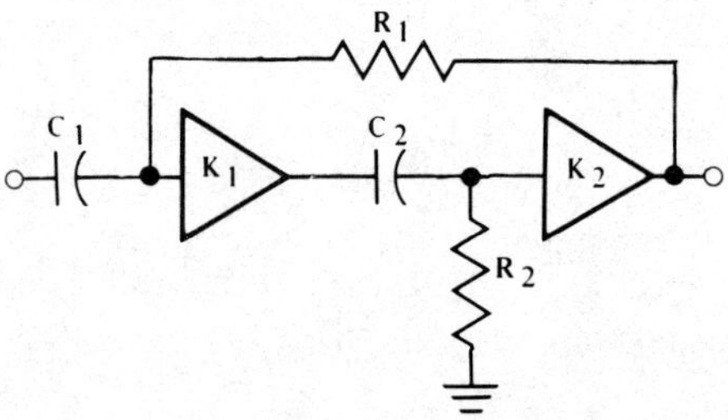

CLASS 1C: HIGH-PASS

Transfer Function:

$$H(s) = \frac{K_1K_2s^2R_1C_1R_2C_2}{s^2R_1R_2C_2[(C_1 + C_3 + C_4) + K_1(K_2C_4 + C_3)] + s\left\{R_1[C_1 + C_3(1 + K_1) + C_4] + R_2C_2\right\} + 1}$$

Parameters:

$$\omega_o = \frac{1}{\left\{R_1R_2C_2[(C_1 + C_3 + C_4) + K_1(K_2C_4 + C_3)]\right\}^{1/2}} \qquad H_o = \frac{K_1K_2C_1}{C_1 + C_3(1 + K_1) + C_4(1 + K_1K_2)}$$

$$\zeta = \frac{R_1[C_1 + C_3(1 + K_1) + C_4] + R_2C_2}{2\left\{R_1R_2C_2[(C_1 + C_3 + C_4) + K_1(K_2C_4 + C_3)]\right\}^{1/2}}$$

Design Equations: Set $R_1 = R_2 = R$, $C_1 = C_2 = C_3 = C_4 = C$

Given: ω_o, ζ

Choose: C, K_2

Calculate: $K_1 = -4 + 2\zeta^2(K_2 + 1) \pm 2\zeta[(\zeta^2 - 4)(1 + K_2) - 3]^{1/2}$

$$R = 1/(3 + 5K_1)^{1/2}\omega_o C_1, \qquad H_o = K_1K_2/[3 + K_1(1 + K_2)]$$

Sensitivities: (For $K_2 = 4$) Set $a = 5K_1 + 3$, $b = K_1 + 4$

$S_{K_1}^{\omega_o} = -K_1/2a$

$S_{K_2}^{\omega_o} = S_{K_2}^{\zeta} = -2K_1/a$

$S_{R_1}^{\omega_o} = S_{R_2}^{\omega_o} = S_{C_2}^{\omega_o} = 1/2$

$S_{C_1}^{\omega_o} = -1/2a$

$S_{C_3}^{\omega_o} = -(1 + K_1)/2a$

$S_{C_4}^{\omega_o} = -(1 + 4K_1)/2a$

$S_{K_1}^{\zeta} = K_1/b$

$S_{R_1}^{\zeta} = (2 + K_1)/2b$

$S_{C_1}^{\zeta} = (2 + 9K_1)/2ab$

$S_{R_2}^{\zeta} = -(2 + K_1)/2b$

$S_{C_2}^{\zeta} = -(2 + K_1)/2b$

$S_{C_3}^{\zeta} = (9K_1^2 + 11K_1 + 2)/2ab$

$S_{C_4}^{\zeta} = (4K_1^2 - 7K_1 + 2)/2ab$

$S_{K_1}^{H_o} = 3/a$

$S_{K_2}^{H_o} = (3 + K_1)/a$

$S_{C_1}^{H_o} = (2 + 5K_1)/a$

$S_{C_3}^{H_o} = -(1 + K_1)/a$

$S_{C_4}^{H_o} = -(1 + 4K_1)/a$

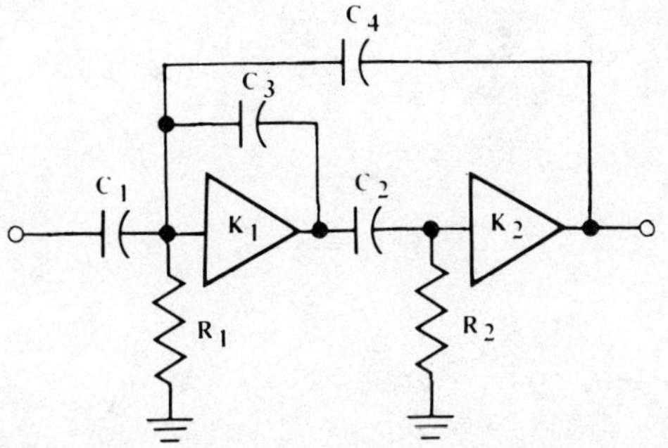

CLASS $1\overline{C}$: HIGH-PASS

Transfer Function:

$$H(s) = \frac{-K_1K_2s^2R_1C_1R_2C_2}{s^2R_1C_1R_2C_2 + s[R_1C_1(1+K_2) + R_2C_2(1+K_1K_2)] + (1+K_2)}$$

Parameters:

$$\omega_o = \left[\frac{1+K_2}{R_1C_1R_2C_2}\right]^{1/2} \qquad H_o = -K_1K_2$$

$$\zeta = \frac{(R_1C_1/R_2C_2)^{1/2}(1+K_2) + (R_2C_2/R_1C_1)^{1/2}(1+K_1K_2)}{2(1+K_2)^{1/2}}$$

Design Equations: Set $R_1C_1 = R_2C_2 = k/\omega_o$

Given: ω_o, ζ, $-H_o$

Choose: C_1, C_2, ρ

Calculate: $K_2 = 2(k\zeta - 1) - H_o$ $\qquad R_1 = k/\omega_oC_1$

$K_1 = -H_o/K_2$ $\qquad R_2 = k/\omega_oC_2$

Sensitivities:

$$S_{R_1}^{\omega_o} = S_{R_2}^{\omega_o} = S_{C_1}^{\omega_o} = S_{C_2}^{\omega_o} = -\tfrac{1}{2} \qquad S_{K_1}^{\zeta} = H_o/2k\zeta$$

$$S_{K_2}^{\omega_o} = K_2/2(1+K_2) \qquad S_{K_2}^{\zeta} = 1 - 1/2k\zeta - K_2/2(1+K_2)$$

$$S_{R_1}^{\zeta} = -S_{R_2}^{\zeta} = S_{C_1}^{\zeta} = -S_{C_2}^{\zeta} = \tfrac{1}{2}[1 - (H_o+1)/k\zeta]$$

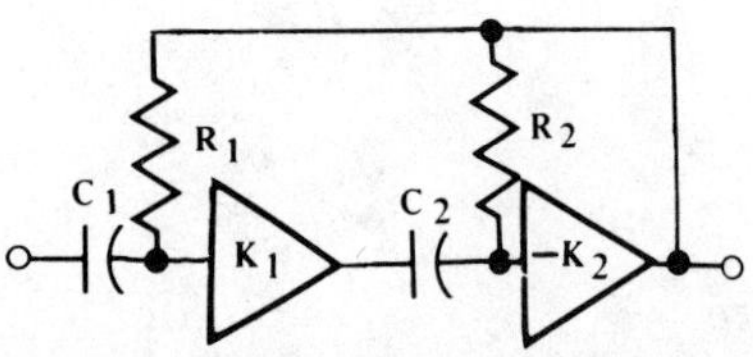

CLASS 1E: HIGH-PASS

Transfer Function:

$$H(s) = \frac{1 + R_6/R_5}{1 + R_3/R_4} \frac{s^2 R_1 C_1 R_2 C_2}{s^2 R_1 C_1 R_2 C_2 + s R_2 C_2 [(1 + R_6/R_5)/(1 + R_4/R_3)] + R_6/R_5}$$

Parameters:

$$\omega_o = \left[\frac{R_6/R_5}{R_1 C_1 R_2 C_2}\right]^{1/2} \qquad H_o = \frac{1 + R_6/R_5}{1 + R_3/R_4}$$

$$\zeta = \frac{1}{2} \frac{1 + R_6/R_5}{1 + R_4/R_3} \left[\frac{R_5}{R_6} \frac{R_2 C_2}{R_1 C_1}\right]^{1/2}$$

Design Equations: Set $R_1 = R_2 = R$, $C_1 = C_2 = C$, $R_3 = R_5 = R_6$

Given: ω_o, ζ

Choose: C, R_3

Calculate: $R = 1/\omega_o C$

$R_4 = (1/\zeta - 1)R_3$

$H_o = 2(1 - \zeta)$

Sensitivities:

$$S_{R_1}^{\omega_o} = S_{R_2}^{\omega_o} = S_{R_5}^{\omega_o} = -S_{R_6}^{\omega_o} = S_{C_1}^{\omega_o} = S_{C_2}^{\omega_o} = -1/2$$

$$S_{R_1}^{\zeta} = -S_{R_2}^{\zeta} = -S_{R_3}^{\zeta} = S_{C_1}^{\zeta} = -S_{C_2}^{\zeta} = -1/2$$

$$S_{R_3}^{H_o} = -S_{R_4}^{H_o} = -\zeta$$

$$S_{R_5}^{H_o} = -S_{R_6}^{H_o} = -1/2$$

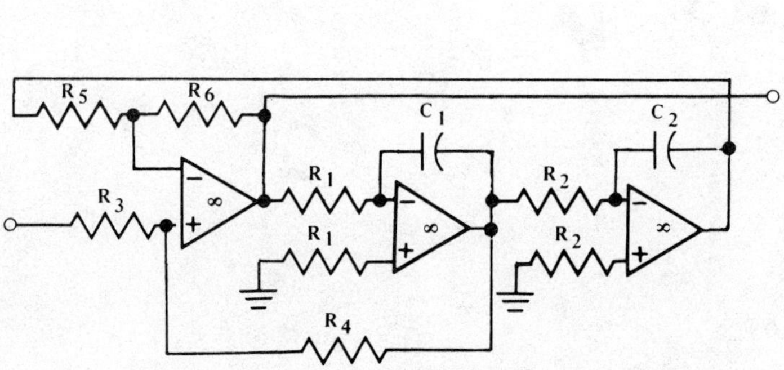

L. P. Huelsman, J. G. Graeme, and G. E. Tobey, *Operational Amplifiers*, Chap. 8.3.3, McGraw-Hill, NY, 1971.

CLASS 2A: HIGH-PASS

Transfer Function:

$$H(s) = \frac{-Ks^2R_1C_1R_2C_2}{s^2[1 + (C_3/C_1)(1 + K)]R_1C_1R_2C_2 + s[R_1C_1(1 + C_3/C_1) + R_2C_2(1 + R_1/R_2)] + 1}$$

Parameters:

$$\omega_o = \frac{1}{\{[1 + (C_3/C_1)(1 + K)]R_1C_1R_2C_2\}^{1/2}} \qquad H_o = \frac{-K}{1 + (C_3/C_1)(1 + K)}$$

$$\zeta = \frac{(R_1C_1/R_2C_2)^{1/2}(1 + C_2/C_1) + (R_2C_2/R_1C_1)^{1/2}(1 + R_1/R_2)}{2[1 + (C_3/C_1)(1 + K)]^{1/2}}$$

Design Equations: Set $R_1 = R_2 = R$, $C_1 = C_2 = C_3 = C$

Given: ω_o, ζ

Choose: C

Calculate: $K = (2/\zeta)^2 - 2$

$R = \zeta/2\omega_o C$

$H_o = -K/(2 + K)$

Sensitivities:

$S_K^{\omega_o} = S_K^{\zeta} = -K/2(2 + K)$ $\qquad S_{R_1}^{\zeta} = -S_{R_2}^{\zeta} = 1/4$ $\qquad S_K^{H_o} = 2/(2 + K)$

$S_{R_1}^{\omega_o} = S_{R_2}^{\omega_o} = S_{C_2}^{\omega_o} = -1/2$ $\qquad S_{C_1}^{\zeta} = K/4(2 + K)$ $\qquad S_{C_1}^{H_o} = -S_{C_3}^{H_o} = (1 + K)/(2 + K)$

$S_{C_1}^{\omega_o} = -1/2(2 + K)$ $\qquad S_{C_2}^{\zeta} = 1/2$

$S_{C_3}^{\omega_o} = -(1 + K)/2(2 + K)$ $\qquad S_{C_3}^{\zeta} = -(3 + 2K)/2(2 + K)$

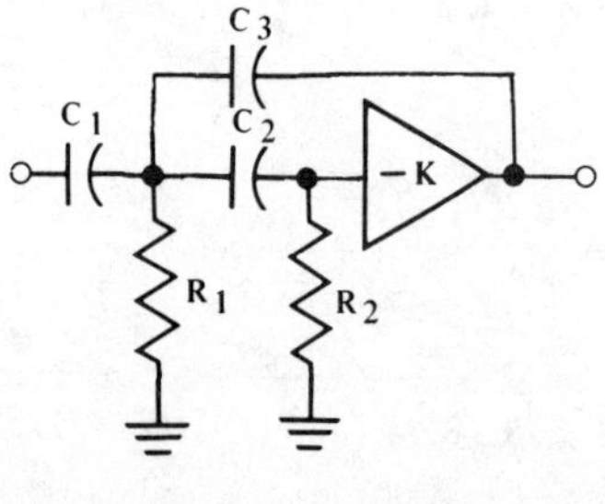

CLASS $2\overline{A}$: HIGH-PASS

Transfer Function:

$$H(s) = \frac{\tfrac{1}{2} K s^2 R_1 C_1 R_2 C_2}{s^2 R_1 C_1 R_2 C_2 + s[R_1 C_1(1 + C_2/C_1) + R_2 C_2] + (1 + K)}$$

Parameters:

$$\omega_o = \left[\frac{1 + K}{R_1 C_1 R_2 C_2}\right]^{1/2} \qquad H_o = K/2$$

$$\zeta = \frac{(R_1C_1/R_2C_2)^{1/2}(1 + C_2/C_1) + (R_2C_2/R_1C_1)^{1/2}}{2(1 + K)^{1/2}}$$

Design Equations: Set $R_1 = R_2 = R$, $C_1 = C_2 = C$

Given: ω_o, ζ

Choose: C

Calculate: $R = 3/2\zeta\omega_o C$

$K = 9/4\zeta^2 - 1$

$H_o = K/2$

Sensitivities:

$$S_{R_1}^{\omega_o} = S_{R_2}^{\omega_o} = S_{C_1}^{\omega_o} = S_{C_2}^{\omega_o} = -\tfrac{1}{2}$$

$$S_K^{\omega_o} = -S_K^{\zeta} = \tfrac{1}{2}(1 - 4\zeta^2/9)$$

$$S_{R_1}^{\zeta} = -S_{R_2}^{\zeta} = -S_{C_1}^{\zeta} = S_{C_2}^{\zeta} = -1/6$$

$$S_K^{H_o} = 1$$

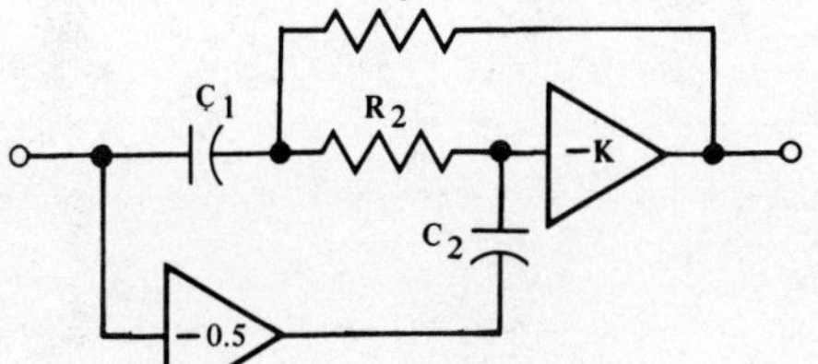

M. A. Soderstrand and S. K. Mitra, loc. cit.

CLASS 2B: HIGH-PASS

Transfer Function:

$$H(s) = \frac{Ks^2R_1C_1R_2C_2}{s^2R_1C_1R_2C_2 + s[R_1C_1(1 + C_2/C_1) + R_2C_2(1 - K)] + 1}$$

Parameters:

$$\omega_o = \frac{1}{(R_1C_1R_2C_2)^{1/2}} \qquad H_o = K$$

$$\zeta = \tfrac{1}{2}\,[(R_1C_1/R_2C_2)^{1/2}(1 + C_2/C_1) + (R_2C_2/R_1C_1)^{1/2}(1 - K)]$$

Design Equations: Set $C_1 = C_2 = C$

Given: ω_o, ζ, H_o

Choose: C

Calculate: $R_1 = \dfrac{\zeta \pm [\zeta^2 + 2(H_o - 1)]^{1/2}}{2\omega_o C} = \dfrac{F}{\omega_o C}$

$R_2 = 1/F\omega_o C$

$K = H_o$

Sensitivities:

$$S_{R_1}^{\omega_o} = S_{R_2}^{\omega_o} = S_{C_1}^{\omega_o} = S_{C_2}^{\omega_o} = -\tfrac{1}{2} \qquad S_K^{\zeta} = -H_o/2\zeta F$$

$$S_{R_1}^{\zeta} = -S_{R_2}^{\zeta} = \tfrac{1}{2} + (H_o - 1)/\zeta F \qquad S_K^{H_o} = 1$$

$$S_{C_1}^{\zeta} = -S_{C_2}^{\zeta} = F/\zeta - \tfrac{1}{2}$$

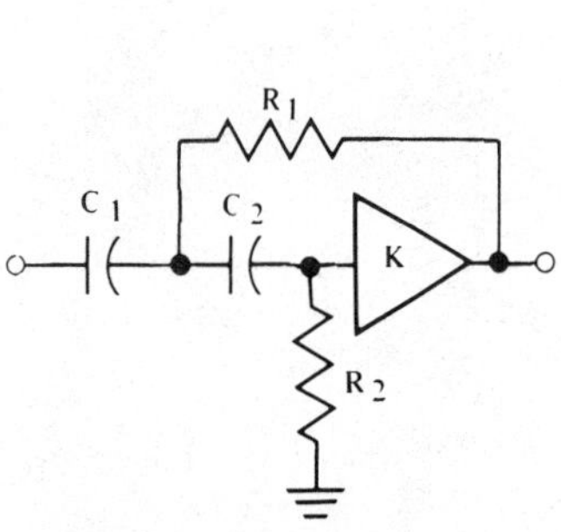

J. L. Hilburn and D. E. Johnson, *Manual of Active Filter Design*, Chap. 3, McGraw-Hill, NY, 1973.

CLASS 2C: HIGH-PASS

Transfer Function:

$$H(s) = \frac{Ks^2R_1C_1R_2C_2}{s^2R_1R_2\left\{C_4[C_1 + C_2 + C_3] + C_3[C_1 + C_2(1 - K)]\right\} + s\left\{R_1(C_1 + C_2 + C_3) + R_2[C_3 + C_4(1 - K)]\right\} + 1}$$

Parameters:

$$\omega_o = \frac{1}{\left\{R_1R_2[C_4(C_1 + C_2 + C_3) + C_3(C_1 + C_2(1 - K))]\right\}^{1/2}}$$

$$\zeta = \frac{R_1(C_1 + C_2 + C_3) + R_2(C_3 + C_4(1 - K))}{2\left\{R_1R_2[C_4(C_1 + C_2 + C_3) + C_3(C_1 + C_2(1 - K))]\right\}^{1/2}}$$

$$H_o = \frac{KC_1C_2}{C_4(C_1 + C_2 + C_3) + C_3(C_1 + C_2(1 - K))}$$

Design Equations: Set $R_1 = R_2 = R$, $C_1 = C_2 = C_3 = C_4 = C$

Given: ω_o, ζ

Choose: C

Calculate: $R = 1/2\zeta\omega_o C$

$K = 5 - 4\zeta^2$

$H_o = K/(5 - K)$

Sensitivities: Let $a = 5 - K$

$S_K^{\omega_o} = K/a$

$S_{R_1}^{\omega_o} = S_{R_2}^{\omega_o} = -½$

$S_{C_1}^{\omega_o} = -1/a$

$S_{C_2}^{\omega_o} = -(2 - K)/2a$

$S_{C_3}^{\omega_o} = -(3 - K)/2a$

$S_{C_4}^{\omega_o} = -3/2a$

$S_K^{\zeta} = -2K/a$

$S_{R_1}^{\zeta} = S_{C_3}^{\zeta} = (1 + K)/2a$

$S_{R_2}^{\zeta} = -(1 + 5K)/2a$

$S_{C_2}^{\zeta} = K/2a$

$S_{C_4}^{\zeta} = -(1 + 2K)/2a$

$S_K^{H_o} = 5/a$

$S_{C_1}^{H_o} = S_{C_2}^{H_o} = -S_{C_3}^{H_o} = (3 - K)/a$

$S_{C_4}^{H_o} = -3/a$

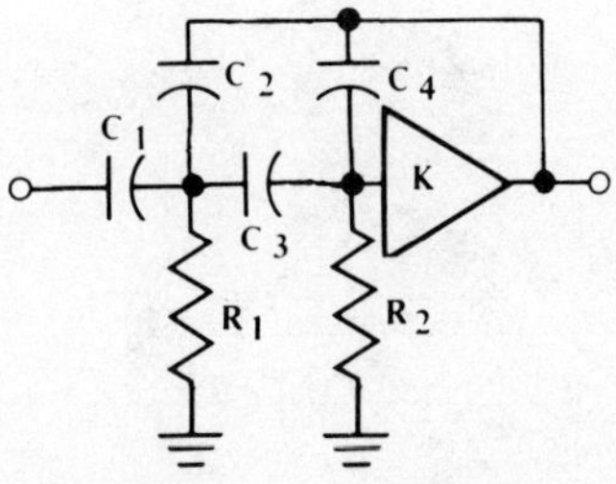

CLASS $2\overline{C}$: HIGH-PASS

Transfer Function:

$$H(s) = \frac{Ks^2R_1C_1R_2C_2}{s^2R_1C_1R_2C_2 + s(1-K)[R_1C_1(1+C_2/C_1)+R_2C_2] + (1-K)}$$

Parameters:

$$\omega_o = \left[\frac{1-K}{R_1C_1R_2C_2}\right]^{1/2} \qquad H_o = K$$

$$\zeta = \tfrac{1}{2}(1-K)^{1/2}[(R_1C_1/R_2C_2)^{1/2}(1+C_2/C_1) + (R_2C_2/R_1C_1)^{1/2}]$$

Design Equations: Set $C_1 = C_2 = C$

Given: ω_o, ζ, H_o

Choose: C

Calculate: $$R_1 = \frac{\zeta \pm [\zeta^2 - 2(1-H_o)]^{1/2}}{2\omega_oC} = \frac{F}{\omega_oC} \qquad K = H_o$$

$$R_2 = \frac{1-H_o}{F\omega_oC}$$

Sensitivities:

$$S_{R_1}^{\omega_o} = S_{R_2}^{\omega_o} = S_{C_1}^{\omega_o} = S_{C_2}^{\omega_o} = -\tfrac{1}{2} \qquad S_{C_2}^{\zeta} = (1-H_o)/2(2F^2-1+H_o)$$

$$S_K^{\omega_o} = S_K^{\zeta} = -H_o/2(1-H_o) \qquad S_K^{H_o} = 1$$

$$S_{R_1}^{\zeta} = -S_{R_2}^{\zeta} = (2F^2-1+H_o)/2(2F^2-1+H_o)$$

$$S_{C_1}^{\zeta} = (F^2-1+H_o)/2(2F^2-1+H_o)$$

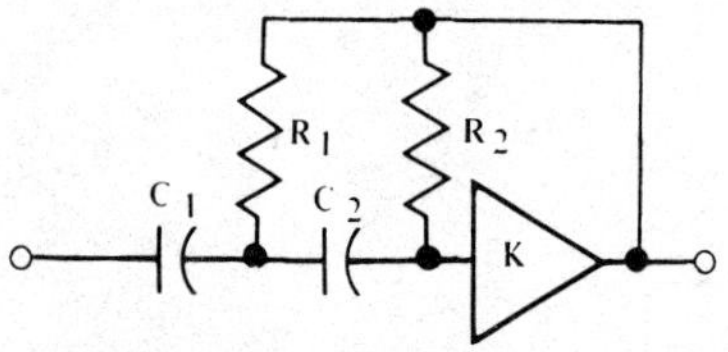

R. M. Inigo, "Active filter realization using finite-gain voltage amplifiers," IEEE Trans. Circuit Theory, vol. CT-17, pp. 445–448, Aug., 1970.

CLASS 2E: HIGH-PASS

Transfer Function:

$$H(s) = \frac{-s^2R_2C_1R_5C_3}{s^2R_2C_4R_5C_3 + s[R_2C_3 + R_2C_4(1 + C_1/C_4)] + 1}$$

Parameters:

$$\omega_o = \frac{1}{(R_2C_4R_5C_3)^{1/2}} \qquad H_o = -C_1/C_4$$

$$\zeta = \tfrac{1}{2}(R_2/R_5)^{1/2}[(C_3/C_4)^{1/2} + (C_4/C_3)^{1/2}(1 + C_1/C_4)]$$

Design Equations: Set $C_1 = C_3 = C$

Given: ω_o, ζ, $-H_o$

Choose: C

Calculate: $C_4 = C/(-H_o)$

$$R_2 = \frac{\zeta}{(0.5 - H_o)\omega_oC} = \frac{1}{F\omega_oC}$$

$$R_5 = \frac{F}{\omega_oC}$$

Sensitivities:

$$S_{R_2}^{\omega_o} = S_{R_5}^{\omega_o} = S_{C_3}^{\omega_o} = S_{C_4}^{\omega_o} = -\tfrac{1}{2} \qquad S_{C_3}^{\zeta} = -(H_o + 1)/2(3H_o + 1)$$

$$S_{R_2}^{\zeta} = -S_{R_5}^{\zeta} = \tfrac{1}{2} \qquad S_{C_4}^{\zeta} = (-2H_o + 1)/2(2H_o + 1)$$

$$S_{C_1}^{\zeta} = H_o/(2H_o - 1) \qquad S_{C_1}^{H_o} = -S_{C_4}^{H_o} = 1$$

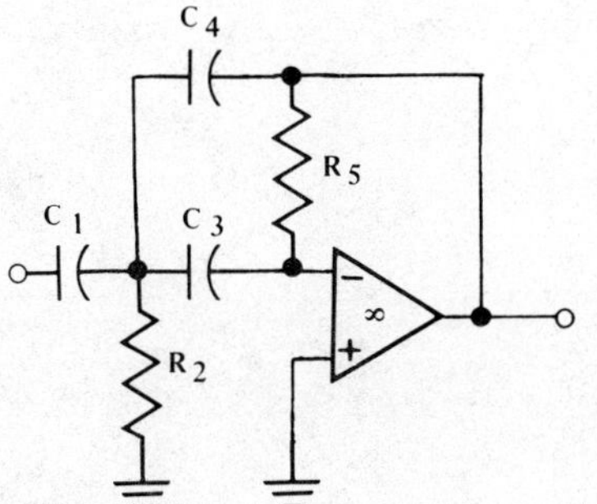

L. P. Huelsman, J. G. Graeme, and G. E. Tobey, op. cit., Chap. 8.3.1.

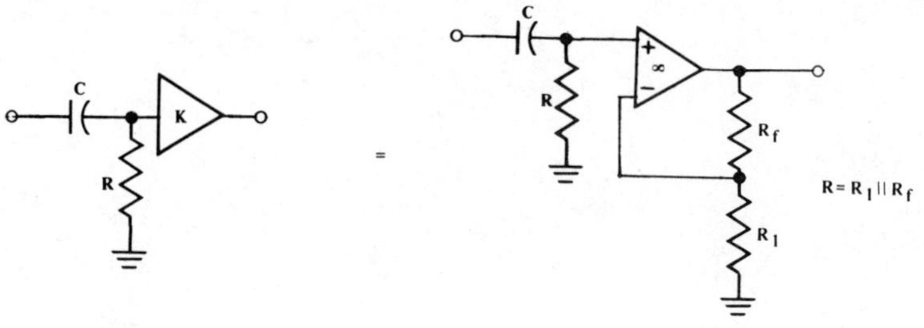

Fig. 9.4.1 First-order high-pass filter (noninverting).

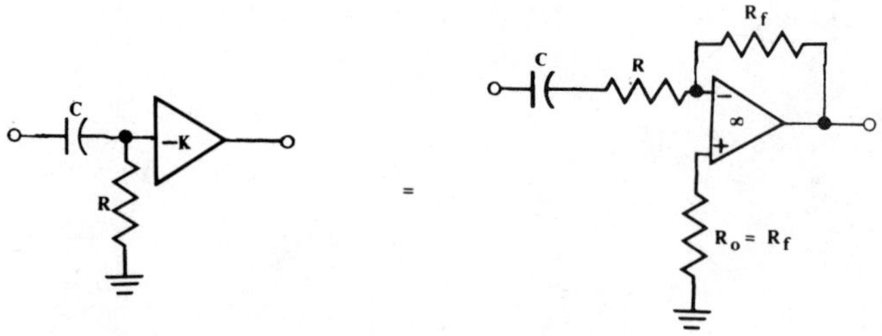

Fig. 9.4.2 First-order high-pass filter (inverting).

EXAMPLE 9.4.1 Design a first-order high-pass filter having a corner frequency of 10 KHz and a dc gain of 10. Use both inverting and noninverting gain blocks.

Solution The design parallels that of the low-pass filters in Examples 8.4.2 and 8.4.3. The noninverting first-order stage was shown in Fig. 9.4.1. Using Eq. 9.4.2 for ω_o, suitable (R, C) combinations are shown in Fig. 8.4.4. Selecting

$$C = 0.001\ \mu F, \qquad R = 15.9\ K\ \text{(use 16 K)} \tag{9.4.3}$$

then

$$R_f = KR = 160\ K, \qquad R_1 = KR/(K-1) = 17.8\ K\ \text{(use 18 K)} \tag{9.4.4}$$

from Table 8.4.1. The completed design is shown in Fig. 9.4.3a.

The inverting first-order stage was shown in Fig. 9.4.2. Since ω_o is also given by Eq. 9.4.2, the same (R, C) combinations can be used. To choose the best set, we must consider dc offset effects. If this is the output stage of the filter, then R_f must not be too large. In this situation,

$$C = 0.01\ \mu F, \qquad R = 1.6\ K, \qquad R_f = 16\ K \tag{9.4.5}$$

would be a good combination where R_f is obtained from Table 8.4.2. The complete filter design is shown in Fig. 9.4.3b. If this is an intermediate stage of the filter which is dc isolated from succeeding stages, then

$$C = 0.001\ \mu F, \qquad R = 16\ K, \qquad R_f = 160\ K \tag{9.4.6}$$

could be used. Note that this is a case where the high-gain arrangement could be used to advantage to increase R in Eq. 9.4.5.

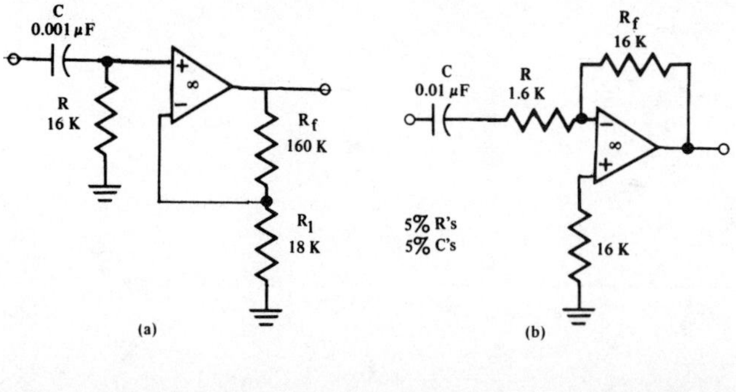

Fig. 9.4.3 Realizations of (a) noninverting and (b) inverting high-pass filters of Example 9.4.1.

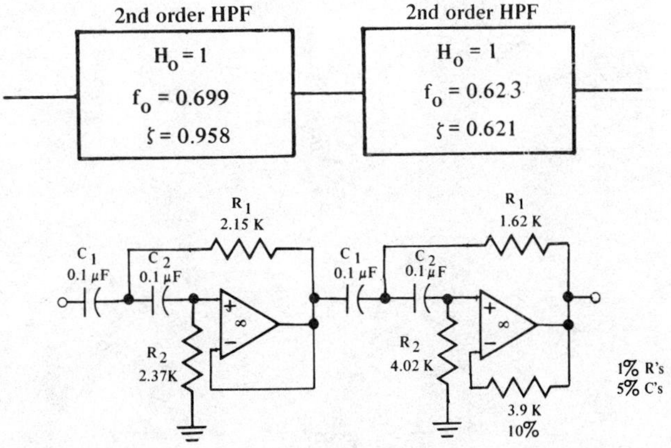

Fig. 9.4.4 Block diagram of fourth-order Bessel high-pass filter and its realization.

EXAMPLE 9.4.2 Design a fourth-order Bessel filter having a 3 dB cutoff frequency of 1000 Hz and unity high-frequency gain. Use a Class 2B realization.

Solution The block diagram for the Bessel high-pass filter is easily drawn in Fig. 9.4.4. The Class 2B filter realization is also shown. The design equations are:

Set: $C_1 = C_2 = C$

Given: ω_o, ζ, H_o

Choose: C

$$\text{Calculate: } R_1 = \frac{\zeta + [\zeta^2 + 2(H_o - 1)]^{1/2}}{2\omega_o C} = \frac{F}{\omega_o C}, \qquad R_2 = \frac{1}{F\omega_o C}, \qquad K = H_o$$

The design of the first stage proceeds as:

$$\begin{aligned} &K = H_o = 1, \qquad F = \zeta = 0.958 \\ &1/R_1C = 2\pi(699\text{ Hz}/0.958) = 2\pi(730\text{ Hz}), \qquad 1/R_2C = 2\pi[0.958(699\text{ Hz})] = 2\pi(670\text{ Hz}) \\ &C = 0.1\ \mu\text{F}, \qquad R_1 = 2.18\text{ K (use 2.15 K)}, \qquad R_2 = 2.38\text{ K (use 2.37 K)} \end{aligned} \tag{9.4.7}$$

The second stage is designed in the same way where:

$$\begin{aligned} &K = H_o = 1, \qquad F = \zeta = 0.621 \\ &1/R_1C = 2\pi(623\text{ Hz}/0.621) = 2\pi(1003\text{ Hz}), \qquad 1/R_2C = 2\pi[0.621(625\text{ Hz})] = 2\pi(388\text{ Hz}) \\ &C = 0.1\ \mu\text{F}, \qquad R_1 = 1.59\text{ K (use 1.62 K)}, \qquad R_2 = 4.10\text{ K (use 4.02 K)} \end{aligned} \tag{9.4.8}$$

The complete filter is shown in Fig. 9.4.4. An important but often overlooked detail of high-pass filter design is dc offset correction. As mentioned before, in cascade design, only the last stage must be compensated for dc offset since the dc offsets of all preceding stages are not transmitted as in low-pass filters. Thus, the offset resistor is not needed in the first stage of Fig. 9.4.4. The only time that dc offset compensation is needed in high-pass filter design is if dc offsets become excessive and cause clipping or limiting of either the positive or negative peaks of the input signal.

EXAMPLE 9.4.3 Design a fourth-order synchronously-tuned high-pass filter having a 3 dB cutoff frequency of 1 KHz and unity high-frequency gain. Use a Class $2\overline{C}$ realization.

Solution The block diagram for the synchronously-tuned high-pass filter is drawn in Fig. 9.4.5 with its Class $2\overline{C}$ realization form. Since two identical stages are required, the design time is reduced. The design equations are:

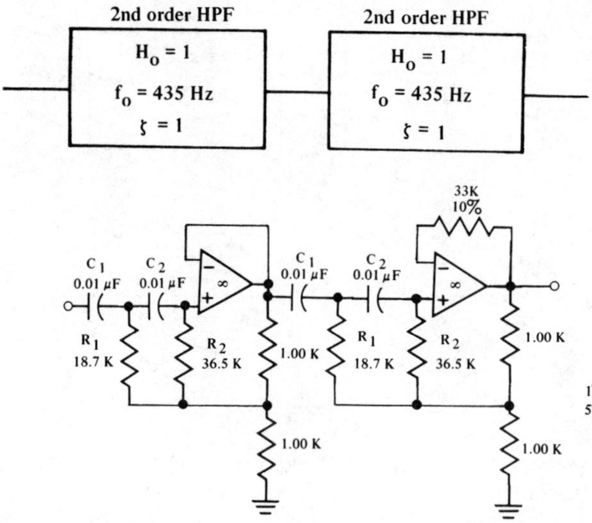

Fig. 9.4.5 Block diagram of fourth-order synchronously-tuned high-pass filter and its realization.

Set: $C_1 = C_2 = C$

Given: ω_o, ζ, H_o

Choose: C

Calculate: $R_1 = \dfrac{\zeta \pm [\zeta^2 - 2(1 - H_o)]^{1/2}}{2\omega_o C} = \dfrac{F}{\omega_o C}$, $\quad R_2 = \dfrac{1 - H_o}{F\omega_o C}$, $\quad K = H_o$

We see from the equation for R_1 and R_2 that the gain H_o is limited as

$$(1 - \zeta^2/2) \leqslant H_o \leqslant 1 \tag{9.4.9}$$

Therefore since $\zeta = 1$, $0.5 \leqslant H_o \leqslant 1$. Choosing $H_o = 0.5$, then the design proceeds as:

$$F = 0.5, \quad 1/R_1C = 2\pi(435\text{ Hz})/0.5, \quad 1/R_2C = 2\pi[0.5(435\text{ Hz})/(1 - 0.5)] = 2\pi(435\text{ Hz})$$
$$C = 0.01\ \mu\text{F}, \quad R_1 = 18.3\text{ K (use 18.7 K)}, \quad R_2 = 36.6\text{ K (use 36.5 K)}, \quad K = H_o = 0.5 \tag{9.4.10}$$

The filter is shown in Fig. 9.4.5. The gain blocks K are realized by using unity-gain amplifiers with voltage dividers at their outputs. Detuning effects are minimized by selecting the resistors of the voltage divider small compared with R_1 and R_2. This is more desirable than using a voltage divider at the input to the amplifier as was done in Example 8.5.4. It also eliminates the need for an output gain block.

EXAMPLE 9.4.4 Design a fourth-order Butterworth high-pass filter having a 3 dB cutoff of 1000 Hz and unity high-frequency gain. Use a Class 2E realization.

Solution The block diagram for the filter is shown in Fig. 9.4.6 with its Class 2E realization. The design equations are:

Set: $C_1 = C_3 = C$

Given: $\omega_o, \zeta, -H_o$

Choose: C

Calculate: $C_4 = C/(-H_o)$, $\quad R_2 = \zeta/(0.5 - H_o)\omega_o C = 1/F\omega_o C$, $\quad R_5 = F/\omega_o C$

Let us design the first stage as:

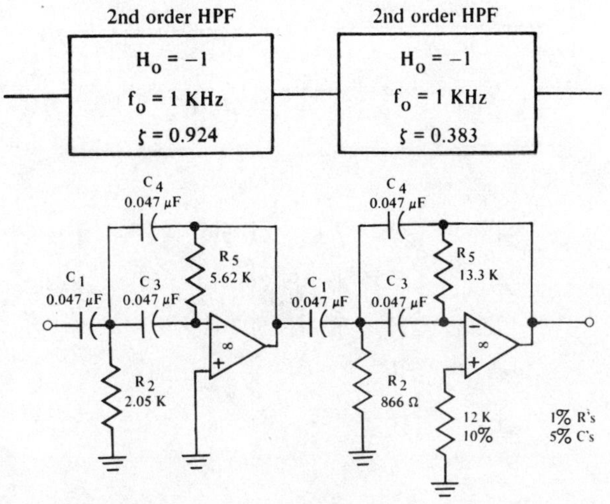

Fig. 9.4.6 Block diagram of fourth-order Butterworth high-pass filter and its realization.

$$F = [0.5 - (-1)]/0.924 = 1.62, \quad 1/R_2C = 2\pi[1.62(1\text{ KHz})] = 2\pi(1.62\text{ KHz})$$
$$1/R_5C = 2\pi(1\text{ KHz}/1.623) = 2\pi(616\text{ Hz}) \tag{9.4.11}$$
$$C = C_4 = 0.047\ \mu\text{F}, \quad R_2 = 2.09\text{ K (use 2.05 K)}, \quad R_5 = 5.50\text{ K (use 5.62 K)}$$

The design of the second stage follows in the same way but where $\zeta = 0.383$:

$$F = [0.5 - (-1)]/0.383 = 3.92, \quad 1/R_2C = 2\pi[3.92(1\text{ KHz})] = 2\pi(3.92\text{ KHz})$$
$$1/R_5C = 2\pi(1\text{ KHz}/3.92) = 2\pi(255\text{ Hz}) \tag{9.4.12}$$
$$C = C_4 = 0.047\ \mu\text{F}, \quad R_2 = 865\ \Omega\text{ (use 866 }\Omega), \quad R_5 = 13.3\text{ K}$$

The complete filter is shown in Fig. 9.4.6.

EXAMPLE 9.4.5 Design a fourth-order Chebyshev high-pass filter having a 3 dB passband ripple, a 3 dB cutoff frequency of 1 KHz, and a maximum high-frequency gain of unity. Use a Class 2E realization.
Solution The block diagram and realization form of the filter is shown in Fig. 9.4.7. The design equations are the same as in Example 9.4.4. The first stage design is:

$$F = [0.5 - (-1)]/0.464 = 3.23, \quad 1/R_2C = 2\pi[3.23(2.26\text{ KHz})] = 2\pi(7.30\text{ KHz})$$
$$1/R_5C = 2\pi(2.26\text{ KHz}/3.23) = 2\pi(700\text{ Hz}) \tag{9.4.13}$$
$$C = C_4 = 0.01\ \mu\text{F}, \quad R_2 = 2.18\text{ K (use 2.15 K)}, \quad R_5 = 22.7\text{ K (use 22.6 K)}$$

The second stage design is:

$$F = [0.5 - (-0.707)]/0.0896 = 13.5, \quad 1/R_2C = 2\pi[13.5(1.05\text{ KHz})] = 2\pi(14.2\text{ KHz})$$
$$1/R_5C = 2\pi(1.05\text{ KHz}/13.5) = 2\pi(77.7\text{ Hz}) \tag{9.4.14}$$
$$C = 0.01\ \mu\text{F}, \quad C_4 = C/0.707 = 0.014\ \mu\text{F (use 0.01 }\mu\text{F} \parallel 3900\text{ pF)}$$
$$R_2 = 1.12\text{ K (use 1.10 K)}, \quad R_5 = 205\text{ K}$$

The complete filter is shown in Fig. 9.4.7. We see that H_o leads to a nonstandard C_4 (0.014 μF) in the second stage, which must be obtained using padding (0.01 μF || 3900 pF). This example points up many design problems which are not uncommon: (1) H_o leads to nonstandard C values. (2) R_2 in the second stage can be small which consumes excessive power and requires large drive current. (3) R_5 in the second stage can be large which causes parasitic detuning problems and large current offsets. (4) Thus, a tradeoff in R_2 and R_5 is required. A better solution is to let $C_3 = kC_1$ and derive a new set of design equations.

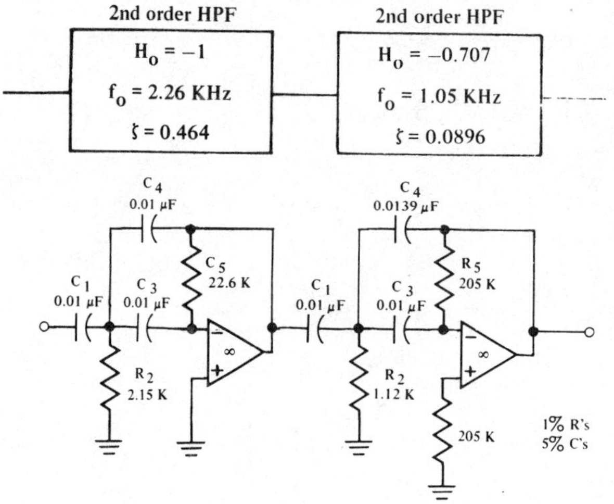

Fig. 9.4.7 Block diagram of fourth-order Chebyshev high-pass filter and its realization.

EXAMPLE 9.4.6 Convert the third-order Butterworth low-pass filter of Example 8.5.1 having $f_o = 1$ KHz and $H_o = 10$ into an equivalent high-pass filter. A Class 1B realization was used for the second-order stage.

Solution The low-pass filter may be converted into a high-pass filter directly using the RC:CR transformation. However, we must be careful to properly perform the frequency scaling required. The low-pass filter is shown in Fig. 9.4.8a so that making the R:1/C interchange results in the high-pass filter of Fig. 9.4.8b. Since we have essentially inverted frequency, the low-pass filter having a corner frequency of 1 KHz becomes a high-pass filter with a corner frequency at $1/(2\pi)^2(10^3 \text{ Hz}) = 0.0253 \times 10^{-3}$ Hz. To move the corner frequency back up to 1 KHz, we must frequency scale the capacitors (for review, see Sec. 1.10) by a factor of $0.0253 \times 10^{-3}/10^3 = 0.0253 \times 10^{-6}$. This results in the high-pass filter shown in Fig. 9.4.9a. We can magnitude scale the components by 10^{-3} so that R = 100 K and C = 0.00156 μF which would be more reasonable. However, the C values are nonstandard which is usually the case using the RC:CR transformation. Therefore, we further magnitude scale the components by 0.156 to yield the final high-pass filter shown in Fig. 9.4.9b. This process can be quickly carried out with a little practice. When low-pass filters are designed and high-pass filters are required, this is a very convenient design method. Occasionally, by comparing the design sheets of the low-pass and the high-pass filters, we will find they have identical design equations. This was the case for the Class 1B filters. Then, simple component interchange completes the design. This is the simplest situation we will encounter. Although taking the direct RC:CR transform usually works well on Class B and D filters where no frequency scaling is involved, it usually works poorly on Class A, $\overline{\text{A}}$, C, $\overline{\text{C}}$, and sometimes E filters. These classes are often used to take advantage of frequency scaling. Taking their RC:CR transforms produces filters in the complementary class which have undesirable component values.

EXAMPLE 9.4.7 Determine the input impedance characteristic to the Class 1B stage in Example 9.4.6.

Solution The input impedance for the Class 1B filter was determined in Example 9.2.5 and is given by

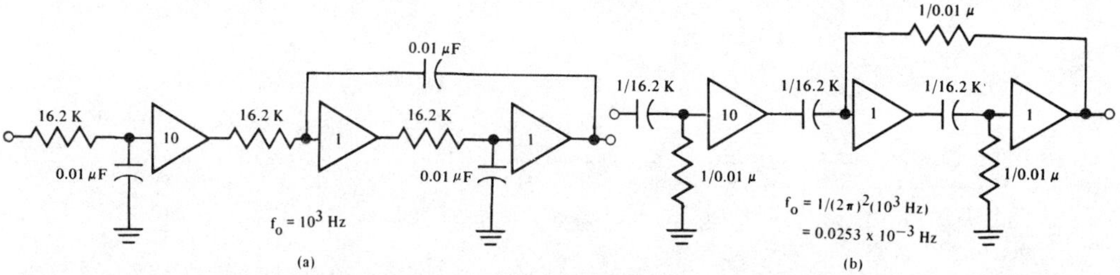

Fig. 9.4.8 Conversion of (a) low-pass filter into (b) high-pass filter before frequency scaling.

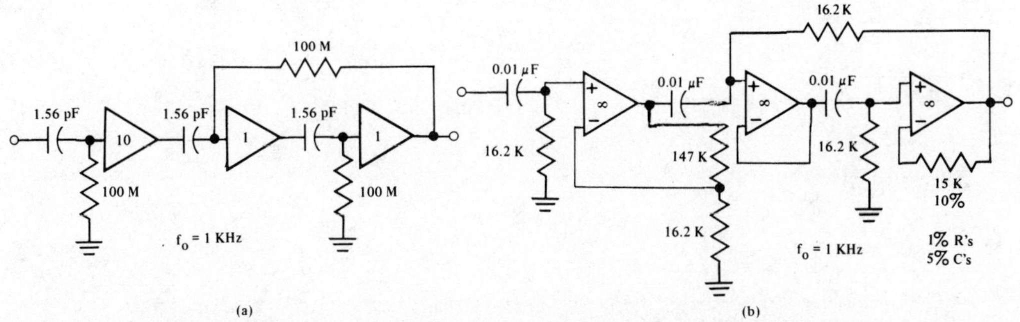

Fig. 9.4.9 Magnitude scaling of components in Fig. 9.4.8 to obtain suitable values.

Eq. 9.2.24. Substituting the component values in Fig. 9.4.9b into Eq. 9.2.24 gives

$$Z_{in} = R\,\frac{s_n^2 + s_n + 1}{s_n} \tag{9.4.15}$$

where R = 16.2 K and $s_n = s/2\pi(1\ \text{KHz})$. The magnitude and phase characteristics for Z_{in} are easily plotted in Fig. 9.4.10. Since $\zeta = 0.5$, the response is close to that of the approximation. At frequencies below 316 Hz, the input appears to be a 0.01 μF capacitor. At frequencies above 3.16 KHz, it appears to be an inductor having a value of

$$L_o = s_n R/s = R^2 C = (16.2\ \text{K})^2(0.01\ \mu\text{F}) = 2.6\ \text{H} \tag{9.4.16}$$

Here is another situation where drawing the magnitude response directly on impedance paper quickly establishes the L_o value without calculation.

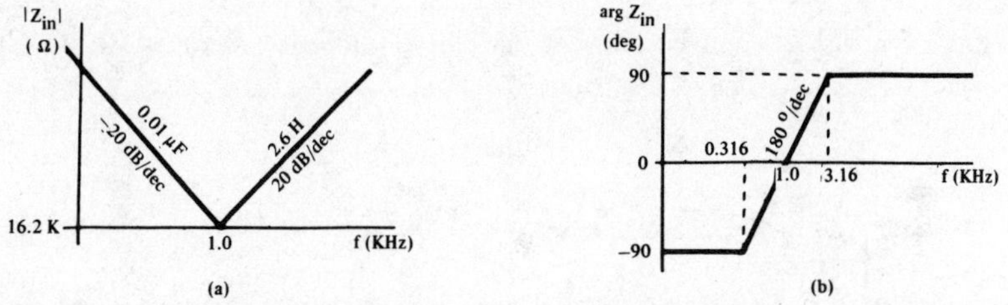

Fig. 9.4.10 Magnitude and phase characteristics of Z_{in} for Example 9.4.7.

9.5 TUNABLE HIGH-PASS FILTERS

Just as with low-pass filters, there are a broad group of applications which require tunable high-pass filters. Generally, tunable ω_o-constant ζ filters are needed. A gain-tuned high-pass filter must have a transfer function

$$H(s) = \frac{H_o K^2 s^2}{K^2 s^2 + aKs + b^2} \tag{9.5.1}$$

so that $\omega_o = b/K$ and $\zeta = a/2b$ by analogy with Eq. 8.6.1. It is important to note that resonant frequency ω_o varies inversely with gain. Gain-tunable high-pass filters are realized approximately using Class C, D, or E filters.

We saw in Sec. 8.6 that there were six canonical gain-tuned filters of the low-pass variety. These were given in Fig. 8.6.3. By performing the RC:CR transformation, we can obtain the

2C

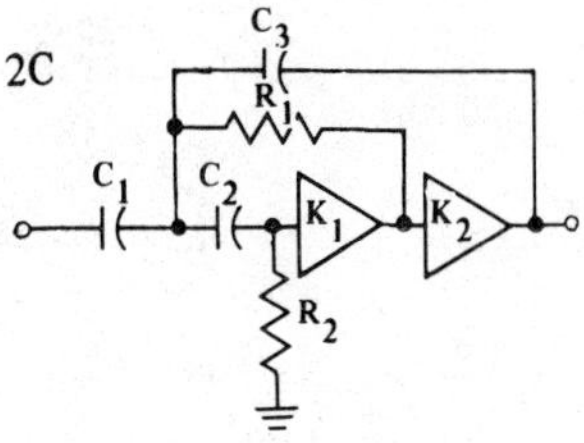

$K_1=-K_2=-K_0<0$

$C_1=C>0,\ C_2=\alpha C,\ C_3=\beta C$

$\beta R_1=\gamma^2 R_2\alpha,\ \gamma>0,\ \beta\gg\alpha$

$Q_0 = \frac{\gamma}{(1+A)}$

$\omega_o = \gamma/\beta K_0 R_1 C$

$K_{0\,min} = \frac{1+\gamma^2(1+\frac{1}{\beta})}{\gamma} Q_0 \frac{1+A}{A}$

HF gain $= -\frac{1}{\beta}$

2C

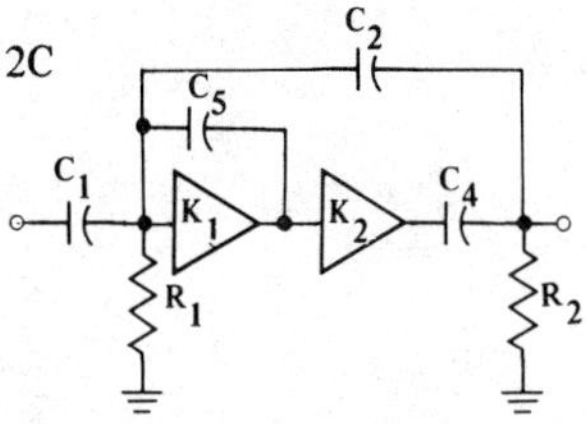

$K_1=-K_2=-K_0<0$

$C_1=C>0,\ C_2=\alpha C,\ C_4=\beta C$

$C_5=\gamma C$

$\beta R_2=\alpha R_1,\ \alpha\gg 1+\gamma$

$Q_0 = \frac{\beta}{\gamma(1+A)}$

$\omega_o = 1/\beta K_0 R_2 C$

$K_{0\,min} = (2+\frac{\alpha}{\beta}) Q_0 \frac{1+A}{A}$

HF gain $= -\frac{1}{\alpha}$

1C

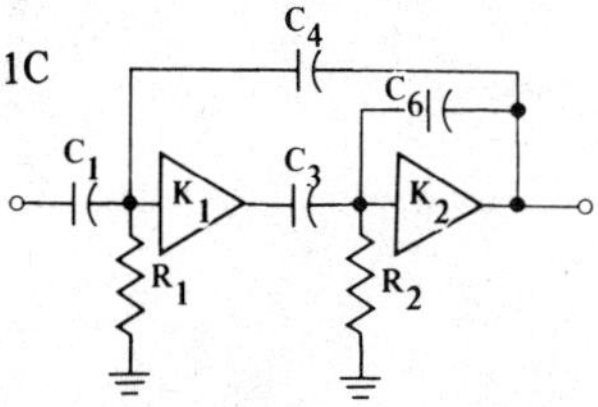

$K_1=-K_2=K_0>0$

$C_1=C>0,\ C_3=\alpha C,\ C_4=\beta C$

$C_6=\gamma C$

$\alpha R_2=\beta R_1,\ \beta\gg 1$

$Q_0 = -\frac{\alpha}{\gamma(1+A)}$

$\omega_o = 1/\beta K_0 R_1 C$

$K_{0\,min} = 2Q_0\frac{1+A}{A} + \frac{1}{A}$

HF gain $= -\frac{1}{\beta}$

1C

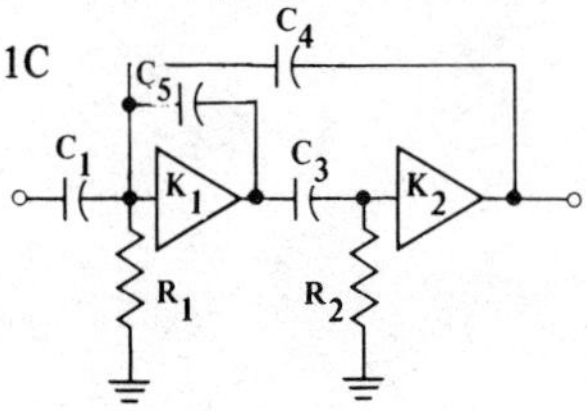

$K_1=-K_2=-K_0<0$

$C_1=C>0,\ C_3=\alpha C,\ C_4=\beta C$

$C_5=\gamma C$

$\alpha R_2=\beta R_1,\ \beta\gg 1$

$Q_0 = \frac{\beta}{\gamma(1+A)}$

$\omega_o = 1/\beta K_0 R_1 C$

$K_{0\,min} = 2Q_0\frac{1+A}{A} + \frac{1}{A}$

HF gain $= -\frac{1}{\beta}$

2E

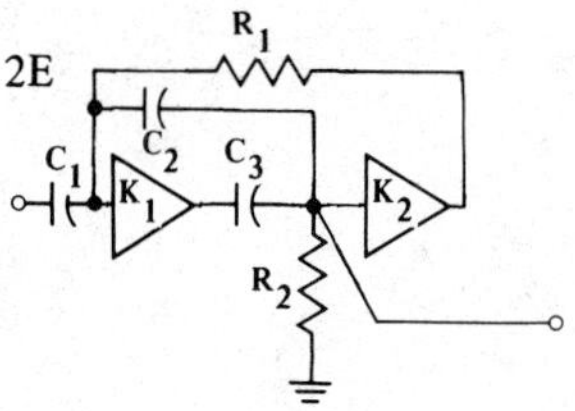

$K_1=-K_0^2,\ K_2=\frac{1}{K_0},\ K_0>0$

$C_1=C>0,\ C_2=\alpha C,\ C_3=\beta C$

$\alpha R_1=\beta\gamma^2 R_2,\ \gamma>0,\ \beta\gg\alpha\gg 1$

$Q_0 = \frac{\gamma}{1+A}$

$\omega_o = \gamma/\alpha K_0 R_1 C$

$K_{0\,min} = \frac{1+\gamma^2}{\gamma} Q_0 \frac{1+A}{A}$

HF gain $= -\frac{1}{\alpha}$

2E

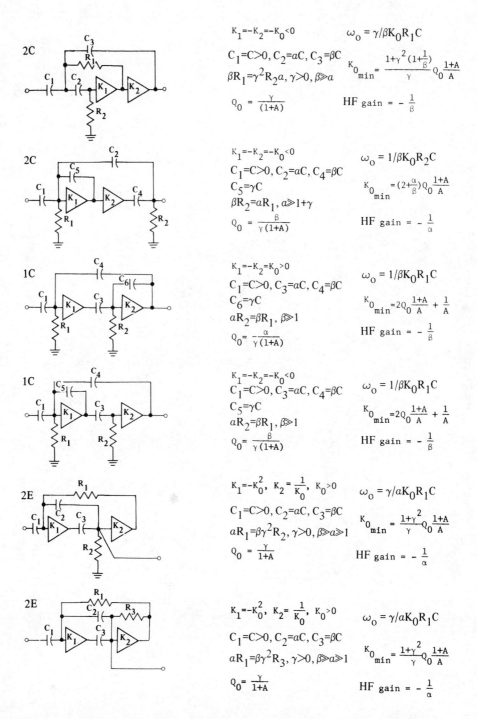

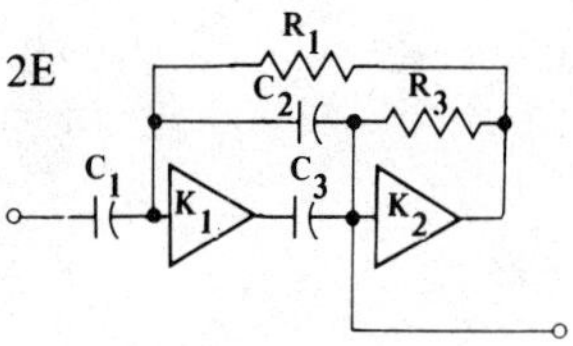

$K_1=-K_0^2,\ K_2=\frac{1}{K_0},\ K_0>0$

$C_1=C>0,\ C_2=\alpha C,\ C_3=\beta C$

$\alpha R_1=\beta\gamma^2 R_3,\ \gamma>0,\ \beta\gg\alpha\gg 1$

$Q_0 = \frac{\gamma}{1+A}$

$\omega_o = \gamma/\alpha K_0 R_1 C$

$K_{0\,min} = \frac{1+\gamma^2}{\gamma} Q_0 \frac{1+A}{A}$

HF gain $= -\frac{1}{\alpha}$

Fig. 9.5.1 Canonical gain-tunable high-pass filters. (Note that $\Delta Q_o/Q_o = \Delta A_o/A_o = A(N-1)/(N+A)$ for all filters.) (Adapted from S. Bruminhent and K. L. Su, "Gain-tuned active filters," Proc. Intl. Symp on Circuits and Systems, pp. 443–447, April, 1974.)

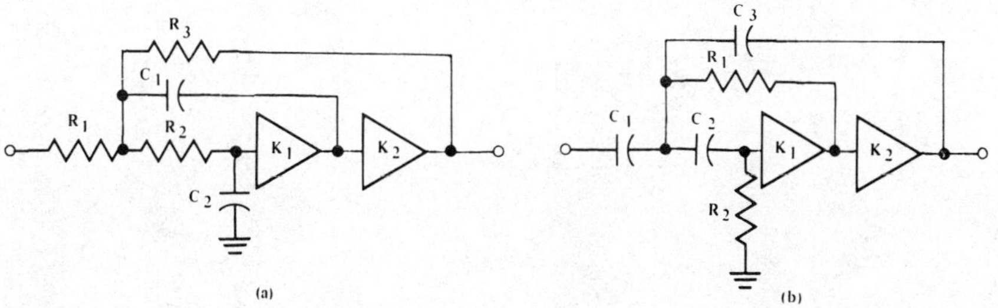

Fig. 9.5.2 Conversion of gain-tuned (a) low-pass filter into (b) high-pass filter.

analogous gain-tuned high-pass filters. These are listed in Fig. 9.5.1. It is easy to make the minor changes in the parameters as we show in the following example. It should be remembered that since these filters are operated as Class C, frequency ω_o is up-scaled by gain K so they are primarily useful for lower-frequency applications.

EXAMPLE 9.5.1 Convert the first gain-tuned low-pass filter of Fig. 8.6.3 into a high-pass filter. Determine its parameters.

Solution Using the RC:CR transformation, the gain tuned high-pass filter shown in Fig. 9.5.2 results. Its component values are obtained by making the R:1/C interchange to give

$$K_1 = -K_2 = -K_o < 0$$
$$C_1 = C > 0, \quad C_2 = aC, \quad C_3 = \beta C, \quad \beta R_1 = \gamma^2 a R_2, \quad \gamma > 0, \quad \beta \gg a \tag{9.5.2}$$

The filter parameters result by inverting ω_o and leaving Q and H_o unchanged to give

$$\omega_o = \frac{\gamma}{K\beta RC}, \quad Q_o = \frac{\gamma}{1 + A}, \quad \text{HF gain} = -1/\beta, \quad K_{o\,min} = \frac{1 + \gamma^2(1 + 1/\beta)}{\gamma} Q_o \frac{1 + A}{A} \tag{9.5.3}$$

The tolerances on Q and A equal

$$\Delta Q_o/Q_o = \Delta A/A = A(N - 1)/(N + A) \tag{9.5.4}$$

It is rather remarkable that these results can be obtained with such ease.

Passive-tuned high-pass filters are generally simpler to design than gain-tuned high-pass filters. The root loci for the denominators of the transfer functions of passive-tuned filters were shown in Figs. 8.7.1 (single-tuned) and 8.7.2 (double-tuned). We saw that passive-tuned filters could be realized in every class. They could be realized exactly using double-tuning or approximately using single-tuning of the time constants. From Eq. 8.7.1, since the passive corner frequencies equal $a_i = 1/R_iC_i$ (in most cases) and $\omega_o \sim a$, then the corner frequencies vary inversely with R. Thus, the tuning is equivalent to that in the gain-tuned filters in Fig. 9.5.1.

EXAMPLE 9.5.2 Design a passive-tuned Butterworth high-pass filter to have a corner frequency of 1 KHz and a tuning range of 10:1. Use a Class 2E realization.

Solution The Class 2E high-pass filter was described by its design sheet in Sec. 9.3. From the design sheet, we see that gain H_o must be properly selected to produce standard resistance values. Since the resistance ratio equals

$$R_5/R_2 = F^2 = [(0.5 - H_o)/\zeta]^2 \tag{9.5.5}$$

selecting $H_o = -0.5$ requires $R_5 = 2R_2$ which is convenient. Of course, other H_o's could be used, or the design equations could be modified so that $C_1 \neq C_3$ (which would be a good option here). However, we shall let $R_5 = 2R_2$. Then the design equations become:

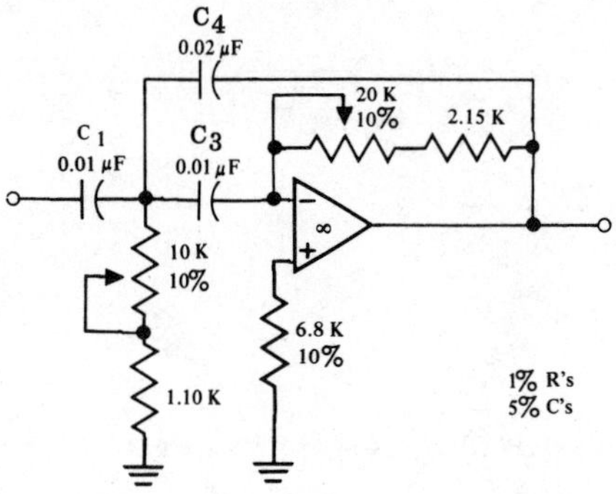

Fig. 9.5.3 Passive-tuned high-pass filter realization of Example 9.5.2.

Set: $C_1 = C_3 = C, \quad H_o = -0.5$

Given: ω_o, ζ

Choose: C

Calculate: $R_2 = 1/2^{1/2}\omega_o C, \quad R_5 = 2R_2, \quad C_4 = 2C$

Recalling that the variation $\Delta R_2 = R_{2max} - R_{2min}$ required for R_2 is given by Eq. 8.7.3, then

$$1/C\Delta R_2 = 2^{1/2}[2\pi(10\text{ KHz})/(10-1)] = 2\pi(1.57\text{ KHz}) \tag{9.5.6}$$

Selecting $C = 0.01\ \mu F$, then from Eqs. 9.5.6 and 8.7.4,

$$\Delta R_2 = 10\text{ K}, \quad R_{2\,min} = \Delta R_2/(N-1) = 1.11\text{ K (use 1.10 K)}, \quad \Delta R_5 = 2\Delta R_2 = 20\text{ K}$$
$$R_{5\,min} = 2R_{2\,min} = 2.22\text{ K (use 2.15 K)}, \quad C_4 = 2C = 0.02\ \mu F \tag{9.5.7}$$

The complete filter is shown in Fig. 9.5.3. If an extended tuning range is acceptable, the padding resistors R_{2min} and R_{5min} can be omitted. Since we have a wide tuning range where $N = 10$, we use the geometric average of R_5 for the bias resistor R_o. Using Eq. 8.7.8b, $R_o = \Delta R_5 \sqrt{N}/(N-1) = 7K$ (use 6.8 K).

9.6 COMPLEMENTARY HIGH-PASS FILTERS

In Sec. 6.3.5, we discussed the low-transient or complementary low-pass to high-pass transformation. The transfer function of the complementary high-pass filter equals

$$H_{CHP}(s) = 1 - H_{LP}(s) \tag{9.6.1}$$

where $H_{LP}(s)$ was the gain of the low-pass filter and $H_{LP}(0) = 1$. If H_o is the dc gain of the low-pass filter, then we subtract H_{LP} from H_o. These filters were useful when the parameters of the step response were to be maintained. We want to briefly discuss complementary high-pass filters which are required by this transformation. We will be concerned with only second-order filter stages. It is also useful to note that complementary high-pass filters can be converted into complementary low-pass filters using the RC:CR transformation.

When the low-pass filter has a transfer function

$$H_{LP}(s) = \frac{\omega_o^2}{s^2 + 2\zeta\omega_o s + \omega_o^2} \tag{9.6.2}$$

then the complementary high-pass filter has a gain from Eq. 9.6.1 of

$$H_{CHP}(s) = \frac{s(s + 2\zeta\omega_o)}{s^2 + 2\zeta\omega_o s + \omega_o^2} \tag{9.6.3}$$

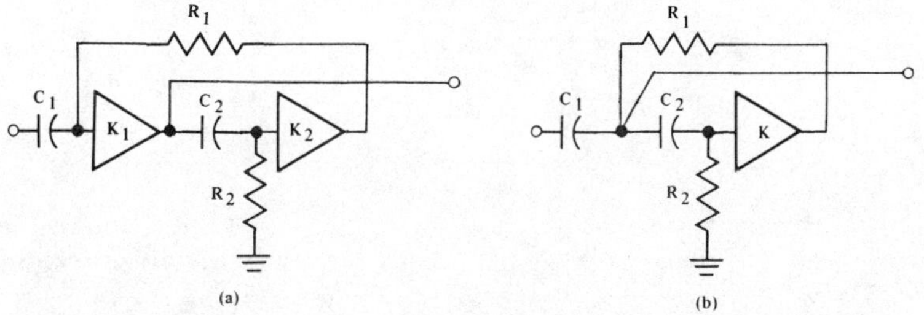

Fig. 9.6.1 (a) Class 1B and (b) Class 2B complementary high-pass filters.

which has the form of Eq. 9.1.2 where $z = 2\zeta\omega_o$ (in more general filters, z is arbitrary). Therefore, the high-pass filter has a second zero which is not at the origin. The question is now, how do we systematically design such filters? We will discuss three different approaches. The first approach will utilize the Class 1X high-pass filters of Sec. 9.3 as we will now show.

The high-pass filters which have been tabulated are described by flow graphs having single forward branches. These flow graphs are shown in Fig. 8.1.1 and have transfer functions given by Eq. 8.1.4. As discussed earlier in this chapter, such Class 1X high-pass filters have a T_{45} which is itself high-pass where

$$T_{45} = \frac{c_{51}s}{a_{50} + a_{51}s} = \frac{H_o's}{s + \tau} \tag{9.6.4}$$

from Eq. 9.1.5. Suppose we utilize the output of the first amplifier K_1 rather than the second amplifier K_2 in Fig. 8.1.1. Then the transfer $H'(s) = H(s)/K_2T_{45}$ where H(s) is given by Eq. 8.1.4. When H(s) is high-pass as given by Eq. 9.1.1, then

$$H_{CHP}(s) = \frac{s + \tau}{K_2H_o's}H_{HP}(s) = \frac{H_o}{K_2H_o'}\frac{s(s + \tau)}{s^2 + 2\zeta\omega_o s + \omega_o^2} \tag{9.6.5}$$

which is complementary high-pass when $\tau = 2\zeta\omega_o$. Therefore, by simply selecting the output of the other amplifier of the Class 1X high-pass filters in Sec. 9.3, Class 1X complementary high-pass filters can be obtained. It is simple to convert the design sheets so they may be used for designing H_{CHP}.

EXAMPLE 9.6.1 Convert the Class 1B high-pass filter into a Class 1B complementary high-pass filter shown in Fig. 9.6.1a. Utilize its design sheet.

Solution The transfer function for the Class 1B high-pass filter equals

$$H_{HP}(s) = K_1K_2\frac{s^2R_1C_1R_2C_2}{s^2R_1C_1R_2C_2 + s[R_1C_1 + R_2C_2(1 - K_1K_2)] + 1} \tag{9.6.6}$$

By inspection of the filter, $T_{45} = sR_2C_2/(1 + sR_2C_2)$. Therefore, the transfer function from the input to the output of the first amplifier (K_1) equals

$$H_{CHP}(s) = \frac{H_{HP}(s)}{K_2T_{45}} = K_1\frac{sR_1C_1(sR_2C_2 + 1)}{s^2R_1C_1R_2C_2 + s[R_1C_1 + R_2C_2(1 - K_1K_2)] + 1} \tag{9.6.7}$$

which has the form of Eq. 9.1.2. The pole parameters remain unchanged. The zero frequency $z = 1/R_2C_2$ and the high-frequency gain $H_o = K_1$. Due to the requirement that the zero must equal twice the real part of the pole, we now have one fewer degrees-of-freedom so the design is more constrained.

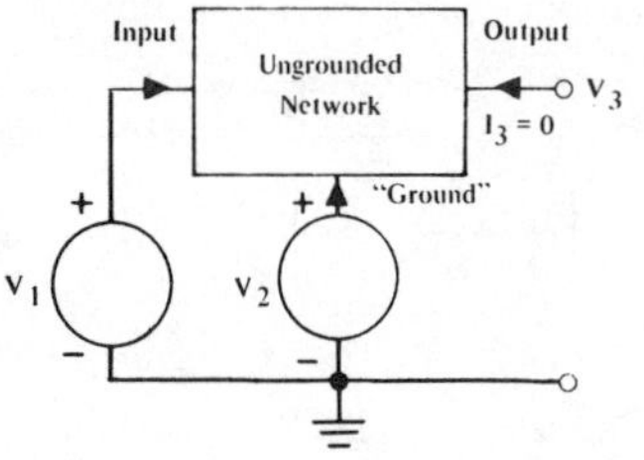

Fig. 9.6.2 Complementary operation of passive ungrounded network.

There are of course many other filter forms having transfer functions like Eq. 9.6.3. We have used this approach so that we could directly utilize some of our tabulated Class 1X high-pass filters. Class 2X filters can also be used by connecting the internal node to the output as shown in Fig. 9.6.1b. However, the transfer functions must be recalculated.

The second approach is to use a differencing amplifier in conjunction with a low-pass filter to perform the subtraction in Eq. 9.6.1. This is easily done using the op amp arrangement shown in Prob. 9.34, which is attractive from a tuning standpoint. Once the low-pass filter is tuned for ω_o and ζ, and the differencing amplifier adjusted so the two channel gains are equal and opposite, the complementary high-pass filter will automatically have the proper ω_o, ζ, z, and H_o (see Eq. 9.6.3).

An alternative approach which does not require the buffer amplifier for obtaining complementary filters was introduced by Hilberman.[4] However, this approach requires filters having a *positive gain of unity*. He observed that in a passive three-terminal network as shown in Fig. 9.6.2, the voltage transfer function from one input to the output must be the complement of that from the other input to the output where

$$T_{13}(s) = 1 - T_{23}(s) \tag{9.6.8}$$

This equation matches Eq. 9.6.1 when $T_{23}(0) = 1$. Thus, if T_{23} is low-pass, then T_{13} will be complementary high-pass. The proof is straight-forward and uses Kirchhoff's current law. If the network is an (n + 1)-port, then Eq. 9.6.8 generalizes to

$$\sum_{i=1}^{n} T_{i,\,n+1}(s) = 1 \tag{9.6.9}$$

Now let us add an amplifier to a three-terminal network as shown in Fig. 9.6.3a. Since

$$V_4 = T_{41}V_1 + T_{42}V_2 + T_{43}V_3 \tag{9.6.10}$$

and noting that $V_3 = KV_4$, then we can write that

$$V_3 = \frac{KT_{41}}{1 - KT_{43}} V_1 + \frac{KT_{42}}{1 - KT_{43}} V_2 = \frac{KT_{41}}{1 - KT_{43}} (V_1 + \frac{T_{42}}{T_{41}} V_2) \tag{9.6.11}$$

Summing the transfer functions at node 4 as $1 = T_{41} + T_{42} + T_{43}$, then substitution into Eq. 9.6.10 yields

$$V_3 = \frac{KT_{41}}{1 - KT_{43}} [V_1 + \left(\frac{1 - T_{43}}{T_{41}} - 1\right) V_2] = TV_1 + \left[\frac{K(1 - T_{43})}{1 - KT_{43}} - T\right] V_2 \tag{9.6.12}$$

where $T = KT_{41}/(1 - KT_{43})$. We see from Eq. 9.6.12 that the closed-loop transfer functions from V_1 to V_3 and V_2 to V_3 are not complementary. Letting $K \to \infty$ yields

$$V_3 = TV_1 + (1 - T - 1/T_{43})V_2 \tag{9.6.13}$$

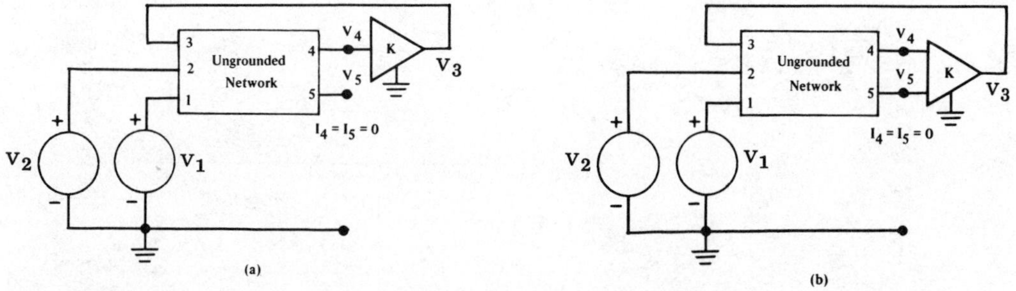

Fig. 9.6.3 Passive ungrounded network with an embedded (a) amplifier and (b) differential-input amplifier.

where $T = T_{41}/T_{43}$. The transfer functions of V_1 and V_2 are almost complementary (within an error $1/T_{43}$). In the low-pass filter case, this assumes $T(0) = 1$.

The error can be cancelled by using a differential input amplifier as shown in Fig. 9.6.3b. Repeating the previous analysis of expressing the voltages and the transfer function sum (given by Eq. 9.6.9) at nodes 4 and 5, and noting that $V_3 = K(V_4 - V_5)$, then Eq. 9.6.13 generalizes to

$$V_3 = TV_1 + \left[\frac{K(T_{53} - T_{43})}{1 + K(T_{53} - T_{43})} - T\right] V_2 \tag{9.6.14}$$

where $T = K(T_{53} - T_{43})/(1 + K(T_{53} - T_{43}))$. Eq. 9.6.14 becomes complementary when $K \to \infty$ so that

$$V_3 = TV_1 + (1 - T)V_2 \tag{9.6.15}$$

where T is positive and equals $(T_{51} - T_{41})/(T_{53} - T_{43})$. This result holds true independent of the number of differential-input infinite-gain amplifiers which are used. In the low-pass filter case, we must assure that $T(0) = 1$.

We can utilize this result in the following way. Complementary filters can be obtained using any noninverting infinite-gain filters. In all our filters, we have used infinite-gain, differential-input op amps to realize our gain blocks. Thus, to obtain complementary high-pass filters, we can use any low-pass filters with unity dc gains which are positive. However, we must be careful to select the proper inputs. We do this by grounding the low-pass filter inputs. We then "lift" the original grounds of the low-pass filter including any op amp grounds. These become the inputs to the complementary high-pass filter. This is shown in the following example.

EXAMPLE 9.6.2 Design a complementary high-pass filter using a Class 1E low-pass filter. Use the complementary input technique.

Solution The Class 1E low-pass filter was described by the design in Sec. 8.3. It is shown in Fig. 9.6.4a. By interchanging the ground and low-pass filter input, a Class 1E complementary high-pass filter results. The transfer function of the low-pass filter is

$$H_{LP}(s) = T = \frac{(1 + R_6/R_5)/(1 + R_3/R_4)}{s^2R_1C_1R_2C_2 + sR_2C_2[(1 + R_6/R_5)/(1 + R_4/R_3)] + R_6/R_5} \tag{9.6.16}$$

For unity dc gain, $H(0) = 1$, which requires that $1 + R_3/R_4 = 1 + R_5/R_6$. The transfer function of the complementary high-pass filter therefore equals

$$H_{CHP}(s) = 1 - T = \frac{sR_2C_2(sR_1C_1R_5/R_6 + 1)}{s^2R_1C_1R_2C_2R_5/R_6 + sR_2C_2 + 1} \tag{9.6.17}$$

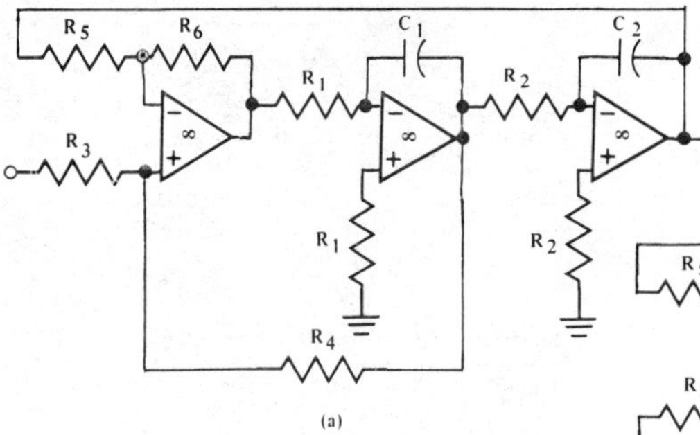

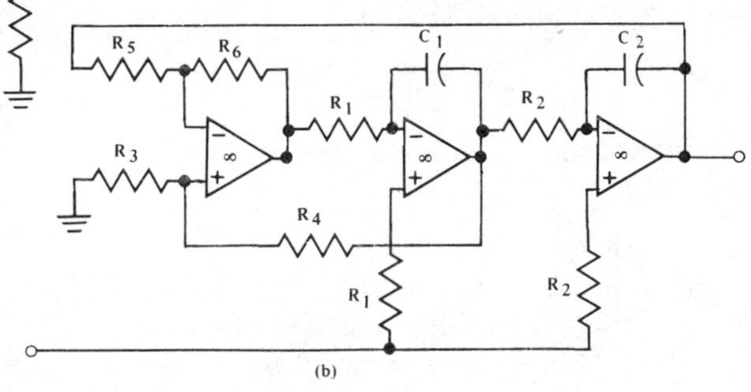

Fig. 9.6.4 Conversion of (a) Class 1E low-pass filter into (b) Class 1E complementary high-pass filter.

Hilberman's approach for designing complementary filters is especially convenient from a tuning standpoint. The filter is first tuned in its original form. Then the inputs are interchanged and it is operated in its complementary form. For instance in Fig. 9.6.4a, the low-pass filter is tuned so $H(0) = 1$ and for the required ω_o and ζ. Then the inputs are interchanged as shown in Fig. 9.6.4b. The complementary high-pass filter is then guaranteed to have $H_o = 1$, the same poles as the low-pass filter, and a zero at $2\zeta\omega_o$ (see Eq. 9.6.3). This procedure is much simpler than that which would be required to tune the complementary high-pass filter directly (e.g., see Eq. 9.6.5). It is equivalent to the tuning required using a differencing amplifier.

PROBLEMS

9.1 High-pass filters have the typical frequency response shown in Prob. 6.1. Describe the parameters required to specify the response.

9.2 The importance of compiling complete filter specifications cannot be overemphasized. A typical specification sheet was shown in Prob. 6.2. Briefly list the reasons for providing each data entry listed on that sheet.

9.3 A Class 1C low-pass filter is shown in Sec. 8.3. Draw its Class $1\overline{C}$ high-pass filter equivalent using the RC:CR transformation. Determine its transfer function and parameters directly from the low-pass filter results.

9.4 A fourth-order Chebyshev high-pass filter having 3 dB passband ripple, a 3 dB corner frequency of 1 KHz, and a maximum passband gain of unity is required. Design the filter using a Class 1E realization.

9.5 A low-pass/high-pass band-splitting filter used in speech analysis was analyzed in Prob. 6.7. The filters are shown in Fig. P8.25 in block diagram form. Design the high-pass filter using a Class 2A realization. Assume that its gain is arbitrary.

9.6 A fourth-order Butterworth low-pass filter having a dc gain of unity and a 3 dB bandwidth of 10 KHz was designed in Example 8.5.2. A Class $2\overline{A}$ realization was used. Redesign the filter in high-pass form directly using the RC:CR transformation and a Class 2A realization. Maintain the passband gain and the 3 dB cutoff frequency. Is the frequency up-scaling excessive and, therefore, is this a practical realization?

9.7 A multipurpose filter which could be operated in low-pass, high-pass, or band-pass modes was analyzed in Prob. 8.32. Repeat that problem for the high-pass filter.

9.8 In most filter designs, we wish to select C values and calculate the required R values. However, some normalized data exists where the R values are selected and the C values are calculated. An example is shown in Fig. P9.8a for a Class 2B Bessel, Butterworth, and Chebyshev low-pass filter where $R_n = R = 1$ and $\omega_o = 1$. The C values are listed in Table P9.8. (a) Describe how the results of Table P9.8 can be used to obtain high-pass filters. (b) Show the realizations for third-order Bessel and Butterworth high-pass filters. (c) Is this a good filter class to use for Chebyshev filters? Discuss, in view of the unity gain condition. (d)

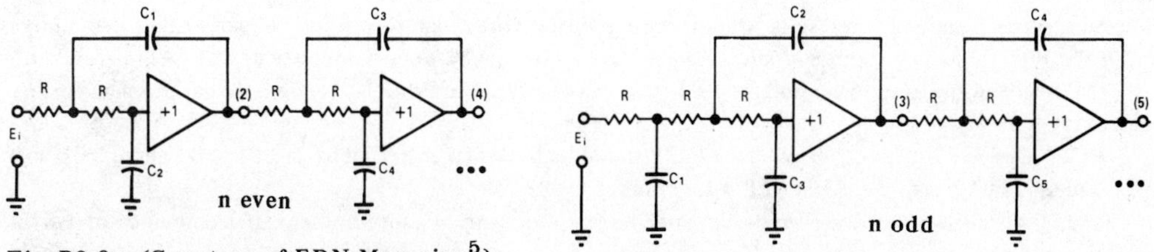

Fig. P9.8a (Courtesy of EDN Magazine[5])

Table P9.8 (Courtesy of EDN Magazine[5])

Butterworth Filter

N	C_1	C_2	C_3	C_4	C_5	C_6	C_7	C_8
1	1.00							
2	1.41	0.707						
3	1.39	3.54	0.202					
4	1.08	0.924	2.61	0.383				
5	1.09	1.80	0.509	3.24	0.309			
6	1.41	0.707	1.04	0.966	3.86	0.259		
7	1.38	2.52	0.288	1.11	0.900	4.49	0.223	
8	1.18	0.846	2.05	0.437	0.965	1.04	4.84	0.207

Chebyshev Filter–1 dB Ripple

N	C_1	C_2	C_3	C_4	C_5	C_6	C_7	C_8
1	1.97							
2	1.82	0.498						
3	2.34	14.8	0.0587					
4	7.17	0.141	2.97	1.21				
5	3.81	8.60	0.246	11.2	0.0905			
6	16.1	0.0628	5.98	0.305	4.31	1.86		
7	5.11	28.6	0.0510	21.9	0.0460	5.40	0.803	
8	28.6	0.0352	10.0	0.138	6.70	0.438	5.68	2.50

Bessel Filter

N	C_1	C_2	C_3	C_4	C_5	C_6	C_7	C_8
1	1.00							
2	0.667	0.500						
3	0.565	0.814	0.145					
4	0.345	0.317	0.475	0.183				
5	0.359	0.736	0.0572	0.298	0.235			
6	0.235	0.226	0.268	0.179	0.397	0.0948		
7	0.262	0.735	0.285	0.210	0.185	0.246	0.141	
8	0.179	0.176	0.229	0.114	0.192	0.151	0.352	0.0586

Chebyshev Filter–2 dB Ripple

N	C_1	C_2	C_3	C_4	C_5	C_6	C_7	C_8
1	1.31							
2	2.49	0.631						
3	3.01	26.9	0.0377					
4	9.53	0.113	3.95	1.14				
5	4.90	12.3	0.194	14.8	0.0708			
6	21.3	0.0486	7.79	0.241	5.70	1.75		
7	6.81	14.1	0.315	28.9	0.0355	10.3	0.152	
8	37.7	0.0270	13.3	0.106	8.86	0.345	7.51	2.36

Chebyshev Filter–0.5 dB Ripple

N	C_1	C_2	C_3	C_4	C_5	C_6	C_7	C_8
1	2.86							
2	1.40	0.470						
3	1.92	0.957	0.762					
4	5.70	0.165	2.36	1.88				
5	3.13	6.46	0.286	8.93	0.108			
6	12.9	0.0759	4.71	0.360	3.45	1.85		
7	4.18	20.6	0.0669	17.5	0.0561	4.33	0.909	
8	22.9	0.0431	8.05	0.168	5.38	0.518	4.56	2.49

Chebyshev Filter–3 dB Ripple

N	C_1	C_2	C_3	C_4	C_5	C_6	C_7	C_8
1	1.00							
2	3.10	0.455						
3	3.63	43.4	0.0253					
4	11.7	0.0943	4.86	1.05				
5	5.92	15.8	0.160	18.2	0.0586			
6	26.2	0.0400	9.57	0.200	7.01	1.61		
7	8.24	17.9	0.262	35.5	0.0291	12.7	0.126	
8	46.3	0.0222	16.3	0.0873	10.9	0.287	9.22	2.16

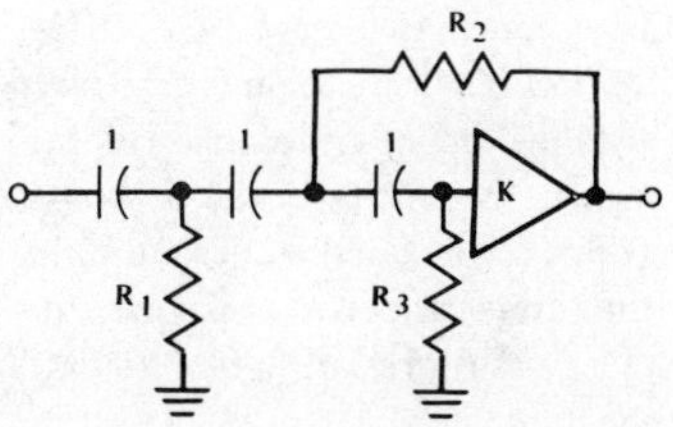

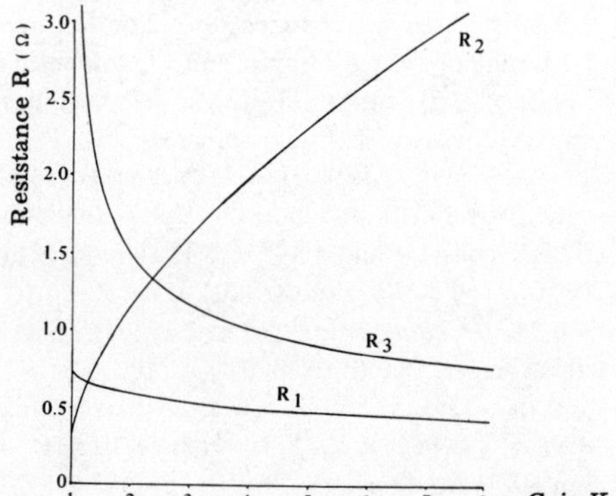

Fig. P9.8b (Courtesy of Proc. IEEE[6])

Stephenson has extended the results for third-order Butterworth high-pass filters for gains other than unity. From the high-frequency loop gain and root locus viewpoint, why does K increase as $R_2 \to \infty$ in Fig. P9.8b?

9.9 A band-splitting low-pass/high-pass filter was analyzed in Prob. 8.28. Repeat that problem for the high-pass filter.

9.10 Design a fourth-order synchronously-tuned high-pass filter having hf gain of unity and a 3 dB cutoff frequency of 1 KHz. Use a Class 2B realization.

9.11 A fourth-order Bessel low-pass filter having a dc gain of unity and a 3 dB bandwidth of 1 KHz was designed in Example 8.5.3. A Class 2B realization was used. Redesign the filter in high-pass form directly using the RC:CR transformation. Maintain the passband gain and the 3 dB cutoff frequency. Compare the result with Example 9.4.2.

9.12 A band-splitting filter was analyzed in Example 6.3.7. If we require M_s = 20 dB and M_p = 1.25 dB, a third-order elliptic filter can be used. A unity-gain third-order elliptic low-pass filter has a block diagram which consists of a first-order LPF stage having parameters $(H_o, f_o) = (0.866/k, 0.593)$ cascaded with a first-order BSF stage having parameters $(H_o, f_{op}, \zeta_p, f_{oz}) = (k, 1.001, 0.147, 1.414)$. Design the analogous high-pass filter having a 1.25 dB corner frequency of 1209 Hz. Use a Class 2B realization.

9.13 A third-order elliptic low-pass filter having a dc gain of unity and a 1.25 dB bandwidth of 1 KHz was designed in Example 8.5.6. A Class 2B realization was used. Redesign the filter in high-pass form directly using the RC:CR transformation. Maintain the passband gain and the 1.25 dB cutoff frequency.

9.14 The Dolby B noise reduction system was described in Prob. 2.10. Two high-pass filters were utilized. One was a high-pass filter having a fixed 3 dB frequency of 1.5 KHz. The other was a tunable high-pass filter. Design the fixed high-pass filter to be fourth-order Butterworth having a 3 dB bandwidth of 1.5 KHz. Use a Class 2C realization.

9.15 In Prob. 6.9, we found that the F1A-weighting curve could be realized as shown in Fig. P9.15. Design the high-pass filter using a Class $2\overline{C}$ realization.

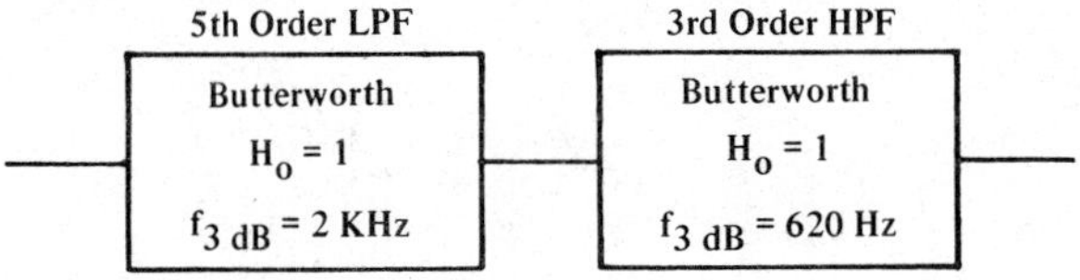

Fig. P9.15

9.16 A third-order parabolic low-pass filter having H_o = 10 and f_{3dB} = 1 KHz was designed in Example 8.5.4. A Class 2C realization was used. Redesign the filter in high-pass form directly using the RC:CR transformation and a Class $2\overline{C}$ realization. Maintain H_o and f_{3dB}. Is the frequency down-scaling excessive and, therefore, is this a practical design?

9.17 In Prob. 6.10, we determined that the C-weighting curve could be realized using a third-order Butterworth high-pass filter cascaded with a fourth-order Chebyshev low-pass filter. The high-pass filter has f_{3dB} = 732 Hz and H_o = 1. Design the entire high-pass filter using a Class 2E realization for the second-order stage.

9.18 Redesign the fourth-order Bessel high-pass filter of Example 9.4.2 using Class 2E stages.

9.19 Redesign the fourth-order synchronously-tuned filter of Example 9.4.3 using Class 2E stages.

9.20 Design a gain-tuned second-order Chebyshev filter to have an upper corner frequency of 2.5 KHz, a 5:1 tuning range, 3 dB ripple, and a Q tolerance of ± 5%. Use the first filter in Fig. 9.5.1. Gain is arbitrary.

9.21 A patient monitoring system was discussed in Prob. 2.22. It uses the second-order low-pass and high-pass Butterworth filters shown in Fig. P9.21. They have variable corner frequencies in the 5 Hz–10 KHz (LPF) and DC–800 Hz (HPF) ranges. (a) Classify the filters used. Is this class a good choice from the sensitivity and drift standpoint? (Hint: Remember the ζ value.) (b) Do the filters use active or passive tuning? Is ζ constant and why? (c) Design the high-pass filter for corner frequencies (in Hz) of 800, 400, 200, 100, 50, 25, 0.5, 0.1, and DC. (d) Is a gain-tuned filter suitable in this application?

9.22 As discussed in Prob. 2.32, high-pass filters must often be "tuned" to obtain their required parameters. Repeat that problem.

9.23 Repeat Prob. 8.41 for the Class 1A high-pass filter of Sec. 9.3.

9.24 Repeat Prob. 8.41 for the Class $1\overline{C}$ high-pass filter of Sec. 9.3. (Hint: To reduce work, should K_1 or K_2 be used?)

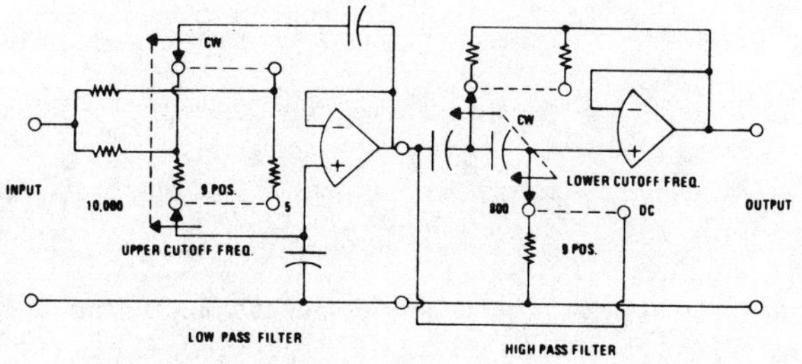

Fig. P9.21 (Courtesy of Western Periodicals Company[7])

9.25 The Class 2B low-pass filter of Prob. 8.4 1 had an input impedance of

$$Z^{(k)} = \frac{R}{(2-K)s_n} \frac{s_n^2 + (3-K)s_n + 1}{1 + s_n/(2-K)}$$

Perform the RC:CR transformation to obtain the input impedance to the Class 2B high-pass filter. Write its input impedance directly from $Z^{(k)}$. Plot and interpret the results.

9.26 Convert the Class 1A high-pass filter of Sec. 9.3 into a Class 1A complementary high-pass filter. Obtain a suitable set of design equations.

9.27 Repeat Prob. 9.26 for a Class $1\overline{C}$ high-pass filter.

9.28 Convert the Class 1B low-pass filter of Sec. 8.3 into a Class 1B complementary high-pass filter. Use the complementary input technique. Compare the result with Example 9.6.1.

9.29 Convert the Class 2B low-pass filter of Sec. 8.3 into a Class 2B complementary high-pass filter. Use the complementary input technique.

9.30 A fourth-order Butterworth low-pass filter having $H_o = 1$ and $f_{3dB} = 10$KHz was designed in Example 8.5.2. Show how it may be converted into a complementary high-pass filter. Plot its step response and compare with that of its associated low-pass filter.

9.31 Repeat Prob. 9.30 for the fourth-order Bessel low-pass filter having $H_o = 1$ and $f_{3dB} = 1$ KHz in Example 8.5.3.

9.32 Repeat Prob. 9.30 for the third-order elliptic low-pass filter having $H_o = 1$ and $f_{1.25dB} = 1$ KHz in Example 8.5.6.

9.33 A fourth-order Chebyshev low-pass filter was realized in Example 8.5.5. We are interested in its complementary high-pass filter. (a) Can the low-pass filter conversion be made using complementary input techniques? (b) Describe how to change the requirements of the block diagrams so that complementary input techniques can be used. (c) Show how a differencing amplifier can be used to obtain the complementary high-pass filter.

9.34 A differencing amplifier is shown in Fig. P9.34. Show that the output equals

$$V_o = \frac{1 + R_f/R_1}{1 + R_2/R_3} V_1 - \frac{R_f}{R_1} V_2$$

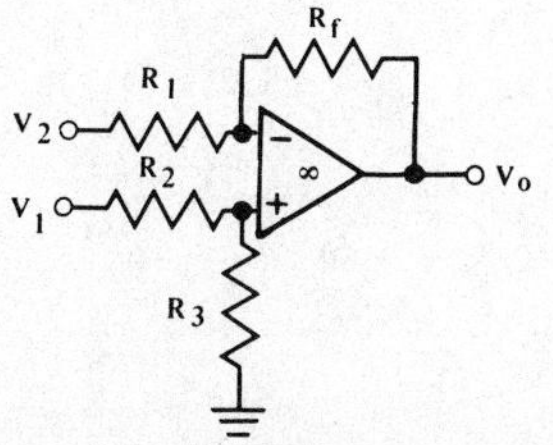

Fig. P9.34

9.35 A low-transient high-pass filter was analyzed in Prob. 6.14. Its normalized transfer function equals

$$H_{CHP}(s) = \frac{s(s^2 + 0.591s + 1.177)}{(s + 0.593)(s^2 + 0.295s + 1.002)}$$

Draw the block diagram of the filter.

REFERENCES

1. Mitra, S. K., "A network transformation for active RC networks," Proc. IEEE, vol. 55, pp. 2021–2022, Nov., 1967.
2. Mitra, S. K., *Analysis and Synthesis of Linear Active Networks*, Sec. 3.2, Wiley, NY, 1969.
3. Cole, L. G., "Practical design of active filters," M.S.E.E. Directed Research, California State Univ., Long Beach, Jan., 1975.
4. Hilberman, D., "Input and ground as complements in active filters," IEEE Trans. Circuit Theory, vol. CT-20, pp. 540–547, Sept., 1973.
5. Al-Nasser, F., "Tables speed design of low-pass active filter," EDN Magazine, pp. 23–32, March 15, 1971.
6. Stephenson, F. W., "High-pass realization of equal-valued capacitor active RC networks," Proc. IEEE, vol. 68, p. 996, Aug., 1972.
7. Koerner, H., and E. F. Furst, "Electrically isolated instrumentation for cardiac cathaterization laboratory," Conf. Rec., pp. 706–710, 7th Asilomar Conf. on Circuits, Systems and Computers, Nov., 1973. Western Periodicals Company.

10 BAND-PASS FILTERS

'It's the oldest rule in the book,' said the King.
'Then it ought to be Number One,' said Alice.
Carroll

The next important class of filter we want to consider is the band-pass variety. We begin by investigating band-pass filters from the classification viewpoint of Chap. 7. We will investigate the intuitive RC:CR half-transformation which can be used to convert low-pass and high-pass filters into band-pass filters. A set of filter design sheets will be compiled. These sheets will be used to investigate and design a variety of band-pass filters. We will compare the gain and sensitivity bounds of the various filters and make qualitative evaluations of the designs. Tunable band-pass filters of various types shall also be considered. We will conclude with a discussion of frequency discriminators and their design.

10.1 BAND-PASS FILTER CLASSES

Band-pass filters of first-order have gains which equal

$$H(s) = H_o \frac{(s/\omega_o)/Q}{(s/\omega_o)^2 + (s/\omega_o)/Q + 1} \tag{10.1.1}$$

Quasi-band-pass filters fail to have zero gain at low and/or high frequencies and are described by the general biquadratic form

$$H(s) = H_o \frac{(1 + s/z_1)(a + s/z_2)}{(s/\omega_o)^2 + (s/\omega_o)/Q + 1} \tag{10.1.2}$$

In quasi-band-pass filters, $Q \gg 1$ or $\zeta \ll 1$ to give significant gain peaking in the vicinity of the center frequency ω_o. Again, band-stop filters are required when designing elliptic filters. When needed, we will simply utilize a band-stop filter from the next chapter and reserve its discussion until later. In general, we shall be concerned with only first-order band-pass filters described by Eq. 10.1.1. Such filters are completely described by their resonant frequency ω_o, the pole Q, and the midband gain H_o. In the filter designs of Chaps. 2–6, we summarized this information in a band-pass filter (BPF) block. We now shall implement these blocks with hardware. It should be noted that we will use filter Q, rather than damping factor ζ, to be consistent with most band-pass filter nomenclature.

We must again select the class of band-pass filter which we want to utilize, so that we can freely make the gain-sensitivity tradeoffs discussed in Chap. 7. This assumes we can realize band-pass filters in any class which is indeed the case as we will now show. Consider the active filters having the simplest topology of a single forward branch using the assumptions listed in Sec. 8.1. These filters have the flow graph of Fig. 8.1.1 and a transfer function given by Eq. 8.1.4. The numerator of the gain function is equal to the numerator of the forward path gain product $K_1K_2T_{13}T_{45}$. Therefore, the form of the numerators of T_{13} and T_{45} determine the filter type. Using the notation of Eqs. 8.1.5–8.1.8, it was shown in Eq. 8.1.9 that the numerator of the transfer function H(s) for first-order decomposition filters is

$$\begin{aligned}\text{Num } H(s) &= K_1K_2(c_{50} + c_{51}s)(d_{30} + d_{31}s) \\ &= K_1K_2[c_{50}d_{30} + (c_{50}d_{31} + c_{51}d_{30})s + c_{51}d_{31}s^2]\end{aligned} \tag{10.1.3}$$

For H(s) to be band-pass, we must set the s^0 and s^2 coefficients of Num H equal to zero. This requires $c_{50}d_{30} = 0$ and $c_{51}d_{31} = 0$ where the s^1 coefficient must be nonzero. Thus, there are two permissible combinations. These are (1) $c_{50} = d_{31} = 0$ and (2) $c_{51} = d_{30} = 0$. Therefore, in the first case,

$$T_{13} = \frac{d_{30}}{a_{30} + a_{31}s} \quad \text{(LPF)}, \qquad T_{45} = \frac{c_{51}s}{a_{50} + a_{51}s} \quad \text{(HPF)} \tag{10.1.4}$$

Interchanging the filter types leads to the second case where

$$T_{13} = \frac{d_{31}s}{a_{30} + a_{31}s} \quad \text{(HPF)}, \qquad T_{45} = \frac{c_{50}}{a_{50} + a_{51}s} \quad \text{(LPF)} \tag{10.1.5}$$

Here we have more flexibility than in low-pass and high-pass filters which allowed only a single case (see Eqs. 8.1.10 and 9.1.4). In second-order decomposition filters, the numerator of the transfer function H(s) was given by Eq. 8.1.11. For H(s) to be band-pass, this requires $d_{30} = d_{32} = 0$ so that

$$T_{13} = \frac{d_{31}s}{a_{30} + a_{31}s + a_{32}s^2} \quad \text{(BPF)}, \qquad T_{45} = \frac{c_{50}}{a_{50}} \quad \text{(constant)} \tag{10.1.6}$$

Again, by investigating the form of T_{45} from Tables 7.19.1 and 7.19.2, we can immediately exclude any classes where T_{45} fails to be of the proper type. For first-order decomposition, T_{45} must be either low-pass or high-pass from Eqs. 10.1.4 and 10.1.5. From Table 7.19.1, *all* Class 1X filters are therefore realizable in band-pass form as long as T_{13} has the proper form. From Table 7.19.2, T_{45} is always constant so that band-pass filters result whenever T_{13} is band-pass. Therefore, band-pass filters are realizable in every class. Thus, we can again choose the filter class best suited to the application.

Let us illustrate the use of these results by formulating a Class 1A band-pass filter having the topological constraints of Fig. 8.1.1. From Table 7.19.1 and Eq. 10.1.4, such filters must have branch transfer functions of

$$T_{13} \ \text{(LPF)}, \qquad T_{63} = \frac{c_{31}s}{a_{30} + a_{31}s} \quad \text{(HPF)}, \qquad T_{45} \ \text{(HPF)} \tag{10.1.7}$$

Arranging RC networks to have these transfer functions and the topology of Fig. 8.1.1 results in one possible filter shown in Fig. 10.1.1a.

The Class 2A band-pass filter is obtained in a similar manner. From Table 7.19.2 and Eq.

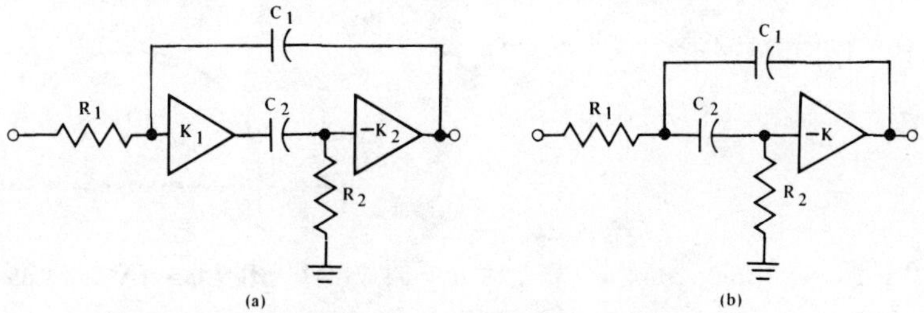

Fig. 10.1.1 (a) Class 1A and (b) Class 2A band-pass filters.

10.1.6,

$$T_{13}\ \text{(BPF)}, \qquad T_{63} = \frac{c_{32}s^2}{a_{30} + a_{31}s + a_{32}s^2}\ \text{(HPF)}, \qquad T_{45}\ \text{(constant)} \tag{10.1.8}$$

A single-amplifier realization is shown in Fig. 10.1.1b. Therefore, we again see that these filters can be easily generated.

10.2 LOW-PASS TO BAND-PASS FILTER TRANSFORMATION

Unfortunately, there is no topological transformation that allows the engineer to transform RC active low-pass filters or high-pass filters into RC active band-pass filters. However, with experience, the engineer can use a variation of the RC:CR transformation to generate band-pass filters from both low-pass and high-pass filters. For sake of terminology, we will call this rather *intuitive* approach an RC:CR half-transformation. Essentially, it consists of performing the RC:CR transformation on only *half* of a low-pass or high-pass filter. When properly applied, this converts the filter into a band-pass form. The transformation can only be used to rearrange the filter and to reformulate its flow graph description. It *cannot* be used to obtain new design equations, sensitivities, etc. We will perform this half-transformation on a few examples to illustrate its use.

EXAMPLE 10.2.1 Transform the Class 1B low-pass filter shown in Fig. 10.2.1a into a Class 1A band-pass filter using the RC:CR half-transformation.

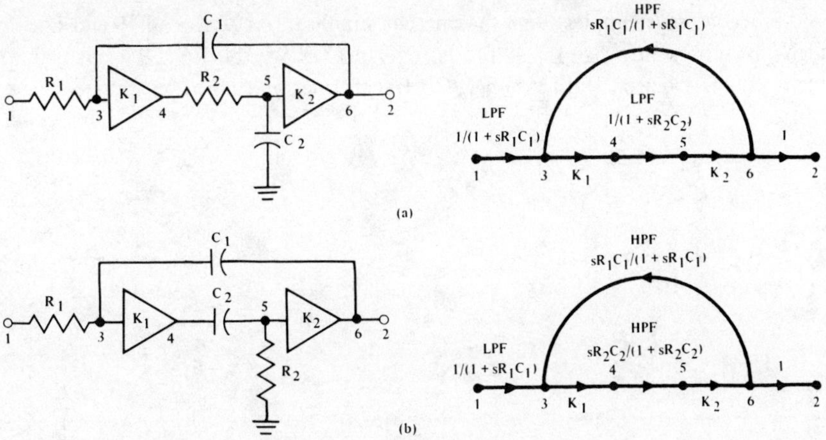

Fig. 10.2.1 Performing an RC:CR half-transformation on (a) Class 1B low-pass filter to produce (b) Class 1A band-pass filter.

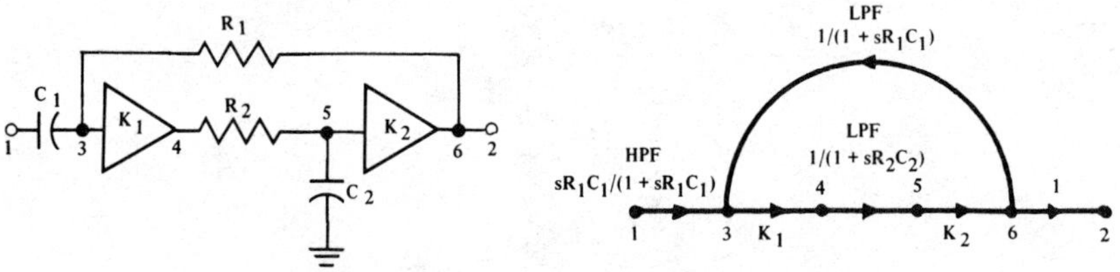

Fig. 10.2.2 Conversion of Class 1B low-pass filter into Class $1\bar{A}$ band-pass filter.

Solution The Class 1B low-pass filter has no local feedback and cross-couplings that are low-pass and high-pass. To generate a Class 1A band-pass filter, T_{45} and T_{63} must both be high-pass and T_{13} low-pass. Since T_{13} and T_{63} already have the proper form, we use the RC:CR transformation on the T_{45} low-pass cross-coupling half of the filter (i.e., the R_2C_2 half). This modifies the T_{45} branch of flow graph and results in the band-pass filter shown in Fig. 10.2.1b.

EXAMPLE 10.2.2 Repeat the previous example but generate a Class $1\bar{A}$ band-pass filter. Determine its transfer function.

Solution To generate a Class $1\bar{A}$ band-pass filter, we must produce low-pass cross-couplings and a high-pass T_{13}. Since T_{13} is low-pass and T_{63} is high-pass in Fig. 10.2.1a, we perform the RC:CR transformation on the R_1C_1 half of the filter. This results in the filter shown in Fig. 10.2.2. From the flow graph, the transfer function equals

$$H(s) = \frac{K_1K_2sR_1C_1}{s^2R_1C_1R_2C_2 + s(R_1C_1 + R_2C_2) + (1 - K_1K_2)} \tag{10.2.1}$$

It is important to re-emphasize that this half-transformation is topological, and is only used on the appropriate portions of the flow graph. It cannot be used directly to generate the gain expressions for the filter.

EXAMPLE 10.2.3 Transform the Class $2\bar{C}$ high-pass filter shown in Fig. 10.2.3a into a band-pass filter. Classify the filter. The analogous Class 2C low-pass filter was analyzed in Example 7.15.1.

Solution From Fig. 10.2.3a, T_{13} is high-pass which must be made band-pass using the RC:CR half-transformation. We therefore either interchange R_1 and C_1, or R_2 and C_2 as shown in Figs. 10.2.3b and c, respectively. The filter classes must be determined from the form of T_{43}. Since T_{43} describes an RC bridged-T network in both cases, T_{43} is biquadratic. Therefore, both band-pass filters are Class 2E.

Since these examples have shown that simple interchanges of R and C convert low-pass and high-pass filters into band-pass filters, why do we say the RC:CR transformation is an *intuitive* method? The reason is that the RC:CR transformation cannot be applied to the entire filter. The

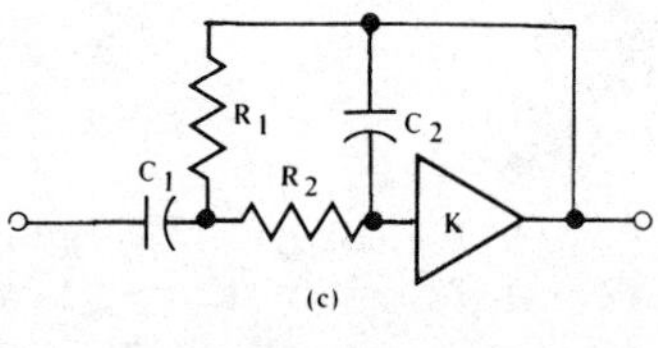

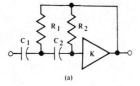

Fig. 10.2.3 Conversion of (a) Class $2\bar{C}$ high-pass filter into two band-pass filters (b) and (c).

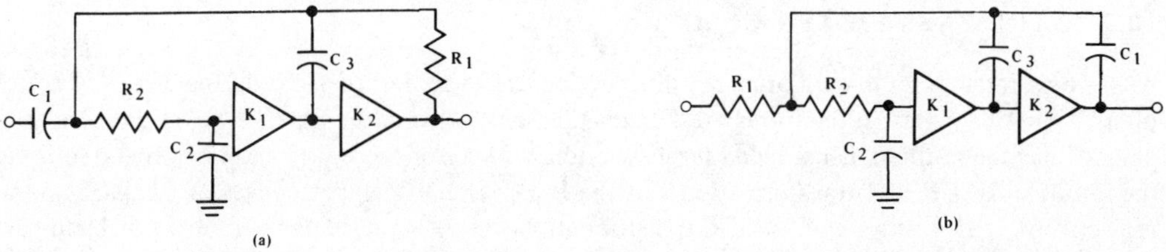

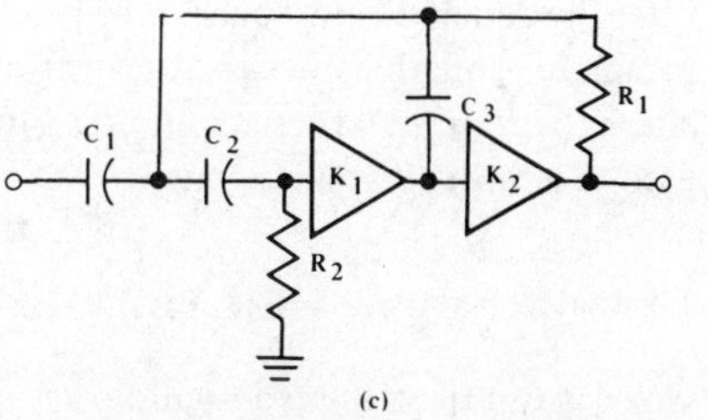

Fig. 10.2.4 Conversion of (a) Class $2\overline{C}$ band-pass filter into (b) Class 2B low-pass filter and (c) Class 2C high-pass filter.

engineer must exercise his judgement and *find* the proper (R, C) interchange which makes the $T_{13}T_{45}$ product band-pass, assuming the filter has the single-forward-branch topology outlined in the last section. He cannot use *any* (R, C) interchange. Therefore, in Class 1X filters, if the original filter is low-pass (high-pass) so that T_{13} and T_{45} are low-pass (high-pass), then the RC:CR half-transformation must be performed on either T_{13} or T_{45} to make it high-pass (low-pass). This was the case in Examples 10.2.1 and 10.2.2. Similarly in Class 2X filters, if the original filter is low-pass or high-pass so that T_{13} is low-pass or high-pass, then the RC:CR half-transformation must be performed on T_{13} to convert it into a band-pass section. This latter situation was the case in Example 10.2.3. When the filter has many components, this can become confusing if the engineer does not understand the RC:CR half-transformation method. Often the easiest approach is to begin with the flow graph of the original filter, find T_{13} and T_{45} and decide which branch gain needs to be converted, and then to finally apply the RC:CR half-transformation to the filter itself. This is illustrated in the next example.

EXAMPLE 10.2.4 The Class $2\overline{C}$ band-pass filter shown in Fig. 10.2.4a was analyzed in Example 7.16.1. Determine the analogous low-pass and high-pass filters which can be found using the RC:CR half-transformation.

Solution The flow graph of the band-pass filter is shown in Fig. 7.16.2. T_{13} is band-pass and T_{45} is a constant. To produce a low-pass filter, we must force T_{13} to be low-pass. From the filter, we see that performing the RC:CR half-transformation on R_1 and C_1 makes T_{13} low-pass. This results in the Class 2B low-pass filter shown in Fig. 10.2.4b. Replacing C_1 by R_3 results in the Class $2\overline{C}$ low-pass filter shown in Fig. 8.6.3a. Another Class $2\overline{C}$ low-pass filter results when we perform the RC:CR half-transformation on R_3 and C_3.

To produce a high-pass filter, we must force T_{13} to be high-pass. From the filter, we see that performing the RC:CR half-transformation on R_2 and C_2 makes T_{13} high-pass. This results in the Class 2C high-pass filter shown in Fig. 10.2.4c. The Class $2\overline{C}$ high-pass filter shown in Fig. 9.5.1a results when we perform the RC:CR half-transformation on R_1 and C_3 in addition to R_2 and C_2. This example shows the wide variety of filters which can be generated from a single form using the concept of the RC:CR half-transformation.

It is also important to note that an RC:CR transformation (*not* half-transformation) can be applied to any band-pass filter to produce another band-pass filter. The filter class remains unchanged for Class B, D, and E filters; however, the class is complemented for Class A, $\overline{A}$, C, and $\overline{C}$ filters. Therefore, applying the RC:CR transformation to band-pass filters and the intuitive RC:CR transformation to low-pass and high-pass filters, gives us considerable latitude in developing band-pass filters.

10.3 BAND-PASS FILTER COMPILATIONS

We have seen that a set of well-prepared filter design sheets are indispensible in the design of active filters. More band-pass filter forms are known than any other filter type. A representative sampling of band-pass filters is compiled in this section.[1] Many of these filters can be generated using the intuitive RC:CR half-transformation and the low-pass and high-pass filters of Chaps. 8 and 9, respectively. Of course, the RC:CR transformation can be applied to any of these band-pass filters producing other band-pass filters. (This is convenient for verifying transfer functions and parameter equations between transformed filter pairs.) Thus, we have great flexibility in choosing alternative forms. These band-pass filters have been found useful in actual design work and can be used in almost all applications.

10.4 BAND-PASS FILTER DESIGN EXAMPLES

Now let us utilize these design sheets to realize a variety of band-pass filters. Their design proceeds in the same fashion as that of low-pass and high-pass filters.

EXAMPLE 10.4.1 A data recorder receives an FSK signal over a telephone line from a remote FSK modem operating at 25 Bps. The data modem transmits a signal of 2012.5 Hz for a "1" of data and 1987.5 Hz for a "0". Design a first-order band-pass filter for the input of the data recorder to eliminate noise and extraneous signals but which will pass the signals. Design for a center frequency of 2000 Hz and a bandwidth of 2(25) = 50 Hz. Design two band-pass filters using Class 1A and 2A realizations. Compare the two designs.

Solution In this application, $f_o = 2000$ Hz, $B = 50$ Hz, and $Q = 2000/50 = 40$. It is therefore a high-Q filter. The design equations for the Class 1A filter are:

Set: $R_1 = R_2 = R, \quad C_1 = C_2 = C$ (For Minimum Gain and Minimum Sensitivity)

Given: ω_o, Q

Choose: C

Calculate: $R = 1/2Q\omega_o C, \quad K_1K_2 = 4Q^2 - 1, \quad H_o = -K_1K_2/2$

Therefore, the design proceeds as:

$$1/RC = 2\pi[2(40)(2\text{ KHz})] = 2\pi(160\text{ KHz}), \qquad C = 0.001\ \mu F, \qquad R = 995\ \Omega\ (\text{use } 1.00\text{ K})$$
$$K_1K_2 = 4(40)^2 - 1 \cong 80^2 = 76\text{ dB}, \qquad H_o \cong -6400/2 = -3200 = 70\text{ dB (inverting)} \tag{10.4.1}$$

The Class 1A realization is shown in Fig. 10.4.1a. If we set the gains equal so that $K_1 = -K_2$, then 38

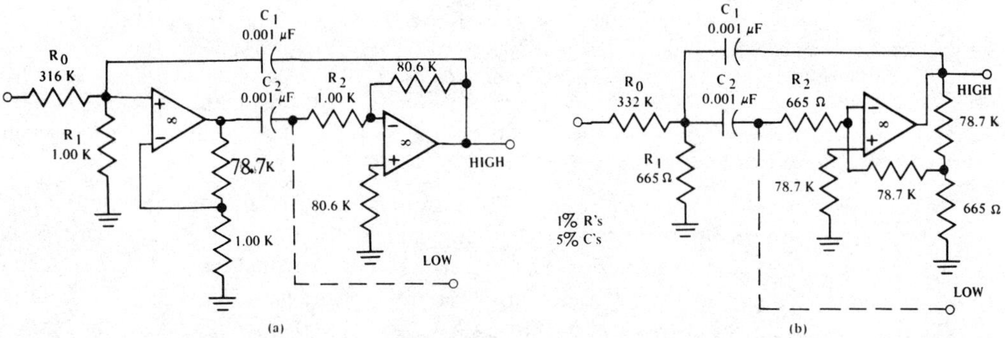

Fig. 10.4.1 Realization of (a) Class 1A and (b) Class 2A first-order band-pass filters.

CLASS 1A: BAND-PASS

Transfer Function:

$$H(s) = \frac{-K_1K_2sR_2C_2}{s^2(1 + K_1K_2)R_1C_1R_2C_2 + s(R_1C_1 + R_2C_2) + 1}$$

Parameters:

$$\omega_o = \frac{1}{[(1 + K_1K_2)R_1C_1R_2C_2]^{1/2}} \qquad H_o = \frac{-K_1K_2R_2C_2}{R_1C_1 + R_2C_2}$$

$$Q = \frac{[(1 + K_1K_2)R_1C_1R_2C_2]^{1/2}}{R_1C_1 + R_2C_2}$$

Design Equations: Set $R_1 = R_2 = R$, $C_1 = C_2 = C$ (For Minimum Gain and Minimum Sensitivity)

Given: ω_o, Q

Choose: C

Calculate: $R = 1/2Q\omega_oC$

$K_1K_2 = 4Q^2 - 1$

$H_o = -K_1K_2/2$

Sensitivities:

$$S_{R_1}^{\omega_o} = S_{R_2}^{\omega_o} = S_{C_1}^{\omega_o} = S_{C_2}^{\omega_o} = -\tfrac{1}{2} \qquad S_{K_1}^{H_o} = S_{K_2}^{H_o} = 1$$

$$S_{K_1}^{\omega_o} = S_{K_2}^{\omega_o} = -S_{K_1}^{Q} = -S_{K_2}^{Q} = -\tfrac{1}{2}(1 - 1/4Q^2)$$

$$S_{R_1}^{H_o} = -S_{R_2}^{H_o} = S_{C_1}^{H_o} = -S_{C_2}^{H_o} = -\tfrac{1}{2}$$

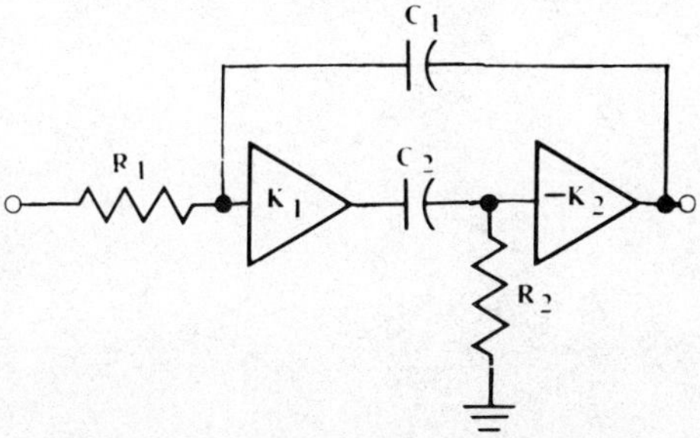

P. R. Geffe, "A Q-invariant active resonator," Proc. IEEE, vol. 57, p. 1442, Aug., 1969; and M. A. Soderstrand and S. K. Mitra, "Extremely low sensitivity active RC filter," Proc. IEEE, vol. 57, pp. 2175–2176, Dec., 1969.

CLASS $1\bar{A}$: BAND-PASS

Transfer Function:

$$H(s) = \frac{-K_1K_2sR_1C_1}{s^2R_1C_1R_2C_2 + s(R_1C_1 + R_2C_2) + (1 + K_1K_2)}$$

Parameters:

$$\omega_o = \left[\frac{1 + K_1K_2}{R_1C_1R_2C_2}\right]^{1/2} \qquad H_o = \frac{-K_1K_2R_1C_1}{R_1C_1 + R_2C_2}$$

$$Q = \frac{[(1 + K_1K_2)R_1C_1R_2C_2]^{1/2}}{R_1C_1 + R_2C_2}$$

Design Equations: Set $R_1 = R_2 = R$, $C_1 = C_2 = C$ (For Minimum Gain and Minimum Sensitivity)

Given: ω_o, Q

Choose: C

Calculate: $R = 2Q/\omega_oC$

$K_1K_2 = 4Q^2 - 1$

$H_o = -K_1K_2/2$

Sensitivities:

$$S_{R_1}^{\omega_o} = S_{R_2}^{\omega_o} = S_{C_1}^{\omega_o} = S_{C_2}^{\omega_o} = -1/2$$

$$S_{K_1}^{\omega_o} = S_{K_2}^{\omega_o} = S_{K_1}^{Q} = S_{K_2}^{Q} = 1/2\,(1 - 1/4Q^2)$$

$$S_{R_1}^{H_o} = -S_{R_2}^{H_o} = S_{C_1}^{H_o} = -S_{C_2}^{H_o} = 1/2$$

$$S_{K_1}^{H_o} = S_{K_2}^{H_o} = 1$$

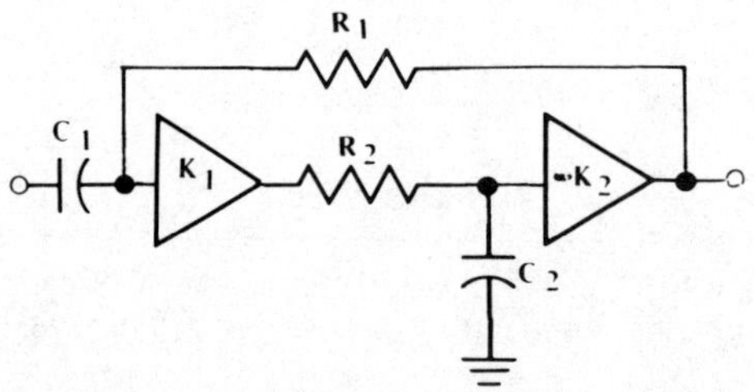

CLASS 1B: BAND-PASS

Transfer Function:

$$H(s) = \frac{K_1K_2sR_2C_2}{s^2R_1C_1R_2C_2 + s\left\{R_1C_1 + R_2C_2[1 + \rho(1 - K_1K_2)]\right\} + (1 + \rho)}, \qquad \rho = R_1/R_3$$

Parameters:

$$\omega_o = \left[\frac{1 + \rho}{R_1C_1R_2C_2}\right]^{1/2} \qquad H_o = \frac{K_1K_2R_2C_2}{R_1C_1 + R_2C_2[1 + \rho(1 - K_1K_2)]}$$

$$Q = \frac{[(1 + \rho)R_1C_1R_2C_2]^{1/2}}{R_1C_1 + R_2C_2[1 + \rho(1 - K_1K_2)]}$$

Design Equations: Set $C_1 = C_2 = C$, $R_2 = R_1R_3/(R_1 + R_3)$ (For Minimum Active Sensitivity)

Given: ω_o, Q

Choose: C, ρ

Calculate: $R_1 = (1 + \rho)/\omega_oC$ $\qquad K_1K_2 = 2(1 - 1/Q)(1 + 1/\rho)$

$R_2 = 1/\omega_oC$ $\qquad H_o = \dfrac{(1 + 1/\rho)(2Q - 1)}{1 + \rho - Q}$

$R_3 = (1 + \rho)/\rho\omega_oC$

Sensitivities:

$S_{R_1}^{\omega_o} = -1/2(1 + \rho)$ $\qquad S_{R_1}^{Q} = (2Q - 1)/2(1 + \rho)$ $\qquad S_K^{H_o} = 1 - Q$

$S_{R_2}^{\omega_o} = S_{C_1}^{\omega_o} = S_{C_2}^{\omega_o} = -1/2$ $\qquad S_{R_2}^{Q} = \dfrac{(1 + 2\rho)Q - (1 + \rho)}{2(1 + \rho - Q)}$ $\qquad S_{R_1}^{H_o} = (1 + \rho - Q)/(1 + \rho)$

$S_{R_3}^{\omega_o} = -\rho/2(1 + \rho)$ $\qquad S_{C_1}^{Q} = [2\rho Q - (1 + \rho)]/2(1 + \rho)$ $\qquad S_{R_2}^{H_o} = (\rho + 2Q - 1)/\rho$

$S_{K_1}^{Q} = S_{K_2}^{Q} = \rho(2Q - 1)/(1 + \rho)$ $\qquad S_{C_2}^{Q} = \rho(Q - 1)/(1 + \rho)$ $\qquad S_{R_3}^{H_o} = 1 - [Q(2 + \rho)/(1 + \rho)]$

$S_{C_1}^{H_o} = Q/(Q - 1)$

$S_{C_2}^{H_o} = Q$

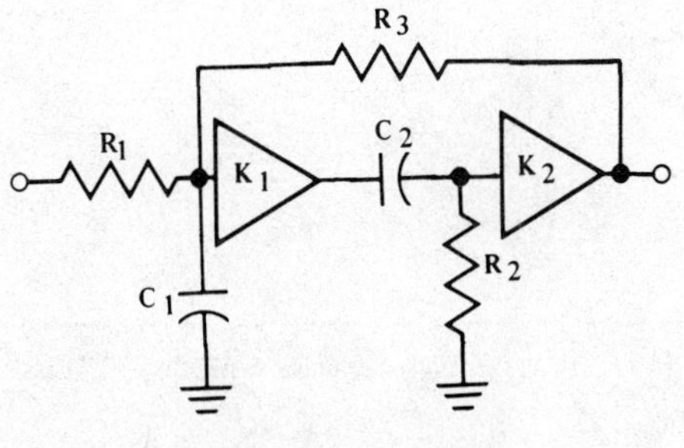

CLASS 1C: BAND-PASS

Transfer Function:

$$H(s) = \frac{-K_1K_2sR_2C_2}{s^2(1+K_1K_2)R_1C_1R_2C_2 + s\left\{R_1C_1 + R_2C_2[1+\rho(1+K_1K_2)]\right\} + (1+\rho)}, \qquad \rho = R_1/R_0$$

Parameters:

$$\omega_o = \left[\frac{1+\rho}{(1+K_1K_2)R_1C_1R_2C_2}\right]^{1/2} \qquad H_o = \frac{-K_1K_2R_2C_2}{R_1C_1 + R_2C_2[1+\rho(1+K_1K_2)]}$$

$$Q = \frac{[(1+K_1K_2)(1+\rho)R_1C_1R_2C_2]^{1/2}}{R_1C_1 + R_2C_2[1+\rho(1+K_1K_2)]}$$

Design Equations: Set $C_1 = C_2 = C$ (For Zero Active Q Sensitivities)

Given: ω_o, Q

Choose: C

Calculate: $$R_1 = \frac{2Q}{[2Q + (4Q^2-1)^{1/2}](4Q^2-1)^{1/2}}\frac{1}{\omega_o C} \cong 1/4Q\omega_o C$$

$$R_2 = \frac{1}{2Q + (4Q^2-1)^{1/2}}\frac{1}{\omega_o C} \cong 1/4Q\omega_o C$$

$$R_0 = 2Q/\omega_o C$$

$$K_1K_2 = 2[2Q + (4Q^2-1)^{1/2}](4Q^2-1)^{1/2} \cong 16Q^2$$

$$H_o \cong -2Q$$

Sensitivities:

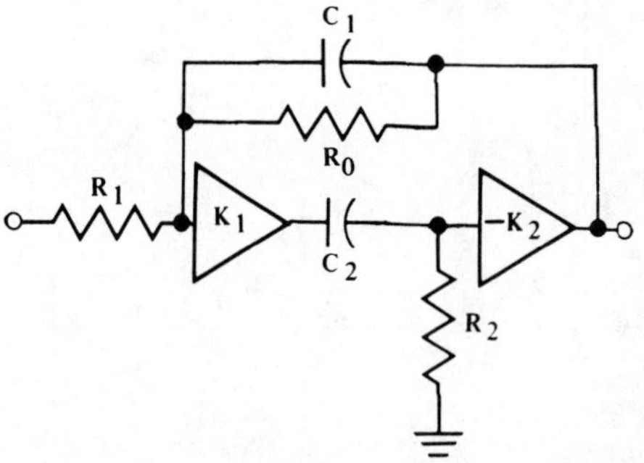

$$S_{R_0}^{\omega_o} \cong 0$$

$$S_{R_1}^{\omega_o} \cong -1/2$$

$$S_{R_2}^{\omega_o} = S_{C_1}^{\omega_o} = S_{C_2}^{\omega_o} = -1/2$$

$$S_{R_0}^{Q} \cong 1/2$$

$$S_{R_1}^{Q} \cong S_{R_2}^{Q} \cong S_{C_1}^{Q} \cong -S_{C_2}^{Q} \cong -1/4$$

M. A. Soderstrand and S. K. Mitra, "Design of active RC filters with zero gain-sensitivity product," IEEE Trans. Circuit Theory, vol. CT-20, pp. 441–445, July, 1973.

CLASS $1\overline{C}$: BAND-PASS

Transfer Function:

$$H(s) = \frac{-K_1K_2sR_1C_1}{s^2R_1C_1R_2C_2 + s\left\{R_1C_1 + R_2C_2[1+\rho(1-K_1)]\right\} + [1 + K_1K_2 + \rho(1-K_1)]}, \qquad \rho = R_1/R_0$$

Parameters:

$$\omega_o = \left[\frac{1 + K_1K_2 + \rho(1-K_1)}{R_1C_1R_2C_2}\right]^{1/2} \qquad H_o = \frac{-K_1K_2R_1C_1}{R_1C_1 + R_2C_2[1+\rho(1-K_1)]}$$

$$Q = \frac{\left\{[1 + K_1K_2 + \rho(1-K_1)]R_1C_1R_2C_2\right\}^{1/2}}{R_1C_1 + R_2C_2[1+\rho(1-K_1)]}$$

Design Equations: Set $R_1C_1 = R_2C_2 = RC = T$

Given: ω_o, Q

Choose: C, T, ρ

Calculate: $R = 1/TC$

$$K_1 = 1 + 2/\rho - \omega_oT/Q$$

$$K_2 = (\omega_o^2T^2 - \omega_oT/Q + 1)/K_1$$

$$H_o = -K_1K_2/[2 + \rho(1-K_1)]$$

Sensitivities:

$$S_{K_1}^{\omega_o} = [\omega_o^2T^2 - (1+\rho)]/2\omega_o^2T^2$$

$$S_{K_2}^{\omega_o} = S_{K_2}^{Q} = (\omega_o^2T^2 - \omega_oT/Q + 1)/2\omega_o^2T^2$$

$$S_{K_1}^{Q} = -[\omega_o^2T^2 - 4Q\omega_oT + (1+\rho)]/2\omega_o^2T^2$$

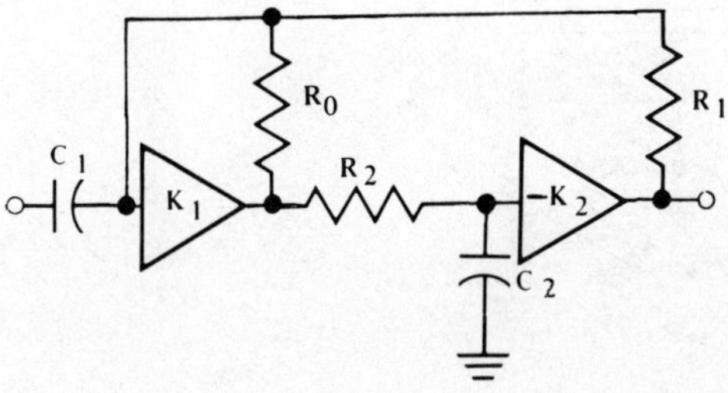

M. A. Soderstrand and S. K. Mitra, "Gain and sensitivity limitations of active RC filters," IEEE Trans. Circuit Theory, vol. CT-18, pp. 600–609, Nov., 1971.

CLASS 1E: BAND-PASS

Transfer Function:

$$H(s) = \frac{1 + R_6/R_5}{1 + R_3/R_4} \frac{-sR_2C_2}{s^2R_1C_1R_2C_2 + sR_2C_2[(1 + R_6/R_5)/(1 + R_4/R_3)] + R_6/R_5}$$

Parameters:

$$\omega_o = \left[\frac{R_6/R_5}{R_1C_1R_2C_2}\right]^{1/2} \qquad H_o = -R_4/R_3$$

$$Q = \frac{1 + R_4/R_3}{1 + R_6/R_5}\left[\frac{R_6}{R_5}\frac{R_1C_1}{R_2C_2}\right]^{1/2}$$

Design Equations: Set $R_1 = R_2 = R$, $C_1 = C_2 = C$, $R_3 = R_5 = R_6$

Given: ω_o, Q

Choose: C, R_3

Calculate: $R = 1/\omega_o C$

$R_4 = (2Q - 1)R_3$

$H_o = -(2Q - 1)$

Sensitivities:

$$S_{R_1}^{\omega_o} = S_{R_2}^{\omega_o} = S_{R_5}^{\omega_o} = -S_{R_6}^{\omega_o} = S_{C_1}^{\omega_o} = S_{C_2}^{\omega_o} = -1/2$$

$$S_{R_1}^{Q} = -S_{R_2}^{Q} = S_{C_1}^{Q} = -S_{C_2}^{Q} = 1/2$$

$$S_{R_3}^{Q} = -S_{R_4}^{Q} = 1/2Q - 1$$

$$S_{R_3}^{H_o} = -S_{R_4}^{H_o} = -1$$

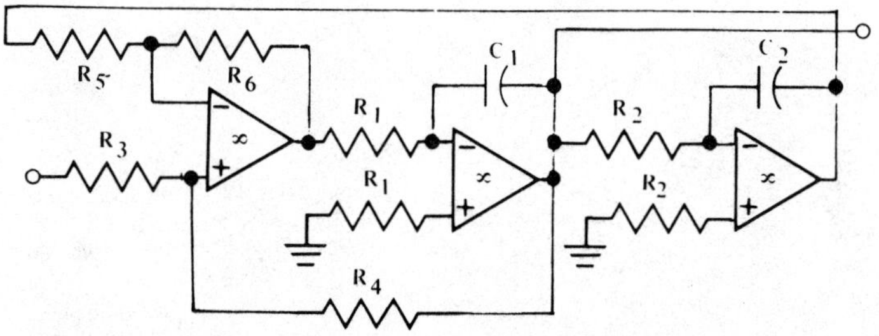

L. P. Huelsman, J. G. Graeme, and G. E. Tobey, *Operational Amplifiers*, Chap. 8.3.3, McGraw-Hill, NY, 1971.

CLASS 2A: BAND-PASS

Transfer Function:

$$H(s) = \frac{-KsR_2C_2}{s^2(1+K)R_1C_1R_2C_2 + s[R_1(C_1+C_2)+R_2C_2] + 1}$$

Parameters:

$$\omega_o = \frac{1}{[(1+K)R_1C_1R_2C_2]^{1/2}}$$

$$H_o = \frac{-KR_2C_2}{R_1(C_1+C_2)+R_2C_2}$$

$$Q = \frac{[(1+K)R_1C_1R_2C_2]^{1/2}}{R_1C_1(1+C_2/C_1)+R_2C_2}$$

Design Equations: Set $R_1 = R_2 = R$, $C_1 = C_2 = C$

Given: ω_o, Q

Choose: C

Calculate: $R = 1/3Q\omega_oC$

$K = 9Q^2 - 1$

$H_o = -K/3$

Sensitivities:

$$S_{R_1}^{\omega_o} = S_{R_2}^{\omega_o} = S_{C_1}^{\omega_o} = S_{C_2}^{\omega_o} = -½$$

$$S_{C_1}^{H_o} = -S_{C_2}^{H_o} = -1/3$$

$$S_K^{\omega_o} = -S_K^{Q} = -½(1 - 1/9Q^2)$$

$$S_K^{H_o} = 1$$

$$S_{R_1}^{Q} = -S_{R_2}^{Q} = -S_{C_1}^{Q} = S_{C_2}^{Q} = -1/6$$

$$S_{R_1}^{H_o} = -S_{R_2}^{H_o} = -2/3$$

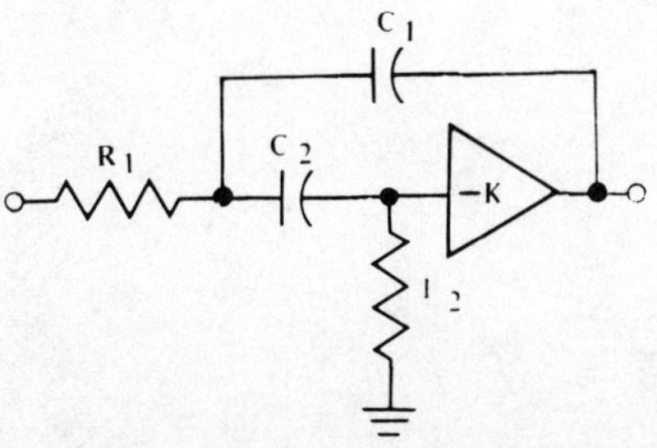

R. P. Sallen and E. L. Key, "A practical method for designing RC active filters," IRE Trans. Circuit Theory, vol. CT-2, pp. 74–85, March, 1955; and P. R. Geffe, "RC-resonators for active filters," IEEE Trans. Circuit Theory, vol. CT-15, pp. 415–419, Dec., 1968.

CLASS $2\overline{A}$: BAND-PASS

Transfer Function:

$$H(s) = \frac{-KsR_1C_1}{s^2R_1C_1R_2C_2 + s[R_1C_1 + R_2(C_1 + C_2)] + (1 + K)}$$

Parameters:

$$\omega_o = \left[\frac{1 + K}{R_1C_1R_2C_2}\right]^{1/2} \qquad H_o = \frac{-KR_1C_1}{R_1C_1 + R_2(C_1 + C_2)}$$

$$Q = \frac{[(1 + K)R_1C_1R_2C_2]^{1/2}}{R_1C_1 + R_2C_2(1 + C_1/C_2)}$$

Design Equations: Set $R_1 = R_2 = R$. $C_1 = C_2 = C$

Given: ω_o, Q

Choose: C

Calculate: $R = 3Q/\omega_oC$

$K = 9Q^2 - 1$

$H_o = -K/3$

Sensitivities:

$$S_{R_1}^{\omega_o} = S_{R_2}^{\omega_o} = S_{C_1}^{\omega_o} = S_{C_2}^{\omega_o} = -\tfrac{1}{2} \qquad S_{C_1}^{H_o} = -S_{C_2}^{H_o} = 1/3$$

$$S_K^{\omega_o} = S_K^{Q} = \tfrac{1}{2}(1 - 1/9Q^2) \qquad S_K^{H_o} = 1$$

$$S_{R_1}^{Q} = -S_{R_2}^{Q} = -S_{C_1}^{Q} = S_{C_2}^{Q} = 1/6$$

$$S_{R_1}^{H_o} = -S_{R_2}^{H_o} = 2/3$$

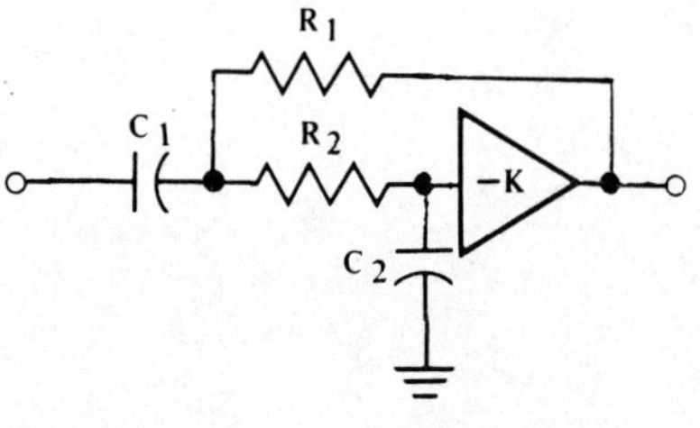

CLASS 2B: BAND-PASS

Transfer Function:

$$H(s) = \frac{KsR_2C_2}{s^2R_1C_1R_2C_2 + s\left\{R_1C_1[R_2/R_3 + (1-K)C_2/C_1] + R_2C_2[1 + R_1/R_3]\right\} + [(R_1 + R_2)/R_3]}$$

Parameters:

$$\omega_o = \frac{1}{\left\{R_3[R_1R_2/(R_1 + R_2)]C_1C_2\right\}^{1/2}}$$

$$Q = \left[\frac{R_1 + R_2}{R_3}\right]^{1/2} \frac{(R_1C_1R_2C_2)^{1/2}}{R_1C_1[R_2/R_3 + (1-K)C_2/C_1] + R_2C_2[1 + R_1/R_3]}$$

$$H_o = \frac{KR_2C_2}{R_1C_1[R_2/R_3 + (1-K)C_2/C_1] + R_2C_2[1 + R_1/R_3]}$$

Design Equations: Set $R_1 = R_2 = R$, $R_3 = 2R$, $C_1 = C_2 = C$

Given: ω_o, Q

Choose: C

Calculate: $R = 1/\omega_o C$

$K = 3 - 1/Q$

$H_o = K/(3 - K)$

Sensitivities:

$$S_{R_1}^{\omega_o} = S_{R_2}^{\omega_o} = S_{R_3}^{\omega_o} = S_{C_1}^{\omega_o} = S_{C_2}^{\omega_o} = -1/2$$

$$S_K^Q = 3Q - 1$$

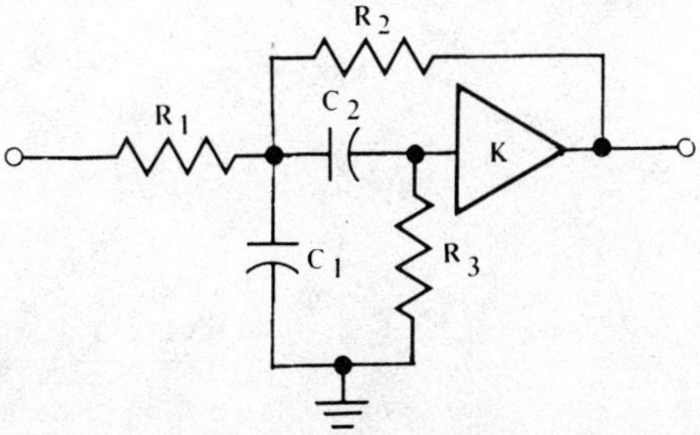

W. J. Kerwin and L. P. Huelsman, "The design of high performance active RC band-pass filters," IEEE Intl. Conv. Rec., vol. 14, part 10, pp. 74–80, 1960; and J. L. Hilburn and D. E. Johnson, *Manual of Active Filter Design*, Chap. 4, McGraw-Hill, NY, 1973.

CLASS 2C: BAND-PASS

Transfer Function:

$$H(s) = \frac{-KsR_2C_2}{s^2(1+K)R_1C_1R_2C_2 + s\left\{R_1C_1(1+C_2/C_1) + R_2C_2[1+\rho(1+K)]\right\} + (1+\rho)}, \qquad \rho = R_1/R_0$$

Parameters:

$$\omega_o = \left[\frac{1+\rho}{(1+K)R_1C_1R_2C_2}\right]^{1/2} \qquad H_o = \frac{-KR_2C_2}{R_1C_1(1+C_2/C_1) + R_2C_2[1+\rho(1+K)]}$$

$$Q = \frac{[(1+K)(1+\rho)R_1C_1R_2C_2]^{1/2}}{R_1C_1(1+C_2/C_1) + R_2C_2[1+\rho(1+K)]}$$

Design Equations: Set $C_1 = C_2 = C$ (For Zero Active Q Sensitivity)

Given: ω_o, Q

Choose: C

Calculate: $R_1 \cong 1/6Q\omega_oC$

$$R_2 = \frac{4Q^2+1}{4Q^2}\,\frac{1}{6Q\omega_oC} \cong 1/6Q\omega_oC$$

$$R_0 = 2Q/\omega_oC$$

$$K = [4Q^2/(4Q^2+1)]\,[36Q^2+3] - 1 \cong 36Q^2$$

$$H_o \cong -4Q$$

Sensitivities:

$$S_{R_0}^{\omega_o} \cong 0 \qquad S_{R_2}^{\omega_o} = S_{C_1}^{\omega_o} = S_{C_2}^{\omega_o} = -\tfrac{1}{2}$$

$$S_{R_1}^{\omega_o} \cong -\tfrac{1}{2} \qquad S_K^{\omega_o} \cong -\tfrac{1}{2}$$

$$S_{R_0}^{Q} \cong \tfrac{1}{2}$$

$$S_{R_1}^{Q} \cong S_{C_1}^{Q} \cong -S_{C_2}^{Q} \cong \tfrac{1}{2}$$

$$S_{R_2}^{Q} \cong 1/6$$

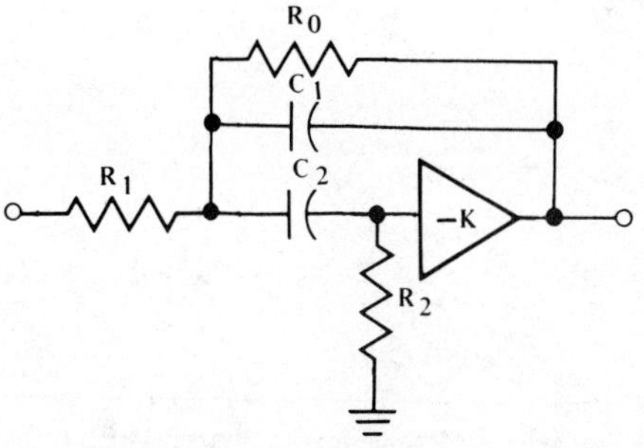

M. A. Soderstrand and S. K. Mitra, "Design of active RC filters with zero gain-sensitivity product," loc. cit.

CLASS $2\overline{C}$: BAND-PASS

Transfer Function:

$$H(s) = \frac{-KsR_1C_1}{s^2R_1C_1R_3C_2 + s\left\{R_1C_1[1 + (R_3/R_2)(1 + K) + C_2/C_1] + R_3C_2\right\} + (1 + K)[1 + (R_1 + R_3)/R_2]}$$

Parameters:

$$\omega_o = \left[\frac{(1 + K)(R_1 + R_2 + R_3)}{R_1C_1R_2C_2R_3}\right]^{1/2} \qquad H_o = \frac{-KR_1C_1R_2}{R_1C_1[R_2 + R_3(1 + K)] + R_2C_2[R_1 + R_3]}$$

$$Q = \frac{[(1 + K)(R_1 + R_2 + R_3)R_1C_1R_2C_2R_3]^{1/2}}{R_1C_1[R_2 + R_3(1 + K)] + R_2C_2[R_1 + R_3]}$$

Design Equations: Set $R_1 = R_3 = R_2/\rho = R$, $C_1 = C_2 = C$

Given: ω_o, Q

Choose: C_1, ρ

Calculate: $K = -1 - 3\rho + [\rho(2 + \rho)/2Q^2] \pm (\rho/Q)[-6 - 3\rho + (\rho + 2)^2/4Q^2]^{1/2}$

$$R = \frac{1}{\omega_o C}\,\frac{[(1 + K)(2 + \rho)]^{1/2}}{\rho^{1/2}}$$

$$H_o = -K/[3 + (1 + K)/\rho]$$

Sensitivities: Let $a = 2 + \rho$, $b = 1 + K + 3\rho$

$S_{K_1}^{\omega_o} = K/2(1 + K)$ $S_K^Q = -K(1 + K - 3\rho)/2b(1 + K)$ $S_{C_2}^Q = (1 + K - \rho)/2b$

$S_{R_1}^{\omega_o} = -(1 + \rho)/2a$ $S_{R_1}^Q = [1 + K(1 + \rho) - \rho^2]/2ab$ $S_K^{H_o} = (1 + 3\rho)/b$

$S_{R_2}^{\omega_o} = -1/a$ $S_{R_2}^Q = -[1 + K + \rho(2 - K)]/ab$ $S_{R_1}^{H_o} = \rho/b$

$S_{R_3}^{\omega_o} = -(1 + \rho)/a$ $S_{R_3}^Q = [1 + K + \rho(4 - K + \rho)]/2ab$ $S_{R_2}^{H_o} = (1 + K)/b$

$S_{C_1}^{\omega_o} = S_{C_2}^{\omega_o} = -1/2$ $S_{C_1}^Q = -(1 + K - \rho)/2b$ $S_{R_3}^{H_o} = -(1 + K + 2\rho)/b$

$S_{C_1}^{H_o} = -S_{C_2}^{H_o} = 2\rho/b$

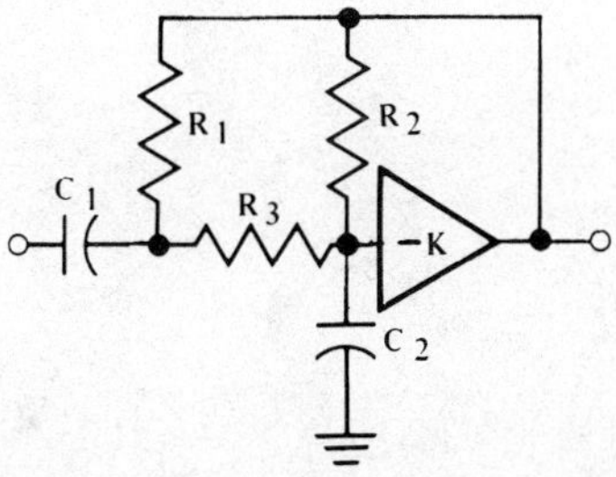

CLASS 2D: BAND-PASS

Transfer Function:

$$H(s) = \frac{-2K(sRC)}{(1+K)(sRC)^2 + 4(sRC) + (1+K)}$$

Parameters:

$\omega_o = 1/RC$ $H_o = -K/2$

$Q = ¼\,(1 + K)$

Design Equations:

Given: ω_o, Q

Choose: C

Calculate: $R = 1/\omega_o C$

$K = 4Q - 1$

$H_o = -K/2$

Sensitivities:

$S_R^{\omega_o} = S_C^{\omega_o} = -1$

$S_K^Q = 1 - 1/4Q$

$S_K^{H_o} = -1$

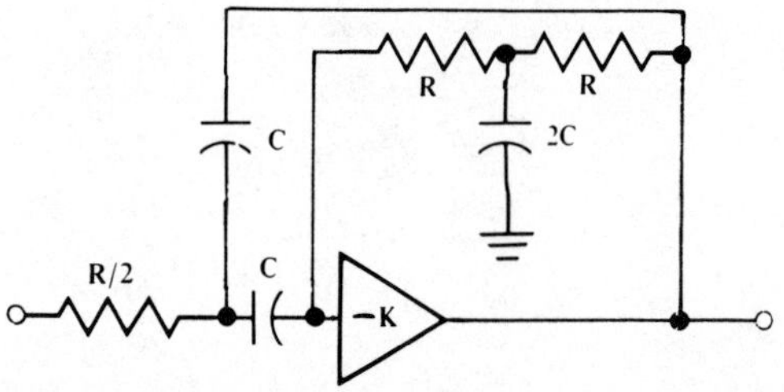

M. A. Soderstrand and S. K. Mitra, "Gain and sensitivity limitations of active RC filters," op. cit.

CLASS 2E: BAND-PASS

Transfer Function:

$$H(s) = \frac{-sR_5C_3}{s^2R_1C_3R_5C_4 + sR_1(C_3 + C_4) + (1 + R_1/R_2)}$$

Parameters:

$$\omega_o = \left[\frac{1 + R_2/R_1}{R_2C_3R_5C_4}\right]^{1/2} \qquad H_o = \frac{-R_5/R_1}{1 + C_4/C_3}$$

$$Q = \frac{(R_5/R_1 + R_5/R_2)^{1/2}}{(C_3/C_4)^{1/2} + (C_4/C_3)^{1/2}}$$

Design Equations: Set $C_3 = C_4 = C$

Given: ω_o, Q, $-H_o$

Choose: C

Calculate: $R_1 = Q/(-H_o\omega_oC)$

$R_2 = 1/(1 + H_o/2Q^2)2Q\omega_oC$

$R_5 = 2Q/\omega_oC$

Sensitivities:

$$S_{R_1}^{\omega_o} = S_{R_1}^{Q} = H_o/4Q^2$$

$$S_{R_2}^{\omega_o} = S_{R_2}^{Q} = \tfrac{1}{2}(1 + H_o/2Q^2)$$

$$S_{R_5}^{\omega_o} = S_{C_3}^{\omega_o} = S_{C_4}^{\omega_o} = -S_{R_5}^{Q} = -\tfrac{1}{2}$$

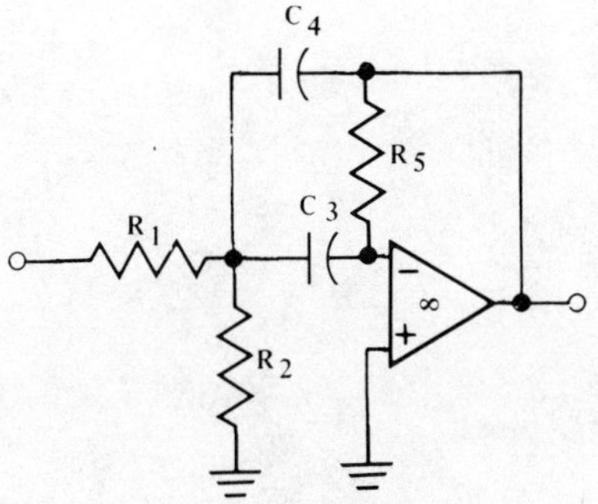

J. L. Hilburn and D. E. Johnson, loc. cit.

dB of gain is required in each stage. For an overall gain of 20 dB, we must insert an attenuator at the filter input with (70 – 20) = 50 dB of loss. This can be obtained using a 316:1 resistor divider at the input as shown. Signal-to-noise ratio (SNR) considerations require close proximity between the divider and K_1 amplifier. An alternative approach for low input levels is to use the unbuffered output in front of K_2 and adjust $K_1 = 10 = 20$ dB. Then $K_2 = 76 - 20 = 56$ dB = 631 (inverting). In this case, the input divider is unnecessary but the bandwidth of the K_2 amplifier is reduced about one decade as we shall discuss in Chap. 14.

Now let us design the Class 2A realization. The design equations are:

Set: $R_1 = R_2 = R, \quad C_1 = C_2 = C$

Given: ω_o, Q

Choose: C

Calculate: $R = 1/3Q\omega_o C, \quad K = 9Q^2 - 1, \quad H_o = -K/3$

Therefore, the design proceeds as:

$$1/RC = 2\pi[3(40)(2\text{ KHz})] = 2\pi(240\text{ KHz}), \qquad C = 0.001\ \mu F, \qquad R = 663\ \Omega \ (\text{use } 665\ \Omega)$$
$$K = 9(40)^2 - 1 \cong 14{,}400 = 83\text{ dB}, \qquad H_o \cong -14{,}400/3 = -4800 = 74\text{ dB (inverting)} \tag{10.4.2}$$

The Class 2A realization is shown in Fig. 10.4.1b. Now the entire gain of 83 dB must be realized with the single amplifier. For an overall gain of 20 dB, an attenuator with (74 – 20) = 54 dB of loss must be inserted at the input (480:1). Again, from a SNR standpoint, this requires careful circuit board layout. Alternatively, we can use the unbuffered output in front of the amplifier without the input attenuator. Since the midband gain is now only 1/3, another gain stage will be needed.

This example exphasizes the fact that Class A filters require high amplifier gains. Thus, the operational amplifiers used to realize these gains must themselves have even larger open-loop gains and wider bandwidths. Therefore, proper op amps must be used as will be discussed in Sec. 14.4.

EXAMPLE 10.4.2 A first-order band-pass filter for decoding Touch-Tone frequencies was analyzed in Example 2.7.2. Its center frequency varied from 697 Hz to 1633 Hz. Assume that Q = 22 and that a midband gain of 10 is required. Design the filter using a Class 1E realization assuming f_o = 697 Hz. What filter components should be changed to most easily modify the center frequency of the filter? Construct a tuning table showing component values required to obtain the different center frequencies.

Solution The filter realization form is shown in Fig. 10.4.2. Its design equations are:

Set: $R_1 = R_2 = R, \quad C_1 = C_2 = C, \quad R_3 = R_5 = R_6$

Given: ω_o, Q

Choose: C, R_3

Calculate: $R = 1/\omega_o C, \quad R_4 = (2Q - 1)R_3, \quad H_o = -(2Q - 1)$

Choosing R_3 = 1.00 K, then:

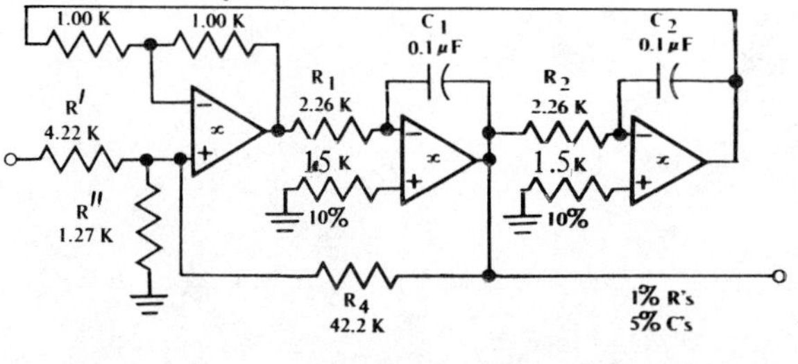

Fig. 10.4.2 Realization of Class 1E first-order band-pass filter.

Table 10.4.1 Resistor selection chart for band-pass filter of Fig. 10.4.2.

f_o (Hz)	697	770	852	941	1209	1336	1477	1633
Calculated	2.28 K	2.06 K	1.87 K	1.69 K	1.31 K	1.19 K	1.08 K	973 Ω
Use	2.26 K	2.05 K	1.87 K	1.69 K	1.33 K	1.21 K	1.05 K	953 Ω

$$1/RC = 2\pi(697\text{ Hz}),\quad C = 0.1\ \mu F,\quad R = 2.28\text{ K (use 2.26 K)}$$
$$R_4 = [2(22) - 1](1\text{ K}) = 43.0\text{ K (use 42.2 K)},\quad H_o = -[2(22) - 1] = -43 \tag{10.4.3}$$

Since $H_o = -43$ and a midband gain of -10 is required, we use a 4.3:1 resistor divider at the filter input. The input resistor values equal

$$R' = R/K = 4.3(1\text{ K}) = 4.30\text{ K (use 4.22 K)}$$
$$R'' = R/(1/K - 1) = 4.22\text{ K}/(4.3 - 1) = 1.28\text{ K (use 1.27 K)} \tag{10.4.4}$$

using Eq. 8.5.26. The filter realization is shown in Fig. 10.4.2.

To modify the center frequency f_o of the filter, we see from the design equation $\omega_o = 1/RC$ that we must vary either R or C. Because resistors are cheaper and have many more standard values, we choose to vary the resistors $R = R_1 = R_2$. Choosing $C = 0.1\ \mu F$ and substituting into $R = 1/\omega_o C$, we calculate the resistor values tabulated in Table 10.4.1. All other component values remain unchanged from those in Fig. 10.4.2. Thus, f_o tuning is easily achieved by simple resistor selection. For the offset resistors in the second and third op amp, we use the average R_o value of

$$R_o = \tfrac{1}{2}(R_{min} + R_{max}) = \tfrac{1}{2}(0.95\text{ K} + 2.26\text{ K}) = 1.61\text{ K (use 1.5 K)} \tag{10.4.5}$$

EXAMPLE 10.4.3 A second-order Butterworth band-pass filter having a center frequency of 1 KHz, a 100 Hz bandwidth, and unity midband gain is required. It has the block diagram realization shown in Fig. 10.4.3. Design the complete filter using Class 2E stages.

Solution The Class 2E realization form for the filter is also shown in Fig. 10.4.3. The design equations for the filter are:

Set: $C_3 = C_4 = C$

Given: $\omega_o, Q, -H_o$

Choose: C

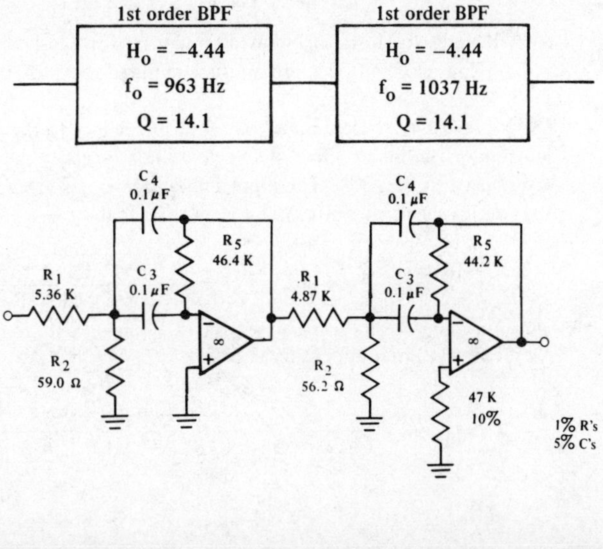

Fig. 10.4.3 Block diagram of second-order Butterworth band-pass filter and its realization.

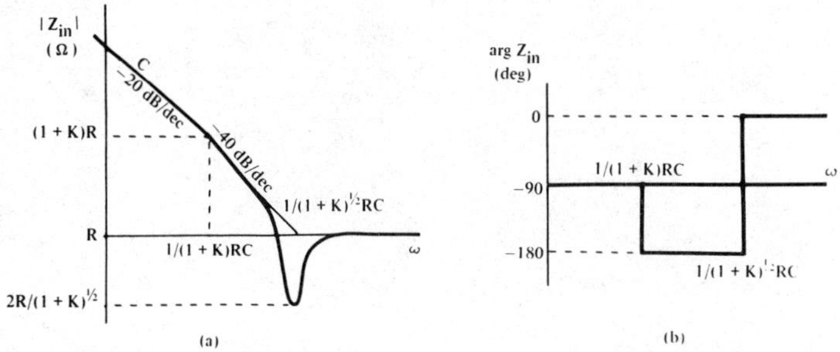

Fig. 10.4.4 Magnitude and phase characteristics of Z_{in} for Class 1A band-pass filter.

Calculate: $R_1 = Q/(-H_o\omega_o C)$, $R_2 = 1/(1 + H_o/2Q^2)2Q\omega_o C$, $R_5 = 2Q/\omega_o C$

The design of the first stage is:

$$\begin{aligned} 1/R_1C &= 2\pi[4.44(963 \text{ Hz})/14.1] = 2\pi(303 \text{ Hz}) \\ 1/R_2C &= 2\pi(1 - 8.88/28.2^2)(28.2)(963 \text{ Hz}) = 2\pi(26.9 \text{ KHz}) \\ 1/R_5C &= 2\pi(963 \text{ Hz}/28.2) = 2\pi(34.1 \text{ Hz}) \end{aligned} \tag{10.4.6}$$

$C = 0.1\ \mu F$, $R_1 = 5.25$ K (use 5.36 K), $R_2 = 59.2\ \Omega$ (use 59.0 Ω), $R_5 = 46.4$ K

The second stage is designed in the same manner where:

$$\begin{aligned} 1/R_1C &= 2\pi[4.44(1037 \text{ Hz})/14.1] = 2\pi(327 \text{ Hz}) \\ 1/R_2C &= 2\pi(1 - 8.88/28.2^2)(28.2)(1037 \text{ Hz}) = 2\pi(28.9 \text{ KHz}) \\ 1/R_5C &= 2\pi(1037 \text{ Hz}/28.2) = 2\pi(36.8 \text{ Hz}) \end{aligned} \tag{10.4.7}$$

$C = 0.1\ \mu F$, $R_1 = 4.87$ K, $R_2 = 55.1\ \Omega$ (use 56.2 Ω), $R_5 = 43.3$ K (use 44.2 K)

The complete band-pass filter is shown in Fig. 10.4.3. It is interesting to note that (R_1, R_2) form an input voltage divider. There is no loss when $R_2 = \infty$ which requires a gain $H_{omax} = -2Q^2$. For less gain than H_{omax}, then the attenuator provides a loss of

$$\frac{R_1 + R_2}{R_2} = 1 + R_1/R_2 = 1 + \frac{[1 + H_o/2Q^2]\,2Q}{-H_o/Q} = -\frac{2Q^2}{H_o}[1 + H_o/2Q^2] \tag{10.4.8}$$

Then R_1 and R_2 form an input attenuator with a loss of about $(2Q^2/H_o){:}1$ followed by a high gain block. Thus, close physical proximity is required to maintain a good SNR.

EXAMPLE 10.4.4 Determine the input impedance to the Class 1A band-pass filter of Example 10.4.1.
Solution The immittances of an active filter are easily calculated using Blackman's impedance relation as discussed in Sec. 8.8. The input impedance Z_{in} is given by Eq. 8.8.1. Using the Class 1A band-pass filter design sheet, we can write by inspection that

$$Z^{(0)} = \frac{1 + sR_1C_1}{sC_1}, \quad T_s = -\frac{K_1K_2s^2R_1C_1R_2C_2}{(1 + sR_1C_1)(1 + sR_2C_2)}, \quad T_\infty = -\frac{K_1K_2sR_2C_2}{1 + sR_2C_2} \tag{10.4.9}$$

Therefore, the input impedance equals

$$Z_{in} = Z^{(0)}\frac{1 - T_s}{1 - T_\infty} = \frac{1}{sC_1}\,\frac{s^2(1 + K)R_1C_1R_2C_2 + s(R_1C_1 + R_2C_2) + 1}{s(1 + K)R_2C_2 + 1} \tag{10.4.10}$$

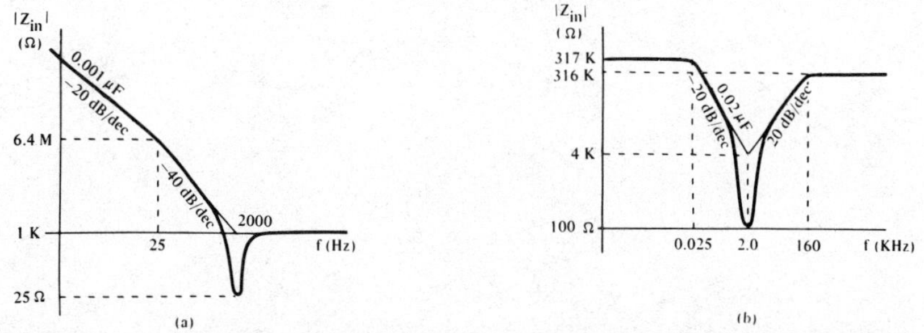

Fig. 10.4.5 Magnitude characteristics for Z_{in} (a) without and (b) with voltage divider in Example 10.4.4.

where $K = K_1K_2$ and $K \gg 1$. From the design sheet, we see the zeros of Z_{in} are the poles of the gain function H(s). Z_{in} has one pole at the origin and one on the negative-real axis. When $R_1 = R_2 = R$ and $C_1 = C_2 = C$, then Z_{in} becomes

$$Z_{in} = \frac{1}{sC}\frac{(1 + K)(sRC)^2 + 2sRC + 1}{(1 + K)sRC + 1} \qquad (10.4.11)$$

The magnitude and phase of Z_{in} are shown in Fig. 10.4.4. At low frequencies, the input is capacitive with value C, while at high frequencies, it is resistive with value R. In the vicinity of the resonant frequency, the impedance level drops to $2R/\sqrt{1 + K}$ which can be very small. However, because arg Z is -90°, little power is dissipated. Neglecting the voltage divider at the filter input in Fig. 10.4.1a, the input impedance characteristic is therefore easily constructed as shown in Fig. 10.4.5a.

When the voltage divider *is* considered, then Z_{in} has another form. Performing calculations as before, it is easy to show that

$$Z_{in} = (R_o + R_1)\frac{s^2(1 + K)R_1'C_1R_2C_2 + s(R_1'C_1 + R_2C_2) + 1}{[1 + sR_1C_1]\,[1 + s(1 + K)R_2C_2]} \qquad (10.4.12)$$

where $R_1' = R_1 \| R_o$. The input impedance characteristic is shown in Fig. 10.4.5b. Again, the impedance becomes very small at the center frequency of the filter due to its relatively large Q of 40.

EXAMPLE 10.4.5 Design a 455 KHz band-pass filter having a bandwidth of 35 KHz for use as an IF amplifier. Assume that the filter is first-order and that its gain is arbitrary.

Solution Due to the center frequency of the filter, a high-frequency version must be used as discussed in Sec. 8.9. Selecting the Class $1\overline{A}$ band-pass filter from Sec. 10.3 (recall that $\overline{A}$, 2B, and $\overline{C}$ classes can be used), the R_2C_2 network and the K_1 and $-K_2$ ideal amplifiers can be replaced by an actual amplifier as shown in Fig. 10.4.6a. Denoting the actual amplifier gain as $K = -K_1K_2$ and its bandwidth as $BW = 1/R_2C_2$, then the Class $1\overline{A}$ filter design equations may be rewritten as:

Given: ω_o, Q

Choose: C

Calculate: $BW = \omega_o/Q$, $\quad R = 2/BWC$, $\quad K = 4Q^2 - 1$, $\quad H_o = -K/2$

Since Q = 455 KHz/35 KHz = 13, the design proceeds as:

$$BW = 2/RC = 2\pi[455\text{ KHz}/\ 13\ ] = 2\pi(\ 35\text{ KHz}), \quad C = 0.001\ \mu F, \quad R = 17.8\text{ K}$$
$$K = 4(13^2) - 1 \cong 676 = 57\text{ dB}, \quad H_o \cong -676/2 = -338 = 51\text{ dB (inverting)} \qquad (10.4.13)$$

The complete high-frequency filter is shown in Fig. 10.4.6b. The open-loop bandwidth BW of the amplifier is adjusted using external op amp compensation as will be discussed in Sec. 14.4.

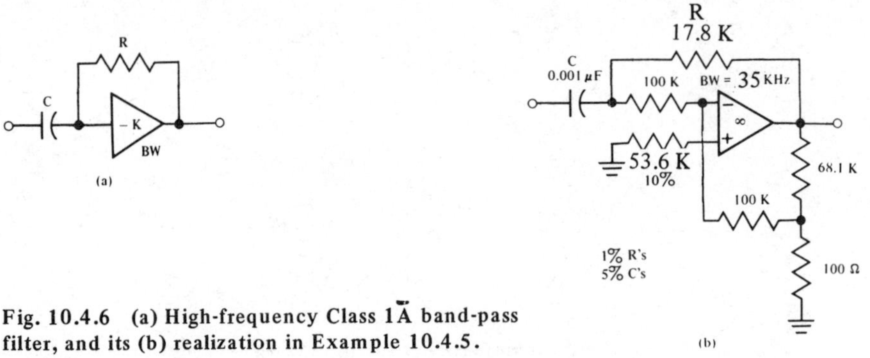

Fig. 10.4.6 (a) High-frequency Class 1$\overline{A}$ band-pass filter, and its (b) realization in Example 10.4.5.

10.5 TUNABLE BAND-PASS FILTERS

There are many applications which require band-pass filters having tunable center frequency ω_o and fixed Q. Unlike low-pass and high-pass filters, other problems require tunable center frequency ω_o. We noted in Sec. 8.6 that from a gain-tuning standpoint, for tunable ω_o/constant B applications, we use Class $\overline{A}$ filters (or adjust Class C–E filters). For tunable Q/constant ω_o applications, we use Class B or D filters (or adjust Class C, $\overline{C}$, and E filters). And for tunable ω_o/almost constant Q, we use Class C–E filters. From a passive-tuning standpoint, we can use every class for these three situations which gives us more design flexibility.[2] The root loci for these three cases were shown in Fig. 8.6.1, and tolerances were shown in Fig. 8.6.2.

10.5.1 TUNABLE CENTER FREQUENCY/CONSTANT Q BAND-PASS FILTERS

We considered Class C, $\overline{C}$, and E gain-tuned filters extensively in Chaps. 8 and 9 for the last case of tunable ω_o/almost constant Q filters. For this type of gain-tuned band-pass filter, it must have a transfer function of

$$H(s) = \frac{H_o aKs}{s^2 + aKs + K^2b^2} \quad \text{or} \quad \frac{H_o aKs}{K^2s^2 + aKs + K^2b^2} \tag{10.5.1}$$

As before, these can be realized only approximately by two-amplifier Class C–E filters. Bruminhent and Su determined that fourteen canonical band-pass filters were possible.[3] These have the minimum number of nodes (i.e., six). Of these, seven band-pass filters were the RC:CR dual of the other seven. The seven possible Class C and E filters are shown in Fig. 10.5.1. The other seven Class $\overline{C}$ and E filters can be obtained using the RC:CR transformation as discussed in Example 9.5.1. The parameters listed in Fig. 10.5.1 are interpreted as discussed in Secs. 8.6 and 9.5. Tunable band-pass filter design is identical to that outlined in Example 8.6.2 so we shall not pursue its design further.

Passive-tuned filters of every class can also be used to realize tunable ω_o/constant Q band-pass filters. As with the analogous low-pass and high-pass filters, exact tuning can be obtained using double-tuning and approximate tuning using single-tuning of the passive time constants. The root loci were shown in Tables 8.7.1 and 8.7.2. Since the design of this type of passive-tuned filter was outlined in Examples 8.7.1 and 9.5.2, they too shall not be pursued further.

10.5.2 TUNABLE CENTER FREQUENCY/CONSTANT BANDWIDTH BAND-PASS FILTERS

Some applications require band-pass filters having variable ω_o/constant B. They have transfer

A_0 = Midband Gain

2C

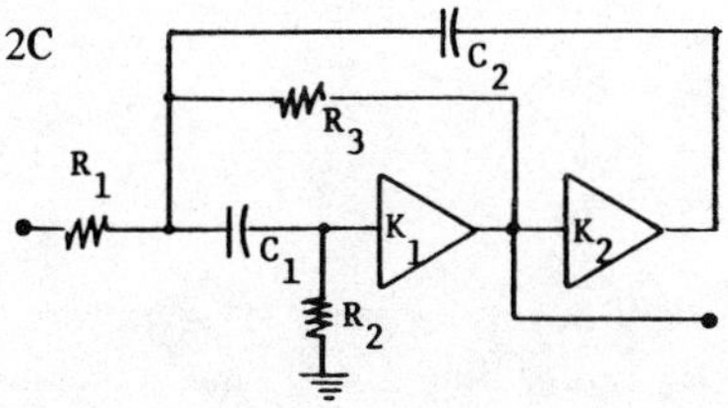

$K_1 = -K_2 = -K_0 < 0$

$C_1 = C > 0,\ C_2 = \alpha C$

$\alpha G_1 = G_3 Q_0 (1+A),\ \alpha >> 1$

$\alpha G_2 = G_1 + G_3$

$\omega_0 = \frac{G_2}{CK_0}$

$K_{0_{min}} = 2Q_0 \frac{1+A}{A}$

$A_0 = \frac{-G_1}{G_3(1+A)}$

2C

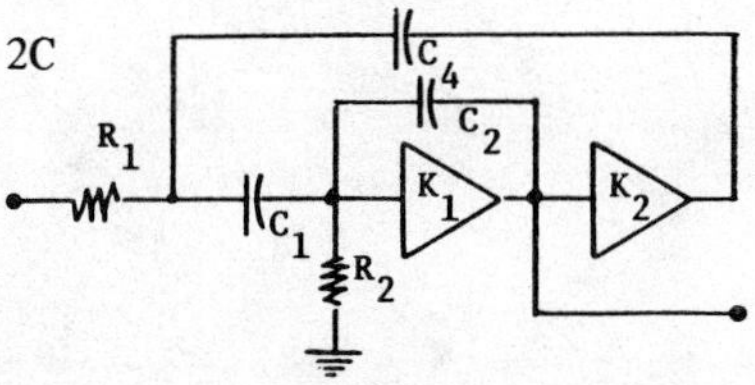

$K_1 = -K_2 = -K_0 < 0$

$C_1 = C > 0,\ C_2 = \alpha C,\ C_4 = \beta C$

$G_1 = \beta G_2,\ \beta >> 1$

$Q_0 = \frac{1}{\alpha(1+A)}$

$\omega_0 = \frac{G_2}{CK_0}$

$K_{0_{min}} = (2+\alpha) Q_0 \frac{1+A}{A}$

$A_0 = \frac{-1}{\alpha(1+A)}$

2C

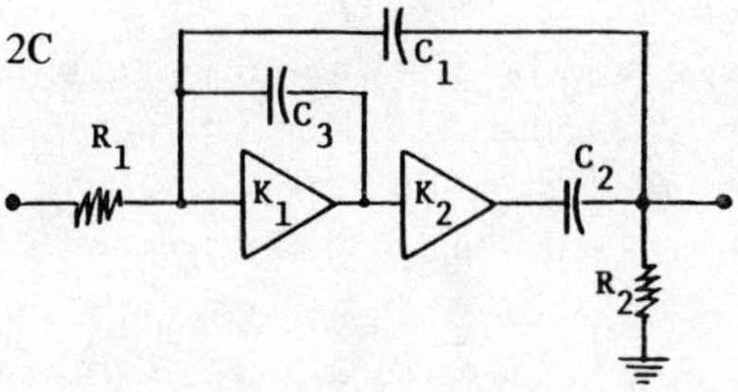

$K_1 = -K_2 = -K_0 < 0$

$C_1 = C > 0,\ C_2 = \alpha C,\ C_3 = \beta C$

$\alpha G_1 = G_2,\ \alpha >> 1$

$Q_0 = \frac{1}{\beta(1+A)}$

$\omega_0 = \frac{G_1}{CK_0}$

$K_{0_{min}} = (2+\beta) Q_0 \frac{1+A}{A}$

$A_0 = \frac{-K_0}{\beta(1+A)}$

$\Delta A_0/A_0 = (1 + A)/N(1 + NA) - 1$

1C

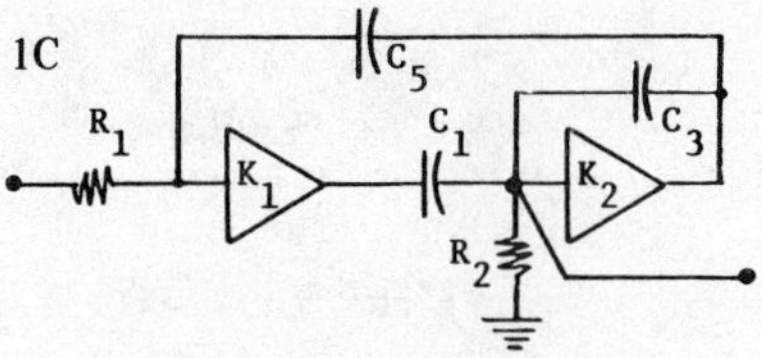

$K_1 = -K_2 = K_0 > 0$

$C_1 = C > 0,\ C_3 = \alpha C,\ C_5 = \beta C$

$G_1 = \beta G_2,\ \beta >> 1$

$Q_0 = \frac{1}{\alpha(1+A)}$

$\omega_0 = \frac{G_2}{CK_0}$

$K_{0_{min}} = (2+\alpha) Q_0 \frac{1+A}{A}$

$A_0 = \frac{1}{\alpha(1+A)}$

1C

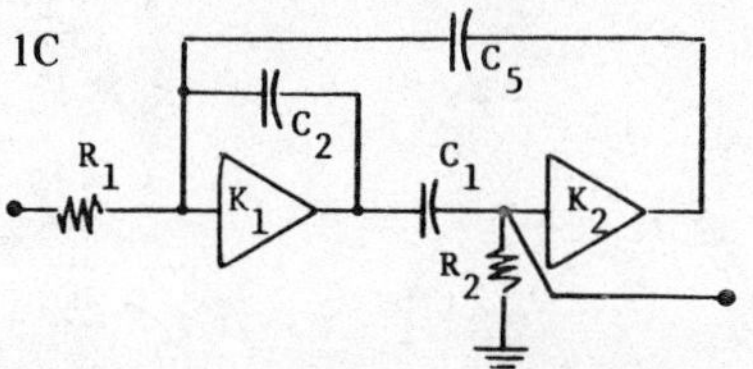

$K_1 = -K_2 = -K_0 < 0$

$C_1 = C > 0,\ C_2 = \alpha C,\ C_5 = \beta C$

$G_1 = \beta G_2,\ \beta >> 1,\ \alpha > 1$

$Q_0 = \frac{\beta}{\alpha(1+A)}$

$\omega_0 = \frac{G_2}{CK_0}$

$K_{0_{min}} = 2Q_0 \frac{1+A}{A} + \frac{1}{A}$

$A_0 = \frac{-\beta}{\alpha(1+A)}$

2E

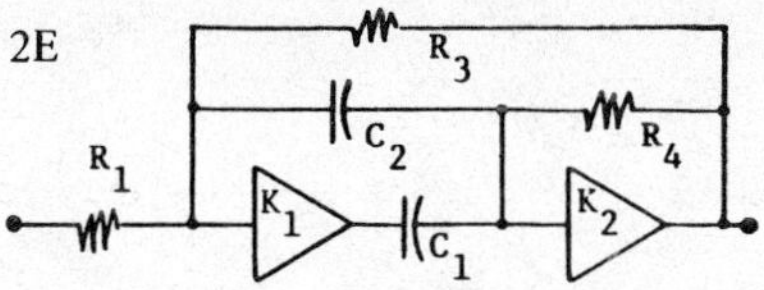

$K_1 = -K_0^2,\ K_2 = \frac{1}{K_0},\ K_0 > 0$

$C_1 = C > 0,\ C_2 = \alpha C$

$G_1 + G_3 = \alpha G_4,\ \alpha << 1$

$Q_0 = \frac{G_1 + G_3}{G_3(1+A)}$

$\omega_0 = \frac{G_4}{CK_0}$

$K_{0_{min}} = 2Q_0 \frac{1+A}{A}$

$A_0 = \frac{-G_1}{(1+A)G_3}$

2E

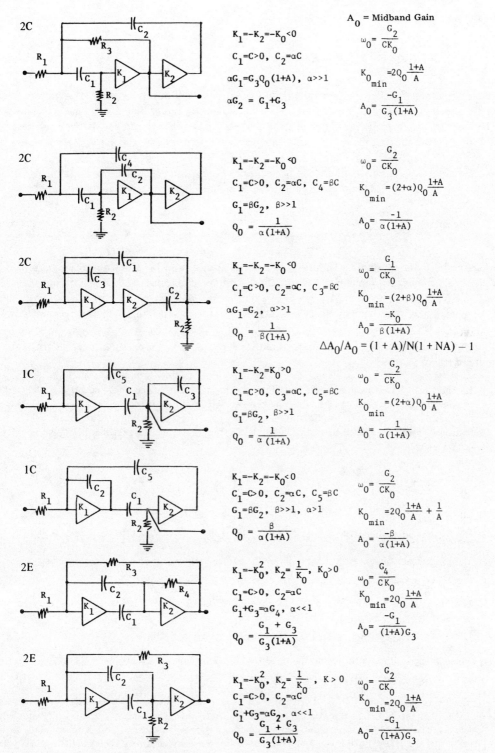

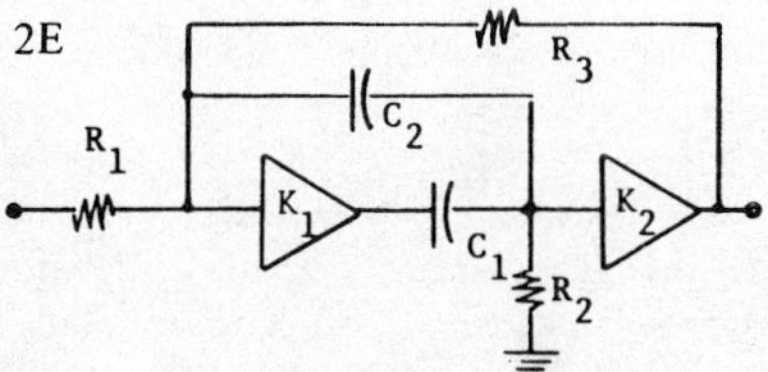

$K_1 = -K_0^2,\ K_2 = \frac{1}{K_0},\ K > 0$

$C_1 = C > 0,\ C_2 = \alpha C$

$G_1 + G_3 = \alpha G_2,\ \alpha << 1$

$Q_0 = \frac{G_1 + G_3}{G_3(1+A)}$

$\omega_0 = \frac{G_2}{CK_0}$

$K_{0_{min}} = 2Q_0 \frac{1+A}{A}$

$A_0 = \frac{-G_1}{(1+A)G_3}$

Fig. 10.5.1 Canonical gain-tunable Class C and E band-pass filters. (Note that $\Delta Q_o/Q_o = \Delta A_o/A_o = A(1 - N)/(1 + NA)$ for all filters except third.) (From S. Bruminhent and K. L. Su, "Gain-tuned active filters," Proc. Intl. Symp. on Circuits and Systems, pp. 443–447, April, 1974.)

functions which equal

$$H(s) = \frac{H_o Bs}{s^2 + Bs + \omega_o^2} \tag{10.5.2}$$

where the center frequency ω_o is varied and the 3 dB bandwidth B is held fixed. Therefore, their design sheets are usually expressed in terms of ω_o, B, and H_o rather than ω_o, Q, and H_o as before. These design sheets are easily obtained from the original design sheets in Sec. 10.3 by substituting $B = \omega_o/Q$ into the various equations. Bandwidth sensitivities can also be easily converted by noting that $S_X^B = S_X^{\omega_o} - S_X^Q$ from Sec. 1.15.

Tunable ω_o/constant B filters can be realized exactly using Class $\overline{A}$ filters or approximately using Class C–E filters. Ideally, such gain-tuned filters must have transfer functions of

$$H(s) = \frac{H_o as}{s^2 + as + K^2 b^2} \tag{10.5.3}$$

where a and b are constants. The filter parameters are $\omega_o = bK$ and $B = a$. ω_o is varied with K while the bandwidth B remains constant. Class $\overline{A}$ filters have transfer function determinant given in Fig. 7.19.1 having parameters $B = a_1 + a_2$ and $\omega_o = [a_1 a_2(k^2 - 1)]^{1/2} \cong k\sqrt{a_1 a_2}$. Although B is constant, ω_o is not exactly linear in K. Of course, Class C–E filters have more general expressions where B varies slightly also. Recalling that $k^2 = K_1 K_2$, then $\omega_o \sim K_1 K_2$ so two-amplifier forms give linear control of ω_o. Single-amplifier forms have $K \sim \sqrt{\omega_o}$ and therefore give square-root control of ω_o.

EXAMPLE 10.5.1 Design a gain-tunable filter which can be used to decode the six MF signalling tones used in the telephone system. The tones lie between 700 and 1700 Hz and have spacings of 200 Hz (see Prob. 2.24). Use a Class 1$\overline{A}$ band-pass filter and design for 20 Hz bandwidths and a midband gain of 10.

Solution From the Class 1$\overline{A}$ band-pass filter design sheet in Sec. 10.3, we see that the design equations can be re-expressed as:

Set: $R_1 = R_2 = R, \quad C_1 = C_2 = C$

Given: ω_o, B

Choose: C

Calculate: $R = 2/BC, \quad K_1K_2 = (2\omega_o/B)^2 - 1, \quad H_o = -K_1K_2/2$

The bandwidth requirement B = 20 Hz allows the passive portion of the filter to be designed as:

$$1/RC = 2\pi(10\text{ Hz}), \qquad C = 1\ \mu F, \qquad R = 15.9\text{ K (use 16.2 K)} \tag{10.5.4}$$

The tuning range N of the filter must equal N = 1700/700 = 2.43. Letting $K = K_1 = -K_2$, then the gain equals

$$K = [(2\omega_o/B)^2 - 1]^{1/2} \cong (2\omega_o/B)[1 - \tfrac{1}{2}(B/2\omega_o)^2] \cong 2\omega_o/B \tag{10.5.5}$$

which is linear with an error of only about $(B/\omega_o)^2/8$. The minimum gain required equals

$$K_{min} \cong 2(700\text{ Hz})/20\text{ Hz} = 70 \cong 37\text{ dB} \tag{10.5.6}$$

which is accurate within 0.01%. The gains must be increased in steps of 20 to shift the center frequencies in steps of 200 Hz. A maximum gain of 170 is required. The complete circuit is shown in Fig. 10.5.2. The resistor R_2 before the second amplifier has been increased to 18.7 K to account for the loading of the 100 K resistor and maintain the corner frequency at 10 Hz. The amplifier gain K_2 has correspondingly been increased 1.19 to account for the loss in the (18.7 K, 100 K) voltage divider. When the pots are adjusted to their upper positions, the center frequency is 700 Hz. This center frequency increases linearly with pot position. It reaches 1700 Hz in the lower positions.

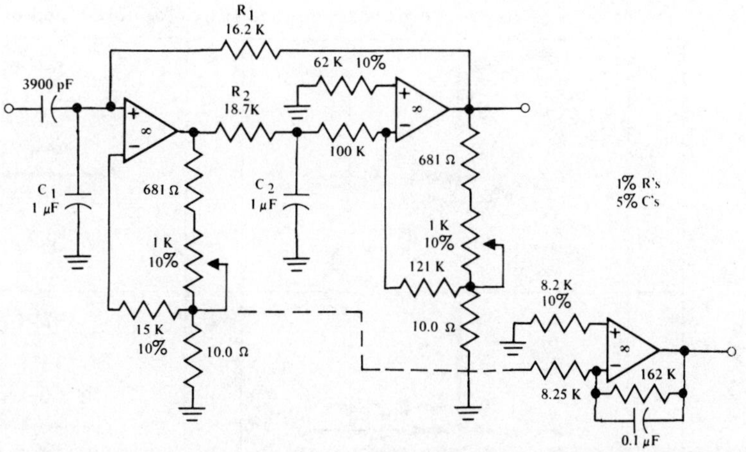

Fig. 10.5.2 Gain-tuned band-pass filter realization of Example 10.5.1.

If the filter gain is to be 10, then an input attenuator is required of value $K^2/2$:10. Since the minimum gain required is 70, then the attenuator ratio is 245:1. This is easily obtained using the (3900 pF, 1 μF) attenuator as shown (see Eq. 8.5.9). The corner frequency of R_1 and C_1 is maintained. However as the filter is tuned, K increases and so does H_o. Without correction, H_o will increase by a factor of $N^2 = 2.43^2$ or 5.9. Taking the output before the K_2 amplifier at the (R_2, C_2) junction modifies the midband gain to equal $H_o = K_1/2$. Then H_o increases by only a factor of 2.43. A better alternative is to use no input attenuator and the output as shown where $H_o = 1/2$. Here the gain is constant over the tuning range. Note that an equivalent (R_2, C_2) network must be added to maintain the corner frequency.

Passive-tuned filters can also be used to realize tunable ω_o/constant B filters. The root loci for single-passive-tuned filters was shown in Tab. 8.7.1. The parameters must be chosen to produce the vertical root locus of Fig. 8.6.1b. Inspecting the root loci of Fig. 8.7.1, we see that by properly choosing finite gain k, we can move the zero to $s = -\infty$ in Class B, C, $\overline{\text{C}}$, and E filters. This produces tunable ω_o/constant B filters. The gain conditions using single-passive-tuning are:

$$\begin{aligned} &\text{Class B: } k = 1; \qquad \text{Class C: } ka_3 = 1,\ k > 1 \\ &\text{Class } \overline{\text{C}}\text{: } ka_3 = 1,\ k < 1; \qquad \text{Class E: } k = 1,\ ka_4 \neq 1,\ ka_3 \neq 1 \end{aligned} \tag{10.5.7}$$

These classes yield constant-bandwidth filters (i.e., those having vertical root loci) while the other classes yield only approximately constant-bandwidth filters (i.e., those having circular root loci). Since $\omega_o \sim \sqrt{a_1}$, tuning of a_1 gives square root control of ω_o.

However, all classes except Class B can be used as single-tuned filters by tuning only a portion of the time constant. This involves setting a gain to some particular value (as in Eq. 10.5.7) so that ω_o is independent of the tuning parameter chosen. Since the active portion must therefore involve s^2 and/or s^0, only Class B filters are not useful with this approach. For example, consider the Class 1$\overline{\text{C}}$ band-pass filter of Sec. 10.3. By setting $K_1 = 1$, B becomes independent of ρ; ρ can then be used as the tuning parameter by varying R_0. In this type of tuning, $Q \sim a^{\pm 1/2}$ so tuning is still nonlinear.

Double-passive-tuned filters have the wedge-shaped root loci of Fig. 8.7.2. They cannot be made vertical (with nonzero real parts) without changing the tuning mode. Thus, double-tuning where $a_1 = a_2 = a$ is not useful for tunable ω_o/constant B filters. However, suppose we tune a_1 and a_2 so their sum is constant (i.e., $a_1 + ca_2 = a$). Then the root loci are shown in Table 10.5.1. They all have constant bandwidth proportional to a as required. Since $\omega_o \sim \sqrt{a_1(a-a_1)} \cong$

Table 10.5.1 Root loci for passive-tuned filters (double-tuned using $a_1 + ca_2 = a$).*

A

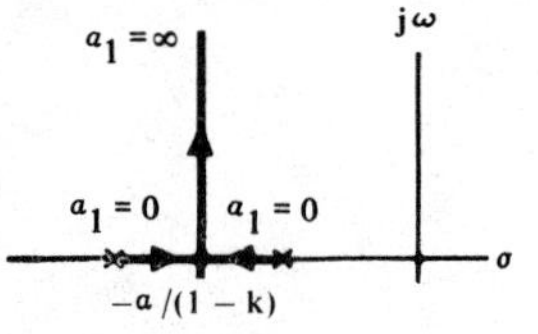

$$\Delta(s) = s[s(1-k)+a] + a_1(a - a_1)$$

$\bar{A}$

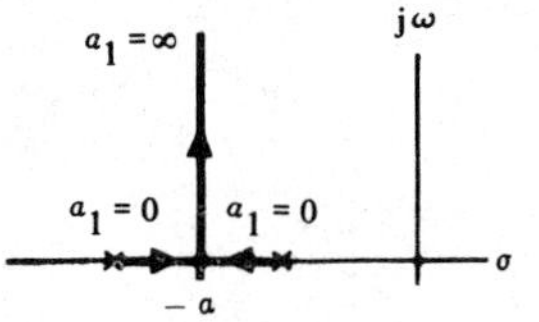

$$\Delta(s) = s(s+a) + a_1(1-k)(a - a_1)$$

B

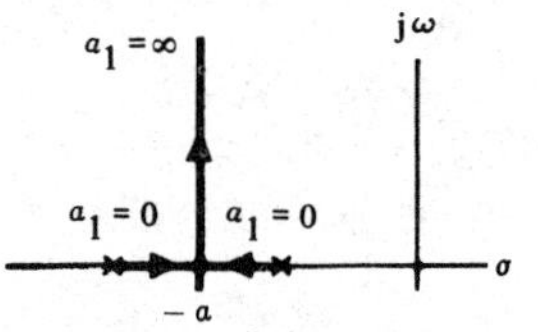

$$\Delta(s) = s(s+a) + a_1[a - a_1(1-k)]$$

C

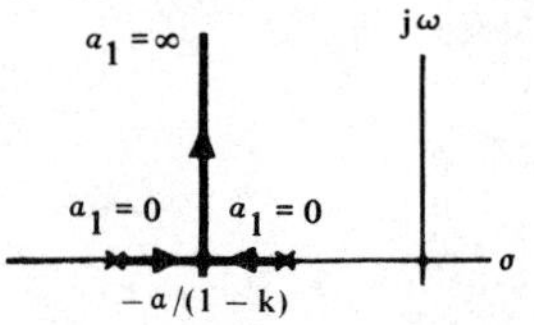

$$\Delta(s) = s[s(1-k)+a] + a_1[a - a_1(1-k)]$$

$\bar{C}$

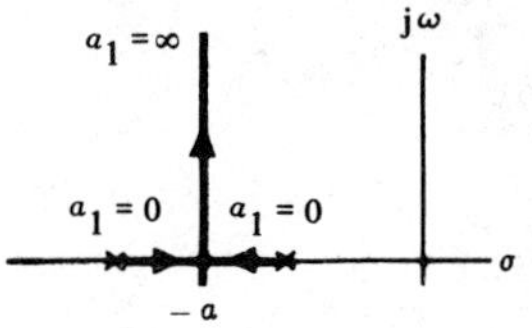

$$\Delta(s) = s(s+a) + a_1(1-k)[a - a_1(1-k)]$$

D

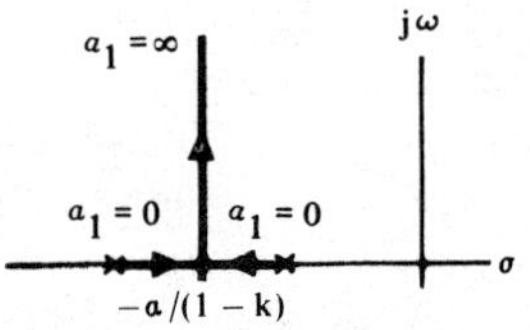

$$\Delta(s) = s[s(1-k)+a] + a_1(1-ka_3^2)(a - a_1)$$

E

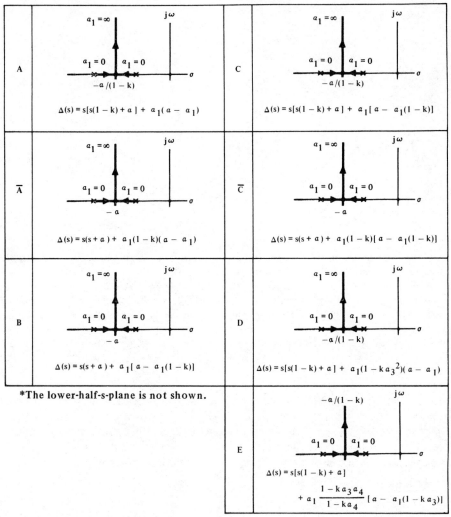

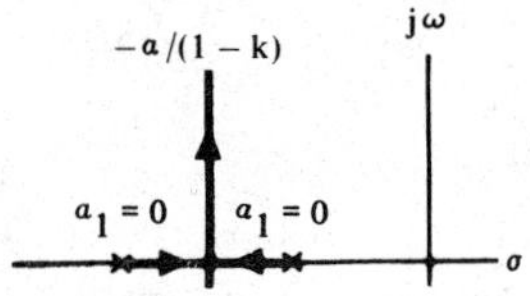

$$\Delta(s) = s[s(1-k)+a] + a_1\frac{1-ka_3a_4}{1-ka_4}[a - a_1(1-ka_3)]$$

***The lower-half-s-plane is not shown.**

$\sqrt{a_1 a}$ where $a_1 \ll a$, then ω_o varies as the square root of a_1 just as in the single-tuned case. To maintain the bandwidth constant requires that the sum of the passive corner frequencies a_1 and a_2 remain constant. Since $a_i \sim 1/R_i$, this requires

$$1/R_1 + 1/R_2 = 1/R \qquad \text{or} \qquad 1/R_2 = 1/R - 1/R_1 \tag{10.5.8}$$

Taking R = 1, then for $n \gg 1$,

$$R_1 = n, \qquad R_2 = (n-1)/n = 1 - 1/n \tag{10.5.9}$$

Potentiometers having these tapers are nonstandard. Therefore, double-tuned filters are less practical than single-tuned filters in tunable ω_o/constant B applications.

Band-pass filters with tunable ω_o have many uses. When properly operated in a closed control loop, they become tracking filters. *Tracking filters* are self-tuning band-pass filters which automatically adjust their center frequency to track the incoming signal frequency. They are analogous to phase-locked loops (PLL) in the sense that they change their *own* center frequency rather than the output frequency of a voltage-controlled oscillator (VCO). Tracking filters are

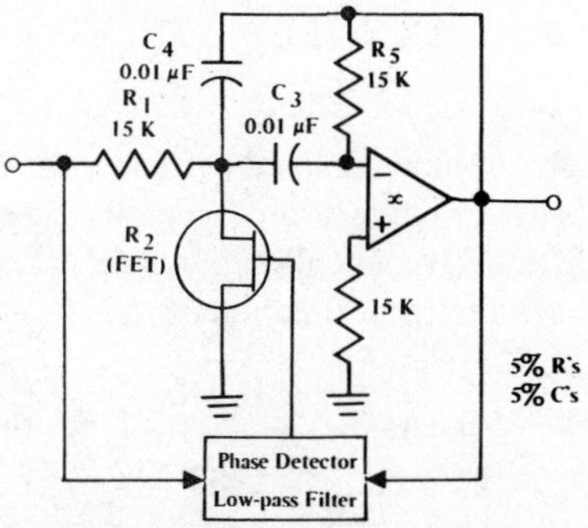

Fig. 10.5.3 Tracking filter realization of Example 10.5.2.

somewhat simpler in design. More importantly, their output signal amplitudes are linear with input signal amplitudes, unlike PLL's. Their design is illustrated in the next example.

EXAMPLE 10.5.2 The Class 2E filter shown in Sec. 10.3 can be modified for self-tuning using a variable resistor (FET) as shown in Fig. 10.5.3.[4] The FET, in turn, is controlled by a phase detector. Determine the component values of the filter if the filter must tune itself over a 1–20 KHz range and have a 2 KHz bandwidth. What gain is obtained?

Solution Setting $C_3 = C_4 = C$ and $R_1 || R_2 = R$, the parameters of the filter equal

$$\omega_o = \frac{1}{C}\left[\frac{1}{R_5}\left(\frac{1}{R_1} + \frac{1}{R_2}\right)\right]^{1/2} = \frac{1}{C(R_5 R)^{1/2}}, \qquad B = \frac{2}{R_5 C}, \qquad H_o = -\frac{R_5}{2R_1} \tag{10.5.10}$$

We see that fixing R_5 fixes the bandwidth of the filter. Then fixing R_1 fixes the midband gain of the filter. The center frequency can then be controlled by R_2. Letting $R_2 = \infty$ and combining the ω_o, B, and H_o equations gives $\omega_{omin}/\sqrt{-2H_o} = B/2$. Therefore, the gain equals

$$-H_o = 2(\omega_{o\,min}/B)^2 = 2Q_{min}{}^2 = 2(1\text{ KHz}/2\text{ KHz})^2 = 0.5 \tag{10.5.11}$$

and the design becomes:

$$1/R_5C = 2\pi(2\text{ KHz}/2) = 2\pi(1\text{ KHz}), \qquad C = 0.01\ \mu F, \qquad R_5 = 15.9\text{ K (use 15 K)}$$

$$R_1 = 15\text{ K}/(2)(0.5) = 15\text{ K}, \qquad 1/C(R_5R_{min})^{1/2} = 2\pi(20\text{ KHz}), \qquad (R_5R_{min})^{1/2} = 796\ \Omega$$

$$R_{min} = R_1||R_2 = 40\ \Omega, \qquad R_2 = \frac{R_{min}R_1}{R_1 - R_{min}} = \frac{15\text{ K} - 40}{(15\text{ K})(40)} = 40\ \Omega \tag{10.5.12}$$

Therefore, we set $C_1 = C_2 = 0.01\ \mu F$ and $R_1 = R_2 = 15$ K. Varying the FET gate voltage so its drain-source resistance decreases from ∞ to 40 Ω, the center frequency of the tracking filter varies from 1 KHz to 20 KHz. This requires gate voltage swings typically of several volts.

Tracking filters can be used to improve SNR of a signal of varying frequency which is contaminated by noise. If the signal is fairly narrowband, but its center frequency varies over a wide range, a wideband fixed-frequency band-pass filter would be required. However, the wideband filter will not reject its in-band noise. Since the tracking filter can be designed to have a narrow bandwidth but a wide tuning range, it will be much more effective in rejecting noise. The improvement in the SNR of a signal using a tracking-filter rather than a fixed-center frequency filter is the square root of their bandwidth ratio. In our example, the improvement would about equal $(20\text{ KHz}/2\text{ KHz})^{1/2} = 10$ dB. The price paid for this improvement is increased complexity and other design requirements such as lock-in time, capture ratio, etc. The engineer can quickly become familiar with these concepts by referring to any text on phase-locked loops.[5]

10.5.3 TUNABLE Q/CONSTANT CENTER FREQUENCY BAND-PASS FILTERS

Let us now briefly consider tunable Q/constant ω_o band-pass filters. These filters are not generally needed in band-pass applications but they will be conceptually useful when we discuss band-stop filters and necessary when designing tunable all-pass filters. Tunable Q/constant ω_o filters have circular root loci shown in Figs. 8.6.1c and 8.6.2c. Using gain-tuning, they must have a transfer function of

$$H(s) = \frac{H_o aKs}{s^2 + aKs + b^2} \quad \text{or} \quad \frac{H_o as}{Ks^2 + as + Kb^2} \tag{10.5.13}$$

In either case, the resonant frequency $\omega_o = b$ where $Q = a/Kb$ or Ka/b, respectively. Therefore, they can be realized exactly using gain-tuning in Class B filters, properly adjusted Class D, two-amplifier Class C, $\overline{C}$, and E filters, or approximately using single-amplifier Class C, $\overline{C}$, and E filters. In any case, Q is only approximately linear in K or 1/K.

Table 10.5.2 Root loci for passive-tuned filters (double-tuned where $\sqrt{a_1 a_2} = \omega_o$).*

A	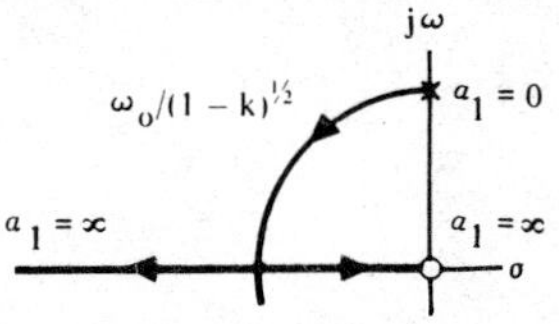 $\Delta(s) = [s^2(1-k) + \omega_o^2] + a_1[1 + (\omega_o/a_1)^2]s$	C	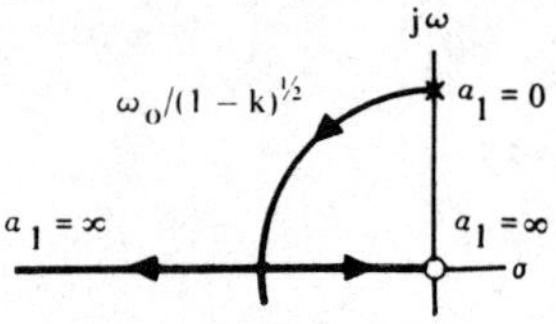 $\Delta(s) = [s^2(1-k) + \omega_o^2] + a_1[1 - ka_3 + (\omega_o/a_1)^2]s$
$\overline{A}$	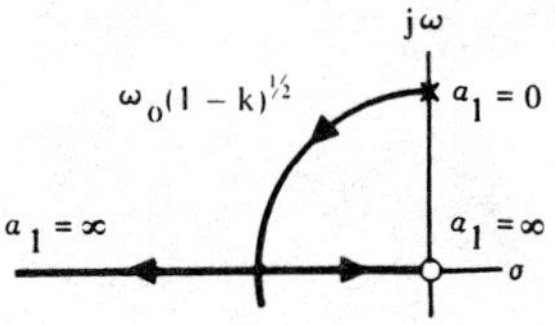 $\Delta(s) = [s^2 + \omega_o^2(1-k)] + a_1[1 + (\omega_o/a_1)^2]s$	$\overline{C}$	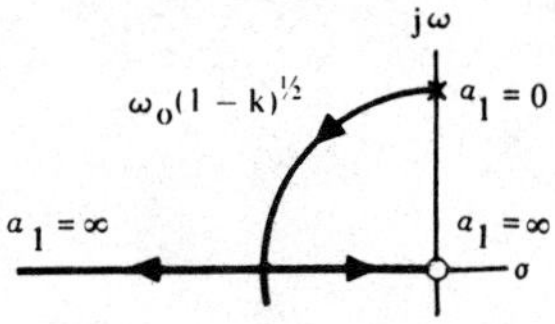 $\Delta(s) = [s^2 + \omega_o^2(1-k)] + a_1[1 - ka_3 + (\omega_o/a_1)^2]s$
B	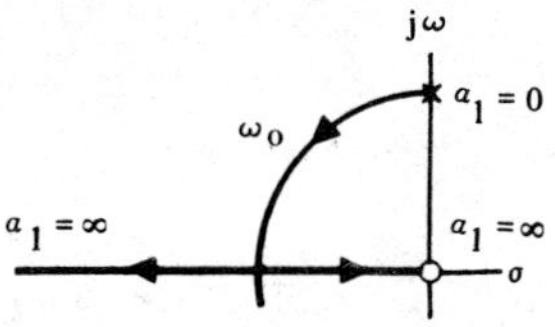 $\Delta(s) = [s^2 + \omega_o^2] + a_1[1 - k + (\omega_o/a_1)^2]s$	D	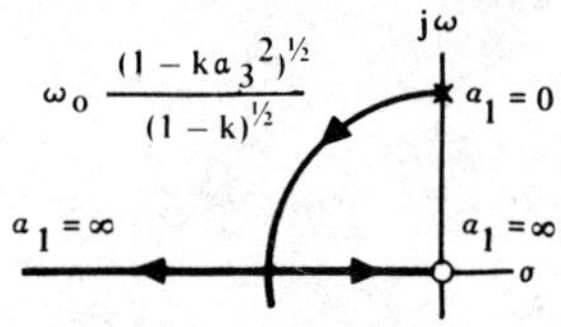 $\Delta(s) = [s^2(1-k) + \omega_o^2(1-ka_3^2)] + a_1[1 + (\omega_o/a_1)^2]s$
		E	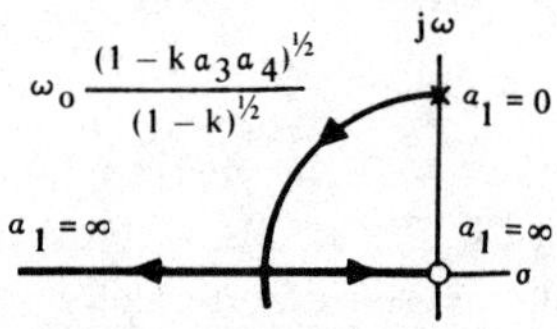 $\Delta(s) = [s^2(1-k) + \omega_o^2(1-ka_3a_4)] + a_1[(1-ka_3) + (1-ka_4)(\omega_o^2/a_1^2)]s$

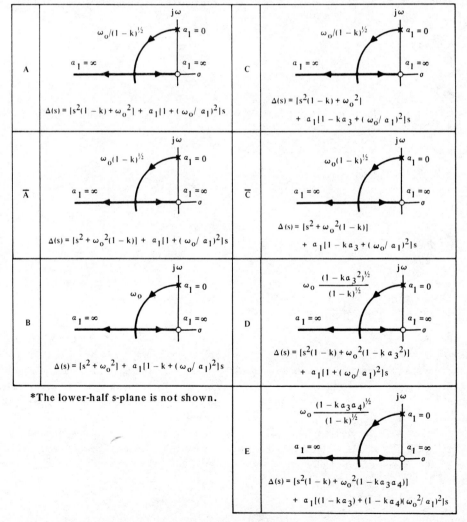

*The lower-half s-plane is not shown.

Let us inspect the design sheets of Sec. 10.3 to illustrate this. The Class 1B and 2B sheets show ω_o is always constant and 1/K controls Q. The Class 2D filter needs no adjustment to have the same behavior where K controls Q. The Class $1\overline{C}$ filter has a constant ω_o when $K_1(K_2 - \rho)$ is constant. This requires K_1 and K_2 to vary as almost reciprocals which is easy to implement. Then K_1 controls Q. The analogous Class 1C filter of Example 7.7.1 has a constant ω_o when the same condition is satisfied. The analogous single-amplifier Class 2C and $2\overline{C}$ filters can only realize constant ω_o approximately.

Passive-tuned filters can also be used to realize tunable Q/constant ω_o filters. The root loci for the single-passive-tuned filters are shown in Figs. 8.7.1. Since the root loci are always centered about the zero (use Prob. 1.43), they can be made circular about the origin only when the zero is placed there. But then there is a pole-zero cancellation and the filter becomes first-order. Thus, this type of single-passive-tuning cannot be used to realize constant ω_o filters. However, a portion of the time constant can be tuned to yield constant-ω_o single-passive-tuned filters. This is the same technique as that used for tunable ω_o/constant B filters and discussed in the last section. All classes can be used except Class B. In this type of tuning, Q is nonlinear in a.

Double-passive-tuned filters have the wedge-shaped root loci of Fig. 8.7.2. They cannot be made circular without changing the tuning mode. Thus, double-tuning where $a_1 = a_2 = a$ is not useful for tunable Q/constant ω_o filters. However, suppose we tune a_1 and a_2 as reciprocals where $a_1 a_2 = \omega_o{}^2$. Then the root loci are shown in Table 10.5.2. They all have constant radii proportional to ω_o as required. Since Q equals

$$Q \cong \left\{(a_1/\omega_o)[1 + (\omega_o/a_1)^2]\right\}^{-1} \cong a_2/\omega_o, \qquad a_1 \gg \omega_o \tag{10.5.14}$$

and $a_2 \sim 1/R_2$, then Q varies as the reciprocal of R_2. To maintain the product of the passive corner frequencies a_1 and a_2 constant, they must be varied in opposite directions. This can be accomplished using potentiometers which have logarithmic tapers where $R_1 = R(10^{x-1})$ where $0 \leqslant x \leqslant 1$. Setting $R_1 R_2 = R^2$, then R_2 must be set equal to $R_2 = R^2/R_1 = R(10^{1-x})$. Therefore, R_1 and R_2 must have tapers in the opposite directions. This will be discussed extensively in Sec. 14.2. Standard logarithmic pots yield 20 dB or 40 dB variations in resistance. Thus, Q has a 20 dB or a 40 dB logarithmic variation. Tracking between R_1 and R_2 is extremely important in this type of tunable filter.

10.6 FREQUENCY DISCRIMINATORS

Frequency discriminators are a type of band-pass filter whose transfer functions vary as s (i.e., linear in ω) over a specified frequency range as discussed in Sec. 6.4.6. Low-pass frequency discriminators have transfer functions

$$H(s) = sH_{LP}(s) \tag{10.6.1}$$

which are linear from dc over some bandwidth B. Low-Q band-pass frequency discriminators have transfer functions

$$H(s) = sH_{BP}(s) \tag{10.6.2}$$

High-Q band-pass frequency discriminators have transfer functions

$$H(s) = \left(\frac{s^2 + \omega_o{}^2}{s\omega_o}\right) H_{BP}(s) \tag{10.6.3}$$

Both are linear over a bandwidth B but are centered at ω_o rather than dc.

The design of frequency discriminators parallels the design of the other filters we have thus far considered. The design is routine once the block diagram of the discriminator is determined.

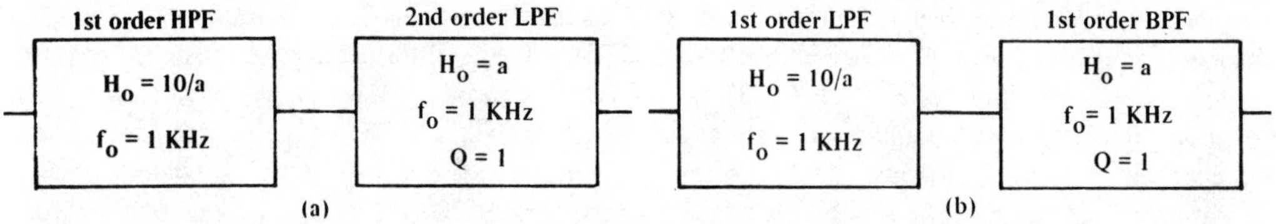

Fig. 10.6.1 Alternative designs for low-pass discriminator.

Consider Eqs. 10.6.1 and 10.6.2. Due to the simple form of their transfer functions which involve s times some standard low-pass or band-pass transfer function, their block diagrams are easy to draw. This simply involves converting a LPF block to a BPF block, or a BPF block to a HPF block in a cascade design. Only one block is thus changed, while the ω_o and Q parameters of all blocks remain fixed. The block gains H_o must generally be modified to obtain the desired gain of the discriminator. To illustrate their design, let us convert the third-order Butterworth low-pass filter of Example 8.5.1 into a Butterworth low-pass discriminator.

EXAMPLE 10.6.1 Design a third-order Butterworth low-pass discriminator having a 3 dB bandwidth of 1 KHz, and a low-frequency gain of

$$m = d\,|H(0)|/d\omega = 10/2\pi(1\text{ KHz}) = 1.59 \times 10^{-3}\ \text{(volt/volt)/(rad/sec)} \tag{10.6.4}$$

The transfer function $H(s) = 10s_n/B_3(s_n)$ where $s_n = 2\pi(1\text{ KHz})$ and B_3 is a third-order Butterworth polynomial. Utilize the low-pass filter of Example 8.5.1.

Solution The low-pass filter was realized in block diagram form in Example 8.5.1. The filter may be therefore realized in either of the two ways as shown in Fig. 10.6.1. In Fig. 10.6.1a, s has been absorbed into the first-order block. In Fig. 10.6.1b, s has been absorbed into the second-order block. Since the low-pass filter of Example 8.5.1 had the form of Fig. 10.6.1a, we can easily convert it into the low-pass discriminator. The second-order stage remains unchanged. We perform an RC:CR transformation on the first-order stage to convert the low-pass filter into a high-pass filter. Since the gains are unchanged, this procedure completes the discriminator design which is shown in Fig. 10.6.2.

EXAMPLE 10.6.2 Design the third-order Butterworth low-pass discriminator of Example 10.6.1 using a Class 2E band-pass filter.

Solution The block diagram of the discriminator is shown in Fig. 10.6.1b. Let us design the band-pass stage first. From the Class 2E design sheet and Eq. 10.4.8, we see that R_2 can be eliminated by setting $H_o = -2Q^2$. Then the design equations become:

Set: $C_3 = C_4 = C, \quad R_2 = \infty$

Given: ω_o, Q

Choose: C

Calculate: $R_1 = 1/2Q\omega_oC, \quad R_5 = 2Q/\omega_oC, \quad H_o = -2Q^2$

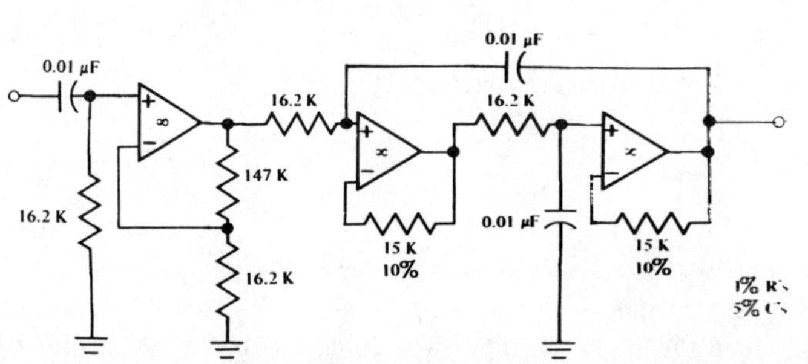

Fig. 10.6.2 Low-pass discriminator realization of Example 10.6.1.

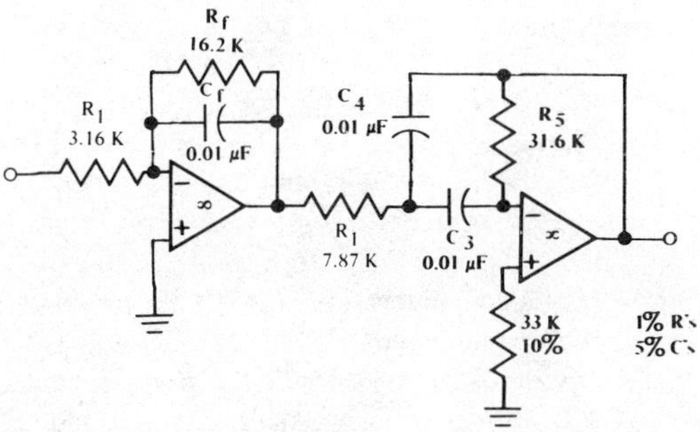

Fig. 10.6.3 Low-pass discriminator realization of Example 10.6.2.

The design proceeds as:

$$1/R_1C = 2\pi[2(1\text{ KHz})] = 2\pi(2\text{ KHz}), \quad 1/R_5C = 2\pi(1\text{ KHz}/2) = 2\pi(500\text{ Hz}), \quad C = 0.01\ \mu F$$
$$R_1 = 7.96\text{ K (use 7.87 K)}, \quad R_5 = 31.8\text{ K (use 31.6 K)}, \quad H_o = -2 \tag{10.6.5}$$

The first stage is also easily designed. The dc gain must equal $H_o = -10/2 = -5$ so that the overall gain is 10. Using an inverting gain block as shown in Fig. 8.4.6, the design proceeds as:

$$1/R_fC_f = 2\pi(1\text{ KHz}), \quad C_f = 0.01\ \mu F$$
$$R_f = 15.9\text{ K (use 16.2 K)}, \quad R_1 = R_f/(-H_o) = 16.2\text{ K}/5 = 3.24\text{ K (use 3.16 K)} \tag{10.6.6}$$

The complete discriminator is shown in Fig. 10.6.3.

The high-Q band-pass frequency discriminator is slightly more complex to design. From Eq. 10.6.3, the transfer function of the band-pass filter must be multiplied by $(s^2 + \omega_o{}^2)/s\omega_o$. In cascade design, this involves simply changing a single band-pass filter stage to a band-stop filter stage. Otherwise the design procedure follows that of the earlier discriminator design examples. Band-stop filters are discussed in the next chapter so we shall not pursue this further.

PROBLEMS

10.1 Band-pass filters have the typical frequency response shown in Prob. 6.1. Describe the parameters required to specify the response.

10.2 The importance of compiling complete filter specifications cannot be overemphasized. A typical specification sheet was shown in Prob. 6.2. Briefly list the reasons for providing each data entry listed on that sheet.

10.3 Frequency discriminators have somewhat different specifications than filters. The important parameters are listed in Prob. 6.3. Modify the specification sheet of Prob. 6.2 so that it can be used for discriminators.

10.4 In filters having $Q \geqslant 2$ or $\zeta \leqslant 0.25$, the sensitivity coefficients $S_x^{\omega_o}$ and S_x^Q for x = R, C, and K become very important. Drifts in ω_o and Q can cause serious detuning. (a) What is the maximum allowable percentage drift in f_o when we restrict $\Delta f_{max} = \pm B/4$ and Q = 22? (b) What are the sensitivity coefficients of ω_o for band-pass filters having $\omega_o = 1/(R_1C_1R_2C_2)^{1/2}$? (c) What are the sensitivity coefficients of ζ where $\zeta = 1/2(R_2C_2/R_1C_1)^{1/2}$? (d) Assuming that the drifts in R_1, R_2, C_1, and C_2 are uncorrelated, what are the maximum temperature coefficients of the R's and C's to meet the part (a) result? (e) What TC's are required to insure that the drift in Q does not exceed ± 5%? Is the TC of part (d) or (e) more stringent?

10.5 A Class 1A band-pass filter is shown in Sec. 10.3. (a) How must the parameters be chosen to obtain minimum sensitivities? What are the gain-sensitivity values with these parameters? (b) How must the parameters be chosen to obtain minimum gain? What are the gain-sensitivity values with these parameters? (c) Which set of parameters are the best? Justify. (d) Now replace K_1 with a short to produce a Class 2A band-pass filter. Repeat parts (a) and (b).

10.6 A Class 1C band-pass filter was analyzed in Example 7.7.1. Its characteristics therefore lie between (or exceed) those of a Class 1A and 1B filter. (a) Determine which components to vary to force it to approach a Class 1A filter, (b) Class 1B filter.

10.7 Repeat Prob. 10.6 for the Class $1\overline{C}$ band-pass filter analyzed in Example 7.8.1. Note that its characteristics lie between (or exceed) those of a Class $1\overline{A}$ and 1B filter.

10.8 A Class 1E filter which could be operated in low-pass or band-pass modes was discussed in Prob. 8.18. Repeat that problem for the band-pass filter.

10.9 A second-order Butterworth band-pass filter having a center frequency of 100 Hz, a bandwidth of 10 Hz, and a midband gain of 10 must be designed. Its block diagram consists of two first-order BPF stages having parameters (H_o, f_o, Q) which equal (4.44, 96.3 Hz, 14.1) and (4.44, 103.7 Hz, 14.1). Should a Class A or $\overline{A}$ realization be used? Design the complete filter using the Class 2A realization.

10.10 Octave and one-third octave band-pass filters were discussed in Prob. 2.21. For frequencies below 100 Hz, the passive component values become large which is undesirable (where $\omega_o = 1/RC$). (a) What class of filters should be used in this application? (b) Design first-order band-pass filters having center frequencies of 16, 31.5, and 63 Hz, Q = 4.3, and unity gains. Use Class 2A realizations. (c) What improvement in component values is obtained using Class 2A filters rather than Class $2\overline{A}$ and 2B filters?

10.11 A temperature measuring system which utilizes the white noise generated by a resistor R_s and a high-Q band-pass filter is shown in Fig. P10.11. (a) Verify that the band-pass filter has $f_o = 20$ Hz, a bandwidth B = 1 Hz, and a midband gain of 40 dB. (b) To reduce the capacitance values required, we shall use the frequency up-scaling properties of a Class 2A filter. Redesign the band-pass filter. (c) What improvement in the component values is obtained using a Class 2A filter rather than Class $2\overline{A}$ and 2B filters?

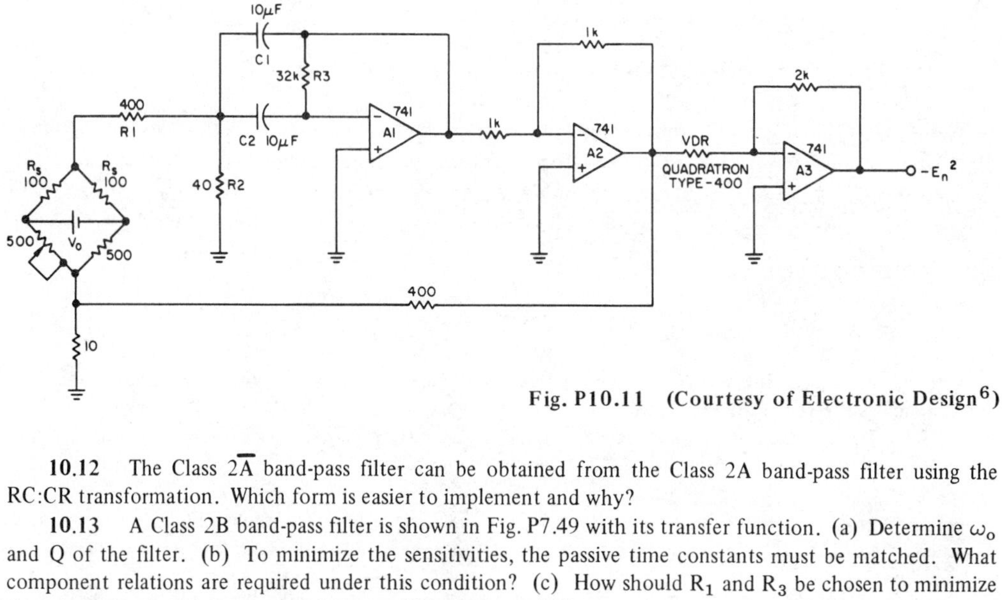

Fig. P10.11 **(Courtesy of Electronic Design[6])**

10.12 The Class $2\overline{A}$ band-pass filter can be obtained from the Class 2A band-pass filter using the RC:CR transformation. Which form is easier to implement and why?

10.13 A Class 2B band-pass filter is shown in Fig. P7.49 with its transfer function. (a) Determine ω_o and Q of the filter. (b) To minimize the sensitivities, the passive time constants must be matched. What component relations are required under this condition? (c) How should R_1 and R_3 be chosen to minimize the gain under the minimum sensitivity conditions of part (b)?

10.14 A multipurpose filter which could be operated in low-pass, high-pass, or band-pass modes was analyzed in Prob. 8.32. Repeat that problem for the band-pass filter.

10.15 Two band-pass filters[7] and their design parameters are shown in Table P10.15. (a) Classify the filters. (b) Compare the minimum sensitivity values with the actual sensitivities. Are these an acceptable set of design equations? (c) The actual drifts in ω_o and Q due to drifts in the R's and C's are also given. What are the component limitations to obtain a stable ω_o and Q?

10.16 Repeat Prob. 10.6 for the first Class 2C band-pass filter shown in Fig. 10.5.1. Its transfer function is given below. Note that its characteristics lie between (or exceed) those of a Class 2A and 2B filter.

$$T_1 = R_1C_2, \quad T_2 = R_2C_1$$

$$H(s) = \frac{sK_1T_2}{s^2(1 - K_1K_2)T_1T_2 + s\{T_1(1 + C_2/C_1) + T_2[1 + (1 - K_1)R_1/R_3]\} + [1 + R_1/R_3]},$$

Table P10.15 (Courtesy of Electronic Design[7])

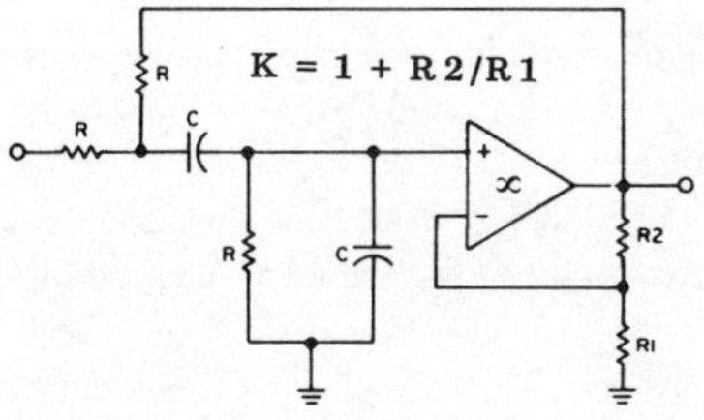

Parameters:

$\omega_o = 2^{1/2}/RC$, $Q = 2^{1/2}/(5 - K)$, $H_o = K/(5 - K)$

Stability Functions:

(a) $\dfrac{\Delta\omega_o}{\omega_o} = -\sqrt{2}\left[\dfrac{\Delta R}{R} + \dfrac{\Delta C}{C}\right]$

(b) $\dfrac{\Delta Q}{Q} = (2\sqrt{2}\,Q\text{-}1)\left[\dfrac{\Delta R_2}{R_2} - \dfrac{\Delta R_1}{R_1}\right]$

(c) $\dfrac{\Delta K_o}{K_o} = (3.54Q)\left[\dfrac{2.84Q - 1}{3.54Q - 1}\right]\left[\dfrac{\Delta R_2}{R_2} - \dfrac{\Delta R_1}{R_1}\right]$

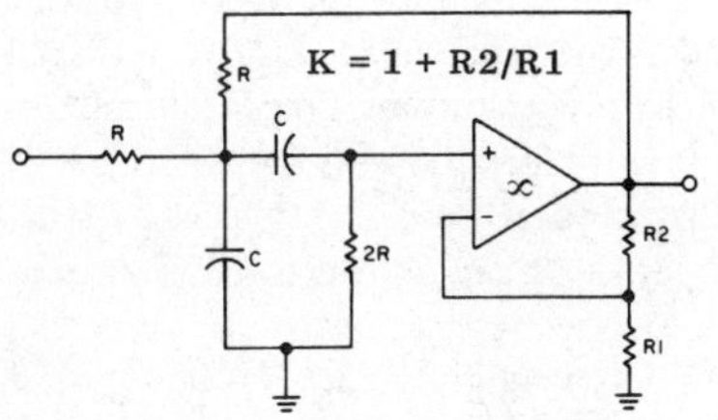

Parameters:

$\omega_o = 1/RC$, $Q = 1/(3 - K)$, $H_o = K/(3 - K)$

Stability Functions:

(a) $\dfrac{\Delta\omega_o}{\omega_o} = -\left[\dfrac{\Delta R}{R} + \dfrac{\Delta C}{C}\right]$

(b) $\dfrac{\Delta Q}{Q} = (2Q\text{-}1)\cdot\left[\dfrac{\Delta R_2}{R_2} - \dfrac{\Delta R_1}{R_1}\right]$

(c) $\dfrac{\Delta K_o}{K_o} = 3Q\left[\dfrac{2Q\text{-}1}{3Q\text{-}1}\right]\left[\dfrac{\Delta R_2}{R_2} - \dfrac{\Delta R_1}{R_1}\right]$

10.17 "Drop-outs" occur when a transmission line fails to transmit signal or when it transmits a much attenuated signal. The block diagram of a drop-out simulator is shown in Fig. P10.17. The required specifications are:[8] (1) 3 dB frequency range: 300 Hz–3.4 KHz, (2) attenuation: –3 dB to –27 dB (in 3 dB steps), and (3) drop-out duration: 1 msec–10 sec (in 1 msec steps). Design a second-order Butterworth band-pass filter to meet the band-limiting requirements. Use a Class 2C realization.

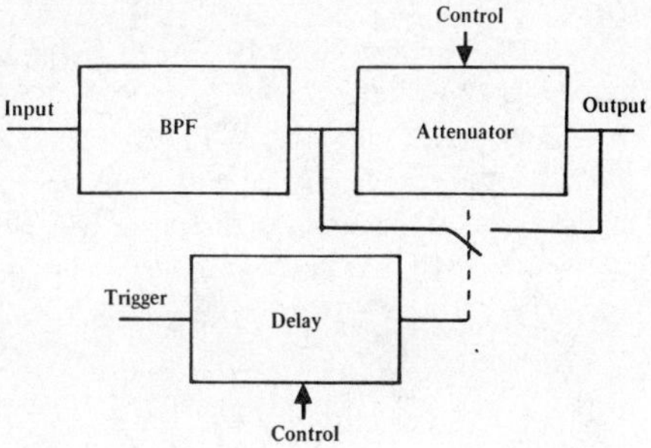

Fig. P10.17

10.18 The 1170/2125 Hz Transmit band-pass filters of an acoustical data coupler were analyzed in Prob. 6.22. The Transmit filters were second-order Chebyshev having 0.5 dB ripples. Their block diagrams consist of two first-order BPF stages having parameters (H_o, f_o, Q) which equal (1.41, 1.05 or 2.00 KHz, 8.3 or 14.9) and (1.41, 1.29 or 2.24 KHz, 8.3 or 14.9). Design the filter using a Class 2C realization having a center frequency of (a) 1170 Hz and (b) 2125 Hz.

10.19 Repeat Prob. 10.6 for the Class $2\overline{C}$ band-pass filter analyzed in Example 7.16.1. Note that its characteristics lie between (or exceed) those of a Class $2\overline{A}$ and 2B filter.

10.20 The 3400/3550 Hz band-pass filter used in the Lenkurt Type 45 signalling system was analyzed in Prob. 6.23. A second-order Butterworth filter having f_o = 3480 Hz and Q = 11.6 can be used. Its block diagram consists of two first-order BPF stages having parameters (H_o, f_o, Q) which equal (1.41, 3.33 KHz, 16.4) and (1.41, 3.63 KHz, 16.4). Design the filter using a Class 2D realization.

10.21 A Class 2E band-pass filter was analyzed in Example 7.18.1. Determine which components to vary to force it to approach a Class 2D filter.

10.22 A Class 2E band-pass filter and its transfer function are shown in Fig. P7.67. Discuss what other classes can be obtained by varying parameter values.

10.23 The input impedance to a Class 1A band-pass filter was determined in Example 10.4.4. Perform the RC:CR transformation to obtain the input impedance to the Class $1\overline{A}$ band-pass filter. Write its input impedance directly from Eq. 10.4.10. Plot and interpret the results.

10.24 Repeat Prob. 8.41 for the Class 2A band-pass filter of Sec. 10.3. Without calculation, does there appear to be any impedance advantage to using the Class $2\overline{A}$ form obtained from the RC:CR transformation?

10.25 Repeat Prob. 8.41 for the Class 1B band-pass filter of Sec. 10.3.

10.26 A tunable band-pass filter is shown in Fig. P10.26. It uses two solid-state multipliers as gain blocks (gain = $0.1V_x$) to control the center frequency ω_o.[9] Determine the parameters of the filter.

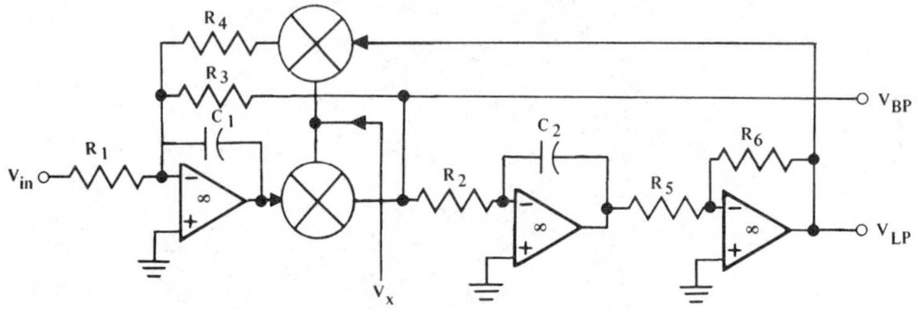

Fig. P10.26

10.27 Design a gain-tuned first-order band-pass filter to have a center frequency of 1 KHz, a 2:1 tuning range, and Q = 5. The variation in Q cannot exceed ± 20%. Use the first filter in Fig. 10.5.1.

10.28 FDM channel banks use band-pass filters having 4 KHz bandwidths with center frequencies in the range between 60–108 KHz as discussed in Prob. 6.27. The variation in Q cannot exceed ± 5%. Design a gain-tuned Class $1\overline{C}$ filter to meet these requirements. Use the RC:CR dual of the fifth filter in Fig. 10.5.1, or equivalently, the Class $1\overline{C}$ filter in Sec. 10.3.

10.29 Audio spectrometers were discussed in Prob. 2.21. Design a one-third octave bandwidth filter to be tunable from 12.5 Hz to 800 Hz. Use a passive-tuned first-order Class 2A band-pass filter having a Q of 6.25.

10.30 Repeat Prob. 10.29 and design the filter so it is tunable from 800 Hz to 40 KHz. Use a passive-tuned Class $2\overline{A}$ filter.

10.31 EEG brain-wave filters were analyzed in Prob. 2.23. The Delta, Alpha, and Beta band-pass filters have center frequencies of about 5.5 Hz, 10.5 Hz, and 19 Hz, respectively. Assume that they have Q's of 2.1. An Alpha filter is shown in Fig. P10.31 where Q = 3.4. Modify the filter so that Q = 2.1. Add passive tuning so that it can be switched into a Delta, Alpha, or Beta filter.

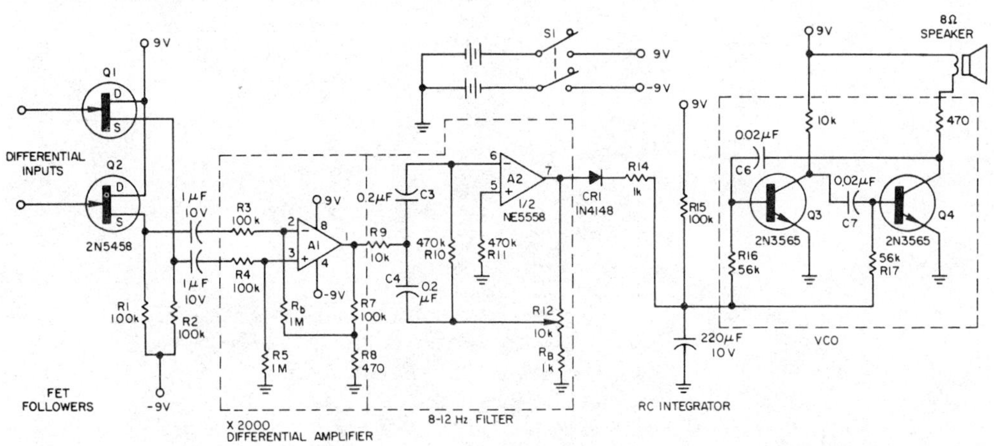

Fig. P10.31 (Courtesy of Electronic Design[10])

10.32 Prepare design sheets for Class $1\overline{A}$ and Class $2\overline{A}$ constant-bandwidth filters.

10.33 Band-pass filters used by the telegraph system were analyzed in Prob. 2.25. They have 120 Hz or 170 Hz tone spacing and are constant-bandwidth. Design a gain-tunable Receive filter for 120 Hz tone spacing which can be tuned from 420 Hz to 3300 Hz. Assume that it is first-order and has a 3 dB bandwidth of 64 Hz. Use a Class $2\overline{A}$ realization.

10.34 Repeat Prob. 10.33 but use a Class $1\overline{A}$ realization. Why is this more advantageous than using a Class $2\overline{A}$ filter?

10.35 Repeat Prob. 10.33 for 170 Hz tone spacing. The filter must be tunable from 425 Hz to 3315 Hz and have a constant bandwidth of 90 Hz. Use a Class $1\overline{A}$ realization.

10.36 Scramblers were discussed in Prob. 6.39. They require band-pass filters having 500 Hz bandwidths which are tunable from 550 Hz to 2950 Hz. Design a tunable first-order band-pass filter using a Class $2\overline{A}$ realization.

10.37 A gas analyzer determines the concentration of a particular component in a gas. One such analyzer has a detector that uses the band-pass filter shown in Fig. P10.36 and which is tuned to have a center frequency of 10 Hz. Classify the filter and determine its characteristics from the component values.

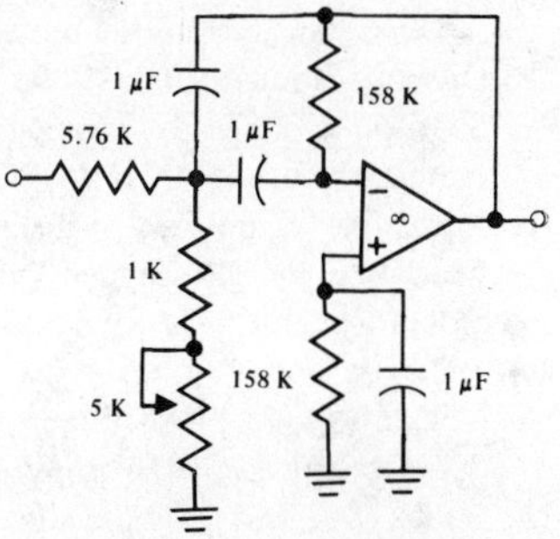

Fig. P10.37 (Courtesy of Beckman Instruments[11])

10.38 Design a gain-tuned first-order band-pass filter having variable Q and constant ω_o. Assume that its center frequency is 1 KHz and its Q must be tuned from 1 to 10 (its response is shown in Fig. 2.7.1). Design the filter using a Class 2D realization.

10.39 Repeat Prob. 10.38 for a passive-tuned filter. Use a Class 1E realization. What taper must the pots have for Q to be linear in R?

10.40 ULF direction finder systems are used in mine rescue operations. A keyed-CW transmitter connected to a large collapsible loop antenna radiates a frequency in the 0.9–3.1 KHz range underground at each mine site. 34 frequencies are used. Above ground, a portable receiver is used to detect the location from which the desired frequency is being transmitted.[12] Assuming that the receiver uses a band-pass filter of first-order (although this is insufficient) with a 2 Hz bandwidth, discuss what type of filter should be used in this application. (Hint: Is tuning necessary?)

10.41 Design a fourth-order Butterworth low-pass discriminator with a cutoff frequency of 500 Hz and a gain of 0.00522 volt/volt/Hz.[13] Its block diagram realization was determined in Prob. 6.49 to consist of a second-order LPF stage having parameters (H_o, f_o, ζ) which equal (–1, 500 Hz, 0.924) cascaded with a first-order BPF stage having parameters (–3.41, 500 Hz, 0.383). Use a Class 2E realization for both stages. (Hint: Set the gain to unity in the first stage. Then $|H(j\omega)| \sim R_5 C_3 \omega$ overall at low frequencies.)

10.42 Design a third-order elliptic low-pass discriminator having a 1.25 dB bandwidth of 1 KHz, an in-band ripple not exceeding 1.25 dB, and a gain of 10^{-2} volt/volt/Hz. Utilize the Class 2B low-pass filter design of Example 8.5.6.

10.43 As discussed in Prob. 2.32, band-pass filters must often be "tuned" to obtain their required parameters. Repeat that problem.

REFERENCES

1. Cole, L. G., "Practical design of active filters," M.S.E.E. Directed Research, California State Univ., Long Beach, Jan., 1975.
2. Tarukachon, D., "Passive-tuned active filters," M.S.E.E. Directed Research, California State Univ., Long Beach, July, 1975.
3. Bruminhent, S., and K. L. Su, "Gain-tuned active filters with constant percent bandwidth," IEEE Trans. Circuit Theory, vol. CAS-22, pp. 587–594, July, 1975.
   ———, "Gain-tuned active filters," Proc. Intl. Symp. on Circuits and Systems, pp. 443–447, April, 1974.
4. Deboo, G. J., and R. C. Hedlund, "Automatically tuned filter uses IC operational amplifiers,"EDN Magazine, Feb., 1970.
5. Viterbi, A. J., *Principles of Coherent Communication*, McGraw-Hill, NY, 1966.
6. Kraus, K., "Measuring system uses white noise to indicate temperature from 10 to 2500°K," Electronic Design, p. 190, Nov. 22, 1973, copyright Hayden Publishing, 1973.
7. Russell, H. T., "Design active filters with less effort," Electronic Design, pp. 82–85, Jan. 7, 1971, copyright Hayden Publishing, 1971.
   ———, "Single-amplifier active filters give stable Q," EDN Magazine, pp. 65–66, Jan. 1, 1972.
8. Dropout Simulator FA-1955, Data Sheet 2845M573, SEG, Electronics, Richmond Hill, NY, 5/73.
9. Sparkes, R. G., and A. S. Sedra, "A tracking biquad active filter," Proc. Intl. Symp. on Circuits and Systems, pp. 585–589, April, 1974.
10. Lutus, P., "Simplified biofeedback circuit detects alpha-wave activity," Electronic Design, p. 154, June 7, 1974, copyright Hayden Publishing, 1974.
11. Model 864 Infrared Analyzer, Inst. Manual 015-082267, Beckman Instruments, Fullerton, CA, Nov., 1972.
12. McDermott, J., "ULF direction finder for miners passes tests at 1500 ft. depth," Electronic Design, pp. 32–34, Sept. 27, 1974, copyright Hayden Publishing, 1974.
13. Budak, A., and K. E. Waltz, "Linear amplitude Butterworth active filter," Proc. IEEE, vol. 58, pp. 274–275, Feb., 1970.

11 BAND-STOP FILTERS

O! throw away the worser part of it,
And live the purer with the other half.
Shakespeare

We now want to consider band-stop filters, which are also called band-reject, band-elimination, or notch filters. We begin by investigating band-stop filters from the classification viewpoint of Chap. 7. We shall see that there are relatively few single-forward-branch band-stop filters and that they have standard twin-T forms. However, using more general topologies, we will have a variety of filters from which to choose. We will then investigate a standard method which allows us to utilize band-pass filters in constructing band-stop filters. A set of filter design sheets will be compiled. These sheets will be used to investigate and design a variety of band-stop filters. We will compare the gain and sensitivity bounds of the various filters and make qualitative evaluations of the designs. Since twin-T's are so important in this class of filter, we shall discuss them in detail. Tunable band-stop filters shall also be investigated. We will conclude with a discussion of biquadratic filters and amplitude equalizers.

11.1 BAND-STOP FILTER CLASSES

Band-stop filters of first-order have gains which equal

$$H(s) = H_o \frac{(s/\omega_{oz})^2 + 1}{(s/\omega_{op})^2 + (s/\omega_{op})/Q_p + 1} \tag{11.1.1}$$

Generally, the dc and high-frequency gains are different. Notch filters having symmetrical gains result when the poles and zeros are equal. Quasi-band-stop filters are described by the biquadratic equation where

$$H(s) = H_o \frac{(s/\omega_{oz})^2 + (s/\omega_{oz})/Q_z + 1}{(s/\omega_{op})^2 + (s/\omega_{op})/Q_p + 1} \tag{11.1.2}$$

We shall only be concerned with first-order band-stop filters described by Eq. 11.1.1 whose poles and zeros may or may not be equal. Such filters are completely described by their resonant frequencies ω_{op} and ω_{oz}, the Q of the pole, Q_p; and the asymptotic passband gain H_o. H_o must be specified as a dc gain ($H_o(0)$) or a high-frequency gain ($H_o(\infty)$). In the filter designs of Chaps. 2–6, this information was summarized in a band-stop filter (BSF) block. We shall now implement these blocks with hardware.

We again want to select the class of band-stop filters to obtain the desired gain/sensitivity tradeoffs. Let us consider the active filters which have the simplest topology of a single forward branch using the assumptions of Sec. 8.1. These filters have the flow graph of Fig. 8.1.1 and a transfer function given by Eq. 8.1.4. The numerator of the gain function is equal to the numerator of the forward path gain product $K_1K_2T_{13}T_{45}$; thus, the form of the numerators of T_{13} and T_{45} determine the filter type. Using the notation of Eqs. 8.1.5–8.1.8, it was shown in Eq. 8.1.9 that the numerator of the transfer function H(s) for first-order decomposition filters is given by

$$\begin{aligned}\text{Num } H(s) &= K_1K_2(c_{50} + c_{51}s)(d_{30} + d_{31}s) \\ &= K_1K_2[c_{50}d_{30} + (c_{50}d_{31} + c_{51}d_{30})s + c_{51}d_{31}s^2]\end{aligned} \tag{11.1.3}$$

For H(s) to be notch, then the s^1 coefficient of Num H must equal zero. This requires $c_{50}d_{31} = -c_{51}d_{30}$ which can never occur (the various a, b, c, and d's are always non-negative by the Fialkow-Gerst conditions of Eq. 8.1.6). Alternatively stated, when a band-stop filter is required, then T_{13} and T_{45} must be notch (i.e., first-order band-stop) and zero-order, respectively, or vice versa. Since Class 1X filters have first-order transfer functions, then T_{13} or T_{45} can never be notch, so Class 1X notch filters cannot be realized.

In second-order decomposition filters, the numerator of the transfer function H(s) was given by Eq. 8.1.11. For H(s) to be notch, this requires $d_{31} = 0$ so that

$$T_{13} = \frac{d_{30} + d_{32}s^2}{a_{30} + a_{31}s + a_{32}s^2} \quad \text{(BSF)}, \qquad T_{45} = \frac{c_{50}}{a_{50}} \quad \text{(constant)} \tag{11.1.4}$$

From Table 7.19.2, we see that constant T_{45}'s are required in all Class 2X filters. Thus, when T_{13} is a notch filter, then Class 2X band-stop filters having a single forward branch can be realized. Since passive notch filters are more constrained topologically than low-pass, high-pass, and band-pass filters (the twin-T is the only standard form), Class 2X band-stop filters physically have fairly standard forms.

However, requiring T_{13} to be a notch filter is a severe restriction. Therefore the question is, can we use some other filter topologies which are more flexible? The answer is yes we can. For example, we can add a T_{12} branch to the flow graph of Fig. 8.1.1 as will be discussed in the next section. This facilitates tuning and band-stop filters can be realized in every class.

Two other possibilities are shown in Fig. 11.1.1. Here T_{15} and T_{42} branches have been added to the single-forward-branch flow graph of Fig. 8.1.1.[1] The transfer function of the flow graph having a T_{15} branch is

$$H(s) = K_2T_{62}\frac{N_{15}D_{43} - K_1(N_{15}N_{43} - N_{13}N_{45})}{D_{43}D_{65} - K_1N_{43}D_{65} - K_2N_{65}D_{43} + K_1K_2(N_{43}N_{65} - N_{45}N_{63})} \tag{11.1.5}$$

while that using a T_{42} branch is

$$H(s) = K_1T_{43}\frac{D_{43}}{D_{42}}\frac{N_{42}D_{65} - K_2(N_{42}N_{65} - N_{45}N_{62})}{D_{43}D_{65} - K_1N_{43}D_{65} - K_2N_{65}D_{43} + K_1K_2(N_{43}N_{65} - N_{45}N_{63})} \tag{11.1.6}$$

Note that adding these branches modifies the gain numerator so that it involves *difference* terms. This gives us the flexibility to force the damping factor ζ_z of the zero to equal zero, or $Q_z = \infty$ as required in band-stop filters. In addition, the T_{13} transfer function need no longer be notch so its filter topology can be simplified.

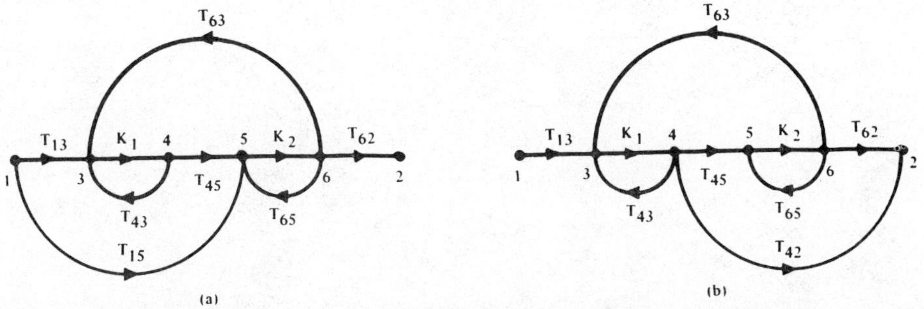

Fig. 11.1.1 Alternative band-stop filter forms using (a) T_{15} branch and (b) T_{42} branch.

Usually, it is more satisfactory to add a T_{15} branch rather than a T_{42} branch. Using a T_{15} branch, the output of the filter corresponds to the K_2 output so that the output impedance is zero. However, when T_{42} is added, a passive voltage divider is required at the output so that the output impedance is nonzero. An additional amplifier is required for impedance buffering which increases the parts count. Thus, we shall be concerned only with adding T_{15} branches.

Let us consider only first-order decomposition band-stop filters. The gain function using a T_{15} branch is given by Eq. 11.1.5. The denominator of the gain function is still given by Eq. 7.3.3. The necessary branch transfer functions are therefore still listed in Table 7.19.1. When $T_{62} = 0$, the numerator of the transfer function of Eq. 11.1.3 equals

$$N(s) = \text{Num } H(s) = K_2[N_{15}D_{43} - K_1(N_{15}N_{43} - N_{13}N_{45})] \tag{11.1.7}$$

Then substituting the appropriate N_{ij} and D_{ij} terms from Eq. 8.1.5 into Eq. 11.1.7, the normalized numerator can be expressed as

$$\begin{aligned} N(s)/K_2 &= [(d_{50} + d_{51}s)(a_{30} + a_{31}s) - K_1(d_{50} + d_{51}s)(b_{30} + b_{31}s) \\ &\qquad + K_1(d_{30} + d_{31}s)(c_{50} + c_{51}s)] \\ &= [a_{31}d_{51} + K_1(c_{51}d_{31} - b_{31}d_{51})]s^2 \\ &\quad + [a_{30}d_{51} + a_{31}d_{50} + K_1(c_{50}d_{31} + c_{51}d_{30} - b_{30}d_{51} - b_{31}d_{50})]s^1 \\ &\quad + [a_{30}d_{50} + K_1(c_{50}d_{30} - b_{30}d_{50})] \end{aligned} \tag{11.1.8}$$

To force N(s) to have zeros of transmission where $\zeta_z = 0$, we must set the s^1 coefficient to equal zero. This requires

$$a_{30}d_{51} + a_{31}d_{50} + K_1(c_{50}d_{31} + c_{51}d_{30} - b_{30}d_{51} - b_{31}d_{50}) = 0 \tag{11.1.9}$$

or

$$K_1 = -\frac{a_{30}d_{51} + a_{31}d_{50}}{c_{50}d_{31} + c_{51}d_{30} - (b_{30}d_{51} + b_{31}d_{50})} \tag{11.1.10}$$

where the s^2 and s^0 coefficients must be nonzero. Thus, gain K_1 will generally be used to adjust $\zeta_z = 0$.

To illustrate the use of these results, let us formulate a Class 1A band-stop filter. Referring to Table 7.19.1, the various feedback transfer functions equal

$$T_{43} = T_{65} = 0, \qquad T_{63} = \frac{c_{31}s}{a_{30} + a_{31}s} \text{ (HPF)}, \qquad T_{45} = \frac{c_{51}s}{a_{50} + a_{51}s} \text{ (HPF)} \tag{11.1.11}$$

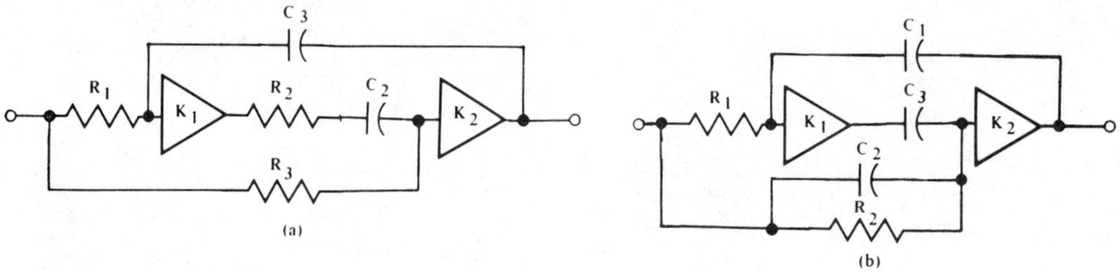

Fig. 11.1.2 Two Class 1A band-stop filters.

Comparing these equations with those of Eq. 8.1.5, we see that

$$D_{13} = D_{63} = a_{30} + a_{31}s, \qquad D_{15} = D_{45} = a_{50} + a_{51}s, \qquad N_{63} = c_{31}s, \qquad N_{45} = c_{51}s \tag{11.1.12}$$

Substituting these results into Eq. 11.1.5, we find that

$$H(s) = K_2 \frac{N_{15}(a_{30} + a_{31}s) + K_1 N_{13} c_{51} s}{(a_{30} + a_{31}s)(a_{50} + a_{51}s) - K_1 K_2 c_{31} c_{51} s^2} \tag{11.1.13}$$

The denominator confirms this is a Class 1A filter. Substituting N_{13} and N_{15} from Eq. 8.1.5 into Eq. 11.1.13, we now adjust the numerator of H(s) given by

$$\text{Num } H(s) = K_2[(a_{30} + a_{31}s)(d_{50} + d_{51}s) + K_1 c_{51} s(d_{30} + d_{31}s)] \tag{11.1.14}$$

to be band-stop. Therefore for $\zeta_z = 0$, K_1 must equal

$$K_1 = -(a_{30}d_{51} + a_{31}d_{50})/c_{51}d_{30} \leq 0 \tag{11.1.15}$$

in which case the numerator reduces to

$$\text{Num } H(s) = K_2[(a_{31}d_{51} + K_1 c_{51} d_{31})s^2 + a_{30}d_{50}] \tag{11.1.16}$$

For the simplest realization, we set $d_{31} = 0$. Then the resulting transfer function equals

$$H(s) = K_2 \frac{s^2 a_{31}d_{51} + a_{30}d_{50}}{s^2(a_{31}a_{51} - K_1K_2c_{31}c_{51}) + s(a_{31}a_{50} + a_{51}a_{30}) + a_{30}a_{50}} \tag{11.1.17}$$

To further obtain $\omega_{op} = \omega_{oz}$, Eq. 11.1.17 shows that

$$\frac{a_{50}d_{51}}{a_{51}d_{50}} = 1 - K_1K_2 \frac{c_{31}c_{51}}{a_{31}a_{51}} \tag{11.1.18}$$

so that K_2 must equal

$$K_2 = \frac{1}{-K_1} \frac{a_{31}a_{51}}{c_{31}c_{51}} \left(\frac{d_{51}/a_{51}}{d_{50}/a_{50}} - 1 \right) \tag{11.1.19}$$

For complex poles, K_1 and K_2 must have opposite signs in Class 1A filters. Since $K_1 \leq 0$, then $K_2 \geq 0$ which requires $d_{51}/a_{51} \leq d_{50}/a_{50}$ so T_{15} is quasi-low-pass. Summarizing the various transfer functions yields

$$T_{13} = \frac{d_{30}}{a_{30} + a_{31}s} \ \text{(LPF)}, \qquad T_{15} = \frac{d_{50} + d_{51}s}{a_{50} + a_{51}s} \ \text{(QHP)} \tag{11.1.20a, b}$$

$$T_{63} = \frac{c_{31}s}{a_{30} + a_{31}s} \text{ (HPF)}, \qquad T_{45} = \frac{c_{51}s}{a_{50} + a_{51}s} \text{ (HPF)} \tag{11.1.20c, d}$$

where gains K_1 and K_2 must satisfy Eqs. 11.1.15 and 11.1.19. All that remains is to choose the proper set of RC networks which have these transfer functions. With practice, this is easily done. We see that for simplicity and minimum parts count, the networks having gains T_{13} and T_{15} should be chosen as simply as possible. From Eq. 11.1.20, T_{15} must be a quasi-low-pass filter. We saw that selecting $d_{31} = 0$ simplifies the transfer functions while still allowing the K_1 and K_2 equations to be satisfied. One filter having these transfer functions is shown in Fig. 11.1.2a. The branch transfer functions equal

$$T_{13} = \frac{1}{1 + s\tau_{11}}, \quad T_{63} = \frac{s\tau_{11}}{1 + s\tau_{11}}, \quad T_{15} = \frac{1 + s\tau_{22}}{1 + s(\tau_{22} + \tau_{32})}, \quad T_{45} = \frac{s\tau_{32}}{1 + s(\tau_{22} + \tau_{32})} \tag{11.1.21}$$

where $\tau_{xy} = R_x C_y$. When

$$K_1 = -(\tau_{11} + \tau_{22})/\tau_{32} \tag{11.1.22}$$

from Eq. 11.1.15, then Eq. 11.1.17 yields

$$H(s) = K_2 \frac{s^2\tau_{11}\tau_{22} + 1}{s^2\tau_{11}[\tau_{22} + \tau_{32}(1 - K_1K_2)] + s(\tau_{11} + \tau_{22} + \tau_{32}) + 1} \tag{11.1.23}$$

An alternative form is shown in Fig. 11.1.2b. Here the gain K_1 is given Eq. 11.1.22 and the transfer function is given by Eq. 11.1.23 where τ_{32} is replaced by τ_{23}. The principle difference between them is that the second form requires three capacitors rather than two.

Following this procedure, a variety of Class 1X filters can be realized. The Class 1X filters listed in Sec. 11.3 were generated using this method. The same approach can be used to realize Class 2X filters of this topology but we shall not pursue this further.

11.2 BAND-PASS TO BAND-STOP FILTER TRANSFORMATION

Band-pass filters can be transformed into band-stop filters using the complementary filter arrangement discussed in Sec. 9.6. There it was shown that if any active filter employing infinite-gain amplifiers has a transfer function H(s), then its complementary transfer function $H_C(s)$ equals

$$H_C(s) = 1 - H(s) \tag{11.2.1}$$

The filter having this complementary transfer function is obtained by grounding the original inputs, lifting the original grounds, and treating these as the new inputs. If the original filter is band-pass with a positive midband gain of unity where

$$H_{BP}(s) = \frac{s_n/Q}{s_n^2 + s_n/Q + 1} \tag{11.2.2}$$

(note the midband gain *must* be +1), then the complementary filter will be band-stop with a transfer function of

$$H_{BS}(s) = \frac{s_n^2 + 1}{s_n^2 + s_n/Q + 1} \tag{11.2.3}$$

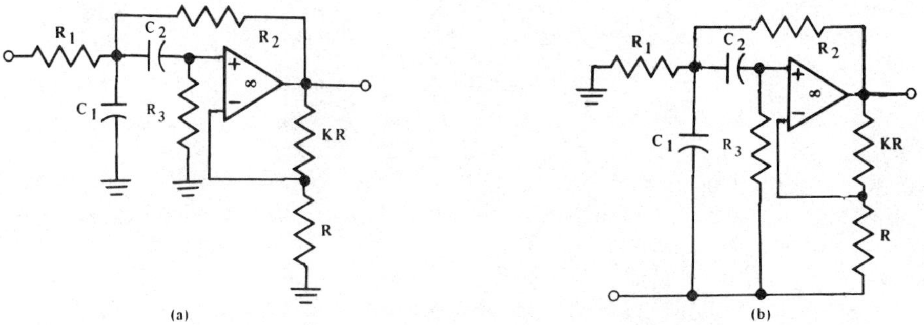

Fig. 11.2.1 Conversion of (a) Class 2B band-pass filter into (b) Class 2B band-stop filter.

This conversion is illustrated in Fig. 11.2.1. In practice, the band-pass filter is tuned to have $H_o = 1$ and the desired ω_o and Q. Then interchanging the input and ground produces a band-stop filter having the same parameters.

There is no other topological transformation that allows the engineer to directly transform RC active low-pass, high-pass, or band-pass filters into band-stop filters. Neither the RC:CR transformation or intuitive RC:CR half-transformation can be used, because these transformations fail to topologically produce band-stop filters from the other filter types.

Although no other topological transformations exist, it is easy to show a general topology in which low-pass, high-pass, and band-pass filters can be utilized to realize band-stop filters. These topologies are shown in Fig. 11.2.2. In the first case, a band-pass filter is inserted in parallel with a unity gain filter. The overall gain equals

$$H(s) = 1 + H_{BP}(s) = 1 + H_o \frac{s_n/Q}{s_n^2 + s_n/Q + 1} = \frac{s_n^2 + (1 + H_o)s_n/Q + 1}{s_n^2 + s_n/Q + 1} \tag{11.2.4}$$

To force H(s) to be band-stop, we must eliminate the s_n^1 term in the numerator. Thus, by setting its coefficient to zero, then the band-pass filter gain required equals $H_o = -1$. Thus, any band-pass filter with a midband gain of -1 can be used in conjunction with a parallel filter of unity gain to produce a band-stop filter. Note that this is equivalent to allowing $T_{12} = 1$ in the flow graph of the inverting band-pass filters analyzed in the previous chapter. Note also that ω_o and Q of the band-stop filter always equal that of the band-pass filter. Both asymptotic passband gains equal unity. Thus, we have two ways to utilize band-pass filters in constructing band-stop filters.

Alternatively, if we connect low-pass and high-pass filters of identical ω_o and Q in parallel, the overall gain equals

$$H_{BS}(s) = H_{LP}(s) + H_{HP}(s) = \frac{H_1}{s_n^2 + s_n/Q + 1} + \frac{H_2 s_n^2}{s_n^2 + s_n/Q + 1} = H_2 \frac{s_n^2 + H_1/H_2}{s_n^2 + s_n/Q + 1} \tag{11.2.5}$$

which is also band-stop.. Again, ω_o and Q of the band-stop filter are identical to that of the low-pass and high-pass filter. Both asymptotic passband gains equal unity. Of these two approaches, the band-pass filter realization is generally preferable because of simplicity (it requires only about half the components due to the unity gain branch), and it has no (ω_o, Q) matching requirement. Note however that the low-pass/high-pass filter approach gives us the flexibility to adjust ω_{oz} relative to ω_{op} using the H_1/H_2 ratio.

These methods of band-stop filter implementation add greatly to our design flexibility. They show that we can realize band-stop filters from the other filters we have considered in Chaps. 8–10. These methods also indicate the variety of realization forms available when we remove the topological single-forward-path restriction of the last section.

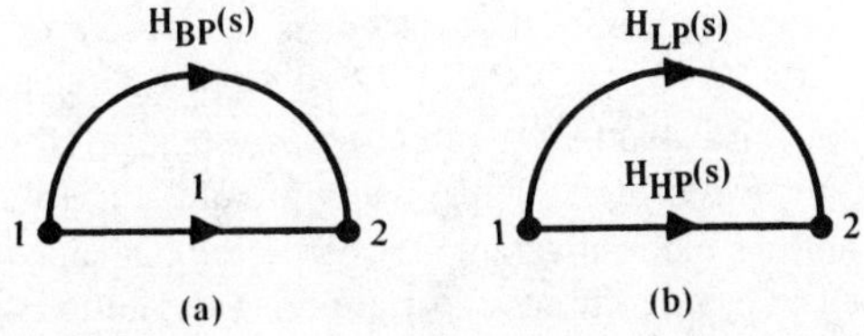

Fig. 11.2.2 Flow graph arrangements of (a) band-pass and (b) low-pass and high-pass filter to realize band-stop filters.

EXAMPLE 11.2.1 Design a Class 2A band-stop filter using a Class 2A band-pass filter and a summer. Obtain the design equations.

Solution The required filter is shown in Fig. 11.2.3. The overall gain equals

$$H(s) = \frac{1}{1+k}[1 + kH_{BP}(s)] \tag{11.2.6}$$

where from Sec. 10.3, the band-pass filter gain equalled

$$H_{BP}(s) = \frac{-KsR_2C_2}{s^2(1+K)R_1C_1R_2C_2 + s[R_1C_1(1+C_2/C_1) + R_2C_2] + 1} \tag{11.2.7}$$

The amplifier gain $-K$ is used to obtain the proper pole Q. To force the damping factor of the zeros to be zero, the summer gain k must equal

$$k = \frac{1}{-H_o} = \frac{R_1C_1(1+C_2/C_1) + R_2C_2}{KR_2C_2} = [1 + (R_1/R_2)(1 + C_1/C_2)]/K \tag{11.2.8}$$

Using the design equations of the Class 2A band-pass filter where:

$$\begin{aligned}
&\text{Set: } R_1 = R_2 = R, \quad C_1 = C_2 = C, \quad k = R_4/R_3 \\
&\text{Given: } \omega_o, Q \\
&\text{Choose: } C \\
&\text{Calculate: } R = 1/3Q\omega_oC, \quad K = 9Q^2 - 1
\end{aligned} \tag{11.2.9}$$

then we augment these equations to determine k and H_o. Substituting the parameter constraints of Eq. 11.2.9 into Eq. 11.2.8 shows that k equals

$$k = [1 + 1(1+1)]/K = 3/K = 3/(9Q^2 - 1) \tag{11.2.10}$$

The overall gain then equals

$$H_o(0) = \frac{1}{1+k} = \frac{9Q^2 - 1}{9Q^2 + 2} \tag{11.2.11}$$

These equations for k and H_o complete the design equations for the band-stop filter. If impedance buffering is required, an inverting or noninverting amplifier is used following the voltage divider.

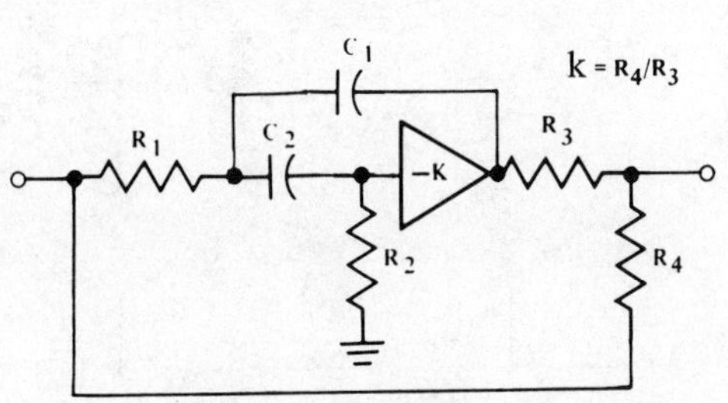

Fig. 11.2.3 Class 2A band-stop filter realization using a Class 2A band-pass filter and summer.

It is important to emphasize that applying the complementary transformation to a general nth-order band-pass filter produces its analogous *low-transient* band-stop filter. To obtain the standard band-stop filter, we must apply the complementary transformtion to the low-transient *band-pass* filter. Thus, when a band-stop filter is to be designed, its transfer function is calculated and its block diagram is constructed. Then each BSF block is realized and tuned using a band-pass filter having the same parameters (assuming $H_o = +1$).

11.3 BAND-STOP FILTER COMPILATIONS

A number of band-stop filters are compiled in this section.[1] These filters represent many of the band-stop filters which are known at the present time. It is useful to remember that the RC:CR transformation can be applied to any band-stop filter to produce another band-stop filter.

11.4 BAND-STOP FILTER DESIGN EXAMPLES

Now let us utilize these design sheets to realize a variety of band-stop filters. Their design proceeds in the same way as that of the other filter types.

EXAMPLE 11.4.1 Test tones are used by the telephone company to test transmission channels. Band-stop filters are used to eliminate these tones as discussed in Example 6.5.9. Design a first-order 1010 Hz filter to have $Q = 20$ and $H_o = -1$. Use a Class 1E realization.

Solution The block diagram of the filter is shown in Fig. 11.4.1. The design equations for the Class 1E filter are:

Set: $R_7 = R_8 = R$

Given: $\omega_{op}, Q_p, \omega_{oz}, -H_o(\infty)$

Choose: C_1, C_2, R

Calculate: $R_1 = Q_p/\omega_{op}C_1$, $R_2 = 1/\omega_{op}C_2$, $R_3 = R_2C_2/C_1$, $R_4 = R_1/(-H_o)$

$R_5 = [\omega_{op}/(-H_o\omega_{oz})]/\omega_{oz}C_2$, $R_6 = R_8/(-H_o)$

The design is easily carried out as:

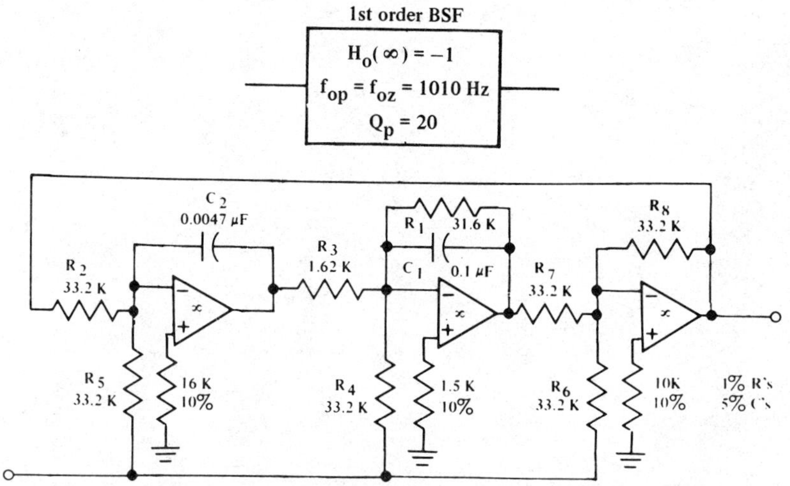

Fig. 11.4.1 Block diagram of first-order band-stop filter and its realization.

CLASS 1A: BAND-STOP ($\omega_{oz} > \omega_{op}$)

Transfer Function:

$$H(s) = K_2 \frac{s^2R_1C_1R_2C_2 + s[R_1C_1 + R_2(C_2 - K_1C_3)] + 1}{s^2R_1C_1[R_2C_2 + R_2C_3(1 + K_1K_2)] + s[R_1C_1 + R_2(C_2 + C_3)] + 1}$$

Parameters:

$$\omega_{op} = \frac{1}{\left\{R_1C_1[R_2C_2 + R_2C_3(1 + K_1K_2)]\right\}^{1/2}} \qquad \omega_{oz} = \frac{1}{(R_1C_1R_2C_2)^{1/2}}$$

$$\zeta_p = \frac{R_1C_1 + R_2(C_2 + C_3)}{2\left\{R_1C_1[R_2C_2 + R_2C_3(1 + K_1K_2)]\right\}^{1/2}} \qquad H_o(0) = K_2$$

$$\zeta_z = \frac{R_1C_1 + R_2(C_2 - K_1C_3)}{2(R_1C_1R_2C_2)^{1/2}} = 0 \text{ so that } \qquad K_1 = \frac{R_1C_1 + R_2C_2}{R_2C_3}$$

Design Equations: Set $R_2C_2 = k^2R_1C_1$

Given: ω_{op}, ζ_p, ω_{oz}

Choose: C_1, C_2, k

Calculate: $R_1 = 1/k\omega_{oz}C_1$

$R_2 = k/\omega_{oz}C_2$

$C_3 = [2\zeta_p\omega_{oz}/k\omega_{op} - (1 + k^2)/k^2]C_2$

$K_1 = [(1 + k^2)/k^2](C_2/C_3)$

$K_1K_2 = (C_2/C_3)[(\omega_{oz}/\omega_{op})^2 - 1] - 1$

$H_o(0) = K_2$

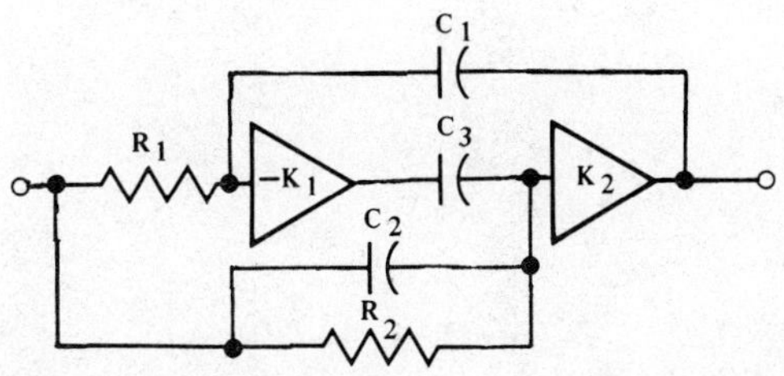

CLASS $1\bar{A}$: BAND-STOP ($\omega_{oz} < \omega_{op}$)

Transfer Function:

$$H(s) = K_2 \frac{s^2R_1C_1R_2C_2 + s[R_1C_1(1 - K_1R_2/R_3) + R_2C_2] + 1}{s^2R_1C_1R_2C_2 + s[R_1C_1(1 + R_2/R_3) + R_2C_2] + [1 + (1 + K_1K_2)R_2/R_3]}$$

Parameters:

$$\omega_{op} = \left[\frac{1 + (1 + K_1K_2)R_2/R_3}{R_1C_1R_2C_2}\right]^{1/2} \qquad \omega_{oz} = \frac{1}{(R_1C_1R_2C_2)^{1/2}}$$

$$\zeta_p = \frac{R_1C_1(1 + R_2/R_3) + R_2C_2}{2\left\{R_1C_1R_2C_2[1 + (1 + K_1K_2)R_2/R_3]\right\}^{1/2}} \qquad H_o(\infty) = K_2$$

$$\zeta_z = \frac{R_1C_1(1 - K_1R_2/R_3) + R_2C_2}{2(R_1C_1R_2C_2)^{1/2}} = 0 \text{ so that} \qquad K_1 = \frac{R_3}{R_2}\left[1 + \frac{R_2C_2}{R_1C_1}\right]$$

Design Equations: Set $R_1C_1 = k^2R_2C_2$

Given: ω_{op}, ζ_p, ω_{oz}

Choose: C_1, C_2, k

Calculate: $R_1 = k/\omega_{oz}C_1$

$R_2 = 1/k\omega_{oz}C_2$

$R_3 = R_2/[2\zeta_p\omega_{op}/k\omega_{oz} - (1 + k^2)/k^2]$

$K_1 = [(1 + k^2)/k^2](R_3/R_2)$

$K_1K_2 = (R_3/R_2)[(\omega_{op}/\omega_{oz})^2 - 1] - 1$

$H_o(\infty) = K_2$

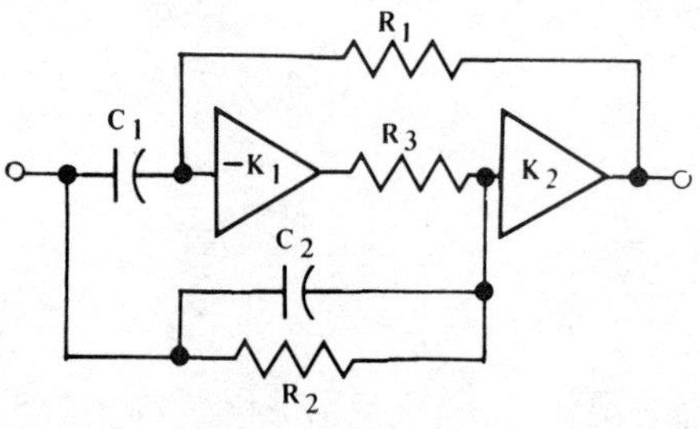

CLASS 1B: BAND-STOP ($\omega_{oz} > \omega_{op}$)

Transfer Function:

$$H(s) = K_2 \frac{s^2R_1C_1R_2C_2 + s\left\{R_1C_1 + R_2[C_2(1 + R_1/R_3) - K_1C_3]\right\} + (1 + R_1/R_3)}{s^2R_1C_1R_2(C_2 + C_3) + s[R_1C_1 + R_2(C_2 + C_3)(1 + R_1/R_3) + K_1K_2R_2C_3R_1/R_3] + (1 + R_1/R_3)}$$

Parameters:

$$\omega_{op} = \left[\frac{1 + R_1/R_3}{R_1C_1R_2(C_2 + C_3)}\right]^{1/2} \qquad \omega_{oz} = \left[\frac{1 + R_1/R_3}{R_1C_1R_2C_2}\right]^{1/2}$$

$$\zeta_p = \frac{R_1C_1 + R_2(C_2 + C_3)(1 + R_1/R_3) + K_1K_2R_2C_3R_1/R_3}{2[(1 + R_1/R_3)R_1C_1R_2(C_2 + C_3)]^{1/2}} \qquad H_o(0) = K_2$$

$$\zeta_z = \frac{R_1C_1 + R_2[C_2(1 + R_1/R_3) - K_1C_3]}{2[(1 + R_1/R_3)R_1C_1R_2C_2]^{1/2}} = 0 \text{ so that } \qquad K_1 = \frac{R_1C_1 + R_2C_2(1 + R_1/R_3)}{R_2C_3}$$

Design Equations: Set $C_1[R_1R_3/(R_1 + R_3)] = R_2[C_2 + C_3]$, $\rho = R_1/R_3$ (For Minimum Active Sensitivity)

Given: ω_{op}, ζ_p, ω_{oz}

Choose: C_1, C_2, ρ

Calculate: $C_3 = C_2[(\omega_{oz}/\omega_{op})^2 - 1]$

$R_1 = (1 + \rho)/\omega_{op}C_1$

$R_2 = (\omega_{op}/\omega_{oz})/\omega_{oz}C_2$

$R_3 = R_1/\rho$

$K_1 = (C_2/C_3)(1 + \rho) + R_1C_1/R_2C_3$

$\rho K_1K_2 = 2(R_1C_1/R_2C_3)(\zeta_p - 1)$

$H_o(0) = K_2$

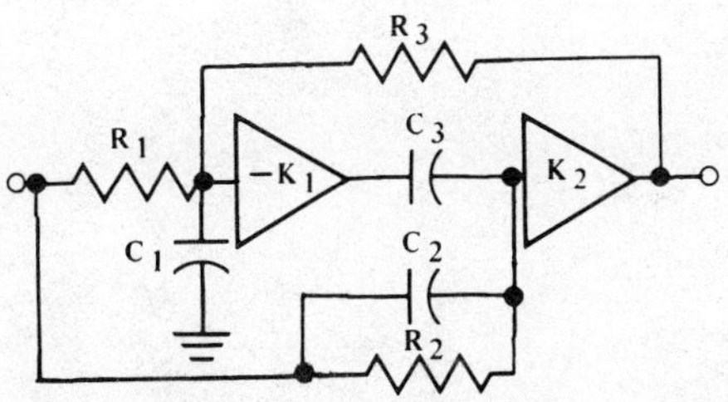

CLASS 1C: BAND-STOP ($\omega_{oz} > \omega_{op}$)

Transfer Function:

$$H(s) = K_2 \frac{s^2R_1C_3R_2C_2 + s\left\{R_1C_3 + [R_2(1 + C_3/C_1) - K_1R_3]C_2\right\} + (1 + C_3/C_1)}{s^2R_1C_3[R_2 + R_3(1 + K_1K_2)]C_2 + s[R_1C_3 + (R_2 + R_3)(1 + C_3/C_1)C_2 + K_1K_2R_3C_2C_3/C_1] + (1 + C_3/C_1)}$$

Parameters:

$$\omega_{op} = \left[\frac{1 + C_3/C_1}{R_1C_3[R_2 + R_3(1 + K_1K_2)]C_2}\right]^{1/2} \qquad \omega_{oz} = \left[\frac{1 + C_3/C_1}{R_1C_3R_2C_2}\right]^{1/2}$$

$$\zeta_p = \frac{R_1C_3 + (R_2 + R_3)(1 + C_3/C_1)C_2 + K_1K_2R_3C_2C_3/C_1}{2\left\{(1 + C_3/C_1)R_1C_3[R_2 + R_3(1 + K_1K_2)]C_2\right\}^{1/2}} \qquad H_o(0) = K_2$$

$$\zeta_z = \frac{R_1C_3 + [R_2(1 + C_3/C_1) - K_1R_3]C_2}{2[(1 + C_3/C_1)R_1C_3R_2C_2]^{1/2}} = 0 \text{ so that} \qquad K_1 = \frac{R_1C_3 + R_2C_2(1 + C_3/C_1)}{R_3C_2}$$

Design Equations: Set $R_1 = R_2 = 2R$, $C_1 = C_2 = C_3 = C$

Given: ω_{op}, ζ_p, ω_{oz}

Choose: C

Calculate: $R = 1/\sqrt{2}\,\omega_{oz}C$

$R_3 = 2R[2\sqrt{2}\,\zeta_p\omega_{oz}/\omega_{op} - (\omega_{oz}/\omega_{op})^2 - 2]$

$K_1 = 6R/R_3$

$K_1K_2 = (2R/R_3)[(\omega_{oz}/\omega_{op})^2 - 1] - 1$

$H_o(0) = K_2$

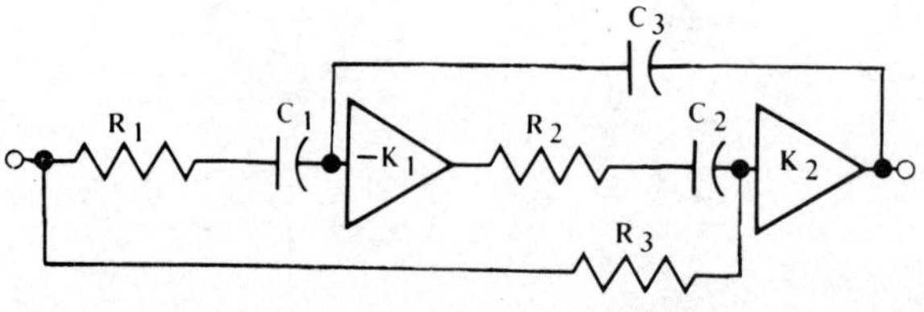

CLASS 1$\overline{\mathrm{C}}$: BAND-STOP ($\omega_{oz} < \omega_{op}$)

Transfer Function:

$$H(s) = K_2 \frac{s^2(R_1 + R_3)C_1R_2C_2 + s[R_3C_1(1 + R_1/R_3 - K_1C_2/C_3) + R_2C_2] + 1}{s^2(R_1 + R_3)C_1R_2C_2 + s[(R_1 + R_3)C_1(1 + C_2/C_3) + R_2C_2 + K_1K_2R_1C_1C_2/C_3] + [1 + (1 + K_1K_2)C_2/C_3]}$$

Parameters:

$$\omega_{op} = \left[\frac{1 + (1 + K_1K_2)C_2/C_3}{(R_1 + R_3)C_1R_2C_2}\right]^{1/2} \qquad \omega_{oz} = \frac{1}{[(R_1 + R_3)C_1R_2C_2]^{1/2}}$$

$$\zeta_p = \frac{(R_1 + R_3)C_1(1 + C_2/C_3) + R_2C_2 + K_1K_2R_1C_1C_2/C_3}{2\left\{[1 + (1 + K_1K_2)C_2/C_3](R_1 + R_3)C_1R_2C_2\right\}^{1/2}} \qquad H_o(\infty) = K_2$$

$$\zeta_z = \frac{R_3C_1(1 + R_1/R_3 - K_1C_2/C_3) + R_2C_2}{2[(R_1 + R_3)C_1R_2C_2]^{1/2}} = 0 \text{ so that} \qquad K_1 = \frac{(R_1 + R_3)C_1 + R_2C_2}{R_3C_1C_2/C_3}$$

Design Equations: Set $R_1 = R_2 = R_3 = R$, $C_1 = C_2 = C/2$

Given: ω_{op}, ζ_p, ω_{oz}

Choose: C

Calculate: $R = \sqrt{2}/\omega_{oz}C$

$$C_3 = C/2[2\sqrt{2}\,\zeta_p\omega_{op}/\omega_{oz} - (\omega_{op}/\omega_{oz})^2 - 2]$$

$$K_1 = 6C_3/C$$

$$K_1K_2 = (2C_3/C)[(\omega_{op}/\omega_{oz})^2 - 1] - 1$$

$$H_o(\infty) = K_2$$

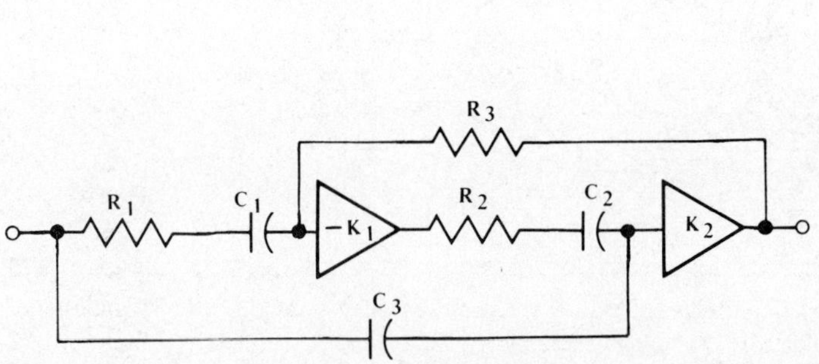

CLASS 1E: BAND-STOP

Transfer Function:

$$H(s) = -\frac{R_2R_8}{R_5R_6}\,\frac{s^2R_3C_1R_5C_2 + s[(R_3/R_1)(1 - R_1R_6/R_4R_7)R_5C_2] + R_6/R_7}{s^2R_3C_1R_2C_2 + s(R_3/R_1)R_2C_2 + R_8/R_7}$$

Parameters:

$$\omega_{op} = \left[\frac{R_8/R_7}{R_3C_1R_2C_2}\right]^{1/2} \qquad \omega_{oz} = \left[\frac{R_6/R_7}{R_3C_1R_5C_2}\right]^{1/2}$$

$$\zeta_p = \tfrac{1}{2}\left[\frac{R_2C_2}{R_1C_1}\,\frac{R_3R_7}{R_1R_8}\right]^{1/2} \qquad H_o(\infty) = -R_8/R_6$$

$$\zeta_z = \tfrac{1}{2}\left[\frac{R_5C_2}{R_1C_1}\,\frac{R_3R_7}{R_1R_6}\right]^{1/2}(1 - R_1R_6/R_4R_7) = 0 \text{ so that} \qquad R_1/R_4 = R_7/R_6$$

Design Equations: Set $R_7 = R_8 = R$

Given: ω_{op}, Q_p, ω_{oz}, $-H_o(\infty)$

Choose: C_1, C_2, R

Calculate:

$R_1 = Q_p/\omega_{op}C_1$ | $R_4 = R_1/(-H_o)$

$R_2 = 1/\omega_{op}C_2$ | $R_5 = [\omega_{op}/(-H_o\omega_{oz})]/\omega_{oz}C_2$

$R_3 = (C_2/C_1)R_2$ | $R_6 = R/(-H_o)$

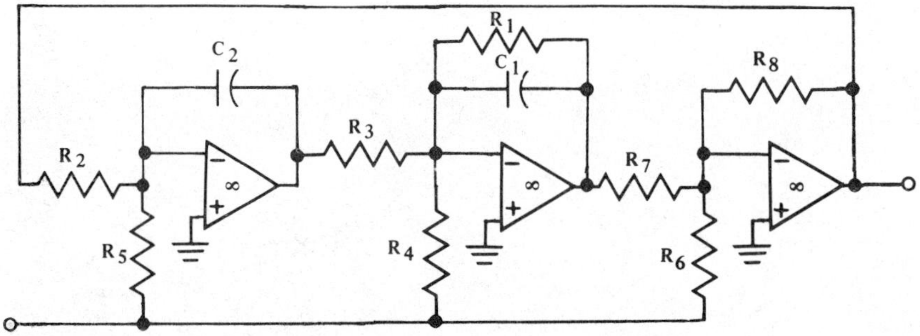

P. E. Fleischer and J. Tow, "Design formulas for biquad active filters using three operational amplifiers," Proc. IEEE, vol. 61, pp. 662–663, May, 1973.

CLASS 2B: BAND-STOP ($\omega_{oz} \leqslant \omega_{op}$)

Transfer Function:

$$H(s) = K \frac{(sRC)^2 + 1}{(sRC)^2 + 2(2 + p - K)(sRC) + (1 + 2p)}$$

Parameters:

$$\omega_{op} = \frac{(1 + 2p)^{1/2}}{RC} \qquad \omega_{oz} = \frac{1}{RC}$$

$$Q_p = \frac{(1 + 2p)^{1/2}}{2(2 + p - K)} \qquad H_o(\infty) = K$$

Design Equations:

Given: ω_{op}, Q_p, ω_{oz}

Choose: C

Calculate: $R = 1/\omega_{oz}C$

$p = 0.5[(\omega_{op}/\omega_{oz})^2 - 1]$

$K = 2 + p - (\omega_{op}/\omega_{oz})/2Q_p$

$H_o(\infty) = K$

Sensitivities:

$$S_R^{\omega_{op}} = S_C^{\omega_{op}} = S_R^{\omega_{oz}} = S_C^{\omega_{oz}} = -1 \qquad S_K^{Q_p} = -K/(2 + p - K)$$

$$S_{R/p}^{\omega_{op}} = -(1 + 3p)/(1 + 2p) \qquad S_R^{Q_p} = S_{R/p}^{Q_p} = \frac{p}{2p + 1} - \frac{p}{2 + p - K}$$

$$S_K^{H_o} = 1$$

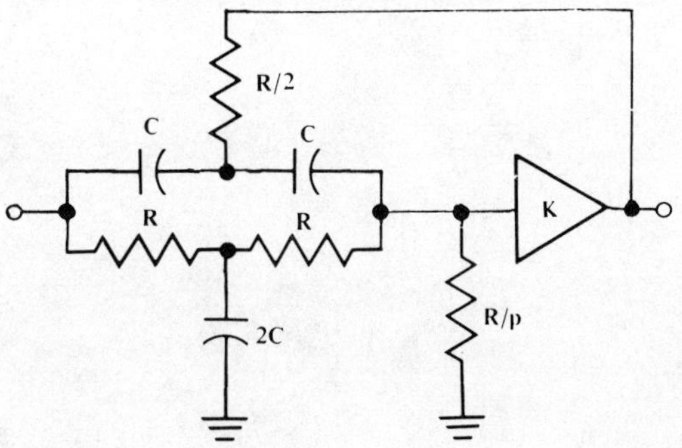

R. W. Newcomb, *Active Integrated Circuit Synthesis*, Chap. 3, Prentice-Hall, NJ, 1968; and S. K. Mitra, *Analysis and Synthesis of Linear Active Networks*, Chap. 8, Sec. 4, Wiley, NY, 1969.

CLASS 2B: BAND-STOP ($\omega_{oz} \geqslant \omega_{op}$)

Transfer Function:

$$H(s) = K \frac{(sRC)^2 + 1}{(1 + 2p)(sRC)^2 + 2(2 + p - K)(sRC) + 1}$$

Parameters:

$$\omega_{op} = \frac{1}{(1 + 2p)^{1/2} RC} \qquad \omega_{oz} = \frac{1}{RC}$$

$$Q_p = \frac{(1 + 2p)^{1/2}}{2(2 + p - K)} \qquad H_o(0) = K$$

Design Equations:

Given: ω_{op}, Q_p, ω_{oz}

Choose: C

Calculate: $R = 1/\omega_{oz}C$

$p = 0.5[(\omega_{oz}/\omega_{op})^2 - 1]$

$K = 2 + p - (\omega_{oz}/\omega_{op})/2Q_p$

$H_o(0) = K$

Sensitivities:

$$S_R^{\omega_{op}} = S_C^{\omega_{op}} = S_R^{\omega_{oz}} = S_C^{\omega_{oz}} = -1 \qquad S_K^{Q_p} = -K/(2 + p - K)$$

$$S_{pC}^{\omega_{op}} = -(1 + 3p)/(1 + 2p) \qquad S_C^{Q_p} = S_{pC}^{Q_p} = \frac{p}{2p + 1} - \frac{p}{2 + p - K}$$

$$S_K^{H_o} = 1$$

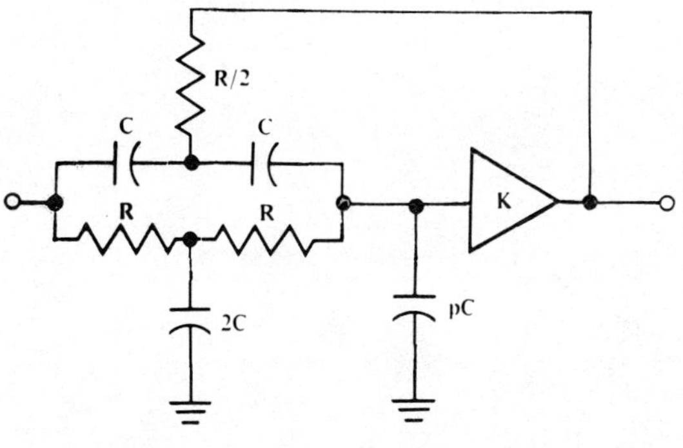

R. W. Newcomb, loc. cit.; and S. K. Mitra, loc. cit.

CLASS 2C: BAND-STOP ($\omega_{oz} \leqslant \omega_{op}$)

Transfer Function:

$$H(s) = K \frac{s^2 R_1 C_3 R_2 C_4 + 1}{s^2[1 + (1-K)(C_5/C_3 + C_5/C_4)] R_1 C_3 R_2 C_4 + s\left\{(R_1 + R_2)C_4 + (1-K)[R_2 C_5 + R_1(C_3 + C_4)]\right\} + 1}$$

Parameters:

$$\omega_{op} = \frac{\omega_{oz}}{[1 + (1-K)(C_5/C_3 + C_5/C_4)]^{1/2}} \qquad \omega_{oz} = \frac{1}{(R_1 C_3 R_2 C_4)^{1/2}}$$

$$\zeta_p = \frac{(R_1 + R_2)C_4 + (1-K)[R_2 C_5 + R_1(C_3 + C_4)]}{2\left\{[1 + (1-K)(C_5/C_3 + C_5/C_4)] R_1 C_3 R_2 C_4\right\}^{1/2}} \qquad H_o(0) = K$$

Design Equations: Set $R_1 = R_2 = R$, $C_3 = C_4 = C$

Given: ω_{op}, ζ_p, ω_{oz}

Choose: C

Calculate: $R = 1/\omega_{oz}C$

$$C_5 = \tfrac{1}{2} C \frac{(\omega_{op}/\omega_{oz})^2 - 1}{1 - \zeta_p(\omega_{op}/\omega_{oz})^3}$$

$$K = 1 + (\omega_{oz}/\omega_{op})^2 - \zeta_p \omega_{op}/\omega_{oz}$$

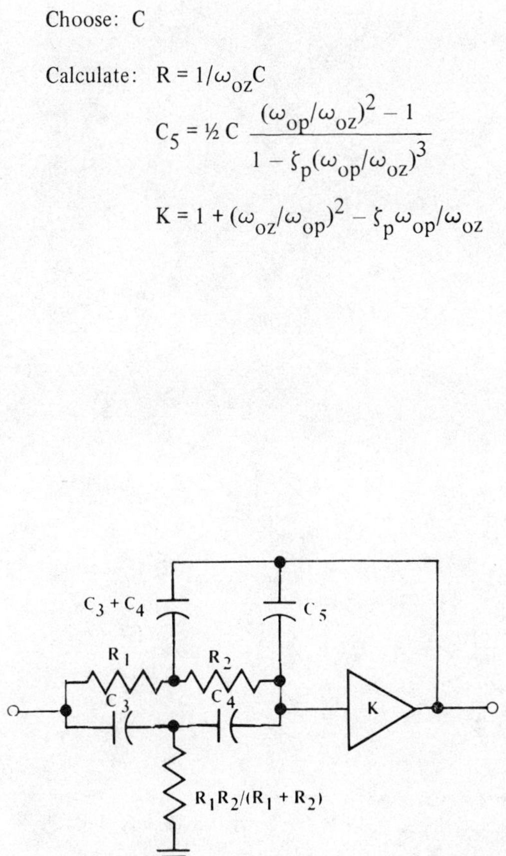

CLASS $2\overline{C}$: BAND-STOP ($\omega_{oz} \geqslant \omega_{op}$)

Transfer Function:

$$H(s) = K \frac{s^2 R_3 C_1 R_4 C_2 + 1}{s^2 R_3 C_1 R_4 C_2 + s\left\{R_3(C_1 + C_2) + (1 - K)[R_3 C_1 (R_4/R_5) + (R_3 + R_4) C_2]\right\} + [1 + (1 - K)(R_3 + R_4)/R_5]}$$

Parameters:

$$\omega_{op} = [1 + (1 - K)(R_3 + R_4)/R_5]^{1/2} \omega_{oz} \qquad \omega_{oz} = \frac{1}{(R_3 C_1 R_4 C_2)^{1/2}}$$

$$\zeta_p = \frac{R_3(C_1 + C_2) + (1 - K)[R_3 C_1 (R_4/R_5) + (R_3 + R_4) C_2]}{2\left\{[1 + (1 - K)(R_3 + R_4)/R_5] R_3 C_1 R_4 C_2\right\}^{1/2}} \qquad H_o(\infty) = K$$

Design Equations: Set $R_3 = R_4 = R$, $C_1 = C_2 = C$

Given: ω_{op}, ζ_p, ω_{oz}

Choose: C

Calculate: $R = 1/\omega_{oz} C$

$$R_5 = 2R \frac{1 - \zeta_p(\omega_{oz}/\omega_{op})^3}{(\omega_{oz}/\omega_{op})^2 - 1}$$

$$K = 1 + (\omega_{op}/\omega_{oz})^2 - \zeta_p \omega_{oz}/\omega_{op}$$

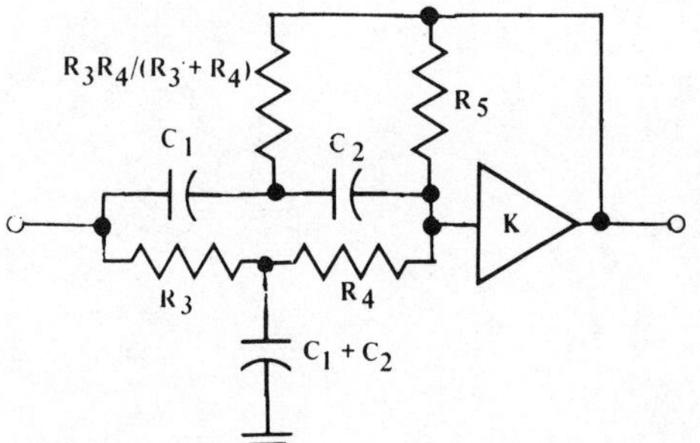

R: M. Inigo, "Active filter realization using finite-gain amplifiers," IEEE Trans. Circuit Theory, vol. CT-17, pp. 445–448, Aug., 1970.

CLASS 2D: BAND-STOP ($\omega_{oz} = \omega_{op}$)

Transfer Function:

$$H(s) = 2K \frac{(sRC)^2 + 1}{(1 + K)(sRC)^2 + 4(sRC) + (1 + K)}$$

Parameters:

$\omega_{op} = \omega_{oz} = 1/RC$ $\qquad$ $H_o(0) = 2K/(1 + K)$

$Q_p = \frac{1}{4}(1 + K)$

Design Equations:

Given: ω_o, Q_p

Choose: C, R_1

Calculate: $R = 1/\omega_o C$

$K = 4Q_p - 1$

$H_o(0) = 2K/(1 + K)$

Sensitivities:

$S_R^{\omega_{op}} = S_C^{\omega_{op}} = S_R^{\omega_{oz}} = S_C^{\omega_{oz}} = -1$

$S_K^{Q_p} = 1 - 1/4Q_p$

$S_K^{H_o} = 1/4Q_p$

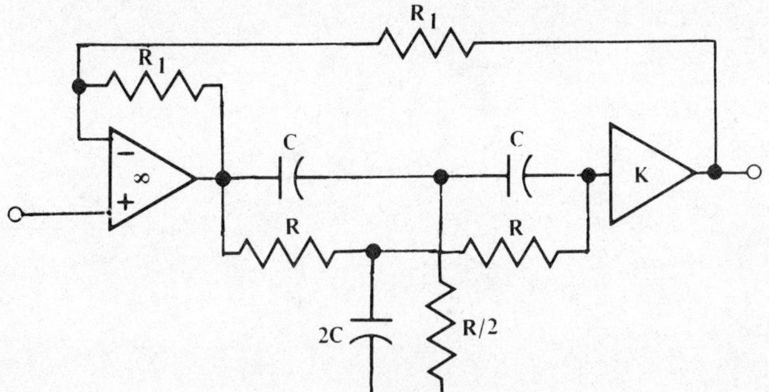

J. Lyman, "Narrow-band rejection filter using twin-T," Electronic Design, p. 127, Oct. 11, 1969, copyright Hayden Publishing, 1969.

CLASS 2E: BAND-STOP ($\omega_{oz} = \omega_{op}$)

Transfer Function:

$$H(s) = \frac{R_B}{R_A + R_B} \frac{s^2 R_1 C_1 R_2 C_2 + s[R_1(C_1 + C_2) - R_2 C_1 R_A/R_B] + 1}{s^2 R_1 C_1 R_2 C_2 + s R_1(C_1 + C_2) + 1}$$

Parameters:

$$\omega_{op} = \omega_{oz} = \frac{1}{(R_1 C_1 R_2 C_2)^{1/2}} \qquad H_o = \frac{R_B}{R_A + R_B}$$

$$\zeta_p = \frac{R_1(C_1 + C_2)}{2(R_1 C_1 R_2 C_2)^{1/2}}$$

$$\zeta_z = \frac{R_1(C_1 + C_2) - R_2 C_1 R_A/R_B}{2(R_1 C_1 R_2 C_2)^{1/2}} = 0 \text{ so that } \qquad \frac{R_A}{R_B} = \frac{R_1(C_1 + C_2)}{R_2 C_1}$$

Design Equations: Set $C_2 = kC_1$ (For Minimum Offset)

Given: ω_o, Q_p

Choose: C_1, k

Calculate: $C_2 = kC_1$ $\qquad H_o = 1/[1 + k/(1 + k)Q_p{}^2]$

$R_1 = 1/(1 + k)Q_p \omega_o C_1$ $\qquad R_A = R_2/H_o$

$R_2 = (1 + k)Q_p/\omega_o C_2$ $\qquad R_B = [(1 + k)Q_p{}^2/k] R_A$

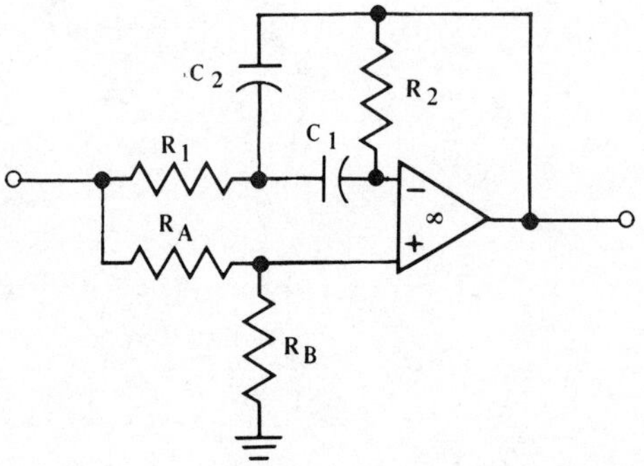

A. Budak and P. Aronhime, "Frequency limitations on an operational amplifier realization of all-pass transfer functions with complex poles," Proc. IEEE, vol. 58, pp. 1137–1138, July, 1970.

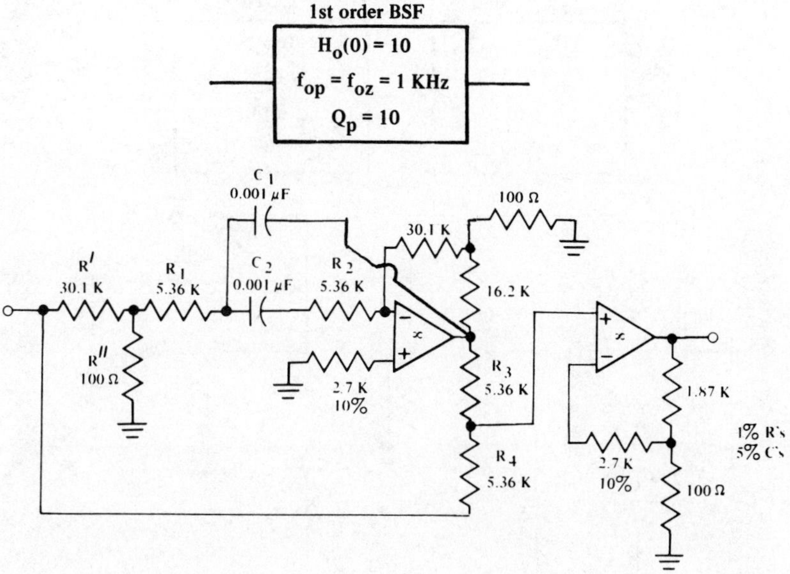

Fig. 11.4.2 Block diagram of first-order band-stop filter and its realization.

$$
\begin{aligned}
&1/R_1C_1 = 2\pi(1010\text{ Hz}/20) = 2\pi(50.5\text{ Hz}), \qquad 1/R_2C_2 = 1/R_5C_2 = 2\pi(1010\text{ Hz})\\
&C_1 = 0.1\ \mu\text{F}, \qquad C_2 = 0.0047\ \mu\text{F}, \qquad R_1 = 31.8\text{ K (use 31.6 K)}\\
&R_2 = R_5 = 33.8\text{ K (use 33.2 K)}, \qquad R_3 = (0.0047/0.1)33.8\text{ K} = 1.59\text{ K (use 1.62 K)}\\
&R_4 = 31.8\text{ K (use 31.6 K)}, \qquad R_6 = R_8 = 33.2\text{ K}
\end{aligned}
\tag{11.4.1}
$$

The complete filter is shown in Fig. 11.4.1.

EXAMPLE 11.4.2 Design a first-order notch filter which will reject 1000 Hz and have a 3 dB bandwidth of 100 Hz. A dc gain of 20 dB is required. Use the Class 2A band-pass filter and summer realization shown in Fig. 11.2.3.

Solution First let us design the notch filter in block diagram form. From the center frequency requirement, $f_{op} = f_{oz} = 1000$ Hz. Since the bandwidth equals 100 Hz, the Q of the notch filter Q_p = 1000 Hz/100 Hz = 10. The dc gain sets $H_o = 10$. The block diagram of the filter is shown in Fig. 11.4.2. From Example 11.2.1, the design equations are:

Set: $R_1 = R_2 = R, \quad C_1 = C_2 = C, \quad k = R_4/R_3$

Given: ω_o, Q_p

Choose: C, R_4

Calculate: $R = 1/3Q_p\omega_oC, \quad K = 9Q_p^2 - 1, \quad k = 3/K, \quad R_3 = R_4/k, \quad H_o(0) = 1/(1+k)$

The design proceeds as:

$$
\begin{aligned}
&1/RC = 2\pi[3(10)(1\text{ KHz})] = 2\pi(30\text{ KHz}), \qquad C = 0.001\ \mu\text{F}, \qquad R = 5.31\text{ K (use 5.36 K)}\\
&K = 9(10^2) - 1 \cong 900 = 59\text{ dB}, \qquad k \cong 3/900 = 1/300\\
&R_4 = 100\ \Omega; \qquad R_3 = 300(100\ \Omega) = 30\text{ K (use 30.1 K)}, \qquad H_o(0) = 300/(1+300) \cong 1
\end{aligned}
\tag{11.4.2}
$$

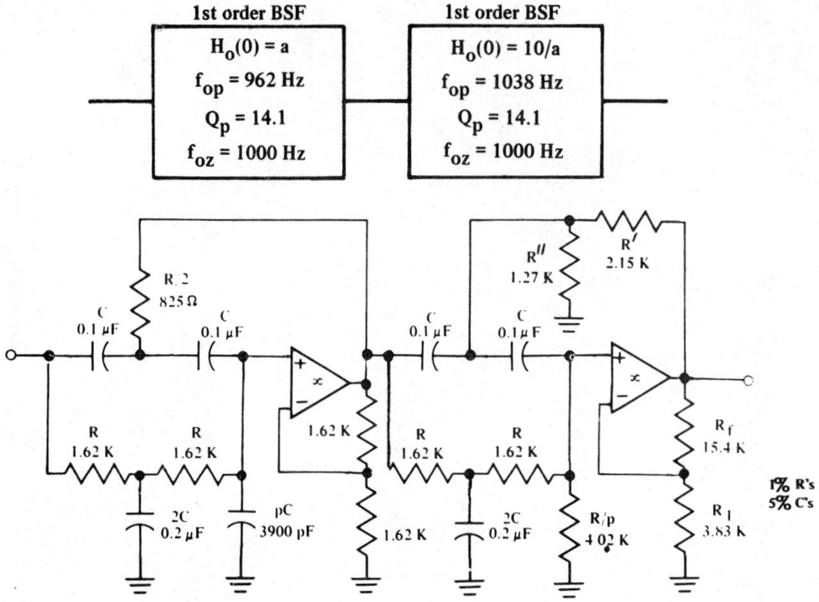

Fig. 11.4.3 Block diagram of second-order Butterworth band-stop filter and its realization.

The basic filter realization is shown in Fig. 11.4.2. The amplifier having gain $-K = 900 = 5.62\,(1 + 159)$ is designed using the (30.1 K, 5.36 K; 16.2 K, 100 Ω) resistor combination shown and the high-gain amplifier of Fig. 8.5.4.

Since the midband gain of the band-pass filter equals $-K/3 = -300$, the amplifier will saturate even at low input levels. Thus, we modify the basic design slightly by setting $R_3 = R_4 = 5.36$ K so that the summer at the filter output has gain 0.5. Then we insert a 300:1 voltage divider at the input of the band-pass filter. This eliminates the saturation problem. To obtain an overall gain of 10, we must then add a buffer amplifier at the filter output with a gain of $10/0.5 = 20$. The complete design is shown in Fig. 11.4.2.

EXAMPLE 11.4.3 A second-order Butterworth band-stop filter having a center frequency f_o of 1 KHz, a bandwidth B of 100 Hz, and a maximum passband gain of 10 was analyzed in Example 6.5.3. Its block diagram was shown in Fig. 6.5.4 which is repeated in Fig. 11.4.3. Design the notch filter using a Class 2B filter. (Due to the higher-Q requirement, another class should be used. Here we have selected a Class B filter to simply illustrate the design procedure.)

Solution From the block diagram, we see that we must design the first stage having $\omega_{op} < \omega_{oz}$ and the second stage having $\omega_{op} > \omega_{oz}$. Thus, both Class 2B filter design sheets will be used. The design equations for the first stage (for $\omega_{oz} \geqslant \omega_{op}$) are:

Given: $\omega_{op}, Q_p, \omega_{oz}$

Choose: C

Calculate: $R = 1/\omega_{oz}C, \qquad p = 0.5[(\omega_{oz}/\omega_{op})^2 - 1]$

$$K = 2 + p - (\omega_{oz}/\omega_{op})/2Q_p, \qquad H_o(0) = K$$

Then the first stage design is:

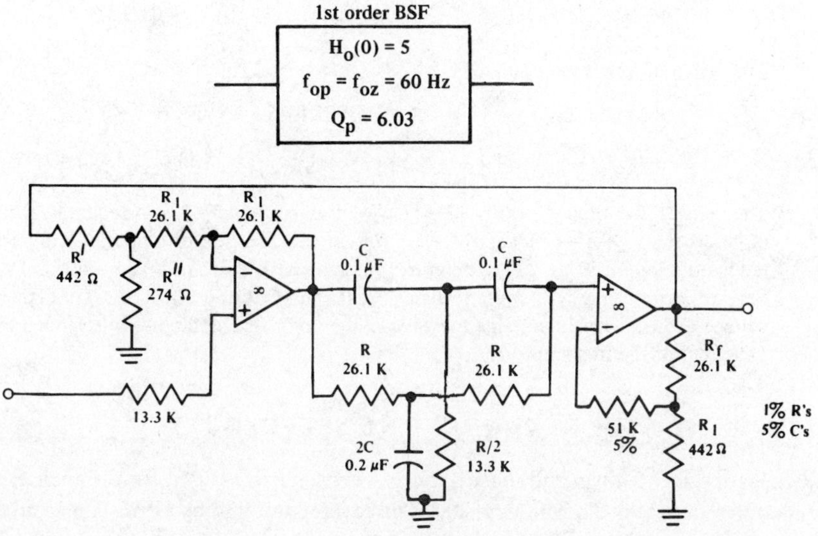

Fig. 11.4.4 Block diagram of first-order band-stop filter and its realization.

$$1/RC = 2\pi(1000\ \text{Hz}), \qquad C = 0.1\ \mu F, \qquad R = 1.59\ K\ \ (\text{use } 1.62\ K)$$

$$p = 0.5[(1000/962)^2 - 1] = 0.08/2 = 0.04, \qquad pC = 0.04(0.1\ \mu F) = 4000\ pF\ \ (\text{use } 3900\ pF) \tag{11.4.3}$$

$$K = 2 + 0.04 - (1000/962)/2(14.1) \cong 2.00, \qquad H_o(0) = 2$$

Since the required amplifier has a gain of 2, we use a voltage follower of gain 2 as shown in Fig. 11.4.3. The design of the second stage follows in the same way (with a minor change in the H_o design equation remembering $\omega_{oz} \leqslant \omega_{op}$):

$$C = 0.1\ \mu F, \qquad R = 1.62\ K, \qquad p = 0.04, \qquad R/p = 1.62\ K/0.04 = 40.5\ K\ \ (\text{use } 40.2\ K)$$

$$K \cong 2.00, \qquad H_o(0) = 2/[1 + 2(0.04)] = 1.85 \tag{11.4.4}$$

To eliminate the need for a gain block of value $10/(2)(1.85) = 2.7$ following the filter, we shall increase the gain of the second amplifier by 2.7 to 5 and insert a 2.7:1 voltage divider in the feedback loop of the second stage. Since we see that $R_2 = 2R||(R/p) = 3.00$ K, the amplifier is designed from Table 8.4.1 as

$$R_f = KR_2 = 5(3.00\ K) = 15.0\ K\ \ (\text{use } 15.4\ K)$$

$$R_1 = R_f/(K - 1) = 15.4\ K/(5 - 1) = 3.85\ K\ \ (\text{use } 3.83\ K) \tag{11.4.5}$$

The 2.7:1 voltage divider is easily designed using Eq. 8.5.26 as

$$R' = R/K = 2.7(1.59\ K/2) = 2.15\ K$$

$$R'' = R'/(1/K - 1) = 2.15\ K/(2.7 - 1) = 1.26\ K\ \ (\text{use } 1.27\ K) \tag{11.4.6}$$

The complete filter is shown in Fig. 11.4.3.

EXAMPLE 11.4.4 A 60 Hz first-order band-stop filter was designed in Example 2.8.1 for a medical electronics system. Its block diagram is shown in Fig. 11.4.4. Design the filter using a Class 2D realization.

Solution The design equations for the Class 2D filter are:

Given: ω_o, Q_p

Choose: C, R_1

Calculate: $R = 1/\omega_o C$, $K = 4Q_p - 1$, $H_o(0) = 2K/(1 + K)$

The design proceeds as:

$$1/RC = 2\pi(60\text{ Hz}), \quad C = 0.1\ \mu F, \quad R = 26.5\text{ K (use 26.1 K)}$$
$$K = 4(6.03) - 1 = 24.1 - 1 = 23.1, \quad H_o(0) = 2(23.1)/(1 + 23.1) = 1.92 \tag{11.4.7}$$

The gain of the filter equals 1.92. However, since a gain of 5 is required, we make a minor design modification as shown in Fig. 11.4.4. We increase the gain of amplifier K by 5/1.92 = 2.6 to 5, and reduce the loop gain by 2.6. Therefore, we increase K to (23.1)(2.6) = 60.1. For the summing amplifier, we introduce a 2.6:1 voltage divider at its input. Choosing R′ = 442 Ω, then R″ = 274 Ω for the voltage divider. This maintains the gain of the noninverting input while reducing the gain of the inverting input of the first amplifier.

11.5 BAND-STOP NETWORKS AND SELECTIVITY

Perhaps the best known and most popular passive network used for producing a band-stop transfer function is the twin-T. The twin-T was discovered in 1934 by H. W. Augustadt while investigating phonograph amplifiers. Since so many active band-stop filters are based upon this circuit, we shall investigate it in more detail.[2]

The twin-T is shown in Fig. 11.5.1. Recall that its admittance parameters were determined in Example 1.11.5. Its transfer function equals

$$H(s) = \frac{[sR_3(C_1 + C_2) + 1] + s^2R_3C_1C_2[sR_1R_2C_3 + (R_1 + R_2)]}{[sR_3(C_1 + C_2) + 1][sR_1C_3 + 1] + [sC_2(1 + sR_3C_2)][sR_1R_2C_3 + (R_1 + R_2)]} \tag{11.5.1}$$

from Eq. 1.11.35. Expressing H(s) as

$$H(s) = \frac{N(s)}{D(s)} = \frac{1 + a_1s + a_2s^2 + a_3s^3}{1 + b_1s + b_2s^2 + b_3s^3} \tag{11.5.2}$$

where

$$\begin{aligned} a_1 &= R_3(C_1 + C_2) & b_1 &= R_3(C_1 + C_2) + R_2C_2 + R_1(C_2 + C_3) \\ a_2 &= R_3(R_1 + R_2)C_1C_2 & b_2 &= R_3[R_1C_3(C_1 + C_2) + (R_1 + R_2)C_1C_2] + R_1R_2C_2C_3 \\ a_3 &= R_1R_2R_3C_1C_2C_3 & b_3 &= R_1R_2R_3C_1C_2C_3 = a_3 \end{aligned} \tag{11.5.3}$$

we see that H(s) is the ratio of two third-order polynomials. The condition for obtaining $j\omega$-axis zeros (or zeros of transmission) of H(s) is found by setting

$$N(s)\big|_{s=j\omega} = \text{Num } H(s)\big|_{s=j\omega} = 0 \tag{11.5.4}$$

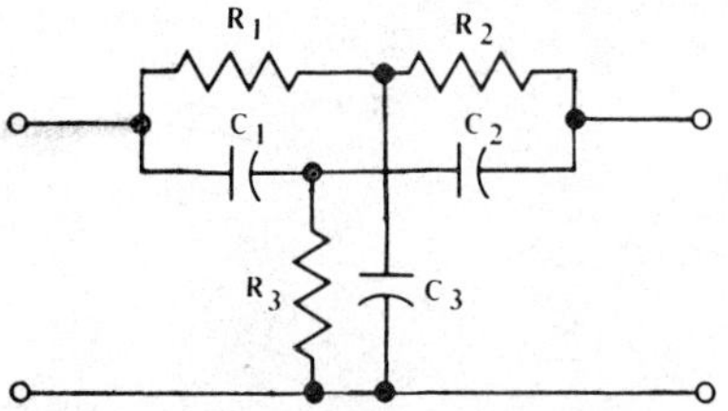

Fig. 11.5.1 General twin-T network.

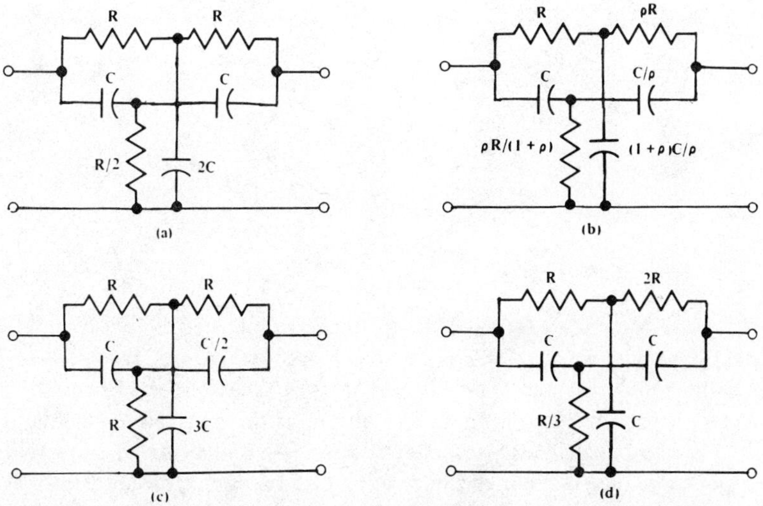

Fig. 11.5.2 Twin-T configurations: (a) symmetrical, (b) potentially symmetrical, (c) equal resistors, and (d) equal capacitors.[2]

Solving this equation leads to the result that the zeros of transmission equal

$$\omega_o = 1/(R_1R_2C_sC_3)^{1/2} \tag{11.5.5}$$

when the tuning condition

$$C_3/R_3 = C_p/R_p \tag{11.5.6}$$

is satisfied. For convenience and to simplify equations, we have defined series and parallel R and C values as

$$C_s = C_1C_2/(C_1 + C_2), \quad C_p = C_1 + C_2, \quad R_s = R_1 + R_2, \quad R_p = R_1R_2/(R_1 + R_2) \tag{11.5.7}$$

Therefore, we see from Eq. 11.5.6 that a zero of transmission can be obtained by equating time constants as $R_pC_3 = R_3C_p$. In the tuned or nulled condition, the third zero is real and is cancelled by a pole, so that the gain equals

$$H(s) = \frac{s^2R_sR_3C_1C_2 + 1}{s^2R_sR_3C_1C_2 + s(R_1C_2 + R_1C_3 + R_2C_2) + 1} \tag{11.5.8}$$

Thus, the resonant frequency ω_o and pole Q_p equal

$$\omega_o = 1/(R_1R_2C_sC_3)^{1/2} = 1/(R_sR_3C_1C_2)^{1/2}, \quad Q_p = (R_sR_3C_1C_2)^{1/2}/(R_sC_2 + R_1C_3) \tag{11.5.9}$$

Several standard twin-T configurations are shown in Fig. 11.5.2. The symmetrical case is the best known where $C_s = C/2$, $C_p = 2C$, $R_s = 2R$, and $R_p = R/2$. This circuit has $\omega_o = 1/RC$ and $Q_p = 1/4$ which cannot be varied. The equal-resistor and equal-capacitor forms have the same parameters.

The potentially symmetrical case uses various component values scaled by ρ and $(1 + \rho)/\rho$. Again, the circuit remains tuned with $\omega_o = 1/RC$ but $Q_p = \rho/2(1 + \rho)$. Thus, the potentially symmetrical twin-T has a Q_p which can be varied between 0 and ½. ρ is often called the *notch sharpness parameter*. As the asymmetry increases, $\rho \to \infty$, $Q_p \to 1/2$, and the poles become coincident. The twin-T magnitude and phase responses are shown in Fig. 2.8.1 for $Q_p = 0.25$ ($\gamma = 2$) and 0.5 ($\gamma = 1$) where $Q_p = 1/2\gamma$.[3]

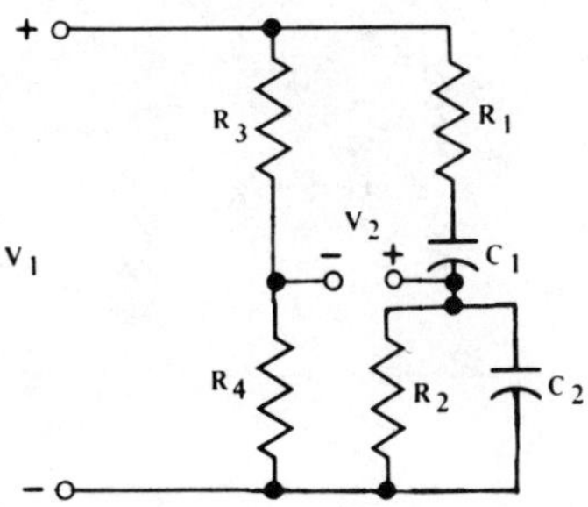

Fig. 11.5.3 Wien bridge network.

The asymmetrical twin-T has the most complicated equations in terms of component relationships for the proper tuning. However, Moschytz observed from Eq. 11.5.9 that a two-stop tuning method could be used.[4] In the first step, R_3 is disconnected from the twin-T and C_3 is tuned for zero phase shift between input and output at the required notch frequency. In the second step, C_3 is disconnected, R_3 is connected, and R_3 is then tuned for zero gain at the required notch frequency. C_3 is then reconnected. This two-step procedure insures that the twin-T has the desired parameters when nonexact (i.e., practical) components are used. Since variable capacitors are very seldom used in discrete active filters, this tuning method is best-used in hybrid active filters where the thin-film capacitors can be trimmed. However, this method can be used for tuning by capacitor substitution.

Passive notch filters can be realized using other topologies. For example, consider the network shown in Fig. 11.5.3 which is a modified version of the network in Fig. 7.18.3. It is called a *Wien bridge* and will yield a notch filter when properly tuned. Its gain equals

$$H(s) = T_{13} - [R_4/(R_3 + R_4)] = [R_4/(R_3 + R_4)]\,[(1 + R_3/R_4)T_{13} - 1] \qquad (11.5.10)$$

where

$$T_{13} = \frac{sR_2C_1}{s^2R_1C_1R_2C_2 + s[R_1C_1 + R_2C_2 + R_2C_1) + 1} \qquad (11.5.11)$$

T_{13} was calculated in Example 7.18.1. Substituting T_{13} into the Eq. 11.5.10 and simplifying yields

$$H(s) = -\frac{R_4}{R_3 + R_4}\,\frac{s^2R_1C_1R_2C_2 + s(R_1C_1 + R_2C_2 - R_2C_1R_3/R_4) + 1}{s^2R_1C_1R_2C_2 + s(R_1C_1 + R_2C_2 + R_2C_1) + 1} \qquad (11.5.12)$$

Setting the coefficient of the s^1 term in the numerator equal to zero gives

$$R_1C_1 + R_2C_2 = R_2C_1R_3/R_4 \qquad (11.5.13)$$

$R_3/R_4 = R_1/R_2 + C_2/C_1$ which is the tuning condition for a notch filter. This circuit is the basis for several Class 2E notch filter designs in Sec. 11.7. Thus, we see that by adding multiple paths (i.e., bridging) to standard circuits, we can produce zeros of transmission.[5] These physically occur when the signal at one side of the output is equal to that at the other side of the output. The difference between these signals is then zero.

The *selectivity* S of a notch or null network is usually defined to equal 2Q. Selectivity is generally intended to be some measure of stopband rejection or rejectivity. However, other figures of merit have been suggested and are sometimes used. These include the shape of the phase response, the magnitude of the complex gain response, the slope of the magnitude response, and weighted versions of these latter two.[6] Considering the first-order notch filter having a gain given by Eq. 11.1.1 and letting $\Delta = 2\gamma = 1/Q_p$, these selectivity indices are tabulated in Table 11.5.1. Notice that the selectivities all have the same value $S = 1/\zeta = 2Q_p$ at the center or null frequency.

Table 11.5.1 Various selectivity definitions for first-order band-stop filters where T = H, ϕ = arg H, x = ω, and u = $\omega + 1/\omega$. (From P. Bowron, "The selectivity of null networks," Proc. IEEE, vol. 59, pp. 1117–1119, July, 1971.)

S Definition	Value	Value at Null Freq.	Value at 3 dB Freq.
$2Q$	$\left(\frac{2}{x_2 - x_1}\right)$	$\frac{2}{\Delta}$	–
$\left\lvert\frac{d\phi(jx)}{dx}\right\rvert$, $\left\lvert\frac{dT(jx)}{dx}\right\rvert$, $\left\lvert\frac{dT(s)}{ds}\right\rvert$	$\frac{\Delta(1 + x^2)}{(1 - x^2)^2 + \Delta^2 x^2}$	$\frac{2}{\Delta}$	$\left(1 + \frac{2}{2 + \Delta^2 \mp \Delta\sqrt{\Delta^2 + 4}}\right) \cdot \frac{1}{2\Delta}$
$\left\lvert\frac{d\lvert T(x)\rvert}{dx}\right\rvert$	$\frac{\Delta^2 x(1 + x^2)}{\lvert(1 - x^2)^2 + \Delta^2 x^2\rvert^{3/2}}$	$\frac{2}{\Delta}$	$\frac{\sqrt{\Delta^2 + 4}}{\sqrt{2 + \Delta^2 \mp \Delta\sqrt{\Delta^2 + 4}}} \cdot \frac{1}{2\Delta}$
$2\left\lvert\frac{d\lvert T(u)\rvert}{du}\right\rvert$	$\frac{2\Delta^2 x^3}{\lvert(1 - x^2)^2 + \Delta^2 x^2\rvert^{3/2}}$	$\frac{2}{\Delta}$	$\frac{\sqrt{\Delta^2 + 4}\sqrt{2 + \Delta^2 \mp \Delta\sqrt{\Delta^2 + 4}}}{4 + \Delta^2 \mp \Delta\sqrt{\Delta^2 + 4}} \cdot \frac{1}{\Delta}$
$2\left\lvert\frac{dT(u)}{du}\right\rvert$	$\frac{2\Delta x^2}{(1 - x^2)^2 + \Delta^2 x^2}$	$\frac{2}{\Delta}$	$\frac{1}{\Delta}$

However, they have different values at the band-edges. Two selectivity indices are plotted in Fig. 11.5.4 along with the gain of a first-order notch filter having $\zeta = 2$ (i.e., $\Delta = 4$ or $Q_p = 0.25$). Recall that in discussing classical filter response, we defined selectivity to equal the band-edge slope of the magnitude response. Thus, the $d|H|/d\omega$ curve in Fig. 11.5.4, when evaluated at ω_{3dB}, is equal to the band-edge selectivity. The definition of sensitivity to be used generally depends not only upon the application, but must also account for any peculiarities in the transfer functions being evaluated.[7]

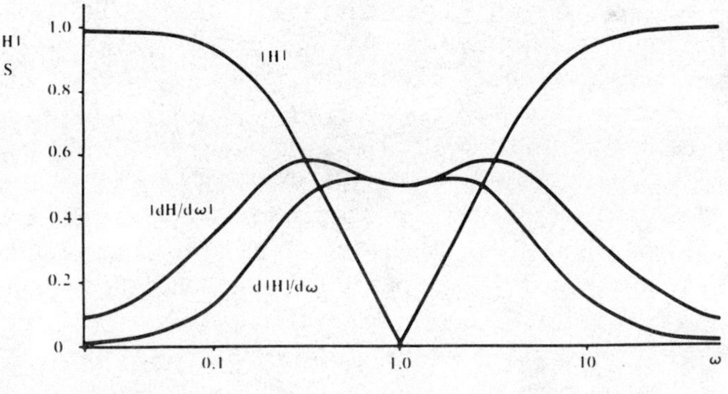

Fig. 11.5.4 Selectivity values versus frequency ($\Delta = 4$). (From P. Bowron, "The selectivity of null networks," Proc. IEEE, vol. 59, pp. 1117–1119, July, 1971.)

11.6 TUNABLE BAND-STOP FILTERS

There are a limited number of applications which require band-stop filters having either tunable ω_o, B, or Q. Designing tunable band-stop filters is more complicated than designing the other filter types. This is due to the need for amplifier K_1 to be properly adjusted to produce a zero of transmission (e.g., see Eq. 11.1.10). In addition, we generally want the zero of transmission to track the poles which compounds the problem. The simplest design method is to use the parallel branch summing method with band-pass filters.

Just as with band-pass filters, we can make the following observations for gain-tuned notch filters. For tunable ω_o/constant B applications, we use Class $\overline{A}$ filters (or adjust Class C–E filters). For tunable Q/constant ω_o applications, we use Class B or D filters (or adjust Class C, $\overline{C}$, and E filters). And for tunable ω_o/almost constant Q, we use Class C–E filters. From a passive-tuning standpoint, we can use every class for these three situations which gives us more design flexibility. The root loci for these three cases were shown in Fig. 8.6.1 and tolerances were shown in Fig. 8.6.2.

11.6.1 TUNABLE CENTER FREQUENCY/CONSTANT Q BAND-STOP FILTERS

We considered Class C, $\overline{C}$, and E gain-tuned band-pass filters in the last chapter. One set of these filters was shown in Fig. 10.5.1. Unfortunately, since their gains are low and usually negative, the complementary band-pass to band-stop transformation cannot be used to convert these filters into band-stop types. However, we can use the parallel branch summing method shown in Fig. 11.2.2, in conjunction with the Class C, $\overline{C}$, and E gain-tuned band-pass filters, to obtain Class C, $\overline{C}$, and E gain-tuned band-stop filters. The process is that outlined in Example 11.2.1. Thus, by simply introducing two additional resistors between the input and output of the gain-tunable band-pass filters shown in Fig. 10.5.1 and using their junction as the new output, we obtain gain-tuned band-stop filters. Using this process, we obtain seven Class C and E, and seven Class $\overline{C}$ and E band-stop filters. The parameter equations are virtually unchanged. This is a practical solution for obtaining gain-tuned band-stop filters. It is suboptimal in the sense that the filters contain seven nodes, rather than six, and two additional resistors.

Passive-tuned filters of every class can also be used to realize tunable ω_o/constant Q band-stop filters. Exact tuning can be obtained using double-tuning, and approximate tuning using single-tuning of the passive time constants. The design of this type of passive-tuned filter was outlined in Examples 8.7.1 and 9.5.2 and shall not be pursued further.

11.6.2 TUNABLE CENTER FREQUENCY/CONSTANT BANDWIDTH BAND-STOP FILTERS

Tunable ω_o/constant B filters can be realized exactly using Class $\overline{A}$ or approximately using Class C–E gain-tuned filters. Two-amplifier forms give linear control of ω_o while single-amplifier forms give square root control. The design of this type of filter was illustrated in Example 10.5.1.

Passive-tuned filters can also be used to realize tunable ω_o/constant B filters. Single-tuned Class B, C, $\overline{C}$, and E filters yield constant-bandwidth filters while the other classes yield only approximately constant-bandwidth. Tuning of a_1 gives square root control of ω_o. Alternatively, all classes except Class B can be used by tuning only a portion of a time constant. ω_o is constant but tuning is nonlinear. Double-tuned filters are impractical since they require pots having non-standard tapers. The design of a single-passive-tuned filter was outlined in Example 10.5.2.

11.6.3 TUNABLE Q/CONSTANT CENTER FREQUENCY BAND-STOP FILTERS

Tunable Q/constant ω_o filters can be realized exactly using Class B, properly adjusted Class D, two-amplifier Class C, $\overline{C}$, and E gain-tuned filters, or approximately using single-amplifier Class C, $\overline{C}$, and E gain-tuned filters. In any case, Q is only approximately linear in K or 1/K.

Passive-tuned filters can also be used. Single-tuned filters of every class except Class B can be used by adjusting only a portion of the time constant. ω_o is constant but tuning is nonlinear. Double-tuned filters of every class can be used to realize tunable Q/constant ω_o filters exactly, but Q is only approximately linear in 1/R.

11.6.4 BAND-STOP FILTERS WITH TUNABLE ZEROS

Another area that has been explored is that in which only the *null* frequency of zero of transmission of the band-stop filter is tunable. The poles remain fixed unlike the tunable filters just discussed. Although the results show that the filter implementations are much simpler, they exhibit distortion in their magnitude responses for wide tuning ranges as we shall see in a moment.

Filters having a tunable-zero frequency have transfer functions of the form

$$H(s) = \frac{s_n^2 + K^2}{s_n^2 + s_n/Q_p + 1} \tag{11.6.1}$$

where K is the gain of an amplifier. Note that the poles remain fixed and only the $j\omega$-axis zeros move since $\omega_{oz} = K$. In many implementations of this type of filter, H(s) has the form[8]

$$H(s) = (1 - K)\frac{s_n^2 + K/(1 - K)}{s_n^2 + s_n/Q_p + 1} \tag{11.6.2}$$

The low-frequency gain equals K, the high-frequency gain equals (1 – K), and the zero or null frequency equals $[K/(1 - K)]^{1/2}$. The magnitude response is asymmetrical except when K = 0.5. Such a transfer function having $Q_p = 1$ is shown in Fig. 11.6.1. Gain K is used to control the zero frequency ω_{oz}; as $K \to 1$, $\omega_{oz} \to \infty$.

An example of a band-stop filter having tunable zeros is shown in Fig. 11.6.2 where H(0) = 1, $\omega_{op} = 1/RC$, $Q_p = 1/4$, and $\omega_{oz} = \omega_{op}/\sqrt{K}$. Inspection of this filter shows that two inputs, v and Kv, are applied to the circuit. In the past, most filters having a tunable zero-frequency have utilized two inputs and were called *dual input filters*. Since K is a gain control, these filters may be viewed as gain-tuned filters. They have also been called voltage-tuned or voltage-controlled filters which is somewhat misleading. Classically, *voltage-tuned filters* are those in which voltage is used to control or tune a passive parameter R or C, or a gain K (e.g., see Example 10.5.2).

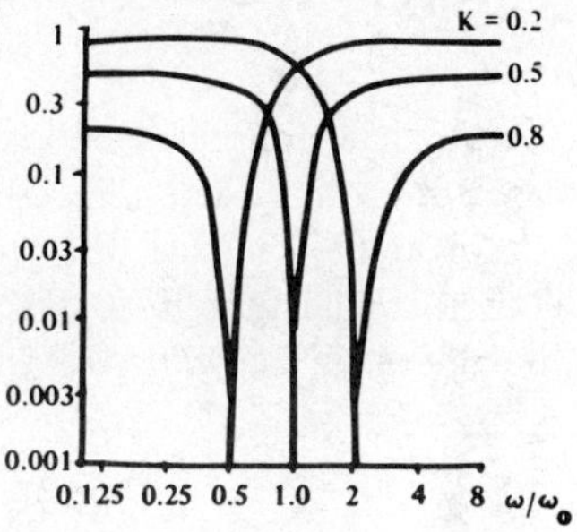

Fig. 11.6.1 Magnitude characteristics of a tunable-zero band-stop filter. (From G. R. Steber and R. J. Krueger, "A voltage-controlled tunable active null network," Proc. IEEE, vol. 57, pp. 233–234, Feb., 1969.)

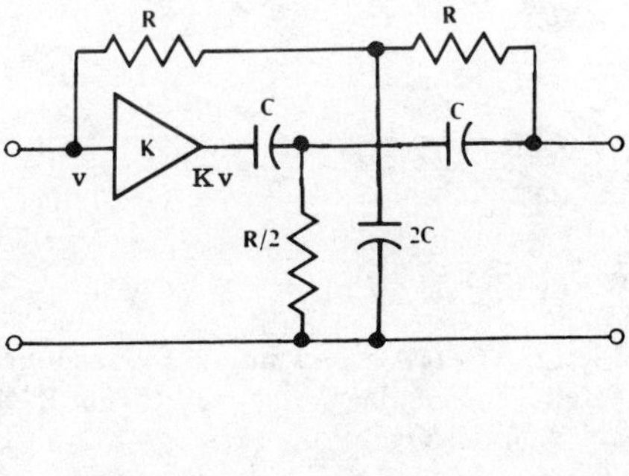

Fig. 11.6.2 A Class 2E tunable-zero band-stop filter.[9]

11.7 AMPLITUDE EQUALIZERS

We discussed delay equalizers in Sec. 2.11. These were all-pass filters whose delay was adjusted to equalize or augment the delay of another filter (or transmission channel) so that the overall delay was constant. By analogy, *amplitude equalizers* are filters whose amplitude is adjusted to augment the amplitude of another filter so that the overall amplitude is constant. They were introduced in 1937 by Bode.[10] Amplitude equalizers usually make use of so-called *biquadratic filters*, or more simply, *biquads*. These filters have biquadratic transfer functions where

$$H(s) = H_o \frac{s^2 + s\omega_{oz}/Q_z + \omega_{oz}^2}{s^2 + s\omega_{op}/Q_p + \omega_{op}^2} \tag{11.7.1}$$

In general, the poles and zeros are made equal so that $\omega_{oz} = \omega_{op}$. The Q of the poles and zeros are adjusted to produce the required magnitude peaking and bandwidth. The magnitude peaking equals

$$M_p = Q_p/Q_z \tag{11.7.2}$$

while the approximate bandwidth equals

$$B = \omega_{op}/Q_p \tag{11.7.3}$$

Band-stop filters are biquads whose $Q_z = \infty$. Therefore, we have chosen to discuss biquads in this chapter rather than elsewhere.

To illustrate the usefulness of amplitude equalizers, consider Fig. 11.7.1. Fig. 11.7.1a shows the actual transmission characteristic of a telephone line. The standard line conditioning limits are shown by the dotted lines (see Prob. 2.27). To reduce the loss and equalize the magnitude response to lie within the allowed limits, we require an amplitude equalizer which has the response shown in Fig. 11.7.1b. The amplitude equalizer has an approximate transfer function of

$$H(s) \cong \frac{s^2 + 2\pi(340)s + [2\pi(300)]^2}{s^2 + 2\pi(210)s + [2\pi(300)]^2} \; \frac{s^2 + 2\pi(6400)s + [2\pi(3000)]^2}{s^2 + 2\pi(4000)s + [2\pi(3000)]^2} \tag{11.7.4}$$

Such transfer functions are usually derived using the optimization criteria of Chap. 5. In simple cases, they can be determined by inspection.

In actual practice, the characteristics of the amplitude equalizers required to produce the desired overall magnitude response are first determined. Then the delay characteristics of the overall system *including* the amplitude equalizer are established. This permits the characteristics

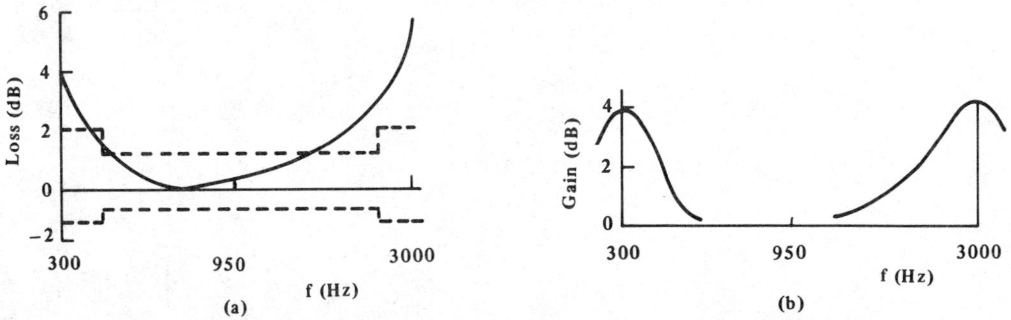

Fig.11.7.1 (a) Actual magnitude response and response bounds and (b) required amplitude equalizer response. (From P. E. Fleischer, "Active adjustable loss and delay equalizers," Proc. Intl. Symp. on Circuits and Systems, pp. 564–568, April, 1974.)

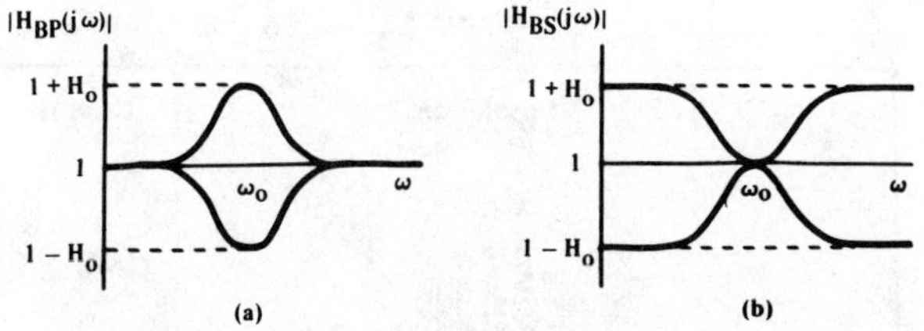

Fig. 11.7.2 Magnitude response of biquadratic filter using (a) band-pass and (b) band-stop filters.

of the delay equalizers required to produce the desired overall delay response to be determined. Delay equalizers will be discussed in the next chapter.

Biquadratic filters are designed in the same manner as the other filters we have discussed. Once design sheets have been assembled, this is a routine matter. In general, most band-stop filters are biquadratic filters whose Q_z's have been tuned to infinity. Thus, their design sheets can be generalized to describe biquad filters. This is true of all the Class 1X band-stop filters tabulated in Sec. 11.3 and the Class 2X filters not having symmetrical twin-T's. For example from the Class 1A band-stop filter design sheet of Sec. 11.3, setting $\omega_{oz} = \omega_{op}$ shows that the gain product $K_1K_2 = -1$ so that $K_2 = -1/K_1$. Since the magnitude peaking equals

$$M_p = \frac{Q_p}{Q_z} = \frac{R_1C_1 + R_2C_2 - K_1R_2C_3}{R_1C_1 + R_2C_2 + R_2C_3} < 1 \tag{11.7.5}$$

this ratio is controlled by K_1. A variety of biquadratic filters are shown in Table 11.7.1 (for others, see Ref. 17).

Another especially convenient method for obtaining biquadratic filters is to utilize band-pass or band-stop filters operated in either the complementary mode or with resistive summers. Expressing $H_{BP}(j\omega_o) = \pm H_o$ (or $H_{BS}(j0) = \pm H_o$), the band-pass (or band-stop) filter provides a midband (or asymptotic) gain which is increased or decreased by H_o from unity. This is illustrated in Fig. 11.7.2.

EXAMPLE 11.7.1 Design an amplitude equalizer having the gain characteristics shown in Fig. 11.7.1b. Use a Class 2A band-pass filter operated in the complementary mode.

Solution The transfer function of the amplitude equalizer is given by Eq. 11.7.4. It is the product of two biquadratic transfer functions so two biquad stages are required. These stages are realized using two inverting band-pass filters as shown in Fig. 11.7.3. Since M_p = 4 dB = 1.6 of peaking is required for each biquad, the band-pass filter gains are set to $H_o = -0.6$. The resonant frequencies are 300 and 3000 Hz as shown in Fig. 11.7.1. Since the required bandwidths are 210 Hz and 4000 Hz from Eq. 11.7.4, then the two required Q_p's are 300/210 = 1.43 and 3000/4000 = 0.75, respectively. This design information is summarized in the block diagram of Fig. 11.7.3.

Now let us design the amplitude equalizer. The design equations for the Class 2A band-pass filter are given by Eq. 11.2.9. The first stage design proceeds as:

$$1/RC = 2\pi[3(1.43)(300\text{ Hz})] = 2\pi(1.29\text{ KHz}), \qquad C = 0.022\ \mu\text{F}, \qquad R = 5.61\text{ K (use 5.62 K)}$$
$$K = 9(1.43^2) - 1 = 17.4, \qquad H_o = -17.4/3 \cong -5.8 \tag{11.7.6}$$

To obtain a gain of −0.6, we must reduce the gain by 5.8/0.6 = 9.67. Thus, we insert a 9.67:1 voltage divider at the input of the filter where

$$R' = R/K = 9.67(5.61\text{ K}) = 54.3\text{ K (use 53.6 K)}$$
$$R'' = R'/(1/K - 1) = 53.6\text{ K}/(9.67 - 1) = 6.18\text{ K (use 6.19 K)} \tag{11.7.7}$$

using Eq. 8.5.26. The second stage is designed in a similar fashion as:

Table 11.7.1 A collection of biquadratic filters.

Class 1B (see Prob. 7.16 solution) (11)

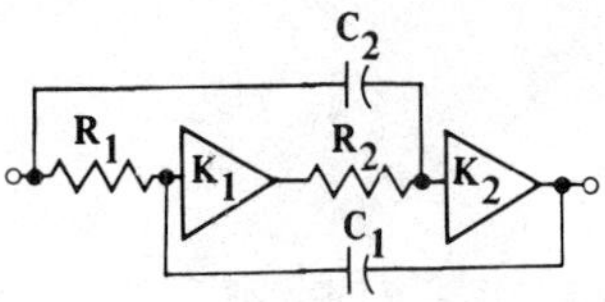

Class 1E (12)

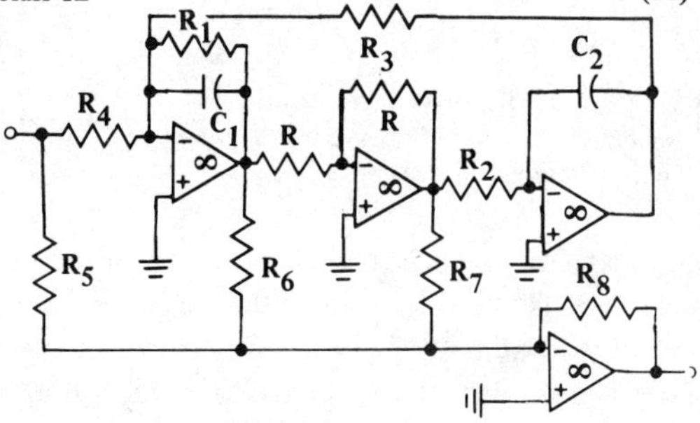

Class 2B (see Prob. 7.50 solution) (11)

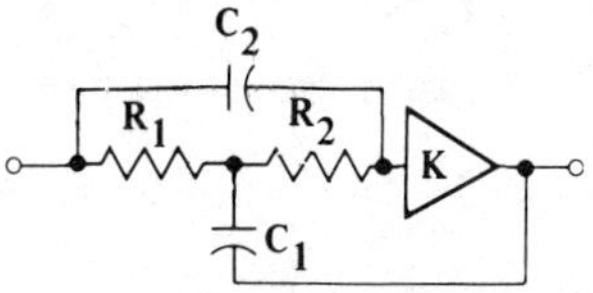

Class 2B not biquad (11)

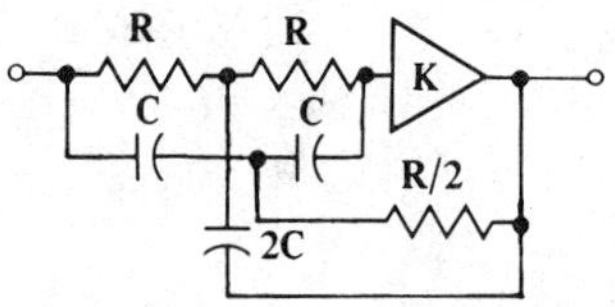

Class 2D (see Prob. 7.61) (13)

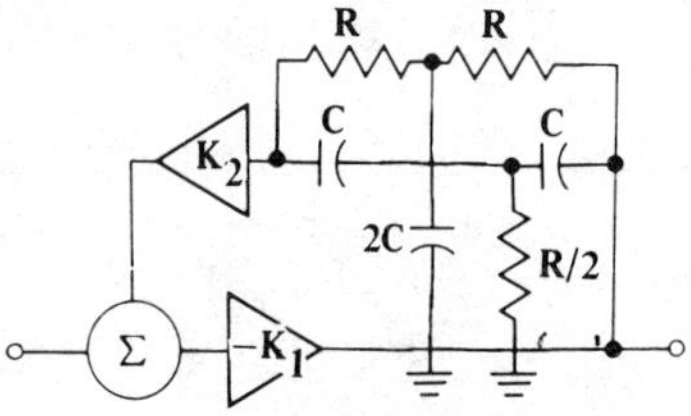

Class 2E (see Prob. 7.68) (13)

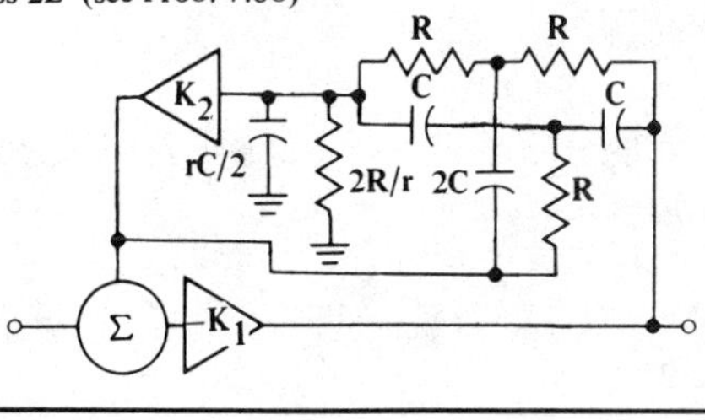

Class 2E (14)

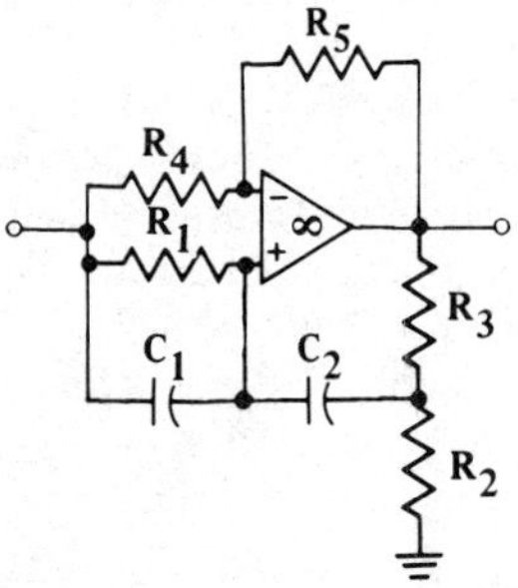

Class 2E (14)

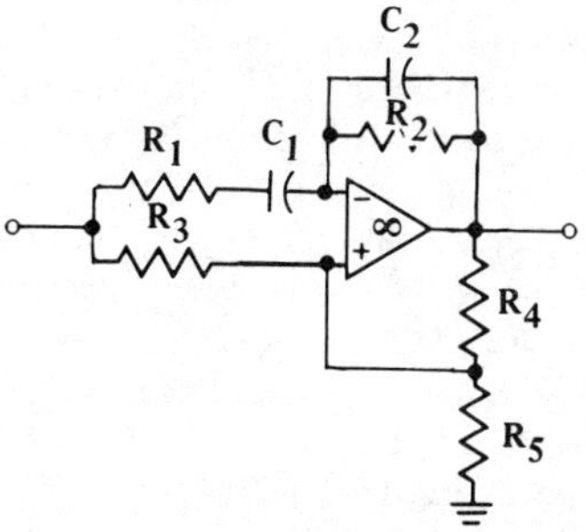

Class 2E (15)

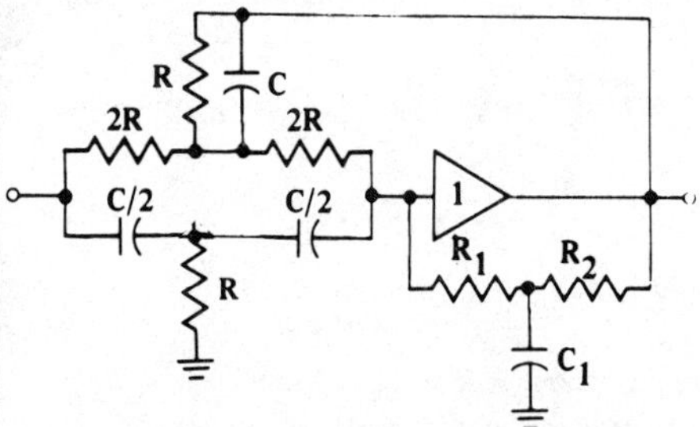

Class 2E (16)

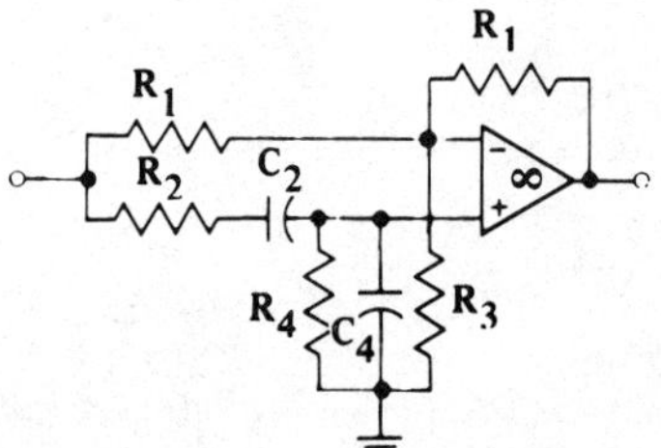

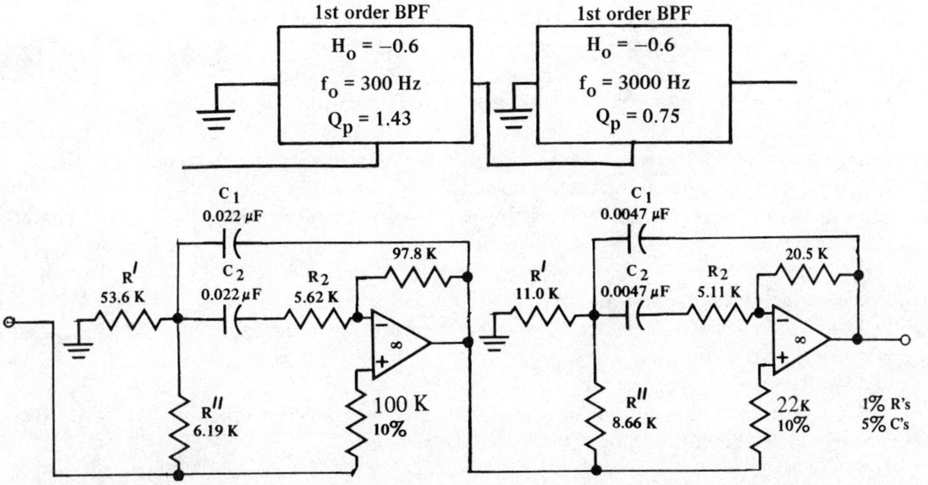

Fig. 11.7.3 Block diagram of fourth-order amplitude equalizer and its realization.

$$1/RC = 2\pi[3(0.75)(3000\text{ Hz})] = 2\pi(6.75\text{ KHz}), \quad C = 0.0047\ \mu F, \quad R = 5.02\text{ K (use 5.11 K)}$$
$$K = 9(0.75^2) - 1 = 4.06, \quad H_o = -4.06/3 = -1.35 \tag{11.7.8}$$

To reduce the gain by 1.35/0.6 = 2.25, we insert a 2.25:1 voltage divider at the filter input where

$$R' = 2.25(5.02\text{ K}) = 11.3\text{ K (use 11.0 K)}$$
$$R'' = 11.0\text{ K}/(2.25 - 1) = 8.80\text{ K (use 8.66 K)} \tag{11.7.9}$$

The complete filter is shown in Fig. 11.7.3. By interchanging the grounds and inputs of the band-pass filters, a biquadratic filter results having the proper characteristics.

PROBLEMS

11.1 Band-stop filters have the typical frequency response shown in Prob. 6.1. Describe the parameters required to specify the response.

11.2 The importance of compiling complete filter specifications cannot be overemphasized. A typical specification sheet was shown in Prob. 6.2. Briefly list the reasons for providing each data entry listed on that sheet.

11.3 A Class 1A band-stop filter was shown in Fig. 11.1.2a. Derive a set of design equations. Compare them with the design equations for the Class 1A filter in Sec. 11.3. Discuss the advantages and disadvantages of the two filters.

11.4 A 200 Hz band-stop filter was analyzed in Prob. 6.52. Assume that a first-order Butterworth band-stop filter with $Q_p = 1/4$ and $H_o = 1$ is required. Design the filter using the Class 1A realization.

11.5 A Class $1\bar{A}$ band-stop filter is compiled in Sec. 11.3. Draw its Class 1A band-stop equivalent using the RC:CR transformation. Express its transfer function and parameters directly from the Class $1\bar{A}$ filter results.

11.6 A 60 Hz first-order band-stop filter was designed in Example 11.4.4. Redesign the filter using a Class 1C band-pass filter operated in the complementary mode. (Hint: Use the output before $-K_2$ so H_o can be adjusted to equal +1.)

11.7 Repeat Prob. 11.5 for the Class $1\bar{C}$ band-stop filter.

11.8 As discussed in Prob. 6.54, 1010 Hz and 2805 Hz test tones are used by the telephone company to test transmission channels. A 1010 Hz band-stop filter was designed in Example 11.4.1 using a first-order Class 1E realization. Now design the 2805 Hz band-stop filter using the same realization form.

11.9 As discussed in Prob. 6.53, a 2600 Hz band-stop filter is required in single-frequency (SF) signalling systems used by the telephone company. A second-order Butterworth band-stop filter having a 3 dB bandwidth of 60 Hz shall be used. Its block diagram was determined in Prob. 6.53 to consist of two first-order BSF stages having parameters (H_o, f_{op}, Q_p, f_{oz}) which equal (1, 2577 Hz, 61.3, 2600 Hz) and (1, 2623 Hz, 61.3, 2600 Hz). Design the filter using the Class 1E realization.

11.10 Repeat Prob. 11.6 using a Class 2A band-pass filter and summer realization.

11.11 A first-order band-pass filter was designed in Example 10.4.1. Design the analogous low-transient band-stop filter. Make use of the complementary transformation and the band-pass filter.

11.12 A 21.6 KHz band-stop filter was analyzed in Prob. 6.52. Assume that a first-order Butterworth band-stop filter with Q_p = 27 and H_o = 1 is required. Design the filter using a Class $2\overline{A}$ band-pass filter and summer realization.

11.13 Repeat Prob. 11.5 for both of the Class 2B band-stop filters in Sec. 11.3. Discuss the advantages and disadvantages of the four filters.

11.14 Design a first-order notch filter to have a center frequency of 1 KHz, Q_p = 10, and a passband gain of 10. Use a Class 2B realization.

11.15 Repeat Prob. 11.5 for the Class 2C band-stop filter.

11.16 A second-order Butterworth band-stop filter was designed in Example 11.4.3. Redesign the filter using Class 2C and $2\overline{C}$ realizations for the respective stages.

11.17 Design a first-order notch filter to have a Q_p of 10 and a center frequency of (a) 120 Hz and (b) 800 Hz. Use a Class 2D realization.

11.18 Notch filters can be constructed using an inverting band-pass filter and a summer. In many cases, the summing can be obtained using an op amp of the filter. This is the case for the Class 2E band-stop filter. Verify the transfer function and parameters listed in Sec. 11.3. (Hint: Use the transfer function for the Class 2E band-pass filter.)

11.19 Notch filters can be constructed using a low-pass filter, a high-pass filter, and a summer. (a) Show the arrangement in block diagram form. Be careful to label completely. (b) A third-order elliptic low-pass filter was designed in Example 8.5.6. The BSF stage was realized with a Class 2B filter. Redesign the stage using this approach and Class 2E low-pass and high-pass filters. (Hint: The summing can be performed in the first-order LPF stage.)

11.20 Repeat Prob. 11.4 using a Class 2E realization.

11.21 Repeat Prob. 11.11 for the second-order Butterworth band-pass filter designed in Example 10.4.3.

11.22 Band-stop filters can be constructed from low-pass and high-pass filters as discussed in Prob. 2.29. Repeat that problem and describe how the band-stop filter can be tuned.

11.23 As discussed in Prob. 2.33, filters having zeros of transmission are more difficult to tune than those having no finite zeros. Repeat that problem.

11.24 A channel substitution filter is used to substitute one channel for another. One application is in telephone systems where 12 voice channels are placed side-by-side in the 60–108 KHz frequency range to form a group as discussed in Prob. 6.27. A channel substitution filter can be used to remove an unwanted channel in the incoming group (with a BSF) and replace it by a local channel (with a BPF) as shown in Fig. P11.24. A single band-pass filter operated in a complementary mode performs this operation (when H_o = +1). Design a first-order band-pass filter with a constant bandwidth of 4 KHz which is tunable from 60–108 KHz. Use passive-tuning and a Class 1E band-pass filter. (Notice that the Class 1E filter has a negative gain. Arrange connections to the band-pass filter so that it can be simultaneously operated in a complementary mode. Modify the filter so that the gain is positive by inputting to the inverting terminal through R_7. Rederive the transfer function using Example 7.10.1.)

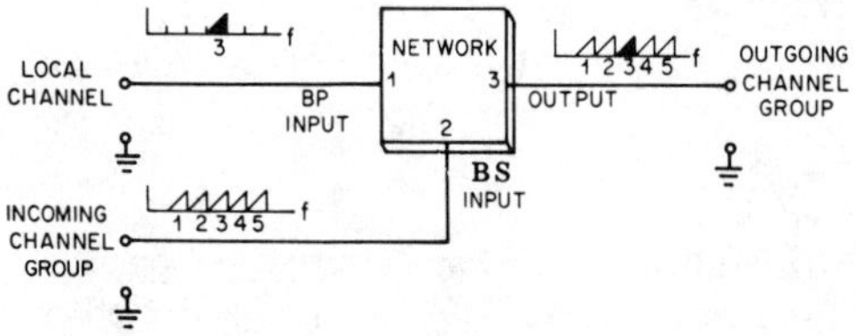

Fig. P11.24 (Courtesy of IEEE[18])

11.25 Tunable-notch filters are used for testing and analysis of voice band telephone channels. One such filter will be described in a moment. (Courtesy of SEG Electronics.[19]) Determine the parameters of the filter. Note the convenient feature that the notch filter can be operated as an oscillator to accurately determine the notch frequency.

"The SEG Model AF-850A Tunable Notch Peak filter provides a versatile filter function for testing and analysis of voice-band telephone channels.

Designed to facilitate notched noise measurements as per Bell Technical Reference Guidelines PUB 41009, harmonic distortion and wave analysis, the 850A is capable of many other measurements in conjunction with standard telephone measurement equipment. Since the 50 dB notch is tunable from 35 Hz to 3500 Hz, a wide variety of test tones can be notched out at the receiving end rather than trying to tune a signal source into the notch from the transmission end.

'Peak' mode provides a constant bandwidth bandpass filter tunable over the same range as the notch. The tunable 'peak' filter is ideal for wave analysis, narrow band noise analysis, and 'cleaning-up' sine wave generators.

Switching into the counter mode causes the filter to oscillate at its center frequency thereby permitting extremely accurate determination of notch frequencies.

Bypass mode bypasses the filtering function so that the effects of filtering can be ascertained without removing the unit from the set-up.

A switchable output amplifier is provided with selectable gain of 0 dB, 10 dB, 20 dB, and 30 dB, to facilitate low level measurements."

Frequency range: 35–350 Hz (Band 1) and 350–3500 Hz (Band 2).

Function: Peak = 3 dB bandwidth is 3.5 Hz (Band 1), 35 Hz (Band 2). Response flat to 0.5 dB.
Notch = 3 dB bandwidth is 32 Hz (Band 1), 320 Hz (Band 2). Notch depth greater than 50 dB.
Counter = Output frequency ± 0.2% of notch frequency.
Gain = 0, 10, 20, 30 dB ± 0.2 dB.
By-pass = By-passes filter functions.

Input/Output: Z_{in} = 600 Ω, 900 Ω, or bridge (100 K) (all balanced). Z_{out} = 600 Ω (unbalanced).
V_{in}, V_{out} = +10 dBM max; DC offset at output = +3 mV with respect to input.

11.26 A commercial hi-Q tunable tracking filter has the following characteristics: (1) f_o = 1 Hz–30 KHz, (2) Q = 1–1000, (3) H_o = 0 dB ± 3 dB, (4) notch depth: 15–50 dB, and (5) Z_{in} = 1 MΩ in parallel with 50 pF. Its block diagram is shown in Fig. P11.26. Design the filter to have decade tuning ranges. Use a Class 2E realization. Arrange the filter so that it will simultaneously provide band-pass and band-stop outputs.

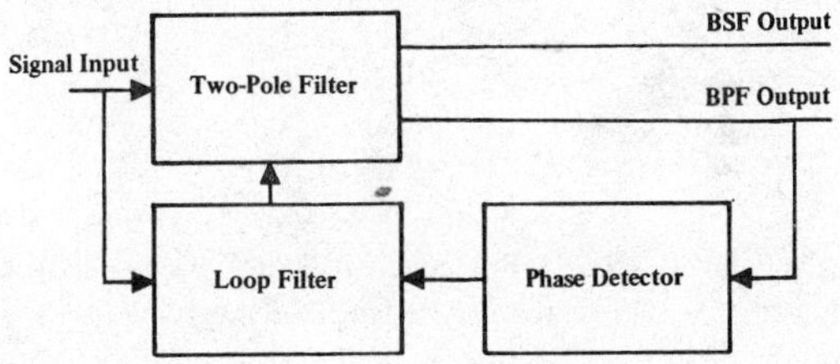

Fig. P11.26 (Courtesy of EDMAC Associates[20])

11.27 Several Class B biquadratic filters were shown in Table 11.7.1. Their transfer functions are also listed. (a) Determine the parameters of the filters. (b) Derive a set of design equations to obtain minimum active sensitivity. (c) In what sequence should the components be tuned when the filters are used as amplitude equalizers?

11.28 Repeat Prob. 11.27 for the Class 2D and 2E twin-T filters of Table 11.7.1. For part (b), derive any set of design equations.

11.29 Design the amplitude equalizer of Example 11.7.1 using (a) Class 2C and (b) Class 2E band-pass filters.

11.30 Hi-fi equalizers use a bank of nine filters centered from 50 Hz to 12.8 KHz (with octave spacing) to cover the audio spectrum from 20 Hz to 20 KHz. These equalizers allow the audiophile to compensate for room acoustics or speaker deficiencies, or to please his personal taste. One such Class 2E equalizer is shown in Fig. P11.30.[21] The equalizer provides boost and cut limits of ±12 dB. (a) What type of filters are used in the filter bank? (b) Determine the transfer function of the filter. (c) How does the center frequency, Q, and midband gain vary with R12? (d) Verify the component values for the 50 Hz filter and

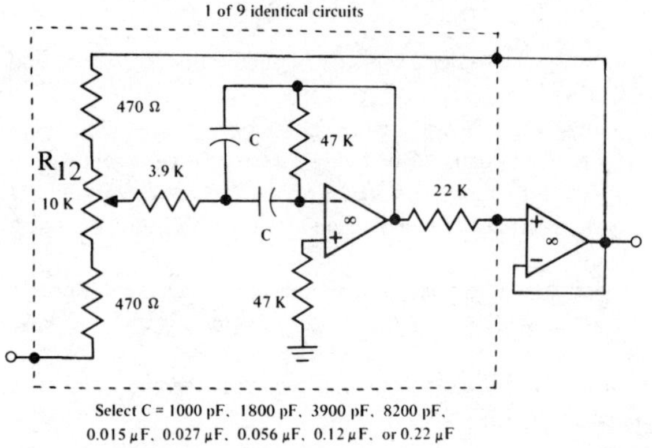

Fig. P11.30

the 12.8 KHz filter.

11.31 Class 1E biquad filters are especially useful for amplitude and delay equalizers. Their topology, in contrast to most others, permits almost independent resistance-tuning of the resonant frequency ω_o and bandwidth B. The three-amplifier Class 1E filter shown in Table 11.7.1 has the gain written below. Show that ω_o can be controlled by R_2 and R_3, B by R_1 and R_4, and the peaking M_p by R_6 or R_7.[22]

$$H(s) = -\frac{R_8}{R_5}\frac{s^2 + s[1 + (R_5/R_7 - R_5/R_6)(R_1/R_4)]/R_1C_1 + 1/R_2C_1R_3C_2}{s^2 + s/R_1C_1 + 1/R_2C_1R_3C_2}$$

11.32 A low-transient third-order Papoulis band-splitting high-pass filter was analyzed in Prob. 6.15. Its transfer function equals

$$H(s) = \frac{s(s^2 + 1.310s + 1.359)}{(s + 0.621)(s^2 + 0.691s + 0.931)}$$

For convenience, should the filter be realized using a biquadratic filter or as a complementary low-pass filter? Justify your answer.

11.33 When the twin-T network of Fig. 11.5.1 is not properly tuned, it does not provide infinite rejection at its center frequency, (a) Setting $R_1 = R_2 = R$, $R_3 = R/\rho$, $C_1 = C_2 = C$, and $C_3 = \rho C$, show that the gain at the center frequency of the notch equals

$$H(j\omega_o) = \frac{(1 - 2/\rho)}{-(1 + 2/\rho + \rho)}$$

where $\omega_o = 1/RC$. (Hint: See Eq. 11.5.2.) (b) For the ideal twin-T, $\rho = 2$ and $|H(j\omega_o)| = 0$. Changes in the impedance ratio ρ strongly affects the insertion loss $|H(j\omega_o)|$ while preserving the basic magnitude and phase response shapes. Show that the insertion loss approximately equals $|1 - 2/\rho|/4$. Verify that the insertion loss equals infinity for $\rho = 2$, about 26 dB for $\rho = 2.5$, and about 22 dB for $\rho = 3.0$. (c) For approximation purposes, express the gain in terms of an equivalent biquadratic transfer function.

11.34 A bridged-T network is a simplified twin-T where R_3 is eliminated, the series "bridging" combination C_1 and C_2 is replaced by C_1, and C_3 is relabelled as C_2. Its transfer function is biquadratic. (a) Derive the transfer function. (Hint: Is Eq. 11.5.2 useful?) (b) Show that the center frequency $\omega_o = 1/\sqrt{R_1C_1R_2C_2}$ and the notch depth $|H(j\omega_o)| = \zeta_1/\zeta_2$. (c) Show that to achieve this notch depth, the tuning conditions are:

$$R_2/R_1 = 1/[4\zeta_1^2(\zeta_2/\zeta_1 - 1) - 1], \qquad C_2/C_1 = [4\zeta_1^2(\zeta_2/\zeta_1 - 1)^2]/[4\zeta_1^2(\zeta_2/\zeta_1 - 1) - 1]$$

(For plots of these ratios, see Ref. 23.) (d) The limiting component values are set when these values approach infinity. Show this occurs when $\zeta_2/\zeta_1 = 1 + 1/4\zeta_1^2$. For example, when $\zeta_1 = 0.1$, then $\zeta_2/\zeta_1 = 26$; and when $\zeta_1 = 0.5$, then $\zeta_2/\zeta_1 = 2$. Show that bridged-T's cannot realize zeros of transmission. (e) In design, we choose ζ_2 and $|H(j\omega_o)|$. Then ζ_1 is determined and if the limit of part (d) is not exceeded, we calculate component values. Choosing R_1, then $C_1 = [\omega_o R_1\sqrt{(R_2/R_1)(C_2/C_1)}]^{-1}$ and R_2 and C_2 are calculated from the ratios of part (c).

REFERENCES

1. Nowell, R. W., "An investigation of active band-stop filters," M.S.E.E. Directed Research, California State Univ., Long Beach, May, 1975.
2. Moschytz, G. S., "A general approach to twin-T design and its application to hybrid integrated linear active networks," Bell System Tech. J., vol. 49, pp. 1105–1149, July–Aug., 1970.
3. Mollinga, T., "Part 1–Active parallel-T networks," EEE, pp. 93–98, April, 1966.
4. Moschytz, G. S., "Two-step precision tuning of twin-T notch filter," Proc. IEEE, vol. 54, pp. 811–812, May, 1966.
   White, C. F., "RC null network requiring only two components of prescribed value," Proc. IEEE, vol. 56, p. 1129, June, 1968.
5. Mitra, S. K., *Analysis and Synthesis of Linear Active Networks*, App. D, Wiley, 1969.
6. Bowron, P., "The selectivity of null networks," Proc. IEEE, vol. 59, pp. 1117–1119, July, 1971.
7. Ramachandran, V., "Design of resistance-capacitance null networks," Proc. IEEE, vol. 55, pp. 1507–1508, Aug., 1967.
   Mitra, S. K., "A note on the design of RC notch networks with maximum gain," Proc. IEEE, vol. 54, p. 1487, Oct., 1966.
8. Chakrabarty, S., and A. K. Choudhury, "State-variable realization of voltage-controlled active notch filters," Proc. IEEE, vol. 57, pp. 2068–2069, Nov., 1969.
   Steber, G. R., and R. J. Krueger, "A voltage-controlled tunable active null network," Proc. IEEE, vol. 57, pp. 233–234, Feb., 1969.
9. Swamy, M. N. S., "A dual input null network," Proc. IEEE, vol. 54, pp. 1117–1118, Aug., 1966.
   ———, "Some observations on dual input null networks," Proc. IEEE, vol. 56, pp. 120–121, Jan., 1968.
10. Bode, H. W., "Amplitude equalizer," U. S. Patent 2,096,027, Oct. 19, 1937.
    ———, "Variable equalizers," Bell System Tech. J., vol. 17, pp. 229–244, 1938.
11. Sallen, R. P., and E. L. Key, "A practical method for designing RC active filters," IRE Trans. Circuit Theory, vol. CT-2, pp. 74–85, March, 1955.
12. Tow, J., "A step-by-step active-filter design," IEEE Spectrum, vol. 6, pp. 64–68, Dec., 1969.
13. Moschytz, G. S., "Miniaturized filter building blocks using frequency emphasizing networks," Proc. Natl. Elec. Conf., pp. 364–369, Oct., 1967.
14. Williams, P., "Notch filters using Wien's bridge," Electronics Letters, vol. 6, pp. 186–187, March 19, 1970.
15. Russell, H. T., "Design active filters with less effort," Electronic Design, pp. 82–85, Jan. 7, 1971, copyright Hayden Publishing, 1971.
16. Inigo, R. M., "A single operational amplifier notch filter," Proc. IEEE, vol. 57, p. 727, April, 1969.
17. Friend, J. J., C. A. Harris, and D. Hilberman, "STAR : An active biquadratic filter section," IEEE Trans. Circuits and Systems, vol. CAS-22, pp. 115–121, Feb., 1975.
    Hamilton, T. A., and A. S. Sedra, "A single-amplifier biquad active filter," IEEE Trans. Circuit Theory, vol. CT-19, pp. 398–403, July, 1972.
    Moschytz, G. S., "A general all-pass network based on the Sallen-Key circuit," IEEE Trans. Circuit Theory, vol. CT-19, pp. 392–394, July, 1972.
18. Hilberman, D., "Input and ground as complements in active filters," IEEE Trans. Circuit Theory, vol. CT-20, pp. 540–547, Sept., 1973.
19. Tunable Notch-Peak Filter AF-850A, Data Sheet 4125M1273, 1 p., SEG Electronics, Richmond Hill, NY, 12/73.
20. EDMAC Model 8010A Hi-Q Tunable Tracking Filter, 1 p. EDMAC Associates, Inc., East Rochester, NY, July, 1974.
21. Kay, G., "Nine-channel stereo equalizer," Popular Electronics, pp. 27–32, May, 1974.
22. Fleischer, P. E., "Active adjustable loss and delay equalizers," Proc. Intl. Symp. on Circuits and Systems, pp. 564–568, April, 1974.
23. Bejach, B., "Design filters in minutes," Electronic Design, pp. 86–88, May 24, 1970, copyright Hayden Publishing, 1970.

12 ALL-PASS FILTERS

Change is not made without inconvenience,
even from worse to better.
Hooker

The last important class of filter we want to consider is the all-pass variety. We begin by investigating all-pass filters from the classification viewpoint of Chap. 7. In general, it will be seen that all-pass filters are at least as difficult and sometimes more difficult to design than notch filters. We will then investigate a standard method which allows us to utilize band-pass filters in constructing all-pass filters. A set of filter design sheets will be compiled which will be used to investigate and design a variety of all-pass filters. We will make qualitative evaluations of the designs. We shall also discuss tunable all-pass filters and delay equalizers.

12.1 ALL-PASS FILTER CLASSES

We saw in Sec. 2.11 that all-pass filters had transfer functions which equal $H(s) = D(-s)/D(s)$ so that their right-half-plane zeros are the reflected images of their left-half-plane poles. First-order all-pass filters have transfer functions which equal

$$H(s) = H_o \frac{(s/\omega_o) - 1}{(s/\omega_o) + 1} \tag{12.1.1}$$

while in second-order all-pass filters,

$$H(s) = H_o \frac{(s/\omega_o)^2 - 2\zeta(s/\omega_o) + 1}{(s/\omega_o)^2 + 2\zeta(s/\omega_o) + 1} \tag{12.1.2}$$

First-order filters are completely described by their resonant frequency ω_o and gain H_o. In second-order filters, the damping factor ζ of the pole is also specified. In the filter designs of Chaps. 2–6, this information was summarized in an all-pass filter (APF) block. We shall now implement these blocks with hardware.

We again want to select the class of all-pass filters to obtain the desired gain/sensitivity trade-offs. Let us consider the active filters having the simplest topology of a single forward branch using the assumptions of Sec. 8.1. These filters have the flow graph of Fig. 8.1.1 and a transfer function given by Eq. 8.1.4. The numerator of the gain function is equal to the numerator of the forward path gain $K_1K_2T_{13}T_{45}$. Thus, the form of the numerators of T_{13} and T_{45} determine the filter type.

Since all-pass filters are closely related to the band-stop filters of the last chapter, we can use many of our previous results. For first-order decomposition filters, the numerator of the transfer function was given in Eq. 11.1.3 and the denominator by Eq. 7.3.3. For H(s) to be all-pass, then the s^1 coefficient of Num H must be negative which can never occur. Therefore, Class 1X filters cannot be realized. In second-order decomposition filters, the numerator of the transfer function H(s) was given by Eq. 8.1.11. Since the s^1 coefficient of Num H can also never be negative, Class 2X filters cannot be realized using topologies of a single forward branch.

As with notch filters, more general topologies must be used. We can add a T_{12} branch to the flow graph of Fig. 8.1.1 as will be discussed in the next section. This is attractive from a tuning standpoint and all-pass filters can be realized in every class. We can also add a T_{15} and T_{42} branches as shown in Fig. 11.1.1. The transfer functions are given by Eqs. 11.1.5 and 11.1.6. We saw from these equations that adding these branches modifies the gain numerator to involve difference terms. This gives us the flexibility to force the damping factor ζ_z of the zero to equal ζ_p of the pole. Since the resonant pole and zero frequencies, ω_{op} and ω_{oz}, must also be set equal, all-pass filters are more highly constrained than notch filters. As before, it is usually preferable to add a T_{15} branch rather than a T_{42} branch in the flow graph to eliminate the need for impedance buffering at the filter output.

All-pass filters are formulated in the same way as notch filters. To show this, let us formulate a Class 1A all-pass filter using a T_{15} branch. The feedback transfer functions are given by Eq. 11.1.11 and the overall gain function equals

$$H(s) = K_2 \frac{s^2(a_{31}d_{51} + K_1c_{51}d_{31}) + s(a_{30}d_{51} + a_{31}d_{50} + K_1c_{51}d_{30}) + a_{30}d_{50}}{s^2(a_{31}a_{51} - K_1K_2c_{31}c_{51}) + s(a_{30}a_{51} + a_{31}a_{50}) + a_{30}a_{50}} \tag{12.1.3}$$

from Eq. 11.1.5. For H(s) to be all-pass, we force the various coefficients of s to equal:

$$\begin{aligned} &s^0\!: \; a_{30}a_{50} = a_{50}d_{50}, \qquad s^1\!: \; a_{30}a_{51} + a_{31}a_{50} = a_{30}d_{51} + a_{31}d_{50} + K_1c_{51}d_{30} \\ &s^2\!: \; a_{31}a_{51} - K_1K_2c_{31}c_{51} = a_{31}d_{51} + K_1c_{51}d_{31} \end{aligned} \tag{12.1.4}$$

Solving for gain K_1 from the s^1 condition gives

$$K_1 = -\frac{a_{30}(a_{51} - d_{51}) + a_{31}(a_{50} - d_{50})}{c_{51}d_{30}} \leqslant 0 \tag{12.1.5}$$

Solving for gain K_2 from the s^2 condition gives

$$K_2 = \frac{a_{31}(a_{51} - d_{51}) - K_1c_{51}d_{31}}{K_1c_{31}c_{51}} \tag{12.1.6}$$

Therefore, K_1 is adjusted to match the damping factors and K_2 is adjusted to match the resonant frequencies of the poles and zeros. The various transfer functions are listed in Eq. 11.1.20. All that remains is to choose the proper set of RC networks which have these transfer functions.

Following the band-stop filter procedure, two possible all-pass filters are shown in Fig. 11.1.2. Substituting the transfer functions given by Eq. 11.1.21 into Eq. 12.1.3, the gain of the all-pass filter in Fig. 11.1.2a equals

$$H(s) = K_2 \frac{s^2\tau_{11}\tau_{22} + s(\tau_{11} + \tau_{22} + K_1\tau_{32}) + 1}{s^2\tau_{11}[\tau_{22} + \tau_{32}(1 - K_1K_2)] + s(\tau_{11} + \tau_{22} + \tau_{32}) + 1} \tag{12.1.7}$$

To match damping factors as $\zeta_z = -\zeta_p$ requires

$$-K_1 = [2(\tau_{11} + \tau_{22}) + \tau_{32}]/\tau_{32} = 1 + 2(\tau_{11} + \tau_{22})/\tau_{32} \tag{12.1.8}$$

which agrees with Eq. 12.1.5. To match resonant frequencies as $\omega_{op} = \omega_{oz}$ requires $K_2 = -1/K_1$ which agrees with Eq. 12.1.6. An alternative all-pass filter is shown in Fig. 11.1.2b. Its transfer function is given by Eq. 12.1.7 and its gain K_1 is given by Eq. 12.1.8 where τ_{32} is replaced by τ_{23}. Gain K_2 still equals $-1/K_1$. The principle difference between the two filters is that the second form requires three capacitors while the first form requires only two.

Following the procedure giving rise to Eq. 12.1.3 for the other classes, it is easy to show that all-pass filters in every class can be realized using T_{15} (or T_{42}) branches.[1] The same approach can be used to realize Class 2X filters of this topology but we shall not pursue this further.

12.2 BAND-PASS TO ALL-PASS FILTER TRANSFORMATION

Band-pass filters can be transformed into all-pass filters using the complementary filter arrangement discussed in Sec. 9.6. There it was shown that if any active filter employing infinite-gain amplifiers has a transfer function H(s), then its complementary transfer function $H_C(s)$ equals

$$H_C(s) = 1 - H(s) \tag{12.2.1}$$

The filter having this complementary function is obtained by grounding the original inputs, lifting the original grounds, and treating these as the new inputs. If the original filter is band-pass with a positive midband gain of +2 where

$$H_{BP}(s) = \frac{2s_n/Q}{s_n^2 + s_n/Q + 1} \tag{12.2.2}$$

then the complementary filter will be all-pass with a transfer function of

$$H_{AP}(s) = \frac{s_n^2 - s_n/Q + 1}{s_n^2 + s_n/Q + 1} \tag{12.2.3}$$

Notice that if the midband gain were instead +1, then a notch filter would result having a transfer function given by Eq. 11.2.3. This conversion was illustrated in Fig. 11.2.1. In practice, the band-pass filter is tuned to have $H_o = 2$ and the desired ω_o and Q. Then interchanging the input and ground produces an all-pass filter having the same parameters except that $H_o = 1$. Of course, we could also use a notch filter having a transfer function

$$H_{BS}(s) = 2\,\frac{s_n^2 + 1}{s_n^2 + s_n/Q + 1} \tag{12.2.4}$$

and a passband gain of +2. Then the complementary filter will also be all-pass with a negative transfer function given by Eq. 12.2.3. In general however, since we have many more band-pass filter forms available to use, they afford more design flexibility.

There is no other topological transformation that allows the engineer to directly transform RC active low-pass, high-pass, band-pass, or band-stop filters into all-pass filters. However, there is a general topology in which low-pass and high-pass, band-pass, or band-stop filters can be utilized to realize all-pass filters. These topologies are shown in Fig. 12.2.1. In the first case, a band-pass filter (or band-stop filter) is inserted in parallel with a unity gain filter as shown in Fig. 12.2.1a. The overall gain equals

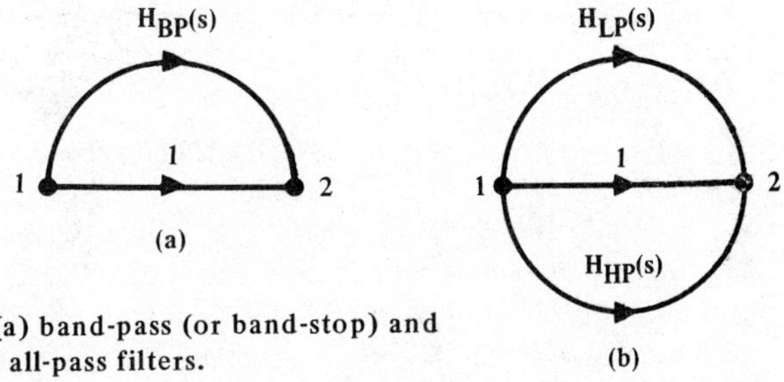

Fig. 12.2.1 Flow graph arrangements of (a) band-pass (or band-stop) and (b) low-pass and high-pass filters to realize all-pass filters.

$$H(s) = 1 + H_{BP}(s) = 1 + H_o \frac{s_n/Q}{s_n^2 + s_n/Q + 1} = \frac{s_n^2 + (1 + H_o)s_n/Q + 1}{s_n^2 + s_n/Q + 1} \tag{12.2.5}$$

To force H(s) to be all-pass, we must insure that the s_n^1 coefficients of the numerator and denominator have opposite signs. Thus, matching coefficients gives $H_o = -2$. Therefore, any band-pass filter with a midband gain of −2 can be used in conjunction with a parallel filter of unity gain to produce an all-pass filter. This is equivalent to allowing $T_{12} = 1$ in the flow graph of the inverting band-pass filters analyzed in Chap. 10. Notch filters having identical ω_{op} and ω_{oz} and a passband gain of −2 can also be used. The ω_o and ζ of the all-pass filter equals that of the band-pass or band-stop filter. The gain of the all-pass filter equals either +1 or −1.

Alternatively, we can connect low-pass and high-pass filters of identical ω_o and Q in parallel with a unity gain filter to produce an all-pass filter. This is shown in Fig. 12.2.1b. Here the gain equals

$$H(s) = 1 + H_{LP}(s) + H_{HP}(s) = 1 + \frac{H_1}{s_n^2 + s_n/Q + 1} + \frac{H_2 s_n^2}{s_n^2 + s_n/Q + 1}$$

$$= \frac{s_n^2(1 + H_2) + s_n/Q + (1 + H_1)}{s_n^2 + s_n/Q + 1} = -\frac{s_n^2(-1 - H_2) - s_n/Q + (-1 - H_1)}{s_n^2 + s_n/Q + 1} \tag{12.2.6}$$

This transfer function is all-pass when $H_1 = H_2 = -2$. As in the analogous band-stop filter design of the last chapter, the band-pass filter approach is more desirable because of decreased complexity and no (ω_o, Q) matching requirement.

This method of all-pass filter implementation adds greatly to our design flexibility. It shows that we can realize all-pass filters from the other filters we have considered in Chaps. 8–11, and vice versa (e.g., see Prob. 12.7).

EXAMPLE 12.2.1 Design a Class 2A all-pass filter using a Class 2A band-pass filter and a summer. Do so by extending the band-stop filter design results in Example 11.2.1.

Solution The required filter is shown in Fig. 11.2.3. By inspection, the overall gain equals

$$H(s) = \frac{1}{1 + k}[1 + kH_{BP}(s)] \tag{12.2.7}$$

where H_{BP} is given by Eq. 11.2.7. To be all-pass, then the midband gain of the band-pass filter must equal $kH_o = -2$ (rather than −1 as in Example 11.2.1). Solving for k gives

$$k = 2/(-H_o) = 2[1 + (R_1/R_2)(1 + C_1/C_2)]/K \tag{12.2.8}$$

from Eq. 11.2.8. Using the design equations that $R_1 = R_2 = R$ and $C_1 = C_2 = C$ given by Eq. 11.2.9, then the summer gain k must equal $k = 6/K = 6/(9Q^2 - 1)$ from Eq. 12.2.9. The gain of the all-pass filter equals $H_o = 1/(1 + k) = (9Q^2 - 1)/(9Q^2 + 5)$. Thus, except for the gains k and H_o, all of the other design equations for the all-pass filter are identical to those in Eq. 11.2.9. When output impedance buffering or gain is required, an inverting or noninverting amplifier is used at the output.

12.3 ALL-PASS FILTER COMPILATIONS

Class 1X all-pass filters can be obtained from the Class 1X band-stop filters compiled in Sec. 11.3 with a simple parameter change (see Probs. 12.3–12.6). Class 2X all-pass filters can be obtained from the Class 2X band-pass and band-stop filters compiled in Secs. 10.3 and 11.3 using either the complementary transformation or resistive summers (see Probs. 12.9–12.19). Therefore, we have minimized redundancy in this section by compiling only two Class E all-pass filters. It is useful to remember that the RC:CR transformation can be applied to any all-pass filter to produce another all-pass filter.

12.4 ALL-PASS FILTER DESIGN EXAMPLES

Now let us utilize these design sheets to realize a variety of all-pass filters. The design proceeds in the same way as that of the other filter types. In cascade design of odd-order all-pass filters, we require a first-order all-pass filter stage which we will now discuss.

In passive synthesis, lattice or bridge circuits are often used to obtain complex zeros. We discussed such an example in Fig. 11.5.3. By proper tuning, these circuits can be used to obtain all-pass filters. For example, let us factor H(s) given by Eq. 12.1.1 as

$$H(s) = \frac{1}{2}\frac{\omega_o - s}{\omega_o + s} = \tfrac{1}{2} - \frac{s}{s + \omega_o} = \tfrac{1}{2} - \frac{1}{1 + \omega_o/s} \tag{12.4.1}$$

An RC bridge realization for H(s) is shown in Fig. 12.4.1. Since $\omega_o = 1/RC$, R is used to tune ω_o; by inspection, $H_o = ½$. The equivalent active first-order all-pass filter is shown in Fig. 12.4.2. The op amp provides the sign inversion for subtracting the bridge outputs. The transfer function equals

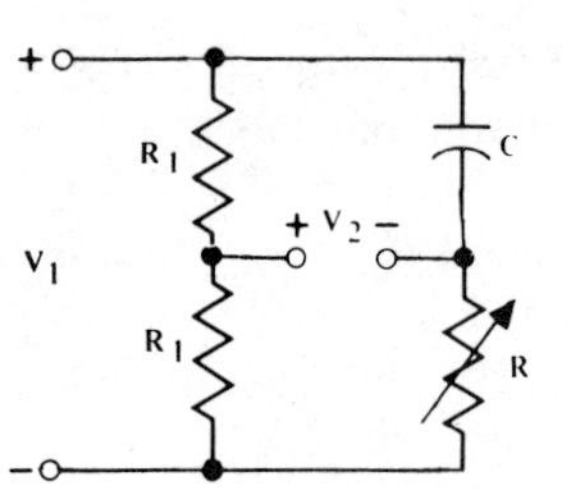

Fig. 12.4.1 Passive first-order all-pass filter.

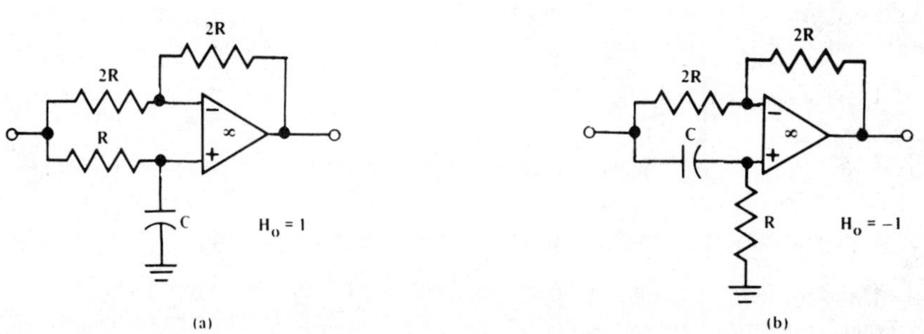

Fig. 12.4.2 Active first-order all-pass filter having an $H_o(0)$ of (a) +1 and (b) −1.[2]

CLASS 1E: ALL-PASS

Transfer Function:

$$H(s) = -\frac{R_2R_8}{R_5R_6}\,\frac{s^2R_3C_1R_5C_2 + s[(R_3/R_1)(1 - R_1R_6/R_4R_7)R_5C_2] + R_6/R_7}{s^2R_3C_1R_2C_2 + s(R_3/R_1)R_2C_2 + R_8/R_7}$$

Parameters:

$$\omega_{op} = \left[\frac{R_8/R_7}{R_3C_1R_2C_2}\right]^{1/2}, \qquad \omega_{oz} = \left[\frac{R_6/R_7}{R_3C_1R_5C_2}\right]^{1/2} \text{ so that } \quad R_8/R_2 = R_6/R_5$$

$$\zeta_p = 1/2\left[\frac{R_2C_2}{R_1C_1}\,\frac{R_3R_7}{R_1R_8}\right]^{1/2} \qquad H_o(\infty) = -R_8/R_6$$

$$\zeta_z = 1/2\left[\frac{R_5C_2}{R_1C_1}\,\frac{R_3R_7}{R_1R_6}\right]^{1/2}(1 - R_1R_6/R_4R_7) = -\zeta_p \text{ so that } \quad R_1/R_4 = 2R_7/R_6$$

Design Equations: Set $R_7 = R_8 = R$, $\quad R_3C_1 = R_2C_2$

Given: ω_o, Q, $-H_o$

Choose: C_1, C_2, R

Calculate: $R_1 = Q/\omega_oC_1$ $\qquad R_4 = R_1/(-2H_o)$

$R_2 = 1/\omega_oC_2$ $\qquad R_5 = R_2/(-H_o)$

$R_3 = (C_2/C_1)R_2$ $\qquad R_6 = R/(-H_o)$

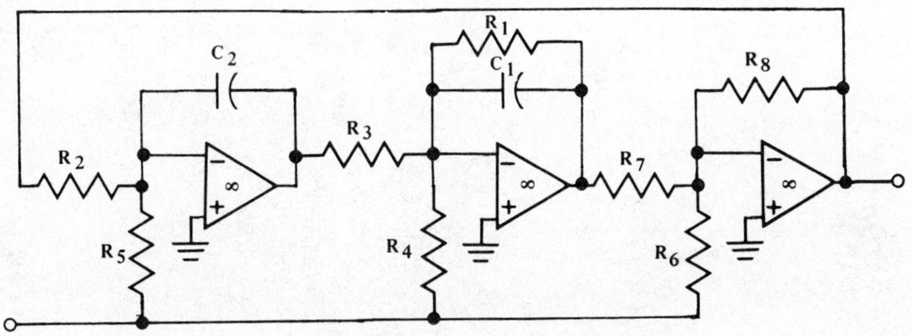

P. E. Fleischer and J. Tow, "Design formulas for biquad active filters using three operational amplifiers," Proc. IEEE, vol. 61, pp. 662–663, May, 1973.

CLASS 2E: ALL-PASS

Transfer Function:

$$H(s) = \frac{R_B}{R_A + R_B} \frac{s^2R_1C_1R_2C_2 + s[R_1(C_1 + C_2) - R_2C_1R_A/R_B] + 1}{s^2R_1C_1R_2C_2 + sR_1(C_1 + C_2) + 1}$$

Parameters:

$$\omega_{op} = \omega_{oz} = \frac{1}{(R_1C_1R_2C_2)^{1/2}} \qquad H_o = \frac{R_B}{R_A + R_B}$$

$$\zeta_p = \frac{R_1(C_1 + C_2)}{2(R_1C_1R_2C_2)^{1/2}}$$

$$\zeta_z = \frac{R_1(C_1 + C_2) - R_2C_1R_A/R_B}{2(R_1C_1R_2C_2)^{1/2}} = -\zeta_p \text{ so that } \qquad \frac{R_A}{R_B} = \frac{2R_1(C_1 + C_2)}{R_2C_1}$$

Design Equations: Set $C_2 = kC_1$ (For Minimum Offset)

Given: ω_o, Q

Choose: C_1, k

Calculate: $C_2 = kC_1$ $\qquad H_o = 1/[1 + 2k/(1 + k)Q^2]$

$R_1 = 1/(1 + k)Q\omega_oC_1$ $\qquad R_A = R_2/H_o$

$R_2 = (1 + k)Q/\omega_oC_2$ $\qquad R_B = [(1 + k)Q^2/2k] R_A$

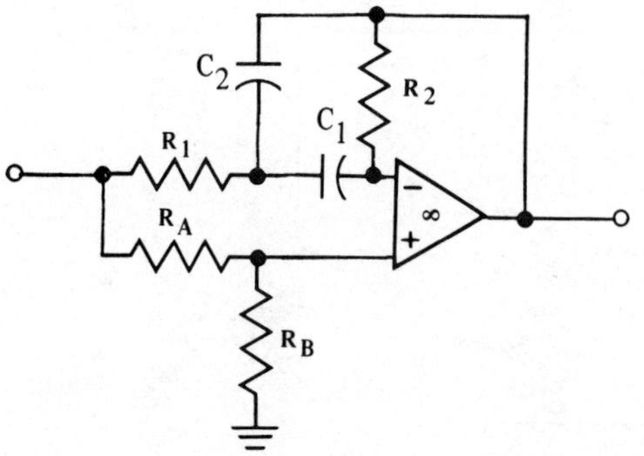

A. Budak and P. Aronhime, "Frequency limitations on an operational amplifier realization of all-pass transfer functions with complex poles," Proc. IEEE, vol. 58, pp. 1137–1138, July, 1970.

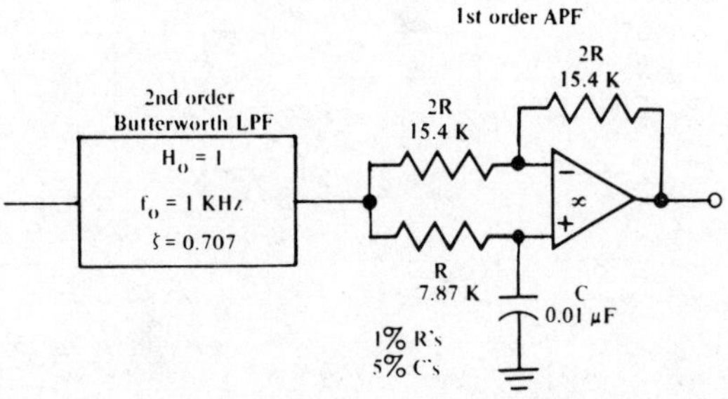

Fig. 12.4.3 Block diagram of first-order all-pass filter and its realization.

$$H(s) = \pm \frac{1 - sRC}{1 + sRC} \tag{12.4.2}$$

where the parameters ω_o and H_o equal

$$H_o = \pm 1, \qquad \omega_o = 1/RC \tag{12.4.3}$$

The sign of the gain expression is selected by the position of R and C. R is used to tune ω_o (note the feedback resistors are equal and can remain fixed). A design utilizing this all-pass filter is considered in the following example.

EXAMPLE 12.4.1 A first-order all-pass filter is needed to equalize (i.e., reduce) the delay variation of a second-order Butterworth low-pass filter having a 3 dB bandwidth of 1000 Hz (see Prob. 2.45). Design the all-pass filter assuming its resonant frequency equals 2000 Hz. The delay-equalized Butterworth filter is shown in Fig. 12.4.3.

Solution The delay equalizer is easily implemented using the all-pass filter in Fig. 12.4.2. Using the design equations given by Eq. 12.4.3, then

$$\begin{aligned} &1/RC = 2\pi(2000 \text{ Hz}), \qquad C = 0.01\ \mu F \\ &R = 7.96 \text{ K (use 7.87 K)}, \qquad 2R = 2(7.87 \text{ K}) = 15.7 \text{ K (use 15.4 K)} \end{aligned} \tag{12.4.4}$$

The complete delay equalizer is shown in Fig. 12.4.3.

EXAMPLE 12.4.2 A second-order all-pass filter is required to decrease the in-band delay variation of the band-pass filter of Example 2.10.6. The delay characteristic of this filter is shown in Fig. 2.10.12. The required all-pass filter is shown in block diagram form in Fig. 12.4.4. Design the filter using a Class 1E realization.

Solution The Class 1E all-pass filter is also shown in Fig. 12.4.4. Its design equations equal:

Set: $R_7 = R_8 = R$

Given: $\omega_o, Q, -H_o$

Choose: C_1, C_2, R

Calculate: $R_1 = Q/\omega_o C_1, \quad R_2 = 1/\omega_o C_2, \quad R_3 = R_2 C_2/C_1, \quad R_4 = R_1/(-2H_o)$

$R_5 = R_2/(-H_o), \quad R_6 = R/(-H_o)$

The design proceeds as:

$$\begin{aligned} &1/R_1C_1 = 2\pi(2.5 \text{ KHz}/1.25) = 2\pi(2 \text{ KHz}), \qquad 1/R_2C_2 = 2\pi(2.5 \text{ KHz}) \\ &C_1 = C_2 = 0.01\ \mu F, \qquad R_1 = 7.96 \text{ K (use 7.87 K)}, \qquad R_2 = 6.37 \text{ K (use 6.49 K)} \\ &R_4 = 7.87 \text{ K}/2 = 3.94 \text{ K (use 4.02 K)}, \qquad R_3 = R_5 = R = R_6 = 6.49 \text{ K} \end{aligned} \tag{12.4.5}$$

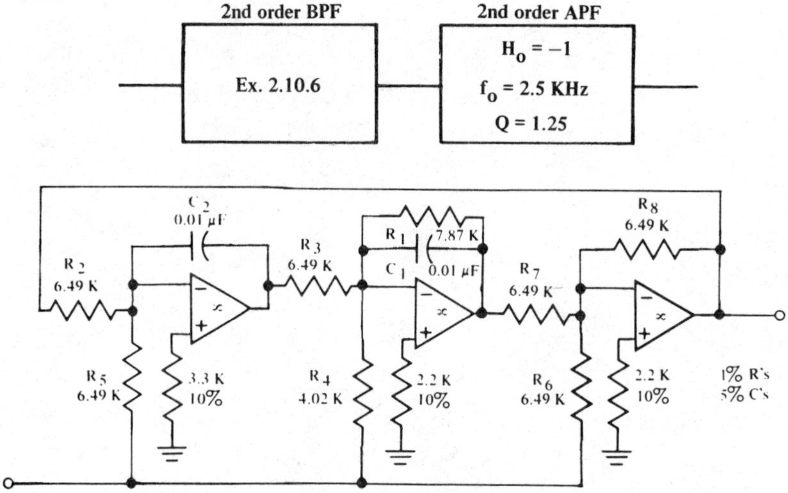

Fig. 12.4.4 Block diagram of second-order all-pass filter and its realization.

The complete filter is shown in Fig. 12.4.4.

EXAMPLE 12.4.3 A low-pass filter having an optimum step response was discussed in Sec. 5.4. The optimum third-order filter had a transfer function

$$H(s) = \frac{s^2 - 6.195s + 16.31}{s^3 + 4.905s^2 + 23.88s + 37.85} \tag{12.4.6}$$

which can be factored as

$$H(s) = \frac{(s+3.10)^2 + 2.59^2}{(s+2.10)[(s+1.40)^2 + 4^2]} \; \frac{(s-3.10)^2 + 2.59^2}{(s+3.10)^2 + 2.59^2} \tag{12.4.7}$$

A second-order all-pass filter can be used to realize the nonminimum phase term. Design the all-pass filter assuming that $\omega_o = 2\pi(1 \text{ KHz})$. Use the Class 2A band-pass filter and summer realization discussed in Example 12.2.1.

Solution We first determine the block diagram of the all-pass filter. From Eq. 12.4.7, the pole parameters are $\omega_n = (3.10^2 + 2.59^2)^{1/2} = 4.04$ and $\zeta = 3.10/\omega_n = 0.767$. Since $\omega_o = 2\pi(1 \text{ KHz})$, its block diagram is easily drawn in Fig. 12.4.5. The design equations for the Class 2A band-pass filter are given by Eqs. 11.2.9 and 12.2.8 as:

Set: $R_1 = R_2 = R, \quad C_1 = C_2 = C, \quad k = R_4/R_3$

Given: ω_o, Q

Choose: C, R_4

Calculate: $R = 1/3Q\omega_o C, \quad K = 9Q^2 - 1, \quad k = 6/K, \quad R_3 = R_4/k, \quad H_o(0) = 1/(1+k)$

The design proceeds as:

$$\begin{aligned} &1/RC = 2\pi[3(4.04 \text{ KHz})/2(0.767)] = 2\pi(7.90 \text{ KHz}), \quad C = 0.001\ \mu\text{F} \\ &R = 20.1\text{ K (use 20.5 K)}, \quad K = 9[1/2(0.767)]^2 - 1 = 3.82 - 1 = 2.82, \quad k = 6/2.82 = 2.13 \\ &R_4 = 20.5\text{ K}, \quad R_3 = 20.5\text{ K}/2.13 = 9.62\text{ K (use 9.53 K)}, \quad H_o(0) = 1/(1+2.13) = 0.319 \end{aligned} \tag{12.4.8}$$

The complete filter realization is shown in Fig. 12.4.5.

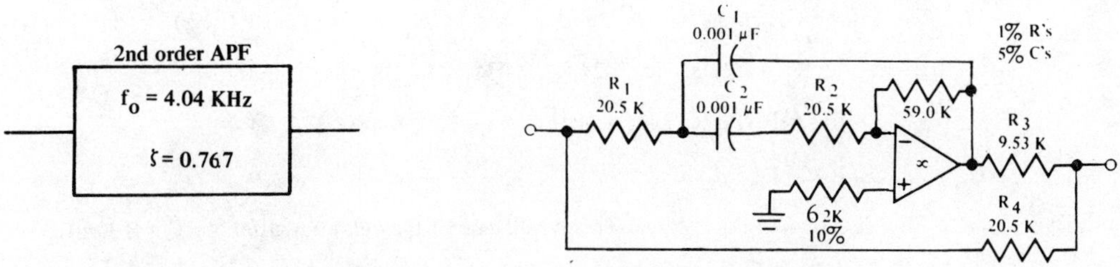

Fig. 12.4.5 Block diagram of second-order all-pass filter and its realization.

EXAMPLE 12.4.4 A fourth-order delay equalizer for a telephone line was analyzed in Example 2.11.5. Its block diagram realization is shown in Fig. 12.4.6. Design the equalizer using a Class 2E realization.

Solution The design equations for the Class 2E all-pass filter are:

Set: $C_2 = kC_1$

Given: ω_o, Q

Choose: C_1, k

Calculate: $C_2 = kC_1$, $R_1 = 1/(1+k)Q\omega_o C_1$, $R_2 = (1+k)Q/\omega_o C_2$

$H_o = 1/[1 + (2k/(1+k)Q^2]$, $R_A = R_2/H_o$, $R_B = R_A(1+k)Q^2/2k$

Setting k = 1, then the first stage design proceeds as:

$$
\begin{aligned}
&1/R_1C_1 = 2\pi(790\text{ Hz}/0.75) = 2\pi(1053\text{ Hz}), \qquad 1/R_2C_2 = 2\pi[0.75(790\text{ Hz})] = 2\pi(593\text{ Hz}) \\
&C = 0.1\ \mu F, \quad R_1 = 1.51\text{ K (use 1.54 K)}, \quad R_2 = 2.68\text{ K (use 2.61 K)} \\
&H_o = 1/[1 + 4(0.75^2)] = 0.308, \quad R_A = 2.61\text{ K}/0.308 = 8.47\text{ K (use 8.66 K)} \\
&R_B = 8.66\text{ K}/4(0.75^2) = 3.85\text{ K (use 3.83 K)}
\end{aligned}
\tag{12.4.9}
$$

The second stage is designed in the same manner, where:

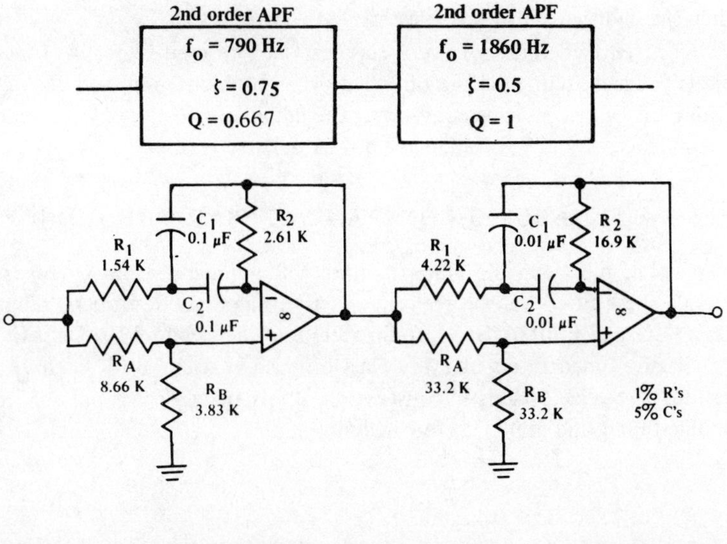

Fig. 12.4.6 Block diagram of fourth-order all-pass filter and its realization.

$$1/R_1C = 2\pi(1860\ \text{Hz}/0.5) = 2\pi(3720\ \text{Hz}), \qquad 1/R_2C = 2\pi[0.5(1860\ \text{Hz})] = 2\pi(930\ \text{Hz})$$

$$C = 0.01\ \mu\text{F}, \quad R_1 = 4.28\ \text{K}\ (\text{use } 4.22\ \text{K}), \quad R_2 = 17.1\ \text{K}\ (\text{use } 16.9\ \text{K}) \tag{12.4.10}$$

$$H_o = 1/[1 + 4(0.5^2)] = 0.5, \quad R_A = 16.9\ \text{K}/0.5 = 33.8\ \text{K}\ (\text{use } 33.2\ \text{K})$$

$$R_B = 33.2\ \text{K}/4(0.5^2) = 33.2\ \text{K}$$

The complete filter is shown in Fig. 12.4.6. The overall gain of the delay equalizer is $H_o' = 0.308(0.5) = 0.154$.

12.5 TUNABLE ALL-PASS FILTERS

There are a wide variety of applications which require all-pass filters having variable Q and constant ω_o or sometimes, vice versa. Just as with band-pass filters, we can make the following observations. For tunable Q/constant ω_o applications, we use Class B or D filters (or adjust Class C, $\overline{\text{C}}$, and E filters). For tunable ω_o/almost constant Q, we use Class C–E filters. From a passive-tuning standpoint, we can use every class for these two situations which gives us more design flexibility.

The root loci for these two cases were shown in Fig. 8.6.1 and the tolerances were shown in Fig. 8.6.2. Designing tunable all-pass filters is even more complicated than designing band-stop filters. This is due to the need for proper adjustment of amplifier K_1 to match damping factors (e.g., see Eq. 12.1.5) and amplifier K_2 to match resonant frequencies (e.g., see Eq. 12.1.6). The simplest design method is to use the parallel branch summing method with band-pass filters.

12.5.1 TUNABLE CENTER FREQUENCY/CONSTANT Q ALL-PASS FILTERS

We considered Class C, $\overline{\text{C}}$, and E gain-tuned band-pass filters in Sec. 10.5. Using the parallel branch summing method shown in Fig. 12.2.1, in conjunction with the Class C, $\overline{\text{C}}$, and E gain-tuned band-pass filters shown in Fig. 10.5.1, we obtain Class C, $\overline{\text{C}}$, and E gain-tuned all-pass filters. By simply introducing two additional resistors between the input and output of the band-pass filters, and using their junction as the new output, gain-tuned all-pass filters result. Using this process, we obtain seven Class C and E, and seven Class $\overline{\text{C}}$ and E all-pass filters. The parameters equations are virtually unchanged. This is a practical solution for obtaining gain-tuned all-pass filters. It is suboptimal in the sense that the filters contain seven nodes, rather than six, and two additional resistors.

Passive-tuned filters of every class can also be used to realize tunable ω_o/constant Q all-pass filters. Exact tuning can be obtained using double-tuning, and approximate tuning using single-tuning of the passive time constants. The design of this type of passive-tuned filter was outlined in Examples 8.7.1 and 9.5.2 and shall not be pursued further.

12.5.2 TUNABLE Q/CONSTANT CENTER FREQUENCY ALL-PASS FILTERS

In general, most tunable all-pass filters will require tunable Q/constant ω_o filters. With gain-tuning, these filters can be realized exactly using Class B, properly adjusted Class D, two-amplifier Class C, $\overline{\text{C}}$, and E filters, or approximately using single-amplifier Class C, $\overline{\text{C}}$, and E filters.

Passive-tuned filters of every class can also be used. Both single-tuning and double-tuning can be used to realize tunable Q/constant ω_o filters exactly. Q is only approximately linear in 1/R for double-tuning and nonlinear for single-tuning.

12.6 DELAY EQUALIZERS

One application requiring tunable all-pass filters is that of delay equalization. We discussed equalizers in Sec. 2.11 and designed several in Sec. 12.4. *Delay equalizers* are all-pass filters whose delay is adjusted to equalize or augment the delay of another filter so the overall delay is constant. This is illustrated in Fig. 12.6.1a which shows the delay response of a telephone line. To reduce the delay variation (i.e., delay distortion), we require a delay equalizer which has the response shown in Fig. 12.6.1b. The overall delay is shown in Fig. 12.6.1c. Now let us determine the parameters of the equalizer.

EXAMPLE 12.6.1 Determine the parameters of the delay equalizer required in Fig. 12.6.1.
Solution As discussed in Example 2.11.5, we can either use stagger-tuning of high-Q stages, or synchronous-tuning of low-Q stages. Due to the form of Fig. 12.6.1b, we shall use stagger-tuning. From Eqs. 2.10.13 and 2.10.19, the maximum delay and resonant frequency equal

$$\tau_{max} \cong 1/\zeta\omega_n = 2Q/\omega_n, \qquad \omega_n \cong \omega_p \tag{12.6.1}$$

assuming $Q \gg 1$ or $\zeta \ll 1$. From Fig. 12.6.1b, the two resonant frequencies approximately equal 1 KHz and 1.4 KHz, respectively. To produce the maximum delays of 500 and 600 μsec shown, then the Q's must equal

$$\begin{aligned} Q_1 &\cong \tfrac{1}{2}\,\omega_n\tau_{max} = \tfrac{1}{2}(2\pi)(1\text{ KHz})(0.5\text{ msec}) = 1.6 \\ Q_2 &\cong \tfrac{1}{2}(2\pi)(1.4\text{ KHz})(0.6\text{ msec}) = 2.6 \end{aligned} \tag{12.6.2}$$

using Eq. 12.6.1. The block diagram of the delay equalizer is shown in Fig. 12.6.2.

In general however, the delay equalizer requirements change from time to time due to changes in transmission line length, transmission and switching equipment, etc. This necessitates changes in the delay equalizer parameters. Thus, by using tunable equalizers in which Q and/or ω_o can be variable, the delay equalizers can be adapted to produce the required equalization. Very often, delay equalizers have center frequencies equally-spaced across the frequency band to be delay equalized. Then the Q of each stage is adjusted to produce the desired response. An example of this is shown in Fig. 2.11.7. Here a multi-stage delay equalizer was used to correct delay so that the delay distortion did not exceed prescribed limits. In one such application, twelve stages were tuned from 923 Hz with a Q of 3, to 3000 Hz with a Q of 10 to maintain the delay distortion below ±100 μsec.[3]

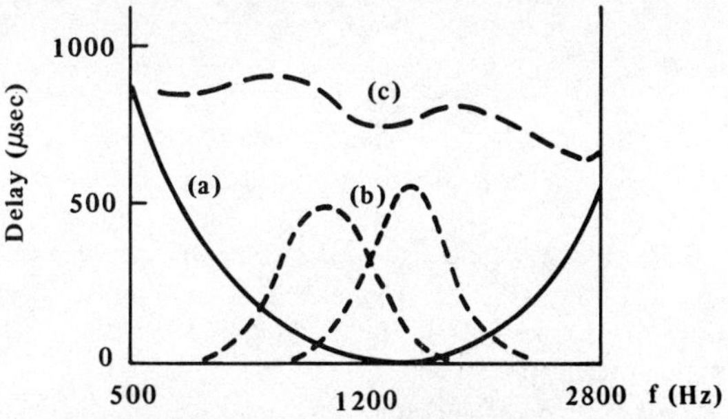

Fig. 12.6.1 (a) Actual delay response, (b) required delay equalizer response, and (c) overall response. (From P. E. Fleischer, "Active adjustable loss and delay equalizers," Proc. Intl. Symp. on Circuits and Systems, pp. 564–568, April 1974.)

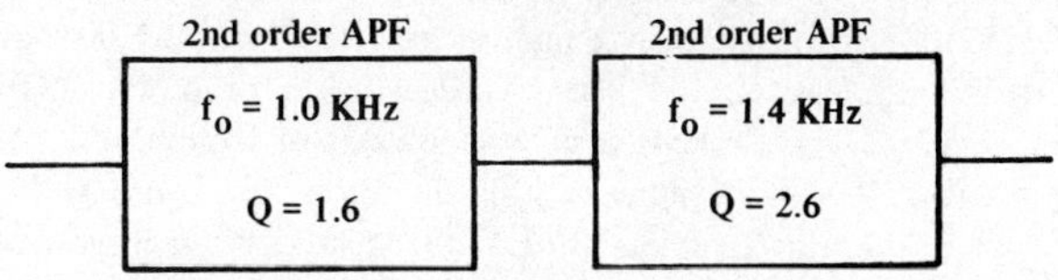

Fig. 12.6.2 Delay equalizer of Example 12.6.1.

PROBLEMS

12.1 The importance of compiling complete filter specifications cannot be overemphasized. A typical specification sheet was shown in Prob. 6.2. Briefly list the reasons for providing each data entry listed on that sheet.

12.2 Delay lines have somewhat different specifications than filters. The important parameters are listed in Prob. 6.3. Modify the specification of Prob. 6.2 so that it can be used for delay lines.

12.3 (a) Show that the Class 1A band-stop filter can be generalized to an all-pass filter by setting $K_1K_2 = -1$ and $K_1 = 1 + 2(R_1C_1 + R_2C_2)/R_2C_3$. Can complex poles be obtained using this filter? (b) Show that the design equations for the Class 1A band-stop filter can be used directly except for K_1 and K_2 which were found in part (a).

12.4 Repeat Prob. 12.3 for the Class $1\overline{A}$ band-stop filter. Show that $K_1K_2 = -1$ and $K_1 = 1 + (2R_3/R_2)(R_1C_1 + R_2C_2)/R_1C_1$.

12.5 Repeat Prob. 12.3 for the Class 1C band-stop filter. Show that $K_1K_2 = -1$ and $K_1 = 1 + 2 \times [R_1C_3 + R_2C_2(1 + C_3/C_1)]/R_3C_2$.

12.6 Repeat Prob. 12.3 for the Class $1\overline{C}$ band-stop filter. Show that $K_1K_2 = -1$ and $K_1 = 1 + (2C_3/C_2)[R_2C_2 + (R_1 + R_3)C_1]/R_3C_1$.

12.7 All-pass filters can be constructed using an inverting band-pass filter and a summer as shown by Eq. 12.2.5.[4] (a) Rearrange the equation to show how a band-pass filter can be obtained using an all-pass filter. (b) A biquadratic filter can be obtained using two first-order all-pass filters as shown in Fig. P12.7. Write the transfer function for the filter. (c) Determine the center frequency ω_o, Q, and midband gain H_o of the filter. What is the maximum stopband rejection obtained?

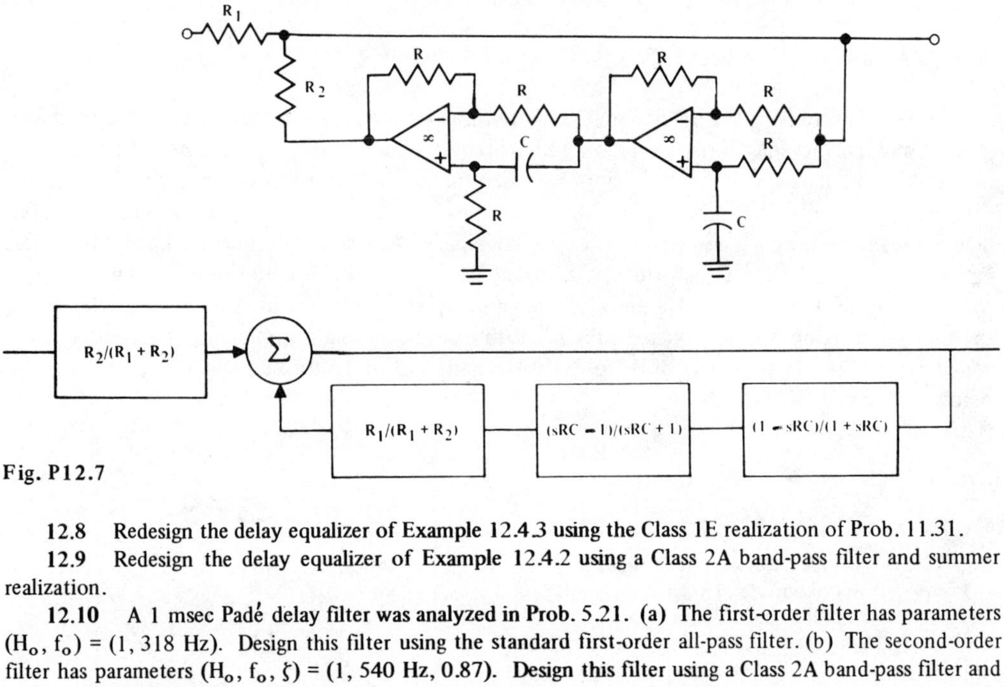

Fig. P12.7

12.8 Redesign the delay equalizer of Example 12.4.3 using the Class 1E realization of Prob. 11.31.

12.9 Redesign the delay equalizer of Example 12.4.2 using a Class 2A band-pass filter and summer realization.

12.10 A 1 msec Padé delay filter was analyzed in Prob. 5.21. (a) The first-order filter has parameters $(H_o, f_o) = (1, 318\text{ Hz})$. Design this filter using the standard first-order all-pass filter. (b) The second-order filter has parameters $(H_o, f_o, \zeta) = (1, 540\text{ Hz}, 0.87)$. Design this filter using a Class 2A band-pass filter and summer realization.

12.11 A second-order delay equalizer was cascaded with a fifth-order Butterworth low-pass filter in Prob. 4.11 to reduce its in-band delay variation. The all-pass filter has parameters $(H_o, f_o, \zeta) = (1, 730\text{ Hz}, 0.87)$. Design the delay equalizer using a Class 2B band-pass filter operating in the complementary mode. (Hint : Increase H_o to 2 with a voltage divider in the feedback loop.)

12.12 Redesign the delay equalizer of Example 12.4.2 using a Class 2B band-stop filter operating in the complementary mode. (Hint: See Prob. 12.11 hint.)

12.13 In Example 2.11.4, the delay of a second-order low-pass filter was equalized using a second-order all-pass filter. The all-pass filter has parameters $(H_o, f_o, \zeta) = (1, 110\text{ Hz}, 0.87)$. Design the filter using a Class 2C band-pass filter and summer realization.

12.14 Redesign the delay equalizer of Example 12.4.2 using a Class 2D band-pass filter and summer realization.

12.15 Redesign the delay equalizer of Example 12.4.2 using a Class 2D band-stop filter operated in the complementary mode. (Hint: See Prob. 12.11 hint.)

12.16 Repeat Prob. 12.11 using a Class 2E band-pass filter and summer realization.

12.17 Redesign the delay equalizer of Example 12.4.2 using a Class 2E realization.

12.18 Redesign the delay equalizer of Example 12.4.3 using a Class 2E realization.

12.19 Redesign the all-pass filter of Example 12.4.4 using a Class 2E band-pass filter and summer realization.

12.20 Op amps have finite gain-bandwidth products $A_o a$. Assuming that the gain of the op amp equals $-A_o a/(s + a)$, it can be shown that the transfer function of the Class 2E filter equals[5]

$$H(s) = a \frac{s_n^2 + s_n[1/Q + Qk(a-1)/a] + 1}{s_n^2(1 + \omega_o Qk/A_o a) + s_n(1/Q + Qk/A_o) + 1}$$

where

$$s_n = s/\omega_o, \quad \omega_o = 1/(R_1C_1R_2C_2)^{1/2}, \quad Q = [C_2/(C_1 + C_2)](R_2C_1/R_1C_2)^{1/2}$$

$$a = R_B/(R_A + R_B), \quad k = (C_1 + C_2)/C_2$$

(a) Compare the resonant frequencies of the poles and zeros. (b) Compare the Q's of the poles and zeros. (c) What condition must be satisfied for the filter to be all-pass? (d) If $A_o = 106$ dB, $a = 2\pi(10\text{ Hz})$, $Q = 20$, and $C_1 = C_2$, what is the percentage error in parts (a) and (b)?

12.21 Determine the input impedance of the first-order all-pass filter shown in Fig. 12.4.2 (use $H_o = +1$ form) using Blackman's impedance relation. Plot the Bode magnitude response of Z_{in}. Can R_1 be chosen to yield a constant Z_{in}?

12.22 The first-order all-pass filter of Prob. 12.21 is driven from a nonideal voltage source V_S with internal resistance R_S. Determine the transfer function $T = V_2/V_S$ for the all-pass filter. Plot the magnitude and phase characteristics of T. Describe the undesirable effects due to R_S and show how these effects can be minimized. (Hint: Use voltage division.)

12.23 As discussed in Prob. 2.33, notch filters are difficult to tune. All-pass filters are even more difficult to tune to obtain $\omega_{op} = \omega_{oz}$ and $\zeta_z = -\zeta_p$. Discuss the tuning sequence.

12.24 It is especially convenient to tune a band-pass filter but much more difficult to tune an all-pass filter.[3] (a) Show how the Class 1E band-pass filter of Sec. 10.3 must be arranged to be operated in a complementary mode. How must the band-pass filter be tuned to produce an all-pass filter having resonant frequency ω_o and an arbitrary Q? (b) A Class 1E all-pass filter is shown in Sec. 12.3. Can it be more easily tuned? (c) Suppose we operate the Class 1E all-pass filter of part (b) in a complementary mode. Can it be more easily tuned? (Hint: Determine the transfer function.)

12.25 The amplifier shown in Fig. P12.25 has its gain controlled by resistor R. Suppose that the amplifier gain and R must have n^2 fixed selectable values. R can be replaced by two resistors, R_B and R_C, each having n values and fixed resistor R_A. This reduces the number of resistor values required from n^2 to $(2n + 1)$. (a) Convert the T network into the Π network, shown in Fig. P12.25, and show that

$$R = R_A + R_C(1 + R_A/R_B)$$

(b) Selecting n values for R_B and R_C as

$$R_{Bi} = R_A/[(1 + \delta)^i - 1], \quad R_{Cj} = R_A(1 + \delta)^{6j}, \quad i, j = 0, 1, \ldots, n-1$$

then show that n^2 values are available for R where[6]

$$R_{i,j} = R_A[1 + (1 + \delta)^{6j + i}]$$

Note that, except for the fixed portion represented by R_A, the equivalent resistance $R_{i,j}$ varies exponentially. When expressed in dB changes, there are nearly constant increments between settings. (c) Show that the Class 1E all-pass filter can be tuned using R_1 for bandwidth B (see Eq. 11.7.3) and R_3 for center fre-

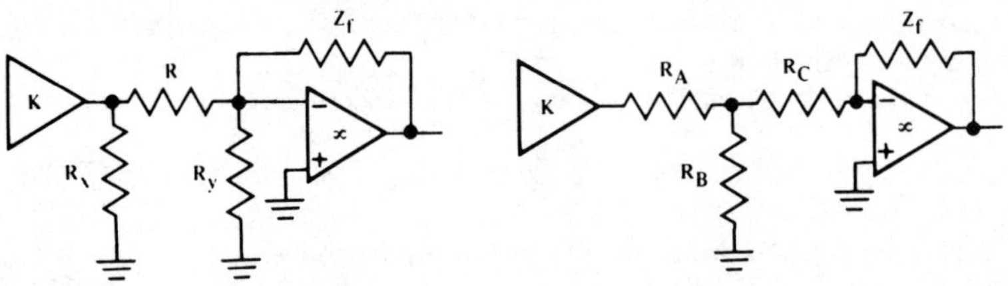

Fig. P12.25

quency ω_o' (note that R_4 must track R_1). Draw the filter using the T networks described in parts (a) and (b) for the tuning resistors.

12.26 The specifications of a conditioning system for a data line are shown in Table P12.26. It is a 14-section state-variable delay and amplitude equalizer. Each delay and amplitude section is controlled by precisely calibrated thumbwheel switches. Discuss the alignment procedure you would use to meet a line conditioning requirement, such as listed in Prob. 2.27.

Table P12.26 (Courtesy of Halcyon[7])

Operating Frequency Range:	0.25 to 3.4 KHz.
Tolerance After Equalization:	Exceeds C3, C4, C5, and S3 requirements.
Typical Equalized Delay Response:	1000 to 2400 Hz, 50 μsec; 1000 to 2600 Hz, 80 μsec; 600 to 2600 Hz, 250 μsec; 500 to 2800 Hz, 500 μsec;
Typical Attenuation Response:	500 to 2800 Hz, –0.5 to +1 dB; 300 to 3000 Hz, –0.8 to +2 dB; 300 to 3200 Hz, –2 to +6 dB.
Maximum Delay Correction Range:	3.5 msec per 14 section circuit spaced at 200 Hz intervals. 6 msec with Bulk Equalizer; 9 msec for tandem applications. Disabling of 600, 3000, and 3200 Hz delay sections controlled by front-panel switches.
Delay Adjustment Range:	Each delay section switchable from 500 to 2183 μsec in 100 precisely repeatable 17 μsec increments.
Maximum Amplitude Correction Range:	–6 to +15 dB between 300 and 3000 Hz (relative to 0 dB at 1000 Hz).
Amplitude Adjustment Range:	*Band-Edges* –6 to +15 dB in 100 precisely repeatable increments at 250 and 3000 Hz or 300 and 3200 Hz. *Shape* Ten switchable high and low frequency shape options.
Ripple Control:	±3 dB per each of 14 discrete frequency bump equalizer sections spaced at 200 Hz intervals between 600 and 3200 Hz.
Delay Amplitude Adjustment Interaction:	Typically less than 0.1 dB at resonant frequency. Less than 20 μsec for ±3 dB amplitude adjustment at resonant frequency of equalizer section.

12.27 Automatic phase control (APC) systems often use all-pass filters as phase-shift networks to maintain the phase difference between two signals of the same frequency over some frequency range.[8] An APC system is shown in Fig. P12.27. Show how an FET and a first-order all-pass filter can be used as the phase-

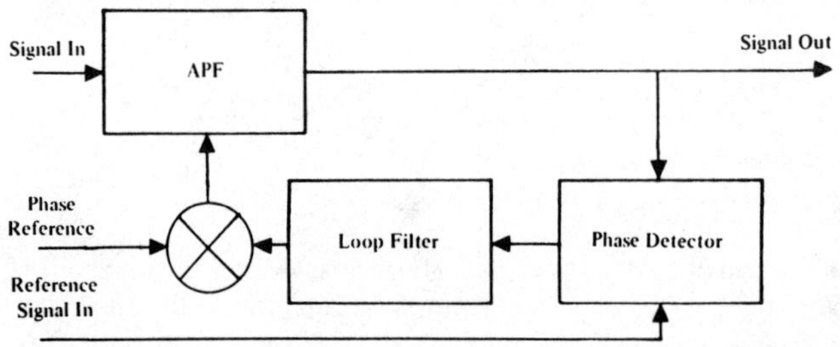

Fig. P12.27

shift block. Design the block to provide 180° of phase shift over the frequency range from 100 Hz to 10 KHz. Plot the phase response. (Hint: See Example 10.5.2.)

REFERENCES

1. Truong, V. S., "Classification and compilation of active RC all-pass filters," M.S.E.E. Directed Research, California State Univ., Long Beach, Jan., 1975.
2. Ponsoby, J. E. B., "Active all-pass filter using a differential operational amplifier," Electronics Letters, vol. 2, pp. 134–135, April, 1966.
   Dutta Roy, S. C., "RC active all-pass networks using a differential-input operational amplifier," Proc. IEEE, vol. 57, pp. 2055–2056, Nov., 1969.
3. Hilberman, D., "Input and ground as complements in active filters," IEEE Trans. Circuit Theory, vol. CT-20, pp. 540–547, Sept., 1973.
4. Comer, D. J., and J. E. McDermid, "Inductorless bandpass characteristics using all-pass networks," IEEE Trans. Circuit Theory, vol. CT-15, pp. 501–503, Dec., 1968.
5. Budak, A., and P. Aronhime, "Frequency limitations on an operational amplifier realization of all-pass transfer functions with complex poles," Proc. IEEE, vol. 58, pp. 1137–1138, July, 1970.
6. Fleischer, P. E., "Active adjustable loss and delay equalizers," Proc. Intl. Symp. on Circuits and Systems, pp. 564–568, April, 1974.
7. Halcyon 112A Data Line Conditioning System, 1 p., Publ. H112-6M-972, Halcyon, Campbell, CA, 9/72.
8. Strauss, G. M., "Design your own dynamic phase shifter," Electronic Design, pp. 60–63, June 8, 1972, copyright Hayden Publishing, 1972.

13 OSCILLATORS

With a name like yours, you might be any shape, almost.
Carroll

In Chaps. 8–12, we considered low-pass, high-pass, band-pass, band-stop, and all-pass filters. Another important area in active filters is that of oscillators. *Oscillators* are conditionally-stable active filters usually of second-order. That is to say they are low-pass, high-pass, band-pass, band-stop, and all-pass filters whose poles are adjusted to lie on the $j\omega$-axis at $s = j\omega_o$, and whose inputs are grounded. Noise in the filter (due to power supply transients, pickup, thermal noise, etc.) causes it to oscillate. Because the poles of the filter are on the $j\omega$-axis, the oscillation at the filter output is sustained. To insure starting, the filter poles are placed slightly in the right-half-plane. This results in oscillations bounded within an exponentially increasing envelope. The envelope continues to grow until it is limited by some nonlinearity in the filter, such as power supply clipping. Usually, nonlinearities are intentionally introduced into the oscillator using zener diodes, nonlinear resistors, or entire circuits, to control the shaping of the output signal. This is called *amplitude stabilization* and often results in reduced distortion.

We will first discuss oscillators from the classification viewpoint of Chap. 7. A variety of oscillators which are useful in design will then be investigated. We will compare their gain and sensitivity bounds with the limits established in Chap. 7. We will make qualitative evaluations of the oscillators and describe situations in which their use is appropriate. A set of oscillator design sheets will be compiled which will be used in designing a number of oscillators. Tunable oscillators will also be investigated. We will conclude with a discussion of amplitude stabilization and distortion.

13.1 OSCILLATOR CLASSES

Oscillators are characterized by their *loop gains* G which equal

$$G(s) = K_1T_{43} + K_2T_{65} - K_1K_2(T_{43}T_{65} - T_{45}T_{63}) \quad (13.1.1)$$

from Eq. 7.2.3, or by their determinants which equal

$$\Delta(s) = 1 - G(s) \quad (13.1.2)$$

This is in contrast to the usual active filter which is characterized by its input/output gain H(s) where $H(s) = N(s)/\Delta(s)$. Oscillators of second-order have determinants which equal

$$\Delta(s) = (s/\omega_o)^2 + 1 \quad (13.1.3)$$

The frequency of oscillation is ω_o. Note that the oscillator poles lie on the $j\omega$-axis so their $\zeta = 0$

Table 13.1.1 Summary of gain-sensitivity relations for Class 2X oscillators. For Class 1X oscillators, add equality signs to the inequalities. (All passive ω_o sensitivities equal ½.)

Class	Loop Gain K	Active θ Sensitivity	Active ω_o Sensitivity	Passive θ Sensitivity
B	$K>1$	$S>2/\pi$	0	$\lvert S\rvert>1/\pi$
C	Tradeoff			
$\overline{C}$	Tradeoff			
E	Tradeoff			

or $Q = \infty$. In general, second-order oscillators are formed from second-order active filters having gain

$$H(s) = \frac{N(s)}{\Delta(s)} = \frac{N(s)}{(s/\omega_o)^2 + 2\zeta(s/\omega_o) + 1} \tag{13.1.4}$$

and the filter parameters are adjusted so $\zeta = 0$ or $Q = \infty$. An oscillator is completely characterized by its resonant frequency ω_o.

Let us determine in what classes oscillators can be realized.[1] From the viewpoint of the transfer function of Eq. 13.1.4, the parameters must be adjusted so that $\zeta = 0$ or $Q = \infty$. Since passive RC networks are characterized by $\zeta > 0$, oscillators can only be realized when the s^1 coefficient involves at least one amplifier gain (K_1 or K_2). Therefore, only filter classes having an active portion which includes s^1 can be used to realize oscillators. From Table 7.2.1, we see that Class B, C, $\overline{C}$, and E oscillators can be realized but Class A, $\overline{A}$, and D types are not realizable.

Now let us view oscillator realizability from a root locus standpoint rather than a gain standpoint. Since oscillators must have a pair of $j\omega$-axis poles, the root locus of their denominator roots must cross the $j\omega$-axis at $\pm j\omega_o$. This is therefore an equivalent realizability condition for oscillators. In Chap. 7, we determined the root locus of the filter poles of the various classes. These root loci were summarized in Fig. 7.19.1 along with the flow graphs. We see that Class A ($\overline{A}$) filters cannot be adjusted to yield (nonzero) imaginary poles. Class D filters require infinite gain to obtain imaginary poles which cannot be physically obtained. Therefore, Class A, $\overline{A}$, and D oscillators cannot be realized. However, all other oscillator classes exist since their root locus can be adjusted to intersect the $j\omega$-axis at $\pm j\omega_o$. Hence, we verify the important observation that oscillators can be realized in only Class B, C, $\overline{C}$, and E forms.

The gain and sensitivity limitations listed in Table 7.19.3 for the various filter classes can be applied to oscillators. All that is required is to let $Q \to \infty$. Rather than using the Q sensitivities S_k^Q and S_a^Q, it is customary to define the pole angle sensitivities S_k^θ and S_a^θ. Using the result $S_x^z = S_x^y S_y^z$ from Table 1.15.1, then the active and passive sensitivities of the pole angle θ equal

$$S_k^\theta = S_k^Q S_Q^\theta, \qquad S_a^\theta = S_a^Q S_Q^\theta \tag{13.1.5}$$

These are easily evaluated once S_Q^θ is known. Since Q, ζ, and θ are interrelated as

$$Q = 1/2\zeta = 1/2\cos\theta = ½\sec\theta, \qquad \theta = \cos^{-1}\zeta = \sec^{-1} 2Q \tag{13.1.6}$$

then the derivative of θ equals $d\theta/dQ = 1/Q\sqrt{4Q^2 - 1}$. Therefore since $\theta = \pi/2$ as $Q \to \infty$, then S_Q^θ equals

$$S_Q^\theta = \frac{d\theta/dQ}{\theta/Q} = \frac{2}{\pi(4Q^2 - 1)^{1/2}} \to 1/\pi Q \tag{13.1.7}$$

Using the Q sensitivities of Table 7.19.3 and Eqs. 13.1.5 and 13.1.7, we can easily determine the θ

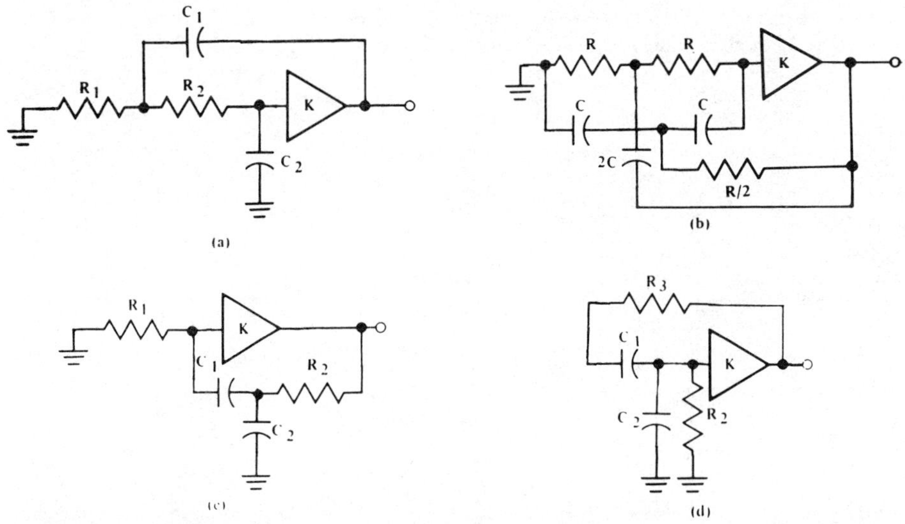

Fig. 13.1.1 Classical oscillators including (a) RC phase shift, (b) twin-T, (c) bridged-T, and (d) Wien bridge types.

sensitivities for the various oscillator classes. The gain-sensitivity limitations are listed in Table 13.1.1.

Class B oscillators require low gains but have higher passive and active ϕ sensitivities. Class C and $\overline{C}$ oscillators require higher gains but have lower passive and active sensitivities (or vice versa depending upon the design equations). Class E oscillators can have passive and active sensitivities approaching zero when sufficiently high gain is used.

Oscillators are often classified or *typed* by the form of their loop gain G given by Eq. 13.1.1. By inspection of the branch gains listed in Tables 7.19.1 and 7.19.2, we see that the various loop gains are: (1) Class B: band-pass (BP), (2) Class C: quasi-high-pass (QHP), (3) Class $\overline{C}$: quasi-low-pass (QLP), and (4) Class E: general (biquadratic). Therefore, Class B oscillators always have band-pass loop gains, Class C (Class $\overline{C}$) oscillators always have quasi-high-pass (quasi-low-pass) loop gains, and Class E oscillators have general biquadratic loop gains.

Historically, the most popular RC active oscillators have been the (two-section) RC phase shift, twin-T, bridged-T, and Wein bridge types. These are shown in Fig. 13.1.1; it is easy to show that these are all Class 2B oscillators. Therefore, these oscillators must all exhibit the characteristics of high ϕ sensitivity but low gains. Using the other classes available, lower ϕ sensitivity oscillators can be designed. This fact has almost always been overlooked in the past. Thus, using the classification concepts of the previous chapters, we now have a new design approach.

13.2 FILTER-TO-OSCILLATOR TRANSFORMATIONS

Any Class B, C, $\overline{C}$ and E filter, whether it be low-pass, high-pass, band-pass, band-stop, all-pass, or a quasi-variety, can be transformed into an oscillator. All that is required is to ground the filter input and to adjust the filter poles so their damping factor ζ equals zero or Q equals infinity. This gives us great flexibility in oscillator design since we can use any of the filters (of appropriate class) discussed in earlier chapters.

EXAMPLE 13.2.1 Design a Class 1B oscillator based upon a Class 1B low-pass filter.
Solution To begin, we review the Class 1B low-pass filter design sheet in Sec. 8.3. Its transfer function equals

$$H(s) = \frac{K_1K_2}{s^2R_1C_1R_2C_2 + s[R_1C_1(1 - K_1K_2) + R_2C_2] + 1} \tag{13.2.1}$$

and its design parameters equal

$$\omega_o = \frac{1}{(R_1C_1R_2C_2)^{1/2}}, \qquad \zeta = \frac{R_1C_1(1 - K_1K_2) + R_2C_2}{2(R_1C_1R_2C_2)^{1/2}}, \qquad H_o = K_1K_2 \tag{13.2.2}$$

To form an oscillator, we set $\zeta = 0$ which requires

$$K_1K_2 = 1 + R_2C_2/R_1C_1 \tag{13.2.3}$$

and ground the input. For minimum sensitivity, we set $R_1C_1 = R_2C_2$ so the design equations become

$$\omega_o = 1/R_1C_1, \qquad K_1K_2 = 2 \tag{13.2.4}$$

Of course, we can also design one- and two-amplifier oscillators using the determinant of Eq. 7.1.12, (which describes) the flow graph of Fig. 7.1.5, and the branch gains listed in Tables 7.19.1 and 7.19.2. The procedure is the same as that used for designing filters of specific classes described in earlier chapters. However, because we have compiled about (2)(4)(5) = 40 Class B, C, $\overline{C}$, and E filters in Chaps. 8–12, we prefer to use our existing filters with grounded inputs.

Oscillator design is facilitated by use of a design sheet which is similar to that used for active filters. The sheet lists: (1) oscillator class: oscillator, (2) determinant, (3) parameters: ω_o, ζ or Q; (4) design equations, (5) sensitivities, (6) schematic, and (7) references. It differs from the design sheet for active filters in items (1) – (3). The oscillator determinant is listed rather than a filter transfer function (there is no input and we are only concerned with filter poles). The oscillator parameters are only ω_o and ζ (or Q) where the gain is adjusted so $\zeta = 0$ (or $Q = \infty$). Note that gain H_o has no meaning in oscillators.

The oscillator design sheets are easily formulated using the design sheets for the various active filters. The oscillator class corresponds to the filter class. The oscillator determinant is simply the denominator of the filter transfer function. Parameters ω_o and ζ or Q equal those of the active filter. The same design equations can be used by specifying $\zeta = 0$ or $Q = \infty$. The ω_o sensitivities are used directly but the Q or ζ sensitivities are replaced by the sensitivities of the pole angle θ. The θ sensitivities are easily formed from the Q sensitivities using Eqs. 13.1.5 and 13.1.7. The schematic remains unchanged except that the input is grounded. References are used when they contain pertinent oscillator design information.

EXAMPLE 13.2.2 Determine the sensitivities of the Class 1B oscillator discussed in Example 13.2.1.
Solution The sensitivities are taken directly from the Class 1B low-pass filter design sheet in Sec. 8.3. The ω_o sensitivities remain unchanged so

$$S_{R_1}^{\omega_o} = S_{R_2}^{\omega_o} = S_{C_1}^{\omega_o} = S_{C_2}^{\omega_o} = -1/2 \tag{13.2.5}$$

The ζ sensitivities of the low-pass filter equal

$$S_{K_1}^{\zeta} = S_{K_2}^{\zeta} = 1 - 1/\zeta, \qquad S_{R_1}^{\zeta} = -S_{R_2}^{\zeta} = S_{C_1}^{\zeta} = -S_{C_2}^{\zeta} = 1/2(1 - 1/\zeta) \tag{13.2.6}$$

However, the θ sensitivities are required for the oscillator. Using analogous equations to Eqs. 13.1.5 and 13.1.7 for ζ (see Prob. 13.2), we multiply S_x^{ζ} by $-(2\zeta/\pi)_{\zeta=0}$ to obtain

$$S_{K_1}^{\theta} = S_{K_2}^{\theta} = 2/\pi, \qquad S_{R_1}^{\theta} = -S_{R_2}^{\theta} = S_{C_1}^{\theta} = -S_{C_2}^{\theta} = 1/\pi \tag{13.2.7}$$

Therefore, we see that forming design sheets for oscillators is very simple based on our earlier work.

13.3 OSCILLATOR COMPILATIONS

Just as with the filter designs, a set of well-prepared oscillator design sheets are indispensible in the design of oscillators. A number of oscillators are compiled in this section. Although the oscillators which have been selected are by no means exhaustive of those available, they are representative of those which can be formed from the filters in Chaps. 8–12. By simply grounding the inputs of these Class B, C, $\overline{C}$, and E filters, and properly adjusting their parameters, they become oscillators. Using this approach, we immediately have about 40 oscillators from which to choose. This increases the number of oscillators ten-fold from those historically available in Fig. 13.1.1. In addition, classes other than B become available to obtain more flexible gain-sensitivity tradeoffs. It is useful to remember that the RC:CR transformation can be applied to oscillators to produce other oscillators.

13.4 OSCILLATOR DESIGN EXAMPLES

With these design sheets, we are now in a position to design a variety of oscillators. Although their design parallels that of active filters, they are usually easier since $\zeta = 0$ (or $Q = \infty$) and H_o is not required.

EXAMPLE 13.4.1 Design a Class 1B oscillator having an output frequency of 1 KHz.
Solution The realization form of the Class 1B oscillator is shown in Fig. 13.4.1. The design equations are:

Set: $R_1 = R_2 = R, \quad C_1 = C_2 = C$

Given: ω_o

Choose: C, K_1

Calculate: $R = 1/\omega_o C, \quad K_2 = 2/K_1$

Therefore choosing $K_1 = 1$, the design is:

$$1/RC = 2\pi(1\text{ KHz}), \quad C = 0.01\ \mu F, \quad R = 15.9\text{ K (use 16.2 K)}, \quad K_2 = 2/1 = 2 \tag{13.4.1}$$

The oscillator realization is shown in Fig. 13.4.1.

EXAMPLE 13.4.2 Design a Class 2E oscillator having an output frequency of 1 KHz.
Solution The Class 2E oscillator is shown in Fig. 13.4.2. The design equations are:

Set: $R_5 = R_6 = R, \quad C_3 = C_4 = C, \quad R_8 = KR_7, \quad K = 2$

Given: ω_o

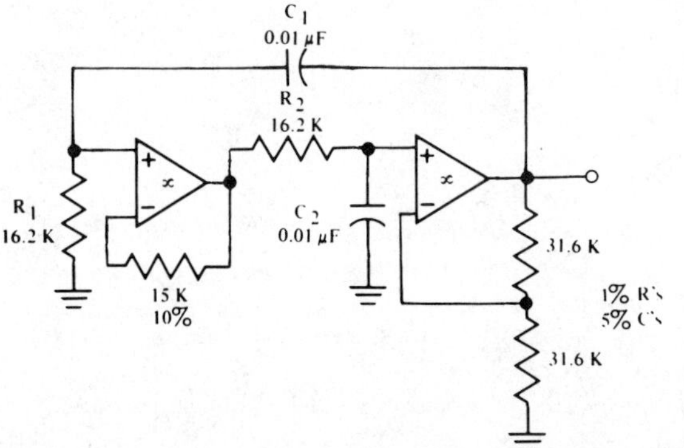

Fig. 13.4.1 Class 1B oscillator realization.

CLASS 1B: OSCILLATOR

Determinant:

$$\Delta(s) = s^2 R_1C_1R_2C_2 + s[R_1C_1(1 - K_1K_2) + R_2C_2] + 1$$

Parameters:

$$\omega_o = \frac{1}{(R_1C_1R_2C_2)^{1/2}}$$

$$\zeta = \frac{R_1C_1(1 - K_1K_2) + R_2C_2}{2(R_1C_1R_2C_2)^{1/2}} = 0 \text{ so that } \qquad K_1K_2 = 1 + \frac{R_2C_2}{R_1C_1}$$

Design Equations: Set $R_1 = R_2 = R$, $C_1 = C_2 = C$ (For Minimum Active Sensitivity)

Given: ω_o

Choose: C, K_1

Calculate: $R = 1/\omega_o C$

$K_2 = 2/K_1$

Sensitivities:

$$S_{R_1}^{\omega_o} = S_{R_2}^{\omega_o} = S_{C_1}^{\omega_o} = S_{C_2}^{\omega_o} = -½$$

$$S_{K_1}^{\theta} = S_{K_2}^{\theta} = 2/\pi$$

$$S_{R_1}^{\theta} = -S_{R_2}^{\theta} = S_{C_1}^{\theta} = -S_{C_2}^{\theta} = 1/\pi$$

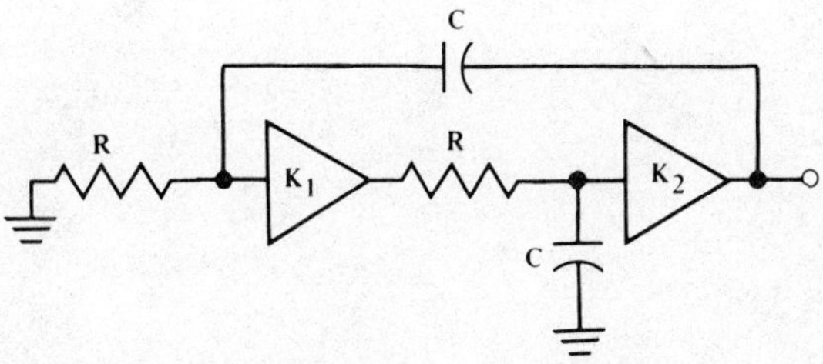

CLASS 1C: OSCILLATOR

Determinant:

$$\Delta(s) = s^2(1 + K_2)R_1C_1R_2C_2 + s[R_1C_1(1 - K_1K_2) + R_2C_2(1 + K_2)] + 1$$

Parameters:

$$\omega_o = \frac{1}{[(1 + K_2)R_1C_1R_2C_2]^{1/2}}$$

$$\zeta = \frac{R_1C_1(1 - K_1K_2) + R_2C_2(1 + K_2)}{2[(1 + K_2)R_1C_1R_2C_2]^{1/2}} = 0 \text{ so that } \qquad K_2 = \frac{R_1C_1 + R_2C_2}{K_1R_1C_1 - R_2C_2}$$

Design Equations: Set $R_1 = R_2 = R$, $C_1 = C_2 = C$

Given: ω_o

Choose: C, K_2

Calculate: $R = \dfrac{1}{(1 + K_2)^{1/2}\omega_o C}$

$K_1 = 1 + 2/K_2$

Sensitivities:

$$S_{K_2}^{\omega_o} = -K_2/2(1 + K_2)$$

$$S_{R_1}^{\omega_o} = S_{R_2}^{\omega_o} = S_{C_1}^{\omega_o} = S_{C_2}^{\omega_o} = -1/2$$

$$S_{K_1}^{\theta} = -K_1K_2/\pi(1 + K_2)^{1/2}$$

$$S_{K_2}^{\theta} = -K_2(1 - K_1)/\pi(1 + K_2)^{1/2}$$

$$S_{R_1}^{\theta} = S_{C_1}^{\theta} = -(1 - K_1K_2)/\pi(1 + K_2)^{1/2}$$

$$S_{R_2}^{\theta} = S_{C_2}^{\theta} = (1 + K_2)^{1/2}/\pi$$

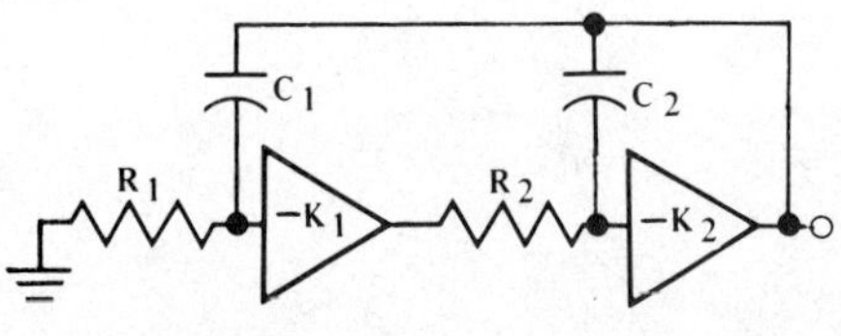

CLASS $1\overline{C}$: OSCILLATOR

Determinant:

$$\Delta(s) = s^2R_1C_1R_2C_2 + s\left\{R_1C_1 + R_2C_2[1 + \rho(1 - K_1)]\right\} + [1 + K_1K_2 + \rho(1 - K_1)], \qquad \rho = R_1/R_0$$

Parameters:

$$\omega_o = \left[\frac{1 + K_1K_2 + \rho(1 - K_1)}{R_1C_1R_2C_2}\right]^{1/2}$$

$$\zeta = \frac{R_1C_1 + R_2C_2[1 + \rho(1 - K_1)]}{2\left\{[1 + K_1K_2 + \rho(1 - K_1)]R_1C_1R_2C_2\right\}^{1/2}} = 0 \text{ so that } \qquad K_1 = 1 + \frac{1}{\rho}\left[1 + \frac{R_1C_1}{R_2C_2}\right]$$

Design Equations: Set $R_1 = R_2 = R$, $\quad C_1 = C_2 = C$

Given: ω_o

Choose: C, ρ, K_2

Calculate: $K_1 = 1 + 2/\rho$

$$R = \frac{[K_1(K_2 - \rho) + (1 + \rho)]^{1/2}}{\omega_o C}$$

Sensitivities: Let $a = 1 + K_1K_2 + \rho(1 - K_1)$

$S_{K_1}^{\omega_o} = K_1(K_2 - \rho)/2a$ $\qquad S_{K_1}^{\theta} = 2/\pi a^{1/2}$

$S_{K_2}^{\omega_o} = K_1K_2/2a$ $\qquad S_{R_0}^{\theta} = -[\rho(1 - K_1)(1 - K_1K_2)]/\pi a^{3/2}$

$S_{R_0}^{\omega_o} = -[1 + K_1K_2 + 2\rho(1 - K_1)]/2a$ $\qquad S_{R_1}^{\theta} = S_{C_1}^{\theta} = 1/\pi a^{1/2}$

$S_{R_1}^{\omega_o} = S_{R_2}^{\omega_o} = S_{C_1}^{\omega_o} = S_{C_2}^{\omega_o} = -1/2$ $\qquad S_{R_2}^{\theta} = S_{C_2}^{\theta} = [1 + \rho(1 - K_1)]/\pi a^{1/2}$

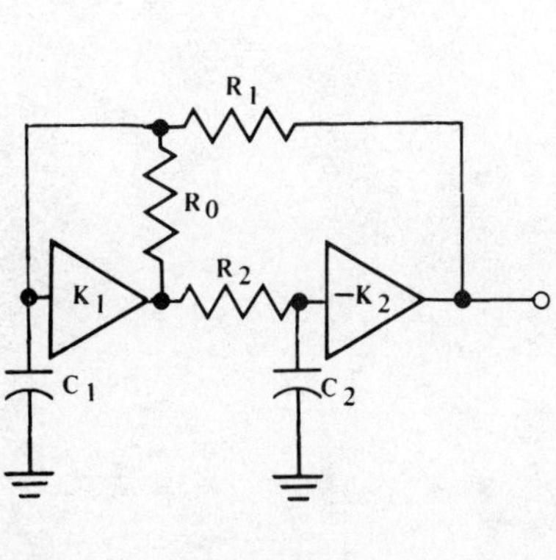

CLASS 1E: OSCILLATOR

Determinant:

$$\Delta(s) = s^2R_1C_1R_2C_2 + sR_2C_2[(1 + R_6/R_5)/(1 + R_4/R_3)] + R_6/R_5$$

Parameters:

$$\omega_o = \left[\frac{R_6/R_5}{R_1C_1R_2C_2}\right]^{1/2}$$

$$\zeta = \frac{1}{2}\,\frac{1 + R_6/R_5}{1 + R_4/R_3}\left[\frac{R_5}{R_6}\,\frac{R_2C_2}{R_1C_1}\right]^{1/2} = 0 \text{ so that} \qquad R_3 = 0 \text{ or } R_4 = \infty$$

Design Equations: Set $R_1 = R_2 = R$, $C_1 = C_2 = C$, $2R_3 = R_5 = R_6$, $R_4 = \infty$

Given: ω_o

Choose: C, R_6

Calculate: $R = 1/\omega_o C$

Sensitivities:

$$S_{R_1}^{\omega_o} = S_{R_2}^{\omega_o} = S_{R_5}^{\omega_o} = -S_{R_6}^{\omega_o} = S_{C_1}^{\omega_o} = S_{C_2}^{\omega_o} = -\tfrac{1}{2}$$

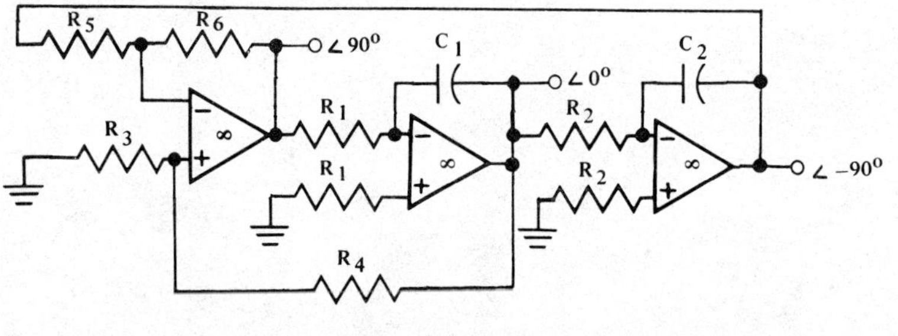

CLASS 2B: OSCILLATOR

Determinant:

$$\Delta(s) = s^2R_1C_1R_2C_2 + s[R_1C_1(1 + C_2/C_1 - K) + R_2C_2] + 1$$

Parameters:

$$\omega_o = \frac{1}{(R_1C_1R_2C_2)^{1/2}}$$

$$\zeta = \frac{R_1C_1(1 + C_2/C_1 - K) + R_2C_2}{2(R_1C_1R_2C_2)^{1/2}} = 0 \text{ so that } \qquad K = 1 + \frac{C_2}{C_1} + \frac{R_2C_2}{R_1C_1}$$

Design Equations: Set $\rho = C_2/C_1 \ll 1$, $R_1C_1 = R_2C_2$ (Towards Minimum Active Sensitivity)

Given: ω_o

Choose: C_1, ρ

Calculate: $R_1 = 1/\omega_o C_1$

$R_2 = R_1/\rho$

$C_2 = \rho C_1$

$K = 2 + \rho$

Sensitivities:

$$S_{R_1}^{\omega_o} = S_{R_2}^{\omega_o} = S_{C_1}^{\omega_o} = S_{C_2}^{\omega_o} = -1/2$$

$$S_K^{\theta} = -(2 + \rho)/\pi$$

$$S_{R_1}^{\theta} = -S_{R_2}^{\theta} = -1/\pi$$

$$S_{C_1}^{\theta} = -S_{C_2}^{\theta} = -(1 + \rho)/\pi$$

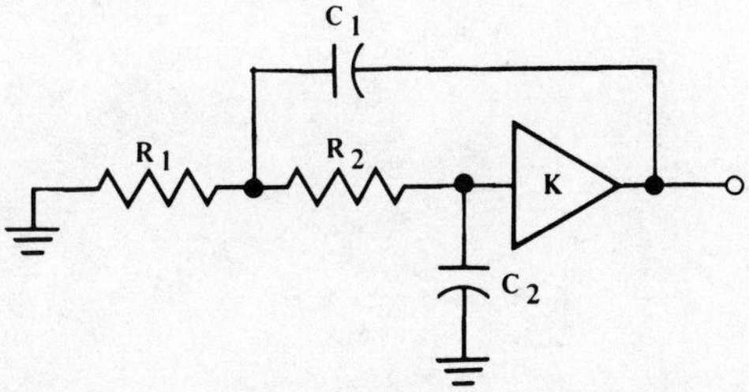

CLASS 2C: OSCILLATOR

Determinant:

$$\Delta(s) = s^2(1 + K_1K_2)R_1C_1R_2C_2 + s[R_1(C_1 + C_2) + R_2C_2(1 - K_1)] + 1$$

Parameters:

$$\omega_o = \frac{1}{[(1 + K_1K_2)R_1C_1R_2C_2]^{1/2}}$$

$$\zeta = \frac{R_1(C_1 + C_2) + R_2C_2(1 + K_1)}{2[(1 + K_1K_2)R_1C_1R_2C_2]^{1/2}} = 0 \text{ so that} \qquad K_1 = 1 + \frac{R_1(C_1 + C_2)}{R_2C_2}$$

Design Equations: Set $\rho = C_2/C_1 \ll 1$, $R_1C_1 = R_2C_2$

Given: ω_o

Choose: C_1, ρ, K_2

Calculate: $K_1 = 2 + 1/\rho$

$$C_2 = \rho C_1$$

$$R_1^{\bullet} = \frac{1}{(1 + K_1K_2)^{1/2}\omega_o C_1}$$

$$R_2 = R_1/\rho$$

Sensitivities:

$$S_{K_1}^{\omega_o} = S_{K_2}^{\omega_o} = -K_1K_2/2(1 + K_1K_2)$$

$$S_{R_1}^{\omega_o} = S_{R_2}^{\omega_o} = S_{C_1}^{\omega_o} = S_{C_2}^{\omega_o} = -1/2$$

$$S_{K_1}^{\theta} = -2K_1/\pi(1 + K_1K_2)^{1/2}$$

$$S_{R_1}^{\theta} = -4/\pi(1 + K_1K_2)^{1/2}$$

$$S_{R_2}^{\theta} = 2(K_1 - 1)/\pi(1 + K_1K_2)^{1/2}$$

$$S_{C_1}^{\theta} = -2/\pi(1 + K_1K_2)^{1/2}$$

$$S_{C_2}^{\theta} = 2(K_1 - 2)/\pi(1 + K_1K_2)^{1/2}$$

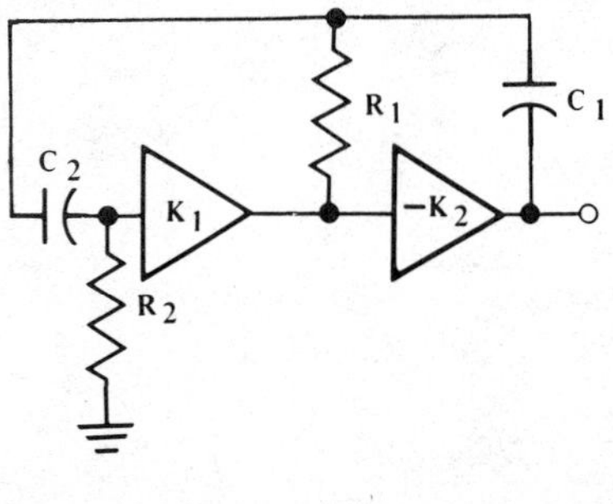

CLASS $2\overline{C}$: OSCILLATOR

Determinant:

$$\Delta(s) = s^2R_1C_1R_2C_2 + s\left\{R_1[C_1(1-K_1)+C_2] + R_2C_2\right\} + (1+K_1K_2)$$

Parameters:

$$\omega_o = \left[\frac{1+K_1K_2}{R_1C_1R_2C_2}\right]^{1/2}$$

$$\zeta = \frac{R_1[C_1(1-K_1)+C_2] + R_2C_2}{2[(1+K_1K_2)R_1C_1R_2C_2]^{1/2}} = 0 \text{ so that } \qquad K_1 = 1 + \frac{C_2}{C_1} + \frac{R_2C_2}{R_1C_1}$$

Design Equations: Set $\rho = C_2/C_1 \ll 1$, $\quad R_1C_1 = R_2C_2$

Given: ω_o

Choose: C_1, ρ; K_2

Calculate: $K_1 = 2 + 1/\rho$

$$C_2 = \rho C_1$$

$$R_1 = \frac{(1+K_1K_2)^{1/2}}{\omega_o C_1}$$

$$R_2 = R_1/\rho$$

Sensitivities:

$$S_{K_1}^{\omega_o} = S_{K_2}^{\omega_o} = K_1K_2/2(1+K_1K_2)$$

$$S_{R_1}^{\omega_o} = S_{R_2}^{\omega_o} = S_{C_1}^{\omega_o} = S_{C_2}^{\omega_o} = -1/2$$

$$S_{K_1}^{\theta} = -2K_1/\pi(1+K_1K_2)^{1/2}$$

$$S_{R_1}^{\theta} = 2/\pi(1+K_1K_2)^{1/2}$$

$$S_{R_2}^{\theta} = -2(K_1-2)/\pi(1+K_1K_2)^{1/2}$$

$$S_{C_1}^{\theta} = 4/\pi(1+K_1K_2)^{1/2}$$

$$S_{C_2}^{\theta} = -2(K_1-1)/\pi(1+K_1K_2)^{1/2}$$

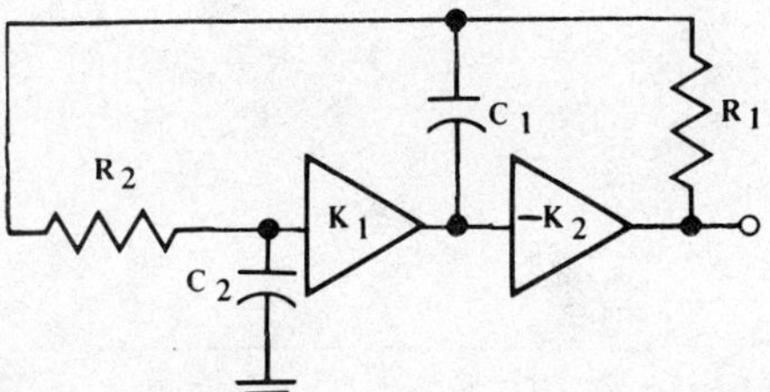

CLASS 2E: OSCILLATOR

Determinant:

$$\Delta(s) = s^2R_6C_3R_5C_4 + sR_6C_3(1 + C_4/C_3 - KR_5/R_6) + 1$$

Parameters:

$$\omega_o = \frac{1}{(R_6C_3R_5C_4)^{1/2}}$$

$$\zeta = \left[\frac{R_6C_3}{R_5C_4}\right]^{1/2}(1 + C_4/C_3 - KR_5/R_6) = 0 \text{ so that } \qquad K = (R_6/R_5)(1 + C_4/C_3)$$

Design Equations: Set $R_5 = R_6 = R$, $C_3 = C_4 = C$, $R_8 = KR_7$, $K = 2$

Given: ω_o

Choose: C, R_7

Calculate: $R = 1/\omega_o C$

$R_8 = 2R_7$

Sensitivities:

$$S_{R_5}^{\omega_o} = S_{R_6}^{\omega_o} = S_{C_3}^{\omega_o} = S_{C_4}^{\omega_o} = -\tfrac{1}{2}$$

$$S_K^{\theta} = -S_{R_5}^{\theta} = S_{R_6}^{\theta} = -2/\pi$$

$$S_{C_3}^{\theta} = -S_{C_4}^{\theta} = -1/\pi$$

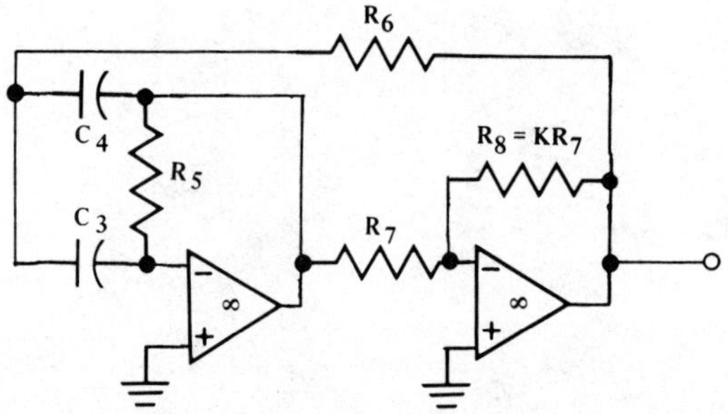

L. P. Huelsman, J. G. Graeme, and G. E. Tobey, *Operational Amplifiers*, Chap. 8.3.1, McGraw-Hill, NY, 1971.

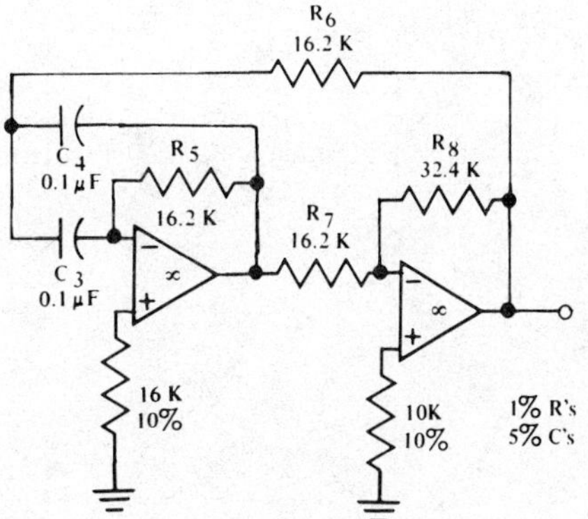

Fig. 13.4.2 Class 2E oscillator realization.

Choose: C, R_7

Calculate: $R = 1/\omega_o C$, $\quad R_8 = 2R_7$

The design proceeds as:

$$1/RC = 2\pi(1\text{ KHz}), \quad C = 0.1\ \mu F, \quad R = R_7 = 15.9\text{ K (use 16.2 K)}$$
$$R_8 = 2(16.2\text{ K}) = 32.4\text{ K (use 31.6 K)} \tag{13.4.2}$$

The completed design is shown in Fig. 13.4.2.

13.5 TUNABLE OSCILLATORS

Tunable oscillators have an output frequency ω_o which can be gain-tuned or passive-tuned. There are a broad group of applications which require such tunable oscillators. Both active and passive tuning are used in practice.

From a gain-tuning standpoint, and the root loci of Fig. 8.6.1, oscillators have:

Class B: Inherently constant ω_o

Class C, $\overline{C}$, E: Can be adjusted to yield tunable ω_o/constant ζ.

Thus, Class C, $\overline{C}$, and E filters are useful for gain-tunable oscillators. In Chaps. 8–10, we discussed gain-tunable low-pass, high-pass, and band-pass filters. By a simple extension, we can utilize these as gain-tunable oscillators. We simply ground the inputs of these filters and adjust their parameters to yield imaginery poles; therefore, these filters become oscillators. Six tunable low-pass filters were considered in Fig. 8.6.3. Grounding their inputs, they can be utilized as oscillators as shown in Fig. 13.5.1a. Six tunable high-pass filters were obtained in Fig. 9.5.1 by applying the RC:CR transformation to the tunable low-pass filters. Thus, analogous oscillators can be obtained by applying the RC:CR transformation in Fig. 13.5.1a. Finally, seven tunable band-pass filters were considered in Fig. 10.5.1. Their analogous tunable oscillators are shown in Fig. 13.5.1b. Seven others can be obtained using the RC:CR transformation. From this discussion, we see that we have 2(6 + 7) = 2(13) = 26 different tunable oscillators from which to select. Recall that the tunable band-stop and all-pass filters used the tunable band-pass filters so no new forms were introduced. Note that although the thirteen oscillators listed in Figs. 13.5.1 contain the minimum number of five nodes, only six are canonical since they contain the minimum number of six components.

The parameters of the oscillators are somewhat different from those of their corresponding filters. To produce oscillators, we must force $Q = \infty$. From Figs. 8.6.3, 9.5.1, and 10.5.1, it is easy to see that this requires $A = -1$ since $(1 + A)$ formed the a portion of the coefficient of the s^1

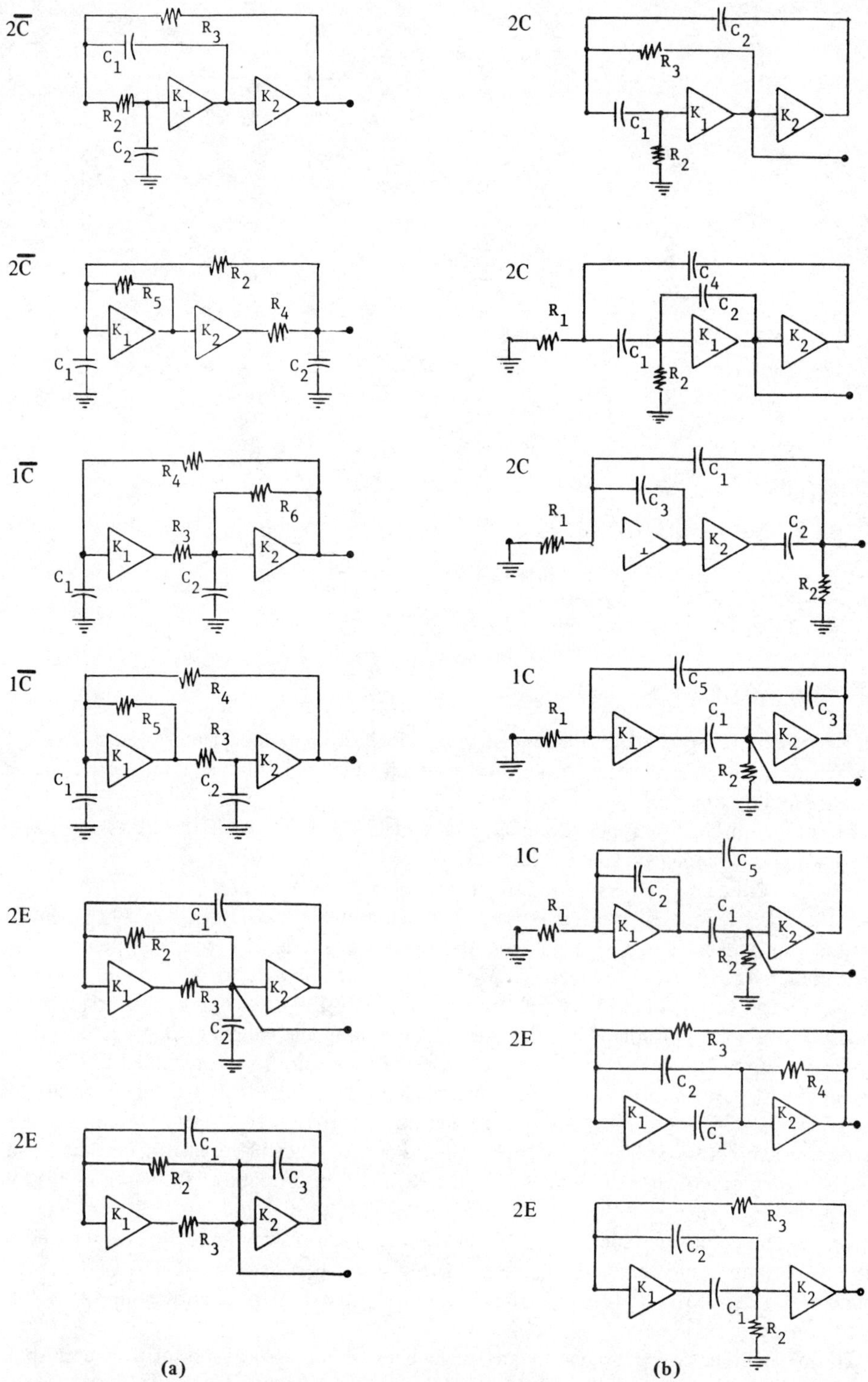

Fig. 13.5.1 Gain-tunable oscillators obtained from (a) low-pass filters, and (b) band-pass filters. (Adapted from S. Bruminhent and K. L. Su, "Gain-tuned active filters," Proc. Intl. Symp. on Circuits and Systems, pp. 443–447, April, 1974.)

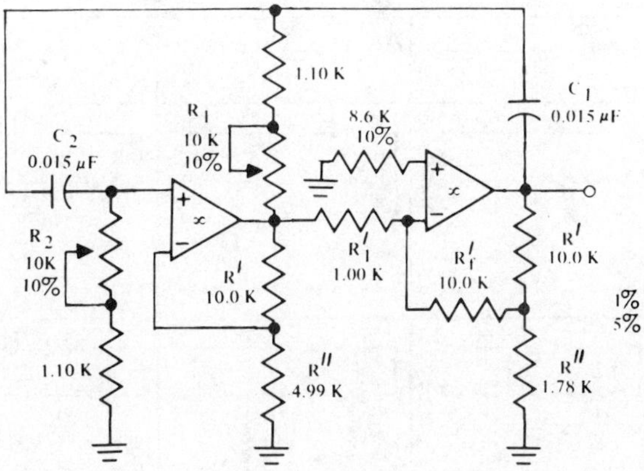

Fig. 13.5.2 Class 2C oscillator realization.

denominator term in the gain expressions of the filters. A was constant for all the filter forms as

$$A = [1 + (\alpha/\gamma)(2 + 1/\beta)]/K_0 \tag{13.5.1}$$

from Eq. 8.6.6. Therefore, the gain K_0 must be negative and equal

$$-K_0 = 1 + (\alpha/\gamma)(2 + 1/\beta) \tag{13.5.2}$$

to produce an oscillator. It is a simple matter to make the changes in the parameters of the filters to meet these conditions.

Passive-tuned Class B, C, $\overline{C}$, and E filters can also be used to realize tunable oscillators. Exact tuning can be used using double-tuning and approximate tuning using single-tuning. Their root loci were shown in Figs. 8.7.1 and 8.7.2. The design of this type of passive-tuned filter follows that outlined in Examples 8.7.1 and 9.5.2 as shown in the following example.

EXAMPLE 13.5.1 Design a passive-tuned 1 KHz oscillator having a 10:1 tuning range. Use a Class 2C realization.

Solution The realization form of the Class 2C oscillator is shown in Fig. 13.5.2. The design equations are:

Set: $R_1C_1 = R_2C_2, \quad \rho = C_2/C_1 \ll 1$

Given: ω_o

Choose: C_1, ρ, K_2

Calculate: $K_1 = 2 + 1/\rho, \quad C_2 = \rho C_1, \quad R_1 = 1/\omega_o C_1[(1 + K_1K_2)/2]^{1/2}, \quad R_2 = R_1/\rho$

Let us select $K_1K_2 = 199$ so that $R_1 = 1/10\omega_o C_1$. Choosing $\rho = 1$, then the design proceeds as:

$$\begin{aligned}
&K_1 = 2 + 1 = 3, \quad K_2 = 199/3 = 66.3, \quad 1/R_1C_1 = 2\pi[10(1\text{ KHz})] = 2\pi(10\text{ KHz}) \\
&1/C_1\Delta R_1 = \omega_{o\,max}/(N-1) = 2\pi[10(10\text{ KHz})/(10-1) = 2\pi(11.1\text{ KHz}) \\
&\Delta R_1 = \Delta R_2 = 10\text{ K}, \quad C_1 = C_2 = 0.0143\ \mu\text{F} \ \ (\text{use } 0.015\ \mu\text{F}) \\
&R_{1\,min} = R_{2\,min} = \Delta R/(N-1) = 10\text{ K}/(10-1) = 1.11\text{ K} \ \ (\text{use } 1.10\text{ K}) \\
&R_{av} = \Delta R\, N^{1/2}/(N-1) = \Delta R\, 10^{1/2}/9 = 3.51\text{ K}
\end{aligned} \tag{13.5.3}$$

The resistors are calculated using Eqs. 8.7.3, 8.7.4, and 8.7.8. The amplifiers are easily designed using the (geometric) average resistance R_{av} and Tables 8.4.1 and 8.4.2. For the first amplifier having $K_1 = 3$, we see

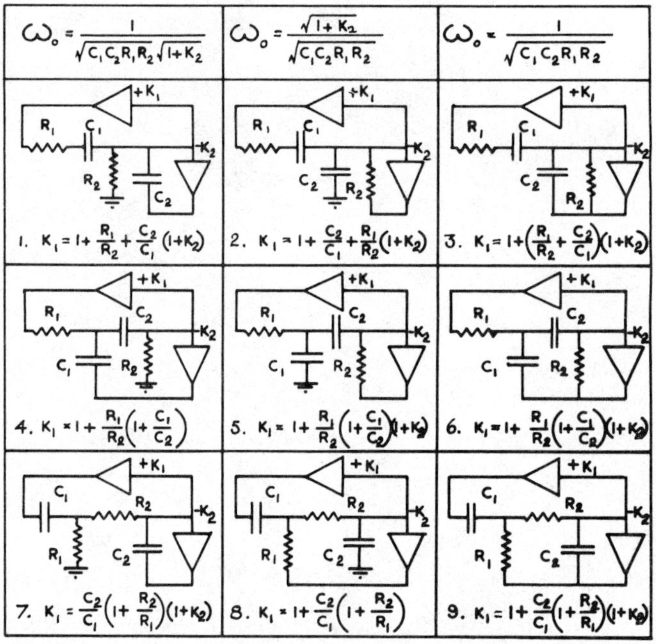

Fig. 13.5.3 Canonical oscillators using paraphase amplifiers. (From A. G. J. Holt and M. R. Lee, "A class of RC oscillators," Proc. IEEE, vol. 55, p. 1119, June, 1967.)

$$R' = KR_{av} = 3(3.51\text{ K}) = 10.5\text{ K} \quad (\text{use } 10.0\text{ K})$$
$$R'' = R_f/(K-1) = 10.0\text{ K}/(3-1) = 5.00\text{ K} \quad (\text{use } 4.99\text{ K}) \tag{13.5.4}$$

For the second amplifier having $K_2 = 66.3$, we see that selecting a resistor ratio $R_f'/R_1' = 10$ and $R' = 10.0$ K, then $R'' = R'/(K-1) = 10.0\text{ K}/65.3 = 1.78$ K. The complete oscillator is shown in Fig. 13.5.2.

An interesting alternative viewpoint for tunable oscillators has been provided by Holt and Lee.[2] They utilized a single paraphase amplifier rather than two individual amplifiers of gains K_1 and $-K_2$. A *paraphase amplifier* is a single amplifier having a common input but two outputs of opposite sign. The two "channels" have gains K_1 and $-K_2$, respectively, In practice, the engineer can only obtain differential-output amplifiers which are paraphase amplifiers having $K_2 = -K_1$. Thus, one of the outputs requires further scaling to obtain unequal gains. Three sets of canonical oscillators using such amplifiers are shown in Fig. 13.5.3. The first set is Class 2C, the second set is Class $\overline{2C}$, and the third set is Class 2B. The second set is RC:CR transform of the first set. These oscillators are also canonical since they contain five nodes and six components.

Thus, we can use a *single* differential-output amplifier in place of two of the usual single-output amplifiers. Although such approaches have been seldom used in practice, it is an interesting viewpoint for expanding our understanding of oscillators.[3] Note that gain-tuning and single-passive tuning give square root of ω_o but that double-passive tuning gives linear control.

EXAMPLE 13.5.2 Design a 16 Hz oscillator. Using Fig. 13.5.3, select the proper oscillator form and justify your choice.

Solution To maintain small C and reasonable R values to insure small size and low cost, we should utilize the frequency up-scaling properties (with respect to ω_o) of the Class 2C oscillator. Although gain-tuning is possible, we choose to use passive-tuning in this application. Let us choose the fourth

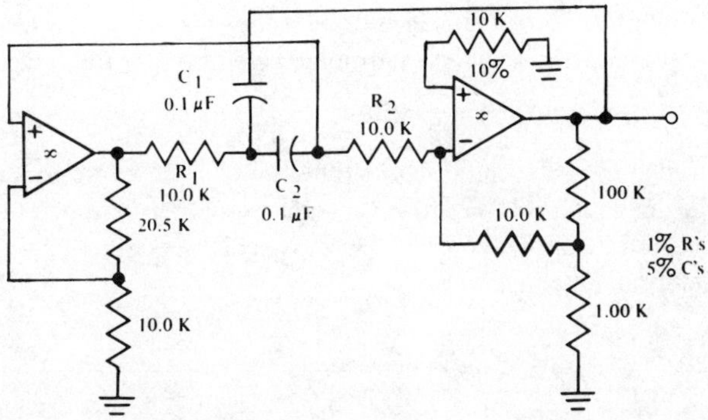

Fig. 13.5.4 Class 2C oscillator realization.

oscillator form from Fig. 13.5.3 where K_1 is independent of K_2. Choosing $R_1 = R_2 = R$ and $C_1 = C_2 = C$, then gain K_1 equals

$$K_1 = 1 + 1(1 + 1) = 3 \tag{13.5.5}$$

Then since the frequency of oscillation $\omega_o = 1/\sqrt{1 + K_2}\,RC$, we can write that $1/RC = \omega_o\sqrt{1 + K_2}$. Selecting $K_2 = 99$, then

$$\omega_o(1 + K_2)^{1/2} = 10\omega_o = 2\pi[10(16 \text{ Hz})] = 2\pi(160 \text{ Hz}) \tag{13.5.6}$$

Choosing $C = 0.1\ \mu F$, then $R = 10.0$ K. The complete oscillator is shown in Fig. 13.5.4 where the gain blocks have been easily implemented. If a Class 2B form had been used instead, then 1 μF capacitors would be required which are costly. Alternatively, the resistors could be scaled up by 10 but that too is undesirable due to offsets.

13.6 HARMONIC DISTORTION

When oscillators are perfectly tuned for imaginary poles, their outputs are perfectly sinusoidal. However to insure starting, the poles are adjusted to lie slightly in the right-half-plane. This results in an exponentially growing output which must be limited by some type of nonlinearity. Since the output is not a perfect sinusoidal signal, the signal is distorted. Because the output is (almost) periodic (signals must exist for all time to be periodic so actual signals cannot be exactly periodic), we can analyze its frequency content in a Fourier series as

$$v(t) = \sum_{n=1}^{\infty} a_n \cos n\omega_o t \tag{13.6.1}$$

If the output is a perfect cosine wave, then $a_n = 0$ for $n = 2, 3$, and so on. If the output contains other frequencies so this condition is not met, it is said to be *distorted*. Since the signal is assumed to be periodic so it contains only harmonics or frequencies which are integer multiples of the fundamental frequency ω_o, the output is said to exhibit *harmonic distortion*. The percentage distortion is defined to equal

$$\%\ \text{Distortion} = \left(\sum_{n=2}^{\infty} a_n^2\right)^{1/2} / a_1 \tag{13.6.2}$$

which is the ratio of the rms value of all the harmonics to the rms value of the fundamental. If the $a_n = 0$, then the distortion equals 0%. Otherwise it is nonzero.

In oscillators, the harmonic distortion is inversely proportional to the Q of the loop-gain expression in Eq. 13.1.1. As the selectivity of the passive feedback network increases, the distortion in the oscillator output decreases. The reason is that harmonics present in the oscillator output may be treated as additional signals which are injected into the feedback network. Each harmonic will be reduced by one minus the loop gain (1 − G) *evaluated at the frequency of the harmonic*. Thus, the *n*th harmonic is reduced by the factor

$$\Delta(jn\omega_o) = 1 - G(jn\omega_o) \tag{13.6.3}$$

In high-Q feedback networks tuned to ω_o, the harmonics are largely rejected (i.e., attenuated) and the distortion is low. However, such networks are much more susceptible to drift.

For example, consider Class B oscillators. Since their loop gain is always band-pass, then their determinant equals

$$\Delta(s) = 1 - \frac{ka_1 s}{(s+a_1)(s+a_2)} = \frac{s^2 + s[a_1(1-k) + a_2] + a_1a_2}{s^2 + s[a_1 + a_2] + a_1a_2} \tag{13.6.4}$$

from Fig. 7.9.1. Since the oscillator poles satisfy $\Delta(s) = 0$, then to place them on the $j\omega$-axis requires a gain $k = 1 + a_2/a_1$ where the center frequency $\omega_o = 1/\sqrt{a_1a_2}$. The harmonics are multiplied by a transfer function

$$\frac{1}{\Delta(s)} = \frac{s^2 + (a_1 + a_2)s + a_1a_2}{s^2 + a_1a_2} = 1 + \frac{(a_1+a_2)s}{s^2 + a_1a_2} \tag{13.6.5}$$

which is an inverse notch filter characteristic. Its reciprocal frequency response is shown in Fig. 2.8.1. The Q of the notch equals

$$Q = 1/[(a_1/a_2)^{½} + (a_2/a_1)^{½}] \tag{13.6.6}$$

Q is maximized as ½ when $a_1 = a_2$. Expressing normalized frequency $\omega = n\omega_o$ so that $\omega/\omega_o = n\omega_o/\omega_o = n$ where n is the harmonic being considered, then the effects of the loop gain can be easily seen from Fig. 2.8.1. For n = 2, 3, . . . , the reciprocal determinant gain equals

$$1/|\Delta(n)| = [(1-n^2)^2 + n^2/Q^2]^{½}/|1-n^2| \tag{13.6.7}$$

which we wish to minimize by properly choosing a_1 and a_2. From Fig. 2.8.1, $1/|\Delta| \sim 1$ as long as Q = 2 for all n. Otherwise, the first few harmonics are *increased* rather than remaining unaltered and distortion increases. Since Q can never exceed ½, this is always the case.

Let us apply these results to the Class 2B oscillator of Sec. 13.3 having $R_1C_1 = R_2C_2$. Using the design sheet,

$$\frac{1}{\Delta(s)} = \left[1 - \frac{3sRC}{(sRC)^2 + 3sRC + 1}\right]^{-1} = \frac{(sRC)^2 + 3(sRC) + 1}{(sRC)^2 + 1} \tag{13.6.8}$$

where the resonant frequency $\omega_o = 1/RC$. Therefore, in terms of the harmonics

$$1/|\Delta(n)| = [(1-n^2)^2 + (3n)^2]^{½}/|1-n^2| \tag{13.6.9}$$

where the Q of passive network equals 1/3. This corresponds to $\gamma = 3/2$ in Fig. 2.8.1. Therefore, since

$$1/\Delta(2) = [(1-4)^2 + 6^2]^{½}/|1-4| = (9+36)^{½}/3 = 2.24 = 7 \text{ dB} \tag{13.6.10}$$

the second harmonic is increased by about 7 dB. If we instead adjust the Class 2B oscillator so $C_2 \ll C_1$, then Q = 1/2 and

$$1/\Delta(2)_{min} = [(1-4)^2 + 4^2]^{½}/|1-4| = (9+16)^{½}/3 = 1.67 = 4.4 \text{ dB} \tag{13.6.11}$$

which is the minimum possible using Class B oscillators. Distortion can be reduced using properly designed Class C, $\overline{C}$, and E oscillators.

Another factor to be considered in harmonic distortion is amplifier gain. To insure start-up,

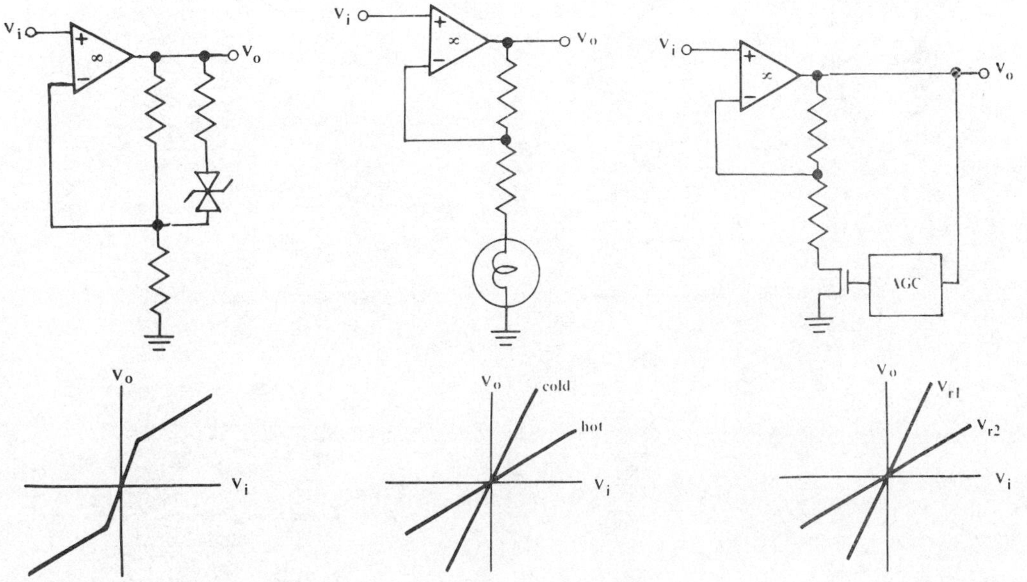

Fig. 13.6.1 Alternative methods to obtain nonlinear amplifier gains.

the gain must be slightly higher than the critical value needed to produce imaginary poles. When oscillations are established, the gain must be reduced to the critical value to insure linear operation of the oscillator. Thus, nonlinear amplifier gains are required. Nonlinear amplifier gains are obtained using zener diodes, nonlinear resistors, or entire circuits such as automatic gain control (AGC). Examples of these three situations are shown in Fig. 13.6.1. The AGC method of amplitude stabilization gives constant amplitude signals having the lowest distortion. Amplitude stabilization usually results in a reduced distortion.

PROBLEMS

13.1 The importance of compiling complete oscillator specifications cannot be overemphasized. A typical specification sheet describing the electrical characteristics of an oscillator is shown in Table P13.1. Briefly list the reasons for providing each data entry.

Table P13.1 (Courtesy of Frequency Electronics[4])

1. Nominal Frequency ______ Accuracy ______	6. Harmonics ______
2. Frequency Stability: Adjustment Range ______	7. Spurious ______
a). Short Term ______	8. Output Waveform ______
b). Long Term (Per Day) ______	9. Operating Temperature ______ to ______
c). Long Term (Per Year) ______	10. Non-Operating Temp. (Storage) ______ to ______
d). Over Temperature Range ______	11. Oscillator Voltage:
e). Input Voltage Variation ______	a). Input Voltage ______ c). Ripple ______
f). Environmental ______	b.) Power ______ d). Regulation ______
3. VCO CHARACTERISTICS:	12. Oven Requirements:
a). Pull Range ______	a). Input Voltage ______
b). Slope ______	b). Input Power ______
c). Modulation Input Voltage ______	c). Other (please specify) ______
d). Modulation Rate ______	13. Oscillator Stabilization Time ______
4. Output Level ______ Load ______	14. EMI Requirements ______
5. Phase Noise ______ Signal/Noise Ratio ______	

13.2 Q sensitivities are converted to θ sensitivities using Eqs. 13.1.5 and 13.1.7. Now we consider ζ sensitivities. Show that for $\theta = \pi/2$ as $\zeta \to 0$, then (a) $d\theta/d\zeta = -1$ and (b) $S_\zeta^\theta = (d\theta/d\zeta)/(\theta/\zeta) \to -2\zeta/\pi$. (c) Obtain the same result using the identity $S_\zeta^\theta = S_Q^\theta S_\zeta^Q$. (Hint: See Eq. 13.1.7.) (d) Verify that $S_K^\theta = -2S_K^\zeta \zeta/\pi$ and $S_a^\theta = -2S_a^\zeta \zeta/\pi$.

13.3 Several figures of merit have been defined for oscillators. These include S_F (frequency stability factor) and M_1,[5] and M_2 (Francini factor),[6] which equal :

$$S_F = \omega_o^{1/2}\, d \arg G(j\omega_o)/d\omega, \qquad M_1 = (\omega_o/2)(d\,|G(j\omega_o)|/d\omega)$$

$$M_2 = [d \operatorname{Im} G(j\omega_o)/d\omega]^{1/2}/[\operatorname{Im} G(j3\omega_o)/3\omega_o]^{1/2}$$

When G is a band-stop transfer function, then $S_F = M_1 = M_2$. Now suppose that G is another type of transfer function as listed in Table P13.3 where

$$G(s) = \frac{a_2 s^2 + a_1 s + a_0}{s^2 + s/Q + 1}$$

(cf. Table 11.5.1). Compare the figures of merit listed for the different filter types.

Table P13.3 (Courtesy of Proc. IEEE[7])

Type of Function	Coefficients	Half-Power Bandwidth	Definition $\frac{1}{2}\cdot\frac{d\lvert H\rvert}{dx}\Big\rvert_{x=1}$	Definition $\frac{1}{2}\cdot\left\lvert\frac{dH}{ds}\right\rvert_{s=j}$	Definition $\frac{1}{2}\cdot\left\lvert\frac{d\angle H}{dx}\right\rvert_{x=1}$
Biquad	a_0 a_1 a_2	$\frac{1}{x_2 - x_1}$	$\frac{(a_0+a_2)\cdot Q}{2\sqrt{1+\left(\frac{a_1}{a_0-a_1}\right)^2}}$	$Q\sqrt{\left[a_1 Q - \frac{a_0+a_1}{2}\right]^2 + Q^2(a_2-a_0)^2}$	$\frac{\frac{1}{2}a_1(a_0+a_2)}{(a_0-a_2)^2 - a_1^2} + Q$
LPF	1 0 0	0	$Q/2$	$Q\sqrt{\frac{1}{4}+Q^2}$	Q
HPF	0 0 1	0	$Q/2$	$Q\sqrt{\frac{1}{4}+Q^2}$	Q
QHP	0 1 1	0	$Q/2\sqrt{2}$	$Q\sqrt{(Q-\frac{1}{2})^2+Q^2}$	∞
BPF	0 1 0	Q	0	Q^2	Q
QLP	1 1 0	$\frac{Q}{\sqrt{2}\sqrt{4Q^2-1+\sqrt{(4Q^2-1)^2+4Q^4}}}$	$Q/2\sqrt{2}$	$Q\sqrt{(Q-\frac{1}{2})^2+Q^2}$	∞
BSF	1 0 1	Q	Q	Q	Q
Biquad	1 1 1	0	0	$Q(Q-1)$	$Q-1$

13.4 Convert the following Class 1B filters into oscillators: (a) low-pass (Sec. 8.3), (b) high-pass (Sec. 9.3), and (c) band-pass (Sec 10.3). Discuss how this conversion can be utilized when tuning the respective filters.

13.5 The RC:CR dual of the Class 1C oscillator has a one less capacitor than the Class $1\overline{C}$ oscillator. Convert the Class 1C oscillator into a Class $1\overline{C}$ form. Compare the two designs. Does one offer any advantage over the other?

13.6 A 2600 Hz oscillator is required in the single-frequency (SF) in-band signalling system discussed in Prob. 6.53. Design the oscillator using a Class 1C realization.

13.7 Class 1E state-variable oscillators are among the most stable of all types available. The oscillator outputs are phase-locked as shown in Sec. 13.3. By tuning resistors, the frequency of oscillation is easily controlled.[8] (a) Determine the transfer function from Example 7.10.1. (b) Write the parameter equations for the oscillator. (c) Verify the Class 1E oscillator design sheet. (d) Design a 12 KHz oscillator.

13.8 A general Class 1E state-variable filter was discussed in Prob. 8.17. Its general transfer functions were listed for low-pass, high-pass, and band-pass operation in both inverting and non-inverting modes. Describe how the filter can be operated as an oscillator to accurately determine the corner frequency.

13.9 Convert the Class 1E band-stop and all-pass filters of Secs. 11.3 and 12.3 into oscillators. Determine their parameters.

13.10 Oscillators can be constructed using two first-order all-pass networks as shown in Fig. P13.10.[9] (For other oscillators, see Ref. 10.) (a) Determine the gain K needed to sustain oscillations. (b) Show how

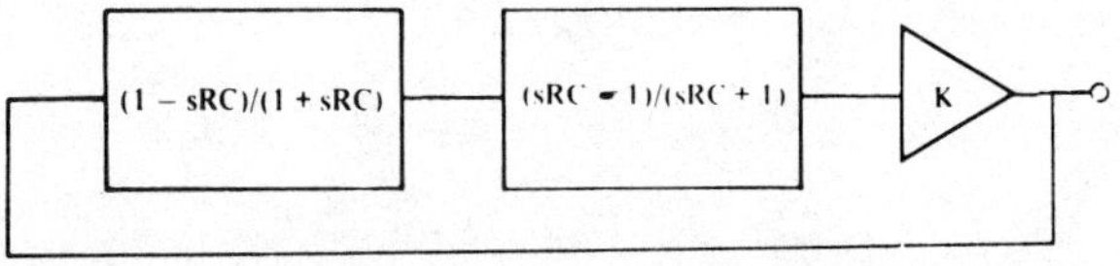

Fig. P13.10

to implement the oscillator using the first-order all-pass filters of Fig. 12.4.2. To conserve op amps, absorb gain K into the all-pass filter blocks.

13.11 Repeat Prob. 13.4 for the Class 2B filters in the chapters listed.

13.12 Write the determinants for the four Class 2B oscillators of Fig. 13.1.1. Compare their parameters. (Hint: From what types of filters have these oscillators been derived?)

13.13 Design a Class 2B Wien bridge oscillator having f_o = 10 KHz. Stabilize the oscillator using AGC such as a light bulb or an FET.

13.14 A tunable-notch filter was discussed in Prob. 11.25. It had the convenient feature that it could be operated as an oscillator to accurately determine the notch frequency. Assuming the notch filter used is Class 2B and is that shown in Sec. 11.3, describe how this feature can be obtained.

13.15 The Bell System Type N, O, and ON out-of-band signalling systems utilize a 3700 Hz oscillator as shown in Fig. P13.15.[11] Design the oscillator using the Class 2C realization (Number 1) in Fig. 13.5.3.

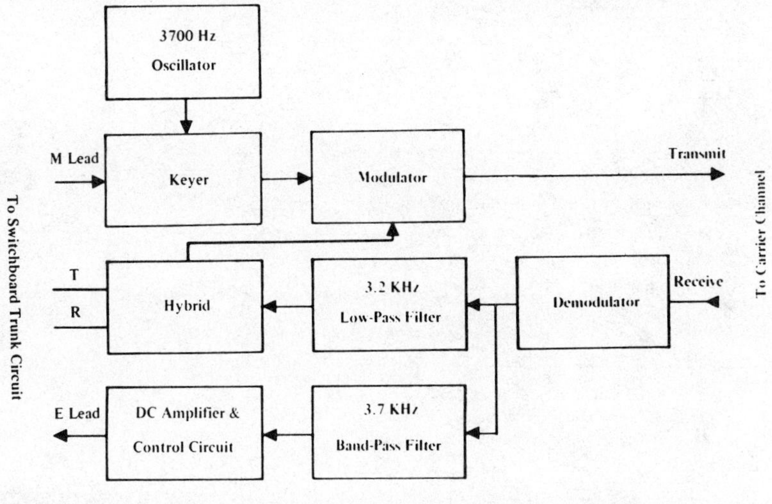

Fig. P13.15

13.16 The Lenkurt Type 45 out-of-band signalling system utilizes a signalling oscillator as shown in Prob. 6.23. This oscillator generates tones at either 3400 Hz or 3550 Hz. Design a gain-tuned Class 2C oscillator using the simplest form in Fig. 13.5.3 (i.e., Number 1, 4, or 7).

13.17 In telephone systems, it is important to consider the effects of frequency and phase jitter upon data transmission. Frequency jitter causes frequency translation while phase jitter varies phase. Assume that the following specifications are required.[12] (1) frequency range: 300–3000 Hz, (2) frequency translation: 1–10 Hz, (3) phase jitter: 0°–45° peak-to-peak, and (4) phase jitter rates: 50, 100, or 150 Hz.

Oscillators are used to control the frequency shift and the phase jitter rates. (a) Design the tunable-frequency-translation oscillator. Use the Class 2C realization (Number 4) in Fig. 13.5.3. (b) Design the 150 Hz phase jitter oscillator. Use the Class 2C realization (Number 7) in Fig. 13.5.3.

13.18 The Polaroid SX-70 camera incorporates a 12 KHz oscillator timer in LSI form having a stability of 1% from 0–50°C.[13] We are interested in designing the oscillator. (a) What class oscillator is most appropriate in the application? (b) Design the oscillator using the best form from Fig. 13.5.3 to obtain minimum C values and R values in the 25K–100K range.

13.19 An electronic watch consists of a 32.768 KHz oscillator, counter, decoder/display, and battery.[14] Due to the precise timing requirements, a crystal oscillator is used. An RC oscillator cannot be used in this application. Nevertheless, for illustrative purposes, let us design a 32.8 KHz oscillator. Repeat Prob. 13.18.

13.20 Design a 50.1 KHz oscillator. Use the Class $2\overline{C}$ realization (Number 8) in Fig. 13.5.3.

13.21 The Class $2\overline{C}$ low-pass filter of Sec. 8.3 has one less amplifier than the Class $2\overline{C}$ oscillator. Convert the low-pass filter into an oscillator and compare the two designs. Does one offer any advantage over the other?

13.22 Two Class 2E band-pass filters are shown in Fig. P13.22. Their transfer functions are listed below. Show how they can be operated as oscillators. Determine a suitable set of design equations.

$$\text{(a)}\quad H(s) = \frac{-Ks/(1-K)R_1C_2}{s^2 + s[1/R_1C_1 + 1/R_2C_2 + 1/R_1C_2(1-K)] + 1/R_1C_1R_2C_2}$$

$$\text{(b)}\quad H(s) = \frac{-Ks/R_1C_2}{s^2 + s(1/R_1C_1 + 1/R_2C_2 - K/R_1C_2) + 1/R_1C_1R_2C_2}$$

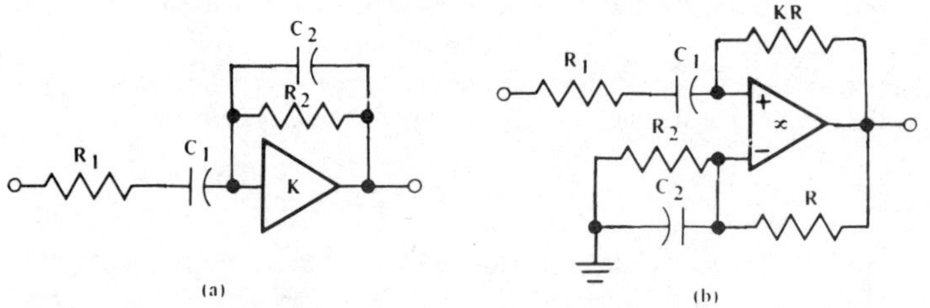

Fig. P13.22

13.23 A Class 2E oscillator was analyzed in Prob. 13.22a. (a) Show that it is topologically similar to a Wien bridge oscillator. Does it affort any advantage in design? (b) Using this form, design a passive-tuned oscillator to meet the requirements of Example 13.5.1.

13.24 A twin-T network having finite loss at its resonant frequency can be operated in a feedback loop to produce an oscillator as shown in Fig. P13.24.[15] The approximate gain of the twin-T is also given in Fig. P13.24 (see Prob 11.33). (a) How much gain K is needed to produce oscillation? (b) Design a 2300 Hz oscillator using $\rho = 2.5$.

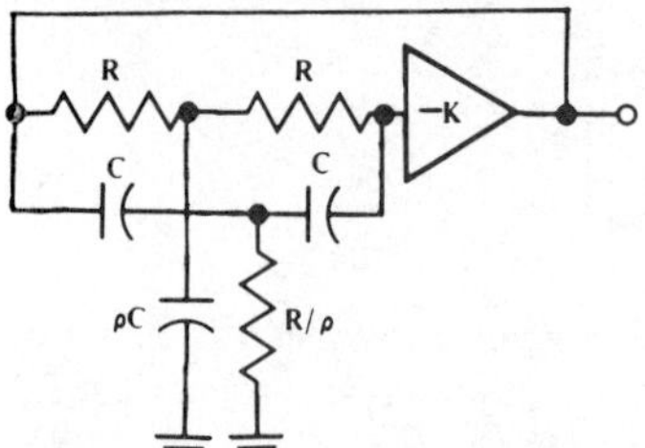

$$H(s) \cong \frac{s_n^2 + (1 - 2/\rho)s_n + 1}{s_n^2 + 4s_n + 1}, \qquad s_n = sRC, \qquad \rho \geqslant 2$$

Fig. P13.24

13.25 Computerized tuning is a popular method for trimming low-cost filters. In one method, resistors are tuned by anodization to increase their values. Since varying one resistor value generally changes all the parameters of a filter, several resistors must be trimmed to maintain parameters. A computer is required to perform the many tedious calculations needed. For example, an audio oscillator and the flow graph of its computer-controlled tuning process is shown in Fig. P13.25. (a) Determine the parameters of the oscillator in terms of the R's and C's. (b) Show how the tuning sequence effects the parameters and that it can indeed be used to tune the oscillator.

13.26 AGC provides amplitude stabilization which results in lower output distortion. An AGC using an FET in a Wien bridge oscillator is shown in Fig. P13.26. FET Q_2 controls the output amplitude over a 100:1 range with typically 0.1% distortion. (a) How much gain is needed for oscillation? (b) What is the frequency of oscillation? (c) Discuss the operation of the AGC in maintaining constant amplitude in the output.

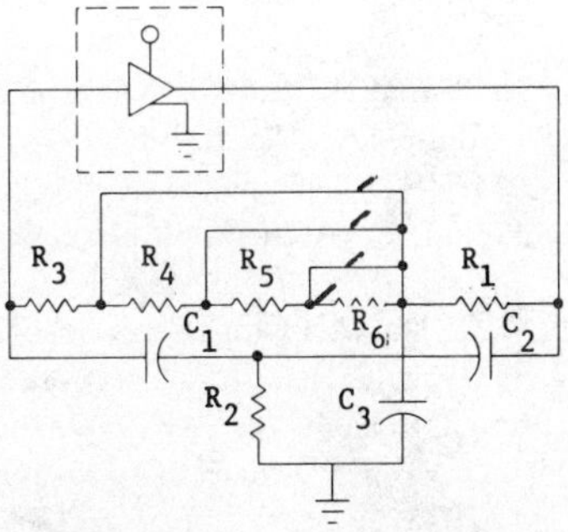

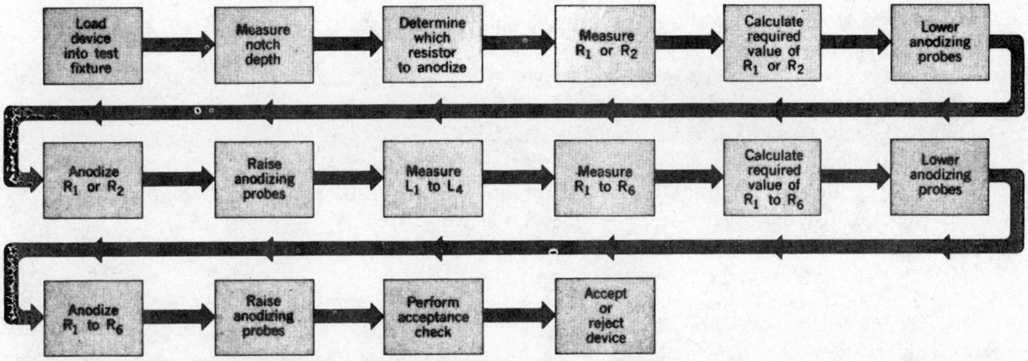

Fig. P13.25 (Courtesy of IEEE Spectrum[16])

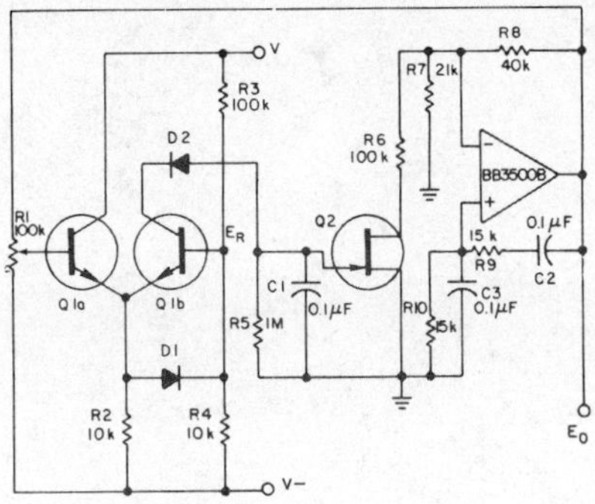

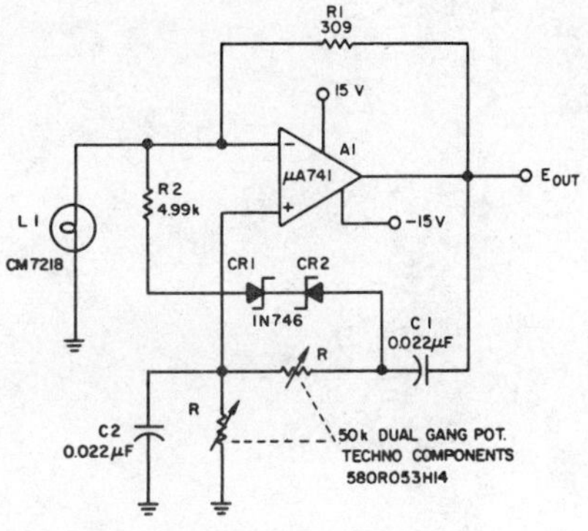

Fig. P13.26 (Courtesy of Electronic Design[17])

Fig. P13.27 (Courtesy of Electronic Design[18])

13.27 Another method of AGC uses nonlinear resistors or zener diodes. One system which uses both is shown in Fig. P13.27. Harmonic distortion is below about 2%. Pot R controls the frequency over a 10:1 range. The zener diodes improve the lamp AGC system by compensating the nonlinearity of the lamp resistance and its low thermal time constant. Repeat Prob. 13.26.

REFERENCES

1. Pearne, H. A., "Classification of active RC oscillators," M.S.E.E. Directed Research, California State Univ., Long Beach, July, 1974.
2. Holt, A. G. J., and M. R. Lee, "A class of RC oscillators," Proc. IEEE, vol. 55, p. 1119, June, 1967.
3. Sun, Y., "Generation of sinusoidal voltage (current)-controlled oscillators for integrated circuits," IEEE Trans. Circuit Theory, vol. CT-19, pp. 137–141, March, 1972.
4. Crystal Oscillator Design Specification, 1 p., Frequency Electronics, Inc., New Hyde Park, NY.
5. Ganguly, U. S., "Null network oscillators," Proc. IEEE, vol. 55, pp. 582–583, April, 1967.
6. Chattopadhyaya, S. K., "Null network oscillator quality," Proc. IEEE, vol. 58, pp. 261–263, Feb., 1970.
7. Bowron, P., "Selectivity measures of second-order networks," Proc. IEEE, vol. 63, pp. 814–815, May, 1975.
8. μAR-2000 Active Resonator Data Sheet, 2 p., Integrated Microsystems, Inc., Mt. View, CA.
9. Kerwin, W. J., and R. M. Westbrook, "Constant-amplitude RC oscillator," NASA, Tech. Brief 70-10338, 2 p., Sept., 1970.
10. Sidorowicz, R. S., "An abundance of sinusoidal RC oscillators," Proc. IEE, vol. 119, pp. 283–293, March, 1972.
11. Talley, D., *Basic Carrier Telephony*, p. 126, Hayden, NY, 1966.
12. Phase Jitter Simulator, Data Sheet, 4 p., SEG Electronics, Richmond Hill, NY.
13. Lapidus, G., "Behind the lens of the SX-70," IEEE Spectrum, vol. 10, pp. 76–83, Dec., 1973.
14. Eleccion, M., "The electronic watch," IEEE Spectrum, vol. 10, pp. 24–32, April, 1973.
15. Claussen, C. H., "FSK oscillator uses twin-T network for high phase sensitivity," Electronic Design, p. 96, Nov. 9, 1972, copyright Hayden Publishing, 1972.
16. Hintzman, F. H., Jr., "Computer tuning of hybrid audio oscillators," IEEE Spectrum, vol. 6, pp. 56–60, Feb., 1969.
17. Graeme, J., "AGC provides 0.1% amplitude stability for Wien-bridge oscillator," Electronic Design, p. 94, May 24, 1975, copyright Hayden Publishing, 1975.
18. Schwerdt, C. B., "Adjustable sinewave audio oscillator employs improved agc for wide frequency range," Electronic Design, p. 82, Feb. 15, 1973, copyright Hayden Publishing, 1973.

14 COMPONENT SELECTION

Much evil can enter through small space
Oriental Proverb

In Chaps. 8–13, we designed a variety of active filters. In general, we observed the guidelines outlined in Sec. 8.4 when selecting component values. Because proper component selection is indispensable in active filter design, we shall now investigate this very important area in great detail.

This chapter will be concerned with all the practical design aspects of resistors, potentiometers, capacitors, and operational amplifiers. Such areas as construction, temperature coefficient, power rating, noise, reliability, and nomenclature will be discussed. All the information which is required when finalizing active filter designs is found here. The engineer will find this chapter to be an indispensable compendium of results.

14.1 RESISTORS

A basic component of the active filter is the resistor. Many different resistor types are available. These include: (1) composition (carbon or cermet), (2) film (metal or carbon), (3) wirewound, (4) thin-film and thick-film, and (5) diffused types. Metal film resistors are the most commonly used in active filters today. Thin-film and thick-film types are used in high-frequency applications. Diffused resistor types are rarely used in active filter design because of their undesirable characteristics and shall not be considered.

14.1.1 CONSTRUCTION

Resistors are formed by making contact between the ends of a resistive material. The resistance R (Ω) of a material of cross-sectional area A (cm^2), length d (cm), and resistivity ρ (Ω-cm) equals

$$R = \rho d/A \tag{14.1.1}$$

Resistor characteristics depend upon the way in which they are physically constructed and upon the nature of their resistive materials.

Composition, wirewound, and metal film resistors are constructed within cylindrical molds or on cylindrical cores as shown in Fig. 14.1.1. Composition resistors consist of a cylinder or slug of resistive material (carbon) in which are embedded end tabs to provide electrical contact with the material. Filament types have resistive material coated on the outer surface of a glass tube with special end tabs. These end tabs have leads (tinned copper, nickel, or gold-plated nickel) welded to them, which are soldered or wrapped to connect the resistor into a circuit. A phenolic case is molded around the resistor body to provide a moisture barrier and mechanical strength.

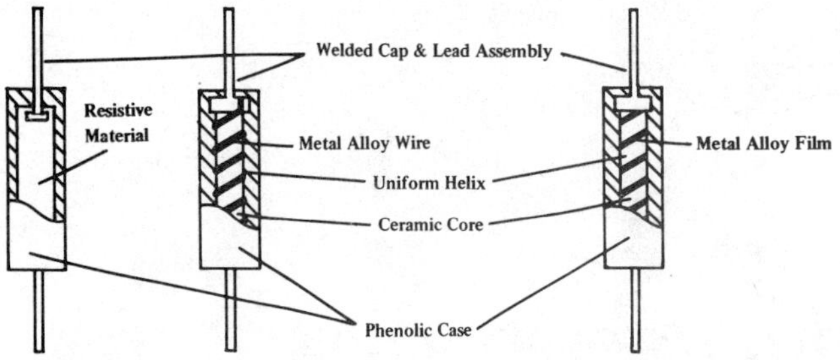

Fig. 14.1.1 Composition, wirewound, and film resistor construction.

Unfortunately, such cases act as thermal insulators. Much of the dissipated energy must be carried away through the leads.

Wirewound resistors are formed by winding resistance wire (a copper-nickel, nickel-chrome, or manganese-copper alloy depending on the resistance value) on a nonconductive core (a ceramic of steatite, aluminum oxide (alumina), or beryllium oxide (beryllia); or fiberglass depending on physical size and grade) and capping the ends (using stainless steel caps). Thermal expansion coefficients are carefully matched. Aryton-Perry winding techniques (two windings in opposite directions and connected in series) are used to obtain low-inductance wirewound resistors.

Film resistors are constructed by depositing a metal film (usually a nickel-chrome alloy) or carbon film of predetermined thickness on a nonconductive core (of the ceramic material listed previously). The core is then scribed along its length in a spiral at a prescribed pitch to obtain the required resistance value, after which the ends are capped. The resistors are then coated (using silicone, epoxy, or vitreous enamel) or hermetically sealed in a glass or ceramic envelope. Longitudinal scribing is used to obtain low-inductance film resistors.

Thin-film and thick-film resistors are formed on chips or large substrates as shown in Fig. 14.1.2.[1] They differ in the method used for forming the resistive material on the chip. Thin-film resistors are formed by evaporating or sputtering resistive materials (such as nickel-chromium (Nichrome), tantalum, tin oxide, or cermet) on a nonconductive substrate (ceramic of alumina or beryllia, glass, or silicon with SiO_2 insulation layer). Silk screening methods of deposition can also be used. Thick-film resistors are formed by depositing special resistive inks (mixtures of metal and glass powder in a binder) on a nonconductive substrate through a photographically formed stencil mask. The substrate is then dried and fired at high temperatures. Both thick-film and thin-film resistors have metal backings (such as gold, platinum gold, or aluminum) which make electrical contact with the film. Metal leads (aluminum or tinned copper) are then bonded to the backings to make the direct connections to metallized substrates. Bonding uses thermocompression, ultrasonic, or eutectic methods.

Some of the key typical characteristics of the various resistor types are summarized in Table 14.1.1. The table shows that metal film and wirewound resistors have low tolerances, low temperature coefficients, and good tracking with temperature. Since metal film resistors are less costly than wirewound types, they are the most widely used in active filters today.

In specifying a resistor, the following parameters are important: (1) resistor value, (2) tolerance, (3) power rating, (4) temperature coefficient, (5) operating temperature range, and (6)

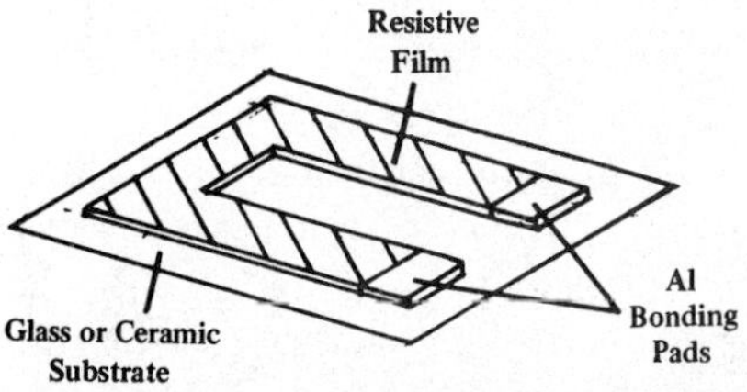

Fig. 14.1.2 Thin-film and thick-film resistor construction.

Table 14.1.1 Typical resistor characteristics.

Resistor Type	Range (Ω)	Tolerance (%)	TC (± PPM/°C)	Tracking (%)	Parasitic Effects	Cost
Composition	1–22 M	10	1000	5	Low	Low
Metal Film	10–1 M	1	50	0.25	Medium	Medium
Carbon Film	10–10 M	5	200	2	Medium	Medium
Wirewound	1–273 K	1	50	0.25	High	High
Thin-Film	25–100 K	2	100	0.5	Low	Medium
Thick-Film	10–1 M	10	25	10	Low	Medium
Diffused	20–50 K	20	500–7000	5	High	Low

style. Other important but often neglected factors include: (7) thermal noise, (8) reliability, and (9) aging. We shall now discuss these parameters to show their importance in design.

14.1.2 STANDARD VALUES AND TOLERANCES

When an active filter is designed, a number of resistor values are generally required. In most cases, the exact values which are calculated are not commercially available. Thus, the filter designer *must* choose from the standard values which *are* available. The standard values available depend upon the tolerance required. The resistor tolerance T is equal to the maximum percentage uncertainty in the resistor value relative to its nominal value R_o. In general, the actual resistor values are grouped close to, but within the tolerance limits. Thus, their distribution is generally described by a bimodal type probability density function rather than a unimodal density function (e.g., a Gaussian distribution[2]) as shown in Fig. 14.1.3. The bimodal type characteristic results from the statistical sorting methods used in industry.

The standard resistor tolerances are ¼, ½, 1, 5, and 10%. The first three significant figures of the standard resistor values available in ¼ and ½% tolerances, and 1% tolerances are listed in Table 14.1.2. Due to their lower cost, 1% values are preferred for active filter designs, but ¼ and ½% values must sometimes be utilized. Some resistor companies provide ¼ and ½% values in their 1% resistor sequence. For example, the 1% resistors available in the vicinity of 10 K are 9.53 K, 9.76 K, 10.0 K, 10.2 K, and 10.5 K.

In certain applications, the resistor value is not critical. In such situations, carbon resistors are often used. The standard 5, 10, and 20% values are listed in Table 14.1.3.

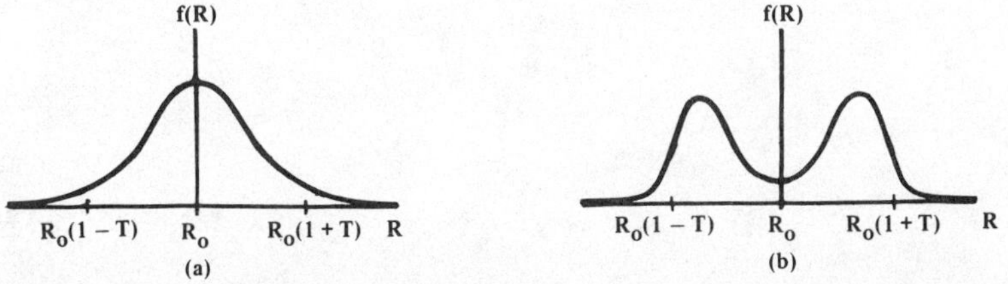

Fig. 14.1.3 Probability density functions showing (a) Gaussian and (b) typical distributions of resistor values.

Table 14.1.2 Standard ¼, ½, and 1% resistor values.

0.25, 0.5%	1%	0.25, 0.5%	1%	0.25, 0.5%	1%
10.0	10.0	21.5	21.5	46.4	46.4
10.2		22.1		47.5	
10.5	10.5	22.6	22.6	48.7	48.7
10.7		23.2		49.9	
11.0	11.0	23.7	23.7	51.1	51.1
11.3		24.3		52.3	
11.5	11.5	24.9	24.9	53.6	53.6
11.8		25.5		54.9	
12.1	12.1	26.1	26.1	56.2	56.2
12.4		26.7		57.6	
12.7	12.7	27.4	27.4	59.0	59.0
13.0		28.0		60.4	
13.3	13.3	28.7	28.7	61.9	61.9
13.7		29.4		63.4	
14.0	14.0	30.1	30.1	64.9	64.9
14.3		30.9		66.5	
14.7	14.7	31.6	31.6	68.1	68.1
15.0		32.4		69.8	
15.4	15.4	33.2	33.2	71.5	71.5
15.8		34.0		73.2	
16.2	16.2	34.8	34.8	75.0	75.0
16.5		35.7		76.8	
16.9	16.9	36.5	36.5	78.7	78.7
17.4		37.4		80.6	
17.8	17.8	38.3	38.3	82.5	82.5
18.2		39.2		84.5	
18.7	18.7	40.2	40.2	86.6	86.6
19.1		41.2		88.7	
19.6	19.6	42.2	42.2	90.9	90.9
20.0		43.2		93.1	
20.5	20.5	44.2	44.2	95.3	95.3
21.0		45.3		97.6	

Table 14.1.3 Standard 5, 10, and 20% resistor values.

5%	10%	20%	5%	10%	20%
10	10	10	33	33	33
11			36		
12	12		39	39	
13			43		
15	15	15	47	47	47
16			51		
18	18		56	56	
20			62		
22	22	22	68	68	68
24			75		
27	27		82	82	
30			91		

14.1.3 POWER RATING

The power rating P (watts) of a resistor is equal to the maximum power which it can continuously dissipate without permanent damage. If the resistor voltage is V (rms volts) and the resistance is R (ohms), then

$$P = V^2/R \tag{14.1.2}$$

or

$$V = \sqrt{PR} \tag{14.1.3}$$

Therefore, the power rating fixes the maximum voltage which the resistor can withstand. Power ratings of 1/8, 1/4, 1/2, 1, and 2 watts are standard. For example, for V = 10 volts, resistors with these power ratings cannot have values of less than 800, 400, 200, 100, and 50 ohms, respectively.

The power rating of a resistor is generally dependent upon (1) its thermal resistance θ between its case and the surrounding environment (usually air), and (2) the temperature of the surrounding environment. The power rating of the resistor must be decreased as the surrounding temperature increases in order that its case temperature not exceed a *critical limit*. The temperature rise ΔT of the resistor equals

$$\Delta T = T_r - T_a = \theta P \tag{14.1.4}$$

where T_r is the resistor temperature, T_a is its ambient surrounding temperature, and θ is its thermal resistance measured in °C/W. This information is generally summarized in a power derating curve similar to that shown in Fig. 14.1.4. These particular curves describe the RN metal film resistor series generally used in active filter design. The letters indicate their temperature coefficients which will shortly be discussed. At ambient temperatures less than the "break" or "corner" temperature, the resistor can dissipate its maximum rated or allowable power. At ambient temperatures exceeding this value, the resistor cannot dissipate rated power without its temperature exceeding the maximum allowable temperature. Therefore, the rated power must be decreased or "derated." The maximum allowable case temperature is that where 0% of rated power can be tolerated. For example, $T_{r\,max}$ in the C, E, and F series equals 175°C.

The thermal resistance is equal to the negative reciprocal of the slope of the curve. For example, the C-, E-, and F-rated metal film resistor has

$$\theta = -\Delta T/P = (-125 + 175)/(1 - 0)P_r = 50/P_r \ ^\circ\text{C/W} \tag{14.1.5}$$

where P_r is the power rating of the resistor. Thus, a ¼ W resistor has a thermal resistance of θ = 200 °C/W. Therefore, if the ¼ W resistor is operated at half-rated power, it will have a temperature rise of

$$\Delta T = \theta P = (200\ ^\circ\text{C/W})(1/8\ \text{W}) = 25^\circ\text{C} \tag{14.1.6}$$

This shows the importance of knowing the operating temperature range of the resistor. In general, the signal levels within the active filter are fixed. The resistor values are calculated, and the required power rating determined from Eq. 14.1.2. Then the required power rating of the resis-

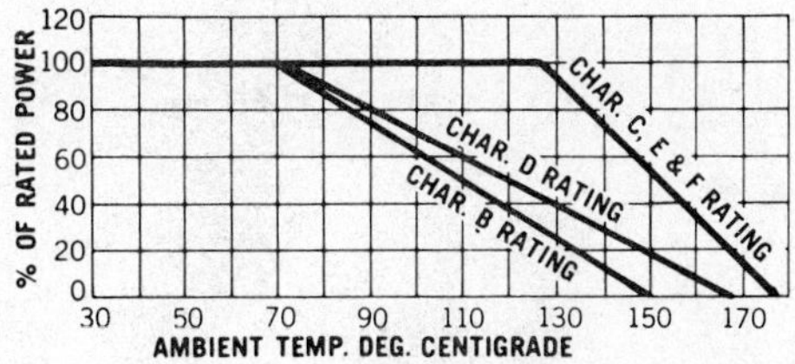

Fig. 14.1.4 Power derating curves for RN metal film resistors. (From the Dale Resistor Guide, p. 149, Dale Electronics, Columbus, NE, Aug., 1970.)

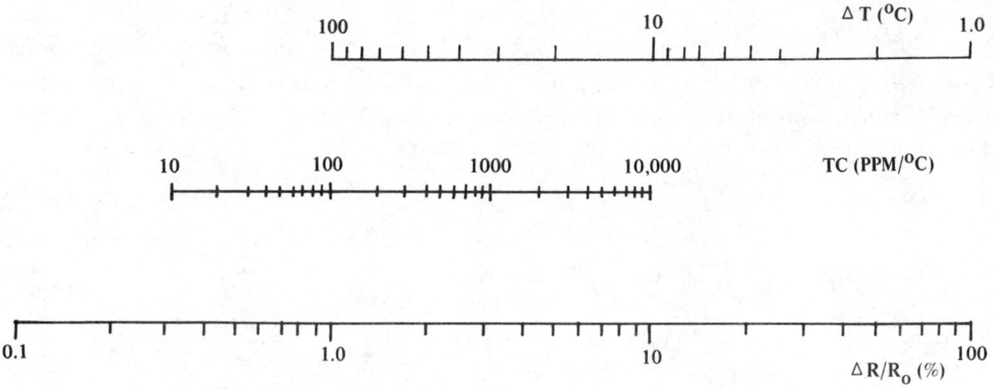

Fig. 14.1.5 Nomograph for calculating the TC of a component.

tor (in watts) is calculated from the manufacturer's derating curve (Fig. 14.1.4 or equivalent) and the operating temperature range. The 1/8 W and 1/4 W sizes are generally used in active filter design. Later in the chapter, we shall relate reliability to both power rating and case temperature.

14.1.4 TEMPERATURE COEFFICIENT

The temperature coefficient (TC) of the resistor measures the drift in the normalized resistor value due to temperature variation. Mathematically, the TC equals

$$TC = \frac{\Delta R/R_o}{\Delta T} 10^6 \text{ PPM/}^o\text{C} \tag{14.1.7}$$

where TC is the temperature coefficient of the resistor in parts per million per degree centigrade (PPM/°C), R_o is the nominal resistor value (usually measured at 25°C), ΔR is the drift in the resistor value, ΔR_o is the normalized resistor drift, and ΔT is the change in temperature producing the drift. For example, a resistor which drifts ± 1% from its nominal value over a 100°C temperature range has a temperature coefficient of

$$TC = (\pm 0.01/100)10^6 = \pm 100 \text{ PPM/}^o\text{C} \tag{14.1.8}$$

Fig. 14.1.5 can be used to estimate the TC of a resistor (or any other component exhibiting drift with temperature). By simply entering the percentage change or drift and temperature variation on the nomograph, the TC is read off directly. Standard TC values for resistors are 25, 50, 100, 200, and 500 PPM/°C.

Three typical types of temperature characteristics are shown in Fig. 14.1.6. The first characteristic shows drifts which can be of either sign. The maximum drifts bound the typical drifts

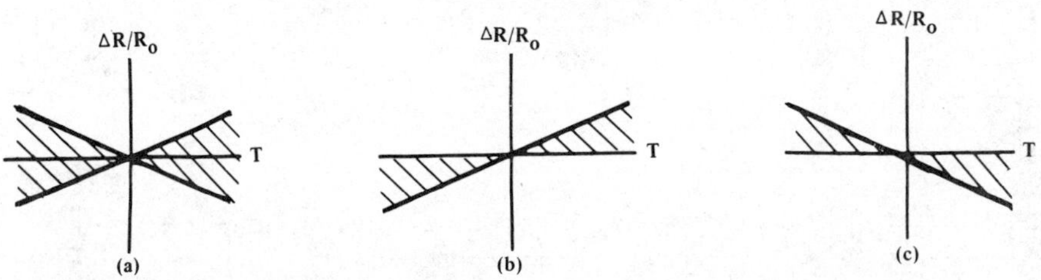

Fig. 14.1.6 Temperature drift of component having (a) ±TC, (b) +TC, and (c) −TC.

which lie within the shaded areas. The second characteristic shows that the drift is monotonically nondecreasing so the TC is positive. In the third characteristic, the TC is negative. Positive and negative TC's are sometimes used to temperature compensate active filters.

14.1.5 NOMENCLATURE

All resistors manufactured meet company, commercial, and/or military specifications. These specifications can be very involved. Often the most demanding are the military (MIL) specifications which are listed in Table 14.1.4. The most universally utilized are the RC (composition), RN (film), and RW (wirewound) types. The more expensive established reliability types are not widely used. Generally, due to mass production techniques, resistors meeting MIL specifications are only slightly more expensive than non-MIL types. Since their characteristics must meet the MIL specifications which are standard, well-defined, and readily available, the design engineer can be reasonably certain of their quality, consistency, and worst-case values.

The standard resistor nomenclature is an alphanumeric code whose format depends upon the resistor style. This format is summarized in Table 14.1.5. Since we are primarily interested in the high-stability (low TC) metal film resistor (RN type) for active filters, the engineer should now verify the decoding of RN60D1003F in Table 14.1.5. In some film resistors and most composition resistors, a color code is utilized rather than an alphanumeric code. We include this code in Table 14.1.6 for convenient reference.

Table 14.1.4 Military type designators and applicable specification numbers for resistors. (Based upon TRW/IRC Resistors Catalog, p. 25, TRW Electronic Components, Philadelphia, PA, 1974.)

Composition		
RC	Resistors, Fixed, Composition (Insulated)	MIL-R-11
RCR	Resistors, Fixed, Composition (Insulated), Established Reliability	MIL-R-39008
Film		
RN	Resistors, Fixed, Film (High Stability)	MIL-R-10509
RNR	Resistors, Fixed, Film, Established Reliability	MIL-R-55182
RL	Resistors, Fixed, Film, Insulated	MIL-R-22684
RLR	Resistors, Fixed, Film, Insulated, Established Reliability	MIL-R-39017
RD	Resistors, Fixed, Film (Power Type)	MIL-R-11804
Wirewound		
RB	Resistors, Fixed, Wirewound (Accurate)	MIL-R-93
RBR	Resistors, Fixed, Wirewound (Accurate), Established Reliability	MIL-R-39009
RW	Resistors, Fixed, Wirewound (Power Type)	MIL-R-26
RWR	Resistors, Fixed, Wirewound (Power Type), Established Reliability	MIL-R-39007
RE	Resistors, Fixed, Wirewound (Power Type, Chassis Mounted)	MIL-R-18546
RER	Resistors, Fixed, Wirewound (Power Type, Chassis Mounted), Established Reliability	MIL-R-39009

Size/Power @ 70° unless otherwise stated)	TC Characteristic	Tolerance
05—1/8 watt 07—1/4 watt 20—1/2 watt 32—1 watt 42—2 watt } MIL-R-11 (RC), MIL-R-39008 (RCR), MIL-R-22684 (RL), MIL-R-39017 (RLR) 50—1/20 watt (@ 125°C) 55—1/8 watt 60—1/4 watt 65—1/2 watt 70—3/4 watt 75—1 watt (@ 125°C) 80—2 watt (@ 125°C) } MIL-R-10509 (RN), MIL-R-55182 (RNR)	B = ±500 ppm/°C C = ± 50 ppm/°C (T2) D = ±200, 500 ppm/°C (T0) E = ± 25 ppm/°C (T9) F = ± 50 ppm/°C } MIL-R-10509 (RN) H = ± 50 ppm/°C (T2) J = ± 25 ppm/°C (T9) K = ±100 ppm/°C (T0) } MIL-R-55182 (RNR) NOTE: RL and RLR resistors are ±200 ppm/°C. There is no temperature coefficient designation in the RL numbering system.	K = ±10% J = ±5% G = ±2% F = ±1% D = ±0.5% C = ±0.25% B = ±0.10% **Failure Rate 1000 Hours (60% Confidence)** M = 1.0% P = 0.1% R = .01% S = .001%

Table 14.1.5 Resistor nomenclature for selected MIL types. (From TRW/IRC Resistors Catalog, p. 9, TRW Electronics Components, Philadelphia, PA, 1974.)

MIL—R—11 (RC) RC07GF153K

RC07	GF	153	K
Style/Power	"G" = 70°C Max. ambient temperature for full load operation. "F" = Temperature Coefficient which varies (with resistance) from ±625 ppm/°C to ±3100 ppm/°C.	Resistance First 2 digits significant, 3rd digit "number of zeros." 153 = 15,000Ω	Tolerance K = ± 10%

MIL—R—22684 (RL) RL07S153J

RL07	S	153	J
Style/Power	Terminal (Lead) "S" = Solderable	Resistance First 2 digits significant, 3rd digit, "number of zeros." 153 = 15,000Ω	Tolerance J = ±5%

MIL—R—10509 (RN) RN60D1003F

RN60	D	1003	F
Style/Power	Characteristic D = ±100 ppm/°C	Resistance First 3 digits significant, 4th digit "number of zeros." 1003 = 100,000Ω	Tolerance F = ±1%

MIL—R—26 (RW)—Numbering System Complex (See MIL spec) RW55U49R9F

RW55	U	49R9	F
Style/Power Size/ Construction	Max. "Hot Spot," derating temperature, insulation resistance and moisture resistance. "U" or "V" characteristic.	Resistance 3 or 4 digits depending on the TC, tolerance, etc. "U" char. has 4 "V" char. has 3	Tolerance Only applicable to "U" char.

MIL—R—39008 (RCR) RCR07G153JS

RCR07	G	153	J	S
Style/Power	Characteristic "G" indicates a max. ambient temperature of 70°C for full load operation, and a TC which varies (with resistance) from ±625 ppm/°C to ±1900 ppm/°C.	Resistance First 2 digits significant, 3rd digit, "number of zeros." 153 = 15,000Ω	Tolerance J = ±5%	Failure Rate S = .001%/ 1000 hours

MIL—R—39017 (RLR) RLR07C153GR

RLR07	C	153	G	R
Style/Power	Terminal (Lead) "C" = Solderable/Weldable	Resistance First 2 digits significant, 3rd digit, "number of zeros." 153 = 15,000Ω	Tolerance G = ±2%	Failure Rate R = ±0.1%/ 1000 hours

MIL—R—55182 (RNR) RNR60H1003FS

RNR60	H	1003	F	S
Style, Terminal and Power RNR = Solderable Leads RNC = Solderable/Weldable Leads RNN = Nickel Leads	Characteristic H = ±50 ppm/°C	Resistance First 3 digits significant, 4th digit "no. of zeros." 1003 = 100,000Ω	Tolerance F = ±1%	Failure Rate S = .001%/ 1000 hours

Table 14.1.6 Resistor color code. (From Hot-Molded Fixed Resistors, Bull. EC 21, p. 5, Allen-Bradley, Milwaukee, WI, Jan., 1972.)

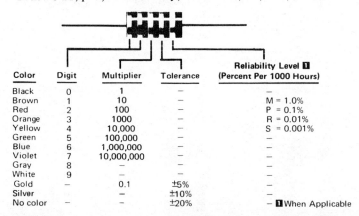

Color	Digit	Multiplier	Tolerance	Reliability Level [1] (Percent Per 1000 Hours)
Black	0	1	–	–
Brown	1	10	–	M = 1.0%
Red	2	100	–	P = 0.1%
Orange	3	1000	–	R = 0.01%
Yellow	4	10,000	–	S = 0.001%
Green	5	100,000	–	–
Blue	6	1,000,000	–	–
Violet	7	10,000,000	–	–
Gray	8	–	–	–
White	9	–	–	–
Gold	–	0.1	±5%	–
Silver	–	–	±10%	–
No color	–	–	±20%	–

[1] When Applicable

14.1.6 IMPEDANCE CHARACTERISTIC

In most active filter applications, the parasitic effects in resistors are negligible. Nevertheless, it is important to recognize the potential problems which can exist. The equivalent circuit of a resistor is shown in Fig. 14.1.7. R is the resistance, L is the series inductance, and C is the shunt capacitance. Wirewound resistors can have a relatively large L, while diffused resistors can have a relatively large C.

To determine the degrading effects of L and C on resistor performance, we first find the impedance Z of the resistor. Z is equal to

$$Z(s) = \frac{1}{sC + 1/(R + sL)} = \frac{R + sL}{s^2LC + sRC + 1} \tag{14.1.9}$$

The impedance has a zero at s = –R/L, and the poles have a resonant frequency of

$$\omega_n = 1/\sqrt{LC} \tag{14.1.10}$$

and a damping factor of

$$\zeta = \tfrac{1}{2}\,[R/(L/C)^{1/2}] = \tfrac{1}{2}\,[RC/(L/R)]^{1/2} = \tfrac{1}{2}\,[(R/L)/(1/RC)]^{1/2} \tag{14.1.11}$$

ζ equals half of two important resistor parameter ratios. The first ratio is that of R to its characteristic impedance $\sqrt{L/C}$;[3] the second is the relative time constant ratio or corner frequency ratio. When ζ is small ($\zeta < 1$ or high resonance) noticable resonance effects occur. When ζ is large ($\zeta > 1$ or low resonance), resonance effects are not evident. Notice that when $\zeta \gg 1$, the poles are real with values

$$a_1 = -1/RC, \qquad a_2 = -R/L \tag{14.1.12}$$

When $\zeta < 1$, they are complex. Notice that ζ always equals $\tfrac{1}{2}\sqrt{a_2/a_1}$ from Eq. 14.1.11.

The pole-zero pattern and magnitude characteristic of the resistor impedance are shown in Fig. 14.1.8. The magnitude characteristic is easily constructed using the techniques of Chap. 2. The difference in peaking between high resonance and low resonance resistors is evident. Note that the maximum useful frequency range is about R/2πL Hz (high resonance) or 1/2πRC Hz (low resonance). We now introduce a simple means for drawing this characteristic which is an invaluable aid in active filter design.

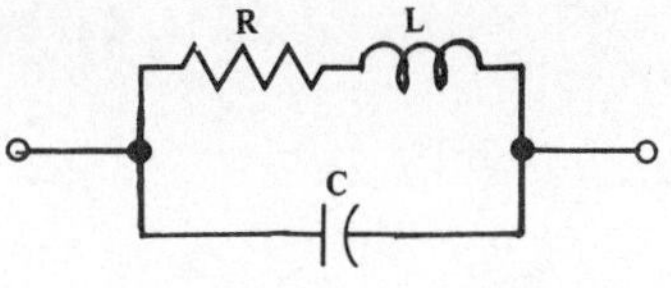

Fig. 14.1.7 Equivalent circuit of resistor.

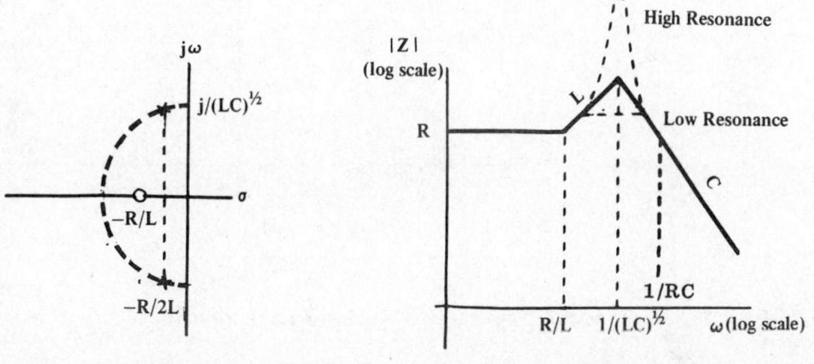

Fig. 14.1.8 Impedance characteristic of resistor.

14.1.7 IMPEDANCE PAPER

One of the simplest, but little-used, design aids is impedance (or reactance) paper.[4] Impedance paper is simply a family of impedance (magnitude) response curves for resistors, inductors, and capacitors plotted as a function of frequency. Since these impedances equal

$$|Z_R(j\omega)| = R, \qquad |Z_L(j\omega)| = \omega L, \qquad |Z_C(j\omega)| = 1/\omega C \tag{14.1.13}$$

their Bode magnitude plots are simply straight lines having slopes of 0, +20, and −20 dB/dec, respectively. These plots make up the impedance paper of Fig. 14.1.9. Note that resistance is constant with frequency as shown by the horizontal lines. Inductors have impedances described by the diagonal lines of positive (+1) slope, while capacitor impedances are described by the diagonal lines of negative (−1) slope. The diagonal family of curves are labelled with their respective inductor values (in μH and H) and capacitor values (in pF and μF). Frequency varies from 1 Hz to

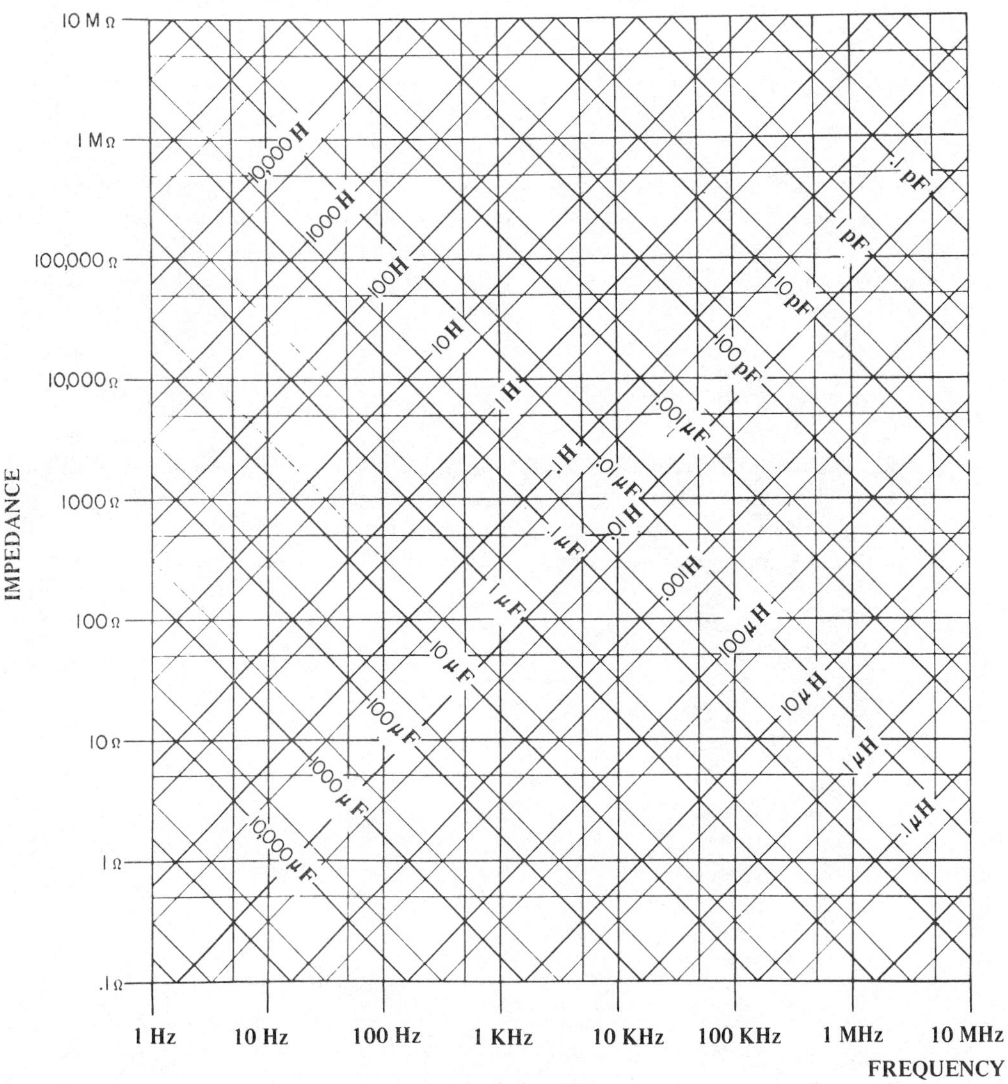

Fig. 14.1.9 Impedance paper. (From GenRad, Concord, MA)

5 MHz. For accurate calculations, a single cycle of the grid, shown in Fig. 14.1.10, is used.

In practice, the "rough" impedance value is obtained from Fig. 14.1.9, and the "exact" impedance value found from Fig. 14.1.10. This paper has been utilized for almost all of the active filter designs in this book. Its importance as a design aid cannot be overemphasized. We shall now utilize the reactance chart in determining the impedance of a wirewound resistor.

EXAMPLE 14.1.1 A wirewound resistor has the following parameters: R = 1 K, L = 200 μH, and C = 20 pF. Plot the impedance characteristic of the resistor. What is its maximum useful frequency range?

Solution We can calculate the zero and poles for the resistor mathematically or we can read them directly off impedance paper. Note that the zero frequency ω_z = R/L which is the frequency where R = ωL. This is the corner frequency where the R = 1 K and L = 200 μH lines intersect on the impedance paper. Thus,

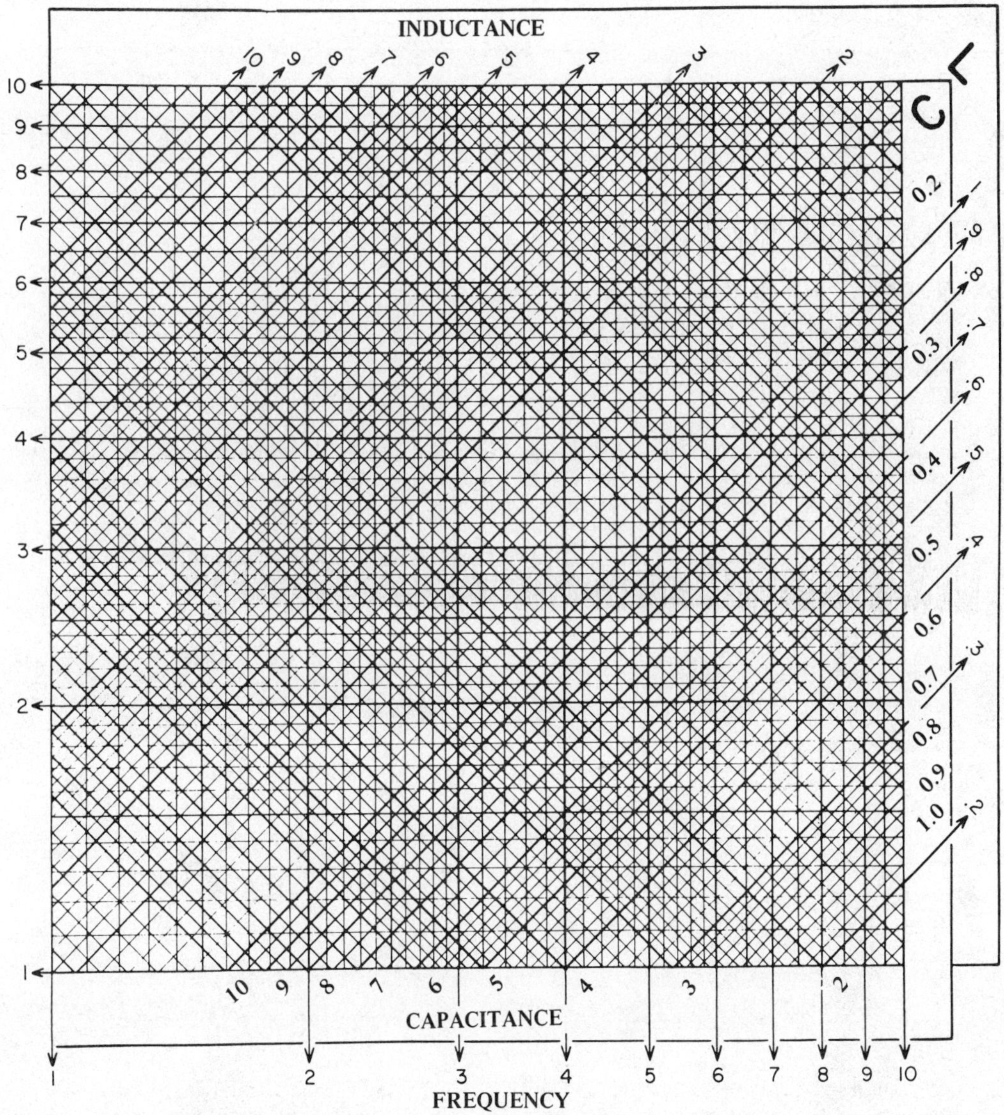

Fig. 14.1.10 Expanded impedance paper. Always obtain the approximate value from Fig. 14.1.9 before using Fig. 14.1.10. (From GenRad, Concord, MA)

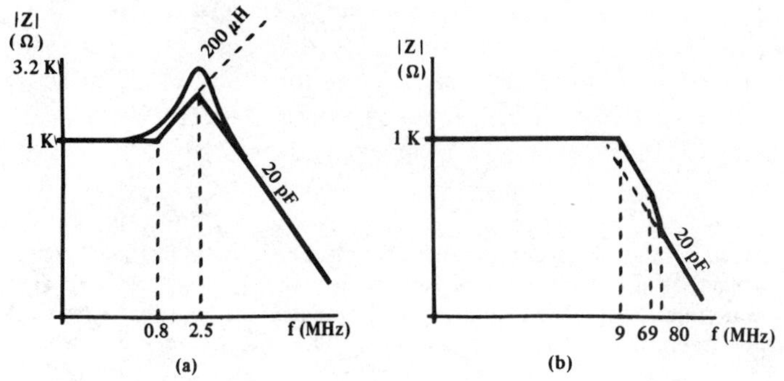

Fig. 14.1.11 Impedance characteristics of wirewound resistors in Examples (a) 14.1.1 and (b) 14.1.2.

$$s_z = a_2 = -R/L = -2\pi(800 \text{ KHz}) \tag{14.1.14}$$

The pole has a resonant frequency $\omega_n = 1/\sqrt{LC}$ which is the frequency where $\omega L = 1/\omega C$. This is the resonant frequency where the L = 200 μH and C = 20 pF lines intersect. Thus,

$$\omega_n = 1/\sqrt{LC} = 2\pi(2.5 \text{ MHz}) \tag{14.1.15}$$

The damping factor of the pole is given by Eq. 14.1.11 which is related to the ratio of two corner frequencies given by Eq. 14.1.13. The first is the zero frequency of 800 KHz. The second is the corner frequency where $R = 1/\omega C$. This is the frequency where the R = 1 K and C = 20 pF lines intersect, or

$$a_1 = -1/RC = -2\pi(8 \text{ MHz}) \tag{14.1.16}$$

Thus, from Eq. 14.1.11, the damping factor equals

$$\zeta = ½ (a_2/a_1)^{½} = ½ (0.8 \text{ MHz}/8 \text{ MHz})^{½} = ½ (0.1^{½}) = 0.16 \tag{14.1.17}$$

and this is the low-loss case. From Fig. 2.4.2, the magnitude characteristic has about 10 dB (or a factor of 3.2) of peaking due to the poles. Therefore, we can now assemble all this information on the impedance paper as shown in Fig. 14.1.11a. It is clear that the maximum useful frequency range for this resistor is about 800 KHz. This is well beyond the range where active filters are generally used. With practice, such plots can often be made directly from the equivalent circuits without the need of writing equations. It is this simplicity and speed which makes impedance paper so useful.

EXAMPLE 14.1.2 Now a "noninductive" style of wirewound resistor is used in Example 14.1.1 where L = 2 μH. Plot the impedance characteristic of the resistor. Is its useful frequency range increased?

Solution The impedance characteristic of the "noninductive" resistor is quite different. The impedance zero is now located at

$$s_z = -R/L = -2\pi(80 \text{ MHz}) \tag{14.1.18}$$

which is increased 100 times. The impedance pole has a resonance frequency

$$\omega_n = 1/\sqrt{LC} = 2\pi(25 \text{ MHz}) \tag{14.1.19}$$

with a damping factor

$$\zeta = ½ (80 \text{ MHz}/8 \text{ MHz})^{½} = ½ (10^{½}) = 1.58 \cong 1.6 \tag{14.1.20}$$

This corresponds now to a high-loss case where the poles are real. Since ζ is close to unity, we calculate the poles using Eq. 2.7.25 where

$$k = \zeta \pm (\zeta^2 - 1)^{½} = 1.58 \pm (1.58^2 - 1)^{½} = 1.58 \pm 1.22 = 0.36,\ 2.8 \tag{14.1.21}$$

so that the impedance poles equal

$$p_1 = -2\pi[0.36(25 \text{ MHz})] = -2\pi(9 \text{ MHz}), \qquad p_2 = -2\pi(25 \text{ MHz}/0.36) = -2\pi(69 \text{ MHz}) \tag{14.1.22}$$

The impedance characteristic is shown in Fig. 14.1.11b. We see that the useful frequency range has been increased by about a decade to 9 MHz. Notice that the asymptotic rolloff still falls on the 20 pF line. However, calculations are required to determine the corner frequencies involved. This example shows why the noninductive resistor is superior to the standard resistor in high-frequency applications.

14.1.8 NOISE

Another important consideration in resistors is that of noise. *Thermal noise*, or equivalently, *Johnson noise* is the result of thermal agitation of electrons in the resistive material.[5] The noise amplitude at any time is random and is described by the Gaussian probability density function

$$f(v) = (2\pi e_n^2)^{-1/2} \exp(-v^2/2e_n^2) \tag{14.1.23}$$

having zero mean and a variance of e_n^2. Thermal noise processes are generally "white" with flat power spectrums (i.e., independent of frequency) having value

$$S_n(\omega) = 2kTR \text{ volts}^2/(\text{rad/sec}) \tag{14.1.24}$$

where R is the resistor value (ohms), T is the resistor temperature (°K), and k is Boltzmann's constant which equals 1.37×10^{-23} (joules/°K). The mean squared voltage density equals

$$e_n^2 = (2\pi/2)S_n(0) = 4kTR \text{ volts}^2/\text{Hz} \tag{14.1.25}$$

In a bandwidth B (Hz), the rms noise voltage equals

$$E_n = [S_n(0)2\pi B/\pi]^{1/2} = (4kTRB)^{1/2} \text{ volts} \tag{14.1.26}$$

At room temperature, the noise density e_n equals $0.13R^{1/2}$ $\mu V/Hz^{1/2}$ for R in MΩ. If we instead express the noise in terms of current, then

$$I_n = E_n/R = (4kTB/R)^{1/2} \text{ amps} \tag{14.1.27}$$

so the noise density i_n equals $0.13/R^{1/2}$ $pA/Hz^{1/2}$ for R in MΩ. At constant measurement bandwidths, the noise voltage and current are constant. Once bandwidth has been defined, the nomograph in Fig. 14.1.12 can be used to simplify noise calculations at room temperature.

EXAMPLE 14.1.3 Determine the inherent thermal noise generated by a 10 K resistor at room temperature in 100 Hz, 1 KHz, and 10 KHz bandwidths. What is the maximum resistor value which can be used if noise cannot exceed 1 μV in a 5 KHz bandwidth?

Solution From Fig. 14.1.12, the inherent rms thermal noise levels equal

$$e_n\,(100\text{ Hz}) = 0.13\ \mu V, \qquad e_n\,(1\text{ KHz}) = 0.41\ \mu V, \qquad e_n\,(10\text{ KHz}) = 1.3\ \mu V \tag{14.1.28}$$

For less than 1 μV of noise in 5 KHz, the maximum resistor value equals 12 K.

In addition to thermal noise, there is 1/f noise which dominates over thermal noise at low frequencies (usually below 100 Hz). *1/f noise* or *contact noise* exhibits a $1/f^2$ power spectrum where the noise density equals

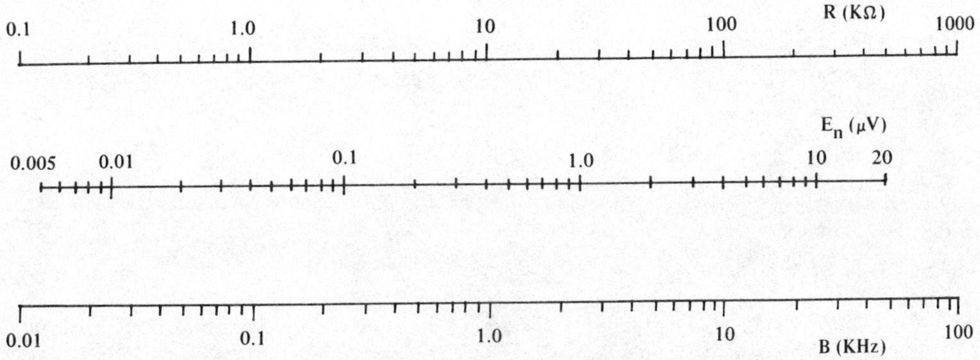

Fig. 14.1.12 Thermal noise nomograph (T = 27°C = 300°K).

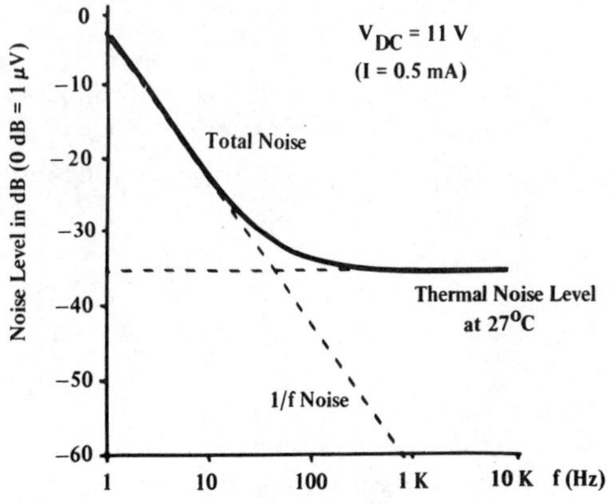

Fig. 14.1.13 Typical thermal and 1/f noise characteristics of 22 K resistor. (From Variable Resistor Catalog ME73VR-2, p. 26, Mepco/Electra, Morristown, NJ, July, 1973.)

$$e_n = K/f \ \mu V/Hz^{1/2} \tag{14.1.29}$$

A more general viewpoint of 1/f noise will be taken in Sec. 14.4.10. The total 1/f noise in a bandwidth B between frequencies f_1 and f_2 equals

$$E_n = \left[\int_{f_1}^{f_2} (K/f)^2 \, df\right]^{1/2} = K\left[-1/f \Big|_{f=f_1}^{f_2}\right]^{1/2} = K(B/f_1 f_2)^{1/2} = KB^{1/2}/f_o \tag{14.1.30}$$

where $f_o = \sqrt{f_1 f_2}$ is the geometric mean of the two corner frequencies. For a constant measurement bandwidth B, e_n varies as $1/f_o$.

The typical noise output of a 22 K resistor at room temperature (T = 300°K) is shown in Fig. 14.1.13. In a 1 Hz bandwidth, the thermal noise equals E_n = 0.019 μV from Fig. 14.1.12 which is 35 dB below 1 μV. For frequencies below 100 Hz, the noise level follows a 1/f power law. The 1/f noise at 1 Hz in a 1 Hz bandwidth is measured as 0.6 μV which is 4.2 dB below 1 μV. Assuming that the various noise sources $e_{n1}, e_{n2}, \ldots$ (or $i_{n1}, i_{n2}, \ldots$) are random and uncorrelated, the noise power due to the various sources is additive. The total rms noise voltage (or current) is the square root of the sum of squares of each separate noise source or

$$e_n = (e_{n1}^2 + e_{n2}^2 + \ldots)^{1/2}, \qquad i_n = (i_{n1}^2 + i_{n2}^2 + \ldots)^{1/2} \tag{14.1.31}$$

Therefore, the total noise is easily drawn in Fig. 14.1.13.

Sometimes the *noise index* of a resistor is specified. The noise index NI, expressed in dB, equals

$$NI = 20 \log_{10} (\text{Noise voltage in } \mu V/\text{DC voltage in V}) \tag{14.1.32}$$

where the noise voltage is measured over one decade of bandwidth at a specified temperature and frequency. Rearranging Eq. 14.1.32, the total noise voltage for a given bandwidth between f_1 and f_2 equals

$$E_n = V_{dc} \times 10^{NI/20} \times [\log_{10} (f_2/f_1)]^{1/2} \tag{14.1.33}$$

Thus, for V_{dc} = 11 volts and a noise index of −20 dB, then the total noise of the 22 K resistor in Fig. 14.1.13 equals

$$E_n = 11 \times 10^{-1} \times (\log_{10} 2)^{1/2} = 0.6 \ \mu V \tag{14.1.34}$$

from 1 to 2 Hz. Typical noise index values are $5 \log_{10}(10^{-10}R)$ for metal film resistors and $10 \log_{10}(10^{-5.5}R)$ for carbon film resistors.[6] For example, the typical NI of a 10 K resistor is −30 dB for metal film types and −15 dB for carbon film types. We see that metal film resistors are much "quieter" than carbon film resistors especially for large resistance values.

When the noise is independent of either the resistor voltage or current level, which is usually the case, we can treat the noise as being generated by an independent source. Thus, we can replace the *unavoidably* noisy resistor by a noiseless resistor and a noise source using either a Thevenin or Norton equivalent. These equivalents are shown in Fig. 1.12.4 and were discussed in Sec. 1.12. It is important to remember that the noise generator n(t) must be described statistically rather than deterministically.

The concept of thermal noise is of paramount importance in active filters because of signal-to-noise ratio (SNR) considerations. Every resistor in an active filter has a noise source associated with it. The noise sources are independent of one another. These noise sources produce an inherent "noise floor" at the output of the active filter. The only way to reduce the noise floor of the filter is to reduce (magnitude scale) the resistors by the same factor. Of course the noise-free capacitors must also be magnitude scaled to preserve the filter parameters. This increases the power consumption of the resistors and their required power rating. We shall discuss SNR when we consider operational amplifiers later in the chapter.

14.1.9 RELIABILITY

The general area of reliability is often neglected by filter designers except those involved in high reliability systems generally associated with the government. A brief introduction to reliability will aid in the proper selection and use of the resistor.

Reliability is defined as the probability that a system will not fail but will operate properly (i.e., survive) at least until some arbitrary time. The operational reliability of a component or system is a function of both its inherent reliability and its usage reliability.[7] As shown in Table 14.1.7, the inherent reliability of a system is determined by the limitations imposed upon its design, the materials and components of which it is made, and the degree to which their quality is assured. The usage reliability is determined by the way in which the system is maintained, and the environment in which it operates.

A number of factors effect these various reliabilities. Some of these factors considered when

Table 14.1.7 Factors to consider in reliability studies.

Operational Reliability

Use Reliability

Inherent Reliability	Limitations	Maintenance Reliability	Environmental Reliability
Quality of material	Cost	Effects of shipping and handling	Mission fulfillment
Manufacturing techniques	Weight	Deterioration in storage	Operational suitability
Component testing	Space	Logistics	Auxiliary and supporting equipment
Circuit selection	Delivery schedule	Installative effect and accessibility	Electrical stress
Standardization and selection of preferred parts	State of the art	Preventive maintenance schedule	Thermal stress
Adequate stress design		Down-time	Shock and vibration
Performance to satisfy specifications		Operating and maintenance procedure	Moisture, humidity, dust, and pH
Debugging procedure		Capability of operating and maintenance personnel	Pressure and altitude
			Radiation
			On-off cycling

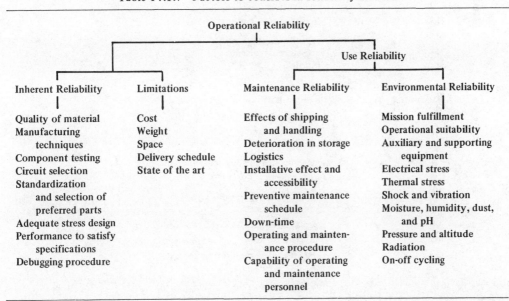

Table 14.1.8 Summary of military test methods. (From "Test methods for electronic and electrical component parts," MIL-STD-202E, p. 3, Dept. of Defense, Washington, DC, April, 1973.)

Method Number	Title
Environmental Tests (100 Class)	
101	Salt spray (corrosion)
102	Cancelled
103	Humidity (steady-state)
104	Immersion
105	Barometric pressure (reduced)
106	Moisture resistance
107	Thermal shock
108	Life (at elevated ambient temperature)
109	Explosion
110	Sand and dust
111	Flammability (external flame)
112	Seal
Physical Characteristic Tests (200 Class)	
201	Vibration
202	Shock (Superseded by Method 213)
203	Random drop
204	Vibration, high frequency
205	Shock, medium impact (Superseded by Method 213)
206	Life (rotational)
207	High impact shock
208	Solderability
209	Radiographic inspection
210	Resistance to soldering heat
211	Terminal strength
212	Acceleration
213	Shock (specified pulse)
214	Random vibration
215	Resistance to solvents
216	Cancelled
Electrical Characteristic Tests (300 Class)	
301	Dielectric withstanding voltage
302	Insulation resistance
303	DC resistance
304	Resistance-temperature characteristic
305	Capacitance
306	Quality factor (Q)
307	Contact resistance
308	Current-noise test for fixed resistors
309	Voltage coefficient of resistance determination procedure
310	Contact-chatter monitoring
311	Life, low-level switching
312	Intermediate current switching

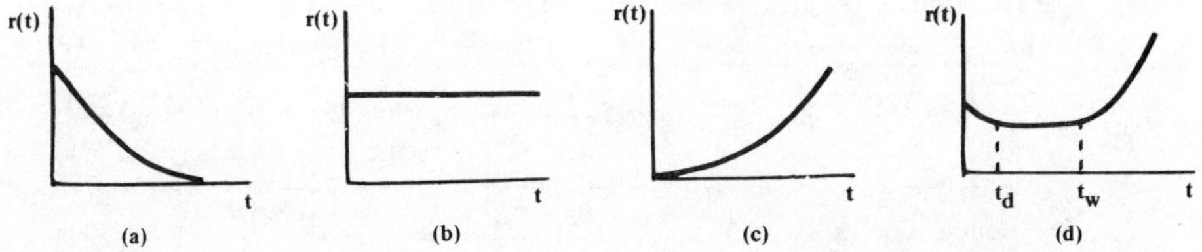

Fig. 14.1.14 (a) Infant mortality, (b) chance mortality, (c) wear-out mortality, and (d) total mortality curves.

characterizing components in military systems are described in MIL-STD-202 and are listed in Table 14.1.8.[8] (It is useful to remember that as additions, deletions, and revisions are made to MIL documents, a letter is added and updated. Hence the 202E document has gone through five updates). The factors listed in the 100 and 200 Classes primarily affect the environmental reliability while those in the 300 Class primarily affect the inherent reliability. The degree to which these factors affect performance is determined using standard test methods. These tests are used to electrically characterize any component (Class 300 tests) and to define its behavior under various conditions (Class 100 and 200 tests). These tests include such factors as humidity, shock, and lifetime. The area which we wish to consider is that of resistor reliability, its useful lifetime, and its failure rate. To do this, we now introduce several general concepts from reliability theory.

Reliability theory categorizes component failures into three classes as (1) infant failure, (2) chance failure, and (3) wearout failure. A component may fail soon after the beginning of operation due to its faulty manufacture, improper use in the electrical design (e.g., incorrect power rating), or many other reasons.[9] These are called *infant failures* and are generally detected during the "burn-in" (i.e., initial operation) of the component. In contrast, a component may operate indefinitely until it begins to wear-out, fatigue, or deteriorate. When a component fails under these conditions, it is called a *wear-out failure.* However, a component may have survived burn-in and yet fail well before wear-out can occur. These are called *chance failures.*

These failure classes are mathematically categorized by their characteristic *force of mortality* curves shown in Fig. 14.1.14. The force of mortality r(t) is defined to equal

$$r(t) = \Pr\,(t = T + dt \mid t > T) = f(t)/[1 - F(t)] \qquad (14.1.35)$$

where f(t) is the mortality probability density function, F(t) is the cumulative mortality probability density function, and t is the time of failure. The force of mortality at time t is equal to the probability that the component will fail at time t (i.e., in the next instant) given that it has survived until time t. The force of mortality is a decreasing function for infant failures, and an increasing function for wear-out failures. However, chance failures are characterized by a constant force of mortality. This is conceptually pleasing since the probability that a component will fail in the next instant is independent of its age if failure is by chance. A typical force of mortality curve for a component is shown in Fig. 14.1.14d.

Since chance failure processes have constant force of mortalities, their probability distribution functions F(t) satisfy

$$\frac{f(t)}{1 - F(t)} = \frac{1}{1 - F(t)}\,\frac{dF(t)}{dt} = k, \qquad t \geqslant 0 \qquad (14.1.36)$$

where F(0) = 0 and F(∞) = 1. Solving this differential equation for F(t) gives

$$F(t) = 1 - e^{-t/k}, \qquad t \geqslant 0 \qquad (14.1.37)$$

Thus, the unique mortality probability density function which describes infant failures is

$$f(t) = dF(t)/dt = e^{-t/k}/k, \qquad t \geqslant 0 \qquad (14.1.38)$$

Table 14.1.9 Typical failure rates for resistors.[10] (Based upon power stress-ambient temperature combinations (P, T) of (0.01, 0°C), (0.5, $T_{max}/2$), and (1.0, T_{max}).

Resistor Type	Failure Rate (failures/10^9 hours) Low	Average	High	T_{max} (°C)
Composition (RC type)	0.35	2.5	30	70
Film (RN type)	1.2	3.4	13	125
Wirewound (RB type)	16	30	230	125

This is the exponential density function with mean k. k is usually referred to as the *mean time between failures* or *MTBF* of the component. Occasionally it is also called the *mean time to failure* or *MTTF*. The reciprocal of the MTBF is the *failure rate* of the component. The probability that the component will not fail before time T, or survive at least until time T, equals

$$\Pr(t \geq T) = 1 - F(t) = e^{-T/k} \tag{14.1.39}$$

For a 90% chance of survival, then T = 0.11k; for 95%, then T = 0.051k; and for 99%, then T = 0.01k.

Extensive testing is required to determine the MTBF or failure rates for various components. In lieu of specific failure rate values for resistors, the typical values listed in Table 14.1.9 can be used. We see that composition and film resistors are the most reliable and wirewound resistors are the least reliable. Composition resistors have an average MTBF of

$$\text{MTBF} = 1/2.5 \times 10^{-9} = 0.40 \times 10^9 \text{ hours} = 45{,}700 \text{ years} \tag{14.1.40}$$

(1 year = 8,760 hours) while film resistors have

$$\text{MTBF} = 1/3.4 \times 10^{-9} = 0.29 \times 10^9 \text{ hours} = 33{,}600 \text{ years} \tag{14.1.41}$$

The lifetimes for a 99% survival probability equal 457 and 336 years, respectively. An extensive listing of failure rates and other reliability data for electronic components can be found in MIL-HDBK-217.[10]

The MTBF and failure rates of most components including resistors is heavily dependent upon (1) their operating (i.e., case) temperature and (2) their operating power relative to their rated power. The failure rates for RN metal film resistors are shown in Fig. 14.1.15. The failure rate increases exponentially with both thermal stress (temperature) and electrical stress (power). Thus, we see the value of adequate heat-sinking and power derating for improving the reliability of a resistor. In general, composition resistors are much more susceptible to these stresses than metal film resistors, and wirewound resistors are only slightly more susceptible.

Derating or π-factors have been empirically obtained to use in conjunction with the failure rates to give more realistic values. These application π-factors are also listed in Fig. 14.1.15. The effective failure rate f is obtained by multiplying the base failure rate f_o, obtained from the figure, by the three π-factors as

$$f = (\pi_E \pi_R \pi_Q) f_o \text{ failures}/10^6 \text{ hours} \tag{14.1.42}$$

The meaning of the π_E-factors are listed in Table 14.1.10. Highest reliability is obtained for benign ground operation and lowest reliability is obtained for missile applications.

EXAMPLE 14.1.4 Determine the failure rates for RN metal film resistors (C types) having values less than 100 K. Assume that they operate in a mobile radio at their maximum rated power levels with maximum permissible case temperatures.

Solution Since they operate at full rated power, their power stress ratios equal R = 1.0. We see from

Table 14.1.10 Types of π_E factors.[12]

Environment	π_E Symbol	Nominal Environmental Conditions
Ground, Benign	G_B	Nearly zero environmental stress with optimum engineering operation and maintenance.
Space, Flight	S_F	Earth orbital. Approaches Ground, Benign conditions without access for maintenance. Vehicle neither under powered flight nor in atmospheric re-entry.
Ground, Fixed	G_F	Conditions less than ideal to include installation in permanent racks with adequate cooling air, maintenance by military personnel and possible installation in unheated buildings.
Ground, Mobile (and Portable)	G_M	Conditions more severe than those for G_F, mostly for vibration and shock. Cooling air supply may also be more limited, and maintenance less uniform.
Naval, Sheltered	N_S	Surface ship conditions similar to G_F but subject to occasional high shock and vibration.
Naval, Unsheltered	N_U	Nominal surface shipborne conditions but with repetitive high levels of shock and vibration.
Airborne Inhabited	A_I	Typical cockpit conditions without environmental extremes of pressure, temperature, shock and vibration.
Airborne, Uninhabited	A_U	Bomb-bay, tail, or wing installations where extreme pressure, temperature, and vibration cycling may be aggravated by contamination from oil, hydraulic fluid, and engine exhaust.
Missile, Launch	M_L	Severe conditions of noise, vibration, and other environments related to missile launch, and space vehicle boost into orbit, vehicle re-entry and landing by parachute.

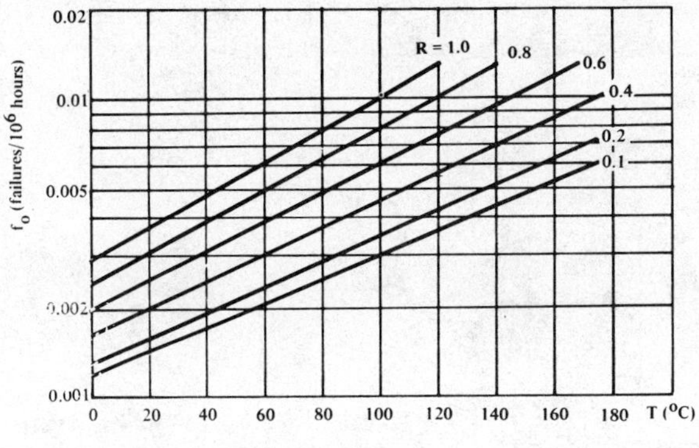

Environment	π_E RL, RLR	π_E RN, RNR
G_B	1.0	1.0
S_F	1.0	1.0
G_F	5.0	2.5
A_I	6.5	5.0
N_S	8.0	7.5
G_M	12.0	10.0
N_U	14.0	11.0
A_U	15.0	12.0
M_L	35.0	18.0

Failure Rate Level (RN)	π_Q
M	1.0
P	0.3
R	0.1
S	0 03

For RL, increase π_Q by 5

Resistance Range (Ω)	π_R
<100 K	1.0
>100 K – 1 M	1.1
>1 M – 10 M	1.6
>10 M	2.5

Fig. 14.1.15 Failure rates for RN, RNR, RL, and RLR film resistors (T_{max} = 125°C).[11]

the derating curve of Fig 14.1.4 that, at the maximum rated power level, the maximum permissible case temperatures equal $T_c = 125°C$. From Fig. 14.1.15, the base failure rates equal

$$f_o = 13 \times 10^{-9} \text{ failures/hour} \tag{14.1.43}$$

A mobile radio is a type of mobile ground application whose environmental factor $\pi_E = 10$. The resistance values are less than 100 K so the resistance factor $\pi_R = 1$. We will assume they are rated at an M failure rate level so that $\pi_Q = 1$. Thus, from Eq. 14.1.42, the resistor failure rate f equals

$$f = (\pi_E \pi_R \pi_Q) f_o = (10)(1)(1)(13 \times 10^{-9}) = 130 \times 10^{-9} \text{ failures/hour} \tag{14.1.44}$$

which is almost 40 times larger than the typical value in Table 14.1.9. The MTBF is reduced to 8780 years so that the lifetimes, for a 99% survival probability, are about 88 years.

14.1.10 AGING AND RADIATION EFFECTS

In addition to temperature drifts, resistors show aging effects. This is illustrated in Fig. 14.1.16. After manufacture and during storage, resistor values drift from their initial values depending upon temperature and humidity. During installation, mechanical and thermal stresses produce further drifts. During operation, the drifts increase as the product of the TC and temperature rise. With age, permanent drifts usually result due to the heat which has been generated during its operation. Because of these factors, resistors operating at 50% power stress for three years typically show the permanent resistance changes listed in Table 14.1.11. Composition resistors have the greatest aging effects while metal film and wirewound have rather small aging effects. Aging effects are vendor dependent. Usually, resistance values tend to somewhat stabilize after the first 500–1000 hours of operation.[13] Reducing the power stress fails to reduce aging (although it increases reliability) significantly.

Resistors are also affected by radiation. Long-term radiation, such as that found in space applications, can cause permanent changes in resistance. Some typical changes are listed in Table 14.1.12. Composition resistors tend to suffer negative changes and metal film resistors show slightly positive changes. Wirewound resistors are virtually unaffected. High-intensity radiation pulses cause temporary decreases in most resistance values. Following the pulse, the resistance usually returns to its normal value.

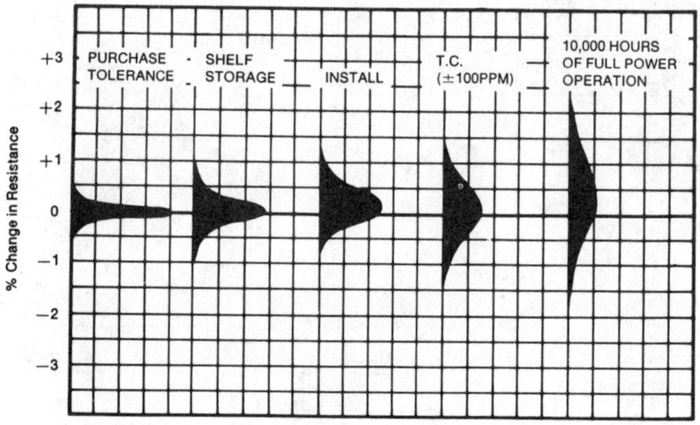

Fig. 14.1.16 Typical resistor aging characteristics over 10,000 hours of operation. (From TRW/IRC Resistors Catalog, p. 6, TRW Electronic Components, Philadelphia, PA, 1974.)

Table 14.1.11 Typical resistance changes in three years (50% power stress).[14]

Type	RB	RB/RV	RD	RL	RN	RW
Change (±%)	1	15	6	5	3 (D) 1 (C & E)	6

Table 14.1.12 Typical resistance changes (%) due to long-term radiation.[14]

Resistor Type	Radiation Intensity (n/cm^2) 10^{15}	10^{18}
Composition	−8.5/+1.6	−11.5/+2.3
Film		
Metal	0/+0.3	0/+0.6
Carbon	−0.2/+1.6	−0.7/+3.2
Wirewound	Negligible	Negligible

14.2 POTENTIOMETERS

Potentiometers are three-terminal devices. Two terminals make contact between the ends of a resistive element. The third terminal is connected to a movable conductive contact (often called the slider or wiper) which slides over the resistive element, thus making contact at some intermediate point between the ends. The output voltage at the wiper is some percentage of the input voltage across the ends. The percentage is controlled by the mechanical angle of the shaft which positions the wiper. In this mode of operation, potentiometers act as voltage dividers. *Rheostats* are two-terminal devices. They are potentiometers in which one end terminal has been omitted. Thus, they can function only as a variable resistor and not as a voltage divider. Potentiometers can be used as variable resistors but not visa versa. Therefore, potentiometers are widely available while rheostats are virtually nonexistent. In certain voltage-divider applications, it is convenient to have one or more fixed outputs in addition to the variable output. These additional outputs are called *taps*.[15]

Historically, George Little patented the rectangular or linear rheostat in 1871, and H. P. MacLagan patented the rotary rheostat in 1907. Although the modern potentiometer has undergone much refinement, it still retains much of the same physical arrangement as its predecessors.

Potentiometers are utilized in active filters for tuning or trimming purposes such as adjusting an amplifier gain K, a center frequency ω_o, or a dc voltage offset. Several types of potentiometers, which are often called simply "pots", are available which include (1) composition (carbon), (2) film (metal, carbon, cermet, conductive plastic), and (3) wirewound. Film potentiometers are used in most active filters today. They have largely replaced wirewound potentiometers except in some low frequency, low cost applications. The low cost composition potentiometers find limited usage because of their large temperature drift. The selection of potentiometers is more difficult than selection of fixed resistors because of the great differences in their electrical characteristics and their wide variety of construction.

14.2.1 CONSTRUCTION

Potentiometers have the general construction shown in Fig. 14.2.1 regardless of their type. They are composed basically of a resistance element, housing, shaft or screw, wiper, exterior terminals, and bushing. The material used to construct the resistance element determines the potentiometer type which we shall discuss in a moment. The housing may be round, square, or rectangular. It is constructed of metal (stainless steel, anodized aluminum, or nickel-plated brass) or plastic (molded plastic–commonly diallyl phthalate, polycarbonate, nylon, epoxy, or laminated phenolic). The shaft or screw which controls the wiper position is also metal (stainless steel or nickel-plated brass) or plastic (nylon, Delrin, or polycarbonate). The wiper is metal (phosphor bronze or tempered brass) as are the three exterior terminals (gold- and silver-plated metal or solder-coated

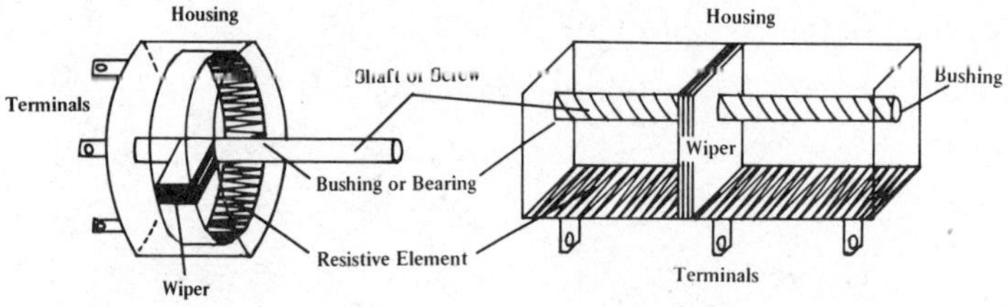

Fig. 14.2.1 Potentiometer construction.

copper). Finally, the bushing which supports the shaft or screw assembly is metal (brass) or simply the housing itself. Occasionally in large assemblies, ball-bearings are used for support. Regardless of the bushing or bearing used, a hermetic seal (an inner O-ring) around the shaft and housing is often used to improve reliability. Now let us review the resistance elements themselves.

Wirewound potentiometers are formed by winding resistance wire (a copper-nickel, nickel-chrome, or manganese-copper alloy depending on the resistance value) on a strip of nonconductive core (an inflexible ceramic of steatite, alumina, or beryllia; or a flexible material such as fiberglass). The flexible core is formed in a circle and mounted in a housing to form a single-turn pot, or the inflexible core is simply laid in a housing to form a rectangular multiturn pot. Alternatively, the resistance wire may be wound on a temporary inner core, and potted or encapsulated within a plastic housing. The inner core is removed and a rotor block assembly inserted.

Composition potentiometers are formed by molding resistive material (carbon) onto a nonconductive disc or strip, or within a hollow nonconductive housing. Generally, end tabs have been previously embedded in the nonconductive cores so the molding insures a solid, integral construction. The rotor block assembly is attached after the molding operation.

Film potentiometers are formed in a manner similar to composition potentiometers. However, the particular film (metal, carbon, cermet, conductive plastic) to be used is deposited on the nonconductive disc, strip, or core rather than molding (except for carbon film). Metal films (usually nickel-chrome (Nichrome) alloy) are usually vapor-deposited on their nonconductive ceramic cores. The films are extremely thin, often only several hundred angstroms thick. Conductive plastic films contain a mixture of conductive particles in a plastic filler. Conductive plastic films and carbon films are molded onto their plastic and ceramic cores using heat and pressure. Cermet films are composed of precious-metal particles suspended in a glass carrier which are screened and later fused to their ceramic cores at 1400° to 2000°F. The thicknesses are 0.0005–0.005 inches.

Some of the key characteristics of the various potentiometer types are summarized in Table 14.2.1. The table shows that cermet and metal film potentiometers have low temperature coefficients, low parasitic effects, and a resonable cost. Since cermet potentiometers have the widest range of values, they are most commonly used in active filters. However, almost all the other types do find specific uses.

Potentiometers are sometimes classified as (1) volume control, (2) trimming, (3) semiprecision, and (4) precision. This classification is from the viewpoint of application and mechanical construction rather than the material of the resistive element. Volume control potentiometers are generally lowest in cost. They are wirewound and carbon types and are generally a single-turn, bushing mount type. Semiprecision potentiometers are intermediate cost pots having a single-turn and bushing mounts. They are generally wirewound or film types. Trimming potentiometers are also intermediate cost pots made of the same materials but which are lead-screw actuated and usually packaged in square or rectangular cases. Precision potentiometers are generally the most costly. They are made of wirewound and film materials having single-turn and multiturn types with bushing mounts. Precision potentiometers have the highest accuracy and are often used in the most adverse environments.

Table 14.2.1 Typical potentiometer characteristics.

Potentiometer Type	Range (Ω)	Tolerance (%)	TC (± PPM/°C)	Power	Parasitic Effects	Cost
Composition	100–5 M	10, 20	1000	Medium	Low	Low
Film						
Metal	50–10 K	5, 10	100	Low	Low	Medium
Carbon	100–5 M	10, 20	1000	Low	Low	Medium
Cermet	10–1 M	5, 10	100	Medium	Low	Medium
Conductive Plastic	1 K–100 K	10, 20	250	Medium	Low	Medium
Wirewound	10–100 K	5, 10	100	High	High	High

In specifying a potentiometer, the following parameters are important: (1) potentiometer value, (2) power rating, (3) temperature coefficient, (4) operating temperature range, and (5) style. Other important but often neglected parameters include: (6) slider current, (7) end resistance, (8) linearity, (9) resolution, (10) noise, (11) reliability, and (12) aging. We shall now discuss these parameters to show their importance in potentiometer selection.

14.2.2 STANDARD VALUES AND TOLERANCES

Because potentiometers are generally used as voltage dividers or as variable resistors, their overall or end-to-end resistance need not be available in a large number of standard values. For this reason, potentiometers have standard values of only 1, 2, and 5 (first significant figure). The range of the values depends on potentiometer type as listed in Table 14.2.1. For the same reason, their tolerance values need not be stringent. The standard tolerances are 5, 10, and 20%.

14.2.3 POWER RATING, TEMPERATURE COEFFICIENT, AND OPERATING TEMPERATURE RANGE

The power rating P_{max} of a potentiometer having total resistance R_p is given by Eq. 14.1.2, and the maximum voltage V_{max} by Eq. 14.1.3 when the slider current is zero. When the potentiometer is used as a rheostat of minimum value KR_p, where K is the minimum percentage of the total resistance, then the most conservative power and voltage ratings become

$$P = KP_{max}, \qquad V = KV_{max} \tag{14.2.1}$$

This assumes that the heat generated in KR_p is not transferred to the unused portion of the pot $(1 - K)R_p$ This "hot-spot" assumption is realistic in practice. On a volume basis, cermet and conductive plastic film and wirewound pots have higher power ratings than metal and carbon film and composition pots. Nevertheless, pots of every variety having standard power ratings of ¼, ½, 1, and 2 watts are available.

Temperature coefficients measure drifts in potentiometer values just as in resistors. The TC's corresponding to various drifts and temperature changes were determined using Fig. 14.1.5. From Table 14.2.1, we see that cermet, metal film, and wirewound potentiometers have low TC's but composition, carbon, and conductive plastic film potentiometers have large TC's.

The operating temperature range of potentiometers is described in the same manner as that for resistors. Typical power derating curves for potentiometers are shown in Fig. 14.2.2 for composition and wirewound resistors.

Another important parameter of a potentiometer is the maximum slider current. This is the

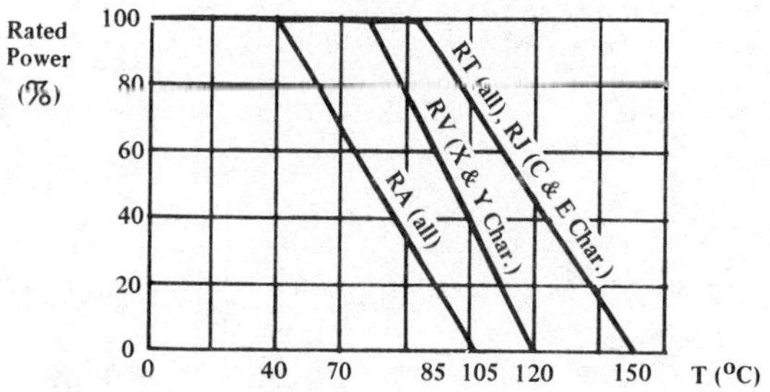

Fig. 14.2.2 Power derating curves for composition film (RV and RJ) and wirewound (RT and RA) potentiometers.

maximum current which can flow into or out of the slider terminal without damaging the pot or significantly altering its characteristics. Large current ratings require sliders having large-area and high pressure to maintain low current densities in the slider/resistance element interface. This current usually ranges from 1–100 mA depending upon the pot design. Therefore, both the maximum power rating and the maximum current rating must be considered when specifying a potentiometer.

14.2.4 MODEL

The equivalent circuit of a potentiometer is shown in Fig. 14.2.3. It is usually adequate to frequencies of 10–100 MHz. The parameters are the (1) end-to-end resistance or (total resistance), (2) active resistance, (3) end resistance, (4) contact resistance, and the (5) contact resistance variation.

The *end-to-end* or *total resistance* is the resistance R_{ab} between the end terminals A and B. This is measured with terminal C open (the slider or wiper current is equal to zero). The *end resistances* R_{ea} and R_{eb} of the potentiometer are the residual resistances of the resistance element when the slider is adjusted to its end points (extreme upward and downward positions). The end resistances are measured using voltage division between the input (terminals A and B) and output (terminal C) when the slider current is zero. The *active portion* of the total resistance, R_p, is the difference between the total resistance R_{ab} and the end resistances R_{ea} and R_{eb}, so that

$$R_{ab} = R_p + R_{ea} + R_{eb} \tag{14.2.2}$$

In ideal potentiometers, R_{ea} and R_{eb} equal zero so that $R_{ab} = R_p$. In actual potentiometers, R_{ea} and R_{eb} are nonzero. End resistance is generally expressed as the maximum value of R_{ea} and R_{eb} (i.e., the worst-case value). Typically, the end resistances are 0.1–1% of R_p.

The contact resistance R_c is the average resistance between the slider and the resistance element. In practice, small variations in contact resistance occur as the slider moves over the resistance element. The contact resistance variation ΔR_c is equal to the average variation in R_c.

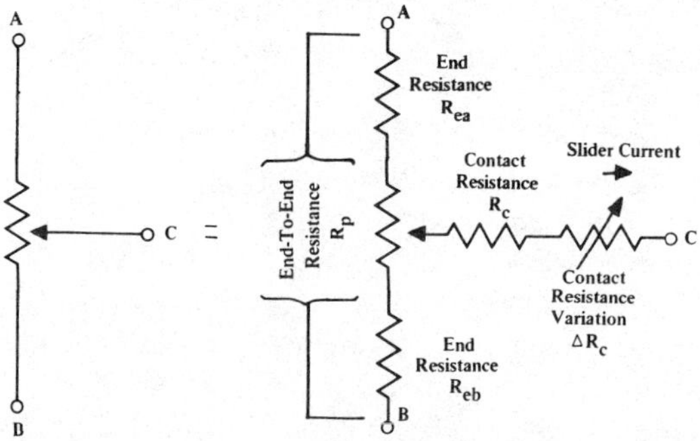

Fig. 14.2.3 Equivalent circuit of potentiometer.

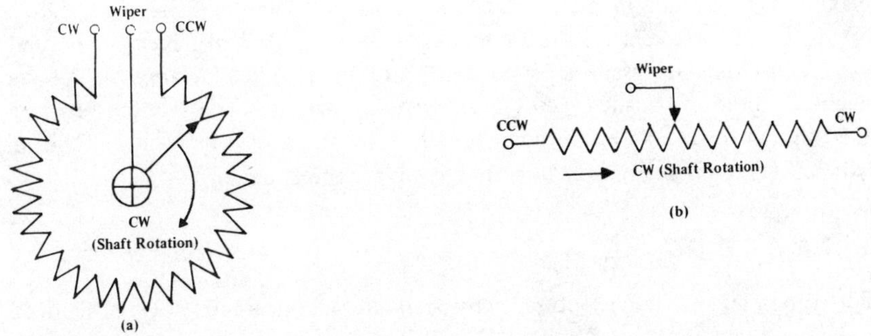

Fig. 14.2.4 View of shaft and resistance element from specified mounting end.

Typically, the contact resistance R_c is 1–10% of R_p while its variation ΔR_c is 1–5% of R_p. (For experimental plots, see Ref. 15.)

14.2.5 ROTATION AND TRANSLATION

The physical or mechanical construction of a potentiometer is extremely important. Not only does it largely control reliability and aging characteristics, but it also effects the electrical characteristics of the potentiometer. The general construction of the pot was shown in Fig. 14.2.1. The *direction of travel* of the shaft and wiper for rotary pots is denoted by CW (clockwise) and CCW (counterclockwise) rotation. When the pot is viewed from the designated end (usually the mounting or adjustment end), the end terminals are labelled in the direction of the shaft and wiper travel. This is shown in Fig. 14.2.4a. In translational pots, CW and CCW correspond to the extending and retracting directions of travel as shown in Fig. 14.2.4b.

The *total mechanical travel* or *angle of rotation* is the total angular travel of the shaft between travel stops. It is usually measured in degrees. For example, one-turn pots generally have total mechanical travels of 200°–300°. In multiturn pots, mechanical travel is generally expressed in turns. In some pots, slip clutches are used on the slider assembly to prevent its damage when travel beyond the travel stops is attempted. In these pots, the total mechanical travel is measured between the points where clutch action begins.

The total *electrical travel* or *effective angle of rotation* is the total angular travel of the shaft between two specified index or end points. The *index points* serve simply as reference points to allow the input/output relation versus shaft position to be established. The total electrical travel is never greater than the total mechanical travel. This is shown in Fig. 14.2.5. When the mechanical travel falls outside the electrical travel index points, it is termed *mechanical overtravel* which results in *electrical overtravel.*

When the shaft is moved to the same electrical travel point from opposite positions, the mechanical travel points will not in general be equal. This is called *backlash* and is defined to be the

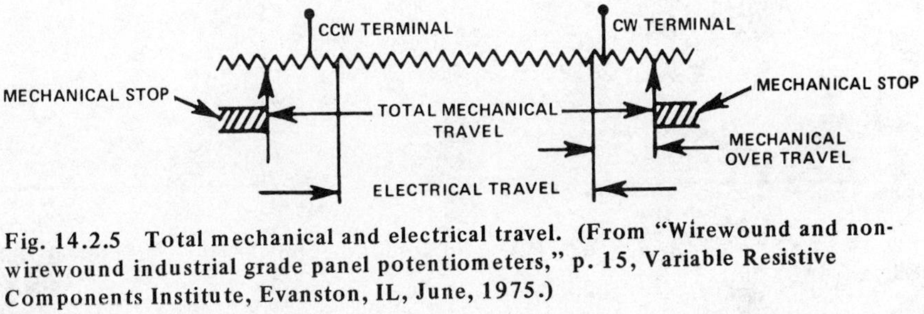

Fig. 14.2.5 Total mechanical and electrical travel. (From "Wirewound and nonwirewound industrial grade panel potentiometers," p. 15, Variable Resistive Components Institute, Evanston, IL, June, 1975.)

maximum difference in mechanical shaft positions for the same electrical output. Backlash is caused by imperfect mechanical coupling between shaft and wiper and is typically from 1°–20°.

The torque necessary to start shaft rotation is called *starting torque,* and that necessary to maintain rotation is called *running* or *operating torque*. The starting torque is usually 1–5 times the running torque which is typically 0.1–1 oz-in. Most pots are also rated for *maximum torque*, which if exceeded, can result in permanent mechanical damage.

14.2.6 TAPER

Potentiometers are manufactured with standard gain characteristics. The ideal gain is expressed as

$$V_2/V_1 = f(\theta/\theta_T) \tag{14.2.3}$$

where f is the standard function and θ is the electrical travel. In most pots, f is a linear or logarithmic function. f is often referred to as the *taper*. The actual gain equals $f(\theta/\theta_T) \pm C$, where C is the *tolerance* or *conformity* of the actual gain to the ideal gain or taper.

The standard tapers for most potentiometers are linear and logarithmic (commonly called audio). These are shown in Fig. 14.2.6. Although these are the standard tapers, a large number of other tapers can be obtained to fit specific applications:[17]

1. Linear

$$f(x) = x \tag{14.2.4}$$

2. Exponential or Logarithmic

$$f(x) = 10^{x-1} \text{ (one-cycle or 20 dB)}, \qquad f(x) = 10^{2(x-1)} \text{ (two-cycle or 40 dB)} \tag{14.2.5}$$

3. Square (one-sided or two-sided)

$$f(x) = x^2 \tag{14.2.6}$$

4. Sine and/or Cosine (90°, 180°, or 360°)

$$f(x) = \sin\theta(x), \qquad \cos\theta(x) \tag{14.2.7}$$

5. Empirical (Data points)

$$f(x) = \text{data points where f is piecewise linear where line segments have nonnegative slopes} \tag{14.2.8}$$

In wirewound resistors, the tapers are obtained by varying the winding pitch (i.e., the center-to-center turn spacing), shaping the winding form, changing the wire resistivity (i.e., the alloy), and/or

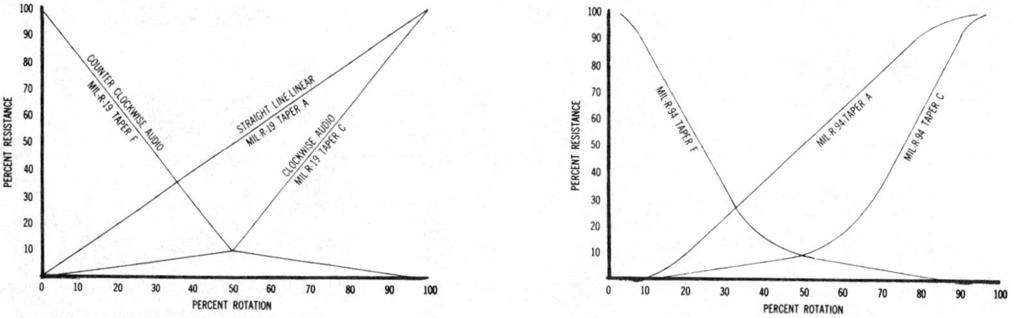

Fig. 14.2.6 Standard tapers for wirewound potentiometers. (From Data Sheet 7004, CTS Corp., Elkhart, IN, 1-70.)

cross-sectional area (i.e., its diameter) from time to time throughout the winding, changing the mechanical arrangements to cause the wiper to traverse varying wire lengths for each degree of shaft rotation, or by tapping and padding. Of these, controlling pitch and tapping are the simplest. The other techniques involve manufacturing difficulties.

In nonwirewound resistances, tapers are more easily achieved since the resistive material is continuous and can be shaped in width and depth as a function of length.

Some of these tapers are obtained using two outputs. In these situations, *tandem* or *ganged* pots are often employed which are constructed of two sections or cups and whose wipers operate off a single shaft. The *phasing* or relative alignment of the wipers is carefully controlled to insure conformity to the required gain characteristics.

Of course, any number of sections can be used to suit a requirement. For example, constant impedance-variable attenuators are often constructed using two- or three-section pots. The individual sections are connected in either L, T, or bridged-T configurations.[18]

14.2.7 LINEARITY AND RESOLUTION

Linear pots have ideal gains described by

$$f(\theta/\theta_T) = A(\theta/\theta_T) + B \tag{14.2.9}$$

The linearity of a pot is a measure of how closely its gain follows Eq. 14.2.9 as illustrated in Fig. 14.2.7. Industry uses four standard linearity definitions: (1) absolute linearity, (2) independent linearity, (3) zero-based linearity, and (4) terminal-based linearity. The only difference between the four definitions is in the position of the line. Absolute and independent linearity are the most widely used. The definitions are:

1. *Absolute linearity*: Maximum deviation of the gain from a straight line drawn through specific minimum and maximum gain values which are separated by the theoretical electrical travel.
2. *Independent linearity*: Maximum deviation of the gain from a straight line whose slope and intercept are chosen to minimize error (i.e., deviations).
3. *Zero-based linearity*: Maximum deviation of the gain from a straight line drawn through a specific minimum gain value and whose slope is chosen to minimize error (i.e., deviations).
4. *Terminal-based linearity*: Maximum deviation of the gain from a straight line drawn through specific minimum and maximum gain values which are separated by the actual electrical travel.

Thus, absolute and terminal-based linearity differ only in the electrical travel used. Independent and zero-based linearity differ only in the end point used to minimize error.

Wirewound pots with linear tapers have quite different gain characteristics than the other types of pots. This is illustrated in Fig. 14.2.8 where wirewound and nonwirewound pots are

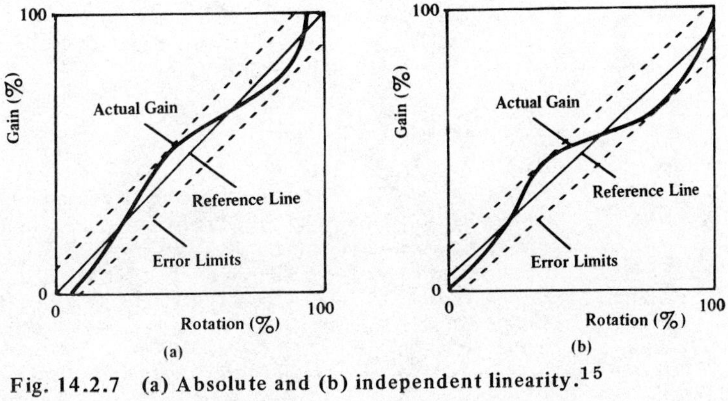

Fig. 14.2.7 (a) Absolute and (b) independent linearity.[15]

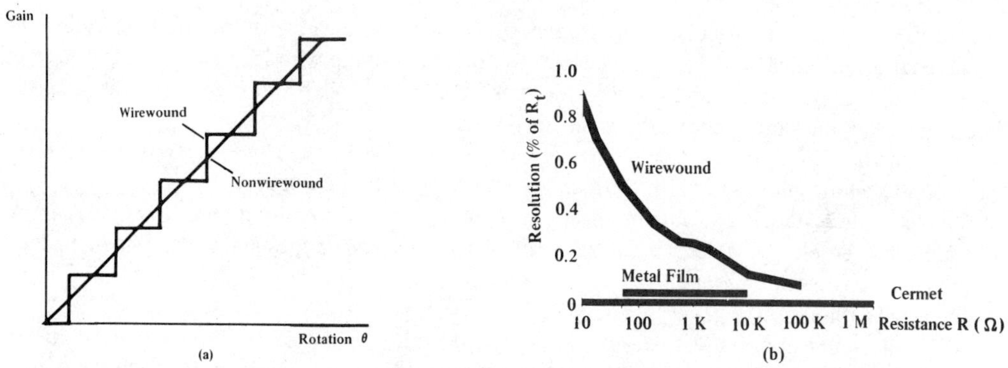

Fig. 14.2.8 (a) Gain of wirewound and nonwirewound potentiometers for small mechanical travel and (b) resolution of wirewound, metal film, and cermet potentiometers. ((b) from Trimmer Tech. Bull., H731168-474-35GF, p. 46, Beckman, Fullerton, CA, April, 1974.)

rotated in both directions, and their gains are plotted. We see the gain of the wirewound pot moves in discrete steps as the wiper moves from turn-to-turn. However, the gain is linear in nonwirewound pots since the resistive element is continuous. *Resolution* (or setting ability) is a measure of the continuity of the gain, or alternatively, the tolerance within which the gain can be adjusted. It is defined to equal the maximum incremental change in gain as the wiper moves over the resistance element. For this reason, nonwirewound pots are often said to have infinite resolution.[20] The best resolution of a wirewound pot is about 0.2%, while for cermet film pots, it is about 0.01% as shown in Fig. 14.2.8b.

14.2.8 NOMENCLATURE

Potentiometer nomenclature is difficult to decipher because it has not been standardized by industry. Generally, potentiometers are described by listing their style, value, tolerance, power, construction; bushing diameter, length, and type (when applicable); shaft diameter, length, and type (when applicable); turns, and taper. We see that potentiometers are much more difficult to specify than resistors. This is primarily due to the mechanical parameters which must be described.

The military nomenclature is standard but rather involved as we shall see. The military designations and specifications which apply are listed in Table 14.2.2. The newer film type potentiometers (excluding cermet types) have not yet been assigned specific designations or numbers.

Table 14.2.2 Military type designators and applicable specification numbers for potentiometers.

Composition		
RV	Resistors, Variable, Composition	MIL-R-94
RJ	Resistors, Variable, Non-wirewound (Lead Screw Actuated)	MIL-R-22097
RJR	Resistors, Variable, Established Reliability	MIL-R-39035
Film		
RVC	Resistors, Variable, Cermet	MIL-R-23285
Wirewound		
RA	Resistors, Variable, Wirewound (Low Operating Temperature)	MIL-R-19
RK	Resistors, Variable, Wirewound, Semi-Precision	MIL-R-39002
RP	Resistors, Variable, Wirewound (Power Type)	MIL-R-22
RR	Resistors, Variable, Wirewound, Precision	MIL-R-12934
RT	Resistors, Variable, Wirewound (Lead Screw Actuated)	MIL-R-27208
RTR	Resistors, Variable, Wirewound (Lead Screw Actuated), Established Reliability	MIL-R-39015

Usually, they are qualified under the RJ type.

In general, each potentiometer type is described using a different nomenclature. Thus, it is necessary to refer to the MIL specification listed in Table 14.2.2 to determine the proper form. The standard potentiometer nomenclature is an alphanumeric code whose format depends upon the potentiometer style. This format is summarized in Table 14.2.3 for the RJ type. We see the nomenclature compactly summarizes many of the important parameters necessary when selecting a potentiometer.

Table 14.2.3 Potentiometer nomenclature for RJ type.
(From Trimmer Tech. Bull. H731168-474-35GR, Beckman, CA, April, 1974.)

Style	Description
RJ11	1 ¼" Rectangular multi-turn with either leads, pins, or lugs.
RJ12	1 ¼" Thin rectangular multi-turn with leads or pins.
RJ22	½" Square multi-turn with leads, bottom, or edge-mount pins.
RJ24	3/8" Square multi-turn with bottom or edge-mount pins.
RJ25	¼" Square multi-turn with bottom or edge-mount pins.
RJ50	¼" Diameter (or square) single-turn with bottom pins.

Terminals: P –Printed circuit pins; L – Flex leads.

Resistance Value: First 2 digits significant, 3rd digit "number of zeros."

EXAMPLE: RJ24CP102 RJ24 C P 102

Resistance Change (±%)			
Environment	A	B	C
Thermal shock	3	4	2
Moisture resistance	10	10	2
Shock	2	2	1
Vibration	2	2	1
Load life	10	10	3
Low temp. operation	2	2	2
High temp. exposure	12	5	3
Rotational life	5	5	2

Power Rating (watts)			
Style	A	B	C
RJ11	0.25	0.25	0.75
RJ12	–	0.25	0.75
RJ22	–	0.25	0.50
RJ24	–	0.25	0.50
RJ25	–	0.25	0.25
RJ50	–	0.25	0.25

Temperature Characteristics			
Parameter	A	B	C
Max. TC (± PPM/°C)	400–1250	600	250
Max. ambient temp. at rated load (°C)	70	70	85
Max. ambient temp. at zero load (°C)	125	125	125
Contact resistance variation (when there are two, use the greater vaiue)	2%	3% or 20 Ω	3% or 20 Ω

14.2.9 MECHANICAL PARAMETERS

To further discuss nomenclature, we will now briefly review the mechanical parameters of potentiometers. These will include their case style, terminal style, adjustment type, and orientation.

Potentiometers have *case styles* which are: rectangular, square (or cube), round, and panel. These are illustrated in Fig. 14.2.9a. The case styles refer to the shape of the cases as shown. The panel style is perhaps the most well-known with its round case and long shaft. It is generally used for wirewound pots. However, the most widely available case is the rectangular style, although all case styles are used.

Potentiometers have a variety of *terminals* which are available. These are: lead, pin, lug, DIP, and wire-wrap as shown in Fig. 14.2.9b. Flexible wire lead types are used for soldering to printed circuit cards. Pin types mount directly to PC boards. DIP types mount in DIP receptacles. Lug types require wires to be soldered to them. Wire-wrap types require wires to be wire-wrapped to them. Thus, a great variety of lead types are available.

Potentiometers have *adjustments* using: screwdriver, shaft, fingertip, and gear as shown in Fig. 14.2.9c. The shaft types are used primarily in panel-mounted pots. Most pots have screwdriver adjustments. Some special types use fingertip and gear adjustments.

Potentiometers are mounted either vertically or horizontally with respect to their shaft adjustments. Almost all rectangular types are horizontally mounted, while round, square, and panel types are usually vertically mounted.

Although these mechanical parameters are sufficient to describe most potentiometers, the panel-mounted types require further description which we shall now review. Panel-mounted pots have *shaft trims* shown in Fig. 14.2.9d. They include round, flat, slotted, knurled, or slotted and knurled varieties. Round and one flat type (a shallow cut) are used for a setscrew knob. The flat surface is diametrically opposite the moving contact. The other flat type (a deep cut) is used for a push-on knob. Again, the flat surface is opposite the moving contact. One slotted type (a shallow slot) is aligned with the moving contact. The other slotted type (a deep slot is used) for a push-on knob. Usually, the slot is located at random. The knurled type is for finger adjustment.

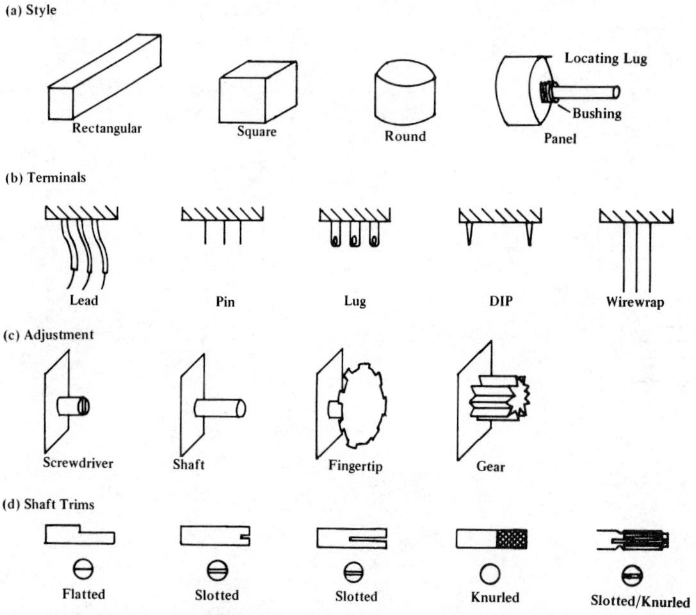

Fig. 14.2.9 Mechanical parameters of potentiometers.

The slotted and knurled types are for push-on knobs. Ganged pots have concentric shafts of the flat or slotted variety for push-on knobs.

Panel-mounted pots are mounted using *bushings*. The types of bushings include nonlocking (standard), locking, and watersealed varieties. All varieties use lockwashers and mounting nuts to mount the pot. However, the locking types allow the shaft to be locked into position (using locknuts) to prevent a change in position under vibration and acceleration. The watersealed varieties provide waterseals for the mounting itself and/or bearing (i.e., a shaft seal).

In addition to bushings, panel-mounted pots also have *locating lugs*. These lugs or tabs are small metal protrusions of the case (parallel to the bushing) which extend beyond the mounting surface. They serve to both orient the case to the proper angle when mounting, and to prevent the case from turning. Most panel-mounted pots use single lugs. Thus, we see the engineer has even more parameters to specify when selecting a panel-mounted pot.

14.2.10 NOISE

We discussed resistor noise in Sec. 14.1.8. Now we wish to consider noise in potentiometers. Using the model of Fig. 14.2.3, the potentiometer is simply a T formed by three resistors. Since each resistor has an equivalent noise source associated with it from Fig. 1.12.4, we insert a noise source in each of the three resistor branches and denote them as e_{na}, e_{nb}, and e_{nc}. The total rms noise of each source (Eq. 14.1.31) depends upon the thermal noise (Eq. 14.1.26) and 1/f noise (Eq. 14.1.30) levels. For example, the total thermal noise generated by the resistance $R_t \cong R_p$ equals

$$e_n = (4kTR_tB)^{1/2} \cong (4kTR_pB)^{1/2} \tag{14.2.10}$$

When the pot setting is K percent of the total, then the two primary thermal noise sources equal

$$e_{na} = (1-K)^{1/2}e_n, \qquad e_{nb} = K^{1/2}e_n \tag{14.2.11}$$

Since R_c and ΔR_c are much less than R_p, then $e_{nc} \ll e_n$ and the e_{nc} noise source can be omitted.

14.2.11 RELIABILITY

Potentiometers are electromechanical devices. They are subject to both electrical and mechanical malfunctions. Electrical failures are caused primarily by hot-spots and lead terminations; mechanical failures are caused primarily by the slider assembly, and O-rings. Let us examine these failures in more detail.

Hot-spots are caused by abnormally high currents (especially through the slider) and/or imperfections in the resistive element itself. A reduced cross-sectional area is the common defect. These imperfections cause localized temperature rise which result in thermal hot-spots. In time, hot-spots degrade and weaken the resistive element and can eventually cause the resistance element to open. They also cause resistance increase. This is especially true in wirewound resistors where wires expand due to temperature changes. Diameters less than 0.0008 inches are reliability hazards.

Lead terminations in the resistive element also cause failures. Generally these failures result from intermittent operation or open-circuits.

The mechanical slider assembly can also be damaged by frequent use. The lead screw can be stripped or the slider assembly itself jammed.

The O-rings form the hermetic seals between the interior of the pot and the environment. Defects in the O-rings or in the other sealed seams of the enclosure can allow excessive moisture and foreign matter to enter the pot (e.g., salt water and fungi). This can result in an increased amount of leakage around the resistive element. With time, it can also cause increased contact resistance and eventually cause open-circuits between the slider and the resistance element due to

Table 14.2.4 Typical failure rates for potentiometers.[10] (Based upon power stress-ambient temperature combinations (P, T) of (0.1, 30°C), (0.5, 55°C), and (1.0, T_{max}).)

Potentiometer Type	Failure Rate (failures/10^6 hours) Low	Average	High	T_{max} (°C)
Composition/Film				
RV type	0.08	0.15	0.41	70
RJ type	0.51	0.72	1.27	85
Wirewound				
RA type	0.06	0.15	0.22	40
RT type	0.05	0.10	0.31	85

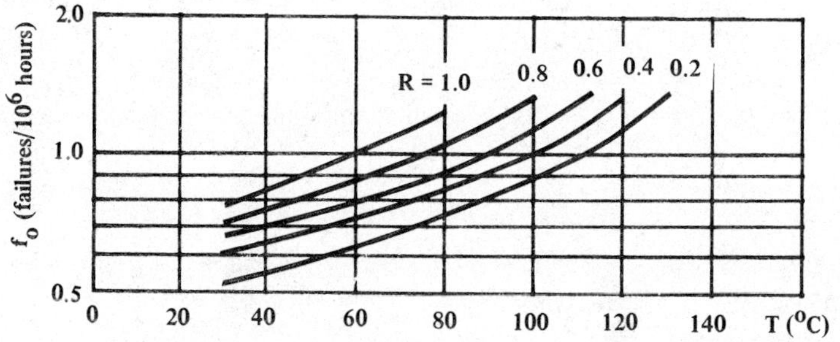

Environment	π_E
G_b	1.0
S_f	N/A
G_f	3.0
A_i	6.0
N_s	8.0
G_m	10.0
N_u	12.5
A_u	15.0
M_l	80.0

Quality Level	π_Q
Upper	1
MIL-SPEC	2
Lower	4

Resistance Range (Ω)	π_R
10 – 50 K	1.0
>50 K – 100 K	1.1
>100 K – 200 K	1.2
>200 K – 500 K	1.4
>500 K – 1 meg	1.8

Ratio of Applied* Voltage to Rated Voltage	π_V
1.0	1.20
0.9	1.05
0.8 to 0.1	1.00

*V_{rated} = 200 V for RJ26, RJ50
= 300 V for RJ12, RJ22, RJ24

Fig. 14.2.10 Failure rates for RJ nonwirewound potentiometers.[21]

corrosion and oxidation of the slider. In wirewound pots, the exposed wire over which the slider moves suffers the same degradations.

The typical failure rates for several types of potentiometers are listed in Table 14.2.4. The RJ type has failure rates that are higher than those of the other types. In general, we see that the RA types are the most susceptible, RV and RT types are less susceptible, and RJ types are the least susceptible to increases in temperature and power stresses. Comparing these failure rates with those of the various resistor types listed in Table 14.1.9, we see that potentiometers (excluding RT types) have worst-case values that are about two orders of magnitude higher than the equivalent fixed resistors. Thus, potentiometers must be carefully selected to be reliable and have long lifetimes. Reliability calculations for potentiometers (and most other electronic components) use the same equations as those described for the resistor. The mortality probability density function is given by Eq. 14.1.38, the probability distribution functions by Eq. 14.1.37, and the survival probability by Eq. 14.1.39.

The MTBF and failure rates of potentiometers (and most other electronic components) is heavily dependent upon their (1) thermal stress (temperature) and (2) electrical stress (power). The failure rates of RJ nonwirewound potentiometers are shown in Fig. 14.2.10. The π-factors are also listed in the figure. The effective failure rate is obtained by multiplying the base failure rate, obtained from the figure, by the π-factors as given by Eq. 14.1.42. Note that one additional factor, π_V, is used in failure rate calculations for potentiometers.

One additional comment should be made. The most recent development in potentiometers has been that of the cermet type. Although cermet potentiometers are qualified under the RVC or RJ type, they exhibit failure rates lower than the typical values listed for the other potentiometer types. Thus, more representative numbers should be used in their failure rate analysis.

14.2.12 AGING AND RADIATION EFFECTS

In potentiometer aging analysis, we are interested in the long-term stability of the total resistance and voltage setting of a potentiometer under environmental changes. Important considerations include load life, high and low temperature extremes, humidity, shock, and vibration. The relative stability factors are listed in Table 14.2.5.

The *load life* of a pot is the time during which it can be operated at rated power, while remaining within allowable degradations. The load life of wirewound, cermet, and metal film pots is the best while that of composition pots is the worst. Typical changes in the total resistance and voltage setting are shown in Fig. 14.2.11. Cermet pots exhibit the best characteristics with average total resistance changes of 0.3% with maximum changes of 1.25% over 1000 hours.

Under high- and low-temperature operation and humidity, cermet and metal film pots are the best and composition pots are the worst. The poor performance of conductive plastic film, carbon

Table 14.2.5 Relative stability of potentiometers on a scale from 1 (best) to 5 (worst).[22]

Operating Characteristics	Wirewound	Cermet	Conductive Plastic	Carbon Film	Metal Film	Carbon Composition
Expected Rotational Life	5	2	1	3	4	2
Humidity	2	1	3	4	1	5
Vibration, Shock, Acceleration	2	1	1	1	1	2
Load Life	1	1	2	2	1	5
Thermal Shock	1	1	2	3	1	3
High Temperature Operation	3	1	2	2	1	4
Low Temperature Operation	2	1	1	1	1	3

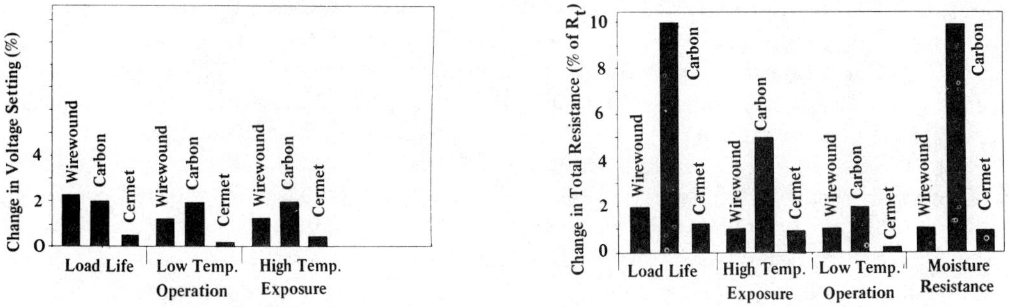

Fig. 14.2.11 Environmental stability of several potentiometers. (From Trimmer Tech. Bull., H731168-474-35GF, Beckman, Fullerton, CA, April, 1974.)

film, and carbon composition pots is due primarily to the temperature characteristics of the carbon and organic binders used in their construction and their affinity for moisture absorption.

Another aging consideration in pots which are continuously or frequently trimmed is *rotational life* which is measured in shaft revolutions (in millions). Conductive plastic and cermet types have the longest life (> 50 M and 20 M, respectively) and wirewound types the shortest (2 M). The long life of the conductive plastic type is due to its smooth surface, lubricity of the carbon film, and large material bulk. The long life of the cermet type is due to its thick, hard, and smooth surface. However, the wirewound types have sudden failures caused by wire wear which leads to eventual breakage. The metal film types (5 M life) have very thin films of vapor-deposited metals which make then susceptible to slider abrasion.

Pots react in the same way to radiation as resistors made of the same material. Resistance changes were listed in Table 14.1.12. Wirewound pots are virtually unaffected while metal film and cermet pots show small changes. Carbon film and especially composition pots exhibit greater changes. Conductive plastic pots are unsuitable since radiation deteriorates most plastics. This will be discussed fully in Sec. 14.3.11 (see Fig. 14.3.17).

14.3 CAPACITORS

Capacitor selection for active filter design is much more difficult than resistor selection because of the large variety of capacitors available and their greatly differing characteristics. These capacitor types include: (1) polycarbonate, (2) polyester (Mylar or polyethylene teraphythalene (PETP)), (3) polypropylene, (4) polystyrene, (5) polysulfone, (6) parylene, (7) Kapton (polymides), (8) Teflon (polytetrafluoroethylene or (P)TFE), (9) mica, (10) glass, (11) porcelain, (12) ceramic, (13) paper (Kraft), (14) aluminum, (15) tantalum, (16) thin-film and thick-film, and (17) diffused.

General purpose ceramic, Mylar, and paper capacitors are used in economical general purpose active filters. Polycarbonate, polystyrene, temperature compensating ceramic, and mica capacitors are used in the more expensive high stability, low drift active filters. Mica capacitors are often used for tuning purposes. Glass and porcelain capacitors are not often used. In very limited filter areas requiring large capacitor values and where large drifts can be tolerated, aluminum and tantalum capacitors are sometimes used. Thin-film and thick-film capacitors are used in high-frequency applications. Diffused types are rarely used in active filter designs and will not be considered.

14.3.1 CONSTRUCTION

Capacitors are formed by making contacts with two metallized plates separated by a dielectric material. The capacitance C (picofarads or pF) between two plates of area A (in^2) separated by a dielectric of thickness d (in) having a relative dielectric constant K equals 0.225KA/d. This is a

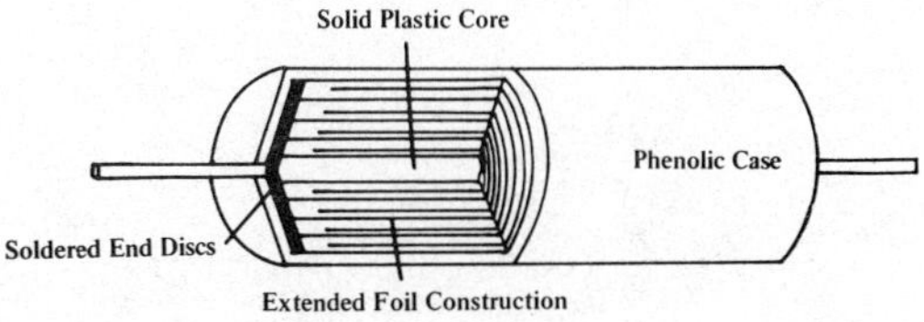

Fig. 14.3.1 Film capacitor construction.

computationally more convenient form than the usual form

$$C = K\epsilon_0 A/d \tag{14.3.1}$$

where MKS units are used and ϵ_o is the permittivity of free space ($\epsilon_o = 8.85 \times 10^{-12}$ coul ^{2}/n-m^2). The capacitor types previously listed refer to the type of dielectric used in their construction. Capacitor characteristics depend primarily upon their dielectric properties as we shall see.

All capacitors are physically constructed in either stacks or cylindrical (or rectangular) rolls, with the exception of diffused types. In polycarbonate, polyester or Mylar, polypropylene, polystyrene, polysulfone, parylene, Teflon, and Kapton types, the dielectric film is either metallized (with aluminum, silver) on one side or used as the insulator with a layer of conductive foil (of aluminum, tantalum). The metallized film or film and foil combination is rolled on a core (solid plastic or hollow plastic) with alternate layers slightly offset or extended. This offset permits electrical connections to be made later at both ends. The wound core is then heat-treated to shrink the film into a hard, uniform mass. End caps or disks (tinned copper) are soldered to the extended ends using induction heating to make contact with the foil. In metallized film, they are press-fitted to the ends with conductive pastes. Axial- or radial-lead wires (tinned copper, nickel, gold-plated nickel, or dumet) are welded to the end caps before soldering. The end-capped capacitor is then sealed. It may be dipped (in epoxy, phenolic resin); wrapped (in Mylar film, plastic, or paper) and end-filled with dipping material; encapsulated in cases or jackets (of molded polypropylene, polystyrene, or other plastic) and end-filled; molded; or hermetically sealed in metal (or glass) tubes or cans with glass-to-metal end seals. Paper capacitors are formed in the same way but have no heat treating and are generally of wrap-and-fill construction.

Mica, glass, porcelain, and ceramic capacitors are usually constructed in stacks or layers as shown in Fig. 14.3.2. In mica, glass, and procelain capacitors, the dielectric is either metallized (with silver) on one side or used in conjunction with foil. The layers are cut, stacked with slighted offset or extended layers, press-fitted with end caps using conductive pastes, and encapsulated in cases. Ceramic capacitors, named from the Greek word "keramos" meaning "to burn", are formed by blending and casting a "green" dielectric film slurry (of barium titanate and binders) onto a flat, smooth surface. The flexible film is dried, stripped from the casting surface, and screened with an ink containing metal (palladium, silver, gold, platinum) to form the electrode layer. The film is stacked into layers, fired in ovens, and separated (dicing or punching) into individual capacitor chips. A conductive ink (as used for screening) containing powdered glass is applied to the electrodes at both ends which connects the electrodes in parallel. The units are fitted with end caps having radial or axial leads welded to them, fired to firmly bond the end caps to the electrodes, and encapsulated by dipping, potting, or molding.[23] Monolithic ceramic chip capaci-

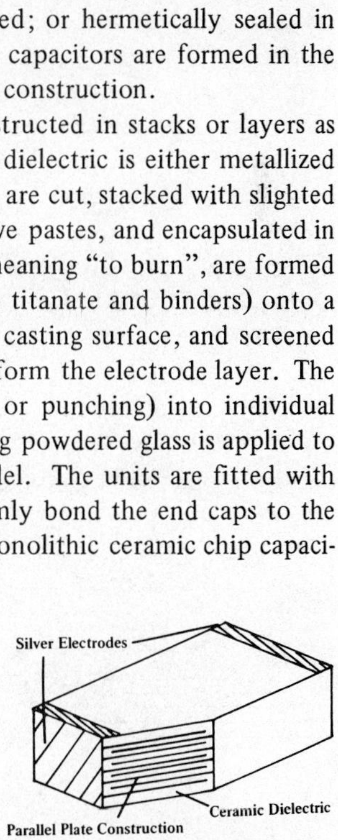

Fig. 14.3.2 Ceramic, mica, glass, and porcelain capacitor construction.

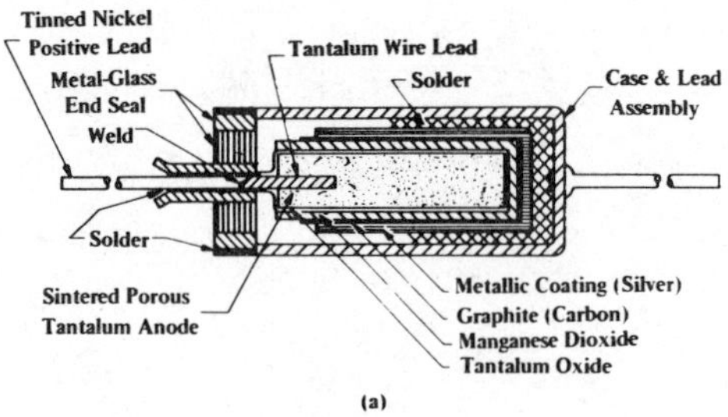

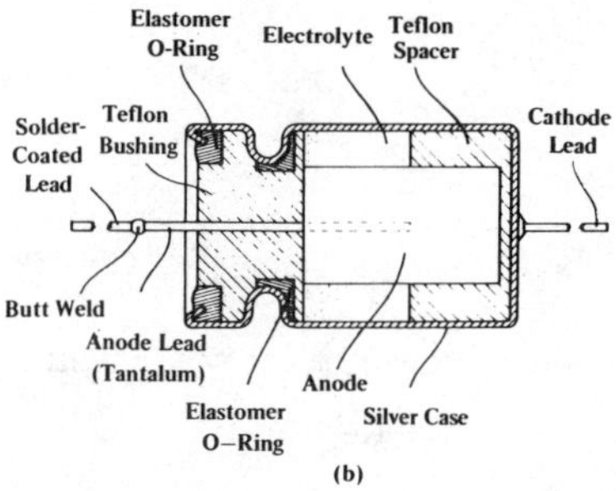

Fig. 14.3.3 Construction of (a) solid and (b) wet tantalum capacitors. ((a) from Capacitor Facts No. 7, GET-2682B, 29 p., 1-65; (b) from Tabular Tantalum Wet-Slug Capacitors, GEP-1814, 11 p., 8/72, General Electric Co., Columbia, SC.)

tors are constructed in similar fashion and fitted with end caps suitable for direct bonding to a metallized substrate.

Tantalum capacitors are available in dry (foil), wet (wet-slug), and solid forms, and aluminum capacitors in a dry (foil) form. The *dry (foil) forms* consist of foil anodes and cathodes (aluminum or tantalum) which are stacked or rolled together using a paper spacer. The forms are then impregnated with electrolyte (sulphuric or phosphoric acid, lithium or calcium chloride, glycol) which is absorbed by the paper. The oxygen from the electrolyte combines with the metal anode to form the oxide dielectric (Al_2O_3 of Ta_2O_5).[24] They are then hermetically sealed in tubs or cans (aluminum, molded polypropylene, polystyrene, or other plastic). *Solid forms* consist of tantalum metal powder pressed into anode slabs or cylinders with an embedded tantalum lead which is welded to a solder-coated lead as shown in Fig. 14.4.3a. A dielectric layer of tantalum pentoxide is formed on the tantalum surfaces by immersion in an electrolyte and positively charging the tantalum anode. The dielectric thickness is controlled by the voltage level applied and the time duration. To minimize the effects of faults (holes and voids) in the dielectric film, the anode is next impregnated with a protective solution (manganese nitrate). A carbon coating, silver paint, and solder dip complete the cathode. The capacitor is either hermetically sealed in cans (aluminum with molded phenolic end seals), encapsulated in jackets (plastic), or dipped (epoxy).[25] Tantalum chip capacitors are constructed in monolithic (chip) form and fitted with end caps for direct bonding to metallized substrates. *Wet forms* are constructed similarly to solid forms as shown in Fig. 14.3.3b. However, their anode slugs are permanently immersed in a wet electrolyte and separated from the case (silver-coated) by a spacer (Teflon).

The thick-film capacitors are generally ceramic chip types previously discussed. Thin-film capacitors are formed in a fashion similar to that used for thin-film resistors as shown in Fig. 14.3.4. A metallization layer (of Nichrome, aluminum, chromium, gold, nickel, tantalum, copper, or tin oxide) is deposited (by evaporation, sputtering, or plating) on top of an insulating substrate (of glass, ceramic, or silicon protected by glass); or a metal layer may be used directly. A dielectric layer (of silicon monoxide, silicon dioxide, alumina, or tantalum oxides) is evaporated, plated, or oxidized on the metallization layer. Finally, another metallization layer is formed on top of the dielectric. A metal backing pad (such as gold or aluminum) makes electrical contact with the

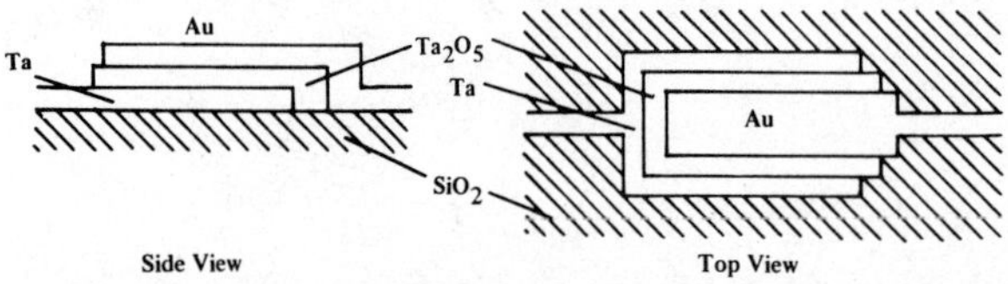

Fig. 14.3.4 Thin-film and thick-film capacitor construction.

Table 14.3.1 Typical capacitor characteristics.

Capacitor Type	Range (μF)	TC (PPM/°C)	Tolerance (±%)	Insulation Resistance (MΩ–μF)	Dissipation Factor (%)	Dielectric Absorption (%)	Temperature Range (°C)	Cost
Polycarbonate	0.001 – 5	±50	10	5×10^5	0.2	0.1	–55/125	High
Polyester/Mylar	0.001 – 5	+400	10	10^5	0.75	0.3	–55/125	Medium
Polypropylene	0.001 – 1	–200	10	10^5	0.2	0.1	–55/105	High
Polystyrene	0.001 – 1	–100	10	10^6	0.05	0.04	–55/85	Medium
Polysulfone	0.001 – 1	+80	5	10^5	0.3	0.2	–55/150	High
Parylene	0.005 – 1	±100	10	10^5	0.1	0.1	–55/125	High
Kapton	0.001 – 1	+100	10	10^5	0.3	0.08	–55/220	High
Teflon	0.001 – 1	–200	10	5×10^6	0.04	0.04	–70/250	High
Mica	5 pF – 0.01	–50	5	2.5×10^4	0.001	0.75	–55/125	High
Glass	5 pF – 0.001	+140	5	10^6	0.001	–	–55/125	High
Porcelain	5 pF – 0.001	+120	5	5×10^5	0.10	4.2	–55/125	High
Ceramic (NPO)	100 pF – 1	±30	10	5×10^3	0.02	0.75	–55/125	Medium
Paper	0.01 – 10	±800	10	5×10^3	1.0	2.5	–55/125	Low
Aluminum	1 – 1000	+2500	–10/+100	100	10	8.0	–40/85	High
Tantalum (Foil)	1 – 1000	+800	–10/+100	20	4.0	8.5	–55/85	High
Thin-Film	10 – 200 pF	+100	10	10^6	0.01	–	–55/125	High
Diffused	10 – 500 pF	–	20	–	–	–	–	Low

top layer to allow external electrical connections to be made. External leads are bonded using thermo-compression, ultrasonic, or eutectic techniques.[26]

Some of the key typical parameters of the various capacitor types are summarized in Table 14.3.1. The table shows that polycarbonate, polystyrene, mica, NPO ceramic, and thin-film capacitors have low temperature coefficients, and good tracking with temperature. Polypropylene and parylene capacitors are similar to polystyrene but have an extended temperature range. The same is true of polysulfone capacitors which are similar to polycarbonate. Kapton and especially Teflon capacitors are used at very high temperatures.

Capacitances have large tolerances which complicates active filter design and tuning procedures. As mentioned before, as a general rule polycarbonate, polystyrene, temperature compensating ceramic, and mica capacitors are used in high-stability higher-cost filters; and general purpose ceramic, Mylar, and paper capacitors in economical general purpose filters.

In specifying a capacitor, the following parameters are important: (1) capacitor value, (2) tolerance, (3) voltage rating, (4) temperature coefficient, (5) operating temperature range, and (6) style. Other important but often neglected factors include (7) insulation resistance, (8) dissipation factor and Q, (9) dielectric absorption, and (10) reliability. We shall now discuss these parameters to show their importance in capacitor selection.

14.3.2 STANDARD VALUES AND TOLERANCES

In active filter design, we usually *choose* the capacitor value and the capacitor ratios. Then the required resistor values are calculated. Seldom do we perform the reverse operation. This is due to the small selection of standard capacitor values which are commercially available. Again, the standard values depend upon the tolerance required. The standard capacitor tolerances are 5, 10, and 20%. The first two significant figures of the standard values for each of these tolerances coincide with those of resistors and are listed in Table 14.1.3. Because of their lower cost, 20% capacitor values are the most desirable. Capacitors have bimodal distributions rather than unimodel distributions just as resistors shown in Fig. 14.1.3. Thus, capacitors tend to be grouped close to, but within, their tolerance values. Because of their large tolerance values, capacitors are often measured and tagged with their actual value. Then only the proper values are used in the filters. Another technique utilizes potentiometer tuning of the filter to compensate for the capacitor error. At times, design engineers may choose to use higher-priced low tolerance capacitors to eliminate the need for tuning.

Precision capacitors having ¼, ½, 1, 2, and 3% tolerances are available but tend to become increasingly expensive with decreasing tolerance. These low tolerance capacitors have standard values which generally correspond with the 10% values of Table 14.1.3. Thus, there are no additional values available in the low tolerance ranges. The actual capacitor values simply have "tighter" distributions, i.e., smaller variances in their probability density functions.

14.3.3 VOLTAGE RATING

Ideal capacitors are energy storage devices and dissipate no power. They store energy in the form of an electric field in the dielectric. If the capacitor voltage becomes excessive, the electric field intensity in the dielectric exceeds the critical breakdown value and the dielectric usually becomes permanently damaged. Thus, capacitors have a maximum voltage rating which is analogous to the maximum power rating in resistors. If the dielectric breakdown electric field intensity is E_{max}, then the maximum voltage rating equals

$$V_{max} = E_{max} d \tag{14.3.2}$$

where d is the dielectric thickness. E_{max} is generally in the range of 100–1000 KV/inch. To increase the voltage rating of a capacitor, the dielectric thickness must be increased. To maintain the same capacitor value, the area must also be increased. Thus, the volume increases with voltage rating. Most capacitors have standard voltage ratings of 50, 100, 200, 400, and 600 VDC. However, the rarely-used tantalum and electrolytic capacitors have ratings of 6, 10, 12, 15, 20, 25, 35, 50, 75, and 100 VDC (and higher as listed above). Since active filters usually process signals of ±15 volts or less, most capacitors are operated at only a small fraction of their rated voltage. This increases the capacitor's reliability and lifetime.

14.3.4 TEMPERATURE COEFFICIENT

The temperature characteristics of capacitors depend primarily upon the nature of the dielectric used in their construction. The dielectric constant K relates the permittivity of the dielectric to that of free space ϵ_o as $\epsilon = K\epsilon_o$ where $\epsilon_o = 8.854$ pF/m. From Eq. 14.3.1, the capacitance varies directly with K. Some capacitance materials have a very temperature-sensitive K. The materials also have nonzero thermal coefficients of expansion so that both A and d vary with temperature. However, their changes tend to track one another and cancel. Thus, the temperature variation in C is due primarily to the variation in K.

Film, mica, glass, porcelain, and paper capacitors all have K's in the 2–7 range, while aluminum and tantalum electrolytic capacitors have K's in the 7–25 range. The notable exception is NPO ceramic capacitors where K is the 25–100 range; in medium-K ceramic types, K varies from 300–1800; and high-K ceramic types have K's from 2500–15,000. Because of their large K values, ceramic capacitors are usually much smaller than the other types.

The typical temperature characteristics of the various capacitor types are shown in Fig. 14.3.5. These curves show that polycarbonate, polystyrene, glass, and mica capacitors have the smallest variation with temperature. Tantalum and aluminum capacitors have extremely large variations and, for this and other reasons, are not often used in active filters. Ceramic capacitors have temperature characteristics which depend upon the dielectric mixture and stabilization technique used. Since ceramic capacitors are the most widely used type in economical filter designs, they warrant further discussion.

The basic dielectric material used in ceramic capacitors is barium titanate ($BaTi0_3$) which is a mixture of Ba0 and $Ti0_2$. This material has a K from 1500–3000 at room temperature and is extremely sensitive to temperature. K can become as large as 10,000 at 125°C as shown by curve A in Fig. 14.3.6a. The temperature at which the peak occurs is called the Curie point. The Curie point can be shifted downward by adding strontium dioxide and upward by adding lead monoxide to the barium titanate dielectric. These compounds are called "shifters". The K variation can be reduced by adding "depressors" such as calcium monoxide, titanium dioxide, and zirconium dioxide as shown in Fig. 14.3.6b. Although the K variation is reduced, K is also.[27] Thus, the temperature characteristics of ceramic capacitors can be tailored by adding the proper shifter and depressor trace elements (under carefully controlled temperature conditions).

The temperature characteristics of several general purpose ceramic capacitors are shown in Fig. 14.3.7. The nomenclature will be described later. K's usually range from 300 to over 10,000.

High stability NPO and temperature compensating ceramic capacitors are also available which have specific temperature characteristics. These are sometimes used for the temperature compensation of active filters. The standard temperature characteristics of these capacitors are shown in Fig. 14.3.8. They are labelled in terms of their nominal TC which is obtained using Fig. 14.1.5 based upon capacitance changes from 25°C to 85°C. A wide variety of negative TC's and a few positive TC's are available. High stability types have values in the P100 to N080 range while the so-called temperature compensating types have values in the N150 to N750 range. Those having TC's in the N1500 and over range are called extended temperature compensating types. The NPO types have almost negligible drift. These types of capacitors have K's in the 8–150 range.

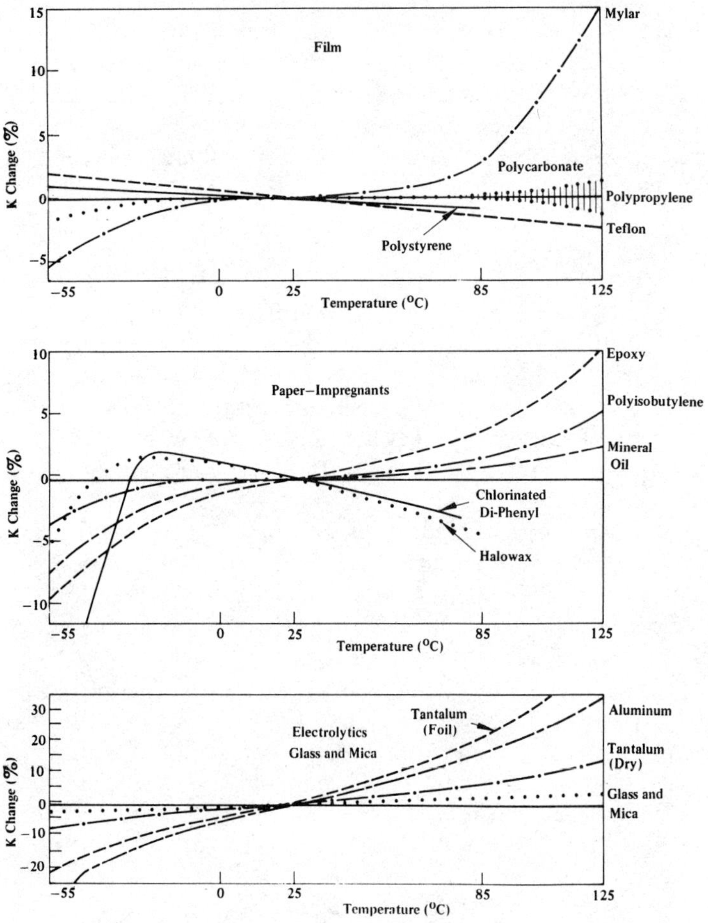

Fig. 14.3.5 Typical temperature characteristics of various capacitor types. (From F. L. Johnson, "Capacitors . . . capacitance changes–Why?," Tech. Bull. No. 03, Electro-Cube, Inc., San Gabriel, CA.)

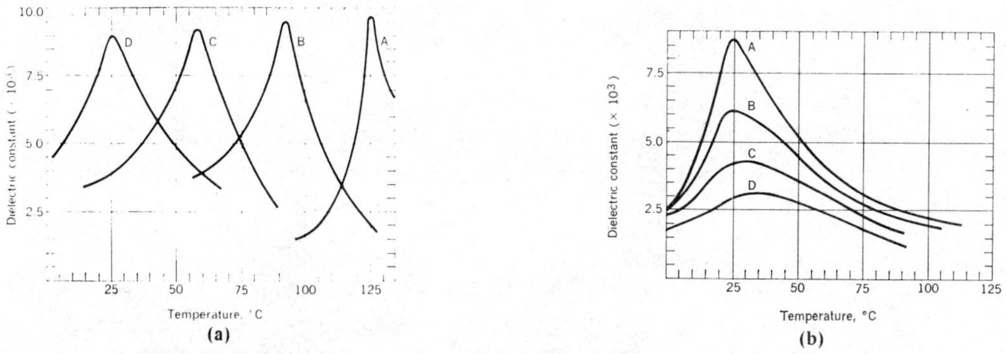

Fig. 14.3.6 Effects of (a) "shifters" and (b) "depressors" on ceramic dielectrics. (From D. W. Hamer, "Ceramic capacitors for hybrid integrated circuits," IEEE Spectrum, vol. 6, pp. 79–84, Jan., 1969.)

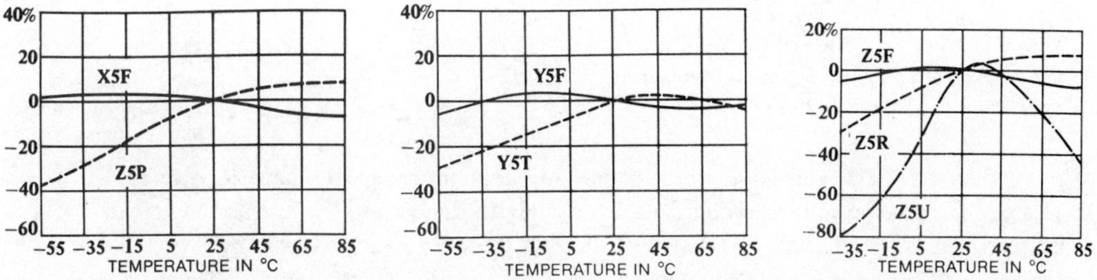

Fig. 14.3.7 Typical temperature characteristics for selected general purpose ceramic capacitors. (From "Capacitors and Ceramic Substrates," Catalog 42D741, 36 p., Centralab Electronics Div., Globe-Union Inc., Milwaukee, WI, 1973.)

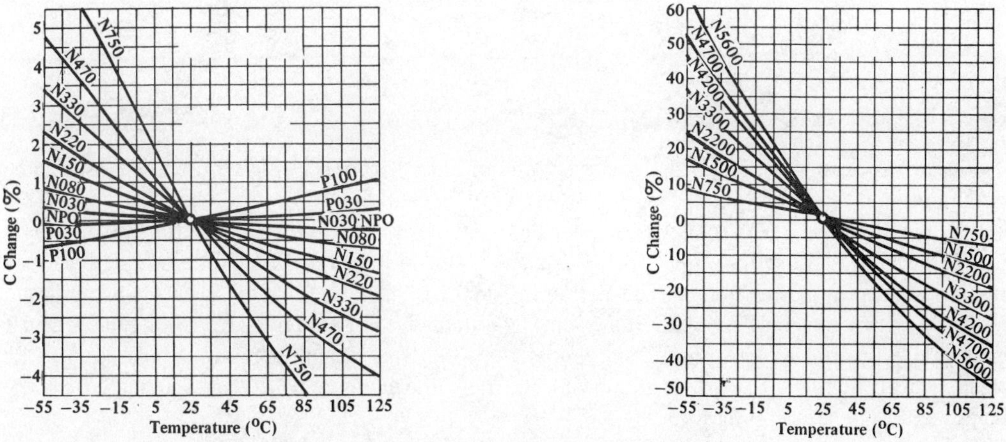

Fig. 14.3.8 Temperature characteristics for temperature compensating and high stability (NPO) ceramic capacitors. (From Fixed Ceramic Capacitors, Catalog 0570 R1, p. 28, Erie Technological Products, Erie, PA, 5/72.)

14.3.5 INSULATION RESISTANCE

Capacitors are more prone to exhibit parasitic effects than resistors. These effects can be particularly degrading in active filters if they are not properly accounted for. The equivalent circuit of the capacitor is shown in Fig. 14.3.9. In addition to C, there exists series inductance L, series resistance R_s, and shunt resistance R_p. The shunt resistance R_p is often referred to as the *insulation resistance* of the capacitor. It accounts for dielectric leakage current and dielectric power losses. For example, if the capacitor is charged to V(0) volts and allowed to discharge "through itself," the time constant is then R_pC.

A common figure of merit for a capacitor is its R_pC product. Since the capacitance $C = \epsilon A/d$ from Eq. 14.3.1 and leakage resistance $R_p = \rho d/A$ from Eq. 14.1.1 where ρ is the resistivity of the dielectric, then their product equals

$$R_pC = \rho\epsilon \tag{14.3.3}$$

The R_pC product is strictly a function of the dielectric properties ρ and ϵ, and has the units of MΩ-μF. Thus, when the capacitance C and dielectric material is known, R_p can be estimated. Typical R_pC products are shown in Fig. 14.3.10 as a function of temperature. Film capacitors and especially Teflon have high R_pC products.

These curves are very useful. For example, consider a 1 μF capacitor. Then its R_p is equal to the value read directly off the figure. In this case, Teflon and polystyrene capacitors have an R_p

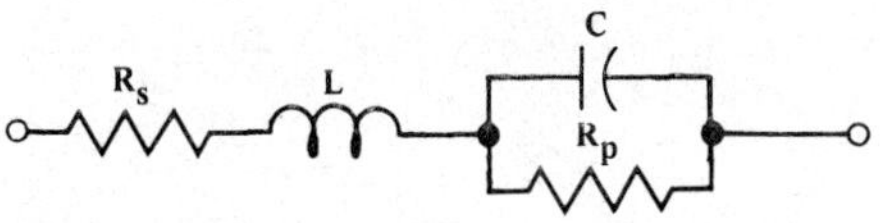

Fig. 14.3.9 Equivalent circuit of capacitor.

of more than 10^6 MΩ, and glass, mica, paper, and ceramic capacitors have R_p's in the 10^3–10^5 MΩ range. Increasing K in ceramic capacitors leads to decreasing R_p in this range. Electrolytic capacitors have R_p's as small as 10 MΩ. Note that these R_p's increase as C decreases below 1 μF, and the R_p's decrease as C increases above 1 μF.

The R_pC product is measured by charging the capacitor C to V(0) volts and allowing it to discharge through itself (i.e., through R_p). The initial and final voltages are measured with a high impedance voltmeter (e.g., an electrometer). Since the capacitor voltage v(t) at any time t equals

$$v(t) = V(0)[1 - \exp(-t/R_pC)] \tag{14.3.4}$$

then the R_pC product equals

$$R_pC = -t \ln [1 - v(t)/V(0)] \tag{14.3.5}$$

The time t is commonly referred to as the "time of electrification" which is usually chosen to be two minutes.

In practice, the R_pC product is not constant but varies with the electrification time. This is due to dielectric absorption effects to be discussed, and reflects itself in a time-varying R_p. As a result of dielectric absorption, the insulation resistance is small at the start of electrification and increases with time until a steady-state value is obtained. For example, R_p for a typical Mylar capacitor estimated at two minutes is almost two orders of magnitude low compared with its steady-state value.[28] Thus, it is important to know the measurement techniques used by the manufacturer in determining R_p.

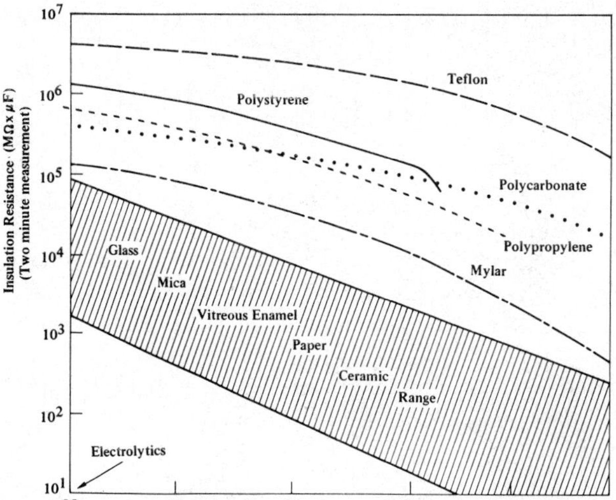

Fig. 14.3.10 Typical temperature characteristics of R_pC products for various capacitor types. (From F. L. Johnson, "Capacitors . . . insulation resistoance can be confusing," Tech. Bull. No. 04, Electro-Cube, Inc., San Gabriel, CA.)

14.3.6 IMPEDANCE CHARACTERISTIC

We shall now determine the degrading effect of the insulation resistance R_p and other parasitic components R_s and L on the impedance characteristic. The results will be utilized in the next section for determining the dissipation factor and Q of a capacitor. The input impedance of the capacitor in Fig. 14.3.9 equals

$$Z(s) = R_s + sL + \frac{R_p}{1 + sR_pC} = \frac{s^2R_pLC + s(L + R_sR_pC) + (R_p + R_s)}{1 + sR_pC}$$
$$= L\,\frac{s^2 + s(1/R_pC + R_s/L) + (1 + R_s/R_p)/LC}{s + 1/R_pC} \qquad (14.3.6)$$

The impedance pole is located at

$$s_p = -1/R_pC \qquad (14.3.7)$$

which is the reciprocal of the insulation resistance-capacitance product plotted in Fig. 14.3.10. The impedance zeros are complex and have a resonant frequency of

$$\omega_n = (1 + R_s/R_p)^{1/2}/(LC)^{1/2} \cong 1/(LC)^{1/2} \qquad (14.3.8)$$

since $R_s \ll R_p$ in all capacitors. Their damping factor ζ equals

$$\zeta = \tfrac{1}{2}\,\frac{1/R_pC + R_s/L}{(1 + R_s/R_p)^{1/2}/(LC)^{1/2}} \cong \tfrac{1}{2}\,\frac{R_s}{(L/C)^{1/2}} = \tfrac{1}{2}\,\frac{(R_sC)^{1/2}}{(L/R_s)^{1/2}} \qquad (14.3.9)$$

since $1/R_pC \ll R_s/L$ in all capacitors. This is similar to the resistor results discussed earlier. ζ equals half of either of two important capacitor parameters. One involves the relative time constant or corner frequency ratio; the other involves the relative characteristic impedance ratio as discussed in Sec. 14.1.6. When the ratios are small (and $\zeta < 1$ or low loss), noticable resonance effects occur. When the ratios are large (and $\zeta > 1$ or high loss), the resonance effects are not noticable. In the high-loss case where $\zeta \gg 1$, the zeros are real with values

$$a_1 = -1/R_sC, \qquad a_2 = -R_s/L \qquad (14.3.10)$$

where $\omega_n = \sqrt{a_1 a_2}$ and $a_2 \gg a_1$. In either low-loss or high-loss capacitors, the input resistance at frequency ω_n is (almost) R_s; at dc, the input resistance is (almost) R_p.

Capacitors have the pole-zero pattern and impedance characteristics shown in Fig. 14.3.11. It is clear that the capacitor has a maximum usable frequency range between $1/R_pC$ and $1/R_sC$ or $1/\sqrt{LC}$. For most practical filter applications, the range is considerably less as we shall see. Ideally, these frequencies equal zero and infinity, respectively.

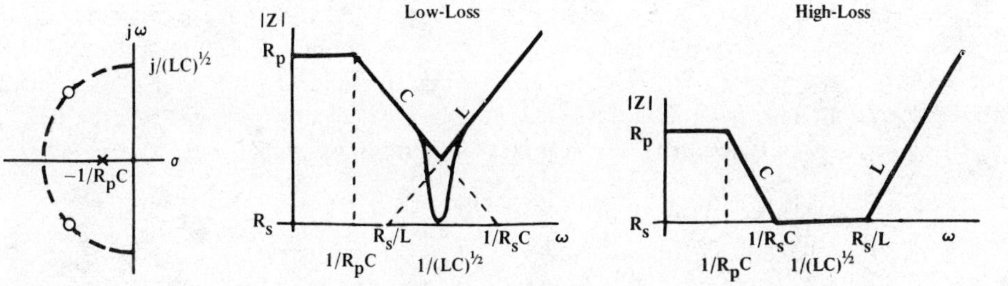

Fig. 14.3.11 Impedance characteristic of capacitor.

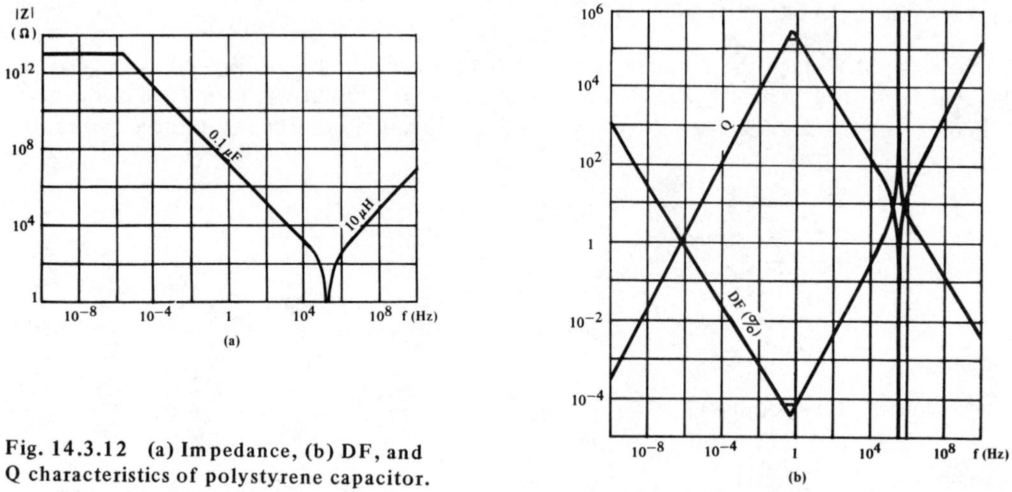

Fig. 14.3.12 (a) Impedance, (b) DF, and Q characteristics of polystyrene capacitor.

In Fig. 14.3.10, we saw that most capacitors have R_pC products in the 10^3–10^6 second range. This corresponds to $2\pi/R_sC$ frequencies in the 10^{-4}–10^{-7} Hz range and determines the lower cutoff frequency. The upper cutoff frequency is determined by R_s, L, and C. High-loss capacitors (excluding electrolytics) have $2\pi/R_sC$ frequencies in the 20 KHz–1 MHz range, while low-loss types have $2\pi/\sqrt{LC}$ frequencies in the 500 KHz–1 GHz range.

EXAMPLE 14.3.1 A polystyrene capacitor has the following parameters: $C = 0.1\ \mu F$, $R_p = 10^7\ M\Omega$, $R_s = 1\ \Omega$, and $L = 10\ \mu H$. Determine the impedance characteristics of the capacitor. What is the maximum useful frequency range over which the capacitor can be used?

Solution The lower cutoff (pole) frequency in Fig. 14.3.1 equals

$$f_p = 1/2\pi R_pC = 0.16 \times 10^{-6}\ \text{Hz} \tag{14.3.11}$$

The resonant (zero) frequency equals

$$f_z = 1/2\pi\sqrt{LC} = 160\ \text{KHz} \tag{14.3.12}$$

The damping factor of the complex zeros equals

$$\zeta = 1/2(100^{1/2}) = 1/20 = 0.05 \tag{14.3.13}$$

so this is a low-loss capacitor. Its dc resistance is 10^7 MΩ and its resistance at resonance is 1 Ω. The impedance characteristic of the capacitor is drawn in Fig. 14.3.12a. The maximum frequency range of operation is 0.16×10^{-6} Hz to 160 KHz. We shall see in the next example that in active filter applications, the range is considerably less. Note that we could have drawn $|Z(j\omega)|$ by inspection on impedance paper.

14.3.7 DISSIPATION FACTOR AND Q

In the ideal capacitor, R_p is infinite and R_s is zero so that the power losses are zero. A measure of the energy losses due to R_s and R_p relative to the energy storage in C and L would, therefore, be a useful figure of merit for the capacitor. Several figures of merit for the capacitor in ac steady-state operation have become industrial standards. These are the power factor PF, dissipation factor DF, and quality factor Q. Expressing the input impedance of the capacitor as

$$Z = R + j(X_L - X_C) \tag{14.3.14}$$

then the various factors are defined as:[29]

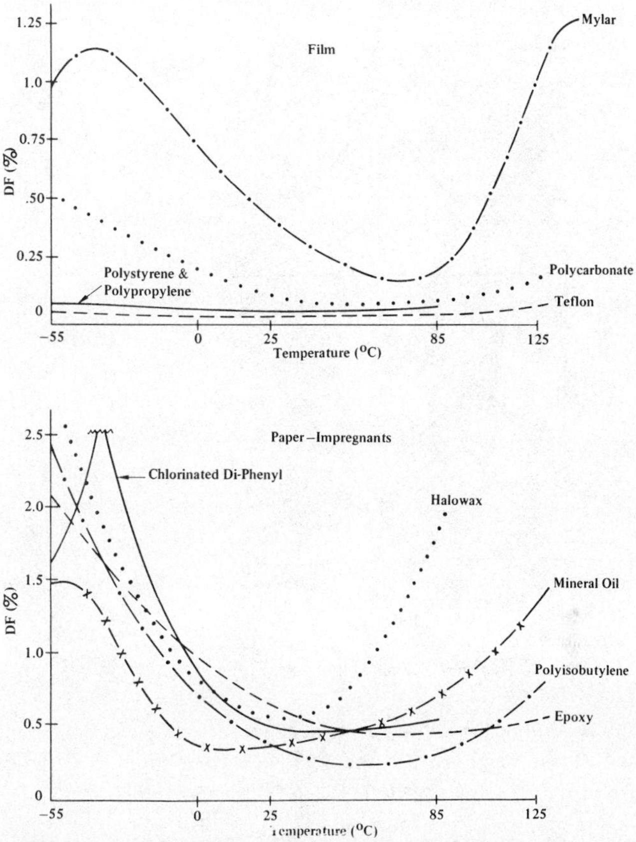

Fig. 14.3.13 **Typical temperature characteristics of dissipation factors for various capacitor types. (From F. L. Johnson, "Capacitors. . . dissipation factor," Tech. Bull. No. 06, Electro-Cube, Inc., San Gabriel, CA.)**

$$PF = \frac{\text{Power Loss}}{\text{Apparent Power In}} = \frac{I^2R}{I^2|Z|} = \frac{R}{|Z|} = \cos\theta$$

$$DF = \frac{\text{Power Loss}}{\text{Reactive Power Stored}} = \frac{I^2R}{I^2X} = \frac{R}{X} = \cot\theta, \qquad Q = 1/DF = X/R = \tan\theta \tag{14.3.15}$$

When $R/|Z|$ approaches zero so that the power loss becomes small, then θ approaches 90°, and PF $\cong$ DF = 1/Q. When PF is less than 10% ($84° \leqslant |\theta| \leqslant 90°$), the error in the approximation is less than ½%. Ideally, when there are no losses, then PF = DF = 0 and Q = ∞. PF, DF, and Q have frequency dependencies which we shall analyze in a moment.

Some typical dissipation factor curves are shown in Fig. 14.3.13 for several different capacitor types. Since R_p and C are heavily dependent upon temperature (and to some extent R_s), DF and Q change with temperature. Teflon and polystyrene types are fairly stable with temperature, but Mylar and paper types exhibit large variations with temperature. To standardize measurement of DF and Q, industry uses a measurement frequency of 1 KHz with a one volt rms input level at room temperature. The design engineer must be very careful in specifying the capacitor Q or DF which he requires.

Now let us analyze the frequency dependency of DF and Q. Since the dissipation factor equals

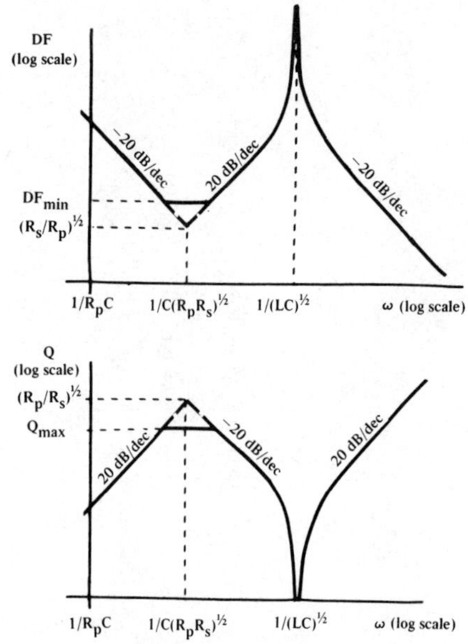

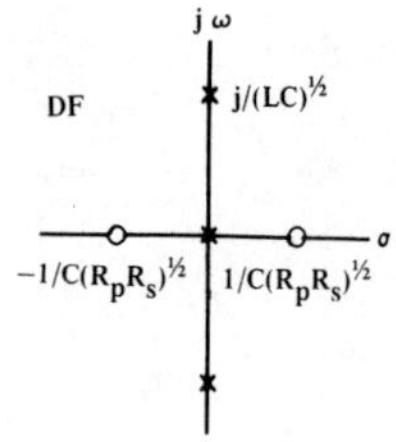

Fig. 14.3.14 Frequency characteristics of the dissipation factor and Q of capacitor.

$$\mathrm{DF}(j\omega) = \mathrm{Re}\, Z(j\omega)/\mathrm{Im}\, Z(j\omega) = j\, \mathrm{Ev}\, Z(s)/\mathrm{Od}\, Z(s)\,\big|_{s=j\omega} = \mathrm{DF}(s)\,\big|_{s=j\omega} \tag{14.3.16}$$

and we know the capacitor impedance Z(s), we can determine DF(jω) by direct substitution. We choose, however, to use the indirect approach of first determining the poles and zeros of D(s). We can then draw the Bode magnitude characteristic DF(jω). We first rationalize Z(s) to make its denominator an even function as

$$\begin{aligned} Z(s) &= \frac{s^2 + s(1/R_pC + R_s/L) + (1 + R_s/R_p)/LC}{1/R_pC + s}\;\frac{1/R_pC - s}{1/R_pC - s} \\ &= \frac{-s^3 - s^2R_s/L + s[1/(R_pC)^2 - 1/LC] + (1 + R_s/R_p)/R_pLC^2}{1/(R_pC)^2 - s^2} = \mathrm{Ev}\, Z(s) + \mathrm{Od}\, Z(s) \end{aligned} \tag{14.3.17}$$

Thus, the dissipation factor equals

$$\mathrm{DF}(s) = \frac{s^2R_s/L - (1 + R_s/R_p)/R_pLC^2}{s[s^2 + (1/LC - 1/(R_pC)^2]} \cong \frac{R_s}{L}\,\frac{s^2 - 1/R_pCR_sC}{s(s^2 + 1/LC)} \tag{14.3.18}$$

The poles and zeros of DF are shown in Fig. 14.3.14. Assuming that $\sqrt{R_pR_s} \gg \sqrt{L/C}$ which is the case for most capacitors, the magnitude characteristic is easily drawn. Since Q(s) = 1/DF(s), the magnitude characteristic of Q is also drawn. We see that DF(s) has poles which are always imaginary and zeros which are always real. At frequencies of dc and $1/\sqrt{LC}$, DF = ∞, and Q = 0.

We see that over the maximum useful frequency range of the capacitor ($1/R_pC$ to $1/\sqrt{LC}$), Q has a maximum and DF a minimum. These occur in the vicinity of $1/2\pi C\sqrt{R_pR_s}$ Hz. It can easily be shown that they are bounded by

$$\mathrm{DF}_{min} \cong 2(R_s/R_p)^{1/2}, \qquad Q_{max} \cong 0.5(R_p/R_s)^{1/2} \tag{14.3.19}$$

using the asymptotes in Fig. 14.3.14 and accounting for the 6 dB error at the corner frequency. (For examples of some other DF curves, see Ref. 30.)

EXAMPLE 14.3.2 Determine the dissipation factor and Q for the polystyrene capacitor in Example 14.3.1.

Solution DF is minimum and Q is maximum at a frequency of

$$f_o = 1/2\pi C(R_p R_s)^{1/2} = 0.5 \text{ Hz} \qquad (14.3.20)$$

Their values equal

$$DF_{min} = 2(R_s/R_p)^{1/2} = 2(10^{-13})^{1/2} = 0.63 \times 10^{-6} = 0.63 \times 10^{-4}\%$$
$$Q_{max} = 1/DF_{min} = 1/(0.63 \times 10^{-6}) = 1.6 \times 10^{6} \qquad (14.3.21)$$

DF is infinite and Q zero at the resonant frequency of

$$f_z = 1/2\pi\sqrt{LC} = 160 \text{ KHz} \qquad (14.3.22)$$

DF and Q are plotted in Fig. 14.3.12b. If the active filter in which the capacitor is to be used requires capacitor Q's greater than 100, then this capacitor can meet this requirement only over a frequency range of about 10^{-4} Hz to 10 KHz. Note that the range is greatly reduced from that in Example 14.3.1 where Q was not considered. It is shown in Prob. 14.17 that the Q and DF curves can be easily drawn on impedance paper.

14.3.8 DIELECTRIC ABSORPTION

Dielectric absorption is a phenomenon that occurs in all solid dielectric capacitors.[31] When a capacitor is charged for some period of time, discharged for some period of time, and allowed to remain open-circuited for a time, then a recovery voltage can be measured across the capacitor with a high impedance voltmeter. This recovery voltage is due to residual charge stored in the dielectric which is not released during the original discharge period. Dielectric absorption is very important in pulse and high-frequency filters where rapid charge and discharge characteristics are necessary.

Dielectric absorption is explained by the Debeye theory of polarization. This theory states that the molecules of all substances (except nonpolar types) possess a characteristic electric moment. When an electric field is applied, the molecules tend to align themselves in the direction of the field. However, the viscous forces within the molecule tend to impede this alignment. This introduces time lags in charging (polarizing) and discharging (depolarizing). It is the failure of the dielectric to completely depolarize in a given time period that results in the recovery voltage.

The dielectric absorption coefficient DA measures the degree of depolarization in a material, and is equal to the ratio of the recovery voltage to the initial charging voltage. Thus,

$$DA = \text{Recovery Voltage/Charging Voltage} \qquad (14.3.23)$$

Typical values for various capacitor types are listed in Table 14.3.1. Polystyrene and Teflon types have only a 0.04% value while mica and NPO ceramic types have a 0.75% value. Paper and electrolytic types have excessive dielectric absorptions. These coefficients are determined by charging the capacitor for five minutes, discharging for ten seconds through 5 Ω, and measuring the recovery voltage.

14.3.9 NOMENCLATURE

Capacitor nomenclature is particularly difficult to decipher because, with the exception of ceramic capacitors, it has not been standardized by industry. However, the military nomenclature is standard for many types of capacitors. The bulk of capacitors must be described by listing their type, dc voltage, value, tolerance, TC, temperature range, frequency range, failure rate, and case size. Thus, specifying capacitors is much more difficult than specifying resistors. Due to the large variability in capacitor characteristics from manufacturer to manufacturer, the design engineer

Table 14.3.2 Military type designators and applicable specification numbers for capacitors.

Style	Type Number	MIL-C-
Paper/Plastic Film		
paper	CP	25
paper/plastic	CH & CQ	18312 & 19978
	CTM	55514 (replaces 27287)
established reliability	CHR & CQR	39022 & 11978
bypass	CZ & CDF	11693 & 15733
established reliability	CZR	39011
Ceramic		
general purpose	CK	11015
established reliability	CKR	39014
temperature compensating	CC	20
Mica		
general purpose	CM	5
established reliability	CMR	39001
dipped	CD	5
button	CB	10950
Glass/Porcelain		
general purpose	CY	11272
established reliability	CYR	23269
Tantalum		
dry (foil), wet	CL	3965
established reliability	CLR	39006
solid	CS	26655
established reliability	CSR	39003
Aluminum		
dry (foil)	CE, CU, & CG	62, 39018, & 23183
Variable		
ceramic	CV	81
air	CT & PC	92 & 14409

must be careful to obtain adequate information to insure that the capacitors he utilizes have the proper characteristics.

The military designations and specifications which apply to the various capacitor types are listed in Table 14.3.2. The capacitors which have obtained wide usage in military equipment in the past have received their own MIL-SPEC numbers. However, the newer film types have not yet been assigned specific designations or numbers. Sometimes, film capacitors are considered to be nonstandard parts which require specific approval for their use. They are usually qualified under one of the several MIL numbers shown.

The typical nomenclature used for capacitors is listed in Table 14.3.3. It is important to emphasize that each capacitor type generally has a different nomenclature. Thus, it is usually necessary to refer to the MIL specification listed in Table 14.3.2 to determine the proper form. Industrial standards have been established by the Electronic Industries Association (EIA) to describe the temperature range and capacitance variation of general purpose (or Class 2) ceramic capacitors.[32] These are listed in Table 14.3.4. A three-letter alphanumeric code is used where the first two letters indicate the minimum and maximum temperatures, and the third letter, the maximum allowable capacitance variation over that range. From Table 14.3.5, we see for example that Y5 types can be used over an extended commercial temperature range (−30 to 85°C). However, X7 (formerly designated W5) types can be used over the standard military temperature range

Table 14.3.3 Typical capacitor nomenclature.

CK	Case/Lead Style	Temp. Range	C Change	C (pF)	Tolerance			
CC	Case/Lead Style	Nominal TC	C Change	C (pF)	Tolerance			
CM	Case/Lead Style	Nominal TC	Rated V	C (pF)	Tolerance	Temp. Range	Freq. Range or Grade	Failure Rate

TYPE

From Table 14.3.2

CASE/LEAD STYLE (Refer to MIL-C-Number)

Case	Shape
Metal	Round
Epoxy	Flat Oval
Wrap-and-Fill	Rectangular
Phenolic	

Lead	Type
Axial	Tinned Copper
Radial	Tinned Nickel
	Gold-Plated Nickel
	Gold-Plated Dumet

TEMPERATURE COEFFICIENT

Symbol	PPM/°C
B	Not Specified
C	−200/+200
D	−100/+100
E	−20/+100
F	0/+170

RATED VOLTAGE

Symbol	VDC
Z	30
A	50
B	100
C	200
E	400
F	600
G	1000

TOLERANCE

Symbol	±%
Z	+100/0
P	+80/−20
M	20
K	10
J	5
H	3
G	2
F	1
D	0.5
B	0.25
A	0.1

TEMPERATURE RANGE

Symbol	°C
M	−55/+70
N	−55/+85
O	−55/+125
P	−55/+150

FREQUENCY RANGE OR GRADE

Refer to MIL-C–Number

FAILURE RATE

Symbol	%/10^3 hours
L	2.0
M	1.0
P	0.1
R	0.01
S	0.001

(−55 to 125°C). The maximum capacitance variation is then specified by letters A, B, etc. Thus, if a capacitor is required which would vary no more than ± 7.5% from −30 to 85°C, then a Y5F type (or better) is required. Several characteristics were shown in Fig. 14.3.7. Typically, K has a value falling in the following ranges based upon capacitance variation: A–E types (< 300); F–R types (300–2400); S–T types (2500–5000); U–V types (5000–10,000); and W type (> 10,000).

Temperature compensating (or Class 1) capacitors had the characteristics shown in Fig. 14.3.8. They are often specified using a three-letter alphanumeric code given in Table 14.3.5. Here the first two letters indicate the TC (based upon the capacitance change from 25°C to 85°C), and the third letter the tolerance on the TC. Thus, a P3K capacitor has a TC of −1500 ± 250 PPM/°C, while a COG capacitor has a TC of 0 ± 30 PPM/°C.

Table 14.3.4 EIA nomenclature for temperature characteristics of general purpose ceramic capacitors.

Low Temp. (^oC)	EIA Code	High Temp (^oC)	EIA Code
+10	Z	+45	2
−30	Y	+65	4
−55	X	+85	5
		+105	6
		+125	7

EIA Code	MIL Code	Range (^oC)
X5	A	−55/+85
X7 (W5)	B	−55/+125
V5	C	−55/+150

EIA Code	MIL Code	Max. C Change (±%)
A		1.0
B		1.5
C		2.2
D		3.3
E		4.7
F		7.5
P		10.0
R		15.0
S		22.0
T		+22/−33
U	W	+22/−56
V		+22/−82
W		+22/−90
	X	+15/−15
	Y	+30/−70
	Z	+30/−20

Table 14.3.5 EIA nomenclature for temperature characteristics of temperature compensating and high stability ceramic capacitors.

Nominal TC (PPM/^oC)	EIA Code	MIL Code
P100	M7	A
P030	B6	
NPO	C0	C
N030	B1	H
N080	U1	L
N150	P2	P
N220	R2	R
N330	S2	S
N470	T2	T
N750	U2	U
N1500	P3	
N2200	R3	
N3300	S3	
N4200	G3	
N4700	T3	
N5600	H3	

TC Tolerance (±PPM/^oC)	EIA Code	MIL Code
30	G	G
60	H	H
120	J	J
250	K	K
400	A	
500	L	
650	B	
850	C	
900	D	
1000	M	

14.3.10 RELIABILITY

Capacitors must be carefully selected and utilized to insure their reliability. MIL-HDBK-217 states that: "About ¼ of the parts in any electronic equipment failures are capacitor failures, and one-half of all failures are caused by improper selection and application."[33] Some typical causes of capacitor failure are: (1) voltage overload/current overload, (2) frequency effects, (3) high temperatures, (4) shock and vibration, (5) humidity, and (6) pressure.

Voltage overload transients produce high voltage gradients within the dielectric which can result in its permanent damage or reduced insulation resistance. Not only should the dc voltage rating be observed, but the peak ac voltage should not exceed the ac rating of the capacitor at that frequency and temperature.

Rapid voltage variations result in current transients. If these currents are of sufficient amplitude and duration, they can permanently damage the dielectric, deform the capacitor case, and permanently change the capacitor value. Since ac capacitor current increases directly with frequency, current overloads can occur when the capacitor is operated at frequencies higher than those for which it was designed. Thus, the maximum rated current versus frequency specification must be observed.

High temperatures and overheating are prime causes of capacitor failure. Regardless of the cause of the overheating (whether it be voltage or current overloads or high ambient temperature), the high temperatures reduce capacitor lifetime, lower the insulation resistance, and cause capacitance drift. Excessive temperature accelerates the aging of many dielectric materials, especially the plastic film types which become brittle with age and crack. Hermetic seals may be broken which allows moisture to penetrate.

Moisture and humidity cause corrosion, nourish fungus growth (paper, wax, and some impregnants are fungus nutrients), reduce the dielectric strength, and lower insulation resistance.

Pressure variations, shock, and vibration may also cause hermetic seals to break, and capacitor cases to fracture. Capacitors have greater mass and moments of inertia than resistors and so are much more susceptible to mechanical stress.

Capacitors failing by chance have lifetimes which are exponentially distributed just as resistors. The mean of the distribution is the MTBF, and the reciprocal of the MTBF equals the failure rate. The MTBF must be determined by extensive testing. Typical failure rates for various capacitor types are listed in Table 14.3.6. These show that paper/film, ceramic, and glass capacitors are the most reliable; mica capacitors are moderately reliable; and aluminum and tantalum capacitors are unreliable.

Table 14.3.6 Typical failure rates for capacitors.[10] (Based upon voltage stress-temperature combinations (P, T) of (0.1, 0°C), (0.5, $T_{max}/2$), and (1.0, T_{max}).)

Capacitor Type	Failure Rate (failures/10^6 hours) Low	Average	High	T_{max} (°C)
Paper/Film (CQ)	.0006	.002	.66	125
Ceramic (CK)	.017	.11	.92	150
(CC)	.0006	.008	.41	100
Mica (CM)	.0004	.013	1.0	125
Glass (CYR)	.0001	.0042	.49	125
Tantalum (CL)	.042	.15	1.7	85
(CSR)	.0033	.011	.35	85
Aluminum (CE)	.0096	.047	1.8	85
(CU)	.0072	.03	.59	85

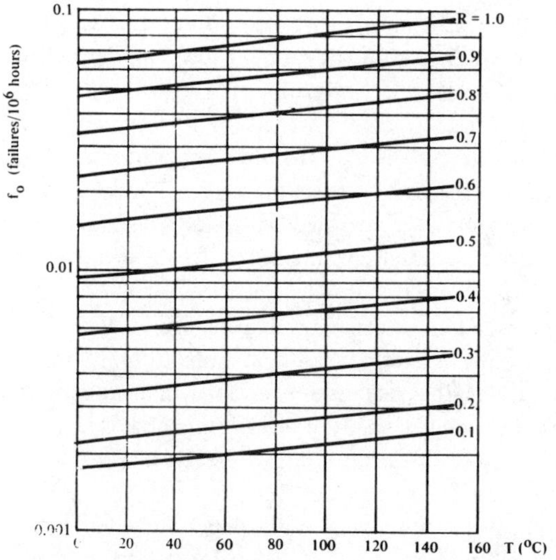

Environment	π_E
G_B	1
S_F	1
G_F	2
A_I	4
N_S	4
G_M	4
N_U	8
A_U	10
M_L	15

Failure Rate Level (CKR)	π_Q
L	1.5
M	1.0
P	0.3
R	0.1
S	0.03

For CK, increase π_Q by 10

Fig. 14.3.15 Failure rates for general purpose ceramic capacitors (CK and CKR types) having 150°C temperature rating.[34]

In resistors, we saw that thermal stress (temperature) and electrical stress (power) essentially determined the failure rate. The same is true of capacitors although they have an electrical stress which is dependent upon voltage rather than power. The failure rates for ceramic capacitors are shown in Fig. 14.3.15. We see that the failure rates of ceramic types are relatively insensitive to temperature increases. Film capacitors have failure rates fairly close to those of ceramic capacitors. Again we see the great desirability for voltage derating to obtain more reliable operation and longer lifetime.

14.3.11 AGING AND RADIATION EFFECTS

Capacitors exhibit aging effects of varying degree depending upon their type. For example, ceramic capacitors exhibit negative changes since their dielectric constant decreases logarithmically with age. The magnitude of the changes increases with the dielectric constant. This is illustrated in Fig. 14.3.16. The changes are exponential in time and are often expressed in percentage change per decade of time. NPO types show negligible change while mid-K and high-K types show changes of −2 and −5 %/hour decade, respectively. Due to the exponential aging rate, little aging takes place after 1000 hours (about 1.4 months). Thus, when ceramic capacitors are sorted, "preaging" allowances are made for the rapid initial aging to maintain shelf life tolerances. The aging process can be reversed by exposing the ceramic capacitor to 125°C. Complete deaging occurs at 150°C for about 30 minutes where the capacitance and dissipation factor revert to their one hour levels. The aging process then repeats itself.

Other capacitor types do not exhibit this peculiar behavior. Data must be obtained from the

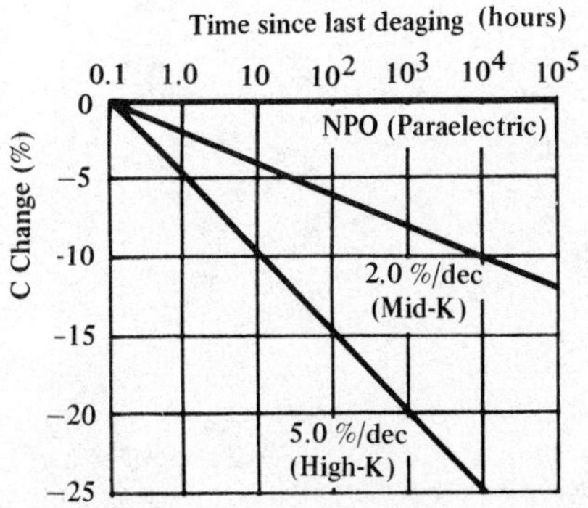

Dielectric Constant	Aging Rate (%/hr dec)
700	1.50
1200	2.00
2000	2.00
2500	3.25
8000	4.00

Fig. 14.3.16 Typical aging characteristics of ceramic capacitors.

manufacturer. When MIL capacitors are utilized, the aging limits are specified so that the design engineer can have some assurance of worst-case values. Because of increased leakage, the insulation resistance of a capacitance decreases with age. Therefore, the DF increases[35] and Q decreases.

Capacitors, in space applications, must also be selected to withstand prolonged radiation. Radiation gradually deteriorates certain plastic film and ceramic dielectrics. Organic dielectrics are much more susceptible than inorganic dielectrics. Radiation reduces the insulation resistance. Many impregnates in paper capacitors (e.g., oil) decompose under radiation and liberate gas (e.g., hydrogen) which can rupture hermetically sealed cases. The same problem exists in wet electrolytic capacitors. The radiation susceptibility of capacitors is illustrated in Fig. 14.3.17. Glass, mica, and ceramic capacitors are the least susceptible. Film and electrolytic capacitors are average (tantalums are better than aluminums), and paper capacitors are the most susceptible.

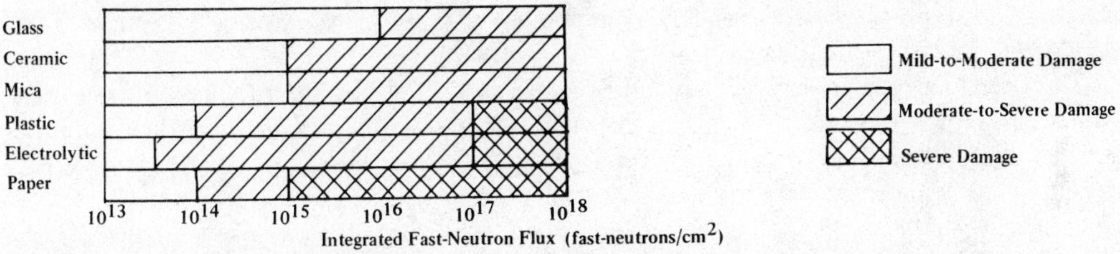

Fig. 14.3.17 Radiation susceptibility of capacitors. (From "The effect of nuclear radiation on capacitors," ASTIA No. AD 252608, p. 6, Battelle Memorial Inst., Columbus, OH, Feb. 15, 1961.)

14.4 OPERATIONAL AMPLIFIERS

The active component in the active filter is the operational or differential amplifier. The proper amplifier must be chosen to insure that the active filter will perform as designed. Fortunately, the electrical characteristics of operational amplifiers are usually well documented by their manufacturer. Once the design engineer becomes familiar with their most important characteristics, he can choose the amplifier best suited to his needs.

Three types of operational amplifiers (i.e., op amps) are used in active filters. These are the monolithic integrated circuit type, the hybrid type, and the discrete type.

The integrated circuit (IC) type operational amplifier is an "integrated" form of the discrete op amp. IC op amps are fabricated[26] on small chips (typically 0.15 inches × 0.15 inches) and packaged in cans (0.32 inches diameter), dual-in-line packages (DIP's of 0.25 inches × 0.75 inches), or flat-packs (0.25 inches X 0.25 inches).

Hybrid operational amplifiers are constructed using several (but not all) thin-film or thick-film resistors and capacitors, in conjunction with discrete transistors or IC active elements in chip form. Hybrid op amps are packaged in the same form as discrete op amps.

Discrete operational amplifiers are designed using discrete components including resistors, capacitors, and transistors. These components are mounted on printed circuit (PC) boards made of fiberglass. The complete circuit is then either coated (with plastic), encapsulated (in epoxy), or hermetically sealed in cans or tubs.

Due to their small size, low cost, and excellent electrical characteristics, the integrated circuit op amp is used in most active filters today. The most important parameters of the operational amplifier in active filter applications are the: (1) open-loop gain/bandwidth and (2) input offset voltage/current. Parameters which also must often be considered include: (3) maximum output voltage/current, (4) slew rate, (5) input bias current, (6) common-mode input voltage/rejection ratio, (7) input impedance, (8) output impedance, (9) noise, and (10) reliability. These characteristics must be thoroughly understood if the op amp is to be properly selected. (For a comparison of about 500 IC types, see Ref. 36.) Therefore, we shall now discuss these various parameters. In order to show the similarities and differences in op amps and the importance of proper selection, we have arbitrarily chosen several standard commercial IC op amps which shall be compared throughout this chapter. These are the μA741,[37] LM101,[38] HA2500,[39] MC1433,[40] μA709,[41] MC1431, and MC1430.[42] At the present time, the 741 and 101 varieties are the most widely used types in active filters and are available from many manufacturers.

14.4.1 OPEN-LOOP GAIN/BANDWIDTH

We utilized the ideal operational amplifier model shown in Fig. 7.1.2 for our filter analysis and design in Chaps. 7–13. The gain constant K is called the *open-loop gain* of the op amp. Since no portion of the output is fed back to either input, the op amp of Fig. 7.1.2 is said to be operating open-loop. Ideal op amps have open-loop gain K equal to infinity. Nonideal op amps have finite gain usually in the 80–120 dB range.

The open-loop gain of a typical op amp is shown in Fig. 14.4.1. It is frequency dependent and decreases toward zero as frequency is increased. Therefore, the actual op amp not only has finite gain but finite bandwidth. The *dc open-loop gain* equals K_o. The *open-loop bandwidth* ω_o is equal to the frequency where the gain is down 3 dB from K_o. ω_o may be as low as 1 Hz or higher than 1 MHz depending upon the op amp used. The open-loop gains and bandwidths for several standard op amps are listed in Table 14.4.1. We should note that K_o varies with temperature (typically 5 dB over a 100°C range) and supply voltage (typically 5 dB for a 50% increase or decrease in supply voltage). For analysis purposes, the open-loop gain K is expressed as

$$K(s) = \frac{K_o}{1 + s/\omega_o} \tag{14.4.1}$$

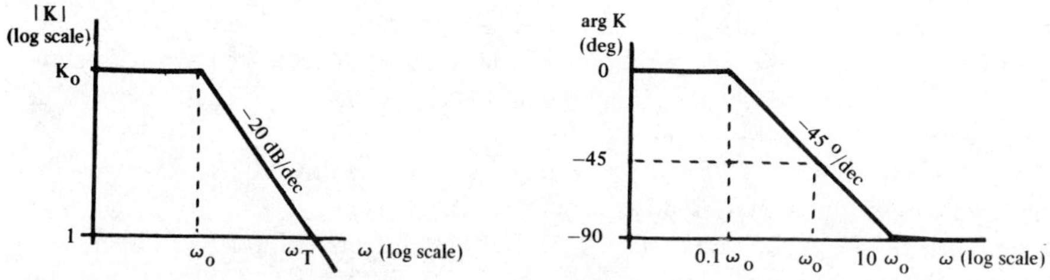

Fig. 14.4.1 Gain and phase characteristics of op amp.

Table 14.4.1 Typical open-loop gains and bandwidths for various op amps. (±15 volt power supplies and wideband compensation used unless otherwise noted.)

Op Amp	DC Open-Loop Gain K_o (dB)	Open-Loop Bandwidth (Hz)
μA741	106	10
LM101	106	500
HA2500	90	250
MC1433	100	2.5 K
μA709	95	10 K
MC1431 (±6 V)	70	200 K
MC1430 (±6 V)	75	2 M

Some manufacturers specify the open-loop *gain-bandwidth product* ($K_o\omega_o/2\pi$) in MHz as a useful figure of merit. The *unity-gain crossover frequency* is also sometimes specified, and is equal to the frequency ω_T at which the open-loop gain equals unity or 0 dB. These are useful figures of merit provided they are used with caution as we shall now see.

Actual op amps have high-frequency gains that decrease at rates faster than −20 dB/dec. This introduces additional phase lag and increases susceptibility to instability. The open-loop gain and phase characteristics for two op amps are shown in Fig. 14.4.2. Many op amps can be *externally compensated* to adjust the shape of these gain and phase curves to suit the application. Usually one or two C's (10 pF–0.1 μF) and/or R's (1 K–100 K) are required for compensation (e.g., see the MC1430 in Fig. 14.4.2).

14.4.2 CLOSED-LOOP GAIN/BANDWIDTH

In active filters, an op amp is used to realize a gain block. The gain may be positive or negative and will lie between zero and infinity. To obtain this gain block, the op amp is embedded within surrounding circuitry and operated in a closed-loop mode (e.g., see Figs. 7.1.3 and 7.1.4). Consider the single op amp described by the flow graph shown in Fig. 14.4.3. The *closed-loop gain*

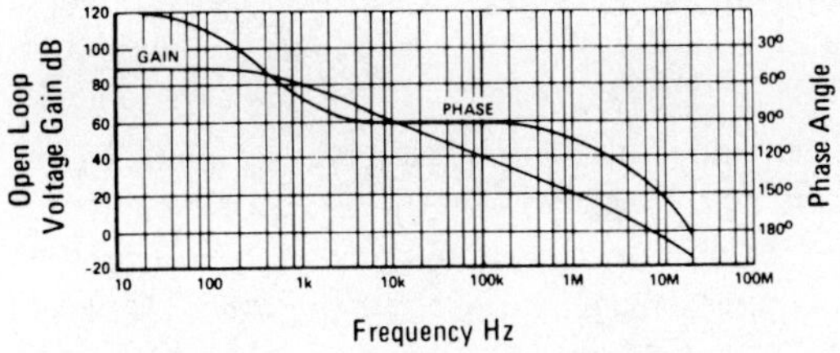

(a)

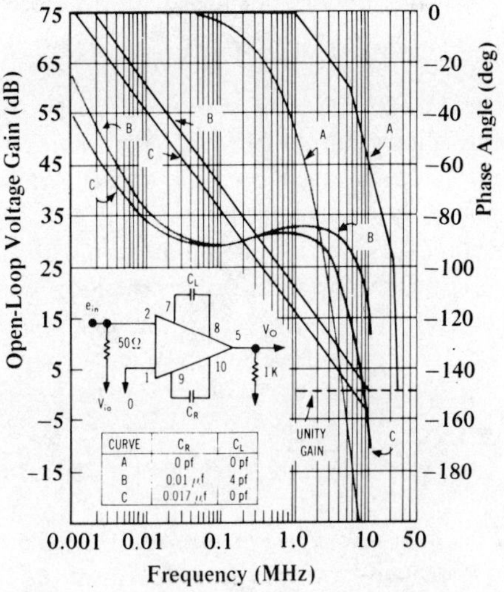

(b)

Fig. 14.4.2 Gain and phase characteristics of the (a) HA2500 and (b) MC1430 (various external compensations used). (Courtesy of Harris[39] and Motorola[42])

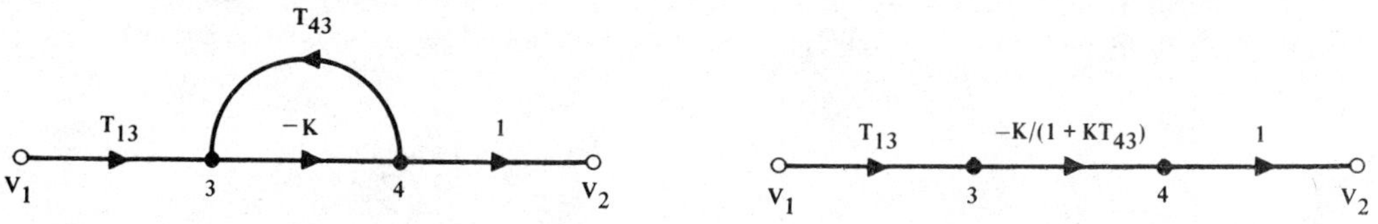

Fig. 14.4.3 Flow graph description of closed-loop op amp.

G(s) of the op amp equals

$$G(s) = -T_{13}\frac{K}{1+KT_{43}} = -\frac{T_{13}}{T_{43}}\frac{KT_{43}}{1+KT_{43}} \tag{14.4.2}$$

The product $-KT_{43}$ is called the loop-gain. When $T_{43} = 0$, then the op amp is said to be operating *open-loop*. When T_{43} is nonzero, the op amp is said to be operating *closed-loop*. When $T_{13} = 1$, the closed-loop gain of the op amp equals

$$G(s) = \frac{K}{1+KT_{43}} \tag{14.4.3}$$

Thus, the closed-loop gain G of the op amp is equal to the open-loop gain $-K$ reduced by the loop gain factor $(1 + KT_{43})$. This is illustrated in Fig. 14.4.4. Substituting K given by Eq. 14.4.1 into Eq. 14.4.3, and assuming that T_{43} is a real constant (e.g., the voltage gain of a resistor divider network), then the closed-loop gain equals

$$G(s) = \frac{K_o}{1+K_oT_{43}+s/\omega_o} \tag{14.4.4}$$

The dc closed-loop op amp gain G_o equals

$$G_o = \frac{K_o}{1+K_oT_{43}} \tag{14.4.5}$$

The 3 dB corner frequency ω_n of the closed-loop op amp equals

$$\omega_n = (1+K_oT_{43})\omega_o \tag{14.4.6}$$

Thus, the closed-loop bandwidth of the op amp is extended by the loop gain factor $(1 + K_oT_{43})$. This allows narrow-bandwidth op amps to be used at frequencies several orders of magnitude beyond their open-loop corner frequency. Thus, we now see the importance of selecting the proper op amp to insure constant gain over the required frequency range of the filter. (For an example of inverting and noninverting op amp design, see Example 8.4.1.)

Another advantage of closed-loop operation is the reduced sensitivity of the closed-loop op amp gain G with respect to the open-loop op amp gain K. Applying the sensitivity relations of Sec. 1.15 to Eq. 14.4.3, we can write that

$$S_K^G = \frac{\partial G/G}{\partial K/K} = 1 - \frac{KT_{43}}{1+KT_{43}} = \frac{1}{1+KT_{43}} \tag{14.4.7}$$

Thus, the percentage change $\Delta G/G$ in the closed-loop gain G equals the percentage change $\Delta K/K$ in the open-loop gain K, reduced by the loop gain factor $(1 + KT_{43})$. Therefore, as long as we maintain our loop-gain large enough, we can reduce the effects of variable gain, ΔK, to any desired

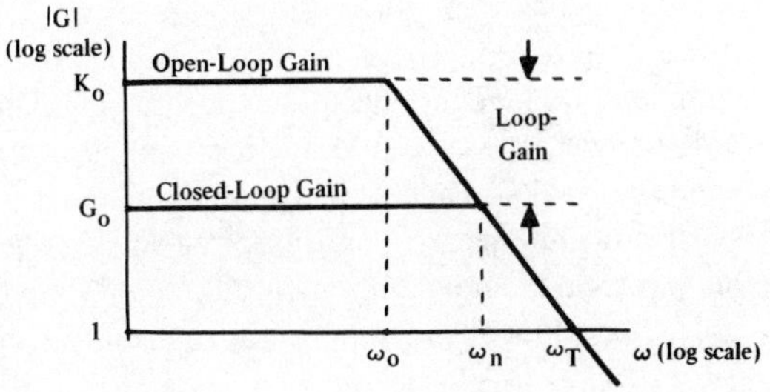

Fig. 14.4.4 Relation between open-loop and closed-loop op amp gains.

level. However, note that

$$S_{T_{43}}^{G} = -\frac{KT_{43}}{1+KT_{43}} = -\frac{1}{1+1/KT_{43}} \cong -1 + \frac{1}{KT_{43}}, \qquad |KT_{43}| \gg 1 \tag{14.4.8}$$

so that the closed-loop op amp gain changes directly with changes in the feedback gain T_{43} (for large loop-gain). In most applications, however, the tolerance on T_{43} is much smaller than that on K so this is a desirable tradeoff.

14.4.3 STABILITY

One disadvantage of operating under closed-loop conditions can be increased op amp susceptibility to instability. To show this, we shall determine the poles of the closed-loop op amp gain G(s). From Eq. 14.4.3, the gain G(s) has poles which satisfy

$$1 + K(s)T_{43}(s) = 0 \tag{14.4.9}$$

Usually T_{43} is a real constant (e.g., a resistive divider is used for feedback). The closed-loop gain poles depend upon the form of the open-loop gain K(s) of the op amp. For modelling purposes, we shall set $T_{43} = 1$ and use the following first-, second-, and third-order gain expressions:

$$K_1(s) = \frac{K_o}{1+s\tau_1}, \qquad K_2(s) = \frac{K_o}{(1+s\tau_1)(1+s\tau_2)}, \qquad K_3(s) = \frac{K_o}{(1+s\tau_1)(1+s\tau_2)(1+s\tau_3)} \tag{14.4.10}$$

For example, we would use the first-order model for the op amp having the open-loop gain of Fig. 14.4.1, and the second- and third-order models for the op amp gains in Fig. 14.4.2. Using the root locus analysis technique of Sec. 1.16, we can easily determine the effect of T_{43}, K_o, τ_1, τ_2, and τ_3 on the closed-loop gain poles. The root loci can be constructed as shown in Fig. 14.4.5. After τ_1, τ_2, and τ_3 are fixed, we see that the dc open-loop gain $-T_{43}K_o$ determines the closed-loop

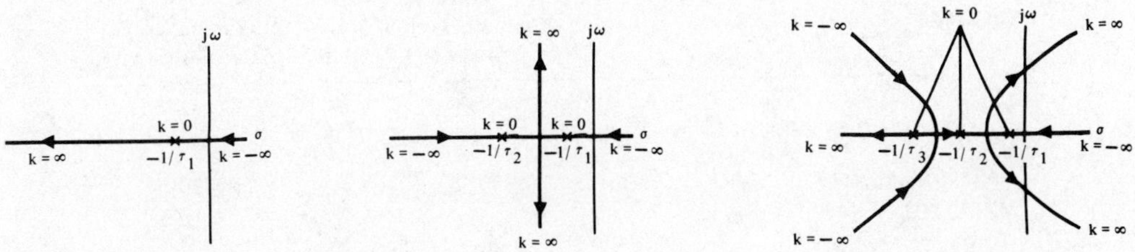

Fig. 14.4.5 Root locus for closed-loop poles of an op amp having one, two, and three open-loop poles (T_{43} = 1).

poles of the system. Note that $T_{43}K_o$ is positive when the op amp is operated in a noninverting mode. Considering negative $T_{43}K_o$ and fixed τ_1, the effect of finite τ_2 and τ_3 is to produce complex poles. These poles have decreasing damping factors as $T_{43}K_o$ is increased. In the third-order model, the closed-loop poles actually migrate into the right-half-plane, so the op amp becomes unstable. Thus, a design tradeoff must be made between using large loop-gain to maintain small closed-loop gain variation, yet small enough to insure adequate stability margin. The stability margin of an op amp operating closed-loop can be determined using either the Bode, Nyquist, or Nichols plots of the loop gain KT_{43}, but we shall not pursue this further.[43]

14.4.4 MAXIMUM OUTPUT VOLTAGE/CURRENT

Ideal op amps amplify any input signal by their gain K so that any output level is possible. As a practical matter, however, the output voltage can be no larger or smaller than the power supply voltages that bias the op amps. Thus, the *maximum output voltage* swing is defined to equal the peak output voltage swing that can be obtained without op amp clipping or limiting. Typically, the maximum output voltage swing will be 90% of the supply voltage. Typical values are listed in Table 14.4.2. The maximum output voltage is plotted versus frequency in many op amp specifications. We shall postpone a discussion of this plot for the next section on slew rate.

The op amp also has maximum current drive capabilities (*maximum output current*) which is fixed by the maximum output voltage and output impedance of the op amp. Typical values are listed in Table 14.4.2. Most op amps have values in the 10–30 mA range. High current-drive op amps having internal current buffering must be used to obtain larger values.

14.4.5 SLEW RATE

Not only is the peak output voltage of the op amp limited, but also is its maximum rate of change under large-signal conditions. This maximum rate of change is called the *slew rate* S, which is expressed in volts/μsec. If we write the output voltage v_2 of the op amp as $v_2 = V_p \cos \omega t$ so that $dv_2/dt = \omega V_p \sin \omega t$, then the slew rate equals

$$S = dv_2/dt \,\Big|_{max} = \omega V_p \tag{14.4.11}$$

The maximum output voltage V_p at frequency ω for an op amp having slew rate S therefore equals

$$V_p = S/\omega = S/2\pi f \tag{14.4.12}$$

V_p decreases for increasing frequency f for a fixed slew rate op amp. Typical slew rates are listed in Table 14.4.3. Slew rate is generally measured under unity gain conditions which yields a worst-case value.

Table 14.4.2 Typical maximum output voltage and current for various op amps ($V_s = \pm 15$ V, $R_L = 2$ K).

Op Amp	Maximum Output Voltage (V)	Maximum Output Current (mA)
μA741	13	25
LM101	13	26
HA2500	12	20
MC1433	12	10
μA709	13	–
MC1431 ($V_s = \pm 6$ V, $R_L = 1$ K)	5	10
MC1430 ($V_s = \pm 6$ V, $R_L = 1$ K)	5	10

Table 14.4.3 Typical slew rates for various op amps in unity-gain mode.

Op Amp	Slew Rate S (V/μsec)
μA741	0.5
LM101	0.2
HA2500	30
MC1433	2
μA709	0.3
MC1431	1.4
MC1430	1.7

In most active filter applications, the peak output V_p and maximum frequency f are known. The designer must then insure that the op amp which he is using has a slew rate S which will meet the requirement of Eq. 14.4.12. The nomograph of Fig. 14.4.6 is extremely useful in such slew rate analysis. When any two of the three parameters V_p, f, and S are specified and entered as points on the chart, a straight line connecting the points is drawn. The third parameter is then read off from the third intersection point as a later example will show.

Slew rate limiting occurs when the output voltage swing becomes so large that the amplifier can no longer respond within its small-signal rise time. These large-signal conditions result in nonlinear amplification and bias disturbances which greatly alter its operation. The output response speed is determined by the circuit capacitances, and the ability of the circuit to provide charging current to these capacitances. Very often this limit is fixed by compensation capacitors used to adjust the open-loop gain and phase characteristics of the op amp. If the limiting capacitor has value C and can be driven by maximum current I_p, then its maximum rate of voltage change cannot exceed $dv_c/dt = I_p/C$. Thus, if the internal gain of the amplifier between C and the output is k, then the output slew rate limit $S = k dv_c/dt = kI_p/C$. This dependency of S upon C is shown in Fig. 14.4.7.

When the op amp is operated closed-loop as shown by the flow graph in Fig. 14.4.3, then the output voltage $V_2 = G_o V_3$ where $G_o = -K/(1 + KT_{43})$ is the closed-loop gain. Thus, the slew rate equals

$$S = dv_2/dt\,|_{max} = G_o\, dv_3/dt\,|_{max} = G_o S_o \qquad (14.4.13)$$

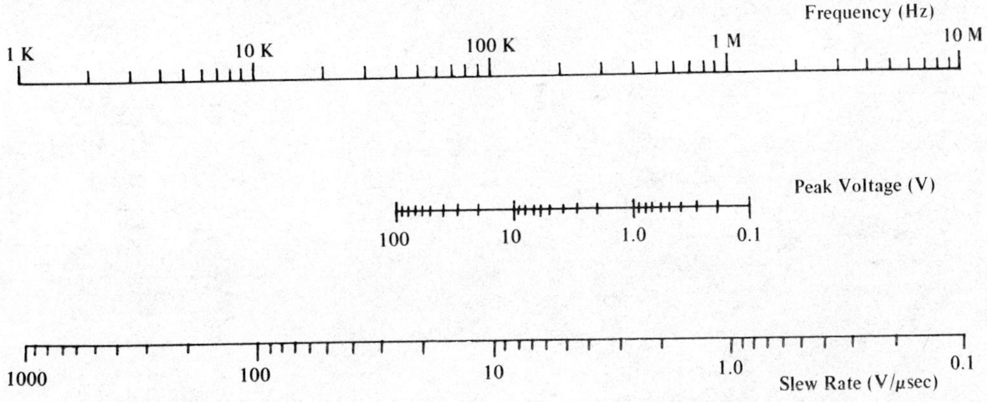

Fig. 14.4.6 Slew rate nomograph.

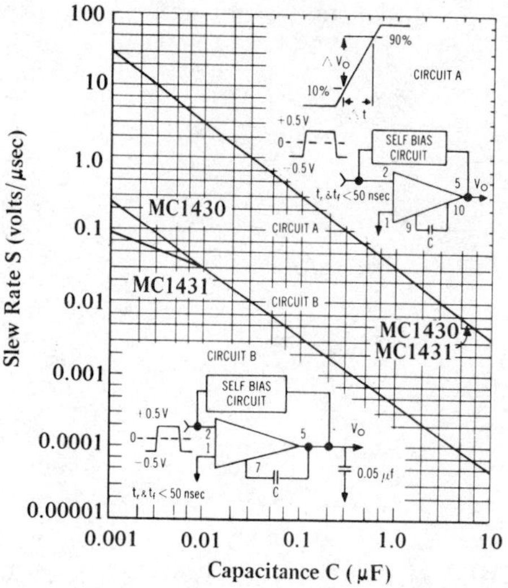

Fig. 14.4.7 Effect of compensation capacitor C on slew rate S for the MC1430 and 1431. (Courtesy of Motorola[42])

where S_o equals the maximum internal slew rate $dv_3/dt|_{max}$ of the op amp. In unity-gain operation (i.e., the op amp is a voltage follower), $G_o = 1$ so $S = S_o$. Thus, S_o can be evaluated from the op amp specification for the unity-gain slew rate. Eq. 14.4.13 shows that increasing the closed-loop op amp gain G_o increases its slew rate S. This is illustrated in Fig. 14.4.8.

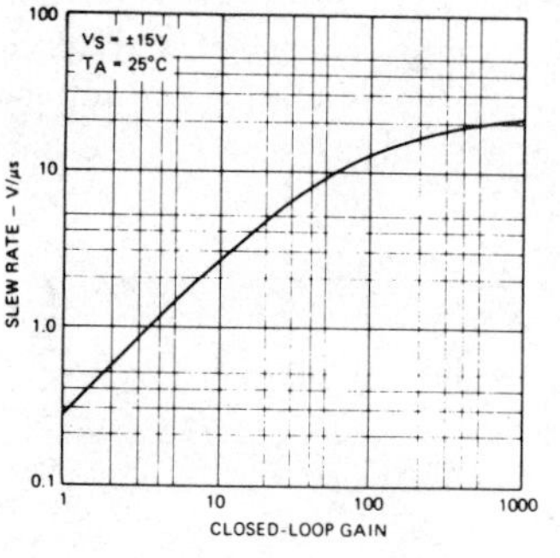

Fig 14.4.8 Slew rate versus closed-loop gain for the μA709 using recommended compensation networks. (Courtesy of Fairchild[41])

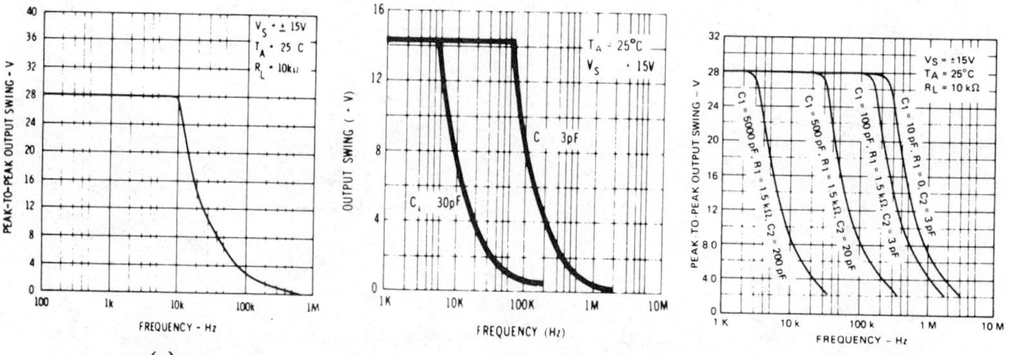

(a) (b) (c)

Fig. 14.4.9 Maximum output voltage for the (a) μA741, (b) LM101, and (c) μA709 using various compensations. (Courtesy of Fairchild[37, 41] and National[38])

In op amp specifications, the maximum output voltage versus frequency will often be plotted in addition to the slew rate. Several examples are shown in Fig. 14.4.9. The curved portion of the characteristic satisfies Eq. 14.4.12. In these situations, it is just as easy to obtain V_p from these figures as from the nomograph of Fig. 14.4.6.

EXAMPLE 14.4.1 A μA709 is to be used for a 20 dB gain block in an active filter which operates to 100 KHz. What is the maximum output level which can be obtained without distortion?
Solution From Table 14.4.3, $S_o = 0.3$ V/μsec under unity-gain conditions. Since we require 20 dB gain, then $G_o = 10$ and $S = 3$ V/μsec from Eq. 14.4.13. This is verified by Fig. 14.4.8. Since f = 100 KHz, we can determine V_p from Fig. 14.4.6. Entering the data and drawing the line gives $V_p = \pm 2$ volts. Thus, we can provide no more than a ±2 volt peak output signal at 100 KHz to the load without slew rate limiting effects. Yet at low frequencies, we can provide $V_p = \pm 13$ volts from Table 14.4.2.

14.4.6 INPUT OFFSET VOLTAGE/CURRENT AND BIAS CURRENT

Ideal op amps have zero output for zero input. Actual op amps exhibit some output for zero input. This output is the sum of a dc component called *offset* and an ac component called *noise*. Noise shall be considered later in the chapter.

Offset analysis in op amps utilizes three op amp parameters: input bias current, input offset current, and input offset voltage. The *input bias current* I_b of an op amp is the average of the two input bias currents. The *input offset current* I_{os} is the difference of the input bias currents. The input bias current depends upon the type of differential input stage (bipolar or FET) used in the op amp, and its current gain. The offset current depends upon the degree of matching of the input stage. Bipolar op amps have I_b in the vicinity of 100 nA and I_{os} in the vicinity of 20 nA. In op amps having FET inputs, these currents are reduced by typically two orders of magnitude.

The *input offset voltage* V_{os} is that voltage which must be applied to the input to obtain zero output voltage. This is typically in the vicinity of 1 mV. The nominal V_{os}, I_{os}, and I_b values for various op amps are listed in Table 14.4.4.

Now we want to determine the op amp model to allow us to analyze offset effects. It is obvious from the definition of V_{os}, I_{os}, and I_b that they are defined relative to the input of the op amp. This is customary to make them independent of the op amp gain K. However, it is not necessary. Recall we saw in Fig. 1.12.1 that any *linear* two-port network having internal independent sources (such as dc offset or noise) can be represented as sourceless networks (having no internal independent sources) with two independent generators connected to the ports in an appropriate manner. Six representations were possible. However, if we wish to refer these sources to the input, the chain matrix description of the two-port must be used. The resulting op amp model is shown in Fig. 14.4.10.[44] When the op amp is operated closed-loop, the offset of the

Table 14.4.4 Typical offset voltage, offset current, and bias current at 25°C for various op amps.

Op Amp	Offset Voltage V_{os} (mV)	Offset Current I_{os} (nA)	Bias Current I_b (nA)
μA741	1	20	80
LM101	1	40	120
HA2500	2	10	100
MC1433	1	100	500
μA709	1	50	200
MC1431	5	10	100
MC1430	2	400	5000

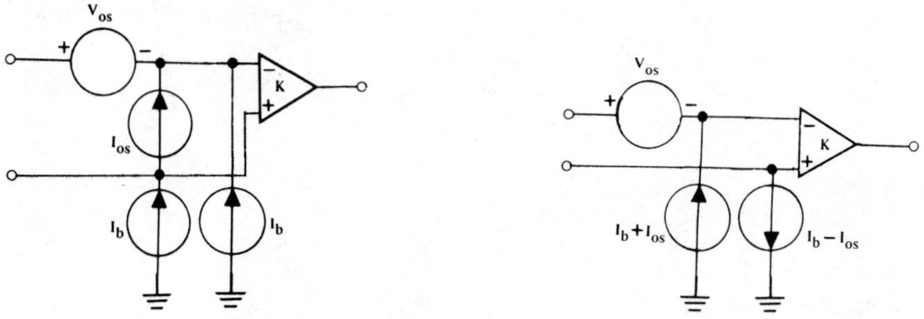

Fig. 14.4.10 Op amp models to represent voltage and current offset effects and bias current effects.

output depends only upon the resistive network in which the op amp is embedded. We shall consider op amps which are operated in both the inverting and noninverting modes.

Consider the inverting op amp of Table 8.4.2 which is redrawn in Fig. 14.4.11. R_{in} is the dc input impedance of the op amp. The flow graph for the op amp including offset and bias effects can easily be drawn as shown. We can obtain greatest insight by reflecting the offset generators to the input V_1 as shown in Fig. 14.4.12. This can easily be accomplished in the flow graph by moving the branches originating at nodes V_{os}, I_{os}, and I_b and terminating on node 3 to node 1 using the star/mesh transformation rule discussed in Table 1.14.1. By inspection, the effective input voltage equals

$$V_1' = V_1 + \frac{1 + R_1/R_f'}{1 + (R_1 || R_f)/R_{in}} V_{os} + R_1 I_{os} + (1 + \frac{R_1}{R_f'})\Delta R I_b$$
$$= V_1 + (1 + R_1/R_f)V_{os} + R_1 I_{os} + (1 + R_1/R_f')\Delta R I_b \tag{14.4.14}$$

This shows that the effective input voltage offset due to I_{os} is dependent only upon R_1. The effective input offset due to V_{os} is dependent only upon $(1 + R_1/R_f)$. Thus, both input offsets are independent of the op amp dc input resistance R_{in} and gain K.[45] The input offset due to bias current I_b is dependent upon the resistance unbalance ΔR that is seen by the op amp inputs. In this case, $\Delta R = R_1 || R_f'$ since the noninverting input is grounded directly. If it were grounded through a resistor of value $R_1 || R_f'$, then $\Delta R = 0$.

The closed loop gain of the op amp equals

$$-\frac{V_2}{V_1'} = \frac{R_f'}{R_1 + R_f'} \frac{K}{1 + KR_1'/(R_1' + R_f')} = \frac{R_{in}}{R_1 + R_{in}} \frac{K}{1 + K(R_1 || R_{in})/(R_f + R_1 || R_{in})} \tag{14.4.15}$$

After manipulation, the closed-loop gain given by Eq. 14.4.15 may be re-expressed as

$$-H_o = -\frac{V_2}{V_1'} = \frac{R_f/R_1}{1 + [1 + R_f/(R_1 || R_{in})]/K} \to \frac{R_f}{R_1} \tag{14.4.16}$$

The effect of finite dc input resistance R_{in} is only to reduce the closed-loop gain H_o. This effect is usually negligible since $R_{in} \gg R_f$. Under limiting gain and impedance conditions where K and $R_{in} \to \infty$ which is the usual case of interest, Eq. 14.4.16 becomes $H_o = -R_f/R_1$. Substituting this result into Eq. 14.4.14, the effective input voltage then equals $V_1' = V_1 + \Delta V_1$ and the total input offset error ΔV_1 equals

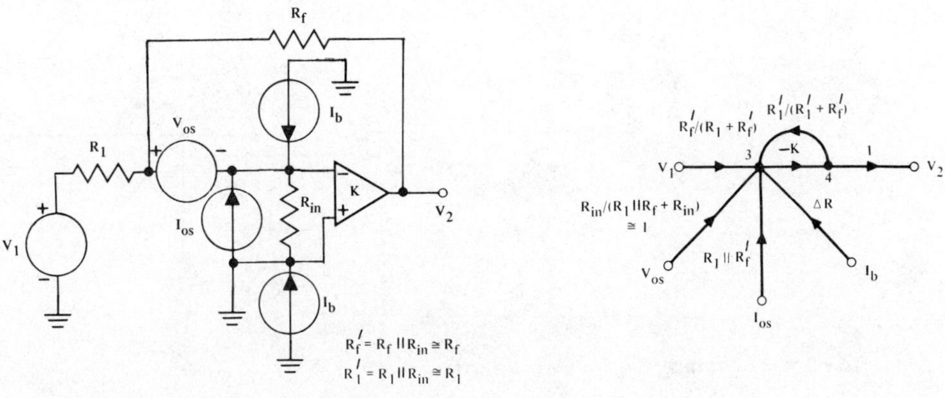

Fig. 14.4.11 Simple inverting op amp with flow graph.

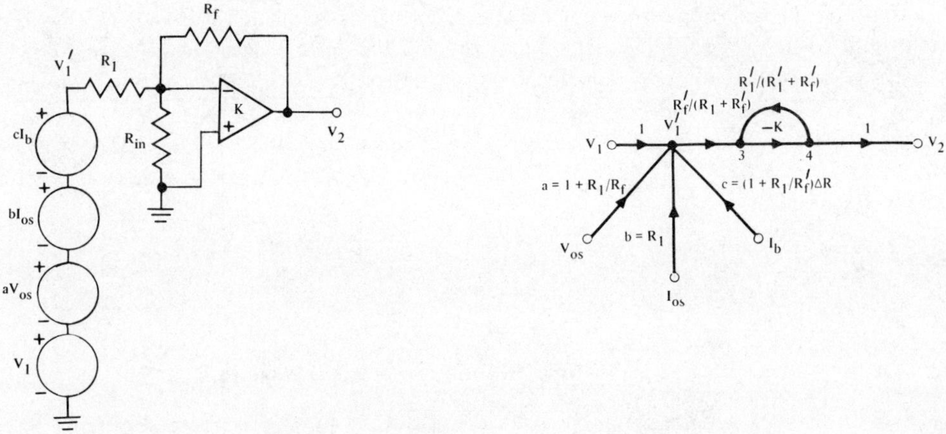

Fig. 14.4.12 Inverting op amp with offset and bias errors referred to input.

$$\Delta V_1 = (1 - 1/H_o)(V_{os} + \Delta R I_b) + R_1 I_{os} \tag{14.4.17}$$

When the first term dominates, the error is primarily due to voltage offset or bias current and/or resistance unbalance. When the second term dominates, the error is primarily due to current offset. We also see that for dc gains H_o less than unity, voltage offset error can become excessive. Bias current offset is eliminated by setting $\Delta R = 0$. This was common practice in Chaps. 8–13 where the noninverting op amp terminal was returned to ground through a resistor of value $R_1 || R_f'$.

Now consider the noninverting op amp of Table 8.4.1 which is redrawn in Fig. 14.4.13. Referring the offsets to the input V_1 in Fig. 14.4.14, the effective input voltage V_1' equals

$$V_1' = V_1 + V_{os} + \Delta R\left(1 + \frac{R_2 + R_1 || R_f}{R_{in}}\right)I_b + \left(R_2 + \frac{R_1 R_f}{R_1 + R_f}\right)I_{os} \tag{14.4.18}$$

Several points should be noted. The input voltage and current offsets are independent of R_{in} and K as in the inverting amplifier case. The input offset due to I_{os} is directly dependent upon R_2 and $R_1 || R_f$. The input voltage offset due to V_{os} is V_{os} and is independent of all resistors unlike the inverting amplifier case. The closed-loop gain equals

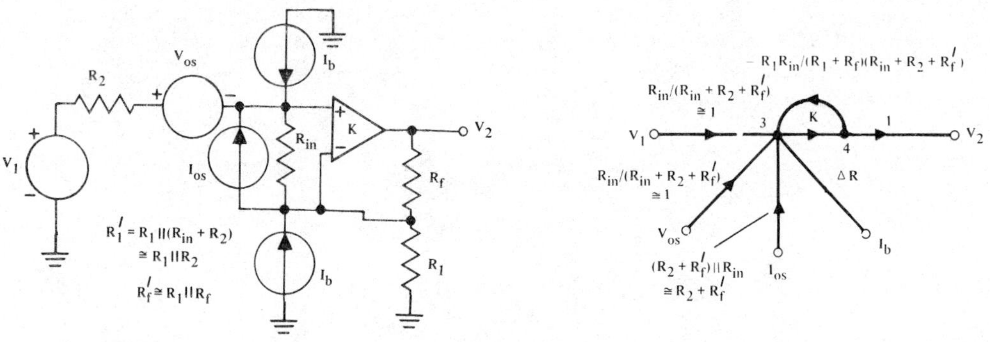

Fig. 14.4.13 Simple noninverting op amp with flow graph.

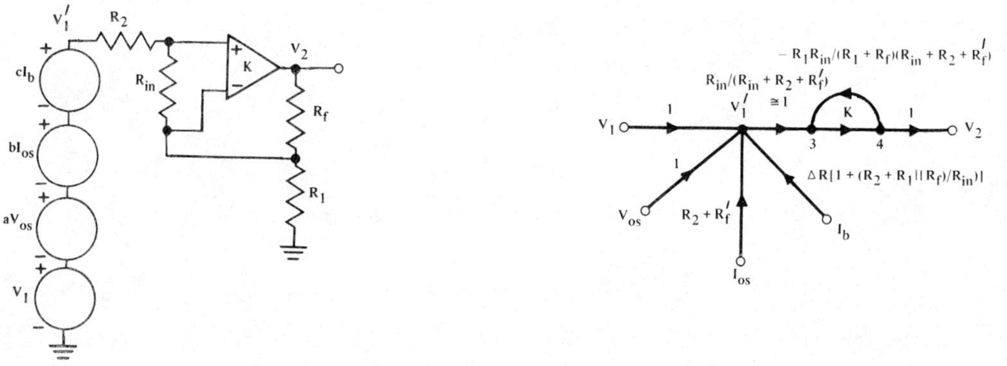

Fig. 14.4.14 Noninverting op amp with offset and bias errors referred to input.

$$H_o = \frac{V_2}{V_1'} = \frac{R_{in}}{R_{in} + R_2 + R_f'} \frac{K}{1 + KR_1R_{in}/(R_1 + R_f)(R_{in} + R_2 + R_f')} \tag{14.4.19}$$

After manipulation, the closed-loop gain given by Eq. 14.4.19 can be re-expressed as

$$H_o = \frac{1 + R_f/R_1}{1 + (1 + R_f/R_1)[1 + (R_2 + R_f')/R_{in}]/K} \to 1 + \frac{R_f}{R_1} \tag{14.4.20}$$

R_{in} decreases the closed-loop gain, but its effect is negligible when $R_{in} \gg R_2 + R_f'$. As $K \to \infty$, then Eq. 14.4.20 reduces to $H_o = 1 + R_f/R_1$. Substituting this result into Eq. 14.4.18, the effective input voltage then equals $V_1' = V_1 + \Delta V_1$ and the total input offset error ΔV_1 equals

$$\Delta V_1 = (V_{os} + \Delta R I_b) + (R_2 + R_f/H_o)I_{os} \tag{14.4.21}$$

This shows that the input voltage offset due to V_{os} and I_b is independent of gain, unlike the inverting op amp. The input offset due to I_{os} is directly dependent upon the sum of R_2 and R_f/H_o, where H_o is the closed-loop gain. For dc gains less than unity, the offset due to I_{os} can become excessive. Unlike the inverting op amp, very large input impedance can be obtained without increasing offset errors as we shall see.[45] A series of nomographs have been developed which can be used to calculate the output offset voltage due to V_{os}, I_{os}, and I_b for both inverting and noninverting operations.[46]

EXAMPLE 14.4.2 Calculate the resistors needed to obtain a dc closed-loop gain of ±10 using an op amp having a dc input impedance R_{in} of 50 KΩ. Assume that its open-loop gain K equals infinity.
Solution From Eqs. 14.4.16 and 14.4.20, the closed-loop gains H_{oI} (inverting mode) and H_{oN} (noninverting mode) equal

$$-H_{oI} \cong (R_f/R_1)(1 - R_f/R_{in}), \qquad H_{oN} \cong 1 + (R_f/R_1)(1 - R_f/R_{in}) \tag{14.4.22}$$

assuming $R_2 < R_f < R_{in}$. Neglecting the second-order effects due to R_{in}, then the gains given by Eq. 14.4.22 reduce to

$$-H_{oI} \cong R_f/R_1 = 10, \qquad H_{oN} \cong 1 + R_f/R_1 = 10 \tag{14.4.23}$$

Choosing R_f = 10 K, then R_1 = 1 K (inverting mode) or R_1 = 1.11 K (noninverting mode). Recalculating R_1 to include second-order effects using R_f = 10 K and $R_2 = R_1 || R_f \cong 1$ K, and Eqs. 14.4.16 and 14.4.20, gives

$$R_{1I} = \frac{R_f/(-H_o)}{1 + R_f/R_{in}} = \frac{10\text{ K}/10}{1 + 0.2} = 833\ \Omega \qquad (825\ \Omega)$$
$$R_{1N} = \frac{R_f}{H_o(1 + R_2/R_{in}) - 1}\,\frac{1 + R_2/R_{in}}{1 + (R_2 + R_f)/R_{in}} = \frac{10\text{ K}}{10(1.02) - 1}\,\frac{1 + 0.02}{1 + 0.22} = 909\ \Omega \tag{14.4.24}$$

EXAMPLE 14.4.3 Assume that the op amp used in Example 14.4.2 has ΔR = 0, V_{os} = 3 mV, and I_{os} = 100 nA. Calculate the equivalent offset voltage at the input. What must the input level be to obtain less that 1% of offset?
Solution From Eqs. 14.4.17 and 14.4.21, the equivalent input offset voltages ΔV_{1I} (inverting mode) and ΔV_{1N} (noninverting mode) equal

$$\begin{aligned}\Delta V_{1I} &= (1 + R_1/R_f)V_{os} + R_1 I_{os} = (1 + 825/10\text{ K})(3\text{ mV}) + (825)(10^{-7}\text{ A}) \\ &= 3.3\text{ mV} + 83\ \mu\text{V} = 3.4\text{ mV} \\ \Delta V_{1N} &= V_{os} + (R_2 + R_1 || R_f)I_{os} = 3\text{ mV} + (1\text{ K} + 909 \,||\, 10\text{ K})(10^{-8}\text{ A}) \\ &= 3\text{ mV} + (1.83\text{ K})(10^{-8}\text{ A}) = 3\text{ mV}\end{aligned} \tag{14.4.25}$$

Both offsets are due primarily to V_{os}. For less than 1% offset, then the input level V_1 must exceed 300 mV rms.

In both the inverting and noninverting op amp cases, the offset errors can be cancelled by proper biasing of an input. However, variations in temperature, supply voltage, and aging change the equivalent offset voltage at the input. To estimate the variations in V_{os} and I_{os}, we use[45]

$$\begin{aligned}\Delta V_{os} &= (\partial V_{os}/\partial T)\Delta T + (\partial V_{os}/\partial V_{sp})\Delta V_{sp} + (\partial V_{os}/\partial V_{sn})\Delta V_{sn} + (\partial V_{os}/\partial t)\Delta t \\ \Delta I_{os} &= (\partial I_{os}/\partial T)\Delta T + (\partial I_{os}/\partial V_{sp})\Delta V_{sp} + (\partial I_{os}/\partial V_{sn})\Delta V_{sn} + (\partial I_{os}/\partial t)\Delta t\end{aligned} \tag{14.4.26}$$

where the various derivatives are the drift coefficients of V_{os} and I_{os} with respect to temperature, positive and negative power supply voltages, and age.

EXAMPLE 14.4.4 Calculate the maximum daily drift in the input offset voltage for the inverting and noninverting op amps of Example 14.4.2 having closed-loop gains of ±10 and open-loop dc input resistances of 50 K. The op amps are operated over the commercial temperature range and have the following drift coefficients:

$$\begin{aligned}&\Delta V_{os}/\Delta T = \pm 20\ \mu\text{V}/^{o}\text{C}, \quad \Delta V_{os}/\Delta V = \pm 20\ \mu\text{V}/\%, \quad \Delta V_{os}/\Delta t = \pm 50\ \mu\text{V/day} \\ &\Delta I_{os}/\Delta T = \pm 1\text{ nA}/^{o}\text{C}, \quad \Delta I_{os}/\Delta V = \pm 2\text{ nA}/\%, \quad \Delta I_{os}/\Delta t = \pm 5\text{ nA/day}\end{aligned} \tag{14.4.27}$$

The power supply is regulated to 0.5%.

Solution The initial offset was calculated in Example 14.4.3 to equal about 3 mV. It can be adjusted to zero at 25°C. Since the commercial temperature range is 0–70°C, we must calculate the offset drifts for (70–25) = +45°C, and (0–25) = –25°C temperature changes. From Eq. 14.4.26, these offsets equal

$$\Delta V_{os} = (\pm 20\ \mu V/^{o}C)(45^{o}C) + (\pm 20\ \mu V/\%)(0.5\%) + (\pm 50\ \mu V/day)(1\ day) = \pm 0.96\ mV \cong \pm 1\ mV$$

$$\Delta I_{os} = (\pm 1\ nA/^{o}C)(45^{o}C) + (\pm 2\ nA/\%)(0.5\%) + (\pm 5\ nA/day)(1\ day) = \pm 51\ nA \cong \pm 50\ nA \qquad (14.4.28)$$

where temperature drift effects predominate. The equivalent input offsets depend upon the resistors R_1, R_2, and R_f calculated in Example 14.4.2.

In the inverting mode where R_1 = 825 Ω and R_f = 10 K, then Eq. 14.4.25a gives

$$\Delta V_{1I} = (1 + 825/10\ K)(\pm 0.96\ mV) + (825)(\pm 51\ nA) = \pm 1.04\ mV \pm 42\ \mu V = \pm 1.08\ mV \qquad (14.4.29)$$

In the noninverting mode, where R_1 = 853 Ω, R_2 = 1 K, and R_f = 10 K, then Eq. 14.4.25b gives

$$\Delta V_{1N} = (\pm 0.96\ mV) + (1\ K + 853\ ||\ 10\ K)(\pm 51\ mA) = \pm 0.96\ mV + (1.78\ K)(\pm 51\ nA)$$
$$= \pm 0.96\ mV \pm 91\ \mu V = \pm 1.05\ mV \qquad (14.4.30)$$

In either case, the equivalent input drift is about ±1 mV which is due primarily to temperature drifts in V_{os}. Because the resistances R_1 and R_2 are so low, the offset increment due to I_{os} is negligible. If the offset is to be less than 1% of the input signal, then V_{in} must be greater than 100 mV rms.

14.4.7 COMMON-MODE INPUT VOLTAGE/REJECTION RATIO

The *common-mode input voltage* (or *maximum input voltage*) is equal to the maximum input voltage which can be applied to either op amp input without causing damage or nonlinear operation. Typical values are listed in Table 14.4.5 and are generally about 70% of the power supply voltage. The common-mode input voltage is usually limited by saturation of the input stage of the op amp.

The *common-mode rejection ratio* (CMRR) is defined as the ratio of the change in output voltage due to a change in common-mode input voltage divided by the open-loop gain K_o. Alternatively stated, it is the ratio of the differential (i.e., difference) voltage gain to the common-mode voltage gain. The CMRR is a figure of merit which compares the gain received by differential signals to that received by common-mode signals. The parameter gives an indication of the degree of balance in the differential input stages of the op amp. A perfectly balanced op amp would have a zero output voltage (i.e., infinite CMRR) since a common-mode input voltage would be identically amplified by both channels of the op amp. Typical CMRR values are 90 dB as shown in Table 14.4.5.

Table 14.4.5 Typical input voltage range and CMRR for various op amps.

Op Amp	Maximum Input Voltage (±V)	Common-Mode Rejection Ratio CMRR (dB)
μA741	13	90
LM101	12	90
HA2500	10	90
MC1433	9	100
μA709	10	90
MC1431 (±6V)	2.2	75
MC1430 (±6V)	2.5	75

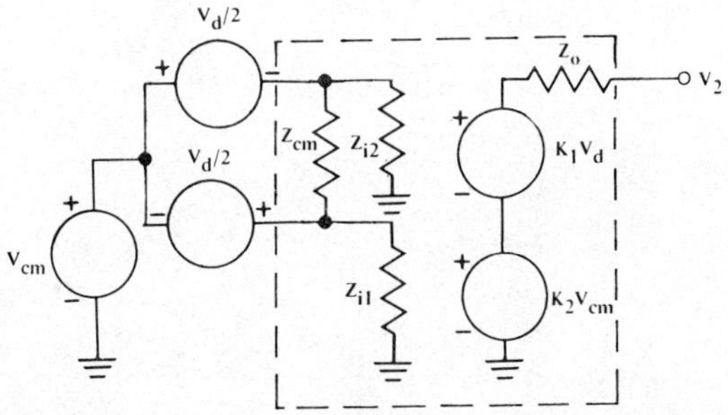

Fig. 14.4.15 Op amp model for common-mode analysis.[47]

A useful model for common-mode analysis is shown in Fig. 14.4.15. Here the input voltages V_{i1} and V_{i2} to the op amp, are expressed as the sum of the common-mode input voltage V_{cm} and differential input voltage V_d where

$$V_d = V_{i1} - V_{i2}, \quad V_{cm} = ½(V_{i1} + V_{i2}) \tag{14.4.31}$$

The actual op amp has a differential voltage gain K_1 with respect to the differential voltage input V_d, and a common-mode voltage gain K_2 with respect to the common-mode voltage input V_{cm}. An ideal op amp would have $K_2 = 0$. The output voltage of the op amp therefore equals

$$V_2 = K_1V_d + K_2V_{cm} \tag{14.4.32}$$

The common-mode rejection ratio can be expressed as

$$\text{CMRR} = K_1/K_2 = (V_2/V_d)/(V_2/V_{cm}) = V_{cm}/V_d \tag{14.4.33}$$

Thus, the output voltage can be re-expressed as

$$V_2 = K_1(V_d + V_{cm}/\text{CMRR}) \tag{14.4.34}$$

and the error due to a finite CMRR can easily be calculated. For example, the common-mode gain K_2 of a μA741 equals (106–90) = 16 dB = 6 from Tables 14.4.1 and 14.4.5. For a common-mode input voltage of 1 volt, the open-loop output voltage equals 1(6) = 6 volts. In closed-loop operation, the CMRR is determined primarily by the resistor unbalance in the input networks rather than the K_1/K_2 ratio of the op amp.

14.4.8 INPUT IMPEDANCE

The input impedance of the op amp is characterized by two parameters. The first is the differential input impedance Z_{id} connected between its two input terminals. The second is the common-mode input impedance Z_{icm} connected between either input terminal and ground. This is shown in Fig. 14.4.16. Most manufacturers specify the input impedance Z_i to the op amp measured at either input with other input grounded. We see that Z_i is equal to $Z_{id} || Z_{icm}$, so that Z_i must be

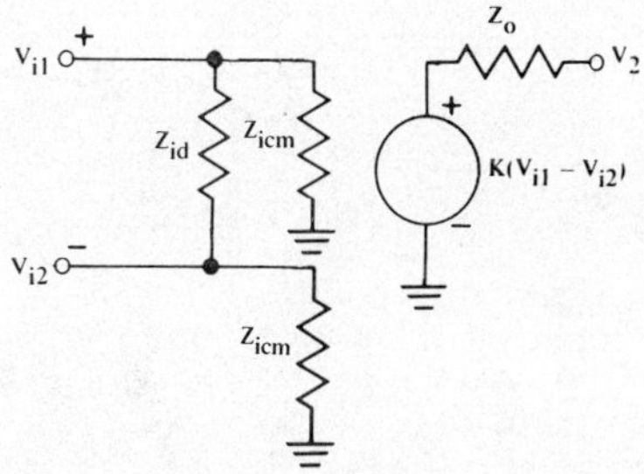

Fig. 14.4.16 Op amp model showing input and output impedances.

Table 14.4.6 Typical input and output impedances of various op amps.

Op Amp	Input Impedance Z_i (MΩ)	Output Impedance Z_o (Ω)
μA741	2	75
LM101	0.8	–
HA2500	50	–
MC1433	0.3	100
μA709	0.4	150
MC1431	0.6	25
MC1430	15 K	25

less than Z_{id} and Z_{icm}. Typical Z_i values are listed in Table 14.4.6 and are in the 250 K–1 M range. Z_i is temperature and frequency dependent. It has a magnitude slope of –20 dB/dec at high frequencies. Using impedance paper, the equivalent C_i can be estimated which is typically in the 1–5 pF range. The Z_i characteristics for a μA741 are shown in Fig. 14.4.17. The temperature characteristic for Z_i shows the importance of insuring that Z_i is large compared with the source impedance of the input networks so that negligible drift and detuning occur.

The input impedance Z_{in} to a closed-loop op amp is of considerable importance to insure that adequate current drive is provided and to facilitiate impedance matching calculations. Let us calculate the input impedance to each channel of the closed-loop op amp shown in Fig. 14.4.18.[48] For convenience, we neglect the common-mode input impedance Z_{id}. To facilitate later generalizations, we shall drive the noninverting channel using a dependent voltage source AV_b.

The input impedance Z_a of the noninverting channel equals

$$Z_a = V_1/I_1 = Z_2 + Z_3 || Z_{i2} \cong Z_2 + Z_3 \tag{14.4.35}$$

under the condition that $Z_{i2} \gg Z_3$ which is usually the case. Thus, the input impedance Z_a to the noninverting channel is the sum of Z_2 and Z_3, and is independent of the op amp parameters (except second-order effects due to Z_{i2}).

However, this is not the case for the input impedance Z_b to the inverting channel as we shall now see. Z_b is easily calculated using Blackman's impedance relation (Eq. 1.10.18a) and choosing the voltage source $K(V_{i2} - V_{i1})$ as the source of interest having strength K. Under limiting conditions where Z_{i1}, Z_{i2}, and $K \to \infty$ and $Z_o \to 0$, then Z_b reduces to the simple expression[48]

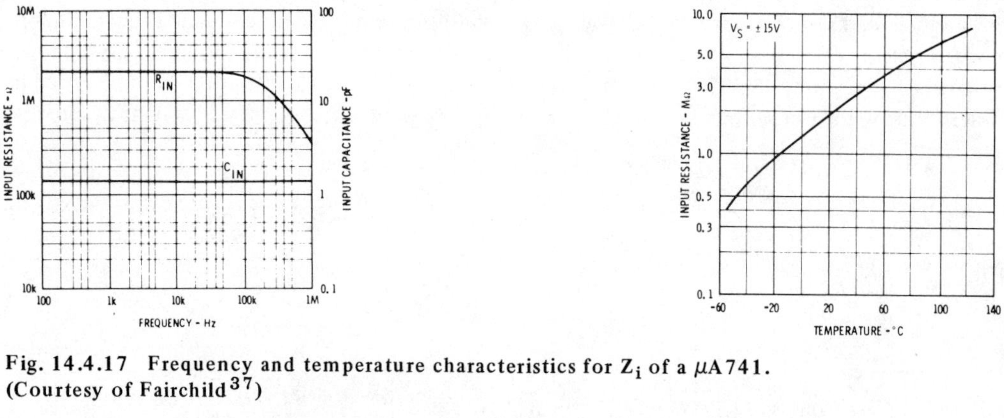

Fig. 14.4.17 Frequency and temperature characteristics for Z_i of a μA741. (Courtesy of Fairchild[37])

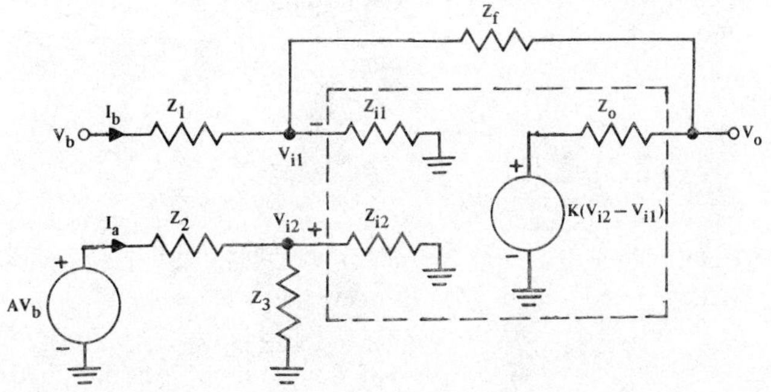

Fig. 14.4.18 Op amp model for calculating input impedance of amplifier.

$$Z_b = Z_b(\infty) = \frac{Z_1}{1 - AZ_3/(Z_2 + Z_3)} = \frac{Z_1}{1 - AG_2} \tag{14.4.36}$$

where $G_2 = Z_3/(Z_2 + Z_3)$ equals the voltage gain of the impedance divider to the noninverting channel for $Z_{i2} \to \infty$. If we normalize the input impedance Z_b by Z_1, then Eq. 14.4.36 may be expressed as

$$Z_{bn} = |Z_{bn}| \exp{(j \arg Z_{bn})} = Z_b/Z_1 = 1/(1 - AG_2) \tag{14.4.37}$$

Therefore, when $AG_2 = 0$, then $Z_b = Z_1$ which is the often-quoted result. However, under non-zero AG_2 conditions, Z_1 must be reduced by $1/(1 - AG_2)$. In ac steady-state, if we express the AG_2 gain product as

$$AG_2 = |AG_2| \exp{(j \arg AG_2)} = |AG_2| \exp{(j\theta_2)} \tag{14.4.38}$$

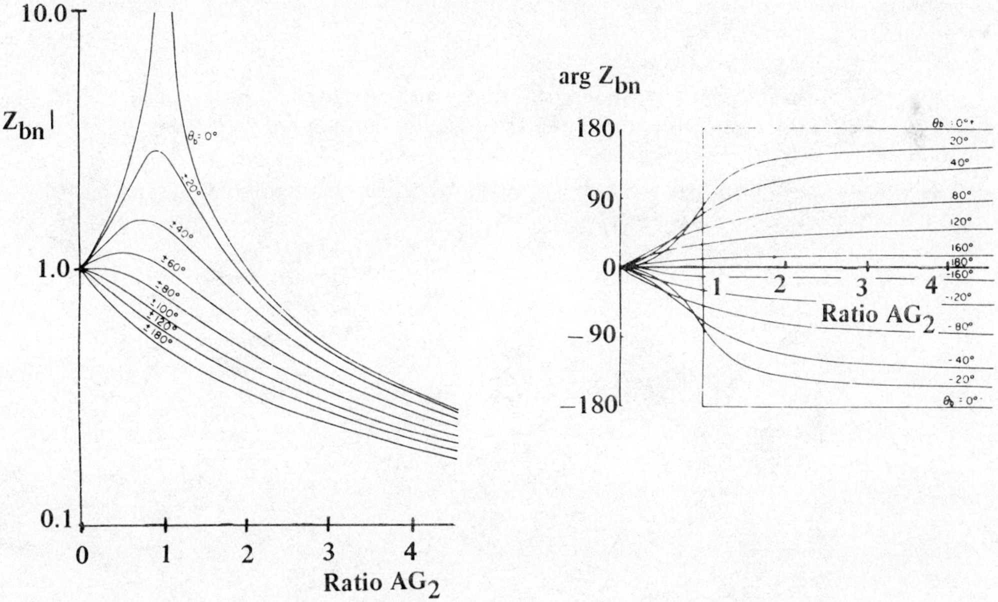

Fig. 14.4.19 Magnitude and phase of Z_{bn} as a function of AG_2. (From C. S. Lindquist, "Differential amplifier input impedance and Blackman's impedance relation," IEEE Trans. on Electron Devices, vol. ED-19, pp. 990–993, Aug., 1972.

then the normalized input impedance to the inverting channel is plotted in Fig. 14.4.19 as a function of $|AG_2|$ and θ_2. It is interesting to note that the input impedance is infinite when $AG_2 = 1$.

14.4.9 OUTPUT IMPEDANCE

The output impedance Z_o of the op amp is equal to the impedance seen by the load in open-loop operation. Typical values are listed in Table 14.4.6 and are usually less than 100 Ω. The output impedance is frequency dependent and increases for large frequencies as shown in Fig. 14.4.20. At these frequencies the output appears inductive but at higher frequencies, it becomes capacitive.

When the op amp is operated closed-loop, the output impedance is reduced by the loop-gain of the op amp as we shall see. Excessive output impedance reduces the closed-loop gain of the op amp. The closed-loop output impedance of the op amp of Fig. 14.4.18 can be easily calculated using Blackman's impedance relation. Since we are calculating impedance at the output port, we set input voltage $V_1 = 0$ and $AV_1 = 0$. Then from Fig. 14.4.18, we can write by inspection that $Z^{(0)}$, T_s, and T_∞ equal

$$Z^{(0)} = Z_b||(Z_1||Z_i + Z_f) \cong Z_o, \qquad T_s = 0, \qquad T_\infty = \frac{-KZ_1||Z_{i1}}{Z_o + Z_f + Z_1||Z_{i1}} \cong \frac{-K}{1 + Z_f/Z_1} \tag{14.4.39}$$

Substituting Eq. 14.4.39 into Eq. 1.10.18a, the closed-loop output impedance Z_{out} of the op amp equals

$$Z_{out} = \frac{Z_o||(Z_1||Z_{i1} + Z_f)}{1 + (KZ_1||Z_{i1})/(Z_o + Z_f + Z_1||Z_{i1})} \cong \frac{Z_o}{1 + K/(1 + Z_f/Z_1)} \tag{14.4.40}$$

so that Z_o is reduced by the loop-gain factor $(1 - T_\infty)$. It is also clear that increasing Z_o decreases the loop-gain.

14.4.10 NOISE

We discussed *thermal* or *Johnson noise* in Sec. 14.1.8 which was given by Eqs. 14.1.26 and 14.1.27. In addition to thermal noise, other types of noise exist within op amps.[49]

Shot (or *Schottky*) *noise* is generated at semiconductor junctions and is caused by random fluctuations in the rate of arrival of charge. Schottky likened it to the noise of a hail of shot striking a target. Shot noise has a value of

$$I_n = (2qI_{dc}B)^{1/2} \text{ amps} \tag{14.4.41}$$

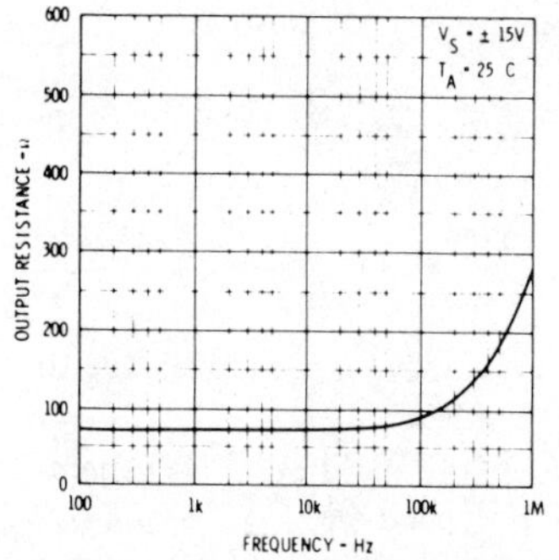

Fig. 14.4.20 Frequency characteristic for Z_o of the μA741. (Courtesy of Fairchild[37])

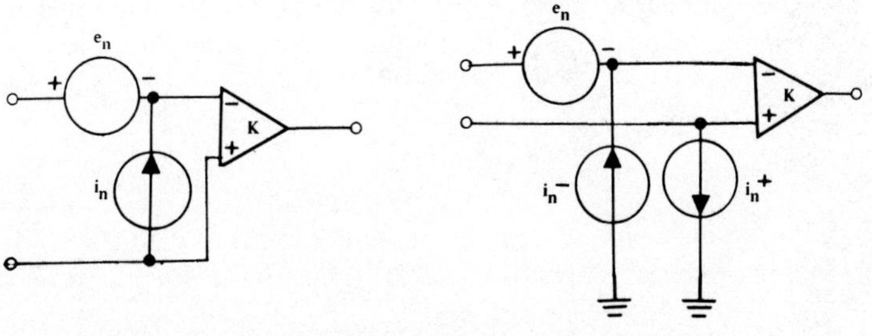

Fig. 14.4.21 Equivalent noise generators in op amp model.

where I_{dc} (amps) is the quiescent junction current and B (Hz) is the measurement bandwidth. The shot noise density i_n equals $570 I_{dc}^{1/2}$ $\mu A/Hz^{1/2}$ for I_{dc} in pA. Thus, the shot noise spectrum is constant (as is thermal noise) up to frequencies where charge transit time must be considered.

Flicker noise occurs in all conducting materials and has several other names including *1/f noise*, *excess noise*, *modulation noise* (in semiconductors), and *contact noise* (in resistors). It generally dominates over thermal and shot noise at low frequencies (usually below 100 Hz). Flicker noise exhibits a $1/f^n$ power spectrum characteristic where n is usually in the range from 0.8 to 1.5. Thus, the flicker noise density equals

$$e_n = Kf^{-n/2} \ \mu V/Hz^{1/2} \tag{14.4.42}$$

We see that the flicker noise density follows a $-n/2$ power law; it has a slope of $-3n$ dB/oct or $-10n$ dB/dec when plotted on log-log paper. The total flicker noise in bandwidth B falling between frequencies f_1 and f_2 (where $B = f_2 - f_1$) equals

$$E_n = k\left[\int_{f_1}^{f_2} f^{-n}\, df\right]^{1/2} = k\left[\frac{f^{1-n}}{1-n}\Bigg|_{f=f_1}^{f_2}\right]^{1/2} = k\left[\frac{f_2^{\,1-n} - f_1^{\,1-n}}{1-n}\right]^{1/2} \tag{14.4.43}$$

from Eq. 14.4.42. Whenever noise has a 1/f power spectrum, it is called *pink noise*. Thus for $n = 1$, the noise is "pink" with value

$$E_n = k\int_{f_1}^{f_2} f^{-1}\, df = k[\ln(f_2/f_1)]^{1/2} = 1.52k[\log_{10}(f_2/f_1)]^{1/2} = 1.52kD^{1/2} \tag{14.4.44}$$

where D is the frequency separation between f_1 and f_2 in decades. Therefore, pink noise increases 3 dB for every doubling of decade separation. Every decade or octave of pink noise will have the same rms noise as every other decade or octave. For example, if the pink noise from 0.01–1 Hz (one decade) is 1 μV, then the pink noise from 10^{-4}–1 Hz or any other four-decade interval will be 2 μV. Note that this differs from thermal noise which depends upon the frequency difference (bandwidth) rather than the frequency ratio. The thermal noise in the band from 10^{-4}–1 Hz would be only 5% more than that in the band from 0.1–1 Hz. Many op amps exhibit pink noise at low frequencies.

Burst or *popcorn noise* is also generated at semiconductor junctions and appears to be due to modulation of the barrier height. It has a $1/f^2$ power spectrum and seems to be related to flicker or 1/f noise.[50]

Assuming that the various noise sources are random and uncorrelated, the noise power due to the various sources is additive and is calculated using Eq. 14.1.31.

Noise is modelled in the same manner as dc offset discussed in Sec. 14.4.6. Two noise generators, e_n and i_n, are connected to the op amp input as shown in Fig. 14.4.21. These sources augment the offset generators, V_{os} and I_{os}, so that the total series voltage is $(V_{os} + e_n)$ and the

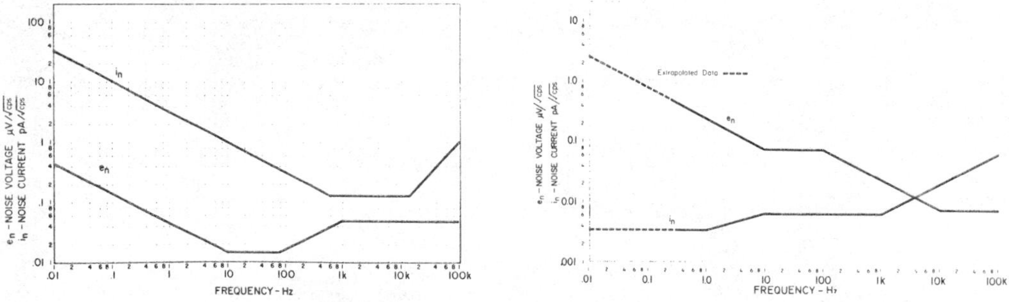

Fig. 14.4.22 **Voltage and current noise densities for Analog Devices (a) 183 (bipolar), and (b) 144 (FET input) op amps. (From L. Smith and D. H. Sheingold, "Noise and operational amplifier circuits," Analog Dialogue, vol. 3, no. 1, Analog Devices, Cambridge, MA.)**

total shunt current is $(I_{os} + i_n)$. However, since the op amp is a linear system, we can calculate the generator effects separately and then superimpose (add) the results. The actual values of e_n and i_n are determined experimentally over fixed bandwidths at various frequencies. The noise density curves of e_n and i_n are plotted and later integrated to determine the total noise E_n and I_n within a specified frequency band.

Typical noise density curves are shown in Fig. 14.4.22. Examining the AD183 voltage density curve, we see that flicker noise (having -10 dB/dec slope) dominates at frequencies below 10 Hz. White noise dominates from 10–80 Hz. The noise rises from 80–1 KHz to reach the shot noise level at 1 KHz and above. The current density curve shows that the flicker noise dominates to 1 KHz. Shot noise sets the noise floor from 600 Hz to 15 KHz. The 20 dB/dec rise in noise above 15 KHz is due to the constant voltage noise level divided by the capacitive loading of the op amp input impedance.[51]

After the noise characteristics of the op amp have been determined, the noise characteristics of the active filter must be found. For example, consider the single op amp filter of Fig. 14.4.23a. To analyze noise, we use the flow graph description of the active filter as derived in Chap. 7. These flow graphs described "noiseless" filters since they only had a V_1 input. Then to account for the noise sources of the op amp, and all the noise sources associated with the filter resistances within the three-port, we add corresponding "noise" nodes to the flow graph. If the network is described by its impedance matrix **Z**, then from Fig. 1.12.1, V_{1n}, V_{2n}, and V_{3n} are the equivalent noise sources at the input ports which account for all noise effects within the three-port network. e_n and i_n account for all noise effects within the op amp. The flow graph of the active filter including all noise sources is shown in Fig. 14.4.23b. The noise sources can also be referred to the filter input as shown in Fig. 14.4.23c. Thus, the input noise ΔV_{1n} due to the three-port network, and the input noise ΔV_{1a} due to the op amp, equal

$$\Delta V_{in} = V_{1n} + (T_{23}/T_{13})V_{2n} + (T_{33}/T_{13})V_{3n}, \qquad \Delta V_{1a} = (T_{e3}/T_{13})e_n + (T_{i3}/T_{13})i_n \tag{14.4.45}$$

The rms noise present, $\Delta V_1 = (\Delta V_{1n}^2 + \Delta V_{1a}^2)^{1/2}$ depends upon the noise densities e_n, i_n and V_{jn}, the measurement bandwidth B, and the form of the transfer functions T_{e3}, T_{i3}, and T_{j3}. They are calculated using Eqs. 4.18.1 and 4.18.2.

A useful figure-of-merit for the filter is the *signal-to-noise ratio* SNR which is defined to equal

$$\text{SNR} = 20 \log_{10} (\text{RMS Signal}/\text{RMS Noise}) \tag{14.4.46}$$

and is expressed in dB. Thus, if the input voltage to the filter is V_1, then the SNR of the filter equals

$$\text{SNR} = 20 \log_{10} [V_1/(\Delta V_{1n}^2 + \Delta V_{1a}^2)^{1/2}] \tag{14.4.47}$$

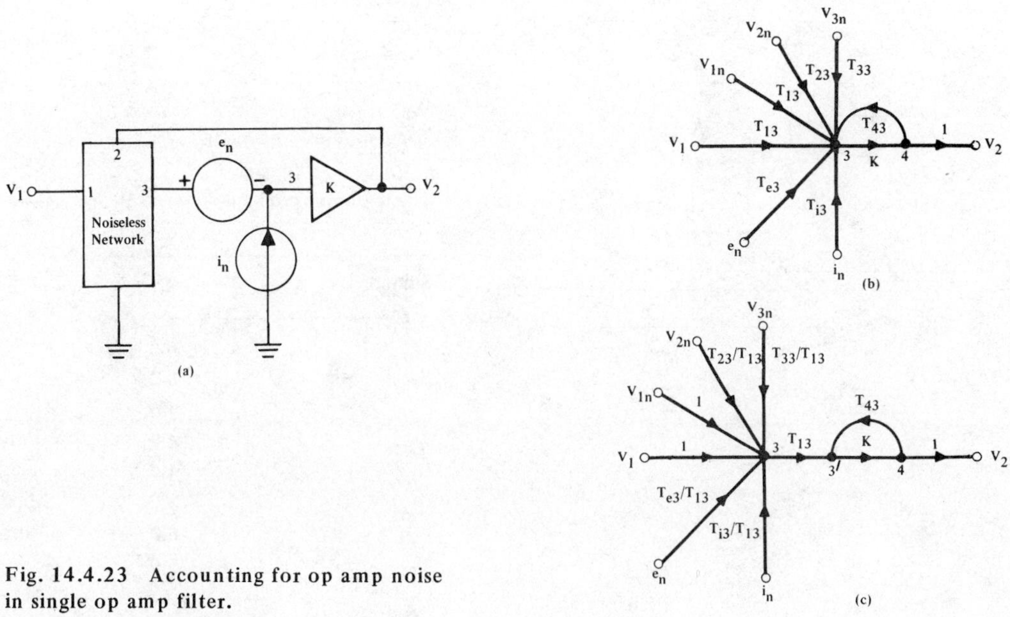

Fig. 14.4.23 Accounting for op amp noise in single op amp filter.

From Eqs. 14.4.46 and 14.4.47, notice that the SNR of the filter is independent of the op amp gain.

The noise figure NF of the amplifier is a measure of the relative levels of ΔV_{1a} and ΔV_{1n}.[52] The NF is defined to equal

$$NF = SNR_o - SNR_i \tag{14.4.48}$$

in dB where SNR_i is the input SNR to the op amp (which is independent of e_n and i_n) and SNR_o is the output SNR of the op amp (which is dependent upon e_n, and i_n). A noiseless op amp would have NF = 1 = 0 dB. From Fig. 14.4.23c,

$$SNR_i = 20 \log_{10} [V_1/\Delta V_{1n}], \qquad SNR_o = 20 \log_{10} [V_1/(\Delta V_{1n}{}^2 + \Delta V_{1a}{}^2)^{1/2}] \tag{14.4.49}$$

so

$$NF = 20 \log_{10} [(\Delta V_{1n}{}^2 + \Delta V_{1a}{}^2)^{1/2}/\Delta V_{1n}] = 20 \log_{10} [1 + (\Delta V_{1a}/\Delta V_{1n})^2]^{1/2} \tag{14.4.50}$$

If the op amp adds no noise to the system, then $e_n = i_n = 0$, so $\Delta V_{1a} = 0$. Thus, NF = 0 dB. Since $SNR_o = SNR_i + NF$, minimizing the SNR_o of the system requires minimizing the sum of the input SNR_i and the op amp NF. When $SNR_i \gg NF$, there is no reason to use low NF op amps. However, when $SNR \ll NF$, the NF of the op amp determines the SNR_o of the system.

14.4.11 RELIABILITY

In addition to temperature, IC op amp failure causes include: (1) contaminates and impurities not removed during manufacture destroy conductors (aluminum) and cause shorts and intermittant operation; (2) moisture content within the package causes increased leakage currents and short circuits. Poor hermetic seals allow moisture to enter the package with the same results; and (3) ceramic substrates crack due to stresses set up by scribing and excessive bonding temperature and pressure.

Table 14.4.7 π-factors in IC op amp failure rate analysis.[53]

Level	π_Q
A	1
B	2
B-1	5
B-2	10
C	16
D (Commercial)	150

T_j (°C)	π_T
25	1
50	8.2
75	50
100	240
125	940
150	3100
175	9200

Description	π_L
Experience with more than 6 months production	1
Inexperience with less than 6 months production	10

Symbol	π_E
G_B	0.2
S_F	0.2
G_F	1.0
A_I	4.0
N_S	4.0
G_M	4.0
A_U	6.0
N_U	5.0
M_L	10.0

The failure rate f_o of IC op amps is given by

$$f_o = \pi_Q \pi_L (f_1 \pi_E + f_2 \pi_T) \text{ failures}/10^6 \text{ hours} \tag{14.4.51}$$

where π_Q is a quality factor, π_L a learning factor, π_E an environmental factor, π_T a temperature acceleration factor, and f_1 and f_2 are failure rates. f_1 and f_2 equal

$$f_1 = 0.0026n^{0.55}, \qquad f_2 = 0.000056n^{0.76} \tag{14.4.52}$$

where n is the number of transistors in the IC op amp. Typically, n = 20 so that $f_1 = 0.0135$ and $f_2 = 0.000546$. The various π factors are listed in Table 14.4.7. The $f_1 \pi_E$ term in Eq. 14.4.51 is constant, but the $f_2 \pi_T$ term varies exponentially with temperature as

$$\pi_T = \exp\left[-8121\left(\frac{1}{T_j + 273} - \frac{1}{298}\right)\right] \tag{14.4.53}$$

At elevated temperatures, this term essentially determines f_o. Assuming that $\pi_Q = \pi_L = \pi_E = 1$ and n = 20, then the failure rates equal

$$f_o = 0.0135 \text{ failures}/10^6 \text{ hours at } T_j = 25^\circ\text{C}, \qquad 0.514 \text{ failures}/10^6 \text{ hours at } T_j = 125^\circ\text{C} \tag{14.4.54}$$

Note also from Table 14.4.7 that the quality level π_Q is very important in determining f_o. If a commercial op amp is used with no screening beyond that used for quality assurance, f_o is increased by 150 on the average. MIL screening can reduce π_Q to unity.

The failure rates of op amps are determined in the same way as those for resistors, potentiometers, and capacitors. Thus, we shall not pursue them further. Instead, let us now determine the failure rate for an entire active filter.

Active filters are composed of a number of components. The filter fails when one or more of its components fail. Thus, the filter survives only when all of its components survive. Assuming that the component failures are independent, the survival probability P of the filter therefore equals

Table 14.4.8 Failure rate calculation for filter of Example 8.5.5.

Number	Component	25°C	70°C	125°C
8	Resistors (RN) $S_P = 0.1, \pi_E = 2.5, \pi_R = 1, \pi_Q = 1$	8(2.5)(0.0015) = 0.030	8(2.5)(0.0023) = 0.046	8(2.5)(0.0038) = 0.076
4	Capacitors (CK) $S_V = 0.3, \pi_E = 2, \pi_Q = 10$	4(20)(0.0036) = 0.29	4(20)(0.0040) = 0.32	4(20)(0.0045) = 0.36
2	IC Op Amps (n = 20) $f_1 = 0.0135, f_2 = 0.000546$ $\pi_Q = 1, \pi_L = 1, \pi_E = 1$	2(1)[0.0135 + 0.000546(1)] = 0.028	2(1)[0.0135 + 0.000546(36)] = 0.066	2(1)[0.0135 + 0.000546(940)] = 1.05
14	Total Failure Rate (failures/10^6 hours)	0.35	0.43	1.5
Lifetime (Pr = 99%)		29×10^3 hours = 3.3 years	23×10^3 hours = 2.7 years	6.7×10^3 hours = 0.76 years

$$\Pr(t \geqslant T) = \Pr_1(t \geqslant T) \ldots \Pr_n(t \geqslant T) \tag{14.4.55}$$

where the P_i are the survival probabilities of its individual components. Thus, using Eq. 14.1.37, the filter also has an exponential density function, where

$$1/\text{MTBF} = \sum_{i=1}^{n} 1/\text{MTBF}_i, \qquad f_o = \sum_{i=1}^{n} f_i \tag{14.4.56}$$

relate the MTBF and failure rate f_o of the filter to those of its individual components.

EXAMPLE 14.4.5 Calculate the failure rates for the fourth-order Chebyshev filter of Example 8.5.5 at temperatures of 25, 70, and 125°C. Assume a fixed ground application.

Solution The filter realization is shown in Fig. 8.5.11. It uses eight R's, four C's and two op amps. Let us assume that the resistors are metal film (RN) with a ¼ W power rating, and that the capacitors are ceramic with a 50 V voltage rating. If the maximum input/output voltage is –15 V, then the worst-case power dissipation in the resistors is about $15^2/12\ \text{K} \cong 20$ mW so there is at most a $20/250 \cong 0.1$ power stress. The worst-case voltage stress in the capacitors is 15/50 = 0.3. We can now calculate the failure rates of each component in the filter as shown in Table 14.4.8. The resistor data is obtained from Fig. 14.1.15, the capacitor data from Fig. 14.3.18, and the op amp data from Table 14.4.7. The total failure rate is the sum of all the individual failure rates using Eq. 14.4.56. Here we have selected a Class A screening on the op amp so its failure rate is compatible with those of the passive components.

Now let us estimate the lifetime T of the filter. For a 99% chance of survival, then $T \geqslant 0.01/f_o$ from Eq. 14.1.39. The lifetimes are also listed in Table 14.4.8. At room temperature, the lifetime is about 3.3 years. At 70°C, the lifetime is reduced to 1.7 years, while at 125°C, the lifetime is only 0.76 year. At elevated temperatures, the op amps determine the lifetime so their reliability must be increased if we wish to extend the life of the filter.

PROBLEMS

14.1 The typical frequency response of metal film resistors is shown in Fig. P14.1. The response depends upon the resistance value. Determine the equivalent circuits for the 10 Ω and 100 KΩ resistors.

14.2 The typical frequency response of composition resistors is shown in Fig. P14.2. The response depends upon their wattage value. To obtain the widest bandwidth impedance characteristics, the ratio of the cross-sectional area to resistor length is minimized. (a) Comparing Fig. P14.2 with Fig. 14.1.8, does C or L dominate the response? (b) The impedance axis is |Z|/R and the frequency axis is Rf × 10^6. Based upon part (a), what is the significance of the 3 dB frequencies? (c) What are the C values for the different resistor types?

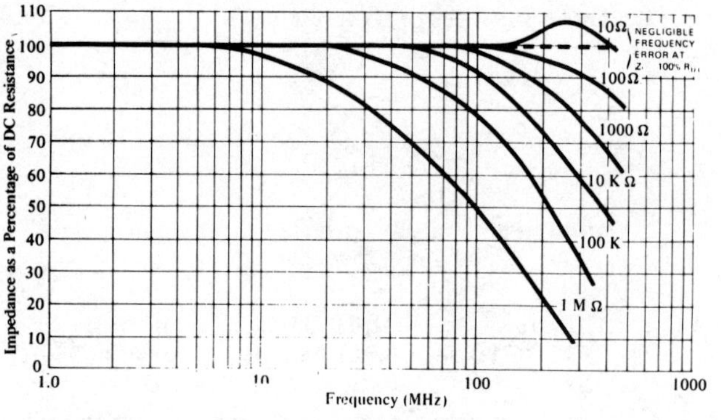

Fig. P14.1 (Courtesy of Mepco/Electra[54])

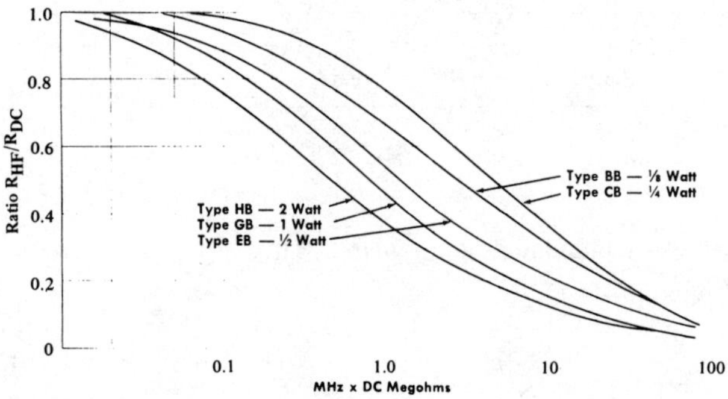

Fig. P14.2 (Courtesy of Allen-Bradley[55])

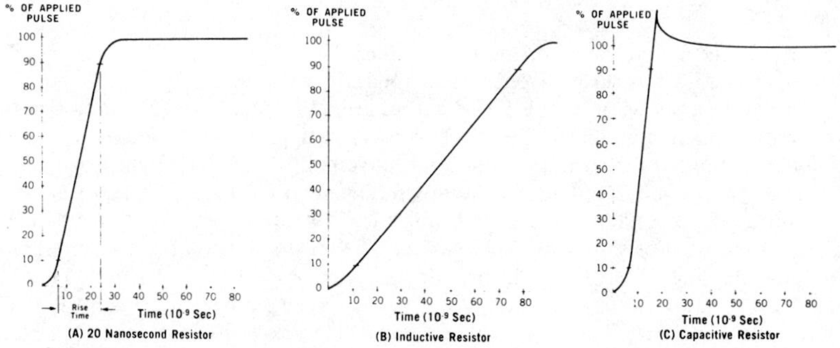

Fig. P14.3 (Courtesy of RCL[56])

14.3 Wirewound resistors exhibit the largest parasitic inductance and capacitance and must be properly constructed to obtain good high-frequency performance. For low resistance, inductance predominates while for high resistance, capacitance predominates. This is illustrated by the step responses shown in Fig. P14.3. (a) Determine the impedance expression for an ideal resistor, an inductive resistor, and a capacitive resistor. (b) Calculate the current response due to a unit voltage step input. Compare the responses with those shown in Fig. P14.3.

14.4 Power and temperature derating is often used to extend the lifetime and reliability of electronic parts. Resistors have the typical temperature rise versus rated power and temperature derating curves shown in Fig. P14.4. (a) Determine the thermal resistance of these resistors using the temperature rise curve. (b) Show how the temperature derating curve is obtained from part (a). (c) Normalize the temperature derating curves to percent of rated power. Compare with Fig. 14.1.4. (d) Draw the derated power curve in part (c) for 50% power stress such that the maximum case temperature is never exceeded (this is called power derating). (e) Draw the derated curve in part (c) so that a case temperature of 150°C is never exceeded (this is called temperature derating).

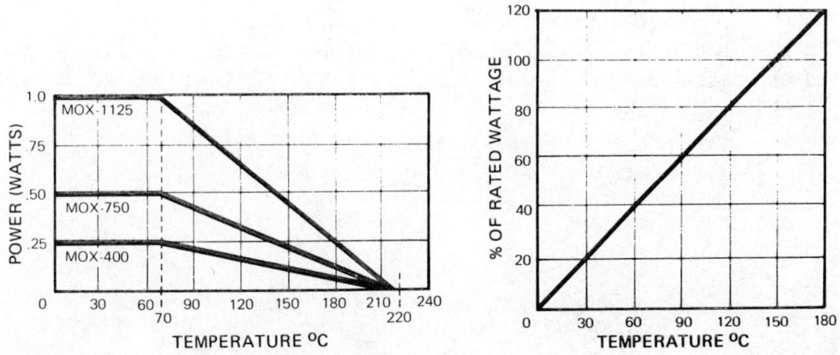

Fig. P14.4 (Courtesy of Victoreen[57])

14.5 Power and temperature derating improves the reliability of electronic parts. In some situations, power derating is more effective than temperature derating. In others, the situation is reversed. Reliability curves can be used to judge which derating method is more effective. (a) Considering the power derating curves for C-, E-, and F-rated RN metal film resistors shown in Fig. 14.1.4, what is the maximum case temperature allowable? (b) Extrapolating the failure rate curves in Fig. 14.1.15, what is the failure rate reduction obtained by derating power stress from 1 to 0.2 at maximum allowable temperature? (c) What reduction in temperature is required from the maximum allowable to obtain the same failure rate reduction? (d) Which derating method is more effective? Discuss the relative ease and tradeoffs in using power stress or temperature derating.

14.6 Failure rate can be mathematically described by the equation $f = f_o R^a \exp(bT_n)$ where a and b are constants, f is the failure rate under operating conditions, f_o is the base failure rate (obtained when $R = 1$ and $T_n = 0$), R is the power stress ($0 \leq R \leq 1$), and T_n is the normalized temperature where $T_n = (T - 25)/T_{max}$. a and b can be easily determined using curve matching techniques. (a) Show that

$$a = \left.\frac{\ln(f_1/f_2)}{\ln(R_1/R_2)}\right|_{T_n=0}, \qquad b = \left.\frac{\ln(f_1/f_2)}{T_{n1} - T_{n2}}\right|_{R=1}$$

(b) Determine the sensitivity of f with respect to R and T_n.

14.7 Using the failure rate expression of Prob. 14.6, (a) determine the failure rate equation for the RN metal film resistors in Fig. 14.1.15. (b) Determine the sensitivity of f with respect to R and T_n. (c) From part (b), determine which sensitivity predominates. Based upon this result, is power or temperature more effective in reducing failure rate?

14.8 Prepare a parts list for the resistors of the low-pass filter in Fig. 8.5.8. Assume that the 1% resistors are metal film and that the 10% resistors are composition. Both types must have ¼ W power ratings and TC's such that they drift no more than ± ½% over a 100°C temperature range.

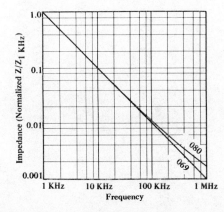

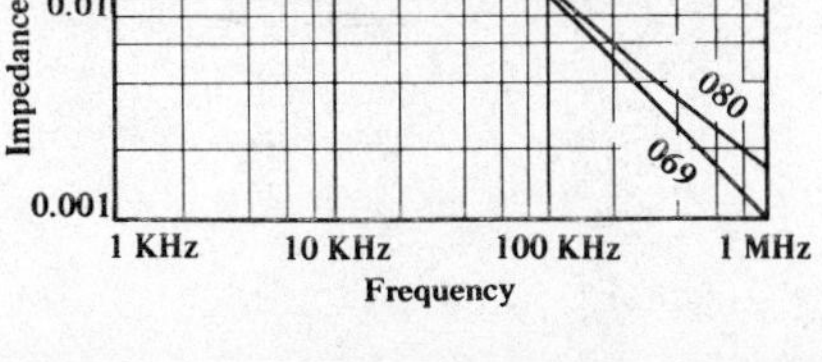

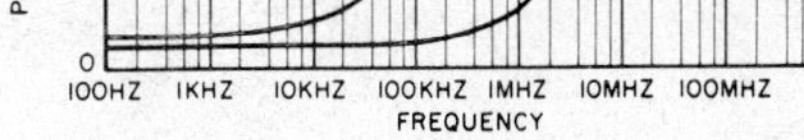

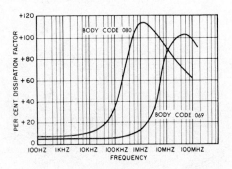

Fig. P14.9 (Courtesy of Sprague[58])

14.9 The impedance characteristic and dissipation factor characteristics of some ceramic disc capacitors are shown in Fig. P14.9. Compare the DF curves with the theoretical curves shown in Fig. 14.3.14 and discuss the discrepancies. (Note: 069 = ± 22%, 080 = ± 33% change in C from −30 to + 85°C.)

14.10 The typical impedance characteristics for several polyester film (410P and 192B) and ceramic (3C023, 7C023, and C080B) 0.1 μF capacitors are shown in Fig. P4.10. Determine their equivalent circuits.

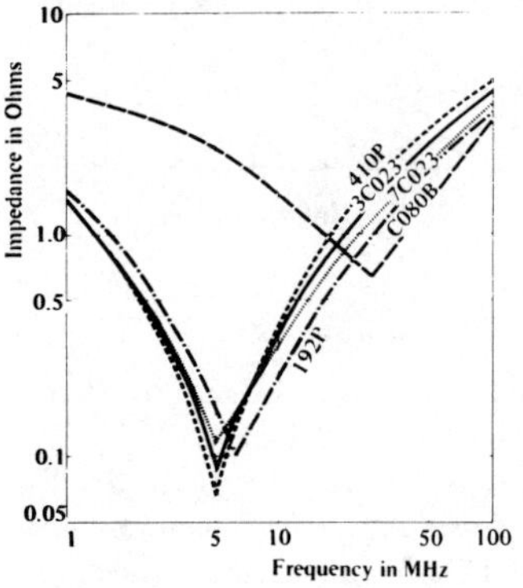

Fig. P14.10 (Courtesy of Sprague[59])

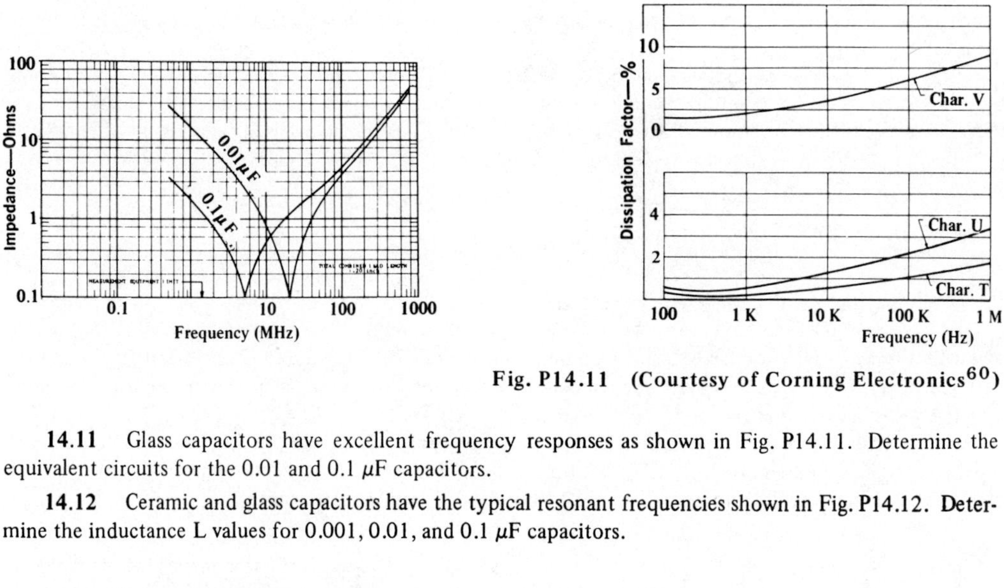

Fig. P14.11 (Courtesy of Corning Electronics[60])

14.11 Glass capacitors have excellent frequency responses as shown in Fig. P14.11. Determine the equivalent circuits for the 0.01 and 0.1 μF capacitors.

14.12 Ceramic and glass capacitors have the typical resonant frequencies shown in Fig. P14.12. Determine the inductance L values for 0.001, 0.01, and 0.1 μF capacitors.

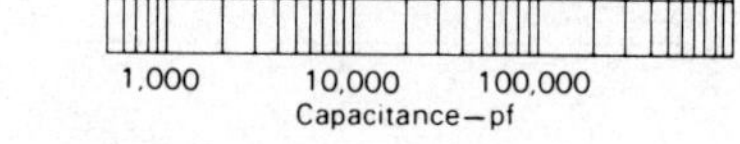

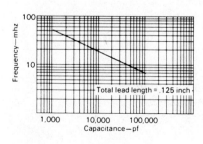

Fig. P14.12 (Courtesy of Corning Electronics[61])

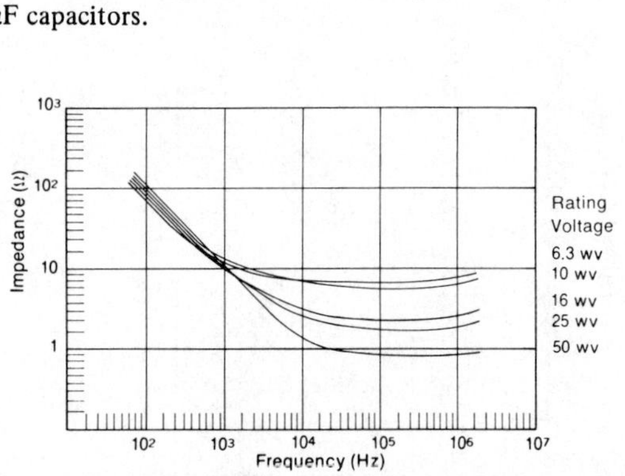

Fig. P14.13 (Courtesy of Nichicon[62])

14.13 Electrolytic capacitors are used primarily for decoupling purposes. The typical frequency responses of 10 μF aluminum electrolytic capacitors are shown in Fig. P14.13. Determine the equivalent circuit for the capacitor having a 50 volt rating. Is this a high- or low-loss capacitor?

14.14 The impedance characteristics of capacitors are sensitive to temperature. The typical frequency response of 220 μF wet-slug tantalum capacitors is shown in Fig. P14.14. Determine the equivalent circuit for the capacitor at -55, 25, and 125°C.

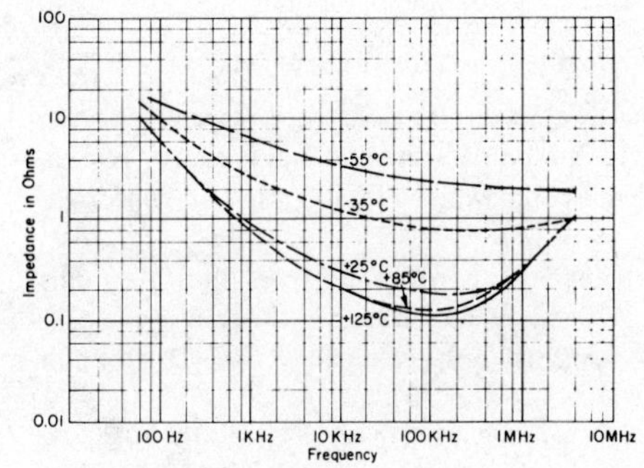

Fig. P14.14 (Courtesy of General Electric[63])

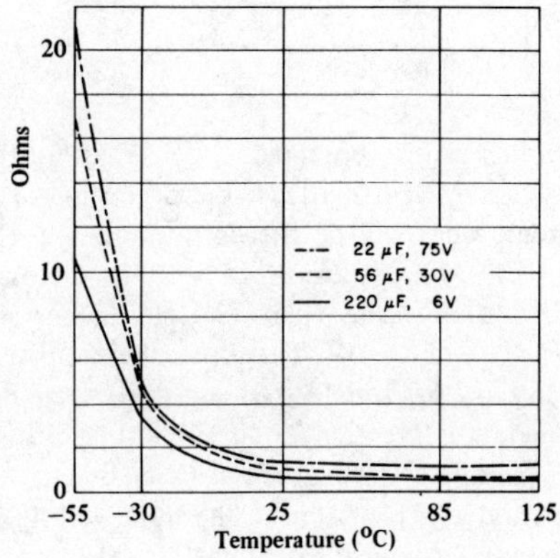

Fig. P14.15 (Courtesy of General Electric[63])

14.15 The series resistance R_s and insulation resistance R_p of capacitors decrease with temperature. The change in R_s of a wet-slug tantalum capacitor is shown in Fig. P14.15. Discuss the effects that decreases in R_s and R_p produce on the impedance, DF, and Q characteristics of the capacitor. (Hint: Use the results of Prob. 14.17.)

14.16 Determine the equivalent circuit for the 0.1 and 110 μF solid tantalum capacitors having the characteristics shown in Fig. P14.16.

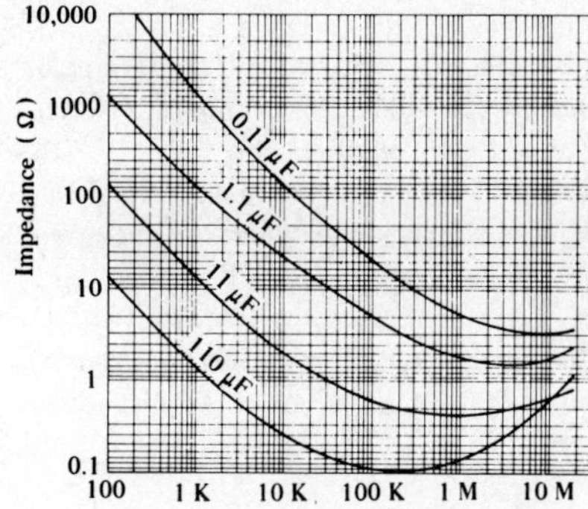

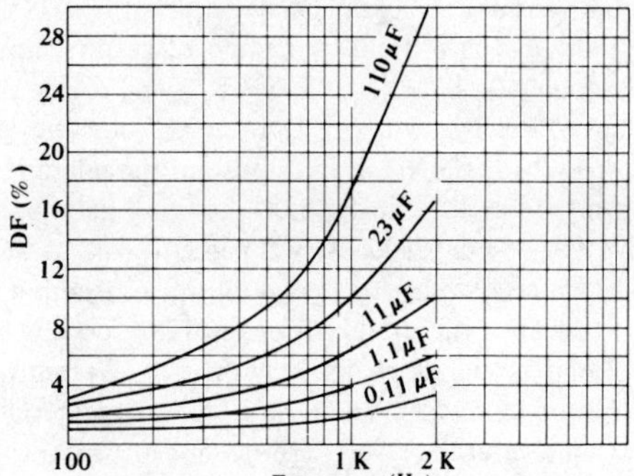

Fig. P14.16 (Courtesy of Union Carbide[64])

14.17 The Q and DF of a capacitor were drawn in Fig. 14.3.14. Show that Q and DF may be drawn directly on impedance paper using the component values shown in Fig. P14.17. (Hint: Use Eq. 14.3.18.)

14.18 Using the failure rate expression of Prob. 14.6, determine the failure rate expression for the CK ceramic capacitors in Fig. 14.3.15.

14.19 Several capacitors carry the following labels: (a) CK21AX103K, (b) CC27LJ104J, and (c) CM04CC104K03. Decode the labels.

14.20 The open-loop gains and bandwidths for several standard op amps were listed in Table 14.4.1. (a) Plot the magnitude responses of these op amps. (b) For a closed-loop gain of 10, what closed-loop band-

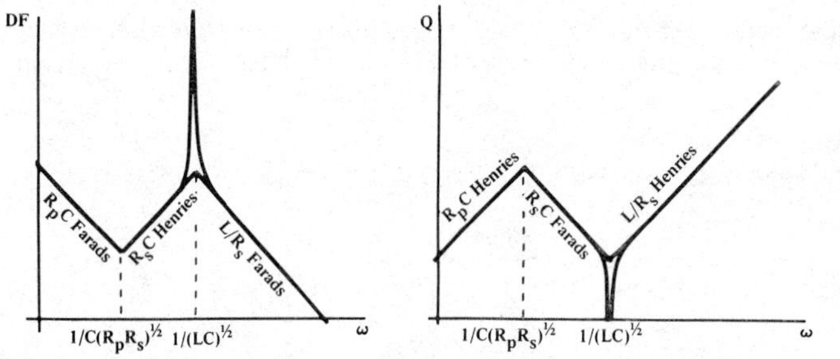

Fig. P14.17

widths can be obtained? (c) What are the sensitivities of the dc closed-loop gains with respect to the dc open-loop gains? (d) If the dc open-loop gain varies ±10 dB due to temperature and power supply fluctuations, what will be the corresponding variations in the dc closed-loop gains? (e) Why is this important?

14.21 Repeat Prob. 14.20 for a closed-loop gain of 100.

14.22 The open- and closed-loop gains of an amplifier depend upon frequency as shown by Eqs. 14.4.1 and 14.4.4. Therefore, their sensitivities are also frequency dependent. Rederive the gain sensitivities (Eqs. 14.4.7 and 14.4.8) and draw their Bode magnitude plots to show this dependency. Why is this consideration important?

14.23 Several of our Class B active filter designs required a gain block K = +2. To realize this gain, we use a 741 op amp in the noninverting mode. If the dc open-loop voltage gain K_o of the op amp varies between a typical value of 200,000 to a minimum value of 50,000 calculate the corresponding variation in K. Since the active gain sensitivity for Class B filters equals $S_K^Q > 2Q - 1$, calculate the corresponding minimum change in Q. Is this an acceptable drift in most applications? What is the maximum useful frequency range of the gain block?

14.24 Op amps are often used to convert balanced (or double-ended) systems into unbalanced (or single-ended) systems using the amplifier arrangement shown in Prob. 9.34. (a) Expressing $G_1 = -Z_f/Z_1$, and $G_2 = Z_3/(Z_2 + Z_3)$, show that $V_o = G_2(1 - G_1)V_1 + G_1V_2$ where V_1 and V_2 are the inputs to the noninverting and inverting channels, respectively. (b) If we use this op amp configuration to eliminate the common-mode signal in V_1 and V_2 and amplify their difference by H_o, how must G_1 and G_2 be related? (c) How must the resistors be chosen for equal channel loading? (Hint: See Eqs. 14.4.35 and 14.4.36.) (d) What are the resistor values if H_o = ½ and R_1 = 10 K? (e) What are the resistor values if H_o = 10 and the input resistance to each channel equals 110 K?[65]

14.25 The stability margin of an op amp can be calculated using Bode, Nyquist, or Nichols plots of the loop gain KT_{43}. (a) For $T_{43} = 1$, sketch these plots for the first-, second-, and third-order gain expressions of Eq. 14.4.10. (b) Draw and discuss the gain and phase margins of the op amps.

14.26 CMRR is an important parameter in many op amp designs.[66] (a) Calculate the CMRR of the balanced amplifier in Prob. 14.24 using the model of Fig. 14.4.18 where the input impedances are neglected. (b) If G_2 is unbalanced by Δ percent, what is the CMRR? (c) If Δ = 1%, calculate the CMRR. Show that it is much worse than the open-loop values listed in Table 14.4.5.

14.27 An alternative way of interpreting CMRR is obtained by viewing the inverting and noninverting op amp inputs as channels with gains A_1 and A_2. Then the open-loop gain $K_1 = (A_1 + A_2)/2$ and the common-mode gain $K_2 = A_2 - A_1$. Draw an alternative model to that shown in Fig. 14.4.15 using A_1 and A_2. Interpret the result. (Hint: Substitute A_i sources for K_i sources.)

14.28 (a) Derive the input impedance Z_b to the amplifier in Fig. 14.4.18. Show that it reduces to Eq. 14.4.36 under limiting conditions. (b) Assuming the limiting conditions exist, derive Eq. 14.4.36 directly by treating AV_b as the controlled source of interest.

14.29 One effect of a nonzero output impedance Z_o is to reduce the loop-gain of the amplifier. In addition to increasing the output impedance, it also reduces the stability margin of the amplifier.[67] (a) Using the op amp in the inverting mode in Fig. 14.4.18, show that a load capacitance C_L produces an additional gain pole at about $s = -1/R_oC_L$. (b) Show how this effects the closed-loop gain of the amplifier. (Hint: See Figs. 14.4.4 and 14.4.5.) (c) Discuss ways to increase the relative stability of the amplifier.

14.30 Noise in active filters is often set by the characteristics of the input stage. Typical voltage e_n and current i_n noise densities are shown in Fig. P14.30 for several preamplifiers (Models 143–168) and filters (Series 4110–4251). (a) Discuss the types of input voltage noise. (b) Discuss the types of input current noise. (c) Since the total input noise $E_n = B[e_n^2 + (i_n R_s)^2]^{1/2}$ where R_s is the source resistance and B the bandwidth of interest, combine and sketch the curves in parts (a) and (b) to show the total noise characteristic.

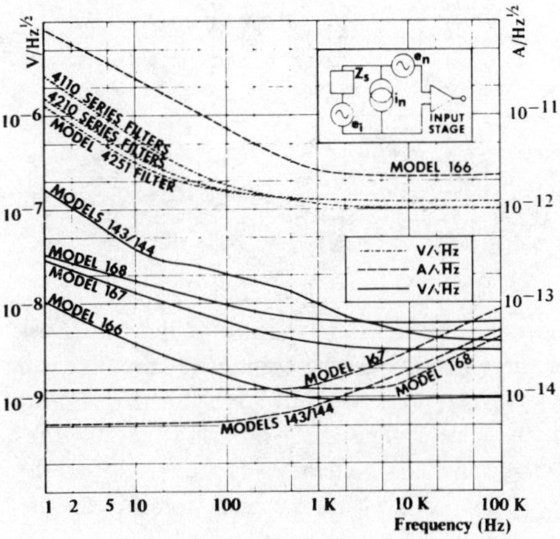

Fig. P14.30 (Courtesy of Ithaco[68])

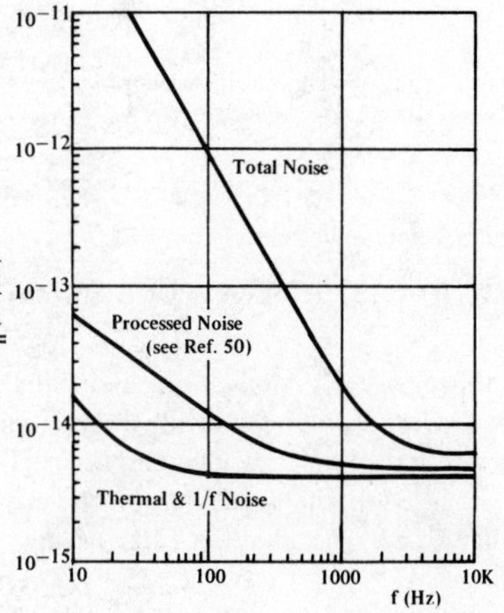

Fig. P14.31 (Courtesy of Proc. IEEE[50])

14.31 The typical e_n^2 noise spectrum in a 741 op amp is shown in Fig. P14.31. The noise has been separated into white, 1/f, and burst noise components. Discuss the form of the power spectrums.

14.32 Most op amps in integrated circuit form are available in TO-5 cylindrical cases or DIP rectangular packages. The thermal resistance of the op amp can be reduced by the use of heat sinks. Generally heat sinks are finned sprung-on assemblies which resemble paddle-wheels. Heat sinks effectively increase the area of the device which in turn lowers its thermal resistance. The typical temperature rise versus power curve for a TO-5 case (and others) is shown in Fig. P14.32. Similar curves are shown for a variety of sprung-on fittings (Models 201–224). (a) Assume perfect thermal coupling between the TO-5 case and the heat sink. Given the thermal resistance of each individually, θ_c and θ_s, determine the effective thermal resistance of the combination. (b) Determine the thermal resistance of the TO-5 case. (c) Determine the thermal resistance for the 202 and 215 heat sinks. (d) Determine the effective thermal resistance for the TO-5 case when equipped with a 202 and 215 heat sink.

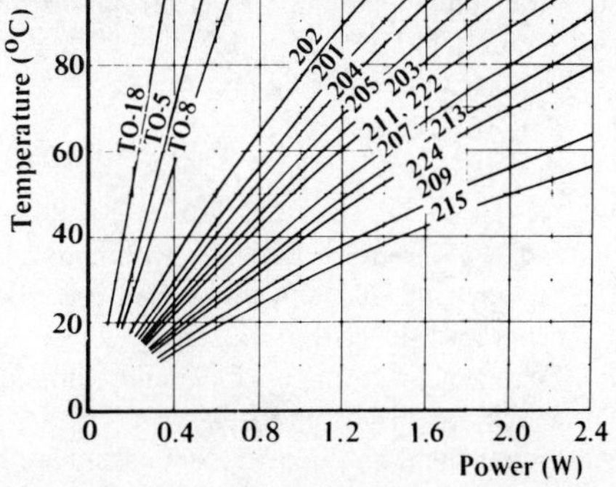

Fig. P14.32 (Courtesy of Wakefield Engineering[69])

14.33 One method of increasing the reliability of a component is by redundancy. The reliability of inverting and noninverting amplifiers can be increased by connecting several amplifiers in parallel. The composite or redundant amplifier (composed of the individual amplifiers) will continue to perform even after one or more individual amplifiers fail. The amplifiers are connected as shown in Fig. P14.33. (a) Determine

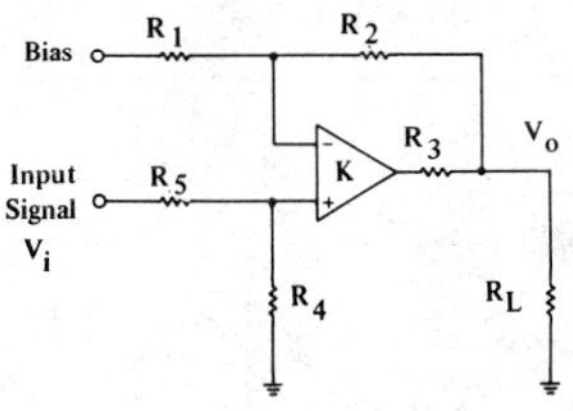

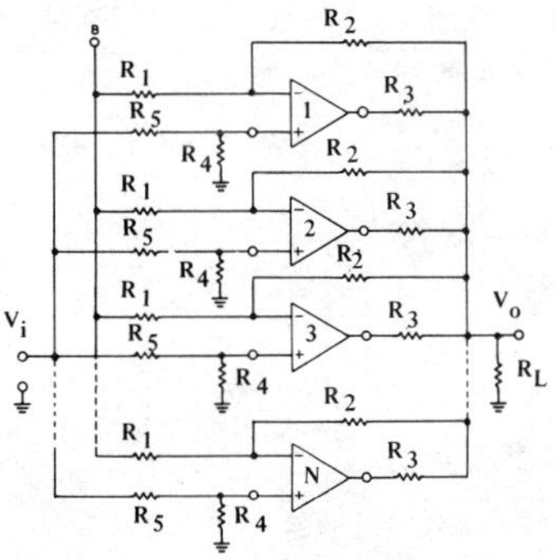

Fig. P14.33 (Courtesy of Electronic Design[70])

the transfer function of the individual amplifiers. (b) Determine the transfer function of the composite amplifier. (c) If n individual amplifiers are used, show that the reliability of the composite amplifier is n times that of the individual amplifiers. (This simplification is an exaggeration. See Ref. 70 for further details.)

14.34 The reliability of an active filter is easily calculated. Determine the MTBF and the 99% lifetime of a single-amplifier filter having the following number of passive components: (a) R = 4, C = 2; (b) R = 5, C = 3; (c) R = 6, C = 3. The resistors are metal film (see Table 14.1.9) and the capacitors are ceramic (see Table 14.3.6). The failure rate of the amplifier is given by Eq. 14.4.54.

REFERENCES

1. Thun, R. E., "Thick films or thin?" IEEE Spectrum, vol. 6, pp. 73–79, Oct., 1969.
   Glang, R., et al., "Pulse trimming of thin-film resistors," IEEE Spectrum, vol. 6, pp. 71–81, Aug., 1969.
2. Parzen, E., *Modern Probability Theory and Its Applications*, Chaps. 5 and 6, Wiley, NY, 1960.
3. Potter, J. L. and S. J. Fich, *Theory of Networks and Lines*, Chap. 1, Prentice-Hall, NJ, 1963.
4. Reactance-frequency paper, Product No. 46 7960 or 46 7963, Keuffel & Esser Co., Morristown, NJ.
5. Papoulis, A., *Probability, Random Variables, and Stochastic Processes*, Chap. 10, McGraw-Hill, NY, 1965.
6. Film Resistors, Bull. RE74F4-3, p. 40, Mepco/Electra, Morristown, NJ, Feb., 1974.
7. Lindquist, C. S., "A mathematical method of evaluating the reliability of electronic equipment, " M. S. Thesis, Oregon State Univ., Corvallis, July, 1964.
8. "Test methods for electronic and electrical component parts," MIL-STD-202E, Dept. of Defense, Washington, DC, April, 1973.
9. Pieruschka, E., *Principles of Reliability*, Chaps. 1–3, Prentice-Hall, NJ, 1963.
10. "Reliability prediction of electronic equipment," MIL-HDBK-217B, Dept. of Defense, Washington, DC, Sept., 1974.
11. Ref. 10, pp. 2.5.2-1 and 2.5.2-4.
12. Ref. 10, p. 2-4.
13. Ref. 10, p. 9-7.
14. "Reliability stress and failure rate data for electronic equipment," MIL-HDBK-217A., pp. 7.5-4, 7.5-6, and 7.4-8, Dept. of Defense, Washington, DC, Dec., 1965.
15. "Wirewound and non-wirewound precision potentiometers," Rev. A, 31 p., Variable Resistive Components Inst., Evanston, IL, Mar., 1974.
    "Wirewound and non-wirewound trimming potentiometers," Rev. A, 19 p., Variable Resistive Components Inst., Evanston, IL, Mar., 1974.
    "Wirewound and non-wirewound industrial grade panel potentiometers," 25 p., Variable Resistive Components Inst., Evanston, IL, June, 1975.
16. Product Data-Model 12 Potentiometer, 42-DO-1374P, Centralab, Div. of Globe-Union, Inc., Milwaukee, WI, 1969.
17. Bourns Custom Precision Potentiometer Catalog, p. 3, Bourns, Riverside, CA, 1972.
18. Type J and Type K Variable Resistors and Attenuators, Publ. EC12, pp. 12–13, Allen-Bradley, Milwaukee, WI, Sept., 1968.

19. Peart, L. T., "Picking the right potentiometer," Electronics, pp. 78–83, June 14, 1965.
20. Schneider, S., and D. Silverman, "Resolution and noise–their significance and measurement in non-wirewound potentiometers," Proc. Natl. Elec. Conf., pp. 900–905, 1964.
21. Ref. 10, pp. 2.5.6-2 to 2.5.6-4.
22. Ref. 19.
Trimmer Tech. Bull., H731168-474-35GF, Beckman, Fullerton, CA, April, 1974.
23. Hamer, D. W., "Ceramic capacitors for hybrid integrated circuits," IEEE Spectrum, vol. 6, pp. 79–84, Jan., 1969.
West-Cap Ceramic Chip Capacitor Handbook, San Fernando Electric Manufacturing Co., San Fernando, CA, 1970.
24. McManus, R. P., "Aluminum electrolytic capacitors," Tech. Paper TP 72-2, Sprague Electric Co., North Adams, MA, 1970.
25. Whitman, A., and D. G. Thompson, "Molded solid tantalum capacitors for printed circuit board and hybrid circuit applications," Tech. Paper TP 70-3, Sprague Electric Co., North Adams, MA, 1970.
26. Stern, L., *Fundamentals of Integrated Circuits*, Chap. 6, Hayden, NY, 1968.
27. Ref. 23, D. W. Hamer.
28. Johnson, F. L., "Capacitors . . . insulation resistance can be confusing," Tech. Bull. No. 04, Electro-Cube, Inc., San Gabriel, CA.
29. Skilling, H. H., *Electrical Engineering Circuits*, 2nd ed., Chaps. 5 and 6, Wiley, NY, 1965.
30. Catalog U, pp. 105–106, General Radio Co., West Concord, MA, Feb., 1970.
31. Ref. 23, West-Cap Ceramic Chip Capacitor Handbook, p. 73.
32. "Ceramic dielectric capacitors classes 1, 2, and 3," EIA Number RS-198-B (or ANSI C83.4-1972).
33. "Reliability stress and failure rate data for electronic equipment," MIL-HDBK-217, p. 97, Dept. of Defense, Washington, DC, Aug.,1962.
34. Ref. 10, pp. 2.6.4-1 and 2.6.4-4.
35. "The Pyranol II Story," Publ. GEA-8849, General Electric Co., Hudson Falls, NY, 6-70.
36. "Product source directory–operational amplifiers," Electronic Design, pp. 103–116 and 187–189, June 21, 1970, copyright Hayden Publishing, 1970.
37. Linear Integrated Circuits Data Catalog, pp. 3-53 to 3-59, Fairchild Semiconductor, Mt. View, CA, Feb., 1973.
38. Linear Integrated Circuits, pp. 2-112 to 2-114, National Semiconductor Corp., Santa Clara, CA, Feb., 1975.
39. "HA-2500/2502/2505 high-slew rate operational amplifiers," 4 p., Harris Semiconductor, Melbourne, FL, Jan., 1972.
40. "MC1533, 1433 operational amplifier monolithic silicon integrated circuit," Data Sheet DS9060R2, 6 p., Motorola, Phoenix, AZ, Nov., 1970.
41. Ref. 37, pp. 3-16 to 3-22.
42. "MC1530, MC1430, MC1531, MC1431 operational amplifiers integrated circuit," Data Sheet DS9049R2, 4 p., Motorola, Phoenix, AZ, Jan., 1972.
"Getting more value out of an integrated operational amplifier data sheet," Appl. Note AN-273, Motorola, Phoenix, AZ, April, 1968.
43. D'Azzo, J. J., and C. H. Houpis, *Control System Analysis and Synthesis*, Chap. 8, McGraw-Hill, NY, 1960.
Dorf, R. C., *Modern Control Systems*, 2nd ed., Chap. 8, Addison-Wesley, Reading, MA, 1974.
44. Conant, R., "Equivalent circuits for operational amplifier drift and noise," Analog Dialogue, vol. 2, no. 1, pp. 8–9, March, 1968, Analog Devices, Cambridge, MA.
45. Stata, R., "Operational amplifiers–Part IV," Appl. Note, Analog Devices, Cambridge, MA.
46. Huber, W. H., "Nomographs ease circuit designing with op amps," EDN Magazine, pp. 37–42, Feb. 1, 1970.
47. "Instrumentation amplifiers and data amplifiers," p. 5, Burr-Brown Research Corp., Tucson, AZ, July, 1971.
48. Lindquist, C. S., "Differential amplifier input impedance and Blackman's impedance relation," IEEE Trans. on Electron Devices, vol. ED-19, pp. 990–993, Aug., 1972.
49. Letzler, S., and N. Webster, "Noise in amplifiers," IEEE Spectrum, vol. 7, pp. 67–75, Aug., 1970.
Smith, L., and D. H. Sheingold, "Noise and operational amplifier circuits," Analog Dialogue, vol. 3,

no. 1, Analog Devices, Cambridge, MA.

50. Strasilla, U. J., and M. J. O. Strutt, "Measurement of white and 1/f noise within burst noise," Proc. IEEE, vol. 62, pp. 1711–1713, Dec., 1974.
51. Ref. 49, L. Smith and D. H. Sheingold, p. 14, App. II.
52. "Noise figure primer," Appl. Note 57, Hewlett-Packard, Palo Alto, CA, 1/15/65.
53. Ref. 10, pp. 2.1.5-1 to 2.1.5-5.
54. Ref. 6, p. 38.
55. Hot-Molded Fixed Resistors, Bull. EC 21, p. 5, Allen-Bradley, Milwaukee, WI, Jan., 1972.
56. Precision and Power Wire-Wound Resistors, Engr. Catalog No. R73, p. 16, RCL, Irvington, NJ, 1973.
57. Victoreen Mini-Mox Resistors, Publ. 2268-5-72, Victoreen, Cleveland, OH, 5-72.
58. Hypercon® Ultra-High Capacitance Disc Ceramic Capacitors, Engr. Bull. 6141G, pp. 3–4, Sprague, North Adams, MA, 1969.
59. Herzig, R. W., "Capacitor impedance characteristics at high frequencies," Tech. Paper TP71-9, 6 p., Sprague, North Adams, MA, 1971.
60. CYK Capacitors, Ref. File CCA-1.02, Corning Electronics, Corning, NY, 5/71.
61. General Design Guide, Publ. EPD GDG-1, p. 14, Corning Electronics, Corning, NY, 3/73.
62. Aluminum Electrolytic Capacitors, Catalog NAC- AEE574, Nichicon, Chicago, IL, 5/74.
63. Extended-Capacitance Tabular Tantalum Wet-Slug Capacitors, Bull. GEP-1842, p. 6., General Electric Co., Columbia, SC, 7/71.
64. Kemet Electronic Products Engr. Bull., Form F-1852-D, Union Carbide, New York, NY.
65. Renschler, E., "Analysis and basic operation of the MC1595," Appl. Note AN-489, Motorola, Phoenix, AZ, 9-69.
    Welling, B., and L. Kinsey, "Using the MC1595 multiplier in arithmetic operations," Appl. Note AN-490, Motorola, Phoenix, AZ, 9-69.
66. Demrow, R., "Evolution from operational amplifier to data amplifier," Tech. Bull., Analog Devices, Cambridge, MA, 9/68.
67. Wojslaw, C. F., "Prevent op-amp output instability," Electronic Design, vol. 17, Aug. 16, 1974, copyright Hayden Publishing, 1974.
68. Variable Electronic Filters, Catalog IPS-104, p. 15, Ithaco, Ithaca, NY, 6/74.
69. Semiconductor Heat Sinks and Thermal Products, Cat. 103A, p. 21, Wakefield Engineering, Inc., Wakefield, MA.
70. Huber, W. H., "Yes, redundancy increases reliability," Electronic Design, pp. 70–77, June 7, 1970, copyright Hayden Publishing, 1970.

ANSWERS TO SELECTED PROBLEMS

Chapter 1

1.4 (a) $r = 3.7\ \Omega$, $c = 3.6$ pF.

1.9 For $H = 10\ \text{mW/cm}^2$, $i_o = 4$ nA, $i = 0.083H$ mA, $r = 109$ K.

1.12 Neither is realizable.

1.21 (a) Eq. 1.9.25; (b) $0 \leqslant \omega \leqslant 1/T$, rolloff = – 20 dB/dec;

(c) $F(j\omega) = (T/2)[\sin(\omega T/4)/(\omega T/4)]^2$; (d) $0 \leqslant \omega \leqslant 2/T$, rolloff = – 40 dB/dec.

1.22 See Examples 8.8.1–8.8.3.

1.27 Using Fig. 1.11.1e: $h_{11} = 2$ K, $h_{12} = 800 \times 10^{-6}$, $h_{21} = 50$, $h_{22} = 35\ \mu$.

1.28 $y_{11} = y_{22} = Z_o^{-1} \coth \gamma d$, $y_{12} = y_{21} = -Z_o^{-1} \operatorname{csch} \gamma d$

$A = D = \cosh \gamma d$, $B = Z_o \operatorname{sech} \gamma d$, $C = Z_o^{-1} \operatorname{sech} \gamma d$

1.31 (a) See Prob. 1.47, (b) same except that $K = R/dr$.

1.37 See Table 1.11.3.

1.39 See Example 7.14.1.

Chapter 2

2.2 (a) Slope = –20 dB/dec,

(b) $H(s) = [s + 2\pi(60\ \text{Hz})]\,[s + 2\pi(3.0\ \text{KHz})]\,/\,[s^2 + 2(0.8)(2\pi(60\ \text{Hz}))\,s + (2\pi(60\ \text{Hz}))^2]$.

2.9 (a) $H_{PRE}(s) = 0.63/[s_n^2 + 2(0.18)s_n + 1]$, $s_n = s/2.6$, (b) $H_{DE}(s) = 1/H_{PRE}(s)$.

2.11 CCIR responses: $H_{REC}(s) = 10[1 + s/2\pi(2\ \text{KHz})]\,/\,[1 + s/2\pi(50\ \text{Hz})]$,

$H_{REP}(s) = [s/2\pi(20\ \text{Hz})]\,[1 + s/2\pi(10\ \text{KHz})]\,/\,[1 + s/2\pi(20\ \text{Hz})]$.

2.16 (a) $B_o/f_n = 2.85$, $S(2) = 0.644$, $\zeta = 2.21$, $\omega_n = 2\pi(949\ \text{Hz})$. Design two 1st order BPF stages both having $H_o = 10^{1/2}$, $f_o = 949$ Hz, $\zeta = 2.21$. (b) $\zeta = 0.5$. Design two 1st order BPF stages both having $H_o = 70.6^{1/2}$, $\zeta = 0.5$. Stage 1 – $f_1 = 357$ Hz. Stage 2 – $f_2 = 2520$ Hz.

2.18 (c) Cascade: 2nd order HPF having $H_o = 1$ dB, $f_1 = 600$ Hz, $\zeta_1 = 0.71$; and 2nd order LPF having $H_o = 1$ dB, $f_2 = 2$ KHz, $\zeta_2 = 0.71$.

2.22 Asymptotic rolloffs are ±40 dB/dec. Widest band-pass filter has $f_L = 0.1$ Hz and $f_U = 10$ KHz; narrowest band-pass filter has $f_L = f_U = f_o$ where bandwidth $B = 1.4f_o$.

2.26 $f_o = [950(1050)]^{1/2} = 1000$ Hz, $\Delta\theta = (-27/\zeta)[\log_2(1050/950)] \leqslant -20^\circ$ so $\zeta \geqslant 0.2$. Use $\zeta = 0.2$ for maximum selectivity.

2.31 (a) Observe phase θ (phase meter or Lissajous figure) and tune ω_n until $\theta = -90^\circ$. (b) Observe gain peaking M_p and tune ζ until it has the required value.

2.36 (a) $H(s) \cong e^{-0.63s}/(1 + s/0.75)$.

2.41 $\tau(0) = 1/p - 1/z$, $\tau(j\sqrt{pz}) \cong 0$, $\tau(j\omega) = (p - z)/\omega^2$ for $\omega \gg \max(p, z)$.

2.48 Consider the Butterworth filter having $\tau(0) = 2.61$ and $\tau(j0.9) = 3.8$. Using the 1st order APF described by Eq. 2.11.8 and setting $\tau_{total}(0) = \tau_{total}(j0.9)$ leads to $H_{AP}(s) = (0.87 - s)/(0.87 + s)$.

Chapter 3

3.4 Elmore's results: $pt_d = 1 - 0.5 = 0.5$, $pt_r = 2.51[1 - (1/2)^2]^{1/2} = 2.2$. Exact results: $pt_D = 0$, $pt_R = 2.3 - 0 = 2.3$. Good agreement on rise time but poor on delay time. Since h(t) is very asymmetrical, Elmore's approach should not be expected to give good results.

3.5 Consider A filter. (a) $H(s)/H_o$ is given by Eq. 3.7.28 where $H_o = 35$ dB $= 56$, $p = 2\pi(90$ Hz) and $z = 2\pi(3$ KHz). (b) $r(t) = 56[1 - (1 - 0.03\ )e^{-pt}]U_{-1}(t)$ from Eq. 3.7.30. (c) $H(s) \cong 56e^{-s/z}/[1 + s/2\pi(90\text{ Hz})]$ from Eq. 3.7.36. (d) $r(t) \cong 56[1 - (1 - 0.03\ )e^{-pt}]U_{-1}(t - 1/z)$ from Eq. 3.7.38.

3.10 (a) $\zeta = [2(1 - (t_r/t_d)^2/2\pi)]^{1/2}$, $\omega_n = 2\zeta/t_d$; (b) $\zeta = 0.77$, $\omega_n = 308$, $f_n = 49$ Hz; (c) $\zeta = 0.72$, $\omega_n = 144$, $f_n = 23$ Hz.

3.15 $r(\infty) = 10$, $r(t)_{max} = 12.5$, $\omega_n = 2\pi(10$ KHz); $\omega_n t_D \cong 1.5$ so $t_D = 24$ μsec, $\omega_n t_R \cong 1.2$ so $t_R = 19$ μsec, $\omega_n T_s \cong 5$ so $T_s = 120$ μsec.

3.24 $\gamma = 20\%$ requires $\zeta = 0.7$. $\omega_n T_s = 4.5$ for $\delta = 5\%$ so $\omega_n = 4.5/1$ msec $= 4500$ rad/sec or $f_n = 716$ Hz.

3.30 $r_{HP}(t) = 1 - r_{LP}(t)$ where $r_{LP}(t)$ is shown in Fig. 3.8.12. $\omega_n = 2\pi(1$ KHz) and $\zeta = 0.2$ so that: $\gamma \cong 55\%$, $\omega_n t_D \cong 0.7$ so $t_D = 0.11$ msec, $\omega_n t_R \cong 1$ so $t_R = 0.16$ msec, $\omega_n T_s \cong 13.5$ so $T_s = 2.2$ msec.

3.36 $r_{BP}(t)$ is given by Eq. 3.10.6 where $B = 2\pi(50$ Hz) and $\omega_o = 2\pi(700$ Hz) or $2\pi(1700$ Hz). $r_{LP}(Bt/2)$ is given by Eq. 3.7.2. Then $Bt_D/2 = 0.69$ so $t_D = 4.4$ msec, $Bt_R/2 = 2.2$ so $t_R = 14$ msec, $BT_s/2 = 3$ so $T_s = 19.1$ msec. Fill in envelope shown in Fig. 3.10.1a with 700 Hz or 1700 Hz sine wave.

3.40 $f_o = 398$ Hz, $\gamma = 91$ (real poles), $Q = 1/2\gamma \cong 0.005$. Extremely low-Q filter so cannot use high-Q approximation.

Chapter 4

4.1 D filter: Butterworth, n = 17; Chebyshev, n = 7; elliptic, n = 4.

4.2 A filter: Bessel, n = 6; Gaussian, impossible.

4.12 (b) Cascade two 2nd order LPF stages both having H_o=.97. Stage 1 – f_1 = 1.75 KHz, ζ_1 = 0.71. Stage 2 – f_2 = 3.02 KHz, ζ_2 = 0.17.

4.13 $H(s) = P_3(s/2\pi(0.1\text{ Hz}))/P_3(s/2\pi(0.01\text{ Hz}))$ where $P_3(s)$ is the third-order (a) Butterworth and (b) Chebyshev filter polynomial.

4.15 (a) Butterworth, n = 10; Chebyshev, n = 5; elliptic, n = 3. (b) Using Table 4.8.2 where M_s = 20.4 dB or $\theta = 51^o$, then the filter consists of two stages. Stage 1 – 1st order LPF having $H_o = 1/k$, f_o = 558 Hz. Stage 2 – 2nd order BSF having H_o = k, f_{op} = 943 Hz, ζ_p = 0.147, f_{oz} = 1330 Hz.

4.20 (a) Butterworth, n = 6; Chebyshev, n = 4; elliptic, n = 4. (b) Set f_p = 4/5 = 0.8 Hz.

4.32 To meet the magnitude requirements: Chebyshev, n = 3; Papoulis, n = 3. Denormalizing time: Chebyshev, Ω_{1dB} = 1.0 so $\omega_{1dB} = 2\pi(1.0\text{ KHz})$, then (0, 1, 1.5) msec become (0, 6.28, 9.42) rad. Papoulis, Ω_{3dB} = 1.2 so $\omega_{3dB} = 2\pi(1.2\text{ KHz})$, then (0, 1, 1.5 msec) become (0, 7.54, 11.3) rad. Transferring the step responses from Figs. 4.4.7 and 4.6.3 onto the r(t) specifications as shown in Fig. 4.3.7, they can both be satisfied.

4.36 (a) $U_{-1}(t-1)$, (b) use the n = 4 step response from Fig. 4.10.5 where t_D = 1. (c) The 4th order Bessel filter has a $\tau(0) \cong (7 \ln 2)^{1/2}$ = 2.2 sec and a 3 dB bandwidth of 1 rad/sec. To obtain 1 msec of delay, select $\omega_n = 2.2 \times 10^3$. Then using Table 4.10.1, cascade two 2nd order LPF stages each having H_o = 1. Stage 1 – ω_1 = 3150, ζ_1 = 0.958. Stage 2 – ω_2 = 3530, ζ_2 = 0.621.

4.45 $|H_n| = [1 + (\omega/\omega_o)^2]^{n/2}$ where $\omega_o \cong 1.2n^{1/2}$. Then $|H_n| = (1 + \Omega^2/n)^{n/2}$ where $\Omega = \omega/1.2$. Applying the binomial theorem and letting $n \to \infty$, $|H| = \exp(-\Omega^2/2) = \exp(-0.347\omega^2)$ which is Gaussian.

4.53 B/w_{omax} = 1000/600 = 1.67 and B/w_{omin} = 1000/1400 = 0.71. From Fig. 4.18.3, $w_oT \gg 1$. Therefore, select pulse length $T \gg 1/2\pi(600\text{ Hz})$ = 0.27 msec.

Chapter 5

5.3 (a) Nonminimum-phase. (b), (c) Cascade three stages. Stage 1 – 1st order LPF having H_o = 1. ω_o = 2.10. Stage 2 – 2nd order biquadratic having H_o = 1, ω_{op} = 4.24, ζ_p = 0.33, ω_{oz} = 4.04, ζ_z = 0.77. Stage 3 – 2nd order APF having H_o = 1, ω_o = 4.04, ζ = 0.77.

5.7 A tradeoff is required. Use variable ω_d and ω_c = 1 in Table 5.6.2. Cascade two 2nd order LPF stages each having H_o = 1. Stage 1 – f_1 = 745 Hz, ζ_1 = 0.73. Stage 2 – f_2 = 1340 Hz, ζ_2 = 0.33.

5.10 (a) $n \geqslant 4$ from Fig. 5.7.1. Cascade two 2nd order LPF stages having H_o = 1. Stage 1 – f_1 = 1.33 KHz, ζ_1 = 1.20. Stage 2 – f_2 = 991 Hz, ζ_2 = 0.371. (b) Delay is shown in Fig. 5.7.1 where $\omega_n = 2\pi(1\text{ KHz}/0.87) = 2\pi(1150\text{ Hz})$ and $\tau(0) = 3/\omega_n$ = 0.42 msec.

5.13 (a) n = 4, m = 2, ω_{3dB} = 0.45 in Fig. 5.8.2. Cascade two filters both having H_o = 1. Stage 1 – 2nd order LPF having f = 804 Hz, ζ = 0.86. Stage 2 – 1st order BSF having f_{op} = 1370 Hz, ζ_p =

0.30, f_{oz} = 2420 Hz. (c) They exhibit large delay distortion yet have excellent step response.

5.15 (a) Delay characteristics differ only at dc. (b) Use Table 5.9.1 and denormalize poles by $\omega_n = 1000$. Cascade two 2nd order LPF stages both having $H_o = 1$. Stage 1 – f_1 = 317 Hz, $\zeta_1 = 0.81$. Stage 2 – f_2 = 608 Hz, $\zeta_2 = 0.35$.

Chapter 6

6.4 Yes. For D filter, see solution to Prob. 4.1.

6.7 3rd order LPF and 2nd order HPF.

6.12 For the low-pass filter, see solution to Prob. 4.55. For the high-pass filter, $B/\omega_o = 1209/941 = 1.28$. From Fig. 4.18.3, $\omega_o T \geqslant 100$ so $T \geqslant 13.2$ msec. To satisfy both requirements simultaneously, select $T \geqslant 16.9$ msec.

6.18 Yes. For A_1 filter, use nomographs in Chap. 4 where $M_p = 3$, $M_{s1} = 20$, $M_{s2} = 40$, $\Omega_{s1} = 2$, and $\Omega_{s2} = 4$. Then Butterworth, n = 4; Chebyshev, n = 3; Bessel, impossible.

6.22 Transmit – 2nd order Chebyshev BPF. Receive – 4th order Chebyshev BPF. Both have 0.5 dB ripple, center frequencies of 1170 or 2125 Hz, bandwidths of 200 Hz, and midband gains of 0 dB.

6.30 (a) Cascade two 1st order BPF both having $H_o = 4.47$ and Q = 14.1. Stage 1 – f_1 = 963 Hz. Stage 2 – f_2 = 1037 Hz.

6.34 (a) Cosine step response in Fig. 3.10.1 and envelope response in Fig. 4.3.6. Denormalize time by $B/2 = \omega_o/2Q$. (b) Since Q = 25, $B/\omega_o = 1/Q = 0.04$, so $\omega_o T \geqslant 80$ from Fig. 6.4.16. Then for $\omega_{o_{max}} = 2\pi(1633\text{ Hz})$, $T_{min} \geqslant 7.8$ msec.

6.41 $H(s) = s_n(1/2Q)^2/[s_n^{\,2} + s_n/Q + (1 + 1/4Q^2)]$ where $s_n = s/\omega_o$.

6.49 Cascade two filter stages. Stage 1 – 2nd order LPF having $H_o = 1$, f_1 = 500 Hz, $\zeta_1 = 0.924$. Stage 2 – 1st order BPF having $H_o = 3.41$, f_2 = 500 Hz, $\zeta_2 = 0.383$.

6.53 $S_3^{40} = 2$ so Butterworth, n = 7; Chebyshev, n = 5; elliptic, n = 3.

6.56 (a) Cascade two 1st order BSF both having $H_o = 1$, $Q_p = 14.1$, f_{oz} = 1000 Hz. Stage 1 – f_{op} = 963 Hz; Stage 2 – f_{op} = 1037 Hz.

6.62 See solution to Prob. 2.48.

6.65 Exact: $r(t) = (1 - 2e^{-t})U_{-1}(t)$. Dominant pole approximation is $H(s) = e^{-2s}$ for $|s| \ll 1$ and $-e^{-2/s}$ for $|s| \gg 1$. Therefore, approximation yields $-J_1(2\sqrt{2t})/\sqrt{t/2}\,U_{-1}(t)$ for $t \ll 1$ and $U_{-1}(t)$ for $t \gg 1$.

Chapter 7

7.2 See Class 1A high-pass filter, Sec. 9.3.

7.10 See Class $1\overline{A}$ band-stop filter, Sec. 11.3.

7.12 See Class 1B high-pass filter, Sec. 9.3.

7.16 Class 1B biquadratic filter having

$$H(s) = K_2 \frac{s^2R_1C_1R_2C_2 + sR_2C_2 + K_1}{s^2R_1C_1R_2C_2 + s[R_1C_1(1 - K_1K_2) + R_2C_2] + 1}$$

7.23 See Class 1C band-pass filter, Sec. 10.3.

7.27 See Class $1\overline{C}$ high-pass filter, Sec. 9.3.

7.33 Class 1E band-pass filter having

$$H(s) = \frac{K_1K_2sR_2C_2}{s^2(1 - K_1K_2)R_1C_1R_2C_2 + s[R_1C_1(1 - K_2) + R_2C_2] + (1 - K_2)}$$

7.39 See Class 2A high-pass filter, Sec. 9.3.

7.42 See Class $2\overline{A}$ band-pass filter, Sec. 10.3.

7.47 See Class 2B high-pass filter, Sec. 9.3.

7.50 Class 2B biquadratic filter having

$$H(s) = K \frac{s^2R_1C_1R_2C_2 + s(R_1 + R_2)C_2 + 1}{s^2R_1C_1R_2C_2 + s[R_1C_1(1 - K + C_2/C_1) + R_2C_2] + 1}$$

7.54 See Class 2C high-pass filter, Sec. 9.3.

7.59 See Class $2\overline{C}$ band-pass filter, Sec. 10.3.

7.60 See Class 2D band-pass filter, Sec. 10.3.

7.63 Class 2E band-pass filter having

$$H(s) = \frac{KsR_2C_2}{s^2(1 - K)R_1C_1R_2C_2 + s[(R_1C_1 + R_1C_2)(1 - K) + R_2C_2] + (1 - K)}$$

Chapter 8

8.5 (a) $[I^a] = [y^a][V^a]$ and $[I^b] = [y^b][V^b]$, (b) $I_2{}^a = y_{21}{}^aV_1{}^a$ and $I_3{}^b = y_{12}{}^bV_3{}^b$, (c) $H(s) = -y_{21}{}^a/y_{12}{}^b$, (d) poles must lie on negative-real axis but zeros can lie anywhere. (e) $Z_f = 1/(s + 10)$ so use 1/10 Ω in parallel with 1 F; $Z_1 = (s + 1)/s$ so use 1 Ω in series with 1F.

8.9 (a) See Sec. 8.3. (b) Tune ω_o with R_1 or R_2; tune ζ with K_1 or K_2; H_o cannot be independently specified. (c) $R_1 = R_2 = 16.2$ K, $C_1 = C_2 = 0.01\ \mu$F, $K_1 = K_2 = 1.38$.

8.12 (a) Stage 1 – C = 0.01 μF, R = 10.0 K, $K_1K_2 = 0.758$. Therefore, let $K_1 = K_2 = 1$ (voltage followers) and replace R_2 by (13.3 K, 42.2 K) voltage divider. Stage 2 – C = 0.01 μF, R = 11.0 K, $K_1K_2 = 0.084$. Therefore, let $K_1 = K_2 = 1$ (voltage followers) and replace R_2 by (133 K, 12.1 K) voltage divider. Add gain block of 1/(0.084)(0.758) = 15.7.

8.19 Stage 2 – C = 0.001 μF, $R = R_3 = 8.66$ K, $R_4 = 44.2$ K, $H_o = 1.67$. Stage 1 – C = 0.01 μF, R = 2.61 K; for noninverting amplifier having $H_o = 5.99$, use $R_f = 15.4$ K, $R_1 = 3.16$ K.

8.22 (a) Class 2B; (b), (c) $H(s) = K_2/[s^2R_1C_1R_2C_2 + s[R_1C_1(1 - K_2K_4) + (R_1 + R_2)C_2] + 1]$; (c) set H_o with K_2, tune ω_o with R, scale ω_o with C, and set ζ with K_4.

8.25 Stage 2 – $C_1 = 0.01\ \mu F$, $C_2 = 0.001\ \mu F$, $R_1 = 7.87$ K, $R_2 = 78.7$ K; for noninverting amplifier having K = 1.1, use $R_f = 7.87$ K, $R_1 = 78.7$ K, pad with 82 K, 10% to negative input. Stage 1 – C = 0.01 μF, R = 7.87 K; use K = 1 (voltage follower) and replace R by (8.66 K, 86.6 K) voltage divider.

8.34 (a) $\omega_o = 1/(R_1C_2R_4C_5)^{1/2}$, $\zeta = \frac{1}{2}(C_5/C_2)^{1/2}[(R_1/R_4)^{1/2} + 2(R_4/R_1)^{1/2}]$, $H_o = -R_4/R_1$. (b) $C_2/C_5 = (1 - 2H_o)^2/4\zeta^2(-H_o)$ which is determined when ζ and $-H_o$ are specified (see Fig. P8.34). (c) C_2/C_5 is minimized when $H_o = -0.5$. The ratio is large for large $-H_o$ and/or small ζ.

8.36 Stage 1 – $C_2 = 0.01\ \mu F$, $C_5 = 0.0047\ \mu F$, $R_1 = R_4 = 22.6$ K, $R_3 = 11.5$ K; $R_o = 22$ K, 10%. Stage 2 – $C_2 = 0.01\ \mu F$, $C_5 = 0.0018\ \mu F$, $R_1 = R_4 = 34.8$ K, $R_3 = 16.2$ K; $R_o = 33$ K, 10%.

8.41 $Z^{(k)} = [R/(2 - K)]\,[s_n^2 + (3 - K)s_n + 1]/[1 + s_n/(2 - K)]$, $s_n = sRC$.

Chapter 9

9.5 2nd order Butterworth high-pass filter having $f_o = 2$ KHz and $\zeta = 0.707$. H_o is arbitrary. C = 0.01 μF, R = 2.87 K, $H_o = -0.75$; for inverting amplifier having K = 6, use $R_f = 16.9$ K, R = 2.87 K for R_1, and $R_o = 18$ K, 10 %.

9.9 3rd order Chebyshev high-pass filter having 1 dB ripple. Frequency scale by $b = 2\pi(350\ \text{Hz})$. Magnitude scale C's to $C_n = 1$ by a. $b = C_n/aC = 1/2\pi(350\ \text{Hz})(0.0015\ \mu F) = 0.303$ M. Then $R = bR_n$ so actual normalized resistor values equal $R_{n1} = 0.495$, $R_{n2} = 0.0726$, $R_{n3} = 18.5$ in Fig. P8.28. Theoretical values equal $R_{n1} = 1/2.34 = 0.427$, $R_{n2} = 1/14.8 = 0.0676$, $R_{n3} = 1/0.0587 = 17.0$ so there is fairly close agreement.

9.12 Convert stages as 1st order HPF having parameters (0.866/k, 1.686) and 2nd order HPF having parameters (k, 0.999, 0.147, 0.707). Stage 2 – C = 0.01 μF, 2C = 0.02 μF, R = 18.7 K, R/2 = 9.53 K, p = 0.5, R/p = 36.5 K. For noninverting amplifier having K = 2.2, use $R_f = 30.1$ K, $R_1 = 24.9$ K. Stage 1 – C = 0.01 μF, R = 7.81 K. For noninverting amplifier having gain K = 0.866/2.2 = 0.394, use K = 1 (voltage follower) and replace R by (48.7 K, 3.01 K) voltage divider.

9.19 Both stages have $C_1 = C_3 = C_4 = 0.1\ \mu F$, $R_2 = 2.49$ K, $R_5 = 5.36$ K. Let $R_o = 0$ in 1st stage but set $R_o = 5.6$ K, 10% in 2nd stage.

9.24 Use K_2 source. $Z^{(k)} = \dfrac{1}{sC_1}\,\dfrac{s^2R_1C_1R_2C_2 + s[R_1C_1(1 + K_2) + R_2C_2(1 + K_1K_2)] + (1 + K_2)}{sR_2C_2(1 + K_1K_2) + (1 + K_2)}$

9.29 Ground R_1, lift C_2 from ground and drive it along with the ground return point of amplifier K (e.g., R_1 in Table 8.4.1).

9.34 Apply superposition and results from Tables 8.4.1 and 8.4.2.

Chapter 10

10.4 (a) $\Delta f_{max}/f_o = \pm 1/4Q = \pm 1.14\%$, (b) $-\tfrac{1}{2}$, (c) $\pm \tfrac{1}{2}$, (d) $T_{f_o} = \Sigma |S| T_x = |\pm \tfrac{1}{2}|(2T_R + 2T_C) =$ 2T if tolerances are equal. Then component tolerances equal $T = \pm 1.14/2 = \pm 0.57\%$. $TC = (\pm 0.0057/70)10^6 = 81$ PPM/°C. (e) $T = \pm 5/2 = \pm 2.5\%$, $TC = (\pm 0.025/70)10^6 = 3600$ PPM/°C which is less stringent than that required in part (d).

10.8 (a) $H(s) = -sR_BC_2/[s^2R_AC_1R_BC_2 + sR_AC_1/(1 + R_7/R_9) + (1 + R_1/R_3)/(1 + R_7/R_9)]$ where $R_A = R_4(1 + R_1/R_4 + R_1/R_3)$ and $R_B = R_5(1 + R_6/R_5 + R_6/R_8)$. (b) Set: $R_4 = R_5 = R$, $C_1 = C_2 = C$, $R_6/R_8 = R_7/R_9$. Given: ω_o, Q, $-H_o$. Choose: C, R_3, $R_9 \ll R$. Calculate: $R = 1/Q\omega_oC$, $R_1 = [Q^2/(-H_o - 1)]R_3$, $R_6 = R_7 = (Q - 1)R_9$.

10.11 (a) **Error** using Class 2E band-pass filter of Sec. 10.3. (b) $C = 0.01\ \mu F$, $R = 13.3$ K, $K = 3600$, $H_o = -1200$. For inverting amplifier having $K = 3600$, let $R_1 = R_f = 13.3$ K, $R_3 = 100\ \Omega$, $R_2 = 121$ K; $R_o = 6.8$ K, 10%, using high-gain amplifier of Fig. 8.5.4a. Replace R_1 in filter input by (162 K, 14.7 K) voltage divider. (c) Obtain frequency scaling of $3Q = 60$ which reduces C values.

10.18 (a) Stage 1 – $C = 0.0047\ \mu F$, $R_1 = R_2 = 649\ \Omega$, $R_o = 536$ K, $K = 2480$, $H_o = -33.2$. Replace R_1 by (15.4 K, 681 Ω) voltage divider. For inverting amplifier having $K = 2480$, set $R_1 = 649\ \Omega$, $R_f = 68.1$ K, $R_3 = 100\ \Omega$, $R_2 = 2.26$ K, $R_o = 6.8$ K in high-gain amplifier of Fig. 8.5.4a. Stage 2 – $C = 0.0047\ \mu F$, $R_1 = R_2 = 536\ \Omega$, $R_o = 426$ K, $K = 2480$, $H_o = -33.2$. For inverting amplifier having $K = 2480$, set $R_1 = 536\ \Omega$, $R_f = 56.2$K, $R_3 = 100\ \Omega$, $R_2 = 2.26$K, $R_o = 56$ K in high-gain amplifier of Fig. 8.5.4a. Drive 2nd stage from (R_2, R_3, R_f) junction in 1st stage.

10.23 $Z^{(k)} = [s^2R_1C_1R_2C_2 + s(R_1C_1 + R_2C_2) + (1 - K)]/sC_1[sR_2C_2 + (1 - K)]$.

10.30 $C = 0.39\ \mu F$, $R = 10$ K pot, $K = 351$, $H_o = -117$. For inverting amplifier having $K = 351$, set $R_1 = R_f = 100$ K, $R_3 = 100\ \Omega$, $R_2 = 34.8$ K, $R_o = 49.9$ K in high-gain amplifier of Fig. 8.5.4a.

10.32 Class $1\overline{A}$: $R = 2/BC$, $K_1K_2 = (2\omega_o/B)^2 - 1$, $H_o = -K_1K_2/2$; $S^B_{K_1} = S^B_{K_2} = 0$ and $S^B_{R_1} = S^B_{R_2} = S^B_{C_1} = S^B_{C_2} = -\tfrac{1}{2}$. Class $2\overline{A}$: $R = 3/BC$, $K = (3\omega_o/B)^2 - 1$, $H_o = -K/3$; $S^B_K = 0$, $S^B_{R_1} = S^B_{C_2} = -2/3$, and $S^B_{R_2} = S^B_{C_2} = -1/3$. Otherwise, the design sheets of Sec. 10.3 remain intact.

10.37 Using Class 2E band-pass filter of Sec. 10.3: $H_o = -13.7$, f_o varies from 7.4 to 13.7 Hz, Q varies from 3.7 to 6.8, **B is 2 Hz.**

10.41 2nd order LPF stage: $H_o = -1$, $C_2 = 0.1\ \mu F$, $C_5 = 0.039\ \mu F$, $R_1 = R_4 = 5.36$ K, $R_3 = 4.87$ K. 1st order BPF stage: $H_o = -3.41$, $C_3 = C_4 = 0.1\ \mu F$, $R_1 = 1.21$ K, $R_2 = \infty$, $R_5 = 8.25$ K, $R_o = 8.2$ K.

Chapter 11

11.4 Choose k = 1. $C_1 = C_2 = 0.33\ \mu F$, $C_3 = 0.68\ \mu F$, $R_1 = R_2 = 23.7$ K, $K_1 = -K_2 = 1$, $H_o = -1$. For inverting amplifiers set $R_1 = R_f = 100$ K.

11.8 $C_1 = C_2 = 0.022\ \mu F$, $R = R_2 = R_3 = R_5 = R_6 = 26.1$ K, $R_1 = R_4 = 51.1$ K. Ground noninverting op amp inputs through (12 K, 2.7 K, 10 K), 10% resistors, respectively.

11.14 $C = 0.01\ \mu F$, $2C = 0.02\ \mu F$, $R = 16.2$ K, $R/2 = 8.25$ K, $K = H_o = 1.95$. For overall gain of 10, increase amplifier gain to 10 and insert (10/1.95) = 5.13:1 voltage divider in feedback loop. For noninverting amplifier having K = 10, set $R_f = 316$ K, $R_1 = 34.8$ K. For voltage divider, set $R' = 40.2$ K, $R'' = 9.53$ K.

11.17 (a) $C = 0.1\ \mu F$, $2C = 0.2\ \mu F$, $R = 13.3$ K, $R/2 = 6.49$ K, $K = 39$, $H_o = 1.95$. For noninverting gain block having K = 39, set $R_f = 13.3$ K, $R_1 = 348\ \Omega$, pad with 27 K, 10% to negative input.

11.20 Choose k = 1. $C_1 = C_2 = 0.1\ \mu F$, R_1 162 K $= /R_2 = 4.02$K, $H_o = 0.111$, $R_A = 31.5$K, $R_B = 46\,4$ K.

11.27 (b) Class 2B filter has $\omega_{op} = \omega_{oz} = 1/(R_1C_1R_2C_2)^{1/2}$, $\zeta_p = [R_1C_1(1 + K + C_2/C_1) + R_2C_2] \div 2(R_1C_1R_2C_2)^{1/2}$, $\zeta_z = (R_1 + R_2)C_2/2(R_1C_1R_2C_2)^{1/2}$, $H_o = K$. (b) Set $R_1C_1 = R_2C_2$ where $C_2 \ll C_1$.

Chapter 12

12.3 Using Class $1\bar{A}$ band-stop filter design sheet of Sec. 11.3, setting $\omega_{op} = \omega_{oz}$ requires $K_1K_2 = -1$. Setting $\zeta_p = -\zeta_z$ requires the K_1 condition listed in Prob. 12.3.

12.7 (a) $H_{BP}(s) = [H_{AP}(s) - 1]/k$. (b) $H(s) = [R_2/(R_1 + R_2)]/[1 + [R_1/(R_1 + R_2)][(s_n - 1)/(s_n + 1)]^2]$ where $s_n = sRC$. (c) $\omega_o = 1/RC$, $Q = \frac{1}{2} + 1/\rho$ where $\rho = R_2/R_1$, $H_o = 1$. Maximum rejection $= \rho/2$.

12.11 $C = 0.01\ \mu F$, $R = 21.5$ K, $R_3 = 44.2$ K, $K = 1.26$, $H_o = 0.724$. For overall gain of 2, increase amplifier gain to (1.26)(2.76) = 3.48 and insert (2/0.724) = 2.76:1 voltage divider in feedback loop. For noninverting amplifier having K = 3.48, set $R_f = 154$ K, $R_1 = 61.9$ K. For voltage divider, set $R' = 1$ K, $R'' = 562\ \Omega$. For complementary operation, ground input, lift and drive all original grounds including those of amplifier.

12.16 $C = 0.1\ \mu F$, $R_1 = 1.87$K, $R_2 = \infty$, $R_5 = 24.9$ K, $H_o = -0.661$. Summer: $R_3 = 332\ \Omega$, $R_4 = 1$ K.

12.21 $$Z^{(k)} = R_1(K + 2)\frac{1 + sRC}{1 + sRC[(1 + 2R_1/R) + K(1 + R_1/R)]}$$ and let $K \to \infty$.

Chapter 13

13.4 (a), (b) Ground inputs and adjust $K_1K_2 = 2$.

13.6 $K_2 = 1$, $K_1 = 3$, $C = 0.01\ \mu F$, $R = 4.42$ K. For inverting amplifier having $K_2 = 1$, set $R_1 = R_2 = 8.66$ K; $R_o = 5.6$ K, 10%, and change $R_2 = 8.66$ K in oscillator. Then increase $K_1 = 2(3) = 6$ to account for the 2:1 loss at input to K_2. For inverting amplifier having $K_1 = 6$, set $R_1 = 4.22$ K, $R_f = 26.1$ K; $R_o = 27$ K, 10%.

13.10 $K = 1$.

13.13 Using Wien bridge oscillator of Fig. 13.1.1d, $C = 0.001\ \mu F$, $R_2 = R_3 = 16.2$ K, $K = 2$. For noninverting amplifier having $K = 2$, set $R_f = 750\ \Omega$ and replace R_1 with 10 V, 15 mA light bulb such as Dialco No. 8073910 or Eldema No. 1869.

13.15 $K_2 = 1$, $K_1 = 4$, $C_1 = C_2 = 0.01\ \mu F$, $R_1 = R_2 = 3.01$ K. For noninverting amplifier having $K_1 = 4$, set $R_f = 9.09$ K, $R_1 = 3.01$ K. For inverting amplifier having $K_2 = 1$, set $R_1 = R_f = 3.01$ K; R_2 of oscillator becomes R_1 of amplifier.

13.24 (a) $K = 4/(1 - 2/\rho)$. (b) $C = 0.039\ \mu F$, $\rho C = 0.1\ \mu F$, $\rho = 2.56$, $R = 1.78$ K, $R/\rho = 691\ \Omega$, $K = 18.3$. For inverting amplifier having $K = 18.3$, set $R_1 = R_f = 100$ K, $R_3 = 691\ \Omega$, $R_2 = 10.0$ K; $R_o = 47$ K, 10% using high-gain amplifier of Fig. 8.5.4a.

Chapter 14

14.1 (a) $R = 100$ K, $C = 0.013$ pF, L negligible; (b) $R = 10\ \Omega$, $C = 40$ pF, $L = 10$ nH.

14.4 (a) $\theta = \Delta T/\Delta P = 150^{\circ}C/\frac{1}{4}\ W = 600\ ^{\circ}C/W$ (MOX-400), (b) $\Delta P/P = \Delta T/P\theta$, (c) replace vertical axis by $\Delta P/P$. Operate at (a) 50% power to 145°C or (e) 100% power to 0°C and then derate both at 10%/15°C. For both deratings, operate at 50% power to 75°C and then derate at 10%/15°C.

14.11 (a) $C = 0.01\ \mu F$, $R_s = 0.1\ \Omega$, $L = 6.3$ nH, $R_p = 2.8 \times 10^4$ M; (b) $C = 0.1\ \mu F$, $R_s = 0.1\ \Omega$, $L = 10$ nH, $R_p = 280$ M. R_p obtained from Eq. 14.3.20.

14.16 (a) $C = 0.11\ \mu F$, $R_s = 3.5\ \Omega$, $L = 3.6$ nH, $R_p = 91$ M; (b) $C = 110\ \mu F$, $R_s = 0.1\ \Omega$, $L = 3.7$ nH, $R_p = 91$ K. R_p obtained from Eq. 14.3.20 or Fig. 14.3.10.

14.23 (a) $K = K_0/(1 + K_0/2) \cong 2(1 - 2/K_0)$ and $S_{K_0}^{K} = -2/K_0$. Since $\Delta K_0/K_0 = 150\ K/200\ K = 75\%$ and $S_{K_0}^{K} = -10^5$, $\Delta K/K = 0.75 \times 10^{-3}\ \%$. (b) $\Delta Q/Q = 1.5Q \times 10^{-3}\ \%$. For $Q \leqslant 100$, then $\Delta Q/Q \leqslant 0.15 \times 10^{-3}\ \%$ which is acceptable drift. (c) $B = (K_0/2 + 1)f_o \cong K_0 f_o/2$. Then $B = 10^5(10\ Hz) = 1$ MHz.

14.24 (a) Apply superposition and use Tables 8.4.1 and 8.4.2. (b) $G_1 = G_2/(1 + G_2)$. (c) $Z_f = H_o Z_1$, $Z_3 = H_o Z_2$, $Z_1 = (1 + 2H_o)Z_2$, and $Z_{in} = Z_1(1 + H_o)/(1 + 2H_o)$. (d) $R_1 = 10$ K, $R_f = R_2 = 5$ K, $R_3 = 2.5$ K. (e) $R_1 = 210$ K, $R_f = 2.1$ M, $R_2 = 10$ K, $R_3 = 100$ K.

14.34 (a) The low, average, and high estimates for the failure rates are 0.0523, 0.316, and 2.41 failures/10^6 hours, respectively. The corresponding lifetimes (for 99% reliability) are 21.8, 3.6, and 0.47 years, respectively.

INDEX